GUIDE TO
LAW
SCHOOLS

BARRON'S

GUIDE TO LAW SCHOOLS

14TH EDITION

Introduction by
Gary A. Munneke
Professor of Law
Pace University School of Law

BARRON'S

All inquiries should be addressed to:
Barron's Educational Series, Inc.
250 Wireless Boulevard
Hauppauge, New York 11788
http://www.barronseduc.com

Every effort has been made to ensure the accuracy
of the information in this book. Because costs and
statistics change from year to year, prospective
students should contact the schools to verify this
information.

Library of Congress Catalog Card No. 90-40512
International Standard Book No. 0-7641-1396-8
International Standard Serial Number 1062-2489

PRINTED IN THE UNITED STATES OF AMERICA
987654321

Contents

Abbreviations and Degreses

ABBREVIATIONS

AALL—American Association of Law Libraries
AALS—Association of American Law Schools
ABA—American Bar Association
ALAS—Auxiliary Loans to Assist Students
CLEO—Council on Legal Education Opportunity
CPPVE—Council for Private Postsecondary and Vocational Education
CRS—Candidate Referral Service
CSS—College Scholarship Service
CWSP—College Work-Study Program
FAFSA—Free Application for Federal Student Aid
FFS—Family Financial Statement
GAPSFAS—Graduate and Professional School Financial Aid Service
GBBE—Georgia Board of Bar Examiners
GPA—Grade Point Average
GSL—Guaranteed Student Loans
LSAT—Law School Admission Test
LSDAS—Law School Data Assembly Service
MBR—Massachusetts Board of Regents
MSACS—Middle States Association of Colleges and Schools
NASC—Northwest Association of Schools and Colleges
NCACS—North Central Association of Colleges and Schools
NDSL—National Direct Student Loan
NEASC—New England Association of Schools and Colleges
SAAC—Student Aid Application for California
SACS—Southern Association of Colleges and Schools
SBC—State Bar of California
WASC—Western Association of Schools and Colleges
UGPA—Undergraduate Grade Point Average

DEGREES

D.C.L.—Doctor of Civil Law
D.C.L.—Doctor of Comparative Law
J.D.—Doctor of Jurisprudence

J.D./M.B.A.—Juris Doctor/Master of Business Administration
J.M.—Master of Jurisprudence
J.S.D.—Doctor of the Science of Law
J.S.M.—Master of the Science of Law
LL.B.—Bachelor of Laws
LL.M.—Master of Laws
M.A.—Master of Arts
M.Acc.—Master of Accountancy
M.A.L.I.R.—Master of Arts in Labor and Industrial Relations
M.A.P.A.—Master of Arts in Public Administration
M.A.S.—Master of Accounting Science
M.B.A.—Master of Business Administration
M.B.T.—Master of Business Taxation
M.C.J.—Master of Criminal Justice
M.C.L.—Master of Comparative Law
M.C.P.—Master of City Planning
M.C.P.—Master of Community Planning
M.C.R.P.—Master of City and Regional Planning
M.D.—Doctor of Medicine
M.H.A.—Master of Health Administration
M.I.L.R.—Master of Industrial and Labor Relations
M.L.S.—Master of Legal Studies
M.L.S.—Master of Library Science
M.L. & T.—Master of Law and Taxation
M.M.—Master of Management
M.O.B.—Master of Organizational Behavior
M.P.A.—Master of Public Administration
M.P.H.—Master of Public Health
M.P.P.A.—Master of Public Policy Administration
M.P.P.M.—Master of Public and Private Management
M.R.P.—Master of Regional Planning
M.S.—Master of Science
M.S.L.—Master of Studies in Law
M.S.S.A.—Master of Science in Social Administration
M.S.W.—Master of Social Work
M.U.P.—Master of Urban Planning
M.U.R.P.—Master of Urban and Regional Planning
Ph.D.—Doctor of Philosophy
S.J.D.—Doctor of the Science of Law

PART I

Choosing a Law School

CHAPTER 1

Should I Go to Law School?

You picked up this book because you have given some thought to the question of going to law school, or else someone you know is thinking about going to law school. Each year, more than 40,000 students in the United States begin the long and arduous journey associated with attending law school. There was a time when large numbers of attorneys received their legal training by studying law books at home until they were knowledgeable enough to pass an oral examination to become a lawyer. Today, almost all lawyers attend a law school before taking a standardized written bar exam. The educational process takes three or four years, depending on whether the curriculum is full or part time, and whether it is obtained at one of the law schools approved by the American Bar Association, or a handful of other law schools approved in the state where they are located.

Law school is not for everyone. Some individuals cannot cope with the intellectual demands, while others find the psychological stress associated with the study and practice of law to be suffocating. Many bright and ambitious people do not succeed at law because they find other activities more rewarding and challenging. However, many college graduates will find law school to be the most stimulating experience of their lives.

There is a great deal of popular mythology about law school and the legal profession. This book attempts to get past much of the confusing rhetoric facing individuals contemplating a legal education. *Barron's Guide to Law Schools* is full of factual information about law schools and no nonsense devices on the application process, the LSAT, and the decision-making process.

A COMPLEX DECISION

The process of choosing a law school is a complex one, and there are no easy answers along the way. The best choice for one person may be the very worst choice for another.

Accordingly, this Guide should be viewed more as a road map to your destination than as the answer to all your questions. A road map may help you find your way, but it cannot replace the experience of getting there yourself.

This book focuses on the choices that each law school applicant must make during the admission process. While you are considering whether and where to attend law school, you will spend considerable energy weighing various options. The fact that you will feel confused (and at times overwhelmed) is normal. Regardless of your background, you cannot escape facing tough decisions that will affect the rest of your life. If you struggle with the choices, it is a sign that you appreciate the importance of the process.

This basic problem (Which school is best for me?) is the same for every applicant. Whether you have many choices or a single acceptance, so much rests on your decision that it is impossible not to feel the pressure. Particularly in a period of change, both nationally and in the legal profession, the consequences of career decisions seem magnified.

The publisher and authors of this text have no ax to grind and no personal investment in whether you attend law school or not. Our aim is to provide objective information that will help you make an informed choice about a tough decision. We encourage you to listen to other voices who have opinions on this subject. There certainly is room for divergence of viewpoints on many of the subjects addressed here. One person will tell you that you have to be a lawyer, and the next person will tell you that nobody should be a lawyer. In the end, only you can decide on the best course of action. The best way to assure that your final decision will be the right one for you is to become fully informed on all the issues.

WHY GO TO LAW SCHOOL?

You might choose to go to law school for a number of different reasons. In fact, many lawyers were influenced by a variety of factors: They wanted the prestige, power, and panache that a degree in law provides; they wanted a professional career in which they could make enough money to establish and maintain a comfortable lifestyle; they wanted to change the world in order to make it a little better than it was when they arrived; they wanted to pursue a long family tradition; they wanted to do something different from anyone else in their family; they took an aptitude test during college and the career counselor said that they should become a lawyer; or (my personal reason for attending law school) they went to a prelaw association meeting as a favor to a roommate, got elected president, and couldn't back out. Everyone arrives at the law school door for different reasons. Some of these are valid; some are not. Here are a few of the wrong reasons to go to law school:

Don't go to law school because other people expect you to. Spouses, family, friends, and advisors seem perpetually willing to push their loved one, associate, or advisee in this direction. While these people almost always want what is best for you, their personal motives are inevitably more complex. Look at the source and weigh the advice accordingly.

Don't go to law school because of what you see on television or read in the newspapers about lawyers. Media coverage of high profile cases such as the O.J. Simpson trial or President Clinton's impeachment tend to glamorize or demonize lawyers and the law. Popular television shows inevitably portray the law practice in a very different light than most lawyers experience in their daily lives. Lawyers are neither as rich, good-looking, and fast-talking, or as weasly, manipulative, and grasping as the stereotypes suggest. Most practicing lawyers will tell you that these images have little in common with their real lives. The fictional world of *Ally McBeal* has about as much in common with the way real lawyers spend their time as WWF wrestling does with street fighting. We smile bemusedly at the antics of the characters on the popular television series, but in our hearts we know that Ally and her associates could never exist in the flesh. If you want to discover how real-life lawyers work and live, ask them. Visit a law firm, or better yet, get a job in one. Look for lawyers outside the world of work; find out about lawyers in their neighborhoods and communities. Investigate how they live and play when they go home at night. You will probably discover that lawyers are a well-educated and intense (but diverse) lot, who give as much to the community as they do to their jobs.

Don't choose to go to law school because you can't figure out what to do with your life, or because you couldn't find anything else that interested you in four years of college, or you just couldn't find a job. Law school is not the place to go to find yourself. Legal education is no place to buy more time to make a decision because you just can't bear to face the real world.

Whatever other motives may influence your decision to attend law school, make certain that a major consideration is your genuine desire to study law. If you have doubts about whether you want to *study* law (as opposed to *practice* law), do something else for a year or two. Work in a law firm, or join the Peace Corps. If you find you can't get the idea of law school out of your mind, that should be a sign to you. If, on the other hand, you forget about it, forget about it.

These admonitions may fall on deaf ears, but at least you've been warned. Many people find law school to be the most interesting, intellectually stimulating, and challenging experience of their educational lives (despite its many aggravations); others hate it almost more than they can bear. If you find that you fit into the latter group and not the former, don't put yourself through the misery of sitting through three years or more of law school classes.

WHICH LAW SCHOOL?

The decision as to which law school to attend can be even more complicated than the decision to attend law school or not. Beware of law school admissions and recruitment people. They want you—actually they want your seat deposit. Most of them are personable, well-informed, and genuine. They are, however, selling a product: their school. The best defense against the hard sell is comparison shopping. Listen to a number of different pitches before you make a choice. Finally, check out the various claims and promises relying on your own independent investigation rather than stock promotional materials. *Barron's Guide to Law Schools* is particularly suited to help you accomplish this objective (see Part I Chapter 2 and Part III of this Guide for more information).

Beware of family, friends, and prelaw advisors, who push you to attend a particular law school. Utilize impartial advice, particularly guidance from professional counselors and advisors, in making your decision. Their experience and knowledge can be invaluable. But remember! Your prelaw advisor may like a certain school because she graduated from it. Your career counselor may have been particularly impressed by the speech he heard at an open house for a certain law school. Your lawyer friend may or may not be privy to accurate information. Sometimes, opinions masked by objectivity are far from objective. And most important of all, remember that no single school is the right choice for everyone.

Beware of letting your procrastination make decisions for you. There are many critical dates in the law school admission process. Don't be foreclosed from applying to schools, seeking financial aid, or pursuing any alternative because you didn't do it in time. If you want to make the best choice, you should seek to maximize your options, and the best way to maximize your options is to stay on top of the process. Start early. Develop a tickler file to remind you in advance about critical dates. Most calendar programs for personal computers allow you to save important dates. Set aside sufficient time to meet deadlines and accomplish your objectives. Remember that the easiest decision is not always the best one.

Barron's Guide to Law Schools contains chapters on the LSAT (Chapters 10 and 11), the job outlook for graduates, including starting salaries (Chapter 8), financial aid (Chapter 6), and profiles of law schools themselves (Chapters 13 and 14).

The checklist below may help you to clarify your objectives and focus your research efforts as you think about law school. There is simply no single decision that is right for every applicant. If you can determine what choices are best for you, you not only will increase your chances of being accepted, but also improve the likelihood that law school will be a rewarding experience.

Geographical considerations inevitably come into play. A majority of law school graduates accept positions in the region where they went to law school. Those who do not stay in the same geographic area tend to return to the region where they grew up or where they have family. This is true not only for so-called local and regional law schools, but for national law schools as well. It is easier to find a job if you are physically located in the area where your job search occurs. Thus, if you know where you want to settle after graduation, you may want to consider limiting your applications to law schools in that geographic area.

Although most law school graduates settle in the largest metropolitan areas, both law schools and legal employment are found in a variety of settings. You may want to consider, as an alternative to pursuing a legal education at a school in a big city, attending school or working in a smaller city or town, a suburban area within a larger metropolitan population, or a rural area. You may have business, political, or personal ties to a community that would make it advantageous to target that place for postgraduate employment. You or your family may have ties to a university or law school that would lead you to go to school there.

You may want to give thought to what substantive areas of practice interest you. Although many entering law students do not have a clue about what areas of law they wish to pursue, sometime during the tenure of their legal education, they will have to make those choices. Other law students know before they begin law school that they are interested in a particular type of practice, and may choose a law school because of its curricular concentration in that field. Although the first year curriculum and

---

CHECKLIST ON CHOOSING A LAW SCHOOL

Where geograpically do you want to go to school?
- [ ] Family considerations
- [ ] Personal considerations
- [ ] Future job prospects
- [ ] Urban, suburban, rural
- [ ] Current job

What areas of practice interest you?
- [ ] School specialization, course offerings
- [ ] Part-time and summer jobs
- [ ] Other life experiences

What kind of school can you afford?
- [ ] State or private
- [ ] Evening (part-time) program
- [ ] Availability of financial aid, scholarships

What sort of atmosphere do you want?
- [ ] Size of student body and faculty
- [ ] Competitiveness
- [ ] Physical plant
- [ ] Library resources
- [ ] Student services
- [ ] Educational philosphy
- [ ] University community
- [ ] Special programs, concentrations

What schools will accept you?
- [ ] LSAT
- [ ] GPA
- [ ] Special considerations (such as ethnicity)
- [ ] Work, education, or life experiences
- [ ] Other factors that make you unique
- [ ] Recommendations
- [ ] Opportunity for personal interview

many core upper-level electives are common in most law schools, different law schools will have different upper-level course offerings and concentrations. You should look carefully at law school catalogs and talk to school representatives about these differences as part of the decision-making process.

What kind of school can you afford? State law schools are usually less expensive for residents than for nonresidents, or than private schools. Among private schools, tuition may differ considerably depending on the prestige of the institution and other considerations. Schools also differ considerably as to the amount of financial aid and scholarship funds that are available to incoming students. Additionally, schools with part-time or evening programs provide an opportunity for students to attend law school while continuing to work full time.

You should look carefully for information about the school's institutional culture. Although it is hard to discern sometimes, every school has a unique personality. Its geographic location and student body demographic makeup will affect the school's atmosphere. The background of the faculty members will, too. Do most of them have experience practicing law? Or did most come directly into teaching from postgraduate appellate clerkships? What is the size of the student body, the faculty, and average classes? In some ways, a larger law school may seem more vibrant and diverse, while a smaller law school will feel more intimate and supportive. Look at the competitiveness of the institution. Do you want to see how you fare in the most highly charged competitive environment? Do you want to be a big fish in a little pond? Will you be happy just to get accepted? Take a look at the physical plant, the library, and other resources available to the law school. Consider what benefits accrue to the law school from affiliation with its parent university. Think about the history of the university and the law school, and how the institutional roots have molded the law school culture today.

Observe whether current students are satisfied with services, such as financial aid and career services. Consider the availability of cocurricular and extracurricular groups, such as law review, moot court, law school student government, and other student organizations. Ask about the educational philosophy of the institution, whether it is highly theoretical, or practical and skills-oriented. Find out whether the curriculum focuses on the law of a particular jurisdiction, or is concentrated in some other way. All of these factors are important in choosing a law school, and you can learn about many of them through careful research.

Finally, look at which law schools will accept you. If your LSAT and GPA are both very strong, you will have significantly more opportunities than people with less impressive credentials. If either your LSAT or GPA is less stellar, the number of law schools interested in you will inevitably drop. You may need to demonstrate your aptitude through other activities and experiences. If your LSAT and GPA are both low, you may find it challenging to find a single law school that will accept you. A few law schools offer programs that permit applicants to compete for slots during the summer prior to admission.

Some law schools may be located in a geographic area that does not draw as many applications as more populous ones. Some states accredit law schools not approved by the American Bar Association (ABA). Graduates of non-ABA-approved schools usually can only take the bar in the state in which the school is accredited. These schools usually have fewer and less competitive applications, and for some people this may be the only way to go to law school. Before committing to a law school not approved by the ABA you should look carefully at all the factors described in the last paragraph (see also Chapters 14–15).

As you use this book, it will help if you have identified your priorities. Then, as you look at various possibilities, you can judge how closely each school comes to meeting your needs. Although no option may be perfect, you will at least have some organized basis for comparison.

by Gary A. Munneke, Professor of Law at Pace University School of Law where he teaches Torts, Professional Responsibility and Law Practice Management. Prior to joining the Pace faculty in 1988, he served on the faculty of the Widener University School of Law, and as Assistant Dean at the University of Texas School of Law. Professor Munneke is the author of eight books and numerous articles about current issues in the legal profession. His other books provide information about choosing law as a career (*Careers in Law* [1992] and *Opportunities in Law Careers* [1993], VGM Career Horizons, Lincolnwood, IL), what to do after you enter law school (*How To Succeed in Law School*, Barron's, NY, 1994), and what to do after you graduate from law school (*The Legal Career Guide: From Law Student to Lawyer* [1992], and *Nonlegal Careers for Lawyers* [1994], American Bar Association, Chicago). In addition, he has lectured extensively on these topics. Professor Munneke is Past Chair of the American Bar Association Law Practice Management Section and previously chaired its Publishing Board. He has served as President and Research Chair of the National Association for Law Placement as well as Chair of the ABA Standing Committee on Professional Utilizational and Career Development. Professor Munneke received his J.D. from the University of Texas Law School in 1973 and is licensed to practice law in Texas and Pennsylvania. He is a Fellow of the American Bar Foundation, and the College of Law Practice Management.

CHAPTER 2

Where Can I Find Information About Law School?

There is both a wealth and paucity of information about law schools. Books and guides of various sorts abound on the shelves of libraries and bookstores. Increasingly, information is available in electronic formats. Information in the form of advice from well-meaning advisors is also easily accessible. If you are thinking about attending law school, the one thing you will find in abundance is advice. What is often in short supply is any way to tell whether the advice you get is good or not. This informational paradox was apparent to the developers of this Guide. The result is a Guide that is easy to use and understand, containing up-to-the-minute information about law schools.

In addition to the *Guide to Law Schools,* Barron's offers other excellent publications, two of which are excerpted in this book. They are *Barron's How to Prepare for the LSAT* by Jerry Bobrow, an in-depth preparation guide for the law school admission test, and *How to Succeed in Law School* by Professor Gary A. Munneke, which describes what law school will be like and what students need to do to maximize their performance and opportunities. A smaller version of the LSAT book, *Pass Key to the LSAT,* is also available. These books should provide you with enough information to tackle the law school challenge. Many readers, however, will want more. For those with the time, energy, and inclination, the following paragraphs discuss many other sources of information.

Prelaw Advisors

Most colleges and universities designate one or more professors as prelaw advisors. Students thinking about law school are routinely funneled to these professors and administrators for guidance. The question of prelaw school education is addressed in more depth in the next chapter: The comments here are aimed more at assessing the pros and cons of utilizing a prelaw advisor at school.

First of all, it is very difficult to make generalizations about the type of individuals who become prelaw advisors or the quality of advice they dispense. Prelaw advisors may come from almost any discipline, although it seems that a high percentage are political science professors. Many, but certainly not all, possess a law degree themselves, in addition to professional credentials in their teaching field. They may be young professors, barely out of school themselves, or wizened veterans who have been advising generations of prospective law students.

Prelaw advisors often come to the table with a distinct set of biases in favor of or against certain law schools, approaches to the application process, and the qualities that are needed to succeed in law school. Keep in mind, however, that the more definite the advisor is in his or her opinions, the more likely it is that there are differing points of view that make as much sense. Some prelaw advisors diligently collect information about law schools, such as law school catalogs or information about former students who have attended certain law schools. Other advisors may have little in the way of written materials, but willingly commit many hours to give to those who want to talk.

Whether or not you should take the advice of your prelaw advisor is a very personal question. Just as it is with doctors, dentists, psychologists, and other professionals, chemistry is important. You need to find someone with whom it is easy to carry on a conversation, someone whose opinion you value, and someone who strikes you as well informed and objective. The same prelaw advisor might hit it off with one student and turn off another. For this reason, it makes sense to get in to talk to your prelaw advisor as early as you can during your college career. If you are not happy with the advice you get, or not comfortable talking to the advisor, you have an opportunity to find another person to fill this role.

You may find that advice from a trusted faculty mentor, such as a club sponsor, academic advisor, or favorite teacher may work just as well for you as the school's official prelaw advisor. While this mentor may not be as well versed on law schools as the regular prelaw advisor, the benefit that you will derive from being able to speak openly and candidly can be invaluable.

At some institutions, the office of career services may provide information or advice about law schools and legal education. Because career counselors have training and experience in helping people to make career decisions, they may be able to assist you in ways that a faculty member could not. Some career services offices offer testing programs, which attempt to identify things like work values, personality types, and vocational interests. These tests are often validated by comparison to control groups of individuals from particular professions. Thus, you can determine whether your personality type or professional values are similar to the values or personality of other people who have chosen to go into law. Unfortunately, such tests can lay a trap for the unwary. It is one thing to say that you are like other members of a group; it does not necessarily follow that you have to have those traits in order to be successful in a given field. In reality, successful lawyers are as diverse in terms of personality and values as the general population, and while it may be possible to identify characteristics common among typical lawyers, it is not uncommon to find lawyers who do not fit into the mold.

Nor is it necessary to limit the universe of potential advisors to educational settings. Well-informed family members, work supervisors, friends, and business associates all may have qualities that make them good advisors for you. In fact, nowhere is it written that you can seek advice from only one person. You may want to take a sampling of opinions from various people and reach your own decisions.

Law School Career Days

One of the best ways to get information about law schools is to attend a law school career day. These events come in a variety of forms, from those sponsored by a single university, attended by as few as a single law school, to those sponsored by Law Services in major

U.S. cities, sometimes attended by more than one hundred law schools. Law schools typically send representatives to these events, in areas where they hope to draw their students. Individual law schools may schedule a day of interviews through the career service office, or the prelaw advisor. Several colleges may join together to schedule panels or career fairs of law school representatives. The Law Services annual law forums are regional fairs in major cities attended by a large number of American law schools (see page 10 for a listing of the fall 2000 fairs. The dates and cities for 2001 will be similar but not identical. Law school forums allow you to visit a number of law school representatives in person and in close proximity for easy comparison. The law schools usually bring catalogs, applications, and other literature for you to take, thus providing a quick way to receive materials.

Prelaw Associations

Many colleges and universities have a prelaw association or club committed to supporting prelaw students at those institutions. These student organizations may sponsor programs, collect information, and at universities affiliated with a law school, provide opportunities for direct contact with law school faculty and students.

The Internet

An increasing number of law schools provide home pages on the Internet that contain an array of useful segments on various aspects of the law school's life and history. You can find faculty biographies, course descriptions, admission and graduation requirements, schedules, and information about special programs in the law school. Some law schools may provide for on-line application. You may be able to contact the admissions officer or faculty members by e-mail with questions. For individuals who are comfortable operating in an electronic environment, much of the work in applying to law school can be completed on-line.

Law School Visits

If you have narrowed the number of law schools to which you plan to apply to two or three, it may make sense for you to visit the schools in person. When you applied to undergraduate schools, you probably visited campuses before you made your final choice. What you learned about the setting, ambiance, and facilities undoubtedly contributed to your final decision. It is no different with the decision to attend law school. Some law schools encourage on-site visits through open houses on specific dates. Most law schools, however, are happy to arrange for a campus visit at any time. It makes sense to try to schedule your visit at a time when classes are in session in order to get a sense of what law school life is like at the school. You may be able to visit classes, talk to students and faculty, and meet with officials about such matters as applications and financial aid.

Law-Related Jobs

Part of the information gathering process may include finding out more about what lawyers do. If you grew up in a family of one or more lawyers, you probably learned a great deal about the legal profession and the practice of law through contact with these family members. You probably learned more about lawyers than you realized at the time. The fact that you remain interested in a career in law suggests that something about the lifestyle of a lawyer appeals to you.

If you did not grow up in such a family, or if you did and you want to learn more, one of the best ways to find out whether you want to practice law is to work in a law firm or other legal organization. Even if you visited a law office as part of a career day in high school or college, nothing will give you a first-hand view of legal work better than a job in the law. You might be surprised at how many opportunities there are in the law firms, corporate law departments, government law departments, district attorney and public defender offices, and public service organizations. These organizations include, in addition to the legal staff, a support staff of people who have not attended law school, including, for example, legal assistants, legal secretaries, and file clerks.

The jobs may be full time or part time, depending on the needs of the employer, and the pay may vary widely depending on the qualifications for the job and the marketplace for workers in the area. You may be able to find a job with a law firm or other employer for the summer, or as part of a school-sponsored internship. If you are already working for a company, you may be able to arrange for temporary assignments with the company's legal department, or to take on other law-related tasks.

The greatest number of opportunities in the legal marketplace is probably for permanent support staff positions. For legal assistants (paralegals as they are sometimes called) or legal secretaries, training or experience in the field will be helpful; however, there are no state or national standards for these positions such as there would be for becoming a lawyer in the organization. Some firms try to hire highly intelligent and motivated people, who possess basic skills such as keyboarding, word processing, and other computer skills, and provide the training to these individuals themselves.

It is not uncommon for law students today to have spent two to three years, or more, working in a law firm or other organization, before coming to law school. Many law students continue these prelegal positions while they go to law school, either cutting back on their work hours to part-time status while they are in school, or continuing to work full time, but attending law school part time in the evening. One potential advantage of working in a law-related position before or during law school, is that there may be an increased probability of obtaining employment with that organization as a lawyer after graduation. Even more important, however, employment in a legal setting may help you to decide whether you want to work in the law at all. You will see up close that the practice of law is very different from the images of legal work garnered from books, television, and secondhand anecdotal information.

U.S. News and Other Rankings

Each year *U.S. News and World Report* produces a ranking of law schools that is relied on extensively by many law school applicants and their advisors. The rankings, based on both statistical data and surveys of lawyers, judges and legal educators, have a tendency to imbue a degree of certainty into the process of evaluating law schools that does not exist in reality. Other similar surveys, reported by different publications, fall into the same trap. They all presume that a single set of measurable criteria will work for all applicants. This is simply not the case.

The American Bar Association has circulated a statement warning students against the uncritical use of law school rankings (see box on page 12). This position is supported by the Law School Admissions Council and most law school deans and admissions officers.

Law School Forums in 2000*

If you're considering law school, come to a Law School Forum. Free admission. No preregistration. In one place, you can:

- talk with representatives of LSAC—member law schools from across the United States;
- obtain admission materials, catalogs, and financial aid information;
- view video programs about the law school admission process, legal education and careers, and minority perspectives on legal education;
- attend informational sessions on the law school admission process, financing a legal education, and issues of importance to minority applicants; and
- purchase Law Services publications and LSAT® preparation materials.

Atlanta, GA	Friday, September 22, 2000: Noon–6 P.M. Saturday, September 23, 2000: 10 A.M.–4 P.M. Grand Hyatt Atlanta Buckhead 8300 Peachtree Road Atlanta, GA
Boston, MA	Friday, October 27, 2000: Noon–6 P.M. Saturday, October 28, 2000: 10 A.M.–4 P.M. Marriott Copley Place 110 Huntington Avenue Boston, MA
Chicago, IL	Friday, September 8, 2000: Noon–6 P.M. Saturday, September 9, 2000: 10 A.M.–4 P.M. Chicago Hilton and Towers 720 South Michigan Avenue Chicago, IL
Dallas, TX	Saturday, November 4, 2000: 10 A.M.–4 P.M. Hyatt DFW DFW Airport Dallas, TX
Los Angeles, CA	Friday, November 10, 2000: Noon–6 P.M. Saturday, November 11, 2000: 10 A.M.–3 P.M. Los Angeles Airport Marriott 5855 West Century Boulevard Los Angeles, CA
New York, NY	Friday, September 15, 2000: Noon–7 P.M. Saturday, September 16, 2000: 10 A.M.–4 P.M. New York Marriott World Trade Center Three World Trade Center New York, NY
Washington, DC	Saturday, July 15, 2000: 10 A.M.–5 P.M. Renaissance Washington DC Hotel 999 9th Street, NW Washington, DC
Oakland, CA (Tentative, check web site for information)	Monday, November 13, 2000 Oakland Marriott City Center 1001 Broadway Oakland, CA
For further information contact:	**Law School Forums** Law Services Box 40 Newtown, PA 18940-0040 215.968.1001 Internet: *http://www.lsac.org*

* A schedule of dates for 2001 will be published by the Law School Admissions Council later in 2001.

LSAT Dates and Registration Deadlines

Domestic & Canadian Published Test Centers (US/Puerto Rico/US Territories/Canada) — Foreign Published Test Centers

Test Dates	Regular Registration by Mail (postmark deadline), and Telephone (receipt deadline), and Online (receipt deadline)	Late Registration by Mail (postmark deadline)	Late Registration by Telephone and Online (receipt deadline)	Foreign Published Test Centers — Registration Deadline** by Mail (postmark deadline), Telephone (receipt deadline), and Online (receipt deadline)
Monday, June 12, 2000	May 12, 2000	May 13–19, 2000	May 13–24, 2000	May 5, 2000
Saturday, October 7, 2000 / Wednesday, October 11, 2000†**	September 8, 2000	September 9–15, 2000	September 9–20, 2000	September 1, 2000
Saturday, December 2, 2000 / Monday, December 4, 2000†*	November 3, 2000	November 4–10, 2000	November 4–15, 2000	October 27, 2000
Saturday, February 10, 2001* / Monday, February 12, 2001†**	January 12, 2001	January 13–19, 2001	January 13–24, 2001	January 5, 2001

Other LSAT Options

Test Dates	Test Center Change†† by Mail (postmark deadline) Telephone (receipt deadline) See page 6 $28	Test Date Change by Mail (postmark deadline) See page 6 $28	Nonpublished Test Centers— Domestic & Canadian Test Centers (postmark deadline) See page 4 $199 plus $90 LSAT fee	Nonpublished Test Centers— Foreign Test Centers (postmark deadline) See page 4 $266 plus $90 LSAT fee	LSAT Registration Refunds partial only (postmark deadline) See page 8 $39
Monday, June 12, 2000	May 19, 2000 (mail) / May 24, 2000 (telephone)	June 27, 2000	May 5, 2000	April 14, 2000	June 9, 2000
Saturday, October 7, 2000 / Wednesday, October 11, 2000†**	September 15, 2000 (mail) / September 20, 2000 (telephone)	October 11, 2000	September 1, 2000	August 11, 2000	October 6, 2000
Saturday, December 2, 2000 / Monday, December 4, 2000†*	November 10, 2000 (mail) / November 15, 2000 (telephone)	December 9, 2000	October 27, 2000	October 6, 2000	December 1, 2000
Saturday, February 10, 2001* / Monday, February 12, 2001†**	January 19, 2001 (mail) / January 24, 2001 (telephone)	February 17, 2001	January 5, 2001	December 15, 2000	February 9, 2001

††Center changes to foreign centers must meet the foreign registration deadline.

LSAT Score Release Dates

Test Dates	LSAT TelScore 215.968.1200 See page 12 $10 fee	Score Report Mailed (approximated date)
Monday, June 12, 2000	July 30, 2000	July 11, 2000
Saturday, October 7, 2000 / Wednesday, October 11, 2000†**	October 28, 2000	November 6, 2000
Saturday, December 2, 2000 / Monday, December 4, 2000†*	December 21, 2000	January 4, 2001
Saturday, February 10, 2001* / Monday, February 12, 2001†**	March 3, 2001	March 9, 2001

■ **For Telephone Services: 215.968.1001** (see page 2 for hours)
■ **On Online Services: www.LSAC.org**
Registration closes midnight EST on deadline date

† This test is for Saturday Sabbath observers only. For details, please see page 4, Saturday Sabbath Observers.

* This test is nondisclosed. Persons who take a nondisclosed test receive only their scores. They do not receive their test questions, answer key, or individual responses. For details, please see page 12, Your Score Report and Test Disclosure.

** Late registration is not available for foreign centers.

Note
Walk-in registration on the day of the test is not permitted at any test center for any test administration.

Rating of Law Schools

No rating of law schools beyond the simple statement of their accreditation status is attempted or advocated by the American Bar Association. Qualities that make one kind of school good for one student may not be as important to another. The American Bar Association and its Section of Legal Education and Admissions to the Bar have issued disclaimers of any law school rating system. Prospective law students should consider a variety of factors in making their choice among approved schools.

If you look at a ranking system such as *U.S. News,* do so with a skeptical eye. Remember that reputations in legal education are established over decades. Recognize that different schools are ""best" for different people. And accept the fact that all ABA-approved law schools go through the same rigorous accreditation process.

LITERATURE AND THE MEDIA

Lawyers are portrayed in a variety of lights in literature and the media. Many of the images of lawyers in television and film, as well as in books and the news, are exaggerated, distorted, and stereotypical. It is very difficult to capture the essence of legal work through a literary or cinematic eye. Notwithstanding this limitation, the pervasiveness of media images of lawyers makes it inevitable that we are influenced by these images. Even lawyers themselves are sometimes influenced by their own media hype.

There are a number of excellent books and films on the legal profession, and regular viewing of court proceedings and discussion of legal issues on Court TV, CNN, and C-SPAN can be highly illuminating. Here are a few specific recommendations on books and films:

- *The Bramble Bush* by Carl Llewellyn. Still a classic on the thought process of legal analysis.

- *The Paper Chase* by John Jay Osborne. The book, or the movie with John Houseman as the quintessential law professor who does intellectual battle with his less-than-equal first-year student nemesis, Hart.

- *One L* by Scott Turow. Probably a more realistic picture of law school, based on Turow's school notes about the first year of law school.

- *A Civil Action* by Jonathan Harr. A riveting account of the colossal battle between a brash, aggressive plaintiff lawyer and an icon of the Boston legal establishment in an environmental pollution case in the town of Woburn, Massachusetts—a true story. Read the book; skip the movie.

- *Inherit the Wind.* The book, the play, the movie, all three a fictionalization of the Scopes Monkey Trial, in which a Tennessee science teacher was prosecuted for teaching evolution. The lawyers in the real case were three-time presidential candidate William Jennings Bryan and famed defense counsel Clarence Darrow.

- *A Few Good Men,* with Jack Nicholson and Tom Cruise, tells the story of military justice, after a commander's rigid discipline leads to a soldier's death. We all know that the villain doesn't usually break down on the stand in real life, but Jack makes us believe anyway.

- *Gideon's Trumpet* by Anthony Lewis. If ever you wanted a reason to become a lawyer, this is it: indigent man fights to the Supreme Court for the right to be represented by counsel.

- *To Kill a Mockingbird* by Harper Lee, or the movie with Gregory Peck. A classic in print or film: small town Southern lawyer stands for courage and dignity as he represents a black man accused of raping a white woman.

- Anything by John Grisham. Sure, the plots are far-fetched, and the dialogue hardly Hemingway, but each one of Grisham's tales provides great imagery on different practice settings from plaintiff practice (*The Rainmaker*), to elite corporate work (*The Firm*), to high profile criminal cases (*A Time to Kill*).

- *Kramer v. Kramer.* Dustin Hoffman and Meryl Streep fight for custody in a courtroom drama that demonstrates how justice isn't always easy to find in the courtroom.

The list could go on and on, because lawyers, trials, and the stories of people who encounter the justice system provide such fertile soil for intriguing plotlines. Whether the source is books, movies, or TV (depictions of lawyers on the small screen are legion), it is possible to learn about the work of lawyers by watching how they are depicted in various media. What you learn may not dictate your choices about law school, but it may provide useful clues to help you answer your questions.

It should be apparent to you that in order for you to gather information about law schools, you need to evaluate information from a variety of sources in light of your own aspirations. The decision to attend law school may involve the outlay of one hundred thousand dollars, or more, in direct costs, and require you to forego other income for a period of three or four years. For this reason, the decision to go to law school should not be made lightly. This chapter has provided an overview of the primary sources of information available to help you make this decision. The rest is up to you.

by Gary A. Munneke, Professor of Law, Pace University School of Law (see page 6).

CHAPTER 3

What Course of Prelaw Study Should I Take?

There is no standard prelaw curriculum. Law schools do not require any particular undergraduate degree, course of study, or particular courses in order to gain admission. Statistics on the entering class of every law school will demonstrate that students come from a wide variety of backgrounds. Perhaps the largest number of law students started out as political science majors, but other majors from the arts and social sciences are well represented, including history, English, psychology, and sociology. Law schools generally have a high concentration of business majors, including tax and accounting, general business, economics, criminal justice, and international relations. There are usually smaller but significant numbers from the hard sciences like physics, chemistry, and biology, or engineering. Other majors, such as journalism, environmental science, and art, music, or drama, are likely to be found in a typical first-year class.

Because law schools only require that you complete an undergraduate degree, every degree program is equal, at least in theory. In practice, law schools may find that they have had better success with graduates from certain degree programs at certain universities than others. Individual admissions committee members at different schools may have their own ideas about what kind of prelaw training will prepare students best for law school. Undergraduate advisors may channel prelaw students into certain majors that they perceive to have a nexus with law school. If your research discloses that certain concentrations or degree programs are likely to receive favorable treatment in the admissions process of schools where you plan to apply, you would be wise to pursue such a course of study. Otherwise, the best advice for your prelegal education is to follow a curriculum that you enjoy and in which you possess an interest independent of law school. There are two important reasons for this: First, chances are that you will do better in a subject area that you enjoy than you will in one that you hate. If you have to struggle each day to get up and go to class, it will undoubtedly be reflected in your grades, and a poor showing will adversely affect your chances to be admitted to law school. Second, if you do not get into law school or decide not to go to law school, you will have pursued a course of study that will help you in some alternative career path.

Much the same advice can be said about specific courses. Take courses that you like, that provide an intellectual challenge for you personally. Study under professors who are interesting and exciting, rather than those who put you to sleep. Take classes that make you want to learn, rather than those that fit into a convenient schedule or guarantee an "A."

There is no washout course for prelaw, like Organic Chemistry for premed majors. There is no one course that every law school applicant must complete. Yet, prelaw students continue to pose the question: What courses will help me most in law school? At the risk of negating the advice of take what you like, the following are this author's personal suggestions:

1. **Logic or reasoning.** Much of law school centers on legal analysis, which is fundamentally deductive logic. Learning about logic and reasoning can help to prepare you for the kind of thinking you will be required to do in law school.

2. **Legal history.** Although you will read historical cases in law school, you may find a paucity of information about the roots of our legal system. A course that traces the development of the law, particularly Anglo-American jurisprudence, will provide you with a useful background throughout your legal career.

3. **Public speaking.** You will be required to speak when called on in class, and you will need to be able to make oral argu-

ments throughout law school. Courses that polish your speaking ability and the skill of thinking on your feet will make the inevitable speaking requirements of law school more palatable. A course like this might be particularly valuable for someone who is not accustomed to, or afraid of, standing up and speaking publicly.

4. **Research and writing.** Any course that imposes a demanding regimen of critiqued writing based upon academic research will help you in law school. All law students are required to complete research and writing assignments during law school—an activity that does not end with graduation, because much of lawyering involves research and writing. In addition, many law school exams are essay tests, which favor effective writers. The more writing experience you get, the better off you will be in law school.

5. **Basic accounting.** Certain law school courses in the areas of contracts, business and tax, assume a fundamental understanding of financial and accounting terms and principles. Legal practitioners are constantly required to deal with their clients' money, as well as their own. Understanding the basics of accounting and business will prove invaluable.

6. **Speed reading.** You will probably be required to do more reading in law school than you ever have before. You will also be expected to understand the material in greater depth than in the past. Accordingly, the ability to pore over a great amount of reading with a high level of retention is important. Many universities offer such courses on either a credit or noncredit basis; if yours does not, consider taking such a course outside of school.

Here are a few other suggestions for course selection in undergraduate school: Do not be afraid of courses that are intellectually demanding; these classes will train your mind for the rigors of a legal education. Get a well-rounded education; take courses outside your major. Legal problems draw from the experience of humankind, and so lawyers inevitably must be renaissance people in order to understand these legal problems. Master technology; most universities are now wired environments, and students use computers in a variety of ways. Do not think that you can avoid technology by attending law school; conversely, if you embrace technology, you will find that there are many applications for your knowledge in law. Do more than go to classes; get involved in extracurricular activities as well. Evidence of learning is found in more places than transcripts.

If it has been several years since you were in school, you may find yourself experiencing some uneasiness about returning to the world of education. Some of this malaise you should discount out of hand. You will find that your reacclimation to school comes quickly. You will also discover that life experiences gained since college give you valuable perspectives that you will use in the law. The discipline of managing life in the real world will undoubtedly help you to organize your time and maximize your performance in law school. If you have been out of school for a long time, or remain nervous about returning to school for any other reason, then take courses before you apply to law school. These might be undergraduate courses at a local community college or a university, or they might be graduate level courses offered through your employer. Such experiences may help to make the transition go more smoothly.

Although the bulk of this section has dealt with undergraduate education, it is worth noting that a significant number of law school entrants possess advanced degrees, including MBAs, CPAs, master's degrees in a variety of other fields, Ph.D.s, MDs and other medical degrees. You should not be surprised in your first year law school class to find yourself sitting between an anesthesiologist and a history professor. You may have obtained a graduate degree yourself, and wondered if there is room in law school for someone like you. The answer is yes.

People who come to law school with professional degree certification usually fall into one of two groups: those who hope to build upon their prior training with a degree in law, and those who hope to make a complete career change because they are not satisfied with their chosen occupation. Both groups are well represented in law school. Graduate level training can be a useful credential for law school admission and an excellent preparation for the study of law. However, because the admission process typically focuses on undergraduate grades, A's in graduate school will not wipe out C's in college.

Finally, a word about *which* college. Law schools take into consideration the reputations of undergraduate institutions just as other graduate programs do. If you went to a school with an excellent reputation, or a highly regarded degree program, it will help you in the application process. Because law schools are able to compare the performance of admitted students with their undergraduate institutions, they may have evidence to show that students from a particular school or college perform above or below the average of admitted students. This may be because the undergraduate school recommends more or fewer of its better students to a particular law school. It may be that a larger number of applicants coming from a particular university (say a local one) means that admitted students fall within the full range of qualifications in the entering class. Whatever the reasons, your school does make a difference. If you think that law schools may not know enough about your prelegal schools or degree programs to be able to make an accurate assessment of your abilities, send informational material about the school or program with your application.

In the final analysis, your prelegal education can help you in a variety of ways to prepare for the rigors of law school. The absence of specific requirements gives you a great deal of freedom in choosing a path. Select one that builds the skills you will need in law school, that is simultaneously interesting and fulfilling on its own.

by Gary A. Munneke, Professor of Law, Pace University School of Law (see page 6).

CHAPTER 4

How Do I Apply to Law School?

Law school and the legal profession are nebulous concepts for most people. The law school application process that you will complete as an applicant is somewhat analogous to what you will be doing as a law student. You will research the issue, you will analyze the results of your research, and you will reach a conclusion.

An attorney has power and position, and thus great responsibility. You are about to embark upon a process that is just the beginning of a lifetime of continued legal education. The law is an ever changing body of statutes and court opinions. You must become socially aware and involved in your community. Today, we face problems that are different from those faced in the past; the problems of the future will be different from those faced today; none are less important than the others.

The application process must be taken seriously and applicants should investigate all options available to them. Fortunately, there are many sources of information for prospective law students to use. See Chapter 2, particularly the schedule of Law School Forums for 2000.

LSATS AND GPAS

Each applicant to law school is required to take the Law School Admission Test (LSAT). The LSAT is administered four times per year, typically June, October, December, and February. For most law schools the LSAT is one of the most important factors in determining entrance as it is a common denominator for every applicant.

In determining whether a particular application is appropriate, law school representatives will release median numbers. Applicants should know that a median means the middle score. Therefore, there are students enrolled with numbers above and below the median. In addition, should the school release average numbers, it would be the sum of the scores divided by the number of enrolled students. Finally, applicants should recognize that the median for the accepted group of students to a particular school is typically higher than the median for the actual enrolled group for that school. For example, if a law school admitted five students with LSAT scores of 180, 172, 151, 148, 143, their median LSAT would be a 151. By way of contrast, the average LSAT would be a 159. If only the bottom three students enrolled, however, the median would be 148, and the average would be 147.

It would appear to be a rather simple matter to compare law schools based on their medians if that were the only criteria used in admission. However, an applicant's undergraduate career typically plays an equally important role in the decision process. A student's academic record must be analyzed very carefully. Factors such as school(s) attended, classes taken, major, minor, number of hours worked while in school, as well as grade progression are all important factors. Therefore, applicants should acknowledge particular strengths in their academic performance, and point out events such as a change of major that may have had a significant impact on the progression of grades.

FACTORS TO CONSIDER

Choosing a law school is a complex process. You must analyze your own needs and desires. You should consider the atmosphere in which you function well, the location, the reputation, the support services, housing options, financial aid packages, placement opportunities, faculty, student body characteristics, activities, and library facilities. Each will be more or less important to each individual.

Are you happiest in an urban, suburban, or rural area? Is the prestige value of the institution you attend of great importance to you? Do you do best where there is a fair degree of interaction between you and your faculty members? Do you want to attend a large school or a small school? (Keep in mind that a law school with over 1,000 students is considered large.) Do you need a nearby support system of family and friends? Is cost important to you? This list of questions barely scratches the surface. Be honest with yourself in order to assess what law school best suits your needs.

As you begin to review the catalogs, keep in mind the factors that are most important to you. However, remember that you shouldn't base your decision solely on the availability of certain elective courses. Your interest may change once you're in law school.

Review the faculty. Do they come from a wide range of schools? Do they have advanced degrees? Have they clerked for a judge or worked in a law firm? Are there women and members of minority groups on the faculty? Do they teach the substantive required courses? There are no right or wrong answers to these and other questions. But the answers to these and other questions you pose will give you a better picture of the law school.

Next, review the student organizations as they can enrich your legal education experience. The variety and types available will give you a sense of the student body at that given law school.

Review the law school placement office. What type of services do they offer? What type of jobs do the graduates take? Where geographically are they employed? Are you able to speak to alumni who practice in various areas of the law, e.g., environmental, health, criminal, etc.? (An overview of law school placement services appears in Chapter 8 of this Guide).

The catalog will also give detailed information on the library: the number of volumes, the advanced technology available, and any specialized collections unique to the school. Most law school libraries have access to the national legal data bases, and law school students are trained to use this valuable research tool.

Items such as faculty-to-student ratio, the ratio of library seats to students, or the number of volumes in the library are factors that are scrutinized by the American Bar Association (ABA). All ABA-approved law schools must meet or exceed national standards as determined by the ABA. (Profiles of ABA-approved law schools appear in Chapters 12 and 13 of this Guide).

At this point the question of attending a non-ABA-approved school may be raised and the answer generally is no. There are some non-ABA-approved law schools that are accredited in their own state. Graduates of state certified schools are usually eligible to take the bar exam in that state. However, problems arise when one of these graduates wants to practice law in another state. The state board of bar examiners in each state sets the requirements for admission to practice in their state as there is no national bar exam. The graduate of a non-ABA-approved law school will find that it is difficult, if not impossible, to get admitted to the bar of any other state. (For more information, see Chapters 14 and 15 of this Guide.)

The number of law schools remaining after this cursory review is probably still too large a number for you to consider applying to all. Therefore, look closely at the schools that meet your needs, based on the preliminary information you have gathered. How well do you match up with the profile of these law schools' most recent incoming class? What are the medians of the schools in which you are interested and how do your numerical predictors match up with their numbers?

It may appear that applicants are judged only on the numbers; however, most law schools consider many other aspects of the application as discussed earlier. Applicants must recognize that the LSAT and GPA are the most common factors to each applicant, thus placing everyone at a starting point or on a level playing field. Other factors then become important, such as major, undergraduate institution, advanced degrees, leadership roles in community or within extracurricular activities, letters of recommendation, and the personal essay.

Most applicants submit anywhere from five to seven applications to various law schools. Applying to one law school is probably unwise; likewise, applying to 100 law schools is not necessary and is very expensive.

FILLING OUT THE APPLICATION

Once you have identified the schools you will be applying to, you must complete the applications in a timely manner. Applicants must read the instructions for each school carefully. Complete all questions that are not identified as optional and provide explanations where necessary. Any questions labeled "optional" may be left blank. (See the sample application provided.)

If you do not have access to a typewriter or word processor, the law school application may be printed clearly. Remember to make copies of each application that is submitted. An increasing number of schools allow you to apply on-line through their web sites. If you are connected to the Internet at your school this option may make sense for you. In addition, applications may be completed by utilizing school specific on-line applications or the LSACD. Produced by Law Services, the LSACD is a Windows(r) compatible, Interactive multimedia CD-ROM. All 176 ABA-approved law schools are included in the LSACD's fully searchable database and easy-to-use application forms.

The Personal Statement

Most law schools in the country do not interview candidates for admission. Therefore, your personal statement is the only place in which you are able to sell yourself to the law school. This may be the only opportunity that the committee has to get to know the person behind the application. It is an opportunity for you to respond to questions you think the admissions committee may have when they review your application and academic record. It is the place to express who you are and what is important to you. You may wish to emphasize any personal or professional experiences and how they have contributed to your growth and/or personal development. Examples of items that applicants might consider including are: a description of work experience and extracurricular activities; explanation of distinct trends or discrepancies among grades; a description of substantial time commitments while attending school; verification that standardized tests have underpredicted academic performance in the past (prior test scores should be provided); cultural, ethnic, educational, or other factors that might cause the LSAT score or GPA to be an inaccurate measure of potential for law study. In addition, you may wish to mention the fact that you are the first member of the family to graduate from college, or you may wish to explain hardships or handicaps that you have overcome in order to achieve your degree.

In sum, the personal statement is a case that you have made for yourself to the admissions committee. Above all, it must be typed carefully and accurately. Correct spelling and grammar are essential.

Letters of Recommendation

Letters of recommendation can be very helpful to the admissions committee. For recent graduates (within two years), at least one faculty appraisal is preferred. Other applicants who would find it difficult to obtain faculty appraisals may request recommendations from individuals who can appraise their ability to perform in law school. Where an institution has a central file for appraisals that are duplicated as needed, or where a committee provides a composite appraisal, typically these alternative procedures are acceptable.

Applicants who have been out of school for a number of years should seek letters of recommendation from individuals who can speak to the applicant's character, leadership abilities, and analytical skills. The quality of the recommendation and content are more important than who writes the letter.

Letters of recommendation are additional pieces of evidence that support your case for admission. Many law schools utilize standard recommendation forms in lieu of or in addition to letters. If the school provides such forms, make sure that your references are complete, then return them.

Most law schools will be utilizing a new service offered by Law Services that will require your letters to be submitted through the LSDAS letter of recommendation service that serves all member schools. The service is included in your LSDAS registration subscription. Your letters will be copied and sent to law schools along with your LSDAS report, or as received. To use this service, follow the directions for submitting letters outlined in the LSAT/LSDAS Registration and Information Book. Be sure to fill out and give each letter writer a letter of recommendation form from the LSAT/LSDAS Registration and Information Book.

DEADLINES, DEADLINES, DEADLINES

All law schools specify deadlines for submission of the application materials to their institution. However, you should begin to explore your options in your junior year of college. This allows you enough time to narrow your choices, gather the appropriate information, and be prepared to submit timely applications in the fall of your senior year. Even if you later decide to work for a period of time after graduation, you keep your choices open by starting early.

First, determine when you are going to take the LSAT exam. Registration materials are available through Law Services. Almost all ABA-approved law schools require the use of the Law School Data Assembly Service (LSDAS), and, therefore, upon registration for the exam, you should register simultaneously

Application for Admission__2000-01

Pace University School of Law
78 North Broadway
White Plains, NY 10603
Admissions Telephone - (914) 422-4210

Application as:

☒ First year student: Fall term _2000_
☐ Reactivation
☐ Transfer student: _____ term 19 _____
☐ Visiting student: _____ term 19 _____
☐ Twenty-four credit student: _____ term 19 _____
(Only for students with foreign law degrees who wish to qualify for bar exam)

Application to enter:

☒ Three-year J.D. (full-time) program*
☐ Four-year J.D. (part-time) program*
  ☐ Day part-time
  ☐ Evening part-time

SAMPLE

Please type or print in ...:

1. Name *SAMPLE* ___ MPLE ___ *A.*
   Last   First   Middle

   If we will be receiving documents under any other name, please indicate name: *NO*

2. Social Security Number *999-99-9999*

3. Are you at least 18 years of age? ☒ Yes ☐ No Birthdate *02 / 04 / 71*
                                                            optional

4. Present Mailing Address *78 North Broadway White Plains NY 10603 USA*
      Number and Street   City   State   Zip Code

   Date when current address no longer applies _____

   Home Telephone: *914-422-4210*   Business Telephone: *914-422-4282*
        Area Code/Number   Area Code/Number

   If we contact you at your business number, may we identify ourselves as calling from Pace University School of Law? ☒ Yes ☐ No

5. Permanent Address *78 North Broadway*   Home Telephone: *914-422-4210*
        Number and Street   Area Code/Number

   White Plains NY 10603 USA
   City   State   Zip Code

6. **Citizenship**
   Are you a U.S. Citizen? ☒ Yes ☐ No
   Are you a permanent resident of the U.S.? ☐ Yes ☐ No
   If you answered NO to either of the above questions, you must complete the Foreign Student Questionnaire attached to the application.

7. Father's Name *Joe Doe*   8. Father's Occupation *Doctor*

9. Mother's Name *Jane Smith*   10. Mother's Occupation *Nurse*

11. If any member of your family has attended Pace University School of Law, please list their name and date of graduation.

   _____

List the name, address and home and business telephone numbers of a person through whom you can be reached

Jane Smith   *Same as above*   *(914) 422-2222*
Name   Address   Telephone #

_____
Name   Address   Telephone #

*If the program you have checked is closed at the time your application is processed, do you wish to be considered for the alternate division?
                                                            ☒ Yes ☐ No

12. Please complete the following summary of your academic history in chronological sequence. This form must be completed.

	Name of Institution	College Code Number (See LSAT/LSDAS registration materials.)	Location of school attended	Dates of attendance	Degree or expected degree	Date awarded or expected	Major field of study
Secondary School(s)	White Plains High School		White Plains NY	09/88		06/99	
College(s) and/or Universities	Pace University	2644	White Plains NY	09/92 06/94	BA		Accounting
Graduate and/or Law School(s)	Pace University	2644	White Plains NY	09/94 06/96	MBA		Accounting

13. Describe in an addendum, if you wish, any or all extracurricular or community activities which were important to you. Indicate your contribution to each activity. We are primarily concerned with those which demonstrate your leadership, communication, and creative thinking abilities as well as your initiative.

14. List any academic honors, awards, prizes or other recognition you have received _Who's Who Among American College Graduates, Alumni Academic Scholarship Program_

15. As an undergraduate, were you employed during the academic year? _Yes_

No. of hours per week: Fr. Year _0_   Soph. Year _10_   Jr. Year _20_   Sr. Year _20_

Position held: _Part-time - Office Assistant_

16. Please state your last four positions (paid or volunteer) of full or part-time employment, including summer employment. You may in addition to, or in place of, the following, submit a current resume. There cannot be any missing or unexplained time periods in our reviewing of items 12, 16, and the personal statement.

From	To	Position held	Name and address of employer	Reason for leaving
06/96	Present	Office Coordinator	Pepsico	N/A
09/94	05/96	Human Resources Assistant	IBM Corporation	Position at Pepsico
09/93	08/94	Office Assistant	Career Development Office - Pace Univ.	Graduated

17. Have you ever applied for admission to this law school? _NO_   If so, in what year and with what result? _____

Answer all of the following questions:

SAMPLE

Answer
Yes or No

Have you ever been enrolled (registered) in another law school?   18. ___No___
School Name_____ Dates of Attendance _____/_____/_____ to _____/_____/_____
_____ I am _____ I am not eligible to return to the above school. If not eligible, briefly state the reason(s)
why you are ineligible on a supplementary sheet.

Have you ever attended a Summer Conditional Admissions Program sponsored by a law school?   19. ___No___
School Name _____ Dates of Attendance _____/_____/_____ to _____/_____/_____

Has your college, university, graduate or professional school course been interrupted for one or more terms for any   20. ___No___
reason? (Interruptions between the end of one degree program and the beginning of another need not be explained.)

Are there any disciplinary charges pending against you?   21. ___No___

Have you ever been placed on academic probation during your college, university, graduate, or professional   22. ___No___
coursework?

Have you ever been placed on academic and or disciplinary probation for actions arising from allegations of   23. ___No___
academic dishonesty, plagiarism, cheating, during your college, university, graduate or professional coursework?

Have you ever been suspended or required to withdraw from any school or college for scholastic or other reasons?   24. ___No___

Have you ever been convicted of a criminal offense other than a minor traffic violation? (NOTE: Repeated moving   25. ___No___
violations, unpaid parking tickets, or driving while intoxicated or impaired may be viewed by some jurisdictions as
serious offenses.)

Are there any criminal charges pending against you?   26. ___No___

*Note: Admission to law school does not mean that you will meet the character and fitness requirements for
admission to the bar of any state. If you are concerned as to whether an event in your life will affect your eligibility
for a license to practice law you should discuss the matter with the Board of Bar Examiners in the state(s) where
you plan to practice.*

If you have ever served on full-time military active duty, was your discharge other than honorable?   27. ___No___

If your answer to any of questions 18 - 27 is "yes," please explain fully on a supplemental sheet.

28. Please indicate when you took (or plan to take) the Law School Admissions Test. Date(s) **02/01/98** Score(s) **155**

29. Ethnic Status (Optional): In order to advance the affirmative action plan of the Law School and in accordance with the national goal
of equal opportunity, please indicate your ethnic and/or racial background (E.E.O. categories). Please check one:
☐ African-American (non-Hispanic)   ☐ Other
☐ American Indian/Alaskan Native (Native American)   ☐ Hispanic (black)
☐ Asian/Pacific Islander   ☐ Hispanic (white)
☒ Caucasian/White (non-Hispanic)   ☐ Puerto Rican
☐ Chicano/Mexican

30. Will you be applying to the Council on Legal Education Opportunity (CLEO) program? *(see description in instructions)*
☐ Yes ☒ No

31. Two appraisals must be submitted on your behalf. Please list the names, titles and addresses of those persons from whom you have
requested an appraisal: PLEASE PRINT CLEARLY.
a. *Jim Burns*   b. *J. White*
   Professor   *Professor*
   Pace University   *Pace University*
   Bedford Rd.   *1 Martin Ave.*

(over)

32. Personal Statement:

On a separate sheet of paper, please complete the required statement as described in the instructions to applicants. The statement must be typed and double-spaced.

33. Please complete. Information regarding the status of my application may be released to the following individual(s). If this section is left blank, information will __not__ be released to anyone except the applicant. Final decisions are __not__ released over the telephone to anyone.

__No__ _____

       Name   *Relationship*

__No__ _____

       Name   *Relationship*

34. Did you meet a representative of Pace University School of Law? ☒ Yes ☐ No
If yes, indicate where _____

☒ LSAC Sponsored Law Forum at:
☒ New York   ☐ Chicago   ☐ Washington, D.C.
☐ Atlanta   ☐ Houston
☐ Boston   ☐ Los Angeles

35. If you are interested in information concerning a specific area of law, indicate below the area of interest:
☐ Certificate in Environmental Law   ☒ J.D./M.B.A.
☐ Certificate in Health Law   ☐ J.D./M.P.A.
☒ Certificate in International Law   __ Health Care
                                                                    __ Government

Please be sure that all of the Instructions to Applicants have been followed. An application will be considered only after it has been completed in full and the Office of Admissions has received all required documents.

I understand that, if I am admitted to the School of Law and register as a student, the School will retain this application and all supporting materials and may make them available to state bar character committees and I consent to such disclosure.

I certify that the information provided by me in this application is true and complete. From time of application through enrollment, I shall promptly advise the Office of Admissions of the School of Law __in writing__ of any change in any of the facts indicated in this application. I understand that matriculation and attendance at any other law school (from time of application through enrollment) would render any offer of admission from Pace University School of Law invalid.

I understand that notification of the application will have for denial or waiver, for dismissal from the School of Law. I further agree and authorize Pace University to publish, for public relations purposes, any photographs in which I appear.

I understand that my admission to Pace University is a privilege and not a right and I agree that my admission, if granted, my registration and continuance on the rolls and graduation are subject to all policies, rules, regulations and procedures set forth in the current bulletins, catalogs, and other publications and notices of Pace University and as they may be amended, and further, subject to the right of the authorities of Pace University to require my withdrawal for scholastic, disciplinary, or other reasons, under circumstances deemed sufficient by them.

_____   _____
    Signature of Applicant   *Date*

for the service. This service analyzes your transcript (you must have one sent to Law Services from each undergraduate institution you have attended) and submits a report of your undergraduate record along with your LSAT score and an unofficial copy of your transcript to the law schools you have indicated.

Send the transcript to Law Services once all your junior year courses have been completed. Typically, upward grade trends occur after the first year of college. Some law schools may even require fall grades in your senior year if a significant trend is noted.

The registration date for the LSAT should be made individually by each applicant. Since test preparation is essential, you should allow adequate time to properly prepare for the test. There are many commercial preparation courses, various books such as Barron's *How to Prepare for the LSAT*, as well as preparation materials through Law Services. (See also Chapters 10 and 11 of this Guide.)

You should be prepared the first time you sit for the exam; never enter the exam with the thought of it being a dry run. Since most law schools average repeated scores, multiple test scores can hurt your application.

THE WAITING PERIOD

When all the appropriate materials are filed with the admissions office, you begin a waiting period. The decision-making process takes time.

Once an application is received, the office of admissions opens a file on you, requests the LSDAS report, and, when all materials are received, reviews your application. The process may be held up if, for example, you have left blank questions on the application that were not marked "optional," or do not file a fee with the application, or do not sign the application form.

When you are notified that the file is complete and ready for review by the admissions committee, the process may take anywhere from two weeks to two months. Patience is essential; however, if you have not heard anything from a law school, do not hesitate to contact that school. You may be missing vital information, or your correspondence may have been delayed by the mail.

Every school employs a slightly different approach to making admissions decisions and notifying applicants of their acceptance. Many schools employ automatic acceptance and rejection categories for very high or low LSAT scores and GPAs. Most applicants fall somewhere in the middle, and their applications are reviewed more carefully by the admissions committee. Some schools may send out all acceptance letters at one time, while others notify applicants as decisions are made. Although the notification process may begin prior to January 1 of the academic year preceding admission, most applicants will hear from law schools between February and April. Later decisions may occur for students who are included on a waiting list, from which they are drawn if other accepted students decide not to matriculate at the school. Waiting list decisions may be made as late as August.

A few schools offer conditional summer programs for students with marginal credentials. Typically, the final decision for these applicants is made on the basis of their performance in the summer courses. Although the experience of attending such programs is good preparation for law school itself, ABA standards do not permit schools to give law school credit for preadmission work.

The admissions office at the schools to which you apply will be able to explain the idiosyncrasies of their procedures, and keep you advised on the progress of your application. Don't call them every day, however, because excessive phone calls actually slow down the admissions process. Use common sense in deciding whether to call for assistance and information.

THE FINAL DECISION

Once the admissions committee reaches a final decision, you must begin your decision-making process. Try to visit the law schools to which you have been accepted. (Please note that most schools will require a deposit no earlier than April but as early as two weeks after your offer of admission is made. Therefore, visiting schools should begin as early as the application process does, if possible.)

A visit might include attendance at a first year class, or a meeting with current students and/or a member of the faculty. You will not have to spend much time at a law school to get a feel for its atmosphere and personality.

Cost is always an issue, and you should recognize the need to submit the required financial aid forms in a timely manner. The submission of financial aid forms (Free Application for Federal Student Aid) does not have an impact on the admission decision. The filing of the appropriate forms should be completed at the time of application to the individual schools or as late as March 15. If all the appropriate financial aid materials have been submitted, a law school should be able to provide you with a financial aid package at the time of acceptance, allowing you to make an educated decision. (See Chapter 6 of this Guide for more information on financial aid.)

by Angela D'Agostino, Assistant Dean and Director of Admissions, Pace University School of Law, White Plains, NY.

Your Chances of Law School Admission

A PROFILE OF RECENT FIRST-YEAR LAW STUDENTS

The table in this section provides basic admissions statistics for the law schools that have been approved by the American Bar Association. All these schools offer the J.D. degree. The information has been compiled from the most recent available information received from schools. If you compare your own GPA and your LSAT score and percentile with those of students recently admitted, and if you note the number of students who applied and the number who were accepted, you will be able to get an idea of your chances of admission to any given law school.

Bear in mind that many law schools take into account factors other than strictly academic qualifications. These are discussed in the profiles of the individual schools.

A blank cell on the chart means that information was not available.

LAW SCHOOL	ACADEMIC STATISTICS				ADMISSION STATISTICS		
	Median LSAT Percentile of Enrolled	Median LSAT Score of Enrolled	Lowest LSAT Percentile of Accepted	Median GPA (4.0 scale) of Enrolled	Total Applicants	Applicants Accepted	Applicants Enrolled
American University (Washington College of Law) 4801 Massachusetts Avenue, N.W. Washington, DC 20016-8186 202-274-4101 Fax: 202-274-4107 wcladmit@wcl.american.edu	70	156		3.4	5093	2117	523
Arizona State University (College of Law/Armstrong Hall) Box 877906 Tempe, AZ 85287-7906 602-965-1474 Fax: 602-965-5550 wanda.decrow@asu.edu	74	157		3.4	1815	441	163
Baylor University (School of Law) P.O. Box 97288 Waco, TX 76798-7288 254-710-1911 Fax: 254-710-2316 becky-beck@baylor.edu	82	157	24	3.4	1247	492	161
Boston College (Law School) 885 Centre Street Newton, MA 02459 617-552-4351 Fax: 617-552-2917 bclawadm@bc.edu	88	162		3.5	5446	1445	273
Boston University (School of Law) 765 Commonwealth Avenue Boston, MA 02215 617-353-3100 bulawadm@bu.edu	84	161		3.4	4885	1620	302
Brigham Young University (J. Reuben Clark Law School) 342 JRCB Brigham Young University Provo, UT 84602 801-378-4277 Fax: 801-378-5897 wilcock@lawgate.byu.edu	83	160	23	3.6	663	246	152
Brooklyn Law School 250 Joralemon Street Brooklyn, NY 11201 718-780-7906 Fax: 718-780-0395 admitq@brooklaw.edu	74	157	37	3.3	3158	1442	515
California Western School of Law 225 Cedar Street San Diego, CA 92101-3046 619-525-1401 Fax: 619-615-1401 rbriscoe@cwsl.edu		150	25		1996	1252	275
Campbell University (Norman Adrian Wiggins School of Law) P.O. Box 158 Buies Creek, NC 27506 910-893-1754 Fax: 910-893-1780 culaw@webster.campbell.edu	64	154		3.2	634	209	112

LAW SCHOOL	ACADEMIC STATISTICS				ADMISSION STATISTICS		
	Median LSAT Percentile of Enrolled	Median LSAT Score of Enrolled	Lowest LSAT Percentile of Accepted	Median GPA (4.0 scale) of Enrolled	Total Applicants	Applicants Accepted	Applicants Enrolled
Capital University (Law School) 303 East Broad Street Columbus, OH 43215-3200 614-236-6500 Fax: 614-236-6972 admissions@law.capital.edu	45	150	36	3.1	922	591	259
Case Western Reserve University (School of Law) 11075 East Boulevard Cleveland, OH 44106 216-368-3600 Fax: 216-368-6144 lawadmissions@po.cwru.edu or lawmoney@po.cwru.edu	67	156		3.2	1411	883	213
Catholic University of America (Columbus School of Law) Cardinal Station Washington, DC 20064 (202) 319-5151 Fax: (202) 319-6285		155	23	3.1	2165	1033	314
Catholic University of Puerto Rico (School of Law) Avenida Las Americas-Station 6 Ponce, PR 00732 809-841-2000	13			2.9			
Chapman University (School of Law) One University Drive Orange, CA 92866 714-628-2500 Fax: 714-628-2501 misles@chapman.edu	64	154	26	3	607	266	87
City University of New York (City University of New York School of Law at Queens College) 65-21 Main Street Flushing, NY 11367-1300 718-340-4210 Fax: 718-340-4372 admissions@maclaw.law.cuny.edu					1543	575	175
Cleveland State University (Cleveland-Marshall College of Law) 1801 Euclid Avenue Cleveland, OH 44115 216-687-2304 Fax: 216-687-6881	50	150	5	3	1220	617	254
College of William and Mary (William and Mary Law School) P.O. Box 8795 Williamsburg, VA 23187-8795 757-221-3785 Fax: 757-221-3261 lawadm@facstaff.wm.edu	90	163	41	3.4	2267	718	201
Columbia University (School of Law) 435 West 116th Street New York, NY 10027 212-854-2670 Fax: 212-854-1109	98	169		3.6	6137		367

LAW SCHOOL	ACADEMIC STATISTICS				ADMISSION STATISTICS		
	Median LSAT Percentile of Enrolled	Median LSAT Score of Enrolled	Lowest LSAT Percentile of Accepted	Median GPA (4.0 scale) of Enrolled	Total Applicants	Applicants Accepted	Applicants Enrolled
Cornell University (Law School) Myron Taylor Hall Ithaca, NY 14853 607-255-5141 Fax: 607-255-7193	94	165		3.6	3219		183
Creighton University (School of Law) 2500 California Plaza Omaha, NE 68178 402-280-2872 Fax: 402-280-3161 admit@culaw.creighton.edu	52	151	18	3.1	718	481	159
De Paul University (College of Law) 25 East Jackson Boulevard Chicago, IL 60604 312-362-6831 lawinfo@wppost.depaul.edu	60	154	23	3.2	2074	1274	363
Drake University (Law School) 2507 University Avenue Des Moines, IA 50311 515-271-1990 lawadmit@drake.edu	52	151	8	3.2	639	428	123
Duke University (School of Law) Science and Towerview Drive, Box 90393 Durham, NC 27708 919-613-7020 Fax: 919-613-7257 admissions@law.duke.edu		165		3.5	3418		236
Duquesne University (School of Law) 900 Locust Street, Hanley Hall Pittsburgh, PA 15282 412-396-6296 campion@duq.edu	60			3.2			240
Emory University (School of Law) Gambrell Hall Atlanta, GA 30322 404-727-6801 Fax: 404-727-2477 jbalej@law.emory.edu	87	161	50	3.4	2773	985	190
Florida Coastal School of Law 7555 Beach Boulevard Jacksonville, FL 32216 904-680-7710 Fax: 904-680-7776 admissions@fcsl.edu	50	150	15	2.9	1036	399	195
Florida State University (College of Law) 425 W. Jefferson St. Tallahassee, FL 32306-1601 850-644-3787 Fax: 850-644-7284 admissions@law.fsu.edu	68	155		3.3	1877	726	233
Fordham University (School of Law) 140 West 62nd Street New York, NY 10023 212-626-6810	90	164	30	3.4	4866	1285	463

LAW SCHOOL	ACADEMIC STATISTICS				ADMISSION STATISTICS		
	Median LSAT Percentile of Enrolled	Median LSAT Score of Enrolled	Lowest LSAT Percentile of Accepted	Median GPA (4.0 scale) of Enrolled	Total Applicants	Applicants Accepted	Applicants Enrolled
Franklin Pierce Law Center 2 White Street Concord, NH 03301 603-228-9217 Fax: 603-228-1074 L.admissions@fplc.edu		150	8	3	790	481	128
George Mason University (School of Law) 3401 North Fairfax Drive Arlington, VA 22201-4498 703-993-8010 Fax: 703-993-8260 arichar5@gmu.edu	81	159		3.2	2006	667	212
George Washington University (Law School) 2000 H Street, N.W. Washington, DC 20052 202-739-0648 jd@main.n/c.gwu.edu	88	162	37	3.5	7126	2048	469
Georgetown University (Law Center) 600 New Jersey Avenue, N.W. Washington, DC 20001 202-662-9010 admis@law.georgetown.edu	95	166	50	3.6	7873	2383	601
Georgia State University (College of Law) P.O. Box 4037 Atlanta, GA 30302-4037 404-651-2096 Fax: 404-651-2096 cjjackson@gsu.edu	74	157	33	3.2	1705	481	202
Golden Gate University (School of Law) 536 Mission Street San Francisco, CA 94105-2968 415-442-6630	48	150		3	1585	923	179
Gonzaga University (School of Law) Box 3528 Spokane, WA 99220-3528 509-323-5532 Fax: 509-323-5710 admissions@lawschool.gonzaga.edu	44	149		3.2	826	576	
Hamline University (School of Law) 1536 Hewitt Avenue St. Paul, MN 55104-1284 651-523-2461 Fax: 651-523-3064 lawadm@gw.hamline.edu	56	152	11	3.2	671	467	184
Harvard University (Harvard Law School) Cambridge, MA 02138 617-495-3109 Fax: 617-495-1110 jdadmiss@law.harvard.edu		170		3.8	5818	845	556
Hofstra University (School of Law) 121 Hofstra University Hempstead, NY 11549 516-463-5916 Fax: 516-463-6264 lawpts@hofstra.edu	72	156	12	3.3	1867	823	291

LAW SCHOOL	ACADEMIC STATISTICS				ADMISSION STATISTICS		
	Median LSAT Percentile of Enrolled	Median LSAT Score of Enrolled	Lowest LSAT Percentile of Accepted	Median GPA (4.0 scale) of Enrolled	Total Applicants	Applicants Accepted	Applicants Enrolled
Howard University (Howard University) 2900 Van Ness Street, N.W. Washington, DC 20008 202-806-8008 Fax: 202-806-8162 admissions@law.howard.edu	50	151		2.9	1225	372	140
Illinois Institute of Technology (Chicago-Kent College of Law) 565 West Adams Street Chicago, IL 60661 312-906-5020 admit@kentlaw.edu	64	154	33	3.2	2160	1299	369
Indiana University-Purdue University (Indiana University School of Law-Indianapolis) 735 West New York Street Indianapolis, IN 46202-5194 317-274-2459 Fax: 317-274-3955 khmiller@iupui.edu	62	155	6	3.2	1078	519	263
Indiana University/Bloomington (School of Law) 211 S. Indiana Avenue Bloomington, IN 47405-1001 812-855-4765 Fax: 812-855-0555 lawadmis@indiana.edu	84	160		3.4	1493	692	203
Inter-American University of Puerto Rico (School of Law) P.O. Box 70351 San Juan, PR 00936-8351 809-751-1912, ext. 2013	13		2	3.1			
John Marshall Law School 315 South Plymouth Court Chicago, IL 60604 312-987-1406 Fax: 312-427-5136 admission@jmls.edu		150		3.4	1543	964	255
Lewis and Clark College (Northwestern School of Law) 10015 Southwest Terwilliger Boulevard Portland, OR 97219 503-768-6613 Fax: 503-768-6671 lawadmss@lclark.edu	78	158	21	3.2	1384	839	200
Louisiana State University (Paul M. Hebert Law Center) Baton Rouge, LA 70803 225-388-8646 Fax: 225-388-8647 bloup@lsu.edu	53	153	6	3.3	847	509	247
Loyola Marymount University (Loyola Law School) 919 S. Albany Street Los Angeles, CA 90015 213-736-1180 admissions@lls.edu	75	157	30	3.3	2897	1240	475

LAW SCHOOL	ACADEMIC STATISTICS				ADMISSION STATISTICS		
	Median LSAT Percentile of Enrolled	Median LSAT Score of Enrolled	Lowest LSAT Percentile of Accepted	Median GPA (4.0 scale) of Enrolled	Total Applicants	Applicants Accepted	Applicants Enrolled
Loyola University - New Orleans (School of Law) 7214 St. Charles Avenue New Orleans, LA 70118 504-861-5575 Fax: 504-861-5772 ladmit@loyno.edu	55	152	15	2.9	1321	725	218
Loyola University Chicago (School of Law) One East Pearson Street Chicago, IL 60611 312-915-7170 Fax: 312-915-7201 law-admissions@luc.edu	78	158	40	3.3	2164	924	231
Marquette University (Law School) Office of Admissions, Sensenbrenner Hall, P.O. Box 1881 Milwaukee, WI 53201-1881 414-288-6767 Fax: 414-288-0676 law.admission@marquette.edu	65	154		3.1	811		198
Mercer University (Walter F. George School of Law) 1021 Georgia Ave. Macon, GA 31201 912-301-2605 Fax: 912-301-2989 Sutton_me@mercer.edu		152	25	3.2	958	470	154
Michigan State University (Detroit College of Law) 316 Law College Bldg. East Lansing, MI 48824-1300 517-432-0222 Fax: 517-432-0098 heatleya@pilot.msu.edu	50	152	20	3.1	1052	600	213
Mississippi College (School of Law) 151 E. Griffith Street Jackson, MS 39201 601-925-7150 pevans@mc.edu	50			3	717	401	143
New England School of Law 154 Stuart Street Boston, MA 02116 617-422-7210 Fax: 617-422-7200 admit@admin.nesi.edu					2097	1521	337
New York Law School 57 Worth Street New York, NY 10013-2960 212-431-2888 Fax: 212-966-1522 admissions@nyls.edu		154		3.1	4194	348	470
New York University (School of Law) 110 West Third Street New York, NY 10012 212-998-6060 Fax: 212-995-4527	98	169		3.6	6481		416

LAW SCHOOL	ACADEMIC STATISTICS				ADMISSION STATISTICS		
	Median LSAT Percentile of Enrolled	Median LSAT Score of Enrolled	Lowest LSAT Percentile of Accepted	Median GPA (4.0 scale) of Enrolled	Total Applicants	Applicants Accepted	Applicants Enrolled
North Carolina Central University (School of Law) 1512 S. Alston Avenue Durham, NC 27707 919-560-6333 Fax: 919-560-6339 jfaucett@wpo.nccu.edu	50	148	143	3.1	1080	258	116
Northeastern University (School of Law) 400 Huntington Avenue Boston, MA 02115 617-373-2395 Fax: 617-373-8865 pbauer@slaw.neu.edu	74	157	10	3.2	1922	715	195
Northern Illinois University (College of Law) Swen Parson Hall De Kalb, IL 60115 815-753-1420 Fax: 815-753-4501 lawadm@niu.edu	60	153		3	836	381	99
Northern Kentucky University (Salmon P. Chase College of Law) Louie B. Nunn Hall Highland Heights, KY 41099 606-572-6476 Fax: 606-572-6081 brayg@nku.edu	56	152	18	3.1	620	275	111
Northwestern University (School of Law) 357 East Chicago Avenue Chicago, IL 60611 312-503-8465 Fax: 312-503-0178 nubwadm@nwu.edu	96	167	45	3.5	4103	744	205
Nova Southeastern University (Shepard Broad Law Center) 3305 College Avenue Fort Lauderdale, FL 33314-7721 954-262-6117 Fax: 954-262-3844 admission@nsu.law.nova.edu	37	147	3	2.8	1416	785	334
Ohio Northern University (Claude W. Pettit College of Law) 525 South Main Street Ada, OH 45810 419-772-2211 Fax: 419-772-1487 g-keener@onu.edu			8	2.8	1115	546	108
Ohio State University (College of Law) 55 West 12th Avenue, John Deaver Drinko Hall Columbus, OH 43210-1391 614-292-8810 Fax: 614-292-1383 roboski.1@osu.edu	74	157		3.6	1482	585	214
Oklahoma City University (School of Law) 2501 North Blackwelder Oklahoma City, OK 73106-1493 405-521-5354 Fax: 405-521-5802 lawadmit@okcu.edu	32	145	10	2.9	878	740	190

LAW SCHOOL	ACADEMIC STATISTICS				ADMISSION STATISTICS		
	Median LSAT Percentile of Enrolled	Median LSAT Score of Enrolled	Lowest LSAT Percentile of Accepted	Median GPA (4.0 scale) of Enrolled	Total Applicants	Applicants Accepted	Applicants Enrolled
Pace University (School of Law) 78 North Broadway White Plains, NY 10603 914-422-4010 Fax: 914-422-4248 adagostino@genesis.law.pace.edu	52	151	21	3.2	1795	871	254
Pennsylvania State University (Dickinson School of Law) 150 South College Street Carlisle, PA 17013 717-240-5207 Fax: 717-241-3503 dsladmit@psu.edu	55	152	17	3.2	1320	691	188
Pepperdine University (School of Law) 24255 Pacific Coast Highway Malibu, CA 90263 310-456-4631 Fax: 310-317-7668 soladmis@pepperdine.edu	71	156		3.3	2520	1200	234
Quinnipiac College (School of Law) 275 Mt. Carmel Avenue Hamden, CT 06518-1948 203-287-3400 Fax: 203-287-3339 ladm@quinnipiac.edu		148	9	3	2004	1044	258
Regent University (School of Law) 1000 Regent University Drive Virginia Beach, VA 23464-9800 757-226-4584 Fax: 757-226-4139 lawschool@regent.edu	45	148	18	3.1	565	368	215
Roger Williams University (School of Law) Ten Metacom Avenue Bristol, RI 02809-5171 401-254-4555 Fax: 401-254-4516 admissions@rwulaw.rwu.edu	40	148	8	3	661	396	148
Rutgers University/Newark (School of Law) S.I. Newhouse Center for Law and Justice, 15 Washington St. Newark, NJ 07102 973-353-5557/5554 Fax: 973-353-1445		157		3.3	2335	765	210
Rutgers, The State University **of New Jersey** (School of Law-Camden) Fifth and Penn Streets Camden, NJ 08102 609-225-6102 Fax: 609-225-6537	74	157	41	3.2	1744	624	206
Saint John's University (School of Law) 8000 Utopia Parkway Jamaica, NY 11439 718-990-6611/6612 Fax: 718-990-2526 rsvp@sjulaw.stjohns.edu	66	154		3	2595	1198	362

LAW SCHOOL	ACADEMIC STATISTICS				ADMISSION STATISTICS		
	Median LSAT Percentile of Enrolled	Median LSAT Score of Enrolled	Lowest LSAT Percentile of Accepted	Median GPA (4.0 scale) of Enrolled	Total Applicants	Applicants Accepted	Applicants Enrolled
Saint Louis University (School of Law) 3700 Lindell Boulevard St. Louis, MO 63108 314-977-2800 admissions@law.slu.edu	64	154	11	3.3	1046	597	250
Saint Mary's University (School of Law) One Camino Santa Maria San Antonio, TX 78228-8601 210-436-3523 Fax: 210-431-4202	46		25	3	1046	603	263
Samford University (Cumberland School of Law) 800 Lakeshore Drive Birmingham, AL 35229 205-726-2702 Fax: 205-726-2673 lawadmissions@samford.edu	52	151	17	3	838	445	190
Santa Clara University (School of Law) 500 El Camino Real Santa Clara, CA 95053 408-554-4800 Fax: 408-554-7897 lawadmission@scu.edu	158	153		3.4	2451	1338	297
Seattle University (School of Law) 900 Broadway Seattle, WA 98122-4340 206-398-4200 Fax: 206-398-4058 lawadmis@seattleu.edu	71	156	15	3.2	1212	769	310
Seton Hall University (School of Law) One Newark Center Newark, NJ 07102-5210 973-642-8747 Fax: 973-642-8876 admitme@shu.edu	65	155	152	3.2	2218	965	384
South Texas College of Law 1303 San Jacinto Street Houston, TX 77002-7000 713-646-1810 Fax: 713-646-2929 acramer@stcl.edu	43	149	15	2.9	1760	1152	515
Southern Illinois University (School of Law) Lesar Law Building, Mail Code 6804 Carbondale, IL 62901-6804 618-453-8767 Fax: 618-453-8769 lawadmit@siu.edu	52	151	26	3.3	669	387	143
Southern Methodist University (School of Law) Office of Admissions, P.O. Box 750110 Dallas, TX 75275-0110 214-768-2550 Fax: 214-768-2549	75	157		3.3			
Southern University and A & M College (Law Center) Post Office Box 9294 Baton Rouge, LA 70813 225-771-5340 Fax: 225-771-2121		146		2.6	589	198	138

LAW SCHOOL	ACADEMIC STATISTICS				ADMISSION STATISTICS		
	Median LSAT Percentile of Enrolled	Median LSAT Score of Enrolled	Lowest LSAT Percentile of Accepted	Median GPA (4.0 scale) of Enrolled	Total Applicants	Applicants Accepted	Applicants Enrolled
Southwestern University (School of Law) 675 South Westmoreland Avenue Los Angeles, CA 90005-3992 213-738-6717 Fax: 213-383-1688 admissions@swlaw.edu	65		29	3.2	1975	1067	353
St. Thomas University (School of Law) 16400 N.W. 32nd Avenue Miami, FL 33054 305-623-2310 lamy@stu.edu	33	145	15	2.7	1524	966	217
Stanford University (Stanford Law School) Crown Quadrangle Stanford, CA 94305-8610 650-723-4985 Fax: 650-723-0838 law.admissions@forsythe.stanford.edu/	96	167		3.7	3824	474	178
State University of New York at Buffalo (University at Buffalo Law School) O'Brian Hall Buffalo, NY 14260 716-645-2907 Fax: 716-645-5940 coxublaw@buffalo.edu	60	153	6	3.2	844	510	232
Stetson University (College of Law) 1401 61st Street South St. Petersburg, FL 33707 727-562-7802 Fax: 727-343-0136 lawadmit@hermes.law.stetson.edu		152		3.4	1943	798	240
Suffolk University (Law School) 120 Tremont Street Boston, MA 02108-4977 617-573-8144 Fax: 617-573-1367	54	153	32	3.2	2100		550
Syracuse University (College of Law) Office of Admissions and Financial Aid Syracuse, NY 13244-1030 315-443-1962 Fax: 315-443-9568	52	151		3.3	1945		265
Temple University (James E. Beasley School of Law) 1719 N. Broad Street Philadelphia, PA 19122 215-204-8925 Fax: 215-204-1185 lawadmis@blue.temple.edu	68	155	21	3.2	2691	1108	343
Texas Southern University (Thurgood Marshall School of Law) 3100 Cleburne Avenue Houston, TX 77004 713-313-7114 Fax: 713-313-1049 cgardner@tsulaw.edu		142		2.7	952	417	322

LAW SCHOOL	ACADEMIC STATISTICS				ADMISSION STATISTICS		
	Median LSAT Percentile of Enrolled	Median LSAT Score of Enrolled	Lowest LSAT Percentile of Accepted	Median GPA (4.0 scale) of Enrolled	Total Applicants	Applicants Accepted	Applicants Enrolled
Texas Tech University (School of Law) 1802 Hartford Lubbock, TX 79409 806-742-3985 Fax: 806-742-1629 xydaw@ttacs.ttu.edu	67	155	17	3.4	1092	536	199
Texas Wesleyan University (School of Law) 1515 Commerce Street Fort Worth, TX 76102 817-212-4040 Fax: 817-212-4002 law-admissions@law.txwes.edu	50	150		3.1	942	238	223
Thomas Jefferson School of Law 2121 San Diego Avenue San Diego, CA 92110 619-297-9700 Fax: 619-294-4713 adm@tjsl.edu		149	9	2.8	1591	1119	243
Thomas M. Cooley Law School 300 South Capitol Avenue Lansing, MI 48901 517-371-5140 Fax: 517-334-5718 admissions@cooley.edu	23	143	6	2.9	2775	2158	769
Touro College (Jacob D. Fuchsberg Law Center) 300 Nassau Road Huntington, NY 11743 631-421-2244 ext. 312 Fax: 631-421-9708 admissions@tourolaw.edu			18		1912	858	219
Tulane University (Law School) Weinmann Hall, 6329 Freret Street New Orleans, LA 70118 504-865-5930 Fax: 504-865-6710 admissions@law.tulane.edu	83	159	25	3.3	2805	1295	323
Union University (Albany Law School) 80 New Scotland Avenue Albany, NY 12208 518-445-2326 Fax: 518-445-2369 admissions@mail.als.edu	47	150	11	3.1	1455	851	254
University of Akron (School of Law) Corner Wolf Ledges and University Avenue Akron, OH 44325-2901 330-972-7331 Fax: 330-258-2343 lawadmissions@uakron.edu	52	151	13	3.2	1149	492	202
University of Alabama (School of Law) Box 870382 Tuscaloosa, AL 35487-0382 205-348-5440 Fax: 205-348-3917 admissions@law.ua.edu	78	158		3.3	621	310	184

LAW SCHOOL	ACADEMIC STATISTICS				ADMISSION STATISTICS		
	Median LSAT Percentile of Enrolled	Median LSAT Score of Enrolled	Lowest LSAT Percentile of Accepted	Median GPA (4.0 scale) of Enrolled	Total Applicants	Applicants Accepted	Applicants Enrolled
University of Arizona **(James E. Rogers College of Law)** Mountain and Speedway P.O. Box 210176 Tucson, AZ 85721-0176 520-621-3477 Fax: 520-621-9140 admissions@nt.law.arizona.edu	85	160	36	3.4	1830	410	150
University of Arkansas **(School of Law)** Robert A. Leflar Law Center, Waterman Hall Fayetteville, AR 72701 501-575-3102		152		3.3	622	338	161
University of Arkansas at Little Rock **(School of Law)** 1201 McAlmont Street Little Rock, AR 72202-5142 501-324-9439 Fax: 501-324-9433	60	153	23	3.3	461	234	109
University of Baltimore **(School of Law)** 1420 North Charles Street Baltimore, MD 21201-5779 410-837-4459 Fax: 410-837-4450 lwadmiss@ubmail.ubalt.edu		149	15	2.9	1473	892	305
University of California **(Hastings College of the Law)** 200 McAllister Street San Francisco, CA 94102 415-565-4623 Fax: 415-565-4863 admiss@uchastings.edu	88	162	23	3.4	3972	1329	416
University of California at Berkeley **(Boalt Hall)** 5 Boalt Hall Berkeley, CA 94720 510-642-2274 Fax: 510-643-6222 admissions@law.berkeley.edu	93	165	37	3.8	4717	867	269
University of California **at Los Angeles** **(School of Law)** P.O. Box 951445 Los Angeles, CA 90095-1445 310-825-2080 Fax: 310-825-9450 admissions@law.ucla.edu	92	164	36	3.7	4721	907	286
University of California, Davis **(School of Law)** King Hall - 400 Mrak Hall Drive Davis, CA 95616-5201 530-752-6477 lawadmissions@ucdavis.edu	81	160	30	3.4	2290	796	161
University of Chicago **(Law School)** 1111 East 60th Street Chicago, IL 60637 773-702-9484 Fax: 773-834-0942 admissions@law.uchicago.edu	97	169		3.7	2972	883	182

LAW SCHOOL	ACADEMIC STATISTICS				ADMISSION STATISTICS		
	Median LSAT Percentile of Enrolled	Median LSAT Score of Enrolled	Lowest LSAT Percentile of Accepted	Median GPA (4.0 scale) of Enrolled	Total Applicants	Applicants Accepted	Applicants Enrolled
University of Cincinnati (College of Law) P.O. Box 210040 Cincinnati, OH 45221-0040 513-556-6805 Admissions@law.uc.edu	84	159	20	3.5	953	416	128
University of Colorado (School of Law) Campus Box 403 Boulder, CO 80309-0403 303-492-7203	86	161	23	3.5	1836	571	168
University of Connecticut (School of Law) 55 Elizabeth Street Hartford, CT 06105 860-570-5159 Fax: 860-570-5153 admit@law.uconn.edu	80	159		3.3	1939	625	184
University of Dayton (School of Law) 300 College Park Dayton, OH 45469-2760 937-229-3555 Fax: 937-229-4194 lawinfo@udayton.edu	56	152	13	3.1	1190	762	167
University of Denver (College of Law) 7039 E. 18th Avenue Denver, CO 80220 303-871-6135 Fax: 303-871-6100	58	154	33	3.2	1751	1161	332
University of Detroit Mercy (School of Law) 651 East Jefferson Avenue Detroit, MI 48226 313-596-0264 Fax: 313-596-0280 udmlawao@udmercy.edu	37	147	15	3	564	312	96
University of Florida (College of Law) 325 Holland Hall P.O. Box 117622 Gainesville, FL 32611-7622 352-392-2087 Fax: 352-392-2087 patrick@law.ufl.edu	75	157		3.5	2328	773	400
University of Georgia (School of Law) Hirsch Hall, 225 Herty Drive Athens, GA 30602-6012 706-542-7060	86	161	20	3.6	1680	532	227
University of Hawaii-Manoa (William S. Richardson School of Law) 2515 Dole Street Honolulu, HI 96822 808-956-7966 Fax: 808-956-3813 lawadm@hawaii.edu	79	159	21	3.4	518	150	77
University of Houston (Law Center) Office of Admissions Houston, TX 77204-6391 713-743-1070 Fax: 713-743-2194 admission@www.law.uh.edu	73	158	18	3.3	2441	881	289

LAW SCHOOL	ACADEMIC STATISTICS				ADMISSION STATISTICS		
	Median LSAT Percentile of Enrolled	Median LSAT Score of Enrolled	Lowest LSAT Percentile of Accepted	Median GPA (4.0 scale) of Enrolled	Total Applicants	Applicants Accepted	Applicants Enrolled
University of Idaho **(College of Law)** P.O. Box 442321 Moscow, ID 83844-2321 208-885-6423 Fax: 208-885-5709 adewitt@uidaho.edu	60	153	23	3.3	479	307	100
University of Illinois **(College of Law)** 504 East Pennsylvania Avenue Champaign, IL 61820 217-244-6415 Fax: 217-244-1478	86	161	33	3.4	1606	609	209
University of Iowa **(College of Law)** 276 Boyd Law Building, Melrose at Byington Street Iowa City, IA 52242 319-335-9095 or 319-335-9142 Fax: 319-335-9019 law-admissions@uiowa.edu	78	158		3.5	1119	537	227
University of Kansas **(School of Law)** 205 Green Hall Lawrence, KS 66045 785-864-4378 Fax: 785-864-5054 lindeman@law.wpo.ukans.edu	69	154	20	3.3			
University of Kentucky **(College of Law)** 209 Law Building Lexington, KY 40506-0048 606-257-7938 dbakert@pop.uky.edu	78	158	33	3.5	843	320	124
University of Louisville **(Louis D. Brandeis School of Law)** University of Louisville Belknap Campus-Wilson W. Wyatt Hall Louisville, KY 40292 502-852-6364 Fax: 502-852-0862 charlene.olivia@louisville.edu	74	157	27	3.4	820	290	125
University of Maine **(School of Law)** 246 Deering Avenue Portland, ME 04102 207-780-4341		154	15	3.1	487	273	77
University of Maryland **(School of Law)** 515 West Lombard Street Baltimore, MD 21201 410-706-3492 Fax: 410-706-4045 admissions@law.umaryland.edu	71	156	10	3.4	2469	984	301
University of Memphis **(Cecil C. Humphreys School of Law)** Campus Box 526513 Memphis, TN 38152-6513 901-678-2073 Fax: 901-678-5210 uofmlaw@profnet.law.memphis.edu	64	154	15	3.2	897	372	139

LAW SCHOOL	ACADEMIC STATISTICS				ADMISSION STATISTICS		
	Median LSAT Percentile of Enrolled	Median LSAT Score of Enrolled	Lowest LSAT Percentile of Accepted	Median GPA (4.0 scale) of Enrolled	Total Applicants	Applicants Accepted	Applicants Enrolled
University of Miami (School of Law) P.O. Box 248087, 1311 Miller Drive Coral Gables, FL 33124-8087 305-284-2523 admissions@law.miami.edu	63	154	13	3.2	2430	1389	435
University of Michigan (Law School) 625 South State Street Ann Arbor, MI 48109-1215 313-764-0537	93	165	40	3.6	3335	1215	343
University of Minnesota (Law School) 229 19th Avenue S., Office of Admissions Minneapolis, MN 55455 612-625-3487 Fax: 612-626-1874	89	162	40	3.6	1773	674	210
University of Mississippi (School of Law) Lamar Hall Oxford, MS 38677 601-915-6910 Fax: 601-915-1289 bvinson@olemiss.edu	60	153	7	3	1122	469	194
University of Missouri-Columbia (School of Law) 103 Hulston Hall Columbia, MO 65211 573-882-6042 Fax: 573-882-9625 umclawadmissions@missouri.edu	62	155	28	3.3	792	445	177
University of Missouri-Kansas City (School of Law) 500 East 52nd Street Kansas City, MO 64110-2499 816-235-1644 Fax: 816-235-5276 klosterman@umkc.edu	52	151	23	3.2	667	386	165
University of Montana (School of Law) Missoula, MT 59812 406-243-2698 lawadmis@selway.umt.edu	60	153	3	3.2	352	235	73
University of Nebraska (College of Law) P.O. Box 830902 Lincoln, NE 68583-0902 402-472-2161 Fax: 402-472-5185 lawadm@unlinfo.unl.edu	60	153	12	4	530	320	133
University of New Mexico (School of Law) 1117 Stanford Drive N.E. Albuquerque, NM 87131-1431 505-277-5072 Fax: 505-277-9958		155		3.2	736	256	120
University of North Carolina at Chapel Hill (School of Law) Campus Box 3380, 101 Van Hecke-Wettach Hall Chapel Hill, NC 27599-3380 919-962-5109 Fax: 919-843-7939 law_admission@unc.edu		160	24	3.6	2481	621	237

LAW SCHOOL	ACADEMIC STATISTICS				ADMISSION STATISTICS		
	Median LSAT Percentile of Enrolled	Median LSAT Score of Enrolled	Lowest LSAT Percentile of Accepted	Median GPA (4.0 scale) of Enrolled	Total Applicants	Applicants Accepted	Applicants Enrolled
University of North Dakota (School of Law) Box 9003 Grand Forks, ND 58202 701-777-2104 Fax: 701-777-2217 linda.kohoutek@thor.law.und.nodak.edu		150	11	3.3	239	129	64
University of Notre Dame (Notre Dame Law School) P.O. Box 959 Notre Dame, IN 46556-0959 219-631-6626 Fax: 219-631-3980 law.bulletin.1@nd.edu	90	163	42	3.4	1869	552	184
University of Oklahoma (College of Law) 300 Timberdell Road Norman, OK 73019 405-325-4726 Fax: 405-325-0502 kmadden@ou.edu	64	154	64	3.4	605	295	187
University of Oregon (School of Law, William W. Knight Law Center) 1515 Agate Street Eugene, OR 97403-1221 541-346-1553 Fax: 541-346-3984 bmcolure@law.uoregon.edu		156	17	3.5	1043	630	177
University of Pennsylvania (Law School) 3400 Chestnut Street Philadelphia, PA 19104-6204 215-898-7400 admissions@oyez.law.upenn.edu	95	166	21	3.6	3422	999	249
University of Pittsburgh (School of Law) 3900 Forbes Avenue Pittsburgh, PA 15260 412-648-1412 Fax: 412-648-2647 admissions@law.pitt.edu	64	154		3.2	1220	765	263
University of Puerto Rico (School of Law) P.O. Box 23349, UPR Station Rio Piedras, PR 00931 787-764-1655 Fax: 787-764-2675	34	146	4	3.6	719	180	168
University of Richmond (The T.C. Williams School of Law) University of Richmond, VA 23173 804-289-8189 admissions@uofrlaw.richmond.edu	74	157		3.2	1246	543	156
University of San Diego (School of Law) 5998 Alcala Park San Diego, CA 92110 619-260-4528 Fax: 619-260-2218 jdinfo@acusd.edu	84	160		3.2	2935		334

LAW SCHOOL	ACADEMIC STATISTICS				ADMISSION STATISTICS		
	Median LSAT Percentile of Enrolled	Median LSAT Score of Enrolled	Lowest LSAT Percentile of Accepted	Median GPA (4.0 scale) of Enrolled	Total Applicants	Applicants Accepted	Applicants Enrolled
University of San Francisco (School of Law) 2130 Fulton Street San Francisco, CA 94117-1080 415-422-6586 Fax: 415-422-6433	68	155		3.2	2445	1148	228
University of South Carolina (School of Law) Main and Greene Streets Columbia, SC 29208 803-777-6605 Fax: 803-777-7751 usclaw@law.law.sc.edu	75	155		3.2	1195	425	223
University of South Dakota (School of Law) 414 East Clark Street Vermillion, SD 57069-2390 605-677-5443 Fax: 605-677-5417 lawreq@usd.edu	56	152	5	3.3	239	116	45
University of Southern California (Law School) Los Angeles, CA 90089-0071 213-740-7331	92	164		3.5	3878	869	199
University of Tennessee (College of Law) 1505 W. Cumblerland Avenue Knoxville, TN 37996-1810 865-974-4131 Fax: 865-974-1572 lawadmit@libra.law.utk.edu	70	156	20	3.5	1049	387	168
University of Texas at Austin (School of Law) 727 East Dean Keeton Street Austin, TX 78705 512-232-1200 Fax: 512-471-6988	88		30		3284	1088	483
University of the District of Columbia (David A. Clarke School of Law) 4200 Connecticut Avenue, N.W. Washington, DC 20008 Null Fax: 202-274-5583 vcanty@law.udc.edu	23	143	2	2.7	362	141	88
University of the Pacific (McGeorge School of Law) 3200 Fifth Avenue Sacramento, CA 95817 916-739-7105 Fax: 916-739-7134 admissionsmcgeorge@uop.edu	48	150	30	3	1680	1174	364
University of Toledo (College of Law) 2801 West Bancroft Street Toledo, OH 43606-3390 419-530-4131 Fax: 419-530-4345 law.utoledo.edu	52	152	15	3.2	633	427	190

LAW SCHOOL	ACADEMIC STATISTICS				ADMISSION STATISTICS		
	Median LSAT Percentile of Enrolled	Median LSAT Score of Enrolled	Lowest LSAT Percentile of Accepted	Median GPA (4.0 scale) of Enrolled	Total Applicants	Applicants Accepted	Applicants Enrolled
University of Tulsa (College of Law) 3120 East Fourth Place Tulsa, OK 74104-2499 918-631-2709 Fax: 918-631-3630	50	149	25	3.1	844	518	181
University of Utah (College of Law) 332 South 1400 East Front Salt Lake City, UT 84112 801-581-7479 Fax: 801-581-6897 gormleyl@law.utah.edu	84	159	32	3.5	805	304	125
University of Virginia (School of Law) 580 Massie Road Charlottesville, VA 22903-1789 804-924-7351 Fax: 804-982-2128 lawadmit@virginia.edu	93	165		3.7	3368	975	353
University of Washington (School of Law) 1100 Northeast Campus Parkway Seattle, WA 98105-6617 206-543-4078	88	162	28	3.5	1770	470	170
University of Wisconsin-Madison (Law School) 975 Bascom Mall Madison, WI 53706 608-262-5914 Fax: 608-262-5485 Admissions@law.wisc.educ		158		3.4	1639	708	310
University of Wyoming (College of Law) P.O. Box 3035 Laramie, WY 82071 307-766-6416 lawadmis@uwyo.edu	55	152	29	3.3	379	249	83
Valparaiso University (School of Law) Wesemann Hall Valparaiso, IN 46383-6493 219-465-7829 Fax: 219-465-7808 heike.spahn@valpo.edu	52	151	17	3.1	734	532	166
Vanderbilt University (School of Law) Nashville, TN 37240 615-322-6452	88	162	29	3.6	2387	760	182
Vermont Law School P.O. Box 96, Chelsea Street South Royalton, VT 05068-0096 802-763-8303 Fax: 802-763-7071 admiss@vermontlaw.edu	52	151	7	3	781	574	179
Villanova University (School of Law) Garey Hall Villanova, PA 19085 610-519-7010	67	157	50	3.4	1511	858	249

LAW SCHOOL	ACADEMIC STATISTICS				ADMISSION STATISTICS		
	Median LSAT Percentile of Enrolled	Median LSAT Score of Enrolled	Lowest LSAT Percentile of Accepted	Median GPA (4.0 scale) of Enrolled	Total Applicants	Applicants Accepted	Applicants Enrolled
Wake Forest University (School of Law) P.O. Box 7206, Reynolda Station Winston-Salem, NC 27109 910-758-5437	86	160	26	3.3	1391	580	163
Washburn University (School of Law) 1700 College Topeka, KS 66621 785-231-1185 Fax: 785-232-8087 admissions@washburnlaw.edu		149		3.1	543	353	141
Washington and Lee University (School of Law) Lewis Hall Lexington, VA 24450 540-463-8504 Fax: 540-463-8586 lawadm@wlu.edu	92	164	26	3.4	1282	488	120
Washington University in St. Louis (School of Law) Box 1120, One Brookings Drive St. Louis, MO 63130 314-935-4525 Fax: 314-935-6959 admiss@walaw.wash.edu	83	161	31	3.4	1961	813	212
Wayne State University (Law School) 468 W. Ferry Mall Detroit, MI 48202 313-577-3937 Fax: 313-577-6000 linda.sims@wayne.edu	65	154		3.2	910	464	213
West Virginia University (College of Law) P.O. Box 6130 Morgantown, WV 26506 304-293-5304 Fax: 304-293-6891 lawaply@wvu.edu	68	156		3.3	515	260	155
Western New England College (School of Law) 1215 Wilbraham Road Springfield, MA 01119 413-782-1406 Fax: 413-796-2067 lawadmis@wnec.edu		148	3	3	962	640	175
Western State University (College of Law) 1111 North State College Blvd Fullerton, CA 92831 714-738-1000, x2909 Fax: 714-526-1062 joel@wsulaw.edu		145		2.9	838	503	214
Whittier College (School of Law) 3333 Harbor Blvd. Costa Mesa, CA 92626 714-444-4141, ext. 121 Fax: 714-444-0250 info@law.whittier.edu		150	8	3	1427	822	233

LAW SCHOOL	ACADEMIC STATISTICS				ADMISSION STATISTICS		
	Median LSAT Percentile of Enrolled	Median LSAT Score of Enrolled	Lowest LSAT Percentile of Accepted	Median GPA (4.0 scale) of Enrolled	Total Applicants	Applicants Accepted	Applicants Enrolled
Widener University (School of Law) 4601 Concord Pike, P.O. Box 7474 and 3800 Vartan Way, Harris Wilmington, DE 19803 302-477-2162 (DE); 717-541-3903 (HBG) Fax: 302-477-2224 (DE); 717-541-3999 (HBG) law.admissions@law.widener.edu	32	147	4	3	1963	1237	520
Willamette University (College of Law) 245 Winter Street S.E. Salem, OR 97301 503-370-6282 Fax: 503-370-6375 law-admission@willamette.edu	64	154		3.2	720	491	150
William Mitchell College of Law 875 Summit Avenue St. Paul, MN 55105-3076 651-290-6476 Fax: 651-290-6414 admissions@wmitchell.edu	56	152	13	3.2	972	638	352
Yale University (Yale Law School) P.O. Box 208329 New Haven, CT 06520-8239 203-432-4995 admissions.law@yale.edu	99	171	71	3.9	3173	259	183
Yeshiva University (Benjamin N. Cardozo School of Law) 55 Fifth Avenue New York, NY 10003 212-790-0274 Fax: 212-790-0482 lawinfo@ymail.yu.edu		157		3.4	2506	1086	347

CHAPTER 6

Is Financial Aid Available?

Unless you are independently wealthy, you are probably having some concerns about financing your legal education. The important thing to keep in mind is that funds are available to help you. The bulk of the assistance for law school students takes the form of student loans. There is very little money available for outright grants. Most law school students and their families are willing to take on a heavy debt load as an investment in the future.

There are certain concepts relative to financial aid that all applicants should know. All programs that are federally funded or sponsored have very strict requirements as to eligibility. Law school financial aid offices process the loan applications in accordance with these rules and regulations. They have very little leeway except in the awarding of institutional funds.

Need Based Need-based loans require a demonstration of need based on Federal Methodology.

Merit Based Merit-based aid does not require a showing of need.

Federal Methodology (FM) Federal Methodology is the federally mandated method of determining financial need.

Base Year Base year is the prior calendar year and is used to calculate need under FM.

Independent Student Law school students are deemed to be independent due to their professional student status.

Budget The budget is set by the financial aid office each year. FM allows only *required* student expenses. These expenses are: tuition, fees, books, living expenses including room and board, transportation costs, an allowance for personal expenses, and miscellaneous expenses. Required student expenses will not cover, in most cases, car payments, credit card monthly payments, alimony, or mortgage payments.

Financial Need Financial need is the difference between expected family contribution and the total cost of attendance.

Packaging Policy Packaging policy is set by each law school and delineates the priorities for awarding financial aid.

CAMPUS-BASED PROGRAMS

Certain financial aid programs are referred to as campus-based. First in this category of aid would be scholarships and grants funded entirely by the law school. At most law schools the amount of money available for this form of aid is small. Since the money comes from the institution, the institution sets the requirements for receiving the aid. In most cases these awards will require a showing of need. Occasionally, a law school will have some merit-based aid.

Carl D. Perkins Loans are another form of campus-based aid. Each year the institution receives an allocation from the federal government for this program. It is basically a loan program administered by the institution in that the institution lends the money to the student and the institution is responsible for collecting the loans from the recipients. Perkins loans carry the lowest interest rate and at most schools are reserved for the neediest students. There is a cumulative limit of $30,000 on all Perkins loans, both graduate and undergraduate.

Another type of campus-based aid is the Federal Work Study Program (FWS). Again, the institution receives a yearly allocation from the federal government to fund this program. FWS is a need-based program and may be reserved for the neediest students. The financial aid award will indicate that the law student is eligible to receive a certain amount of money under the FWS program. This money can be earned either by working on campus or off campus. On-campus jobs take the form of working in the library or other law school offices or as research assistants for faculty members. Off-campus jobs can only be with nonprofit or governmental entities. Some examples would be work at a public defender's office, as a law clerk for a judge, or for a state or federal agency. FWS funds do not have to be repaid.

FEDERAL LOAN PROGRAMS

Other federal loan programs are available through banks, credit unions, savings and loan associations, and other private lenders. The Stafford Student Loan (formerly the Guaranteed Student Loan) is a relatively low-interest federal loan available to law school students. Stafford loans are insured by state guarantee agencies and must be approved by that agency. Subsidized Stafford loans require demonstration of financial need. Law school students can borrow a maximum of $18,500 per academic year under this program but may not exceed $138,500 in total Stafford loans for law school.

OTHER LOAN PROGRAMS

Other loan programs are available to law school students but do not receive federal interest subsidies. These loan programs do not require demonstration of financial need and carry the highest interest rates. An applicant may also have to show a good credit rating or creditworthiness.

The Access Group has developed a loan program specifically designed to fit the needs of law school students. Under this program the student can apply for federally subsidized and unsubsidized Stafford loans as well as a private loan from The Access Group. This private loan is the Law Access Loan (LAL). Students with good credit can borrow up to the total cost of attendance.

There are other private loan programs available. Law Loans is one such program. Your financial aid office will have information on these programs.

OUTSIDE FUNDING

Various foundations and business and professional organizations offer assistance in financing your education. Some programs are geared for minority and disadvantaged students such as the Council on Legal Education Opportunity, the Earl Warren Legal Training Program, and the Mexican American Legal Defense Education Fund. The financial aid office can give you complete information on these other programs. As funds for most of these programs are limited, you should apply early.

Another source of outside funding comes from various state and county bar associations that award scholarships. The amounts and requirements will vary, but this possibility should not be overlooked.

Some states also offer grants to needy graduate students. Contact your local state guarantee agency to explore this option. Your financial aid office (both graduate and undergraduate) can supply you with their names and addresses.

Money is available to finance your legal education. But at what cost? The interest rate increases as you move from the Perkins loan (lowest interest) to the Stafford and the private loans. Borrowing decisions should be carefully made as these loans ultimately have to be repaid.

APPLICATION PROCESS

All law schools require that the financial information necessary to determine financial need be submitted to a national processing center. Most schools use the Free Application for Federal Student Aid (FAFSA).

The FAFSA should be filed as early as possible. Processing time for the FAFSA is approximately four to six weeks. Read the forms carefully and answer all required parts. After the FAFSA has been analyzed, a report will be sent to the schools you have designated.

When the law school financial aid office receives your report generated by the FAFSA, it will review your file in accordance with its packaging policy. This means that the expected student contribution will be subtracted from the school budget to arrive at financial need.

Some schools' packaging policies will require that the first level of need be met by the Stafford loan. If there is any remaining need, you may be eligible for Perkins loan funds and Federal Work Study. After the financial aid office determines your level of eligibility for aid, you will receive notification. This may be four to six weeks or longer after the receipt of the FAFSA report.

The loan applications must be completed, signed, and returned to the lender. If a credit report is required, it is done at this time. If the lender/guarantee agency approves your loan, the check will be disbursed. The approval process can take up to six weeks. For most loans the interest starts to accrue when the check is disbursed. In most cases the check will be made co-payable to the student and the law school. When the check arrives, you will be asked to endorse it, and then the school will endorse it and credit it to your account. If the amount credited is more than is owed, the school will process a refund check for you.

DEFERMENT

It is possible to defer repayment on student loans you received as an undergraduate as long as you are a full-time student. You should request deferment forms from your lender. Take these forms to the registrar at your law school. Federal regulations require that you be a matric-ulated student so these forms will not be signed and sent to your lender until after the semester starts.

It is important to file deferment forms and to know if they have to be filed annually with your lender. If you are not granted a deferment, don't make payments on your undergraduate loans, and are declared in default, you run the risk of being denied loans for your legal education.

REPAYMENT AND CONSOLIDATION

While the money is available to finance your legal education, ultimately it must be repaid. You will have to start making payments six to nine months after graduation. There are several different ways to repay a Federal Direct Loan.

A Standard Repayment Plan has a fixed monthly repayment amount for a fixed period of time, usually 10 years.

An Extended Repayment Plan has a lower fixed monthly payment amount, and loan repayment can be extended beyond the usual 10 years.

A Graduated Repayment Plan usually begins with lower monthly payments, and payment amounts increase at specified times. Payments may be for the usual 10-year period, or they may be extended beyond 10 years.

An Income-contingent Repayment Plan for Direct Stafford loans sets annual repayment amounts based on the borrower's income after leaving school. The loan is repaid over an extended period of time, not to exceed 25 years.

by Angela D'Agostino, adapted from the original article by Christine A. Koterba, Director of Financial Aid, Widener University School of Law.

CHAPTER 7

What Should I Expect in Law School?

[Barron's *How to Succeed in Law School* provides an in-depth look at legal education from the student's point of view, particularly the critical first year. The premise of the book is that being intelligent is not enough; the successful law student needs to know how to play the game. The portion of the book reprinted below provides an overview of the first year; other chapters deal with classroom preparation, studying, test taking, and a variety of other key elements in law school success. Readers who successfully gain admission to law school should read *How to Succeed in Law School* as the next step in their preparation for a career in law. Ed.]

THE LAW SCHOOL CALENDAR

No two people are the same. A key to your success in law school will be your ability to channel the skills you already have into a new educational program, while building new skills that will serve you in the future as a lawyer. It may help you to understand what is happening during the first year of law school by looking at the law school calendar. Although every law school is slightly different from all the others, in many respects they are all much the same. Virtually every law school in the United States models its curriculum, particularly in the first year, after the socratic system promulgated at Harvard Law School in the 1870s. Although legal education has evolved in the past century, the general comment in this chapter will be substantially descriptive of your law school.

Orientation

Law school starts with orientation. Orientation is designed to introduce you to the law school community (and some would say to lull you into a false sense of security about the

upcoming ten months). The first step is check-in. Check-in is run by the Admissions Office, and you will be greeted by the smiling countenance of the admissions officer who recruited you or dealt with you during the admissions process. The Admissions Office will want to make sure that you have paid your tuition, that your financial aid is in order, and that your registration is complete. Depending on how check-in is organized, you may or may not have to wait in a long line. If the line is long, it generally portends three to four years of the same thing.

After checking in, and grabbing a cup of hot coffee, you will proceed to an auditorium where you will be subjected to a series of speeches you will not remember. You will hear from the dean, some associate deans, assistant deans, the financial aid officer, placement director, student bar president, law review editor, moot court board chair, head of security, and other administrators and students too numerous to name. They will all tell you how glad they are to see you, how talented you all are, and how their doors will always be open. You will never see most of them again. While most schools have abandoned the tactic, a few of them may still use the old "Look to the right of you; look to the left of you; one of you won't be here next August." The truth is, 90–95 percent of those who enter law school eventually will graduate.

After this convocation, you may be given a tour of the facilities, including the law library, by engaging upperclass students just dying to tell you what law school is "really like." You also may be solicited by various student organizations; they will all be around and still anxious for your membership after the first year.

One of your first lessons in law school will be to separate the wheat from the chaff. Find out where the assignments are posted. Find out how you can sign up for a locker. Learn to recognize The Dean by sight. (There are many deans, but only one Dean.)

At many schools, class assignments for the first day are posted prior to orientation. An assignment sheet for each class will also tell you what books to buy for the course so you can go to the law school bookstore and pick up your books before the crowds arrive. Don't wait until school has started to obtain your books and start reading.

ORIENTATION CHECKLIST

___Admissions
    ___College transcripts (if needed)
    ___Identification
___Financial aid (if applicable)
___Registrar—class schedule
___Bursar—bring checkbook if not prepaid
___Course assignments
___Bookstore
___Parking Sticker
___Locker
___ID photo
___Law school tour
___Find out who is "The Dean"
___Nearby food
___Library carrel (if available)

First Classes

Unlike classes in undergraduate school, the first classes in law school are generally real classes. The professor may simply walk in and call on a student for the first case. She may give a short speech on what will be expected of you in her course before turning to the cases. Or she may provide a background lecture for most of the first hour. It is likely that the professor will not simply say, "Hello, I'm Professor Jones. Your assignment for Tuesday will be to read the first 30 pages in the book. I'll see you Tuesday." During the first class, the professor may present certain special rules such as the maximum number of class cuts you are allowed, the number of times you may be unprepared before being dropped from the course, what the final exam will be like, what her office hours will be, what outside materials (hornbooks, treatises, etc.) you should read. Such information is important to know.

Such works as *One L* and *The Paper Chase* probably have instilled a sense of fear in the minds of many beginning law students. In reality, not all law professors are as intimidating as Professor Kingsfield, although the terror and alienation described there are very accurate.

You will find yourself in a lecture hall with roughly one hundred more or less equally frightened souls. Your sense of anonymity and privacy will be invaded by the seemingly all-knowing professor armed with a seating chart and an uncanny ability to identify the least prepared student in the class to discuss the case at hand.

During the first week of classes, you will learn the ground rules. Let there be no doubt about it: This is the lions versus the Christians, and regardless of your religious affiliation, you and your classmates are the Christians.

Also, during the first week, you will be introduced to the subject matter to be covered in each course, the professor's unique philosophy of legal education, a new language called legalese, and those ponderous, pictureless tomes called casebooks.

You will also begin to get acquainted with your fellow law students. You may meet a few individuals whom you come to know as real people. Most of your classmates will fall into one of two groups: the nameless faces who fill the classroom and the ones who, by virtue of having been called on or volunteered to speak in class, are identified by name (as in "Mr. Simon, who sits in the first row in Torts"). Custom dictates that you use last names to identify students (as in "Ms. Miller" or "Mr. Musser") and you refer to the teacher as "Professor" or "Dean" as appropriate.

You may encounter some upperclass students who offer with a certain patronizing smugness to teach you the tricks of the trade. A healthy sense of skepticism about the value or motives of such advice is a good sign that you will eventually become a successful lawyer.

Routine

After the first week of classes, you will begin to establish a pattern in each course, and a timetable for your entire life. The reading will average between 10 and 30 pages per night, per class. You may find that the progress in some of the classes is painfully slow, with the professor covering only a portion of the assigned reading each time. Some classes may move along at an almost military clip of three to four cases per class, no matter what. During the first few weeks, you will find yourself spending an inordinate amount of time briefing cases, attempting to fathom the classroom discussion, and wondering secretly if someone in the admissions office hadn't screwed up by sending you an acceptance letter. You will wonder with increasing frequency whether you screwed up in deciding to come to law school. During this phase of school, you may wonder why everyone else in the class but you seems to know what is going on.

When I was in law school, there was a guy named Holtzman, and although Holtzman was only three or four years older than most of the rest of us, it seemed that in every class he had some personal experience relating to the case. If the case involved shoes, he had been in the shoe business; if the case involved clothes, he had been in the clothing business; if the case involved doctors, he had been in the medical business.

Other students will amaze you with their seeming ability to converse freely with the professor in legalese, whereas you find yourself stuck at the *Bonjour Jean* stage. But you will derive hope from the fact that some students' comments will seem totally inane to you, reassuring you that you must be smarter than *someone* in the class. And you will find a wicked satisfaction in seeing a handful of students whose hands are always in the air given their comeuppance by the professor. In every class, there will be at least one individual who, no matter how bloodied by the fray, will keep coming back for more. A pack psychology will come to dominate the class and seek to drive out the weak or the deviant. By mid-semester, the fear of embarrassment in front of the class will inhibit all but the most fearless souls from making rash statements. This mentality is typified by graffito on a bathroom stall at one law school: "After the sixth week of class, if you don't know who the class jerk is, it's you."

These pressures to conform may dissuade some students from ever participating in class discussions unless specifically required to do so by the professor. By laughing at a fellow student, you help to create an environment where one day others may laugh at you.

As the semester wears on, the professor comes to be viewed not so much as a god, but as a common enemy. You learn that the classroom routine is a game the teacher always wins. You learn that the stupidest answers have some value, and you begin to recognize that even the most articulate students really don't know much more than you do. When you come to this realization, you will have reached another milestone in your law school journey.

The Wall

Somewhere between the tenth and twelfth week of classes you will hit the wall. It is during this period that some students actually drop out of school; virtually every student at least contemplates that possibility. By this time in the semester, your work is piling up, final exams are just around the corner, and you still don't

have a clue what you need to know. At this point, when your psychological and physical resources are drained, you will wonder if you can possibly survive for two and a half or three and a half more years. It is critical when you hit the wall to press on. It may help during this period to talk to a sympathetic professor, mentor, or counselor. Family and loved ones, who up until now have been totally supportive, will seem to become part of the problem. Prelaw school friends may find that you have changed, and you may find yourself increasingly irritated that they never see the issue.

Panic

By about the thirteenth week of the semester, you will have no time to worry about such self-indulgent psychological concerns, because finals will be upon you. Some professors, in what is variously perceived as a last minute attempt to catch up with the syllabus or a final effort to break your backs, will increase the reading assignments to two or three times what they were at the beginning of the semester. A full-scale panic attack may threaten to debilitate you before the first test. Somehow, you will survive.

First Semester Finals

At last, final examinations will arrive. As a rule, law school exams average one hour of exam for each credit hour of class. The amount of material you will have to study will be immense. Whole parts of some courses may be incomprehensible when you go back to review them. When you walk out of these exams, your head will feel as if Evander Holyfield had used it as a punching bag. You will have no idea how well you did, but if you thought the test was easy, you probably missed something really big.

Semester Break

Semester break is the time when you regroup. Immediately after your last exam, your impulse will be to engage in the most hedonistic activity possible. Many will actually succumb to this impulse. Next, you will sleep for two days. Then, you will engage in mindless activity such as watching soap operas or football games, reading trashy novels, attending holiday parties, or vegging out with your family. If you are an evening student, you may not have the luxury of all of this R & R. However, to the extent possible, you should try to get away from both school and work for a while.

Toward the end of semester break, you will begin to think about law school again. You may do some reading for class. You may reflect about how you will avoid making the same mistakes you did the first semester. You will rush madly to clear up loose ends in your personal life, in order to give yourself time to devote your full attention to law school.

Renewed Hope

The second semester is better in some ways, and worse in others. It is better in that you know the ropes. You have a better picture of what to expect. You have a clearer idea of what it will take to succeed. On the other hand, the workload will pick up even more. The professors will take off at the same pace they ended the previous semester. In addition, at many schools a required moot court problem will swallow the bulk of your free time.

The January Blues

During January (and sometimes February or March) first semester grades will be posted. The wait for grades may be agonizing. The actual knowledge of your grades may be worse. Most students are disappointed in some or all of their marks. You learn how fast the track really is. Unfortunately, many students do not handle this experience well. They go into a depression from which they do not escape until after the bar exam. Although there is no grade for it, your grade point average may depend on your ability to bounce back psychologically and to learn from this experience.

Falling Behind

In all but the warmest climates, the arrival of spring will bring the last great temptation of the school year. When the flowers begin to bloom and warm winds touch the land, sitting in a law school classroom will not be your first choice of activities. Spring break may help but chances are good that you will fall behind in your reading and studying. If you are not careful, you could find yourself in the proverbial hot water.

The Mad Rush

As March dissolves into April, you will once again find yourself staring at final exams. If you have been diligent, you will simply experience anxiety about finishing the year on a high note; if you find yourself hopelessly behind your

schedule, you will be working feverishly to catch up. The last two weeks of school will pass quickly, and your first year will be almost over.

Finals Again

Final exams in the spring will probably not seem as daunting. The experience will be the same as in the fall, but this time you will be more prepared for it mentally. The amount of work you cover in these exams will be more prodigious than in the fall. But the skills you have developed during the course of the year will make the load seem more manageable. This time, when finals are over, you will just go home, have dinner with friends, and go on about your business.

Over a period of 36 weeks, more or less, you will have been transformed from an ordinary person into a budding lawyer. Whether you want it or not, like it or not, or need it or not, you will never be the same again. The process is in some ways like marine boot camp, taking apart whatever you were before you arrived and rebuilding it into a new person. Whatever other criticisms of law school one might make, it certainly cannot be said that the program does not work.

LAW SCHOOL COURSES

The curricula at most American law schools are comparable. In fact, the first year law school curriculum has not changed appreciably in the past one hundred years. At the same time, there are minor variations in course offerings from school to school, reflecting differences in educational philosophy and institutional tradition.

Most law school courses are offered as 2-, 3-, or 4-semester-hour courses. Full-time first year students take five or six courses for a total of 15-16 credit hours; part-time students generally take one or two fewer courses and 10-11 hours. At some schools, grades are based on an entire year's work for 4- to 6-hour courses. You will study some, if not all, of the following courses during the first year of law school. Some schools will defer certain courses until the second year or not require them at all.

Torts

The word tort comes from an old French term meaning wrong. Torts as a law school subject area refers to a series of legal actions and remedies against wrongdoers for injuries sustained. Torts fall into three broad groups: *intentional torts* where an actor intends conduct that causes injury to another; *negligence torts* where an actor owing a duty to act with reasonable care toward another breaches that duty and causes injury resulting in damages; and *strict liability torts* where an actor causes injury to another without fault or intent but is held liable for policy reasons. You will study a number of distinct tort actions, including assault, battery, false imprisonment, and intentional infliction of emotional distress; negligence actions; misrepresentation; defamation; products liability; and privacy.

Property

The Property course deals with the rights associated with the ownership of property. In the beginning of the course you will probably discuss the origins of property rights in Anglo-American law. You will study such tantalizing questions as who owns the rights to the meteorite: the farmer in whose field it fell or the guy walking down the road who saw it fall? Some of us are still trying to figure that one out. A small portion of the course is devoted to the law of personal property, but the bulk of the year will involve issues relating to real property, or land. In the first semester, you will devote considerable time to basic concepts such as estates in land, transferability of land, and title. Some time during the year you will learn about future interests, those medieval devices for controlling the ownership of land beyond the life of the owner. In the second semester, you will deal with more modern concepts such as easements, zoning, and land use planning.

Contracts

Contracts involves the study of the body of law governing the making and breaking of agreements. You will learn what it takes to create a binding contract with another party. You will spend considerable time discussing what happens when one of the parties breaks its promises, or breaches the contract. You will learn about liquidated damages, specific performance, express and implied warranties, and unilateral contracts. Much of the course will deal with the development of contracts in the commercial setting, including the "battle of forms" and substitution of statutory law in the form of the Uniform Commercial Code for the common law in many situations.

Civil Procedure

Civil Procedure refers to the rules by which the civil courts operate. Most Civ Pro instructors utilize the Federal Rules of Civil Procedure in teaching their courses. Some of the course may touch upon historical material, such as the evolution of the English forms of action into the rules of procedure of today. Most of your time will be spent looking at such concepts as jurisdiction (including subject matter, personal, and diversity), standing, discovery, pleading, appeal, summary judgments, and numerous other provisions of the Rules. A substantial part of the course will address the Erie problem. The case of *Erie Railroad v. Tompkins* held that the federal courts, while applying federal procedural rules, must apply the substantive common law of the state. The ripples from this seemingly simple rule have extended far beyond the original case and have engrossed generations of judges, law professors, legal writers, and students (perhaps *engrossed* is too strong a word for the student response).

Constitutional Law

Many law schools require Constitutional Law during the first year. As the name suggests, Con Law deals with the enforcement of rights and duties established under the United States Constitution. Because there are so many constitutional issues, no two professors will emphasize exactly the same topics. You will look at some fundamental problems such as jurisdiction and standing, separation of powers, the commerce clause, and the privileges and immunities clause. You will deal with cases arising under the first, fifth, and fourteenth amendments as well as others. Perhaps most importantly, you will study the decision-making process in the United States Supreme Court from Chief Justice Marshall's power grab of judicial review in *Marbury v. Madison* to Chief Justice Rehnquist's reshaping the direction of the court in the 1980s.

Criminal Law

Criminal Law is the law of crimes. For a good portion of this course, you will grapple with concepts such as intent, *mens rea,* and lesser included offenses. You will learn the basic elements of crimes you have known about all your life, and a few you have never heard of before. You will study such issues as the right to trial by jury, double jeopardy, the state's burden of proof, and conspiracy.

Professional Responsibility

Although most law schools offer Professional Responsibility during the last year of law school, some require it during the second year, and a few the first. Professional Responsibility deals with the ethical obligations of the lawyer in representing clients. A few of the subjects you will cover in this course are: lawyer/client confidentiality, conflicts of interest, legal fees, advertising and solicitation of business, fitness to practice law, lawyer discipline, and candor to the tribunal. In a broader sense, however, professional responsibility addresses the role of the legal profession in society. What is a lawyer anyway? Are there limits on his or her conduct? Is law a business, a profession, or both? What is the role of the Bar Association? Can one be a good lawyer and a good person at the same time?

Legal Writing

At every law school, there is a course known by a variety of names, but with a general aim of teaching you how to conduct legal research, draft legal briefs and memoranda, prepare and make oral arguments, and gain an understanding of a legal system. These courses are often much maligned by first-year students, but revered by lawyers who come to know the value of the skills they learned in that course. Legal Writing frequently requires a time commitment out of proportion with the amount of credit received. An important consideration during the course of the school year will be your ability to allocate time to Legal Writing in accordance with its relative importance and credit weight, and not to set aside work in other classes for research, writing, and advocacy projects.

THE PROFESSORS

Law students develop a special relationship with their first year teachers. It is not uncommon to experience a love/hate relationship with these professors. Later in law school you will wonder how you placed some of these individuals on such high pedestals. During the first semester of law school they will be like gods— not necessarily in their perfection of appearance, but in their seeming knowledge and omnipotence.

Many of those who become law teachers attained their positions by having done very well academically in law school. Additionally, many of them enter the profession after having served as judicial clerks for the United States Supreme Court or other prestigious tribunals. Increasingly, today, law teachers have some experience in the practice of law. They come from large law firms, corporations, and government agencies. All of them have made an affirmative decision to pursue a career in education, rather than one in a traditional area of law practice. Professors who worked in large law firms or possess more than a few years of experience probably have taken a considerable cut in pay to enter the teaching field. Although law professors as a group have a higher median income than the average of all lawyers, they probably could make more money doing something else.

THE STUDENTS

Classmates

Your classmates can be allies as well as foes during your struggle to master the first year of law school. They can help you to cope in a number of different ways. First, they can help you with assignments. If you happen to miss a class, you need to find someone whose notes you can review. If your own notes have gaps, you may be able to fill them with the help of someone else. If reading assignments or case citations are unclear, you should identify one or more people to call. Even though law school is a competitive environment, most students are willing to help out in this way, as long as their generosity is not abused.

You may study with one of more other students from time to time. Informal small group discussions are common even among students who do not organize formal study groups. In law school, a great amount of learning takes place outside the classroom, and to the extent that your out-of-class conversations are discussions begun during class, the learning process will continue.

If you have ever been to the zoo, you may recall watching a pride of lions or other large cats. The young ones will tussle and play endlessly. Sometimes Mom or Dad will play too, letting the kittens attack and snarl and slap. You know that the older cat can send the kittens flying with a flick of the paw, but they play along until they get bored. You know that the kittens are learning skills they will need as adults in the wild, and the big cats are helping in the process. You also know that the kittens learn from their mock battles with each other just as they do from Mom and Dad. In law school, the professors take on the role of the big cats, and you as kittens should learn from them. However, you should remember that you learn from the rest of the litter as well.

Your classmates can provide an outlet from the pressures of law school. Whether it involves coffee in the morning, eating lunch or dinner, exercising or working out, or partying, you need to socialize from time to time. Those of you who are married to people unconnected with the legal profession, and those who have jobs in nonlegal settings may find it less difficult to break away from law school psychologically. On the other hand, it may be more difficult to find the time to get to know your classmates socially. If you don't want your families and coworkers to despise you because you talk about law all the time, you should try to make some time to get to know your fellow law students in a social setting.

There is an insidious downside to developing relationships with your classmates. Several caveats are in order. Law school is very competitive. Some students will help no one. Some students will promise help, but fail to deliver. Some will take far more than they give. Always remember that the admissions committee did not pick the first year class on the basis of integrity. Although you will meet some of the most honest and honorable people you could hope to know, you may also encounter others who would stoop to any depth to get ahead, and use any means to reach a desired end. Most of you will conclude that you are unwilling to lie, cheat, and steal in order to succeed in law school. Do not be so naive as to believe that everyone feels the same. Beware of the snakes in the grass, and pick your friends carefully.

Your classmates can exert considerable pressure not to succeed. A collective striving for mediocrity may seem to be the norm. Those who study too much, talk too often in class, or don't get into the law school social scene may be branded as outsiders. You have had to deal with similar peer pressure since grade school. The point here is that the pressure to conform does not end in law school. You may have seen the gopher game at the boardwalk or midway. In this game, the gopher pops his head out of one of the number of round holes while the player, wielding a mallet, tries to knock him back into the hole again. If you imagine that the class is the midway player ready to knock down any gopher who has the audacity to stick his head up above the crowd, you get the picture.

One way the group may push you toward mediocrity is by encouraging you to socialize. Although occasional social activity is benefi-cial, too much can be the kiss of death. When study sessions deteriorate into bull sessions like you had when you were a freshman in college, when quick lunches extend into afternoon shopping trips, when an occasional class party becomes an evening ritual, then you will know you have exceeded the bounds of moderation.

Some semblance of self-discipline in the area of time management is absolutely essential. You must decide how much time you are willing to devote to personal and social activities, and live with that decision.

Socializing with other students can take on a more serious note: emotional involvement through love and dependency. Guess what? Law students fall in love. They fall in love with each other and with nonlaw students. It would be futile to say: "Don't fall in love." However, if you do, you will find yourself in turmoil. When you fall in love, your lover tends to become (at least during early stages of infatuation) all-important in your life. Unfortunately, so does law school. Justice Holmes once remarked that the law is a jealous mistress. This conflict appears in the play *Phantom of the Opera*. Christine, the heroine, is torn between her physical relationship with the Vicomte de Chegny and her passion to excel in her career represented by her relationship with the Phantom. It is interesting to note that the author of the book, Gaston Leroux, was himself a lawyer and may have understood the conflict in terms of the law.

A second dangerous emotional involvement is to buy into someone else's problems to the detriment of your own studies. Law students are not immune from the vagaries of life. Some of your friends will have serious problems while they are in school. The stress of law school may compound their anxiety. Some may turn to you to serve as an emotional crutch. In fact, some students are like magnets for those with problems. Lest your friend's difficulties drag you down, the best thing you can do is to get them to go to someone who can really help.

Upperclass Students

When you arrive at law school, you will find a place already populated by students who have gone before you. These upperclass students will be ready and willing to regale you with tales of their own experiences in the first year, to give you the inside scoop on all the profs, and to share the definitive answers on what you need to do to get ahead. Some of them will want you to join their organizations, come to their parties, or buy their old books. They may seem like the smug but grizzled veterans joined in the field by some new recruits in the standard war movie: "Don't worry, kid; I'll show you what you need to do to get out of this place alive." Of course, in the movies, the guy who says that always seems to get killed.

The lesson to learn is to take everything you hear with a grain of salt. You will find out information that is useful. Every law school has a grapevine, and the news, if not always accurate, is at least entertaining. Some of your sources may prove better than others. So use what you can and discard the rest.

Consider the motivation of the upperclass student who offers advice. Is this someone who just likes being a big shot? Someone who needs reaffirmation for his or her own decisions in law school (even if those choices have produced a record of mediocrity)? Someone who would like to ask you out? (Yes, this goes on in law school like everywhere else!) Someone who wants to sell you something (bar reviews, books, bar association memberships)? You do not have to shun all these people, just remember that they want something in return for their information. (In the words of Hannibal Lecter from *The Silence of the Lambs,* "Quid pro quo, Clarice.")

While casual advice should be approached with skepticism, it might be valuable to look for an upperclass mentor. Such a person might well be someone who has similar interests, career aspirations, problems, or background. For example, a first year student with young children at home might encounter an upperclass student who has gone through the same experience and survived. A mentor might be someone you happen to meet and become friendly with during the course of the year. Some schools even offer programs that assign upperclass mentors to first year students. However it occurs that a true mentoring relationship develops, take advantage of it.

A mentor can help to guide you through the law school maze, talk to you when you are down, share your joy when you are flush with success, and set an example for you to follow. Mentoring relationships are built upon a foundation of common interest, molded by walls of trust, and covered by a protective roof of the experience of the mentor for the student. Mentoring relationships are common in the legal profession, not only in law school but in practice as well. To the extent that you find a good mentor, you will discover that the law school experience is a more palatable one.

THE LAW SCHOOL CULTURE

Rules and Procedures

Law school culture is unique, created in part by the intense experience of those involved, and in part by the insular setting of the law school itself. Because most law students did not attend undergraduate school at the university where they attend law school, they tend to have limited interaction with the university community generally. The law school on many campuses is set apart on the edge of campus or on a separate campus altogether. Some law schools are not connected with an undergraduate university at all. There are advantages and disadvantages to attending an independent law school. Such a school can devote all its resources to the law students, but may lack the rich culture of a university setting.

There may be other differences about the physical location or layout of the law building(s) that make the law school environment unique. Does the law school share its campus with undergrads or graduate students? Does the law school share space with other departments? Are law school facilities located in one building or several? The presence or absence of a nonlegal academic community affects not only the type and extent of extracurricular programs and activities, but also the sense of the law school as an insular institution.

In one sense, every law school is different, but in another sense, every law school is the same. Regardless of the idiosyncrasies of different law schools, the process of legal education is similar everywhere.

In this environment, a distinct law school culture has evolved. Law schools have their own student government (the Student Bar Association or SBA), activities, social events, intramurals, and newspapers. Some law schools even have their own yearbooks. At many law schools, the students put on an annual comedy show, generally making fun of the faculty in a singular effort to even the score for a year's worth of abuse.

Within the law school culture, there are several common elements worth noting: First, rules and procedures take on a distinctly legal flavor. Announcements and information may be posted by the registrar, the Dean's Office, or teachers. You will be deemed to know what is in these notices by virtue of the doctrine of constructive notice. The upshot of this concept is that you have to watch out for announcements that pertain to you. The first example of constructive notice during your law school tenure will be the posting of class assignments on a wall or bulletin board prior to the beginning of classes. You will find very little hand-holding by law school teachers and administrators. Students who graduated from small intimate colleges may find this somewhat of a shock.

A second concept that permeates the rules and procedures is the notion of due process. Lawyers, more than those who are not trained in the law, tend to be aware of individual rights to hearings, representation, confrontation of accusers, and appeal. Most law schools operate under some code of conduct for dealing with academic dishonesty, as well as a code of academic standards to cover issues involving academic performance. Both sets of rules tend to focus heavily on due process and protection of the individual.

Another aspect of the law school culture is that it is a small world. The largest law school in the country has around 2,000 students; at most law schools the enrollment is no more than several hundred. The small size of the student body, combined with the nature of the educational process, means that students know much more about each other, law school affairs, and their professors than they did in all but the smallest undergraduate schools. Unlike your high school or college acquaintances, you will tend to maintain contact with many of your law school classmates throughout your career. At every law school there is a student grapevine, laden with information about everything from what courses to take, which firms to interview, to who is sleeping with whom. The old adage, "Believe a tenth of what you hear and half of what you see," is apropos.

Socializing and Breaks

You will find an abundance of opportunities for escape from law school studies in the form of parties and school-sponsored social events. During the year, there will be several receptions, mixers, and even a dance or two sponsored by the SBA. Many student organizations offer periodic social events for their members. And informal groups of students organize their own parties as a break from the grind of law school or meet at a local bar for drinks after class.

In fact, if you are interested, you can find a party almost every night. Unfortunately, partying leads you down a certain path of self-destruction in law school. Everyone needs an occasional break from study; however, the occasional break can easily become a regular habit. The party scene can become an escape

from law school pressures generally, and may shift your values away from learning.

If you were a party animal in college, it may be difficult to break out of old patterns. Unfortunately, most of us cannot get by with the same antics we did in undergraduate school. In law school one all-nighter will not save a semester of neglect.

Law school provides abundant breaks between and during semesters. You will probably have two weeks or more between the end of first semester exams and the start of spring semester classes. Most schools provide a spring break midway through the second semester. And, of course, summers are open.

Students usually use breaks during the year either to get away for a vacation or to get ahead in their work. Sometimes you may not have a choice. If you decide to vacation, leave your guilt at home. If you take your books with you, plan and make time to study. If you have no time to study, do not make a pretense of it by surrounding yourself with symbols of law school while doing nothing to further your cause.

Summer vacation is another matter. Here are 12 to 14 weeks that you can utilize in a variety of different ways. How you choose to spend your summer vacation will have an impact, one way or the other, on your legal education.

A large percentage of law students work for legal employers during the summer. Although it is harder for them to find positions, many first year students take this option, even if they have to work for free. For some students, it is necessary to work in high paying nonlegal jobs in order to earn enough to come back to school the next year.

Many students go to summer school, at their institution or abroad. You may find, however, that you are so burned out that you simply want to relax. And some students do just that after the first year. If you want to travel, this might be the time to do it, before you take your first job.

Competition

A final note about the law school culture is that it is competitive. Entrance to law school was competitive; law school itself is competitive; and law practice by its nature is competitive. Your relationships with other students will be colored by competition. Ironically, many students try to deny the competitive nature of the process. They will say to each other that grades don't matter. They will ostracize fellow students who appear too competitive. They may deny to other students that they study as much as they do. On the other hand, competitiveness can go too far. In all likelihood, before you graduate from law school, you will hear about at least one cheating incident at your school. You will see other examples, such as library books being misshelved by unscrupulous students. If you should be tempted, it's not worth it. In the 1988 presidential campaign, a law school indiscretion may have cost one candidate the nomination for the presidency of the United States.

Excerpted from *How to Succeed in Law School*, by Gary A. Munneke, Barron's Educational Series, Inc. 1994, 1989.

CHAPTER 8

What Are the Career Opportunities in Law?

Although it may seem quite early to begin to think about employment after law school, many prelaw students ask themselves whether they will find employment after investing thousands of dollars in a legal education. Some students understand that the choice of law schools has an impact on the career choices they ultimately make. The school's reputation, geographic location, substantive curriculum, and many other factors go into determining what opportunities are most likely to be available to its graduates. For instance, law schools in the Washington, DC, area typically have more graduates go to work for the federal government than law schools in other areas. Law schools with specialty programs may have a disproportionate number of graduates pursue careers in the specialty field.

First year law students are often surprised to discover that after spending considerable time and energy making a career choice to go to law school, they are now called upon to make additional career choices about what to do with their law degree. Law is practiced in many different ways and many different settings. Some legally trained individuals never practice law at all, but use their legal training in a variety of other fields.

A career counselor at your law school will be able to help you make decisions about your legal career. Although career services for law students may vary from school to school, most law schools employ full-time professionals who possess either a counseling or law degree (or both) to work with law students in developing career plans. Law professors may be able to help, not only with advising, but also with information about contacts and recommendations. The chart beginning on page 60 provides an overview of the career planning and placement services of the law schools included in this guide.

WORK DURING LAW SCHOOL

A great many law students work in legal or law-related jobs while they are in law school. Still others will work in nonlegal jobs that lead them to legal jobs in the area of business where they were working, or into a totally alternative career. Many law students work in law firms, corporate law departments or government law offices. These positions may be full time or part time, and they may be summer jobs, work during the school year, or permanent positions.

Many larger firms, government agencies, and corporate legal departments offer summer internship or clerkship programs as part of a formal recruiting process. These positions tend to be highly competitive, and hiring for them may be heavily influenced by academic performance in law school and the prestige of the law school attended. Many of the organizations that sponsor these summer programs use them as a tool to help make permanent hiring decisions.

Even in law firms and other employers that do not regularly recruit on campus for summer clerks or permanent associates, it is common for students who work in these organizations during law school to accept positions there when they graduate. Even if they do not ultimately stay with the organization where they have worked, the experience they gain is very likely to impress other employers with whom they apply. This kind of hands-on training is an excellent counterbalance to the more esoteric experience of law school.

Types of Employment

The largest segment of the population of law school graduates each year goes to work in private law firms. These firms provide legal services to clients for profit. The owners of the firm may be individual lawyers or partners in multi-lawyer partnerships of several hundred partners, or anything in between. In addition to the partners/owners, law firms also employ salaried junior lawyers or associates. Some of these associates may eventually become partners in the firm; some may remain as permanent associates or staff attorneys; and some may leave the firm to find other employment or start their own practices. The percentage of lawyers in private practice has decreased from around 80 percent in 1950 to around 60 percent today. Additionally, the vast majority of private practitioners in 1950 were solo practitioners, while less than half of them are now. Whereas in 1950, there were only a few law firms with over ten lawyers (partners and associates combined), today there are hundreds of firms with over one hundred lawyers.

Still, the largest law firm in the United States (with slightly over one thousand lawyers and perhaps twice as many support staff) is small compared to business entities in many other fields. There is no big five of law firms like there is in accounting. There is no legal equivalent of Microsoft or General Motors. The reality is that most lawyers will engage in the private practice of law at some point during their careers, but most of these will be in solo practices or small firms. No more than 15 percent of the population of private practitioners work in the largest five hundred law firms in the country.

If six out of ten lawyers work in private practice, the remaining four are employed in a variety of different endeavors. The largest of these other groups are corporations (including both in-house counsel and other corporate positions) and government service in federal, state, and local agencies. Government service also includes work as prosecutors and public defenders in the criminal justice system. Judicial administration is usually listed as a separate category, because of the unique nature of the work performed. While many government lawyers practice law like lawyers in firms (the big difference being that the government is their employer), judges, court administrators, and law clerks engage in a very different kind of activity—running the justice system. Other lawyers work for political action or public interest organizations, serve in legislatures as representatives, or aides, and participate in political parties, campaigns, and other related activities.

Many lawyers go into other lines of work outside the practice of law altogether, having never gone into law, or having left the practice at some time during their careers. Some of these people may simply want a law degree to supplement other qualifications they have. Others may become enticed by personal dreams or business deals along the way. Some, unfortunately, discover after going to law school and practicing law that they are not happy with the career choices they have made, and leave the practice of law for greener pastures. The ranks of these legal expatriates are filled with entrepreneurs, athletes, writers, correspondents, inventors, entertainers, restaurateurs, and even a prominent wine critic. A list of well-known personalities who are also lawyers would surprise most people.

Each year, the National Association for Law Placement, an organization comprised of representatives of the nation's law schools and legal employers, conducts an employment report and salary survey. (See *Jobs and JDs: Employment and Salaries of New Law School Graduates*, National Association for Law Placement, 1999.) The most recent class on which data are available suggests that law graduates go into positions in the percentages not too different from the makeup of the legal profession as a whole. The breakdowns for private practice, corporate, government, and judicial categories are similar to the breakdown for lawyers as a whole, although NALP reported that approximately 55 percent of the 1998 graduates entered private practice, down from a high of 64.3 percent ten years earlier. A very small percentage of law students actually open their own law offices, a practice euphemistically referred to as "hanging out a shingle." More law graduates go to work in law offices of less than 100 lawyers than accept positions in large offices. The judicial cohort is made up of judicial clerks rather than judges and courts administrators for obvious reasons. The largest area of government practice for recent graduates is work in a prosecutor's office. Another area, often listed as a separate category, is the military, which recruits lawyers for the judge advocate generals corps for the service branches, as well as individuals who have completed law school before fulfilling other military obligations. Very few law school graduates go into teaching—particularly law school teaching—directly out of law school, but an appreciable number pursue advanced degrees both in law and other fields.

The 1998 NALP survey accounts for approximately 90 percent of the graduating class, leaving the employment status of 10 percent unknown. Of those whose employment status was known, 90 percent were employed and the remainder unemployed or enrolled in advanced degree programs at the time of the NALP sur-

(*go to page 86*)

THE JOB OUTLOOK

SCHOOL	Law Placement Office	University Placement Office	Employment Counseling	Job Openings Information	Solo Practice Advice	Resume Preparation	Interview Counseling	Employment Planning	Job Interviews Arrangement	Law, Corporate, and Government Contact	Alumni Contacts	Part-Time/Summer Employment	Internships	Alumni Placement	Placement Within 6 to 9 Months	Private Practice 2-10 Attorneys	Private Practice 11-25 Attorneys	Private Practice 26-50 Attorneys	Private Practice 51-100 Attorneys	Judicial Clerkships	Government	Business/Industry	Public Interest	Military	Academic	Other	Average Starting Salary
American University (Washington College of Law) 4801 Massachusetts Avenue, N.W. Washington, DC 20016-8186 202-274-4101 Fax: 202-274-4107 wcladmit@wcl.american.edu	●		●	●	●	●	●	●	●	●	●	●	●	●	96%	7	4	3	3	11	21	13	8	2		18	$24,000–$112,000
Arizona State University (College of Law/Armstrong Hall) Box 877906 Tempe, AZ 85287-7906 602-965-1474 Fax: 602-965-5550 wanda.decrow@asu.edu	●	●	●	●	●	●	●	●	●	●	●	●	●	●	90%	22	6	6	15	16	17	5	1	1	1	11	$34,815–$52,871
Baylor University (School of Law) P.O. Box 97288 Waco, TX 76798-7288 254-710-1911 Fax: 254-710-2316 becky-beck@baylor.edu	●		●	●	●	●	●	●	●	●	●	●	●	●	95%	52	10	4	8	7	8	7				3	$36,500–$65,585
Boston College (Law School) 885 Centre Street Newton, MA 02459 617-552-4351 Fax: 617-552-2917 bclawadm@bc.edu	●		●	●	●	●	●	●	●	●	●	●	●	●	96%	11	6	3	43	18	6	11	2				$18,000–$106,000
Boston University (School of Law) 765 Commonwealth Avenue Boston, MA 02215 617-353-3100 bulawadm@bu.edu	●					●	●		●	●	●	●	●	●	75%	6	9	11	42	9	10	15	2		1		$35,161–$87,462
Brigham Young University (J. Reuben Clark Law School) 342 JRCB Brigham Young University Provo, UT 84602 801-378-4277 Fax: 801-378-5897 wilcook@lawgate.byu.edu	●		●	●	●	●	●	●	●	●	●	●	●	●	94%	23	7	6	1	17	8	16	1	2	1	7	$22,000–$90,000

School	%												Salary
Brooklyn Law School 250 Joralemon Street, Brooklyn, NY 11201, 718-780-7906, Fax: 718-780-0395, admitq@brooklaw.edu	95%	21	4	4	3	6	17	19	4		2	11	$50,000–$100,000
California Western School of Law 225 Cedar Street, San Diego, CA 92101-3046, 619-525-1401, Fax: 619-615-1401, rbriscoe@cwsl.edu	78%	45	15	9	7	4	26	17	2	5	3		$46,773–$78,000
Campbell University (Norman Adrian Wiggins School of Law) P.O. Box 158, Buies Creek, NC 27506, 910-893-1754, Fax: 910-893-1780, culaw@webster.campbell.edu	99%	81	81	81	81	5	9	2	1	1	1		
Capital University (Law School) 303 East Broad Street, Columbus, OH 43215-3200, 614-236-6500, Fax: 614-236-6972, admissions@law.capital.edu	90%	15	3	2	2	5	25	31	1		3	9	$19,000–$140,000
Case Western Reserve University (School of Law) 11075 East Boulevard, Cleveland, OH 44106, 216-368-3600, Fax: 216-368-6144, lawadmissions@po.cwru.edu or lawmoney@po.cwru.edu	95%	25	8	10	30	8	3	13	2		1		$26,000–$125,000
Catholic University of America (Columbus School of Law) Cardinal Station, Washington, DC 20064, (202) 319-5151, Fax: (202) 319-6285	100%	38				18	23	14	2			5	$22,000–$88,000
Catholic University of Puerto Rico (School of Law) Avenida Las Americas-Station 6, Ponce, PR 00732, 809-841-2000											50	50	$14,000–$24,000
Chapman University (School of Law) One University Drive, Orange, CA 92866, 714-628-2500, Fax: 714-628-2501, misles@chapman.edu	82%	34	4	2	2	4	16	24	2		4	8	$31,000–$60,000
City University of New York (City University of New York School of Law at Queens College) 65-21 Main Street, Flushing, NY 11367-1300, 718-340-4210, Fax: 718-340-4372, admissions@maclaw.law.cuny.edu	83%	34				8	24	15	18		1		$22,000–$42,000

PLACEMENT RECORD / PLACEMENT SERVICES

SCHOOL	AVERAGE STARTING SALARY	OTHER	ACADEMIC	MILITARY	PUBLIC INTEREST	BUSINESS/INDUSTRY	GOVERNMENT	JUDICIAL CLERKSHIPS	PRIVATE PRACTICE 51-100 ATTORNEYS	PRIVATE PRACTICE 26-50 ATTORNEYS	PRIVATE PRACTICE 11-25 ATTORNEYS	PRIVATE PRACTICE 2-10 ATTORNEYS	PLACEMENT WITHIN 6 TO 9 MONTHS	ALUMNI PLACEMENT	INTERNSHIPS	PART-TIME/SUMMER EMPLOYMENT	ALUMNI CONTACTS	LAW, CORPORATE, AND GOVERNMENT CONTACT	JOB INTERVIEWS ARRANGEMENT	EMPLOYMENT PLANNING	INTERVIEW COUNSELING	RESUME PREPARATION	SOLO PRACTICE ADVICE	JOB OPENINGS INFORMATION	EMPLOYMENT COUNSELING	UNIVERSITY PLACEMENT OFFICE	LAW PLACEMENT OFFICE
Cleveland State University (Cleveland-Marshall College of Law) 1801 Euclid Avenue, Cleveland, OH 44115, 216-687-2304, Fax: 216-687-6881	$18,000-$90,000		2		2	16	15	4	5	1	9	41	96%	•	•	•	•	•	•	•	•	•	•	•	•		•
College of William and Mary (William and Mary Law School) P.O. Box 8795, Williamsburg, VA 23187-8795, 757-221-3785, Fax: 757-221-3261, lawadm@facstaff.wm.edu	$24,000-$91,000												96%	•	•	•	•	•	•	•	•	•	•	•	•		•
Columbia University (School of Law) 435 West 116th Street, New York, NY 10027, 212-854-2670, Fax: 212-854-1109	$35,000-$160,000	7	1		1	3	2	19	2	1	1	2		•	•	•	•	•	•	•	•	•	•	•	•		•
Cornell University (Law School) Myron Taylor Hall, Ithaca, NY 14853, 607-255-5141, Fax: 607-255-7193	$30,000-$108,000	98	5		5	1	3	21	11	10	1			•	•	•	•	•	•	•	•	•	•	•	•		•
Creighton University (School of Law) 2500 California Plaza, Omaha, NE 68178, 402-280-2872, Fax: 402-280-3161, admit@culaw.creighton.edu	$22,000-$65,000					21	18	8	8	5	20	48	96%	•	•	•	•	•	•	•	•	•	•	•	•		•
De Paul University (College of Law) 25 East Jackson Boulevard, Chicago, IL 60604, 312-362-6831, lawinfo@wppost.depaul.edu	$24,000-$90,000		2	1	2	24	15	4	13	3	11	25	90%	•	•	•	•	•	•	•	•	•	•	•	•	•	
Drake University (Law School) 2507 University Avenue, Des Moines, IA 50311, 515-271-1990, lawadmit@drake.edu	$22,000-$128,000		2	2	2	20	14	12	3	3	9	20	91%	•	•	•	•	•	•	•	•	•	•	•	•		•

School	%	A	B	C	D	E	F	G	H	I	J	K	Salary Range
Duke University (School of Law) Science and Towerview Drive, Box 90393 Durham, NC 27708 919-613-7020 Fax: 919-613-7257 admissions@law.duke.edu	99%		1	2	72	17	2	2	1	2	1	2	$35,000–$95,000
Duquesne University (School of Law) 900 Locust Street, Hanley Hall Pittsburgh, PA 15282 412-396-6296 campion@duq.edu	91%	14	5	5	4	9	12	16	18			16	$20,000–$90,000
Emory University (School of Law) Gambrell Hall Atlanta, GA 30322 404-727-6801 Fax: 404-727-2477 jbaley@law.emory.edu	95%	27	7	8	5	13	14	24	2		1		$30,750–$91,395
Florida Coastal School of Law 7555 Beach Boulevard Jacksonville, FL 32216 904-680-7710 Fax: 904-680-7776 admissions@fcsl.edu													
Florida State University (College of Law) 425 W. Jefferson St. Tallahassee, FL 32306-1601 850-644-3787 Fax: 850-644-7284 admissions@law.fsu.edu	92%	13	6	3	2	5	25	5	3	1	2	35	$24,000–$86,000
Fordham University (School of Law) 140 West 62nd Street New York, NY 10023 212-636-6810	99%	7	7	5	48	6	11	13	1		1		$40,000–$140,000
Franklin Pierce Law Center 2 White Street Concord, NH 03301 603-228-9217 Fax: 603-228-1074 L.admissions@fplc.edu	91%	22	10	22	10	6	12	12	2		2	2	$36,000–$75,000
George Mason University (School of Law) 3401 North Fairfax Drive Arlington, VA 22201-4498 703-993-8010 Fax: 703-993-8260 arichard@gmu.edu	99%	44				10	17	21	1	3	4		$16,000–$240,000
George Washington University (Law School) 2000 H Street, N.W. Washington, DC 20052 202-739-0648 jd@main.nlc.gwu.edu	98%					9	13	6	4		1	62	$67,641

SCHOOL	AVERAGE STARTING SALARY	OTHER	ACADEMIC	MILITARY	PUBLIC INTEREST	BUSINESS/INDUSTRY	GOVERNMENT	JUDICIAL CLERKSHIPS	PRIVATE PRACTICE 51-100 ATTORNEYS	PRIVATE PRACTICE 26-50 ATTORNEYS	PRIVATE PRACTICE 11-25 ATTORNEYS	PRIVATE PRACTICE 2-10 ATTORNEYS	PLACEMENT WITHIN 6 TO 9 MONTHS	ALUMNI PLACEMENT	INTERNSHIPS	PART-TIME/SUMMER EMPLOYMENT	ALUMNI CONTACTS	LAW, CORPORATE, AND GOVERNMENT CONTACT	JOB INTERVIEWS ARRANGEMENT	EMPLOYMENT PLANNING	INTERVIEW COUNSELING	RESUME PREPARATION	SOLO PRACTICE ADVICE	JOB OPENINGS INFORMATION	EMPLOYMENT COUNSELING	UNIVERSITY PLACEMENT OFFICE	LAW PLACEMENT OFFICE
Georgetown University (Law Center) 600 New Jersey Avenue, N.W. Washington, DC 20001 202-662-9010 admis@law.georgetown.edu	$15,800-$200,000	3		1	5	6	8	12	56	4			98%	•	•	•	•	•	•	•	•	•	•	•	•		•
Georgia State University (College of Law) P.O. Box 4037 Atlanta, GA 30302-4037 404-651-2096 Fax: 404-651-2096 cljackson@gsu.edu	$25,000-$101,000	21	2	1	1	21	9	6	6	3	5	25	94%	•	•	•	•	•	•	•	•	•	•	•	•		•
Golden Gate University (School of Law) 536 Mission Street San Francisco, CA 94105-2968 415-442-6630	$44,685		2		5	19	10	2	14	8	8	32	78%	•	•	•	•	•			•	•		•	•		•
Gonzaga University (School of Law) Box 3528 Spokane, WA 99220-3528 509-323-5532 Fax: 509-323-5710 admissions@lawschool.gonzaga.edu	$17,880-$75,800	6	2	3	2	12	22	7	2	3	6	35	85%	•	•	•	•	•	•		•	•	•	•	•		•
Hamline University (School of Law) 1536 Hewitt Avenue St. Paul, MN 55104-1284 651-523-2461 Fax: 651-523-3064 lawadm@gw.hamline.edu	$24,100-$70,000	6	2	1	3	23	12	21	1	1	5	25	96%	•	•	•	•	•	•	•	•	•	•	•	•		•
Harvard University (Harvard Law School) Cambridge, MA 02138 617-495-3109 Fax: 617-495-1110 jdadmiss@law.harvard.edu	$30,000-$135,000	61	1		4	8	2	24						•	•	•	•	•	•	•	•	•	•	•	•		•

School / Contact	Salary Range	Numeric data (as printed, top→bottom)	Placement Rate	Feature columns
Hofstra University (School of Law) 121 Hofstra University, Hempstead, NY 11549; 516-463-5916; Fax: 516-463-6264; lawpls@hofstra.edu	$21,000–$125,000	25, 1, 3, 14, 10, 5, 18, 1, 3, 12	98%	• • • • • • • • • • • • •
Howard University (Howard University) 2900 Van Ness Street, N.W., Washington, DC 20008; 202-806-8008; Fax: 202-806-8162; admissions@law.howard.edu	$30,000–$150,000	1, 1, 3, 19, 30, 16, 3, 3, 1, 5	91%	• • • • • • • • • • • • •
Illinois Institute of Technology (Chicago-Kent College of Law) 565 West Adams Street, Chicago, IL 60661; 312-906-5020; admit@kentlaw.edu	$12,000–$160,000	3, 1, 2, 19, 17, 5, 5, 5, 7, 19	95%	• • • • • • • • • • • • •
Indiana University-Purdue University (Indiana University School of Law-Indianapolis) 735 West New York Street, Indianapolis, IN 46202-5194; 317-274-2459; Fax: 317-274-3955; khmiller@iupui.edu	$24,000–$60,000	2, 3, 16, 12, 4	92%	• • • • • • • • • • • • •
Indiana University/Bloomington (School of Law) 211 S. Indiana Avenue, Bloomington, IN 47405-1001; 812-855-4765; Fax: 812-855-0555; lawadmis@indiana.edu	$19,000–$185,000	80, 3, 1, 5, 11, 12, 9, 9, 9, 5, 19	96%	• • • • • • • • • • • • •
Inter-American University of Puerto Rico (School of Law) P.O. Box 70351, San Juan, PR 00936-8351; 809-751-1912, ext. 2013				•
John Marshall Law School 315 South Plymouth Court, Chicago, IL 60604; 312-987-1406; Fax: 312-427-5136; admission@jmls.edu	$48,900	6, 1, 21, 12, 4, 4, 6, 7, 23	90%	• • • • • • • • • • • • •
Lewis and Clark College (Northwestern School of Law) 10015 Southwest Terwilliger Boulevard, Portland, OR 97219; 503-768-6613; Fax: 503-768-6671; lawadmss@clark.edu	$35,000–$50,000	14, 2, 5, 20, 17, 12, 3, 3, 6, 18	91%	• • • • • • • • • • • • •
Louisiana State University (Paul M. Hebert Law Center) Baton Rouge, LA 70803; 225-388-8646; Fax: 225-388-8647; bloup@lsu.edu	$23,000–$100,000	1, 1, 3, 7, 23, 7, 7, 20, 24	85%	• • • • • • • • • • • • •

SCHOOL	FACILITIES: LAW PLACEMENT OFFICE	FACILITIES: UNIVERSITY PLACEMENT OFFICE	SERVICES: EMPLOYMENT COUNSELING	SERVICES: JOB OPENINGS INFORMATION	SERVICES: SOLO PRACTICE ADVICE	SERVICES: RESUME PREPARATION	SERVICES: INTERVIEW COUNSELING	SERVICES: EMPLOYMENT PLANNING	SERVICES: JOB INTERVIEWS ARRANGEMENT	SERVICES: LAW, CORPORATE, AND GOVERNMENT CONTACT	SERVICES: ALUMNI CONTACTS	SERVICES: PART-TIME/SUMMER EMPLOYMENT	SERVICES: INTERNSHIPS	SERVICES: ALUMNI PLACEMENT	PLACEMENT WITHIN 6 TO 9 MONTHS	PRIV. PRACT. 2-10 ATTORNEYS	PRIV. PRACT. 11-25 ATTORNEYS	PRIV. PRACT. 26-50 ATTORNEYS	PRIV. PRACT. 51-100 ATTORNEYS	JUDICIAL CLERKSHIPS	GOVERNMENT	BUSINESS/INDUSTRY	PUBLIC INTEREST	MILITARY	ACADEMIC	OTHER	AVERAGE STARTING SALARY
Loyola Marymount University (Loyola Law School) 919 S. Albany Street, Los Angeles, CA 90015, 213-736-1180, admissions@lls.edu	•		•	•	•	•	•	•	•	•	•	•	•	•	91%	14	9	12	15	3	10	22	3		4	8	$40,000-$83,000
Loyola University - New Orleans (School of Law) 7214 St. Charles Avenue, New Orleans, LA 70118, 504-861-5575, Fax: 504-861-5772, ladmit@loyno.edu	•	•	•	•	•	•	•	•	•	•	•	•	•	•	93%	50				12	8	10	7		1	12	$42,000-$60,000
Loyola University Chicago (School of Law) One East Pearson Street, Chicago, IL 60611, 312-915-7170, Fax: 312-915-7201, law-admissions@luc.edu	•		•	•	•	•	•	•	•	•	•	•	•	•	96%	10	5	3	2	3	19	18	2	1	1	40	$20,000-$101,000
Marquette University (Law School) Office of Admissions, Sensenbrenner Hall, P.O. Box 1881, Milwaukee, WI 53201-1881, 414-288-6767, Fax: 414-288-0676, law.admission@marquette.edu	•		•	•	•	•	•	•	•	•	•	•	•	•	93%	24	11	7	3	10	8	10	3		1	23	$25,500-$90,000
Mercer University (Walter F. George School of Law) 1021 Georgia Ave., Macon, GA 31201, 912-301-2605, Fax: 912-301-2989, Sutton_me@mercer.edu	•		•	•	•	•	•	•	•	•	•	•	•	•	90%	30	5	5	3	18	9	4	3	1	2	3	$24,000-$78,000
Michigan State University (Detroit College of Law) 316 Law College Bldg., East Lansing, MI 48824-1300, 517-432-0222, Fax: 517-432-0098, heatleya@pilot.msu.edu	•		•	•	•	•	•	•	•	•	•	•	•	•	86%	28	6	2	3	12	10	16	3		1		$30,000-$64,000

School	Salary												%
Mississippi College (School of Law) 151 E. Griffith Street, Jackson, MS 39201 / 601-925-7150 / pevans@mc.edu	$35,000–$48,000			1		2	10	20		10	25	30	90%
New England School of Law 154 Stuart Street, Boston, MA 02116 / 617-422-7210 / Fax: 617-422-7200 / admit@admin.nesl.edu	$27,000–$95,000	2	2	1	3	26	13	9	6	3	4	31	87%
New York Law School 57 Worth Street, New York, NY 10013-2960 / 212-431-2888 / Fax: 212-966-1522 / admissions@nyls.edu	$39,500–$62,500	45	2		3		20	6					93%
New York University (School of Law) 110 West Third Street, New York, NY 10012 / 212-998-6060 / Fax: 212-995-4527	$37,500		1		9		3	16	11	5	1	1	100%
North Carolina Central University (School of Law) 1512 S. Alston Avenue, Durham, NC 27707 / 919-560-6333 / Fax: 919-560-6339 / jfaucett@wpo.nccu.edu	$25,000–$101,000	43	2	2	6	5	18	5					89%
Northeastern University (School of Law) 400 Huntington Avenue, Boston, MA 02115 / 617-373-2395 / Fax: 617-373-8865 / pbauer@slaw.neu.edu	$23,000–$94,000	7		2	18	6	8	23	16	5	4	12	94%
Northern Illinois University (College of Law) Swen Parson Hall, De Kalb, IL 60115 / 815-753-1420 / Fax: 815-753-4501 / lawadm@niu.edu	$27,000–$70,000	4	1	1	16	10	19	4	6	13	6	20	90%
Northern Kentucky University (Salmon P. Chase College of Law) Louie B. Nunn Hall, Highland Heights, KY 41099 / 606-572-6476 / Fax: 606-572-6081 / brayg@nku.edu	$20,000–$100,000	1	1	1	1	26	18	8		1	5	33	94%
Northwestern University (School of Law) 357 East Chicago Avenue, Chicago, IL 60611 / 312-503-8465 / Fax: 312-503-0178 / nubwadm@nwu.edu	$34,200–$125,000		2				6	11				74	99%

SCHOOL	AVERAGE STARTING SALARY	PLACEMENT RECORD — Percentage Breakdown of Type of Employer											PLACEMENT WITHIN 6 TO 9 MONTHS	PLACEMENT SERVICES												FACILITIES	
		OTHER	ACADEMIC	MILITARY	PUBLIC INTEREST	BUSINESS/INDUSTRY	GOVERNMENT	JUDICIAL CLERKSHIPS	PRIVATE PRACTICE 51-100 ATTORNEYS	PRIVATE PRACTICE 26-50 ATTORNEYS	PRIVATE PRACTICE 11-25 ATTORNEYS	PRIVATE PRACTICE 2-10 ATTORNEYS		ALUMNI PLACEMENT	INTERNSHIPS	PART-TIME/SUMMER EMPLOYMENT	ALUMNI CONTACTS	LAW, CORPORATE, AND GOVERNMENT CONTACT	JOB INTERVIEWS ARRANGEMENT	EMPLOYMENT PLANNING	INTERVIEW COUNSELING	RESUME PREPARATION	SOLO PRACTICE ADVICE	JOB OPENINGS INFORMATION	EMPLOYMENT COUNSELING	UNIVERSITY PLACEMENT OFFICE	LAW PLACEMENT OFFICE
Nova Southeastern University (Shepard Broad Law Center) 3305 College Avenue Fort Lauderdale, FL 33314-7721 954-262-6117 Fax: 954-262-3844 admission@nsu.law.nova.edu	$29,914-$38,747	8	1	1	2	15	22	3	4	4	12	28	86%	•	•	•	•	•	•	•	•	•	•	•	•		•
Ohio Northern University (Claude W. Pettit College of Law) 525 South Main Street Ada, OH 45810 419-772-2211 Fax: 419-772-1487 g-keener@onu.edu	$23,300-$77,000		2	2	9	15	16	11	4	2	2	34	50%	•	•	•	•	•	•	•	•	•	•	•	•		•
Ohio State University (College of Law) 55 West 12th Avenue, John Deaver Drinko Hall Columbus, OH 43210-1391 614-292-8810 Fax: 614-292-1383 roboski.1@osu.edu	$28,413-$55,268	2	2	4	3	13	14	10				52	93%	•	•	•	•	•	•	•	•	•	•	•	•		•
Oklahoma City University (School of Law) 2501 North Blackwelder Oklahoma City, OK 73106-1493 405-521-5354 Fax: 405-521-5802 lawadmit@okcu.edu	$27,500-$42,000	14	4		2	12	17	6	1	4	7	27	78%	•	•	•	•	•	•	•	•	•	•	•	•		•
Pace University (School of Law) 78 North Broadway White Plains, NY 10603 914-422-4010 Fax: 914-422-4248 adagostino@genesis.law.pace.edu	$38,000-$65,500	17	2		3	18	16	3	4	3	9	20	86%	•	•	•	•	•	•	•	•	•	•	•	•		•
Pennsylvania State University (Dickinson School of Law) 150 South College Street Carlisle, PA 17013 717-240-5207 Fax: 717-241-3503 dsladmit@psu.edu	$25,000-$80,000	2	1	2	2	6	11	33	14	3	8	18	94%	•	•	•	•	•	•	•	•	•	•	•	•		•

School	Salary Range												%
Pepperdine University (School of Law) 24255 Pacific Coast Highway, Malibu, CA 90263, 310-456-4631, Fax: 310-317-7668, soladmis@pepperdine.edu													92%
Quinnipiac College (School of Law) 275 Mt. Carmel Avenue, Hamden, CT 06518-1948, 203-287-3400, Fax: 203-287-3339, ladm@quinnipiac.edu	$34,000–$38,000	9	1		4	22	16	6	42	42	42	42	94%
Regent University (School of Law) 1000 Regent University Drive, Virginia Beach, VA 23464-9800, 757-226-4584, Fax: 757-226-4139, lawschool@regent.edu		6	8	3	6	14	10	1		2	6	44	79%
Roger Williams University (School of Law) Ten Metacom Avenue, Bristol, RI 02809-5171, 401-254-4555, Fax: 401-254-4516, admissions@rwulaw.rwu.edu	$25,000–$105,000		1		4	28	9	8	2	2	2	44	92%
Rutgers University/Newark (School of Law) S.I. Newhouse Center for Law and Justice, 15 Washington St., Newark, NJ 07102, 973-353-5557/5554, Fax: 973-353-1445	$25,000–$85,000		2		5	20	9	24					92%
Rutgers, The State University of New Jersey (School of Law–Camden) Fifth and Penn Streets, Camden, NJ 08102, 609-225-6102, Fax: 609-225-6537	$30,000–$105,000	3	1	3	2	16	7	41	14	4	4	5	95%
Saint John's University (School of Law) 8000 Utopia Parkway, Jamaica, NY 11439, 718-990-6611/6612, Fax: 718-990-2526, rsvp@sjulaw.stjohns.edu	$24,000–$165,000		7	2	1	12	20	11	8	9	9	21	95%
Saint Louis University (School of Law) 3700 Lindell Boulevard, St. Louis, MO 63108, 314-977-2800, admissions@law.slu.edu	$33,000–$66,000	18	1	1	1	21	10	9	8	6	2	20	95%
Saint Mary's University (School of Law) One Camino Santa Maria, San Antonio, TX 78228-8601, 210-436-3523, Fax: 210-431-4202	$24,000–$55,000	35	2	1	1	4	10	7	7	2	2	29	92%

Placement Record and Placement Services

School	Average Starting Salary	Other	Academic	Military	Public Interest	Business/Industry	Government	Judicial Clerkships	Private Practice 51–100 Attorneys	Private Practice 26–50 Attorneys	Private Practice 11–25 Attorneys	Private Practice 2–10 Attorneys	Placement Within 6 to 9 Months
Samford University (Cumberland School of Law) 800 Lakeshore Drive, Birmingham, AL 35229; 205-726-2702; Fax: 205-726-2673; lawadmissions@samford.edu	$24,600–$100,000		2	3	2	10	10	9	3	4	17	45	92%
Santa Clara University (School of Law) 500 El Camino Real, Santa Clara, CA 95053; 408-554-4800; Fax: 408-554-7897; lawadmission@scu.edu	$65,000				1	21	6	4	7	2	9	17	90%
Seattle University (School of Law) 900 Broadway, Seattle, WA 98122-4340; 206-398-4200; Fax: 206-398-4058; lawadmis@seattleu.edu	$26,000–$75,000	2	1	1	3	15	15	7	12	3	5	36	90%
Seton Hall University (School of Law) One Newark Center, Newark, NJ 07102-5210; 973-642-8747; Fax: 973-642-8876; admitme@shu.edu													96%
South Texas College of Law 1303 San Jacinto Street, Houston, TX 77002-7000; 713-646-1810; Fax: 713-646-2929; acramer@stcl.edu	$36,000–$56,000				1	17	11	6	6	6	6	31	82%
Southern Illinois University (School of Law) Lesar Law Building, Mail Code 6804, Carbondale, IL 62901-6804; 618-453-8767; Fax: 618-453-8769; lawadmit@siu.edu	$25,000–$90,000		1	3	2	8	26	5	5	4	12	27	95%

Placement Services / Facilities

School	Alumni Placement	Internships	Part-Time/Summer Employment	Alumni Contacts	Law, Corporate, and Government Contact	Job Interviews Arrangement	Employment Planning	Interview Counseling	Resume Preparation	Solo Practice Advice	Job Openings Information	Employment Counseling	University Placement Office	Law Placement Office
Samford University (Cumberland School of Law)	•	•	•	•	•	•	•	•	•	•	•	•		•
Santa Clara University (School of Law)	•	•	•	•	•		•	•	•	•	•	•		•
Seattle University (School of Law)	•	•	•	•	•		•	•	•	•	•	•		•
Seton Hall University (School of Law)	•	•	•	•	•	•	•	•	•	•	•	•		•
South Texas College of Law	•	•	•	•	•	•	•	•	•	•	•	•		•
Southern Illinois University (School of Law)	•	•	•	•	•	•	•	•	•	•	•	•		•

School	Salary												%
Southern Methodist University (School of Law) Office of Admissions, P.O. Box 750110 Dallas, TX 75275-0110 214-768-2550 Fax: 214-768-2549	$66,000	5			1	15	8	3	69				95%
Southern University and A & M College (Law Center) Post Office Box 9294 Baton Rouge, LA 70813 225-771-5340 Fax: 225-771-2121	$28,000-$53,000	6	5	4	2	4	32	12	2	1	1	31	10%
Southwestern University (School of Law) 675 South Westmoreland Avenue Los Angeles, CA 90005-3992 213-738-6717 Fax: 213-383-1688 admissions@swlaw.edu	$52,000	10	1		1	16	12	4	9	5	13	28	87%
St. Thomas University (School of Law) 16400 N.W. 32nd Avenue Miami, FL 33054 305-623-2310 lamy@stu.edu	$37,212-$38,559	10	1		2	14	18	2	1	2	5	33	90%
Stanford University (Stanford Law School) Crown Quadrangle Stanford, CA 94305-8610 650-723-4985 Fax: 650-723-0838 law.admissions@forsythe.stanford.edu/		47	2		2	12		25	5	3	2	2	99%
State University of New York at Buffalo (University at Buffalo Law School) O'Brian Hall Buffalo, NY 14260 716-645-2907 Fax: 716-645-5940 coxublaw@buffalo.edu	$27,532-$61,632		12		8	11	13	4	13	2	6	25	95%
Stetson University (College of Law) 1401 61st Street South St. Petersburg, FL 33707 727-562-7802 Fax: 727-343-0136 lawadmit@hermes.law.stetson.edu	$30,000-$67,500	12	5	1	2	5	29	5	5	2	8	26	93%
Suffolk University (Law School) 120 Tremont Street Boston, MA 02108-4977 617-573-8144 Fax: 617-573-1367	$22,000-$60,000	1	3	1	1	28	17	9	3	10	15	12	94%
Syracuse University (College of Law) Office of Admissions and Financial Aid Syracuse, NY 13244-1030 315-443-1962 Fax: 315-443-9568	$20,800-$101,000	27	3	3	3	18	14	8	3	5	4	8	88%

PLACEMENT RECORD / PLACEMENT SERVICES

School	Average Starting Salary	Other	Academic	Military	Public Interest	Business/Industry	Government	Judicial Clerkships	Private Practice 51-100 Attorneys	Private Practice 26-50 Attorneys	Private Practice 11-25 Attorneys	Private Practice 2-10 Attorneys	Placement Within 6 to 9 Months
Temple University (James E. Beasley School of Law) — 1719 N. Broad Street, Philadelphia, PA 19122; 215-204-9925; Fax: 215-204-1185; lawadmis@blue.temple.edu	$30,000–$76,000		2	1	6	20	11	11	22	4	8	15	92%
Texas Southern University (Thurgood Marshall School of Law) — 3100 Cleburne Avenue, Houston, TX 77004; 713-313-7114; Fax: 713-313-1049; cgardher@tsulaw.edu	$47,000				2	4	7					88	72%
Texas Tech University (School of Law) — 1802 Hartford, Lubbock, TX 79409; 806-742-3985; Fax: 806-742-1629; xydaw@ttacs.ttu.edu	$24,000–$87,000						10	5	24	19	29	13	93%
Texas Wesleyan University (School of Law) — 1515 Commerce Street, Fort Worth, TX 76102; 817-212-4040; Fax: 817-212-4002; law-admissions@law.txwes.edu	$33,000–$80,000		1		1	12	14	3		4	9	56	83%
Thomas Jefferson School of Law — 2121 San Diego Avenue, San Diego, CA 92110; 619-297-9700; Fax: 619-294-4713; adm@tjsl.edu	$30,000–$75,000	14	7	1	1	28	12	1	2	2	2	33	90%
Thomas M. Cooley Law School — 300 South Capitol Avenue, Lansing, MI 48901; 517-371-5140; Fax: 517-334-5718; admissions@cooley.edu	$16,500–$104,000		1		4	9	22	1		2	9	50	88%

Placement Services

School	Alumni Placement	Internships	Part-Time/Summer Employment	Alumni Contacts	Law, Corporate, and Government Contact	Job Interviews Arrangement	Employment Planning	Interview Counseling	Resume Preparation	Solo Practice Advice	Job Openings Information	Employment Counseling	University Placement Office	Law Placement Office
Temple University	•	•	•	•	•	•	•	•	•	•	•	•		•
Texas Southern University	•	•	•	•	•	•	•	•	•	•	•	•		•
Texas Tech University	•	•	•	•	•	•	•	•	•	•	•	•		•
Texas Wesleyan University	•	•	•	•	•	•	•	•	•	•	•	•		•
Thomas Jefferson School of Law	•	•	•	•	•	•	•	•	•	•	•	•		•
Thomas M. Cooley Law School	•	•	•	•	•	•	•	•	•	•	•	•		•

School												%	Salary
Touro College (Jacob D. Fuchsberg Law Center) 300 Nassau Road Huntington, NY 11743 631-421-2244 ext. 312 Fax: 631-421-9708 admissions@tourolaw.edu	2	1	1	4	16	17	5	6	2	12	33	78%	
Tulane University (Law School) Weinmann Hall, 6329 Freret Street New Orleans, LA 70118 504-865-5930 Fax: 504-865-6710 admissions@law.tulane.edu	48	2		2	10	12	16					85%	$33,189-$75,000
Union University (Albany Law School) 80 New Scotland Avenue Albany, NY 12208 518-445-2326 Fax: 518-445-2369 admissions@mail.als.edu		2		2	16	21	7	9	6	9	26	95%	$26,500-$101,000
University of Akron (School of Law) Corner Wolf Ledges and University Avenue Akron, OH 44325-2901 330-972-7331 Fax: 330-258-2343 lawadmissions@uakron.edu	5	1	2	1	22	26	6	3	1	5	24	97%	$39,328
University of Alabama (School of Law) Box 870382 Tuscaloosa, AL 35487-0382 205-348-5440 Fax: 205-348-3917 admissions@law.ua.edu		1		3	6	9	10	15	10	9	36	99%	$35,000-$56,000
University of Arizona (James E. Rogers College of Law) Mountain and Speedway P.O. Box 210176 Tucson, AZ 85721-0176 520-621-3477 Fax: 520-621-9140 admissions@nt.law.arizona.edu		5	2	3	13	17	15	15	10	8	12	93%	$28,000-$94,000
University of Arkansas (School of Law) Robert A. Leflar Law Center, Waterman Hall Fayetteville, AR 72701 501-575-3102		2		2	21	14	9	3	1	9	32	95%	$18,000-$82,000
University of Arkansas at Little Rock (School of Law) 1201 McAlmont Street Little Rock, AR 72202-5142 501-324-9439 Fax: 501-324-9433	6	1		2	21	20	11	1	1	4	33	95%	$16,000-$90,000
University of Baltimore (School of Law) 1420 North Charles Street Baltimore, MD 21201-5779 410-837-4459 Fax: 410-837-4450 lwadmiss@ubmail.ubalt.edu				3	6	14	31	47	47	47	47	92%	$39,391

	UC Hastings	UC Berkeley (Boalt Hall)	UCLA	UC Davis	U. Chicago	U. Cincinnati	U. Colorado
FACILITIES							
LAW PLACEMENT OFFICE	•	•	•	•	•		•
UNIVERSITY PLACEMENT OFFICE		•					
SERVICES							
EMPLOYMENT COUNSELING	•	•	•	•	•	•	•
JOB OPENINGS INFORMATION	•	•	•	•	•	•	•
SOLO PRACTICE ADVICE	•	•	•	•	•	•	•
RESUME PREPARATION	•	•	•	•	•	•	•
INTERVIEW COUNSELING	•	•	•	•	•	•	•
EMPLOYMENT PLANNING	•	•	•	•	•	•	•
JOB INTERVIEWS ARRANGEMENT	•	•	•	•	•	•	•
LAW, CORPORATE, AND GOVERNMENT CONTACT	•	•	•	•	•	•	•
ALUMNI CONTACTS	•	•	•	•	•	•	•
PART-TIME/SUMMER EMPLOYMENT	•	•	•	•	•	•	•
INTERNSHIPS	•	•	•	•	•	•	•
ALUMNI PLACEMENT	•	•	•	•	•	•	•
PLACEMENT RECORD							
PLACEMENT WITHIN 6 TO 9 MONTHS	95%	97%	98%	92%	98%	93%	89%
Percentage Breakdown of Type of Employer							
PRIVATE PRACTICE 2-10 ATTORNEYS	15	2	8	15		10	17
PRIVATE PRACTICE 11-25 ATTORNEYS	4	5	7	16		8	3
PRIVATE PRACTICE 26-50 ATTORNEYS	5	3	10	8		5	2
PRIVATE PRACTICE 51-100 ATTORNEYS	8	4	9	8		4	4
JUDICIAL CLERKSHIPS	7	12	8	12	25	9	14
GOVERNMENT	10	8	5	14	1	4	13
BUSINESS/INDUSTRY	13	5	8	1	7	19	10
PUBLIC INTEREST	3	6	3	7	1	4	3
MILITARY				1		3	5
ACADEMIC	1	1	1	1		2	
OTHER	24	54	41	1	67	19	
AVERAGE STARTING SALARY	$26,000-$90,000	$27,000-$145,000	$87,000	$26,400-$95,000	$37,000-$125,000	$23,900-$103,000	$25,000-$94,000

SCHOOL

University of California (Hastings College of the Law)
200 McAllister Street
San Francisco, CA 94102
415-565-4623
Fax: 415-565-4863
admiss@uchastings.edu

University of California at Berkeley (Boalt Hall)
5 Boalt Hall
Berkeley, CA 94720
510-642-2274
Fax: 510-643-6222
admissions@law.berkeley.edu

University of California at Los Angeles (School of Law)
P.O. Box 951445
Los Angeles, CA 90095-1445
310-825-2080
Fax: 310-825-9450
admissions@law.ucla.edu

University of California, Davis (School of Law)
King Hall - 400 Mrak Hall Drive
Davis, CA 95616-5201
530-752-6477
lawadmissions@ucdavis.edu

University of Chicago (Law School)
1111 East 60th Street
Chicago, IL 60637
773-702-9484
Fax: 773-834-0942
admissions@law.uchicago.edu

University of Cincinnati (College of Law)
P.O. Box 210040
Cincinnati, OH 45221-0040
513-556-6805
Admissions@law.uc.edu

University of Colorado (School of Law)
Campus Box 403
Boulder, CO 80309-0403
303-492-7203

School												%	Salary Range
University of Connecticut (School of Law) — 55 Elizabeth Street, Hartford, CT 06105; 860-570-5159; Fax: 860-570-5153; admit@law.uconn.edu	48	2	2	3	19	14	13	9				96%	$28,000–$101,000
University of Dayton (School of Law) — 300 College Park, Dayton, OH 45469-2760; 937-229-3555; Fax: 937-229-4194; lawinfo@udayton.edu	10	2	2	4	24	20	7	3	5	7	27	88%	$23,000–$80,000
University of Denver (College of Law) — 7039 E. 18th Avenue, Denver, CO 80220; 303-871-6135; Fax: 303-871-6100		1	2	2	14	17	4	3	4	10	45	86%	$28,000–$72,000
University of Detroit Mercy (School of Law) — 651 East Jefferson Avenue, Detroit, MI 48226; 313-596-0264; Fax: 313-596-0280; udmlawao@udmercy.edu		3		3	20	20	9	3	2	5	18	85%	$41,000
University of Florida (College of Law) — 325 Holland Hall P.O. Box 117622, Gainesville, FL 32611-7622; 352-392-2087; Fax: 352-392-2087; patrick@law.ufl.edu				1	6	19	6	5	5	7	9	85%	$28,000–$75,000
University of Georgia (School of Law) — Hirsch Hall, 225 Herty Drive, Athens, GA 30602-6012; 706-542-7060	12			4	14	6	16	4	6	11	22	96%	$20,000–$82,000
University of Hawaii-Manoa (William S. Richardson School of Law) — 2515 Dole Street, Honolulu, HI 96822; 808-956-7966; Fax: 808-956-3813; lawadm@hawaii.edu				3	12	15	36	8	7	8	13	93%	$24,000–$70,000
University of Houston (Law Center) — Office of Admissions, Houston, TX 77204-6391; 713-743-1070; Fax: 713-743-2194; admission@www.law.uh.edu		17		1	21	10	27					93%	$45,000–$78,000
University of Idaho (College of Law) — P.O. Box 442321, Moscow, ID 83844-2321; 208-885-6423; Fax: 208-885-5709; adewittl@uidaho.edu		3			8	16	29				42	93%	$36,500

(Each school row also carries a series of "•" marks in the feature/checklist columns that follow; these were present for all listed schools.)

PLACEMENT SERVICES

FACILITIES / SERVICES

School	Law Placement Office	University Placement Office	Employment Counseling	Job Openings Information	Solo Practice Advice	Resume Preparation	Interview Counseling	Employment Planning	Job Interviews Arrangement	Law, Corporate, and Government Contact	Alumni Contacts	Part-Time/Summer Employment	Internships	Alumni Placement
University of Illinois (College of Law)	•	•	•	•	•	•	•	•	•	•	•	•	•	•
University of Iowa (College of Law)	•		•	•	•	•	•	•	•	•	•	•	•	•
University of Kansas (School of Law)	•		•	•	•	•	•	•	•	•	•	•	•	•
University of Kentucky (College of Law)	•		•	•	•	•	•	•	•	•	•	•	•	•
University of Louisville (Louis D. Brandeis School of Law)	•		•	•	•	•	•	•	•	•	•		•	•
University of Maine (School of Law)	•		•	•	•	•	•	•	•	•	•	•		•

PLACEMENT RECORD

Percentage Breakdown of Type of Employer

School	Placement Within 6 to 9 Months	Private Practice 2-10 Attorneys	Private Practice 11-25 Attorneys	Private Practice 26-50 Attorneys	Private Practice 51-100 Attorneys	Judicial Clerkships	Government	Business/Industry	Public Interest	Military	Academic	Other	Average Starting Salary
University of Illinois (College of Law)	96%	11	13	6	12	20	16	21	2	6	5		$22,200-$91,500
University of Iowa (College of Law)	99%	16	6	5	4	14	8	10	7	2	2	25	$30,000-$110,000
University of Kansas (School of Law)	94%	26	14	6	11	7	2	26	4	2	2		$23,000-$52,000
University of Kentucky (College of Law)	98%	30	7	6	7	14	7	14	4	1		10	$22,000-$78,000
University of Louisville (Louis D. Brandeis School of Law)	94%	28	11	9	12	3	18	16	2	1	2		$19,300-$65,000
University of Maine (School of Law)	84%	30	12	4	5	22	10	13	7				$20,000-$50,000

SCHOOL

University of Illinois (College of Law)
504 East Pennsylvania Avenue
Champaign, IL 61820
217-244-6415
Fax: 217-244-1478

University of Iowa (College of Law)
276 Boyd Law Building, Melrose at Byington Street
Iowa City, IA 52242
319-335-9095 or 319-335-9142
Fax: 319-335-9019
law-admissions@uiowa.edu

University of Kansas (School of Law)
205 Green Hall
Lawrence, KS 66045
785-864-4378
Fax: 785-864-5054
lindeman@law.wpo.ukans.edu

University of Kentucky (College of Law)
209 Law Building
Lexington, KY 40506-0048
606-257-7938
dbaker@pop.uky.edu

University of Louisville (Louis D. Brandeis School of Law)
University of Louisville Belknap Campus-
Wilson W. Wyatt Hall
Louisville, KY 40292
502-852-6364
Fax: 502-852-0862
charlene.olivia@louisville.edu

University of Maine (School of Law)
246 Deering Avenue
Portland, ME 04102
207-780-4341

Institution	Salary Range												%	Features
University of Maryland (School of Law) 515 West Lombard Street Baltimore, MD 21201 410-706-3492 Fax: 410-706-4045 admissions@law.umaryland.edu	—	16	2	2	2	14	24	24	4	4	3	7	96%	• • • • • • • • • • •
University of Memphis (Cecil C. Humphreys School of Law) Campus Box 526513 Memphis, TN 38152-6513 901-678-2073 Fax: 901-678-5210 uofmlaw@profnet.law.memphis.edu	$35,068-$60,760		1	1	3	11	11	10	2	6	13	31	96%	• • • • • • • • • • • • •
University of Miami (School of Law) P.O. Box 248087, 1311 Miller Drive Coral Gables, FL 33124-8087 305-284-2523 admissions@law.miami.edu	$20,000-$105,000	7	1	1	4	12	14	3	59	6	13		91%	• • • • • • • • • • • •
University of Michigan (Law School) 625 South State Street Ann Arbor, MI 48109-1215 313-764-0537	(faint)				1	3		15				75	39%	• • • • • • • • •
University of Minnesota (Law School) 229 19th Avenue S., Office of Admissions Minneapolis, MN 55455 612-625-3487 Fax: 612-626-1874	$25,000-$99,000	5	2		3	15	7	24	29	9	5	4	99%	• • • • • • • • • • •
University of Mississippi (School of Law) Lamar Hall Oxford, MS 38677 601-915-6910 Fax: 601-915-1289 bvinson@olemiss.edu	$21,000-$90,000			1	1	9	9	16	4	7	10	26	96%	• • • • • • • • • •
University of Missouri-Columbia (School of Law) 103 Hulston Hall Columbia, MO 65211 573-882-6042 Fax: 573-882-9625 umclawadmissions@missouri.edu	$19,000-$70,000	19	1	1	1	13	23	13	7	10	22	38	90%	• • • • • • • • • • • •
University of Missouri-Kansas City (School of Law) 500 East 52nd Street Kansas City, MO 64110-2499 816-235-1644 Fax: 816-235-5276 klosterman@umkc.edu	$20,000-$70,000	2	1	1		14	21	11	1	1	2	23	94%	• • • • • • • • • •
University of Montana (School of Law) Missoula, MT 59812 406-243-2698 lawadmis@selway.umt.edu	$33,750	1	3		3	9	12	20				43	93%	• • • • • • • • • •

SCHOOL	LAW PLACEMENT OFFICE	UNIVERSITY PLACEMENT OFFICE	EMPLOYMENT COUNSELING	JOB OPENINGS INFORMATION	SOLO PRACTICE ADVICE	RESUME PREPARATION	INTERVIEW COUNSELING	EMPLOYMENT PLANNING	JOB INTERVIEWS ARRANGEMENT	LAW, CORPORATE, AND GOVERNMENT CONTACT	ALUMNI CONTACTS	PART-TIME/SUMMER EMPLOYMENT	INTERNSHIPS	ALUMNI PLACEMENT	PLACEMENT WITHIN 6 TO 9 MONTHS	PRIVATE PRACTICE 2-10 ATTORNEYS	PRIVATE PRACTICE 11-25 ATTORNEYS	PRIVATE PRACTICE 26-50 ATTORNEYS	PRIVATE PRACTICE 51-100 ATTORNEYS	JUDICIAL CLERKSHIPS	GOVERNMENT	BUSINESS/INDUSTRY	PUBLIC INTEREST	MILITARY	ACADEMIC	OTHER	AVERAGE STARTING SALARY
University of Nebraska (College of Law) P.O. Box 830902 Lincoln, NE 68583-0902 402-472-2161 Fax: 402-472-5185 lawadm@unlinfo.unl.edu	•	•	•	•	•	•	•	•	•	•	•	•	•	•	96%	21	9	1	3		23	17	4		4	4	$24,000-$70,000
University of New Mexico (School of Law) 1117 Stanford Drive N.E. Albuquerque, NM 87131-1431 505-277-5072 Fax: 505-277-9958	•			•	•		•		•	•	•	•	•	•	93%	28	8	3	3	16	26	6	1			9	$25,000-$150,000
University of North Carolina at Chapel Hill (School of Law) Campus Box 3380, 101 Van Hecke-Wettach Hall Chapel Hill, NC 27599-3380 919-962-5109 Fax: 919-843-7939 law_admission@unc.edu	•	•	•	•	•	•	•	•	•	•	•	•	•	•	98%	15	4	4	4	10	11	10	6	1	1		$23,000-$100,000
University of North Dakota (School of Law) Box 9003 Grand Forks, ND 58202 701-777-2104 Fax: 701-777-2217 linda.kohoutek@thor.law.und.nodak.edu	•		•	•	•	•	•	•	•	•	•	•	•	•	100%	32	3	2		35	10	14		4			$19,000-$70,000
University of Notre Dame (Notre Dame Law School) P.O. Box 959 Notre Dame, IN 46556-0959 219-631-6626 Fax: 219-631-3980 lawbulletin.1@nd.edu				•	•	•	•	•	•	•	•	•	•	•	96%	5	6	3	6	11	6	9	3	3	3		$60,000
University of Oklahoma (College of Law) 300 Timberdell Road Norman, OK 73019 405-325-4726 Fax: 405-325-0502 kmadden@ou.edu			•	•	•	•	•	•	•	•	•	•	•	•	87%	25	24	6	6	4	19	9	1	3	3	3	$20,000-$80,000

School	Salary Range												%
University of Oregon (School of Law, William W. Knight Law Center) 1515 Agate Street, Eugene, OR 97403-1221 · 541-346-1553 · Fax: 541-346-3984 · bmcclure@law.uoregon.edu													
University of Pennsylvania (Law School) 3400 Chestnut Street, Philadelphia, PA 19104-6204 · 215-898-7400 · admissions@oyez.law.upenn.edu	$30,000–$100,000	1		3	3	5	1	19	70	1			99%
University of Pittsburgh (School of Law) 3900 Forbes Avenue, Pittsburgh, PA 15260 · 412-648-1412 · Fax: 412-648-2647 · admissions@law.pitt.edu	$16,000–$94,000		1	3	3	16	10	13	5	7	5	19	94%
University of Puerto Rico (School of Law) P.O. Box 23349, UPR Station, Rio Piedras, PR 00931 · 787-764-1655 · Fax: 787-764-2675	$28,000–$35,000	5			1	1	30	10	16	15	13	9	
University of Richmond (The T.C. Williams School of Law) University of Richmond, VA 23173 · 804-289-8189 · admissions@uofrlaw.richmond.edu		7		2	4	15	12	14	5	4	5	22	99%
University of San Diego (School of Law) 5998 Alcala Park, San Diego, CA 92110 · 619-260-4528 · Fax: 619-260-2218 · jdinfo@acusd.edu	$30,000–$85,000		1	1	1	15	17	2	11	9	14	29	88%
University of San Francisco (School of Law) 2130 Fulton Street, San Francisco, CA 94117-1080 · 415-422-6586 · Fax: 415-422-6433	$57,073–$52,000	7	1	1	5	15	7	5				60	81%
University of South Carolina (School of Law) Main and Greene Streets, Columbia, SC 29208 · 803-777-7605 · Fax: 803-777-7751 · usclaw@law.law.sc.edu	$26,000–$91,000	6	1	1	2	6	11	24	4	3	11	32	92%
University of South Dakota (School of Law) 414 East Clark Street, Vermillion, SD 57069-2390 · 605-677-5443 · Fax: 605-677-5417 · lawreq@usd.edu	$25,000–$30,000		2			12	18	33	2		2	31	94%

PLACEMENT RECORD

School	Average Starting Salary	Other	Academic	Military	Public Interest	Business/Industry	Government	Judicial Clerkships	Private Practice 51-100 Attorneys	Private Practice 26-50 Attorneys	Private Practice 11-25 Attorneys	Private Practice 2-10 Attorneys	Placement Within 6 to 9 Months
University of Southern California (Law School)	$87,000–$91,000				6	14	5	10	30	20	10	5	95%
University of Tennessee (College of Law)	$28,000–$70,000	11	1	3	6	7	11	14	2	5	11	27	93%
University of Texas at Austin (School of Law)	$61,626	30	1	1	2	9	9	10	5	5	9	10	98%
University of the District of Columbia (David A. Clarke School of Law)		6	1	1	4	17	20	2				50	83%
University of the Pacific (McGeorge School of Law)	$39,000–$55,000		1		2	11	26	4		5	10	56	85%
University of Toledo (College of Law)	$19,200–$75,000		1	2	1	22	18	5	5	5		31	97%
University of Tulsa (College of Law)	$38,000	3	1	2	4	25	11	2	1	2	4	37	91%

PLACEMENT SERVICES

Services: Alumni Placement • Internships • Part-Time/Summer Employment • Alumni Contacts • Law, Corporate, and Government Contact • Job Interviews Arrangement • Employment Planning • Interview Counseling • Resume Preparation • Solo Practice Advice • Job Openings Information • Employment Counseling

Facilities: University Placement Office • Law Placement Office

School	Alumni Placement	Internships	Part-Time/Summer Employment	Alumni Contacts	Law, Corporate, and Government Contact	Job Interviews Arrangement	Employment Planning	Interview Counseling	Resume Preparation	Solo Practice Advice	Job Openings Information	Employment Counseling	University Placement Office	Law Placement Office
University of Southern California	•	•	•	•	•	•	•	•	•	•	•	•		•
University of Tennessee	•	•	•	•	•	•	•	•	•	•	•	•		•
University of Texas at Austin	•	•	•	•	•	•	•	•	•	•	•	•		•
University of the District of Columbia	•	•	•	•	•	•	•	•	•	•	•	•		•
University of the Pacific	•	•	•	•	•	•	•	•	•	•	•	•		•
University of Toledo	•	•	•	•	•	•	•	•	•	•	•	•		•
University of Tulsa	•	•	•	•	•	•	•	•	•	•	•	•	•	•

University of Southern California (Law School)
Los Angeles, CA 90089-0071
213-740-7331

University of Tennessee (College of Law)
1505 W. Cumberland Avenue
Knoxville, TN 37996-1810
865-974-4131
Fax: 865-974-1572
lawadmit@libra.law.utk.edu

University of Texas at Austin (School of Law)
727 East Dean Keeton Street
Austin, TX 78705
512-232-1200
Fax: 512-471-6988

University of the District of Columbia (David A. Clarke School of Law)
4200 Connecticut Avenue, N.W.
Washington, DC 20008
Null
Fax: 202-274-5583
vcanty@law.udc.edu

University of the Pacific (McGeorge School of Law)
3200 Fifth Avenue
Sacramento, CA 95817
916-739-7105
Fax: 916-739-7134
admissionsmcgeorge@uop.edu

University of Toledo (College of Law)
2801 West Bancroft Street
Toledo, OH 43606-3390
419-530-4131
Fax: 419-530-4345
law.utoledo.edu

University of Tulsa (College of Law)
3120 East Fourth Place
Tulsa, OK 74104-2499
918-631-2709
Fax: 918-631-3630

School												%													Salary
University of Utah (College of Law) 332 South 1400 East Front Salt Lake City, UT 84112 801-581-7479 Fax: 801-581-6897 gormley@law.utah.edu		1	1	2	9	33	19	3	7	11	20	93%	•	•	•	•	•	•	•	•	•		•		•	$18,000-$78,000
University of Virginia (School of Law) 580 Massie Road Charlottesville, VA 22903-1789 804-924-7351 Fax: 804-982-2128 lawadmit@virginia.edu	1	1	1	1	5	6	17					97%	•	•	•	•	•	•	•	•	•		•		•	$30,000-$110,000
University of Washington (School of Law) 1100 Northeast Campus Parkway Seattle, WA 98105-6617 206-543-4078	4	3	2	7	12	12	9	13	10	9	19	86%	•	•	•	•	•	•	•	•	•		•		•	
University of Wisconsin-Madison (Law School) 975 Bascom Mall Madison, WI 53706 608-262-5914 Fax: 608-262-5485 Admissions@law.wisc.educ		2	2	2	10	15	9	5	6	8	16	93%	•	•	•	•	•	•	•	•	•		•		•	$37,085-$67,000
University of Wyoming (College of Law) P.O. Box 3035 Laramie, WY 82071 307-766-6416 lawadmis@uwyo.edu	9			2		18	16				53	86%	•	•	•	•	•	•	•	•	•	•	•		•	$18,000-$96,000
Valparaiso University (School of Law) Wesemann Hall Valparaiso, IN 46383-6493 219-465-7829 Fax: 219-465-7808 heike.spahn@valpo.edu		2	2	4	17	16	10	3	2	6	39	95%	•	•	•	•	•	•	•	•	•		•		•	$26,000-$96,000
Vanderbilt University (School of Law) Nashville, TN 37240 615-322-6452		2		1	2	4	20	46	15	8	3	98%	•	•	•	•	•	•	•	•	•		•		•	$62,000
Vermont Law School P.O. Box 96, Chelsea Street South Royalton, VT 05068-0096 802-763-8303 Fax: 802-763-7071 admiss@vermontlaw.edu	13	2	2	6	15	19	11	3	2	5	22	83%	•	•	•	•	•	•	•	•	•		•		•	$33,088-$46,369
Villanova University (School of Law) Garey Hall Villanova, PA 19085 610-519-7010	19	7		1	8	13	19	6	5	20	16	87%	•	•	•	•	•	•	•	•	•		•		•	$35,000-$105,000
Wake Forest University (School of Law) P.O. Box 7206, Reynolda Station Winston-Salem, NC 27109 910-758-5437			2	1	12	16	13	21	6	9	20	96%	•	•	•	•	•	•	•	•	•		•		•	$22,000-$100,000

PLACEMENT SERVICES / PLACEMENT RECORD

School	Law Placement Office	University Placement Office	Employment Counseling	Job Openings Information	Solo Practice Advice	Resume Preparation	Interview Counseling	Employment Planning	Job Interviews Arrangement	Law, Corporate, and Government Contact	Alumni Contacts	Part-Time/Summer Employment	Internships	Alumni Placement	Placement Within 6 to 9 Months	PP 2-10 Attorneys	PP 11-25 Attorneys	PP 26-50 Attorneys	PP 51-100 Attorneys	Judicial Clerkships	Government	Business/Industry	Public Interest	Military	Academic	Other	Average Starting Salary
Washburn University (School of Law) 1700 College, Topeka, KS 66621; 785-231-1185; Fax: 785-232-8087; admissions@washburnlaw.edu	•		•	•	•	•	•	•	•	•	•	•	•	•	91%	26	5	6	5	5	20	13	4	2		6	$24,000–$62,000
Washington and Lee University (School of Law) Lewis Hall, Lexington, VA 24450; 540-463-8504; Fax: 540-463-8586; lawadm@wlu.edu	•		•	•	•	•	•	•	•	•	•	•	•	•	77%	23	6	6	21	27	3	10	2	1			$44,250–$70,000
Washington University in St. Louis (School of Law) Box 1120, One Brookings Drive, St. Louis, MO 63130; 314-935-6959; Fax: 314-935-4525; admiss@walaw.wash.edu	•		•	•	•	•	•	•	•	•	•	•	•	•	95%	17		25		8	11	12	4	1	3		$23,000–$100,000
Wayne State University (Law School) 468 W. Ferry Mall, Detroit, MI 48202; 313-577-3937; Fax: 313-577-6000; linda.sims@wayne.edu	•		•	•		•	•		•	•	•	•	•	•	95%					4	4	20	2		2		
West Virginia University (College of Law) P.O. Box 6130, Morgantown, WV 26506; 304-293-5304; Fax: 304-293-6891; lawaply@wvu.edu	•	•	•	•	•	•	•	•	•	•	•	•	•	•	90%	39	10	7	6	4	18	11	4		1		$36,610–$72,000
Western New England College (School of Law) 1215 Wilbraham Road, Springfield, MA 01119; 413-782-1406; Fax: 413-796-2067; lawadmis@wnec.edu	•		•	•	•	•	•	•	•	•	•	•	•	•	92%	24	2	2	1	10	19	32	1	1	3		$18,000–$95,000

School												%	Salary Range
Western State University (College of Law) 1111 North State College Blvd Fullerton, CA 92831 714-738-1000, x2909 Fax: 714-526-1062 joel@wsulaw.edu	7	1		1	25	16	1	4	5	13	27	92%	
Whittier College (School of Law) 3333 Harbor Blvd. Costa Mesa, CA 92626 714-444-4141, ext. 121 Fax: 714-444-0250 info@law.whittier.edu	6	2		1	18	13	2	1	6	3	46	92%	$25,000-$110,000
Widener University (School of Law) 4601 Concord Pike, P.O. Box 7474 and 3800 Vartan Way, Harris Wilmington, DE 19803 302-477-2162 (DE); 717-541-3903 (HBG) Fax: 302-477-2224 (DE); 717-541-3999 (HBG) law.admissions@law.widener.edu	3	1		2	22	19	17	2	2	4	22	88%	$19,000-$92,500
Willamette University (College of Law) 245 Winter Street S.E. Salem, OR 97301 503-370-6282 Fax: 503-370-6375 law-admission@willamette.edu	14		3	1	16	16	8	3	4	12	24	87%	$16,800-$80,000
William Mitchell College of Law 875 Summit Avenue St. Paul, MN 55105-3076 651-290-6476 Fax: 651-290-6414 admissions@wmitchell.edu		1	2	2	28	13	12	2	4	5	25	94%	$20,800-$260,000
Yale University (Yale Law School) P.O. Box 208329 New Haven, CT 06520-8239 203-432-4995 admissions.law@yale.edu		6		4	4	2	53					98%	$26,664-$100,000
Yeshiva University (Benjamin N. Cardozo School of Law) 55 Fifth Avenue New York, NY 10003 212-790-0274 Fax: 212-790-0482 lawinfo@ymail.yu.edu	20	1		4	16	10	5	7	8	7	22	92%	$30,000-$107,000

vey, approximately nine months after graduation. These numbers have remained fairly consistent over a period of more than twenty-five years, during which NALP has surveyed law school graduates. Not surprisingly, the employment picture is slightly better in years when the general economy is strong, and slightly worse in years with recession. The NALP survey does support the observation that the legal job market is fairly stable and predictable. Competition for the most prestigious and desirable jobs can be fierce, although most people who want jobs as lawyers will eventually get them.

Geographic Locations

Lawyers work almost everywhere. More lawyers are concentrated in the largest population centers, because of the high volume of commercial activity that occurs in those areas. Lawyers are also concentrated in the seats of government, from Washington, DC, to state capitals, to county seats, throughout the United States. Even in rural areas, lawyers can be found with offices close to the clients they serve. An increasing number of U.S. lawyers work outside the boundaries of the United States. With the increasing internationalization of business, lawyers have become a new kind of export.

The NALP statistics for the employment of law school graduates parallel the demographic patterns for lawyers as a whole. The greatest number of legal jobs are found in the largest cities, but law graduates are disbursed to a wide variety of places throughout the country. There is some correlation between law school attended and location of first employment, suggesting that people either choose their law school because of the geographic area or become attached to the area while they are in law school.

The bar exam represents a hurdle to entry into the practice of law, because for most legal positions, it is necessary to pass the bar exam in the state where the lawyer will be working prior to beginning to serve clients. The majority of law graduates take only one bar exam, and are thus limited to the jurisdiction where they become licensed. If graduates have employment in a jurisdiction where they do not pass the bar exam, they will lose those jobs. If they take the exam before they have a job, they will be limited in their job search to positions where they become licensed. Applicants to law school should be aware of these jurisdictional requirements, and investigate the possibilities as appropriate.

Salaries

Lawyers' salaries are reported by various bar associations and consultant surveys, as well as the U.S. Bureau of Labor Statistics and NALP. All of these surveys seem to show that there is a wide range of income among lawyers. Some lawyers, particularly in the rural areas, may not have enough business to sustain a full-time practice. Lawyers in certain metropolitan areas with high lawyer population may find competition for clients to be intense. Some of these lawyers may discover that even after years of practice they do not make a good living practicing law. On the other end of the spectrum are lawyers whose income is in the seven figure range.

Different surveys show discrepancies in reported results that may reflect more on their sampling techniques than actual differences, but most seem to point to an average income for all lawyers of between $100,000 and $150,000. This figure includes not only law firm partners, but also semi-retired senior lawyers and brand new associates as well. It includes not only private practice, but also lower paying government service positions. Within private practice it is generally the case that lawyers in larger firms make more money than lawyers in smaller firms. It is also the case that some areas of practice, notably corporate and tax work, show better returns than other areas, such as criminal law and domestic relations.

Starting salaries nationally range from less than $20,000 to more than $100,000. The NALP's *Jobs and JDs* indicates that the median for all graduates is $45,000. In most cities, the largest firms will pay a standard rate for new associates, and smaller firms will offer salaries somewhat less than the salary leaders. Small firms often pay at or below the median for all graduates. (Remember: a median means that half the scores fall below the midpoint.)

CHAPTER 9

What Trends Are Affecting the Practice of Law?

Like other businesses and professions, the practice of law has changed dramatically in recent years. A revolution in technology has swept the business world. Computers have altered the way law is practiced in countless ways, including how lawyers relate to their clients. Technology has even altered the dynamics of how lawyers relate to each other in organizations.

During the first half of the twentieth century, most lawyers practiced alone. Since World War II, however, more and more lawyers have gone to work in ever-larger law firms. In these firms, partners hired junior lawyers—associates—to assist them in the delivery of legal services. The development of these large law firms paralleled the growth of corporations, which fueled an increase in the need for legal services, and for large firms.

During the same period of time the demographics of the U.S. population was also changing. More and more people were living in large cities or metropolitan areas. Waves of immigrants were producing an increasingly diverse society. Global conflict and worldwide depression illustrated the futility of American isolation on the world stage.

The end of World War II brought new challenges to the legal profession in America. As large numbers of veterans attended law school on the GI bill, there was a rapid increase in the number of lawyers graduating from law school. This growth paralleled a dramatic rise in business opportunity, fueled by post-war prosperity.

In the early 1960s, most lawyers were particularly ill-prepared for the dramatic changes in the practice of law that subsequently occurred in the last half of the twentieth century. Evolution is a good word to use to describe these developments, because they produced a kind of economic Darwinism, in which the fittest adapt and survive, and the less competitive individuals and forms of practice become extinct.

As someone who is thinking about going to law school, you should understand that this evolution is continuing and is likely to continue for the foreseeable future. You should recognize that the changes that have transformed other segments of business and industry have had an impact on the practice of law as well. You should know that some people will succeed in these times and some will not. Law, far from being a refuge from a competitive workplace, is subject to risks like most other fields of endeavor.

What you can do to improve the likelihood that you will be successful in this environment is seek to understand the changes that have occurred and that are likely to take place in the future. Of course, it is impossible to predict the future, but sensitivity to trends and insightful analysis of events can help you to adapt. Several areas are worth watching:

GLOBALIZATION

Electronic communication, air transportation, and global migration have produced a world that is inevitably interconnected. It is possible to know the local news almost anywhere in the world. The distribution of products and services transcends international boundaries, producing at the same time tremendous variety in the marketplace and increased homogeneity in availability. English has increasingly become the default language of world commerce. Stock markets in Asia, wars in Africa, and mergers in Europe all have an impact on business in America. Lawyers increasingly will be called upon to represent clients who have interests outside the United States, or who come from outside the United States and need a lawyer's assistance here. Lawyers themselves will face competition from foreign law firms, and even from organizations that provide law-related services that would be viewed as unauthorized practice of law in the United States.

TECHNOLOGY

The information revolution has transformed the way law is practiced. Today, most lawyers have a computer on their desktop with access to the Internet, legal databases, and software applications. Technology allows lawyers and law firms to practice more efficiently. These new resources also place additional demands on practitioners, particularly older lawyers, who grew up in an era when the most advanced technology needed to practice law was an Underwood typewriter. Technological advancements force lawyers to find new ways to ply their services, and to communicate with clients who are increasingly wired and connected themselves. As legal information and forms become increasingly available on the Internet and other electronic formats, the role of the lawyer shifts to one of information provider, interpreter, and advisor.

DEMOGRAPHICS

After a century of urbanization, there appear to be signs that the American population is disbursing again to the countryside. Unlike the nineteenth century migration westward, which was fueled by farmers and ranchers, this movement is led by lifestyle pioneers, who seek to get away from the pressure of big city life. It is supported by electronic access to goods, services, and entertainment that negate the effects of isolation sometimes associated with country life. A system of good roads and a web of transportation connections mean that no place is more than a few hours from all the cultural attractions that cities have to offer. Yet telecommuting makes it possible for people to do their jobs not only hundreds of miles away, but halfway around the world. Lawyers benefit from this trend as well, because they can remain connected to their offices and their clients. They can commute great distances from homes and can stay in touch while they are out of the office—even on vacation—and can deal with client matters in distant jurisdictions.

A second demographic trend that has had a significant impact on lawyers is the entrance of large numbers of women into the workforce. Until the 1960s, only a handful of women entered the legal profession, and law firms were often an exclusively male domain. Women who did go to work in law firms were often relegated to secretarial and other low-paying jobs. Over the past three decades, the legal profession has experienced a dramatic increase in the number of women lawyers. Today, approximately half of all law students are women, and the percentage of women in the profession as a whole increases each year. This change not only produces more opportunities for women in the practice of law, but it also puts pressure on law firms and other organizations that employ lawyers to assure that these opportunities are meaningful ones.

A related issue is the advent of the two-career family. Since the 1960s, more and more families have become dual-career households, where both spouses either choose to work or have to work in order to sustain a desired lifestyle. When one or both of the people in such a family is a lawyer, there can be a variety of interesting problems, from conflicts of interest between the two lawyers' firms, to employment in different cities, to questions about allocating responsibility for child care and housework.

Since divorce hits one out of two American families, single parents are often forced to raise children without a partner. The problem of single parenting impacts not only the lawyers but also the support staff in law firms. The upheaval can be disruptive to organizations that are trying to provide quality legal services to clients. For law firms, most of which are very small organizations compared to nonlegal businesses, it can be difficult to accommodate the needs of employees in our complex society.

LIFESTYLES

Many young lawyers must face fundamental lifestyle issues, enhanced in part by the great variety of choices available to them. Do they have children or not? If so, when? Who will stay at home with young children and for how long? What kind of childcare and early education will children receive? What kind of geographical setting is most compatible with their interests, hobbies, and professional needs? The beach? The mountains? The big city? A rural county seat? How many hours a week do you and your spouse/partner want to put into the practice of law? Forty? Sixty? Eighty? One hundred? Where do you see yourself in ten or twenty years as your practice matures? And family? Do you want the people you grew up with to be close at hand, or will you be satisfied to see them once or twice a year? Is the type of law that you hope to practice likely to be available in the geographic locale where you would like to live?

CHANGE

One common thread that cuts through all the trends described above is change. The world is changing in unprecedented ways, and will continue to change throughout the professional lives of those students entering law school in the coming years. The changes that we are experiencing are profound; they are transforming. Author Tom Peters, at a 1999 conference on the future of the legal profession, said that humankind may be in the midst of the biggest revolution in the way people live since we came in off the savannahs to live in permanent villages—a 10,000-year sea change. Other observers might not go as far as Peters does, but virtually everyone who has thought about the future believes that we are in the midst of something really big.

It should come as no surprise that the legal profession is undergoing dramatic change in the way legal services are delivered. Just as the industrial base of America has shifted to Third World countries, and the medical profession has endured the rise of managed care, lawyers face an increasingly competitive environment and pressures to deliver better services more economically. Although the number of law school graduates continues to climb, more and more lawyers opt to work in settings outside of private practice (i.e., law firms). An increasing number of graduates accept positions in corporations, government service, private associations, accounting or professional services firms, banks, group legal services, private associations, and a variety of other organizations. Other lawyers start out in law firms, but move to some other type of organization, often one that has been a client of the firm. Some lawyers may abandon the law completely, but the vast majority of them continue to utilize their legal skills and "practice law" in a new environment.

Someone contemplating a career in law should appreciate the fact that the opportunities for lawyers are changing as the world around them changes. All this change creates tremendous challenges and risks, but it also generates unusual opportunities. It will be important for you to stay attuned to how society and the practice of law continue to evolve in order to maximize your opportunities and achieve your goals in the coming years.

These are not simple questions, and there are no easy answers. But both lawyers and applicants to law school will have to face these issues at some time or other. It makes sense to think now about how lifestyle questions will affect the career choices that you make as a lawyer, and try to make decisions that are consistent with your long-term personal needs.

SUBSTANTIVE PRACTICE AREAS

People often ask what are the growing practice areas in the law? There is probably no consensus answer to this question, and many pundits have attempted to predict substantive trends in the law—many with great imprecision. Understanding the risks inherent in such predictions, this author will offer insights into a number of practice areas that are likely to experience growth in the coming decade:

- **Environmental law.** Global environmental issues are protracted; resources are limited. It is inevitable that a world population of six billion will have to confront issues like global warming, extinction of animal species, resource allocation, and sustainable development. Lawyers involved in this process are likely to have their hands full for the foreseeable future.

- **Health care.** In the United States there have been dramatic changes in the way health care services are delivered. The availability of medical treatment, risks associated with scientific advancement, and issues involving death and dying all present health care issues. Decisions about treatment are no longer limited to the patient and provider, but often involve a hospital and/or other corporate employer, and an insurance company or HMO. With a population that is graying demographically, health care issues can be expected to increase during the early part of the twenty-first century.

- **Elder law.** In addition to health care, older citizens have a variety of other issues that they must confront, from increased leisure associated with retirement to legal issues like estate planning, to a variety of other unique problems. An increasing number of lawyers are defining their practice in terms of these clients under the heading of Elder Law.

- **International business.** The growing international interdependence of countries, particularly in the delivery of goods and services, will continue to produce a high level of complex legal work. Lawyers from both this country and others around the world will be involved in solving the legal problems that these commercial transactions create. From the European community to the Pacific Rim, from the former eastern bloc to Central and South America, American lawyers will find opportunities in all these areas.

- **Communications and technology.** The Internet, satellite communications, cable, and other legal problems associated with computers and electronic technology will continue to evolve in the near future. Many of the concepts of common law from copyright to theft must be redefined in the electronic environment. From the antitrust questions confronting Microsoft Corporation to the privacy rights of office workers, without a doubt this area of law will be booming.

- **Leisure law.** Sports and entertainment law, travel law, and related subject areas will experience a period of growth in the coming years, as people have more and more free time. Even those who work long hours will be seeking leisure opportunities during their vacation periods. Many workers will be retiring earlier and looking for leisure activities to fill their time. Although this is a fairly small field of practice today, it is likely to grow in the coming decades.

- **Preventive law.** Estate planning, business planning, tax planning, and other areas where lawyers can advise individuals and businesses on how to avoid legal problems, rather than trying to help once things have fallen apart, will experience considerable growth. This will be not only because lawyers will be seeking these markets, but also because a more sophisticated client base will seek to have this kind of legal help more readily available.

- **Mediation and other alternative dispute resolution.** More and more legal cases will be resolved without going to court, through mediation and alternative dispute resolution processes. Lawyers will be involved in these practice areas as well, because their legal skills of negotiation, persuasion, analysis, and organization will work well to help clients solve problems in a variety of different ways.

- **Employment law.** The proliferation of state and federal law governing the workplace has created a growing practice in employment law. Practice settings in private firms range from small and large law firms devoted exclusively to this area of practice to more general practice firms in which fewer than all of the lawyers specialize in this area. With the growth in business generally, and with large corporate mergers, there will continue to be a need for lawyers to advise clients on employee matters, such as ERISA and pension benefits, to train clients and their employees on prevention (e.g., harassment training) and to litigate or mediate employee complaints and claims arising under the many laws in this area.

- **Intellectual property law.** The growth in certain specialized businesses, particularly in the health care and computer technology industries, will require lawyers who have technological or scientific backgrounds to assist clients in protecting the new technologies they develop. While patent law and copyright law are not new, continued innovations, particularly those triggered by the Internet, and growing technological sophistication, have created an increase in demand for lawyers to help clients secure patents and to help clients protect their intellectual property.

Although the areas of practice described above represent fields where growth can be inferred from a variety of factual indicia, many other specialized or "boutique" practice areas will blossom in the coming years. Because virtually every form of human endeavor has legal implications, it follows that very little in life can be conducted outside the law. This means that there is a substantive practice area for almost anything you can imagine, and if you can imagine it, you can bet that somewhere there is a lawyer practicing in that field. Lawyers today are increasingly becoming specialists, who concentrate their practice in a narrow field of expertise. The general practitioner is a dying breed in law, just as in medicine. And as in medicine, the more complex society becomes, the more specialties emerge.

CONCLUSION

For someone about to enter law school, it should be clear that choosing to become a lawyer is just the beginning of a long path of career choices. Not only will law school graduates have to choose from a variety of practice settings, they will have to decide among an almost infinite array of substantive fields within the law. On top of all this, they will have to be astute enough to understand that the underpinnings of their decisions will be undergoing continual change. The element of change will be a factor in every facet of life, whether you decide to attend law school or not, but if you do elect to go to law school, do not imagine that you will be immune from the forces that are transforming the rest of the world. If you remember that society and the practice of law are both changing, and continually reflect upon how these changes will affect you, you will improve your chances of achieving success professionally and personally.

PART II

Taking the LSAT

The LSAT and the Admissions Process

The Law School Admission Test (LSAT) is required for all law school applicants. Although law school admissions committees consider a variety of criteria, there is little doubt that the LSAT plays a significant role in the selection process.

Preparation for the LSAT is the rule rather than the exception. This section is an introduction to the LSAT preparation process.

ANSWERS TO SOME COMMONLY ASKED QUESTIONS

What does the LSAT measure?

The LSAT is designed to measure a range of mental abilities related to the study of law; therefore, it is used by most law schools to evaluate their applicants.

Will any special knowledge of the law raise my score on the LSAT?

The LSAT is designed so that candidates from a particular academic background are given no advantage. The questions measure reading comprehension, logical reasoning, and analytical reasoning, drawing from a variety of verbal and analytical material.

Does a high score on the LSAT predict success in law school or in the practice of law?

Success on the LSAT demonstrates your ability to read with understanding and to reason clearly under pressure; surely these strengths are important to both the study and the practice of law, as is the ability to write well, measured by the LSAT Writing Sample. To say that success on the LSAT *predicts* success in law school may overstate the case, however, because success in law school also involves skills that are not measured by the LSAT.

When is the LSAT administered?

The regular administration of the test occurs nationwide four times each year, around the beginning of the fall, winter, spring, and summer seasons. Except for the summer month, the test is usually administered on a Saturday morning from 8:30 A.M. to about 1:00 P.M. For the past few years, the *summer exam* has been given on a Monday afternoon. Dates are announced annually by the Law School Admission Council in Newtown, Pennsylvania.

What if I cannot take the test on a Saturday?

Some special arrangements are possible: Check the LSAS General Information Booklet in your registration packet. Those who must take the exam at a time when the regular administration occurs on Saturday, but who cannot participate on Saturday for religious reasons, may arrange for a special Monday administration.

How early should I register?

Regular registration closes about one month before the exam date. Late registration is available up to three weeks prior to the exam date. There is an additional fee for late registration.

Is walk-in registration available?

For security reasons, walk-in registration is no longer permitted. Students may register by telephone by the telephone deadline. The Law School Admission Services (LSAS) will not permit walk-ins the day of the test. Be sure to read very carefully the General Information Booklet section on "registering to take the LSAT."

What is the LSDAS?

The LSDAS (Law School Data Assembly Service) compiles a report about each subscribing applicant. The report contains LSAT results, a summary of the applicant's academic work, and copies of college transcripts. A report is sent to each law school that the applicant designates. Thus, if you register for the LSDAS, you will not need to mail a separate transcript to each of your prospective law schools. REMINDER: You can register for the Candidate Referral Service only at the same time you register for the LSDAS.

How is the LSAT used?

Your LSAT score is one common denominator by which a law school compares you to other applicants. Other factors also determine your acceptance to law school: a law school may consider your personal qualities, grade-point average, extracurricular achievements, and letters of recommendation. Requirements for admission vary widely from school to school, so you are wise to contact the law school of your choice for specific information.

How do I obtain registration forms?

The registration form covering both the LSAT and the LSDAS is available in the LSAT/LSDAS REGISTRATION PACKET. Copies of the packet are available at the admissions offices of most law schools and the testing offices at most undergraduate universities and colleges. You may also obtain the packet by writing to LAW SCHOOL ADMISSION SERVICES, Box 2000, Newtown, PA 18940.

What is the structure of the LSAT?

The LSAT contains five 35-minute multiple-choice sections followed by a 30-minute Writing Sample. The Writing Sample does not count as part of your LSAT score. The common question types that do count toward your score are Logical Reasoning (two sections), Analytical Reasoning (one section), and Reading Comprehension (one section). In addition to these four sections, one experimental or pretest section will appear. This experimental or pretest section, which will probably be a repeat of one of the common question types, will not count in your score.

How is the LSAT scored?

The score for the objective portion of the test ranges from 120 to 180, and there is no penalty for wrong answers. The Writing Sample is unscored, but copies are sent to the law schools of your choice for evaluation.

What about question structure and value?

All LSAT questions, apart from the Writing Sample, are multiple-choice with five choices. All questions within a section are of equal value, regardless of difficulty.

Should I guess?

There is no penalty for guessing on the LSAT. Therefore, before you move on to the next question, at least take a guess. You should fill in guess answers for those you have left blank or did not get to, before time is called for that section. If you can eliminate one or more choices as incorrect, your chances for a correct guess increase.

How often can I take the LSAT?

You may take the LSAT more than once if you wish. But keep in mind that any report sent to you or to law schools will contain scores for any exams taken over the past few years, along with an average score for those exams. The law school receiving your scores will decide which score is the best estimate of your ability; many law schools rely on the average score as a figure.

Is it at all possible to cancel my LSAT score?

You may cancel your score only within five days after taking the test.

How early should I arrive at the test center, and what should I bring?

Arrive at the test center 15 to 30 minutes before the time designated on your admission ticket. Bring three or four sharpened No. 2 pencils, an eraser, and a watch, as well as your LSAT Admission Ticket and proper identification as described in the LSAT Registration/Information Booklet.

Can I prepare for the LSAT?

Yes. Reading skills and test-taking strategies should be the focus of your preparation for the test as a whole. Success on the more specialized analytical sections of the test depends on your thorough familiarity with the types of problems you are likely to encounter and the reasoning process involved. For maximum preparation, work through this book and practice the strategies and techniques outlined in each section.

BASIC FORMAT OF THE LSAT AND SCORING

THE *ORDER* OF THE FOLLOWING MULTIPLE-CHOICE SECTIONS *WILL* VARY. The Experimental Section is not necessarily the last section.

	Section	Number of Questions	Minutes
I.	Logical Reasoning	24-26	35
II.	Analytical Reasoning	22-24 (4 sets)	35
III.	Reading Comprehension	26-28 (4 passages)	35
IV.	Logical Reasoning	24-26	35
V.	Experimental Section	varies	35
	Writing Sample	1 essay	30
TOTALS		118-132 questions (only 96-104 count toward your score)	205 minutes or 3 hours 25 minutes

NOTE: For your convenience, this Barron's text labels each section of this Model Test (e.g., Reading Comprehension, Logical Reasoning, etc.). In contrast, sections of the actual LSAT exam are not usually labeled.

The LSAT is scored on a 120 to 180 scale.

The following simple chart will give you a very general approximation of the LSAT scoring system. It shows the approximate percentage of right answers necessary on the LSAT to be in a certain score range.

Approximate % of right answers	Approximate Score Range
Between 75% and 100%	160-180
Between 50% and 75%	145-159
Between 25% and 50%	130-144
Between 0% and 25%	120-129

Note that this chart is meant to give you an *approximate* score range.

A Closer Look at the Timing—What It Really Means

Although the LSAT is comprised of five 35-minute multiple-choice sections and a 30-minute unscored essay, it is important to understand the timing breakdown and what it means. The test is actually broken down as follows:

105 min. {
    Section I 35 minutes
    Section II 35 minutes
    Section III 35 minutes

Short break—usually 5-10 minutes

70 min. {
    Section IV 35 minutes
    Section V 35 minutes

Very, very short break—usually 1 or 2 minutes

30 min. { Writing Sample (Essay)—30 minutes

Notice that you are given three multiple-choice sections with no breaks in between. When they say "stop" at the end of 35 minutes they will immediately say something like, "Turn to the next section, make sure that you are in the right section, ready, begin." So, in essence, you are working three sections back to back to back. This means that when you practice you should be sure to practice testing for 1 hour and 45 minutes without a break.

After the short break, when you may get up, get a drink, and go to the restroom, you are back for two more back-to-back multiple-choice sections.

For the final 30-minute writing sample you will be given a pen and scratch paper to do your prewriting or outlining.

Keep in mind that there will be some time taken before the exam and after the exam for clerical-type paperwork—distributing and picking up paperwork, filling out test forms, and so on.

Important Reminders

- At least half of your test will contain Logic Reasoning questions; prepare accordingly. Make sure that you are good at Logical Reasoning!
- The experimental or pretest section will usually repeat other sections and can appear in different places on the exam. At the time of the exam, you will not know which section is experimental. Take the test as if all of the sections count.
- Scoring will be from 120-180. This is the score, and the percentile rank that goes with it is what the law schools look at and are referring to in their discussions.
- All questions in a section are of equal value, so do not get stuck on any one question. The scores are determined by totaling all of your right answers on the test and then scaling.
- There is NO PENALTY for guessing, so at least take a guess before you move to the next question.

- The 30-minute Writing Sample will not be scored, but copies will be forwarded to the law schools to which you apply. Scratch paper and a pen will be provided for the Writing Sample only.
- Keep in mind that regardless of the format of your exam, two sections of Logical Reasoning, one section of Analytical Reasoning, and one section of Reading Comprehension always count toward your score.

SOME WORDS TO THE WISE

Ask a Few Questions

Before you actually start your study plan there are four basic questions that you should ask the law schools to which you are applying:

1. Considering my GPA and other qualifications, what score do you think I need to get into your law school?
2. When do you need to get my score reports? Or, When should I take the test to meet your deadlines?
3. What do you do if I take the LSAT more than once? Remember that when the law school receives your score report it will see a score for each time you've taken the test *and* an average of the scores. It is up to the law schools and their governing bodies as to what score(s) they will consider. Try to do your best on the first try and take the LSAT only once, if possible.
4. What do you do with my Writing Sample? Is it used as a tiebreaker? Do you score it yourself? Is it just another piece of the process?

Knowing the answers to most of these questions before you start your study will help you understand what is expected and will help you get mentally ready for the task ahead.

Excerpted from *How to Prepare for the LSAT*, by Jerry Bobrow, Ph.D., Barron's Educational Series, Inc., 1996.

ANSWER SHEET—MODEL TEST
LAW SCHOOL ADMISSION TEST (LSAT)

Section I:
Reading Comprehension

1. Ⓐ Ⓑ Ⓒ Ⓓ Ⓔ
2. Ⓐ Ⓑ Ⓒ Ⓓ Ⓔ
3. Ⓐ Ⓑ Ⓒ Ⓓ Ⓔ
4. Ⓐ Ⓑ Ⓒ Ⓓ Ⓔ
5. Ⓐ Ⓑ Ⓒ Ⓓ Ⓔ
6. Ⓐ Ⓑ Ⓒ Ⓓ Ⓔ
7. Ⓐ Ⓑ Ⓒ Ⓓ Ⓔ
8. Ⓐ Ⓑ Ⓒ Ⓓ Ⓔ
9. Ⓐ Ⓑ Ⓒ Ⓓ Ⓔ
10. Ⓐ Ⓑ Ⓒ Ⓓ Ⓔ
11. Ⓐ Ⓑ Ⓒ Ⓓ Ⓔ
12. Ⓐ Ⓑ Ⓒ Ⓓ Ⓔ
13. Ⓐ Ⓑ Ⓒ Ⓓ Ⓔ
14. Ⓐ Ⓑ Ⓒ Ⓓ Ⓔ
15. Ⓐ Ⓑ Ⓒ Ⓓ Ⓔ
16. Ⓐ Ⓑ Ⓒ Ⓓ Ⓔ
17. Ⓐ Ⓑ Ⓒ Ⓓ Ⓔ
18. Ⓐ Ⓑ Ⓒ Ⓓ Ⓔ
19. Ⓐ Ⓑ Ⓒ Ⓓ Ⓔ
20. Ⓐ Ⓑ Ⓒ Ⓓ Ⓔ
21. Ⓐ Ⓑ Ⓒ Ⓓ Ⓔ
22. Ⓐ Ⓑ Ⓒ Ⓓ Ⓔ
23. Ⓐ Ⓑ Ⓒ Ⓓ Ⓔ
24. Ⓐ Ⓑ Ⓒ Ⓓ Ⓔ
25. Ⓐ Ⓑ Ⓒ Ⓓ Ⓔ
26. Ⓐ Ⓑ Ⓒ Ⓓ Ⓔ
27. Ⓐ Ⓑ Ⓒ Ⓓ Ⓔ
28. Ⓐ Ⓑ Ⓒ Ⓓ Ⓔ

Section II:
Analytical Reasoning

1. Ⓐ Ⓑ Ⓒ Ⓓ Ⓔ
2. Ⓐ Ⓑ Ⓒ Ⓓ Ⓔ
3. Ⓐ Ⓑ Ⓒ Ⓓ Ⓔ
4. Ⓐ Ⓑ Ⓒ Ⓓ Ⓔ
5. Ⓐ Ⓑ Ⓒ Ⓓ Ⓔ
6. Ⓐ Ⓑ Ⓒ Ⓓ Ⓔ
7. Ⓐ Ⓑ Ⓒ Ⓓ Ⓔ
8. Ⓐ Ⓑ Ⓒ Ⓓ Ⓔ
9. Ⓐ Ⓑ Ⓒ Ⓓ Ⓔ
10. Ⓐ Ⓑ Ⓒ Ⓓ Ⓔ
11. Ⓐ Ⓑ Ⓒ Ⓓ Ⓔ
12. Ⓐ Ⓑ Ⓒ Ⓓ Ⓔ
13. Ⓐ Ⓑ Ⓒ Ⓓ Ⓔ
14. Ⓐ Ⓑ Ⓒ Ⓓ Ⓔ
15. Ⓐ Ⓑ Ⓒ Ⓓ Ⓔ
16. Ⓐ Ⓑ Ⓒ Ⓓ Ⓔ
17. Ⓐ Ⓑ Ⓒ Ⓓ Ⓔ
18. Ⓐ Ⓑ Ⓒ Ⓓ Ⓔ
19. Ⓐ Ⓑ Ⓒ Ⓓ Ⓔ
20. Ⓐ Ⓑ Ⓒ Ⓓ Ⓔ
21. Ⓐ Ⓑ Ⓒ Ⓓ Ⓔ
22. Ⓐ Ⓑ Ⓒ Ⓓ Ⓔ
23. Ⓐ Ⓑ Ⓒ Ⓓ Ⓔ
24. Ⓐ Ⓑ Ⓒ Ⓓ Ⓔ

Section III:
Logical Reasoning

1. Ⓐ Ⓑ Ⓒ Ⓓ Ⓔ
2. Ⓐ Ⓑ Ⓒ Ⓓ Ⓔ
3. Ⓐ Ⓑ Ⓒ Ⓓ Ⓔ
4. Ⓐ Ⓑ Ⓒ Ⓓ Ⓔ
5. Ⓐ Ⓑ Ⓒ Ⓓ Ⓔ
6. Ⓐ Ⓑ Ⓒ Ⓓ Ⓔ
7. Ⓐ Ⓑ Ⓒ Ⓓ Ⓔ
8. Ⓐ Ⓑ Ⓒ Ⓓ Ⓔ
9. Ⓐ Ⓑ Ⓒ Ⓓ Ⓔ
10. Ⓐ Ⓑ Ⓒ Ⓓ Ⓔ
11. Ⓐ Ⓑ Ⓒ Ⓓ Ⓔ
12. Ⓐ Ⓑ Ⓒ Ⓓ Ⓔ
13. Ⓐ Ⓑ Ⓒ Ⓓ Ⓔ
14. Ⓐ Ⓑ Ⓒ Ⓓ Ⓔ
15. Ⓐ Ⓑ Ⓒ Ⓓ Ⓔ
16. Ⓐ Ⓑ Ⓒ Ⓓ Ⓔ
17. Ⓐ Ⓑ Ⓒ Ⓓ Ⓔ
18. Ⓐ Ⓑ Ⓒ Ⓓ Ⓔ
19. Ⓐ Ⓑ Ⓒ Ⓓ Ⓔ
20. Ⓐ Ⓑ Ⓒ Ⓓ Ⓔ
21. Ⓐ Ⓑ Ⓒ Ⓓ Ⓔ
22. Ⓐ Ⓑ Ⓒ Ⓓ Ⓔ
23. Ⓐ Ⓑ Ⓒ Ⓓ Ⓔ
24. Ⓐ Ⓑ Ⓒ Ⓓ Ⓔ
25. Ⓐ Ⓑ Ⓒ Ⓓ Ⓔ
26. Ⓐ Ⓑ Ⓒ Ⓓ Ⓔ

ANSWER SHEET—MODEL TEST
LAW SCHOOL ADMISSION TEST (LSAT)

Section IV:
Analytical Reasoning

1. Ⓐ Ⓑ Ⓒ Ⓓ Ⓔ
2. Ⓐ Ⓑ Ⓒ Ⓓ Ⓔ
3. Ⓐ Ⓑ Ⓒ Ⓓ Ⓔ
4. Ⓐ Ⓑ Ⓒ Ⓓ Ⓔ
5. Ⓐ Ⓑ Ⓒ Ⓓ Ⓔ
6. Ⓐ Ⓑ Ⓒ Ⓓ Ⓔ
7. Ⓐ Ⓑ Ⓒ Ⓓ Ⓔ
8. Ⓐ Ⓑ Ⓒ Ⓓ Ⓔ
9. Ⓐ Ⓑ Ⓒ Ⓓ Ⓔ
10. Ⓐ Ⓑ Ⓒ Ⓓ Ⓔ
11. Ⓐ Ⓑ Ⓒ Ⓓ Ⓔ
12. Ⓐ Ⓑ Ⓒ Ⓓ Ⓔ
13. Ⓐ Ⓑ Ⓒ Ⓓ Ⓔ
14. Ⓐ Ⓑ Ⓒ Ⓓ Ⓔ
15. Ⓐ Ⓑ Ⓒ Ⓓ Ⓔ
16. Ⓐ Ⓑ Ⓒ Ⓓ Ⓔ
17. Ⓐ Ⓑ Ⓒ Ⓓ Ⓔ
18. Ⓐ Ⓑ Ⓒ Ⓓ Ⓔ
19. Ⓐ Ⓑ Ⓒ Ⓓ Ⓔ
20. Ⓐ Ⓑ Ⓒ Ⓓ Ⓔ
21. Ⓐ Ⓑ Ⓒ Ⓓ Ⓔ
22. Ⓐ Ⓑ Ⓒ Ⓓ Ⓔ
23. Ⓐ Ⓑ Ⓒ Ⓓ Ⓔ
24. Ⓐ Ⓑ Ⓒ Ⓓ Ⓔ

Section V:
Logical Reasoning

1. Ⓐ Ⓑ Ⓒ Ⓓ Ⓔ
2. Ⓐ Ⓑ Ⓒ Ⓓ Ⓔ
3. Ⓐ Ⓑ Ⓒ Ⓓ Ⓔ
4. Ⓐ Ⓑ Ⓒ Ⓓ Ⓔ
5. Ⓐ Ⓑ Ⓒ Ⓓ Ⓔ
6. Ⓐ Ⓑ Ⓒ Ⓓ Ⓔ
7. Ⓐ Ⓑ Ⓒ Ⓓ Ⓔ
8. Ⓐ Ⓑ Ⓒ Ⓓ Ⓔ
9. Ⓐ Ⓑ Ⓒ Ⓓ Ⓔ
10. Ⓐ Ⓑ Ⓒ Ⓓ Ⓔ
11. Ⓐ Ⓑ Ⓒ Ⓓ Ⓔ
12. Ⓐ Ⓑ Ⓒ Ⓓ Ⓔ
13. Ⓐ Ⓑ Ⓒ Ⓓ Ⓔ
14. Ⓐ Ⓑ Ⓒ Ⓓ Ⓔ
15. Ⓐ Ⓑ Ⓒ Ⓓ Ⓔ
16. Ⓐ Ⓑ Ⓒ Ⓓ Ⓔ
17. Ⓐ Ⓑ Ⓒ Ⓓ Ⓔ
18. Ⓐ Ⓑ Ⓒ Ⓓ Ⓔ
19. Ⓐ Ⓑ Ⓒ Ⓓ Ⓔ
20. Ⓐ Ⓑ Ⓒ Ⓓ Ⓔ
21. Ⓐ Ⓑ Ⓒ Ⓓ Ⓔ
22. Ⓐ Ⓑ Ⓒ Ⓓ Ⓔ
23. Ⓐ Ⓑ Ⓒ Ⓓ Ⓔ
24. Ⓐ Ⓑ Ⓒ Ⓓ Ⓔ
25. Ⓐ Ⓑ Ⓒ Ⓓ Ⓔ

✂ To remove, cut along dotted line.

CHAPTER 11

A Model LSAT

This chapter contains a full-length Model Test. It is geared to the format of the LSAT and it is complete with answers and explanations. It is equivalent to the LSAT in question structure, number of questions, level of difficulty, and time allotments. (The questions used are not taken directly from the LSAT, as those questions are copyrighted and may not be reproduced.)

The Model Test should be taken under strict test conditions. The test ends with a 30-minute Writing Sample, which is not scored.

Section	Description	Number of Questions	Time Allowed
I	Reading Comprehension	28	35 minutes
II	Analytical Reasoning	24	35 minutes
III	Logical Reasoning	26	35 minutes
IV	Analytical Reasoning	24	35 minutes
V	Logical Reasoning	25	35 minutes
	Writing Sample		30 minutes
TOTALS:		127	3 hours 25 minutes

Now please turn to the next page, remove your answer sheets, and begin the Model Test.

| 1 | 1 | 1 | 1 | 1 |

SECTION I
TIME — 35 MINUTES
28 QUESTIONS

Directions: Read the passages and answer the questions following each passage by blackening the appropriate space on the answer sheet. You may refer back to the passages when answering the questions. Answer all questions on the basis of what is stated or implied.

Although statutory law (a law enacted by the legislature) expressly forbids strikes by government workers, the
line constitutional validity of these laws as
(5) well as their interpretative applications have been under attack in various cases, the most publicized case being that of the federal government air traffic controllers.
(10)   The First Amendment to the United States Constitution guarantees the right of free speech. The constitutional issue to be resolved therefore is whether strikes are a form of "symbolic speech"
(15) or "symbolic conduct" that should be accorded the same degree of First Amendment protection as verbal communications. In a case that involved private rather than public employees, a
(20) Texas Court held that picketing as an incident to a labor dispute is a proper exercise of freedom of speech. The court went on to say that only a "clear and present danger of substantive evil will
(25) justify an abridgement of the right to picket." Later, the New Jersey state court concluded that even though picketing is protected by freedom of speech, this does not mean that statutes
(30) prohibiting strikes are constitutionally invalid. This case involved a constitutional interpretation of the New Jersey statute. The court stated that the justification of this statute is based on
(35) the ground of "clear and present danger" that would result to the state if the performance of functions of a public utility was ceased or impaired by a strike. Those in favor of no-strike
(40) clauses seem to concede that strikes are a form of symbolic speech that should be accorded the same degree of First Amendment protection as verbal speech. Their justification for upholding these
(45) clauses is the "clear and present danger" doctrine. They tend to believe that strikes by government employees automatically present a "clear and

present danger of substantive evil."
(50) However, according to the U.S. Supreme Court, legislatures cannot be relied upon to make a determination of what constitutes a "clear and present danger." In effect this is what happened when
(55) President Reagan ordered the firing of the air traffic controllers, based on the antistrike clause pronounced by Congress. The Supreme Court held that courts themselves must determine what
(60) constitutes a clear and present danger. The Supreme Court went on to say that mere public inconvenience or annoyance is not enough to constitute a clear and present danger. Thus, the public
(65) inconvenience and annoyance created by the curtailment of air traffic as a result of the controllers' strike may not be sufficient to constitute such a danger. The argument that a clear and present
(70) danger resulted from the emergency staffing of control towers by military and supervisory personnel is invalidated by the fact that the airlines have run safely since the strike.
(75)   This is not to suggest that every employee should automatically have the right to strike. However, constitutional consideration of due process and freedom of speech should bar denying
(80) government workers, as a class, the right to strike. A close look should be taken at what actually constitutes a "clear and present danger of substantive evil." It is an evasion for courts to allow
(85) legislatures to prejudge all government services to be different for "strike" purposes than those provided by the private sector. The court itself should look at such factors as the nature of the
(90) service in determining whether particular no-strike clauses are constitutionally valid. The nature of the provider of the service (i.e., government v. private) is not a compelling
(95) justification for upholding no-strike clauses.

GO ON TO THE NEXT PAGE ➤

1   1   1   1   1

1. According to the passage, strikes by government workers are

    (A) constitutionally invalid
    (B) forbidden by statutory law
    (C) permissible when there is no danger of substantial evil
    (D) permissible when there is no public inconvenience or annoyance
    (E) permissible when there is no danger to national security and safety

2. If government workers as a class are denied the right to strike, it can be argued that they have been denied all of the following EXCEPT

    (A) due process
    (B) freedom of speech
    (C) the clear and present danger doctrine
    (D) redress from abnormally dangerous working conditions
    (E) an abridgment of the right to picket

3. According to the passage, the "clear and present danger" justification of forbidding a strike has been misapplied for all of the following reasons EXCEPT

    (A) the dangers were determined by the executive branch
    (B) the dangers are often merely inconveniences
    (C) the dangers were determined by the courts
    (D) strikes by government workers do not automatically present dangers
    (E) the inconvenience caused by the air traffic controllers may not have been a danger

4. The fact that there was no rise in the number of airline accidents in the first six months after the firing and replacement of the striking air traffic controllers undermines the

    (A) government's argument that a strike would present a danger to the public
    (B) argument that the no-strike clause violates first amendment rights
    (C) argument that a strike is a form of symbolic speech
    (D) air traffic controllers' argument that they left their jobs because of dangerous working conditions
    (E) argument that no-strike clauses discourage more highly qualified individuals from applying for positions

5. The author of the passage objects to the current situation in which

    (A) all employees equally have the right to strike
    (B) the government regards national security more important than an individual's freedom
    (C) the Supreme Court avoids taking a position in its dealing with regret-to-strike cases
    (D) an unfair burden of proof is placed upon workers who leave jobs they believe to have unsafe working conditions
    (E) a false distinction is made between workers doing similar jobs for the government and private employees

6. Which one of the following might the author cite to exemplify another of the harmful effects of the no-strike rule?

    (A) It deters the highly skilled from taking government jobs.
    (B) It can be used as a precedent in the private sector.
    (C) It places too much power in the hands of the judicial branch of the government.
    (D) It encourages the courts to determine whether or not particular no-strike clauses are valid.
    (E) It protects some workers from abnormally dangerous working conditions.

GO ON TO THE NEXT PAGE ➤

1   1   1   1   1 ➤

Virginia Woolf's development as a
novelist was deeply influenced by her
struggle to reconcile feminism and art.
line Long before the aesthetic creed of
(5) Bloomsbury came into being she had
learned from her father that a work of
literature is no better than the morality
which it is intended to express—a lesson
she never forgot. Virginia Woolf was a
(10) passionate moralist, though she directed
all her fervor into one narrow channel.
The impulse to write Three Guineas
possessed her for years, "violently . . .
persistently, pressingly, compulsorily,"
(15) until she carried it into action. This
moral fervor was not contained within
the limits of her tracts, nor could it have
been. Feminism is implicit in her novels.
The novels are not, of course, didactic in
(20) the narrow sense of pleading for specific
reforms, but they illustrate the dangers
of one-sidedness and celebrate the
androgynous mind.
Virginia Woolf's main emphasis in
(25) her feminist writings, as in the novels,
was on self-reform, and on art as a
means to that end. Novels and tracts
alike grew out of a preoccupation with
her own spiritual dilemma. Fiction was
(30) the medium within which Virginia
Woolf controlled and directed this
intense self-absorption. When she
deserted art for propaganda, as in Three
Guineas, her self-absorption got the
(35) upper hand. Thus, paradoxically, she
was truer to her feminist ideas as a
novelist than as a pamphleteer. Her
social conscience and her aesthetic
vision were mutually dependent. She
(40) could express her feminism only by
means of her art; but her art owed its
character to her feminism.
The contract between Virginia
Woolf's failure in Three Guineas and her
(45) triumph in The Years confirms this
impression. In the first, confining herself
to political and social controversy, she
lost her grasp of reality and ended up
talking to herself. In the second, striving,
(50) as she said, "to give the whole of the
present society . . . facts as well as the
vision," she transcended purely personal
preoccupations and created a lasting
work of art. Virginia Woolf's direct
(55) attack on social evil is too shrill and
self-indulgent to succeed, even as

propaganda. On the other hand, her
symbolic representation of the
Wasteland—pollution, faithlessness,
remorse—has a lucid objectivity that
(60) forces the reader to see through her eyes.
The tract, with all its talk of reform, is
one-sided. The novel is whole.
In Virginia Woolf's case, the myth of
the artist as more or less helpless agent
(65) of his own creative drive seems to have
a foundation in fact. She needed the
discipline of art, because it permitted her
to express her intense moral indignation,
while at the same time controlling the
(70) disintegrating effects of that indignation
upon her personality. Art produced
feelings of release and harmony, such as
she associated with the androgynous
mind. When she avoided that discipline,
(75) as in Three Guineas, her writing tended
to become morbid. In relation to the
radiance of Virginia Woolf's artistic
successes, therefore, Three Guineas
represents a kind of negative definition.
(80) Through it we can glance into the heart
of her darkness.

7. According to the passage, Woolf's father
influenced her

(A) choice of writing as a career
(B) belief in the importance of self-
reform
(C) belief that literature should have a
moral base
(D) desire to write tracts and pamphlets
(E) views on the equality of men and
women

GO ON TO THE NEXT PAGE ➤

8. We can infer from the passage that the "spiritual dilemma" mentioned in line 30 refers to a

   (A) need to transcend one-sidedness and encompass both the masculine and feminine
   (B) desire to retire from the world rather than participate actively in society
   (C) need to choose between artistic endeavors and social work
   (D) desire to pursue a writing career and a desire to raise a family
   (E) need to transcend lucid objectivity and express passion in her work

9. According to the passage, which one of the following best characterizes Woolf's feminism?

   (A) a faith in feminine creativity and intuition
   (B) an integration of the masculine and the feminine
   (C) an indignation toward social institutions
   (D) an emphasis on social equality
   (E) a morbid preoccupation with self

10. The function of the third paragraph of the passage is to provide a

    (A) concrete example of the points made in paragraph 2
    (B) view contrasting with the one presented in paragraph 1
    (C) transition between paragraphs 2 and 4
    (D) subtopic to the main topic of paragraph 1
    (E) exegesis of the works introduced in paragraph 1

11. Which one of the following oppositions does the author principally address in the passage?

    (A) Woolf's aesthetic creed and the aesthetic creed of the Bloomsbury group
    (B) Woolf's novels of social reform and Woolf's novels of individual soul-searching
    (C) masculinity and femininity
    (D) social injustice and self-reform
    (E) Woolf's propaganda and Woolf's art

12. From the passage we can infer that the author

    (A) questions the validity of the Bloomsbury aesthetic creed
    (B) approves of symbolism only when used for social reform
    (C) finds Woolf's fiction more successful than her nonfiction
    (D) believes Woolf's social concerns are trivial
    (E) dislikes literature written in the cause of social reform

13. Which one of the following would be the best title for this passage?

    (A) *Three Guineas* and *The Years:* A Study
    (B) Virginia Woolf's Success
    (C) Virginia Woolf: Problems with Nonfiction
    (D) Virginia Woolf: Reconciling Feminism and Art
    (E) Masculine vs. Feminine: A Study of Virginia Woolf

GO ON TO THE NEXT PAGE ➤

Much as they may deplore the fact, historians have no monopoly on the past and no franchise as its privileged interpreters to the public. It may have been different once, but there can no longer be any doubt about the relegation of the historian to a back seat. Far surpassing works of history, as measured by the size of their public and the influence they exert, are the novel, works for the stage, the screen, and television. It is mainly from these sources that millions who never open a history book derive such conceptions, interpretations, convictions, or fantasies as they have about the past. Whatever gives shape to popular conceptions of the past is of concern to historians, and this surely includes fiction.

Broadly speaking, two types of fiction deal with the past—historical fiction and fictional history. The more common of the two is historical fiction, which places fictional characters and events in a more or less authentic historical background. Examples range from War and Peace to Gone With the Wind. Since all but a few novelists must place their fictional characters in some period, nearly all fiction can be thought of as in some degree historical. But the term is applied as a rule only to novels in which historical events figure prominently. Fictional history, on the other hand, portrays and focuses attention upon real historical figures and events, but with the license of the novelist to imagine and invent. It has yet to produce anything approaching Tolstoy's masterpiece. Some fictional history makes use of invented characters and events, and historical fiction at times mixes up fictional and nonfictional characters. As a result the two genres overlap sometimes, but not often enough to make the distinction unimportant.

Of the two, it is fictional history that is the greater source of mischief, for it is here that fabrication and fact, fiction and nonfiction, are most likely to be mixed and confused. Of course, historians themselves sometimes mix fact with fancy, but it is a rare one who does it consciously or deliberately, and he knows very well that if discovered he stands convicted of betraying his calling.

The writer of fictional history, on the other hand, does this as a matter of course and with no compunction whatever. The production and consumption of fictional history appear to be growing of late. Part of the explanation of this is probably the fragmentation of history by professionals, their retreat into specializations, their abandonment of the narrative style, and with it the traditional patronage of lay readers. Fictional history has expanded to fill the gap thus created but has at the same time gone further to create a much larger readership than history books ever had.

14. We can infer from the passage that the author is probably

(A) a historian
(B) a historical novelist
(C) a literary critic
(D) a social commentator
(E) a literary historian

15. According to the passage, which one of the following is likely to have contributed to the increasing popularity of fictional history?

(A) a change in the demographics of lay readers of history
(B) an increase in the audience for movies and television
(C) a decline in historians' use of a storytelling style
(D) an increase in historians' mixing fact and fancy
(E) a decline in the writing ability of professional historians

GO ON TO THE NEXT PAGE ➤

16. The author's attitude toward fictional history can best be summarized in which one of the following statements?

    (A) Masterpieces such as *War and Peace* and *Gone With the Wind* could not be created in the fictional history genre.
    (B) Fictional history is responsible for leading the reading public away from traditional historical works.
    (C) Fictional history provides a useful service by filling the gap for readers not interested in traditional history.
    (D) Writers of fictional history should not mix historical figures with fictional characters.
    (E) Fictional history can mislead readers about actual historical events.

17. Of the following, which one would the author consider most likely to cause a reader to confuse fact and fiction?

    (A) a book about the Watergate scandal with fictionalized dialogue between President Nixon and his attorney general, John Mitchell
    (B) a book about a fictional platoon in Vietnam during the last days of the war
    (C) a fictional account of the adventures of a group of servants in the White House under Eisenhower, Kennedy, Johnson, and Nixon
    (D) an account of the assassination of President Kennedy as viewed by a Texas adolescent on the parade route
    (E) a book based on newspaper accounts about the reaction to the Cuban missile crisis in the United States, the U.S.S.R., and Western Europe

18. The function of the second paragraph of the passage is to

    (A) reinforce the argument about fictionalized history presented in the first paragraph
    (B) define and contrast fictional history and historical fiction
    (C) emphasize the superiority of historical fiction to fictional history
    (D) provide context for the analysis in the third paragraph
    (E) clarify the difference between history and fiction

19. According to the passage, the author would agree with all of the following statements EXCEPT

    (A) historical fiction and fictional history are of concern to the professional historian
    (B) the works of today's professional historians tend to be more specialized than historical works of the past
    (C) professional historians understand that they should not mix fact and fiction in their works
    (D) a historical event presented as a TV miniseries is likely to be accepted as true by many people
    (E) fictional history has succeeded because of a failure of the academic history curriculum

20. The author's attitude about the issue of fiction and history is presented most clearly in

    (A) paragraph 1, lines 1-7
    (B) paragraph 1, lines 17-20
    (C) paragraph 2, lines 35-41
    (D) paragraph 3, lines 49-53
    (E) paragraph 3, lines 62-64

21. The tone of this passage could best be described as

    (A) hostile and didactic
    (B) moderate and concerned
    (C) pedantic and detached
    (D) ironic and condescending
    (E) philosophical and enlightened

GO ON TO THE NEXT PAGE ➤

Most of our knowledge about how the brain links memory and emotion has been gleaned through the study of so-
line called classical fear conditioning. In this
(5) process the subject, usually a rat, hears a noise or sees a flashing light that is paired with a brief, mild electric shock to its feet. After a few such experiences, the rat responds automatically to the
(10) sound or light even in the absence of the shock. Its reactions are typical to any threatening situation: the animal freezes, its blood pressure and heart rate increase, and it startles easily. In the
(15) language of such experiments, the noise or flash is a conditioned stimulus, the foot shock is an unconditioned stimulus, and the rat's reaction is a conditioned response, which consists of readily
(20) measured behavioral and physiological changes.

Conditioning of this kind happens quickly in rats—indeed, it takes place as rapidly as it does in humans. A single
(25) pairing of the shock to the sound or sight can bring on the conditioned effect. Once established, the fearful reaction is relatively permanent. If the noise or light is administered many times without an
(30) accompanying electric shock, the rat's response diminishes. This change is called extinction. But considerable evidence suggests that this behavioral alteration is the result of the brain's
(35) controlling the fear response rather than the elimination of the emotional memory. For example, an apparently extinguished fear response can recover spontaneously or can be reinstated by an
(40) irrelevant stressful experience. Similarly, stress can cause the reappearance of phobias in people who have been successfully treated. This resurrection demonstrates that the emotional memory
(45) underlying the phobia was rendered dormant rather than erased by treatment.

Fear conditioning has proved an ideal starting point for studies of emotional memory for several reasons. First, it
(50) occurs in nearly every animal group in which it has been examined: fruit flies, snails, birds, lizards, fish, rabbits, rats, monkeys, and people. Although no one claims that the mechanisms are precisely
(55) the same in all these creatures, it seems clear from studies to date that the

pathways are very similar in mammals and possibly in all vertebrates. We therefore are confident in believing that
(60) many of the findings in animals apply to humans. In addition, the kinds of stimuli most commonly used in this type of conditioning are not signals that rats—or humans, for that matter—encounter in
(65) their daily lives. The novelty and irrelevance of these lights and sounds help to ensure that the animals have not already developed strong emotional reactions to them. So researchers are
(70) clearly observing learning and memory at work. At the same time, such cues do not require complicated cognitive processing from the brain. Consequently, the stimuli permit us to
(75) study emotional mechanisms relatively directly. Finally, our extensive knowledge of the neural pathways involved in processing acoustic and visual information serves as an excellent
(80) starting point for examining the neurological foundations of fear elicited by such stimuli.

22. Which one of the following best states the main idea of the passage?

(A) Fear conditioning in animals and humans proves the direct link between emotion and memory.
(B) The mechanisms for linking memory and emotion are the same in mammals and possibly all vertebrates.
(C) Fear conditioning is a helpful starting point to use in studying emotional memory.
(D) Fearful reactions created by a conditioned stimulus are relatively permanent in both animals and humans.
(E) Fear conditioning in rats and other mammals is similar to the creation of phobias in humans.

GO ON TO THE NEXT PAGE ➤

23. Which one of the following statements is best supported by information presented in the passage?

   (A) Fear conditioning requires that the conditioned and unconditioned stimuli are paired on many occasions.
   (B) Emotional mechanisms in the brain are linked to complicated cognitive processing.
   (C) The recurrence of human phobias under stress may be compared to the spontaneous recovery of the fear response in rats.
   (D) A conditioned response is weakened in times of stress provided emotion and memory have been successfully linked.
   (E) A rat's conditioned response to the pairing of conditioned and unconditioned stimuli diminishes over time.

24. A rat is exposed to a buzzer and an electric shock. After pairing the two stimuli 50 times, the rat exhibits a fear response when the buzzer alone is administered. The buzzer is then sounded *without* the shock an additional 200 times. According to the passage, the rat will probably

   (A) continue to exhibit the fear response to the buzzer alone
   (B) initially exhibit the fear response to the buzzer alone but then entirely lose the response
   (C) initially exhibit the fear response to the buzzer alone, then appear to lose the response, then after the buzzer and shock are paired one additional time, exhibit it again to the buzzer alone
   (D) initially exhibit the fear response to the buzzer alone, then appear to lose the response, then exhibit it again after a cat is introduced into the area
   (E) initially exhibit the fear response to the buzzer alone, then begin to exhibit the response erratically, then lose the response entirely

25. The author contends that an apparently extinguished fear response that is recovered under stress indicates

   (A) learning and memory
   (B) complex cognitive processing
   (C) previous strong emotional response to stimuli
   (D) inadequate pairing of conditioned/unconditioned stimuli
   (E) lack of control by the brain

26. The passage lists the nine specific animal groups for which fear conditioning studies have been performed in order to

   (A) suggest the neural basis of the fear response
   (B) show in how wide a range of animals fear conditioning is exhibited
   (C) show the developmental link from fruit flies to people
   (D) raise the question of the role of complex cognitive processes in fear conditioning
   (E) show that emotions are present in simple as well as complex creatures

27. We can infer that the immediate goal of research described in the passage is to understand

   (A) the neural basis of fear
   (B) the relationship between cognition and emotion
   (C) the mechanism of conditioning
   (D) the effects of acoustic and visual stimuli
   (E) the similarities among mammalian cognitive processes

GO ON TO THE NEXT PAGE ➤

1   1   1   1   1

28. Which one of the following best describes the relationship of the third paragraph to the passage as a whole?

(A) It completes the definition of the method begun by the author in the first paragraph and elaborated upon in the second paragraph.

(B) It presents qualifications to the points made in the first and second paragraphs and suggests other possible approaches.

(C) It summarizes the evidence and conclusions described in detail in the second paragraph.

(D) It presents further applications of the method explained in the first and second paragraphs.

(E) It justifies the use of the method explained in the first and second paragraphs.

STOP

IF YOU FINISH BEFORE THE TIME IS UP, CHECK YOUR WORK ON THIS SECTION OF THE TEST ONLY.
DO NOT GO ON TO THE NEXT SECTION OF THE TEST UNTIL TIME IS UP FOR THIS SECTION.

SECTION II
TIME — 35 MINUTES
24 QUESTIONS

Directions: In this section you will be given groups of questions based on different sets of conditions. Drawing a simple diagram may be helpful in answering some of the questions. You are to choose the best answer and mark the corresponding space on your answer sheet.

Questions 1-6

The Bell Canyon Condominium is a four-story building with a single penthouse apartment on the fourth floor. There are two apartments on each of the three other floors. The apartments are owned by A, B, C, D, E, F, and G.

    A's apartment is on one of the floors higher than B's.

    C's apartment is on one of the floors lower than D's.

    C's apartment is on one of the floors lower than E's.

    F and G's apartments are on the same floor.

1. Which one of the following could be the owner of the penthouse?

    (A) B
    (B) C
    (C) E
    (D) F
    (E) G

2. If F's apartment is on the second floor, which one of the following must be true?

    (A) C's apartment is on the first floor.
    (B) D's apartment is on the third floor.
    (C) A's apartment is on the fourth floor.
    (D) G's apartment is on the first floor.
    (E) B's apartment is on the third floor.

3. If D owns the penthouse apartment, on which floor or floors could G's apartment be located?

    (A) the first floor only
    (B) the second floor only
    (C) the third floor only
    (D) the second or the third floor
    (E) the first, second, or third floor

4. If D's and E's apartments are on the same floor, which one of the following must be true?

    (A) D and E are on the third floor.
    (B) D and E are on the second floor.
    (C) A is on the fourth floor.
    (D) B and C are on the first floor.
    (E) F and G are on the second floor.

5. If C's apartment is on the first floor, and A is the owner of the penthouse, which one of the following must be true?

    (A) G's apartment is on the third floor.
    (B) D's apartment is on the second floor.
    (C) E's apartment is on the second floor.
    (D) B's apartment is on the first floor.
    (E) F's apartment is on the second floor.

6. Which one of the following is possible?

    (A) A and C are on the same floor.
    (B) A and E are on the same floor.
    (C) A is on the first floor.
    (D) D is on the first floor.
    (E) C is on the fourth floor.

Questions 7-12

A new bank has decided to stay open only on weekends—all day Saturday and Sunday—and no other days. The bank has hired two managers (U and V), four tellers (W, X, Y, and Z), and two operations officers (S and T), for a total of exactly eight full-time employees. No part-time employees are hired. Each employee works a complete day when working.

A manager must be on duty each day.

The managers cannot work on the same day.

At least two tellers must be working on the same day.

W and X will not work on the same day.

S and Z will only work on Saturday.

No employee can work on consecutive days, but each employee must work on Saturday or Sunday.

7. Which one of the following could be false?

   (A) If U works on Saturday, then V works on Sunday.
   (B) If X works on Saturday, then W works on Sunday.
   (C) T can work either day.
   (D) If W works on Saturday and Y works on Sunday, then X works on Sunday.
   (E) If U works on Sunday, then X works on Saturday.

8. Which one of the following is an acceptable group of employees that could work on Saturday?

   (A) ZWYST
   (B) UVWYZS
   (C) VWXZT
   (D) UZST
   (E) VWZS

9. What is the greatest number of employees that can work on Saturday?

   (A) 2
   (B) 3
   (C) 4
   (D) 5
   (E) 6

10. If W works on Sunday, then which one of the following must be true?

    (A) X works on Saturday.
    (B) Y works on Saturday.
    (C) T works on Sunday.
    (D) Z works on Sunday.
    (E) U works on Saturday.

11. Which one of the following must be true?

    (A) T always works the same day as Y.
    (B) S never works the same day as U.
    (C) Z never works the same day as X.
    (D) If W works on Sunday, then Y always works on Saturday.
    (E) Only two tellers work on Saturday.

12. Which one of the following is a complete and accurate list of the employees who have the possibility of working on Sunday?

    (A) UWYZ
    (B) UWYS
    (C) UVWXT
    (D) UVWXYT
    (E) UVWXYTS

GO ON TO THE NEXT PAGE ➤

2   2   2   2   2

Questions 13-19

Three division office managers, Fred, Al, and Cynthia, draw office assistants each day from the clerical and typing pools available to them. The clerical pool consists of Lyndia, Jim, Dennis, and Sylvia. The typing pool consists of Edra, Gene, and Helen. The office assistants are selected according to the following conditions:

    Fred always needs at least one typist, but never more than two assistants.

    Al always needs at least two assistants, but never more than three.

    Sylvia or Gene and one other assistant always work for Cynthia.

    Gene and Lyndia always work together.

    Dennis and Edra will not work together.

    No more than two typists work for the same manager, but all three typists must work each day.

13. If Gene works for Fred and all of the assistants work, then which one of the following must be FALSE?

    (A) Jim works for Cynthia.
    (B) Sylvia works for Cynthia.
    (C) Lyndia works for Fred.
    (D) Dennis works for Al.
    (E) Edra works for Al.

14. If Sylvia doesn't work for Cynthia, then which one of the following must be true?

    (A) Edra works for Fred.
    (B) Gene works for Al.
    (C) Lyndia works for Cynthia.
    (D) Dennis works for Al.
    (E) Helen works for Cynthia.

15. Assume that Lyndia and Jim work for Al. Which one of the following must be true?

    (A) Gene works for Al.
    (B) Edra works for Cynthia.
    (C) Helen works for Fred.
    (D) Edra works for Fred.
    (E) Helen works for Cynthia.

16. Assume that Sylvia and Jim work for Al. If all of the assistants work, then which one of the following must be true?

    (A) Edra works for Al.
    (B) Gene works for Fred.
    (C) Lyndia works for Al.
    (D) Helen works for Fred.
    (E) Dennis works for Fred.

17. Which one of the following must be FALSE?

    (A) Helen and Edra never work for Cynthia on the same day.
    (B) Edra can work for Cynthia.
    (C) Dennis and Gene never work for Fred on the same day.
    (D) Jim and Sylvia never work for Fred on the same day.
    (E) Lyndia and Sylvia can work for Al on the same day.

18. If Jim works for Cynthia and all of the assistants work, then

    (A) Dennis works for Al.
    (B) Edra works for Al.
    (C) Helen works for Al.
    (D) Lyndia works for Al.
    (E) Sylvia works for Fred.

19. Assume that Al needs only two assistants and Fred needs only one assistant. If Helen works for Fred, then which one of the following must be true?

    (A) Jim works for Al.
    (B) Sylvia doesn't work.
    (C) Dennis doesn't work.
    (D) Edra works for Al.
    (E) Edra works for Cynthia.

GO ON TO THE NEXT PAGE ➤

2   **2**   **2**   **2**   **2**

Questions 20-24

Four teams (Red, Blue, Green, and Yellow) participate in the Junior Olympics, in which there are five events. In each event participants place either 1st, 2nd, 3rd, or 4th. First place is awarded a gold medal, 2nd place is awarded a silver medal, and 3rd place is awarded a bronze medal. There are no ties and each team enters one contestant in each event. All contestants finish each event.

The results of the Junior Olympics are:
  No team wins gold medals in two consecutive events.
  No team fails to win a medal within two consecutive events.
  The Blue team wins only two medals, neither of them gold.
  The Red team only wins three gold medals, and no other medals.

20. If the green team wins only one gold medal, then which one of the following must be true?

    (A) The yellow team wins two gold medals.
    (B) The red team wins only two bronze medals.
    (C) The yellow team wins only one gold medal.
    (D) The yellow team wins only silver medals.
    (E) The green team wins only bronze medals.

21. Which one of the following must be true?

    (A) The yellow team wins only bronze and gold medals.
    (B) The yellow team wins five medals.
    (C) The green team cannot win a silver medal.
    (D) The yellow team cannot win a bronze medal.
    (E) The green team wins exactly three medals.

22. If the yellow team wins five silver medals, then the green team must win

    (A) more silver than gold
    (B) more gold than bronze
    (C) two gold, two bronze, one silver
    (D) two gold, three bronze
    (E) six medals

23. All of the following must be true EXCEPT

    (A) the green team wins five medals
    (B) the yellow team wins five medals
    (C) if the green team wins one gold medal, the yellow team wins one gold medal
    (D) if the green team wins only one silver medal, the yellow team wins only one silver medal
    (E) if the yellow team wins only silver medals, the green team cannot win a silver medal

24. If a fifth team, Orange, enters all events and wins only three consecutive silver medals, which one of the following must be true?

    (A) If green wins a gold in the 2nd event, it also wins a bronze in the 3rd event.
    (B) If green wins a gold in the 2nd event, it also wins a silver in the 4th event.
    (C) If yellow wins a gold in the 2nd event, green wins a bronze in the 3rd event.
    (D) If yellow wins a gold in the 2nd event, blue wins a silver in the 3rd event.
    (E) If red wins a gold in the 1st event, orange wins a silver in the last event.

STOP

SECTION III
Time — 35 minutes
26 Questions

<u>Directions:</u> In this section you will be given brief statements or passages and will be required to evaluate the reasoning involved. In some instances, more than one choice will appear to be a possible answer. You are to choose the *best* answer. Use common sense and reasonableness in making your selection; then mark the proper space on the answer sheet.

1. Though the benefits of the hot tub and the Jacuzzis have been well publicized by their manufacturers, there are also some less widely-known dangers. Young children, of course, cannot be left unattended near a hot tub, and even adults have fallen asleep and drowned. Warm water can cause the blood vessels to dilate and the resulting drop in blood pressure can make people liable to fainting, especially when they stand up quickly to get out. Improperly maintained water can promote the growth of bacteria that can cause folliculitis.

   The main point of this passage is that

   (A) the benefits of the hot tub and the Jacuzzi have been overrated
   (B) the dangers of the hot tub and Jacuzzi outweigh their potential publicized benefits
   (C) users of hot tubs and Jacuzzis should be aware of the dangers connected with their use
   (D) the hot tub and Jacuzzi are dangerous only when improperly maintained
   (E) the hot tub is potentially beneficial in the treatment of high blood pressure

2. *Chariots of Fire* may have caught some professional critics off guard in 1982 as the Motion Picture Academy's choice for an Oscar as the year's best film, but it won wide audience approval as superb entertainment.

   Refreshingly, *Chariots of Fire* features an exciting story, enchanting English and Scottish scenery, a beautiful musical score, and appropriate costumes.

   All of these attractions are added to a theme that extols traditional religious values—without a shred of offensive sex, violence, or profanity.

   Too good to be true? See *Chariots of Fire* and judge for yourself.

   Those who condemn the motion picture industry for producing so many objectionable films can do their part by patronizing wholesome ones, thereby encouraging future Academy Award judges to recognize and reward decency.

   Which one of the following is a basic assumption underlying the final sentence of the passage?

   (A) Academy judges are not decent people.
   (B) The popularity of a film influences academy judges.
   (C) Future academy judges will be better than past ones.
   (D) There are those who condemn the motion picture industry.
   (E) *Chariots of Fire* is a patronizing film.

3   **3**   **3**   **3**   **3**

3. *Andy:* All teachers are mean.
   Bob: That is not true. I know some doctors who are mean too.

Bob's answer demonstrates that he thought Andy to mean that

(A) all teachers are mean
(B) some teachers are mean
(C) doctors are meaner than teachers
(D) teachers are meaner than doctors
(E) only teachers are mean

4. Theodore Roosevelt was a great hunter. He was the mighty Nimrod of his generation. He had the physical aptitude and adventurous spirit of the true frontiersman. "There is delight," he said, "in the hardy life of the open; in long rides, rifle in hand; in the thrill of the fight with dangerous game." But he was more than a marksman and tracker of beasts, for he brought to his sport the intellectual curiosity and patient observation of the natural scientist.

Which one of the following would most weaken the author's concluding contention?

(A) Theodore Roosevelt never studied natural science.
(B) Actually, Theodore Roosevelt's sharpshooting prowess was highly exaggerated.
(C) Theodore Roosevelt always used native guides when tracking game.
(D) Theodore Roosevelt was known to leave safaris if their first few days were unproductive.
(E) Theodore Roosevelt's powers of observation were significantly hampered by his nearsightedness.

5. The following is an excerpt from a letter sent to a law school applicant:

"Thank you for considering our school to further your education. Your application for admission was received well before the deadline and was processed with your admission test score and undergraduate grade report.

"We regret to inform you that you cannot be admitted for the fall semester. We have had to refuse admission to many outstanding candidates because of the recent cut in state funding of our program.

"Thank you for your interest in our school and we wish you success in your future endeavors."

Which one of the following can be deduced from the above letter?

(A) The recipient of the letter did not have a sufficiently high grade point average to warrant admission to this graduate program.
(B) The recipient of the letter was being seriously considered for a place in the evening class.
(C) The law school sending the letter could not fill all the places in its entering class due to a funding problem.
(D) Criteria other than test scores and grade reports were used in determining the size of the entering class.
(E) The school sending the letter is suffering severe financial difficulties.

GO ON TO THE NEXT PAGE ➤

Questions 6-7

At birth we have no self-image. We cannot distinguish anything from the confusion of light and sound around us. From this beginning of no-dimension, we gradually begin to differentiate our body from our environment and develop a sense of identity, with the realization that we are a separate and independent human being. We then begin to develop a conscience, the sense of right and wrong. Further, we develop social consciousness, where we become aware that we live with other people. Finally, we develop a sense of values, which is our overall estimation of our worth in the world.

6. Which one of the following would be the best completion of this passage?

   (A) The sum total of all these developments we call the self-image or the self-concept.
   (B) This estimation of worth is only relative to our value system.
   (C) Therefore, our social consciousness is dependent on our sense of values.
   (D) Therefore, our conscience keeps our sense of values in perspective.
   (E) The sum total of living with other people and developing a sense of values makes us a total person.

7. The author of this passage would most likely agree with which one of the following?

   (A) Children have no self-dimension.
   (B) Having a conscience necessitates the ability to differentiate between right and wrong.
   (C) Social consciousness is our most important awareness.
   (D) Heredity is predominant over environment in development.
   (E) The ability to distinguish the difference between moral issues depends on the overall dimension of self-development.

8. *Editorial:* A previously undisclosed transcript has revealed that Richard Nixon's secret White House slush fund that was used to silence the Watergate burglars came from illegally donated campaign money. After Nixon resigned, his successor, Gerald Ford, pardoned him. The same Gerald Ford has joined Presidents Carter and Bush in urging campaign funding reforms. Recent hearings have shown all too clearly that both parties have been guilty of highly questionable fund-raising practices. Unless the laws are changed, the shoddy practices of the last thirty years will undoubtedly continue.

Which one of the following most accurately states the main point of the argument?

   (A) It is hypocritical of Gerald Ford to urge campaign reform after his pardon of Richard Nixon.
   (B) Both the Democrats and the Republicans have been guilty of unethical campaign fund-raising practices.
   (C) The laws governing campaign fund-raising must be reformed.
   (D) Reform of campaign fund-raising has been supported by former presidents of both parties.
   (E) We cannot expect that those who benefit from a problem will wish to take steps to solve it.

GO ON TO THE NEXT PAGE ➤

3   **3**   **3**   **3**   **3**

Questions 9-10

In a report released last week, a government-funded institute concluded that there is "overwhelming" evidence that violence on television leads to criminal behavior by children and teenagers.

The report based on an extensive review of several hundred research studies conducted during the 1970s, is an update of a 1972 Surgeon General's report that came to similar conclusions.

9. Which one of the following is the most convincing statement in support of the argument in the first paragraph above?

 (A) A 50-state survey of the viewing habits of prison inmates concluded that every inmate watches at least 2 hours of violent programming each day.
 (B) A 50-state survey of the viewing habits of convicted adolescents shows that each of them had watched at least 2 hours of violent programming daily since the age of 5.
 (C) One juvenile committed a murder that closely resembled a crime portrayed on a network series.
 (D) The 1972 Surgeon General's report was not nearly as extensive as this more recent study.
 (E) Ghetto residents who are burglarized most often report the theft of a television set.

10. The argument above is most weakened by its vague use of the word

 (A) violence
 (B) government
 (C) extensive
 (D) update
 (E) overwhelming

Questions 11-12

Violence against racial and religious minority groups increased sharply throughout the county last year, despite a slight decline in statewide figures. Compiling incidents from police departments and private watchdog groups, the County Human Relations Committee reported almost 500 hate crimes in the year, up from only 200 last year. It was the first increase since the committee began to report a yearly figure six years ago. The lower statewide figures are probably in error due to underreporting in other counties; underreporting is the major problem that state surveyors face each year.

11. All of the following, if true, would support the conclusion or the explanation of the discrepancy in the state and county figures EXCEPT

 (A) the number of hate crimes and those resulting in fatalities has increased in neighboring states
 (B) anti-immigration sentiment was fanned this year by an anti-immigration ballot referendum
 (C) funding for police departments throughout the state has decreased
 (D) many law-abiding members of minority groups are fearful or distrustful of the police
 (E) all of the counties in the state have active private watchdog groups that carefully monitor hate crimes

12. The author of this passage makes his case by

 (A) establishing the likelihood of an event by ruling out several other possibilities
 (B) combining several pieces of apparently unrelated evidence to build support for a conclusion
 (C) contrasting a single certain case with several others with less evidence in their support
 (D) assuming that what is only probable is certain
 (E) using a general rule to explain a specific case

GO ON TO THE NEXT PAGE ➤

13. The study of village communities has become one of the fundamental methods of discussing the ancient history of institutions. It would be out of the question here to range over the whole field of human society in search for communal arrangements of rural life. It will be sufficient to confine the present inquiry to the varieties presented by nations of Aryan race, not because greater importance is to be attached to these nations than to other branches of humankind, although this view might also be reasonably urged, but principally because the Aryan race in its history has gone through all sorts of experiences, and the data gathered from its historical life can be tolerably well ascertained. Should the road be sufficiently cleared in this particular direction, it will not be difficult to connect the results with similar researches in other racial surroundings.

Which one of the following, if true, most weakens the author's conclusion?

(A) Information about the Aryan race is no more conclusive than information about any other ethnic group.
(B) The experiences and lifestyle of Aryans are uniquely different from those of other cultures.
(C) The Aryan race is no more important than any other race.
(D) The historical life of the Aryans dates back only 12 centuries.
(E) Aryans lived predominantly in villages, while today 90 percent of the world population live predominantly in or around major cities.

14. Although any reasonable modern citizen of the world must abhor war and condemn senseless killing, we must also agree that honor is more valuable than life. Life, after all, is transient, but honor is ____.

Which one of the following most logically completes the passage above?

(A) sensible
(B) real
(C) eternal
(D) of present value
(E) priceless

Questions 15-16

Bill said, "All dogs bark. This animal does not bark. Therefore it is not a dog."

15. Which one of the following most closely parallels the logic of this statement?

(A) All rocks are hard. This lump is hard. Therefore, it may be a rock.
(B) All foreign language tests are difficult. This is not a foreign language test. Therefore, it is not difficult.
(C) All Blunder automobiles are poorly built. Every auto sold by Joe was poorly built. Therefore, Joe sells Blunder automobiles.
(D) Rocks beat scissors, scissors beat paper, and paper beats rocks. Therefore, it is best to choose paper.
(E) All paint smells. This liquid does not smell. Therefore, it is not paint.

16. Which one of the following would weaken Bill's argument the most?

(A) Animals other than dogs bark.
(B) Some dogs cannot bark.
(C) Dogs bark more than cockatiels.
(D) You can train a dog not to bark.
(E) You can train birds to bark.

3   **3**   **3**   **3**   **3**

17. In the last three years the number of arrests for burglary and robbery in Sandy Beach has declined by more than 30 percent. At the same time, the city has reduced the size of its police force by 25 percent.

Which one of the following helps to resolve an apparent discrepancy in the information above?

(A) Neighborhood Watch programs have always been active in Sandy Beach.
(B) The number of reported burglaries and robberies in Sandy Beach has increased in the last three years.
(C) Compared to other cities in the state, Sandy Beach has one of the lowest crime rates.
(D) By using motorcycles rather than foot patrols, the police are able to cover larger areas of the city using fewer officers.
(E) Many of the residents of Sandy Beach have installed expensive security systems in their homes.

Questions 18-19

California and Nevada officials have questioned the impartiality of the board of scientists from the National Academy of Science who assess the safety of proposed nuclear dumping sites. They claim that the panels are heavily weighted in favor of the nuclear power companies that have been lobbying for the creation of nuclear dump sites in the deserts of the Southwest. At least ten members of the panels are or have been employees of the Department of Energy, but none is associated with any environmental organization. Environmentalists fear that long-lived nuclear wastes may leach into the groundwater and ultimately into the waters of the Colorado River. They also point out that 90 percent of the budget of the National Academy's Radioactive Waste Management Board is provided by the Department of Energy. The inventory of radioactive waste has been growing larger and larger in temporary storage places, but so far there has been virtually no agreement about a permanent dump site.

18. The officials who question the impartiality of the Management Board assume that the Department of Energy

(A) supports the activities of the nuclear power industry
(B) supports the activities of environmental groups
(C) wishes to delay the selection of permanent nuclear waste dumping sites for as long as possible
(D) is indifferent to the growing mass of nuclear wastes in temporary storage sites
(E) has declined to take a stand for or against the use of nuclear power

19. The Nuclear Waste Management Board could best allay doubt of its impartiality if it were to

(A) publish the results of its studies of the feasibility of locating nuclear waste dumps in the deserts of the Southwest
(B) add one or two environmentalists to the panels that assess locations for nuclear dump sites
(C) make public the sources of all its funding
(D) recommend desert sites at a greater distance from the Colorado River
(E) base decisions on feasibility studies by scientists with no connection to the National Academy

20. The law of parsimony urges a strict economy upon us; it requires that we can never make a guess with two or three assumptions in it if we can make sense with one.

Which one of the following is the main point of the author's statement?

(A) Complications arise from economy.
(B) Simplify terminology whenever possible.
(C) Don't complicate a simple issue.
(D) Assumptions are necessarily simple in nature.
(E) Excess assumptions never clarify the situation.

GO ON TO THE NEXT PAGE ➤

21. You can use a bottle opener to open the new beer bottles. You do not need to use a bottle opener to open the new beer bottles.

Which one of the following most closely parallels the logic of these statements?

(A) You must turn on the switch to light the lamp. If you turn on the switch, the lamp may not light.
(B) A cornered rattlesnake will strike, so do not corner a rattlesnake.
(C) If you do not study you will fail the test. If you do study, you may fail the test.
(D) Every candidate I voted for in the election lost his race. I must learn to vote better.
(E) I can move the sofa with my brother's help. If my brother is not available, I'll get a neighbor to help me.

22. To be admitted to Bigshot University, you must have a 3.5 grade-point average (GPA) and a score of 800 on the admissions test, a 3.0 GPA and a score of 1000 on the admissions test, or a 2.5 GPA and a score of 1200 on the admissions test. A sliding scale exists for other scores and GPAs.

Which one of the following is inconsistent with the above?

(A) The higher the GPA, the lower the admissions test score needed for admission.
(B) Joe was admitted with a 2.7 GPA and a score of 1100 on the admissions test.
(C) No student with a score of less than 800 on the admissions test and a 3.4 GPA will be admitted.
(D) More applicants had a GPA of 3.5 than had a GPA of 2.5.
(E) Some students with a score of less than 1200 on the admissions test and a GPA of less than 2.5 were admitted.

23. The Census Bureau's family portrait of America may remind us of the problems we face as a nation, but it also gives us reason to take heart in our ability to solve them in an enlightened way. The 1980 census was the first in history to show that the majority of the population in every state has completed high school. And the percentage of our people with at least 4 years of college rose from 11 percent in 1970 to 16.3 percent in 1980. That's progress—where it really counts.

Which one of the following assumptions underlies the author's conclusion in the above passage?

(A) Greater numbers of high school and college degrees coincide with other firsts in the 1980 census.
(B) Greater numbers of high school and college degrees coincide with greater numbers of well-educated people.
(C) Greater numbers of high school and college degrees coincide with a great commitment to social progress.
(D) Greater numbers of high school and college degrees coincide with a better chance to avoid national catastrophe.
(E) Greater numbers of high school and college degrees coincide with the 1980 census.

24. Add No-NOCK to your car and watch its performance soar. No-NOCK will give it more get-up-and-go and keep it running longer. Ask for No-NOCK when you want better mileage!

According to the advertisement above, No-NOCK claims to do everything EXCEPT

(A) improve your car's performance
(B) increase your car's life
(C) improve your car's miles per gallon
(D) cause fewer breakdowns
(E) stop the engine from knocking

GO ON TO THE NEXT PAGE ➤

3   **3**   **3**   **3**   **3**

25. So many arrogant and ill-tempered young men have dominated the tennis courts of late that we had begun to fear those characteristics were prerequisites for championship tennis.

   Tennis used to be a gentleman's game. What is sad is not just that the game has changed. With so much importance placed on success, it may be that something has gone out of the American character—such things as gentleness and graciousness.

   Which one of the following statements, if true, would most weaken the above argument?

   (A) The American character is a result of American goals.
   (B) Tennis has only recently become a professional sport.
   (C) Some ill-tempered tennis players are unsuccessful.
   (D) The "gentlemen" of early tennis often dueled to the death off the court.
   (E) Some even-tempered tennis players are successful.

26. *Dolores:* To preserve the peace, we must be prepared to go to war with any nation at any time, using either conventional or nuclear weapons.
   Fran: Which shall it be, conventional weapons or nuclear weapons?

   Fran mistakenly concludes that the "either or" phrase in Dolores's statement indicates

   (A) fear
   (B) indecision
   (C) a choice
   (D) a question
   (E) a refusal

STOP

IF YOU FINISH BEFORE THE TIME IS UP, CHECK YOUR WORK ON THIS SECTION OF THE TEST ONLY.
DO NOT GO ON TO THE NEXT SECTION OF THE TEST UNTIL TIME IS UP FOR THIS SECTION.

4   4   4   4   4

SECTION IV
TIME — 35 MINUTES
24 QUESTIONS

Directions: In this section you will be given groups of questions based on different sets of conditions. Drawing a simple diagram may be helpful in answering some of the questions. You are to choose the best answer and mark the corresponding space on your answer sheet.

Questions 1-6

A group of tourists is planning to visit a cluster of islands—U, V, W, X, Y, and Z, connected by bridges. The tourists must stay on each island visited for exactly three days and three nights. Each bridge takes one hour to cross, may be crossed in either direction, and can be crossed only in the morning to give the tourists a full day on the island.
    The islands are connected by bridges only as indicated below:
U is connected to W, X, and Y
V is connected to Y and Z
X is connected to Z and W
Y is connected to X and Z

1. If the group visits island W first, eight days later it could NOT be at which one of the following islands?

   (A) U
   (B) V
   (C) X
   (D) Y
   (E) Z

2. If the group stays on island X for three nights, it CANNOT spend the next three days and nights on island.

   (A) U
   (B) V
   (C) W
   (D) Y
   (E) Z

3. Which one of the following is a possible order of islands visited in 12 days and nights?

   (A) UWYZ
   (B) UVYZ
   (C) UYVX
   (D) UXZV
   (E) UWYX

4. If the group visits island W first and can visit an island more than once, but does not use a bridge more than once, what is the greatest number of visits it can make?

   (A) 5
   (B) 6
   (C) 7
   (D) 8
   (E) 9

5. Assume the group visits island X first, and does not use a bridge more than once. Assume also that the group does stay at island Y twice. What is the greatest number of different islands the group can visit?

   (A) 3
   (B) 4
   (C) 5
   (D) 6
   (E) 7

6. Assume another island, T, is added to the tour. Assume also that T is connected only to U. Which one of the following statements must be true?

   (A) On the eighth day of a tour, starting its visit at island T, the group could be on island V.
   (B) On the fifth day of a tour, starting its visit at island T, the group could be on island X.
   (C) On the seventh day of a tour, starting its visit at island T, the group could be on island U.
   (D) On the eighth day of a tour, starting its visit at island V, the group could be on island T.
   (E) On the tenth day of a tour, starting its visit at island Z, the tour group could be on island T.

GO ON TO THE NEXT PAGE ➤

4   4   4   4   4

Questions 7-13

Teams A and B play a series of 9 games. To win the series, a team must win the most games, but must also win a minimum of 3 games.

There are no ties in the first 3 games.
Team A wins more of the last 3 games than team B.
Team B wins more of the last 5 games than team A.
The last game is a tie.
Games 1 and 3 are won by the same team.

7. Which one of the following must be true?

   (A) One team must win 5 games to win the series.
   (B) There are no ties.
   (C) One team wins at least 2 of the first 3 games.
   (D) The same team wins the last 5 games.
   (E) The last three games are won by one team.

8. Considering all of the conditions mentioned above, game 6

   (A) could be won by team A
   (B) could be won by team B
   (C) could be a tie
   (D) must be won by team A
   (E) must be won by team B

9. If game 7 is won by team A, then

   (A) game 8 is a tie
   (B) game 2 is a tie
   (C) game 4 is won by team A
   (D) game 5 is a tie
   (E) game 6 is won by team A

10. Which one of the following must be true?

    (A) There is only 1 tie in the last 5 games.
    (B) Team A wins 2 of the first 3 games.
    (C) Team B can win 3 of the last 5 games.
    (D) Game 4 is a tie.
    (E) Team A can win only 1 of the last 5 games.

11. If team A wins game 1 and game 4, then which one of the following must be FALSE?

    (A) Team A wins game 3.
    (B) Team A wins game 2.
    (C) Team B wins game 2.
    (D) Team A wins the series.
    (E) Team B wins the series.

12. Assume that game 4 is won by the winner of game 5. If game 2 is not won by the winner of game 3, then which one of the following must be true?

    (A) Team A wins game 7.
    (B) Team B is the winner of the series.
    (C) Team A wins game 2.
    (D) Team B wins game 1.
    (E) Team A wins game 3.

13. Which one of the following must be true?

    (A) For team A to win the series, team A must win exactly two of the first four games.
    (B) For team B to win the series, team B must win exactly one of the first four games.
    (C) For team A to win the series, team A must win only three of the first seven games.
    (D) For team B to win the series, team B must win at least three of the first four games.
    (E) For team A to win the series, team A must win two consecutive games.

GO ON TO THE NEXT PAGE ➤

Questions 14-18

Eight busts of American Presidents are to be arranged on two shelves, left to right. Each shelf accommodates exactly four busts. One shelf is directly above the other shelf. The busts are of John Adams, George Washington, Abraham Lincoln, Thomas Jefferson, James Monroe, John Kennedy, Theodore Roosevelt and Franklin Delano Roosevelt.

   The Roosevelt busts may not be directly one above the other.
   The bust of Kennedy must be adjacent to the bust of a Roosevelt.
   The bust of Jefferson must be directly above the bust of John Adams.
   The busts of Monroe, Adams, Kennedy and Franklin Delano Roosevelt must be on the bottom shelf.
   The bust of Monroe must be third from the left.

14. If the bust of Theodore Roosevelt is second from the left on one shelf, which one of the following must be true?

   (A) The bust of Adams must be first on a shelf.
   (B) The bust of Adams must be third on a shelf.
   (C) The bust of Kennedy must be first on a shelf.
   (D) The bust of Kennedy must be second on a shelf.
   (E) The bust of Kennedy must be third on a shelf.

15. Which one of the following must be true about the bust of Monroe?

   (A) It is next to the bust of Adams.
   (B) It is next to the bust of Kennedy.
   (C) It is next to the bust of Franklin Delano Roosevelt.
   (D) It is directly under the bust of Lincoln.
   (E) It is directly under the bust of Theodore Roosevelt.

16. If the bust of Washington is first, directly above Kennedy's, all of the following must be true EXCEPT

   (A) the bust of Jefferson is fourth
   (B) the bust of Theodore Roosevelt is third
   (C) the bust of Franklin Delano Roosevelt is second
   (D) the bust of Lincoln is third
   (E) the bust of Adams is fourth

17. Which one of the following is not a possible order for the busts on either shelf?

   (A) Washington, Lincoln, Theodore Roosevelt, Jefferson
   (B) Franklin Delano Roosevelt, Kennedy, Monroe, Adams
   (C) Theodore Roosevelt, Lincoln, Washington, Jefferson
   (D) Lincoln, Theodore Roosevelt, Washington, Jefferson
   (E) Kennedy, Adams, Monroe, Franklin Delano Roosevelt

18. If the bust of Lincoln is next to the bust of Jefferson, all of the following are true EXCEPT

   (A) if the bust of Kennedy is first, the bust of Theodore Roosevelt is also first
   (B) if the bust of Washington is first, the bust of Franklin Delano Roosevelt is also first
   (C) if the bust of Washington is second, the bust of Kennedy is also second
   (D) if the bust of Kennedy is second, the bust of Theodore Roosevelt is also second
   (E) if the bust of Washington is second, the bust of Franklin Delano Roosevelt is also second

4   4   4   4   4

Questions 19-24

For a dinner party, a hostess needs several different three-bean salads.

Each salad is to contain three types of beans, chosen from garbanzos, chili beans, wax beans, lima beans, and kidney beans.

Chili beans and lima beans do not taste good together and therefore are never used in the same salad.

Lima beans and kidney beans do not look good together and therefore are never used in the same salad.

19. How many different salads (using the above ingredients) could the hostess serve that contain lima beans?

    (A) 0
    (B) 1
    (C) 2
    (D) 3
    (E) 4

20. How many different salads could she serve that do not contain chili beans?

    (A) 0
    (B) 1
    (C) 2
    (D) 3
    (E) 4

21. How many different salad combinations could she serve at the party?

    (A) 4
    (B) 5
    (C) 6
    (D) 7
    (E) 8

22. Which beans will occur most often in the salad combinations that could be served at the party?

    (A) chili and garbanzos
    (B) chili and limas
    (C) limas and wax beans
    (D) kidney and limas
    (E) garbanzos and wax beans

23. If there are only enough wax beans to go into two salads, what is the total number of salads that can be served?

    (A) 1
    (B) 2
    (C) 3
    (D) 4
    (E) 5

24. If the hostess discovers the garbanzos have gone bad, how many three-bean combinations can she serve without using the rotten garbanzos?

    (A) 0
    (B) 1
    (C) 2
    (D) 3
    (E) 4

STOP

IF YOU FINISH BEFORE THE TIME IS UP, CHECK YOUR WORK ON THIS SECTION OF THE TEST ONLY.
DO NOT GO ON TO THE NEXT SECTION OF THE TEST UNTIL TIME IS UP FOR THIS SECTION.

5   **5**

SECTION V
TIME—35 MINUTES
25 QUESTIONS

<u>Directions:</u> In this section you will be given brief statements or passages and will be required to evaluate the reasoning involved. In some instances, more than one choice will appear to be a possible answer. You are to choose the best answer. Use common sense and reasonableness in making your selection; then mark the proper space on the answer sheet.

1. Chrysanthemums that have not been fertilized in July will normally not blossom in October. In October, the chrysanthemums did not blossom.

   With the premises given above, which one of the following would logically complete an argument?

   (A) Therefore, the chrysanthemums were not fertilized in July.
   (B) Therefore, the chrysanthemums may not have been fertilized in July.
   (C) Therefore, the chrysanthemums may blossom later in the fall.
   (D) Therefore, the chrysanthemums will blossom in the fall.
   (E) Therefore, the chrysanthemums will not blossom later in the fall.

2. When asked about the danger to public health from the spraying of pesticides by helicopters throughout the county, the County Supervisor replied, "The real danger to the public is the possibility of an infestation of harmful fruit-flies, which this spraying will prevent. Such an infestation would drive up the cost of fruits and vegetables by 15 percent."

   Which one of the following is the most serious weakness in the Supervisor's reply to the question?

   (A) He depends upon the ambiguity in the word "danger."
   (B) His response contains a self-contradiction.
   (C) He fails to support his argument concretely.
   (D) He fails to answer the question that has been asked.
   (E) His chief concern is the economic consequences of spraying.

3. So far this year researchers have reported the following:

   Heavy coffee consumption can increase the risk of heart attacks.
   Drinking a cup of coffee in the morning increases feelings of well-being and alertness.
   Boiled coffee increases blood cholesterol levels.
   Coffee may protect against cancer of the colon.

   If all these statements are true, which one of the following conclusions can be drawn from this information?

   (A) Reducing coffee consumption will make people healthier.
   (B) Reducing coffee consumption will make people feel better.
   (C) People at risk for heart attack should limit their coffee drinking.
   (D) Percolated coffee will not affect cholesterol levels.
   (E) People at risk for cancer should reduce their coffee consumption.

GO ON TO THE NEXT PAGE ➤

5   **5**

4. Compared with children in other states, infants born in California weigh more, survive the first years in greater numbers, and live longer. The hysteria about the danger of pesticides in California has attracted attention simply because a few Hollywood stars have appeared on television talk shows. Pesticides are the responsibility of the California Department of Food and Agriculture, and we can be sure its members are doing their job.

The argument of this paragraph would be weakened if all of the following were shown to be true EXCEPT

(A) rates of melanoma and some forms of leukemia in California are above national norms
(B) the three highest positions at the California Department of Food and Agriculture are held by farm owners
(C) synthetic pesticide residues in food cause more cancer than do "natural pesticides" that the plants themselves produce
(D) more Californians suffer the consequences of air pollution than do the citizens in any other state
(E) children of farm workers are three times more likely to suffer childhood cancers than children of urban parents

5. Should we allow the Fire Department to continue to underpay its women officers by using policies of promotion that favor men?

The question above most closely resembles which one of the following in terms of its logical features?

(A) Should the excessive tax on cigarettes, liquor, and luxury goods be unfairly increased again this year?
(B) Should corrupt politicians be subject to the same sentencing laws as blue-collar felons?
(C) Should the police chief be chosen by examination score regardless of gender or seniority?
(D) Should the religious right be allowed to determine the censorship laws for all of society?
(E) Are liberal political values an appropriate basis for all of the social values in this state?

6. If airline fares have risen, then either the cost of fuel has risen or there are no fare wars among competing companies. If there are no fare wars among competing companies, the number of airline passengers is larger than it was last year.

According to the passage above, if there has been a rise in airline fares this month, which one of the following CANNOT be true?

(A) There are no fare wars among competing airlines.
(B) The cost of fuel has risen, and the number of passengers is the same as last year.
(C) The cost of fuel has risen, there are no fare wars, and the number of passengers is larger than it was last year.
(D) There are no fare wars, and the number of passengers is larger than it was last year.
(E) The cost of fuel has risen, there are no fare wars, and the number of passengers is smaller than it was last year.

GO ON TO THE NEXT PAGE ➤

5   **5**

7. Only 75 years ago, the best fishing in the world was the Grand Banks of the North Atlantic. But now overfishing and man's pollution have decimated the area. There will be no fishing industry in the Americas in a very few years. The waters off Newfoundland now yield less than half the catch of five years ago, and less than one quarter of the total of ten years ago. The cod has almost disappeared. The number of fishermen in Newfoundland and New England has declined, and their yearly earnings are now at an all-time low. Yet radar has made fishing methods more efficient than ever.

Which one of the following identifies most clearly a faulty assumption in the reasoning of this passage?

(A) Ten years is too short a time period to use to draw conclusions about the natural world.
(B) The argument assumes that the waters off Newfoundland are representative of all the American oceans.
(C) The pollution of the sea may have been caused by natural as well as by human forces.
(D) The argument does not allow for the possibility that the catch may increase in size in the next five years.
(E) The argument fails to consider that the decline in the catch may be due to factors other than pollution.

8. A cigarette advertisement in a magazine asks, "What do gremlins, the Loch Ness monster, and a filter cigarette claiming 'great taste' have in common?" The answer is "You've heard of all of them, but don't really believe they exist." The advertisement contains no pictures, and no additional text except the words Gold Star Cigarettes and the Surgeon General's warning in a box in the lower corner.

Which one of the following conclusions can be drawn from the information given above?

(A) Cigarette advertising depends upon visual appeal to create images for specific brands.
(B) All cigarette advertising depends on praising a specific brand.
(C) Gold Star Cigarettes are non-filters.
(D) The writers of this advertisement do not believe in advertising.
(E) The writers of this advertisement do not believe the Surgeon General's warning is true.

GO ON TO THE NEXT PAGE ➤

5   **5**

9. The traffic on the Imperial Highway has always been slowed by the dangerous curves in the road. It was built when cars were much smaller and less powerful, and very few drivers traveled between Imperial City and Fremont. All this has changed. The cost of widening and straightening the road would now be many times greater than building the proposed new toll road on the borders of the Imperial Wetlands reserve. Environmentalists fear the construction noise and waste will harm the wildlife in the reserve, and have urged that the toll road not be constructed.

Which one of the following, if true, would most strengthen the case of the environmentalists?

(A) None of the animals living in the Imperial Wetlands is on the list of endangered species.
(B) The traffic congestion on the Imperial Highway increases each year.
(C) The cost of building the new road will be amortized in ten years by the tolls collected.
(D) There are several less direct routes the toll road could take between Fremont and Imperial City.
(E) The environmentalists threaten to bring a lawsuit in federal court to halt construction of the road.

10. Despite the very large increase in the federal tax on luxury items, the value of the stock of Harry Evans, Inc., seller of the world's most expensive jewelry, continues to rise. Six months after the introduction of the tax, Evans's stock is at an all-time high. Moreover, sales in the United States continue to increase. In other countries, where Evans does 30 percent of its business, there have been no rises in excise taxes and the company will open new stores in Tokyo, Monte Carlo, and Singapore. According to a company spokesperson, _____.

Which one of the following most logically completes this paragraph?

(A) American customers who can afford to shop at Evans are not likely to be deterred by a rise in luxury taxes
(B) American customers are expected to spend far less at Evans because of the tax rise
(C) American sales are not significant enough to affect the overall profits of the firm
(D) the company will probably be forced to close most of its stores in America
(E) state taxes are more likely to influence jewelry sales than federal taxes

GO ON TO THE NEXT PAGE ➤

11. A recent study of cigarette smokers has shown that, of cancer patients who are heavy smokers of unfiltered cigarettes, 40 percent will die of the disease. For cancer patients who are light smokers of filter cigarettes, the percentage is 25 percent.

Which one of the following conclusions can be drawn from the information above?

(A) There are more heavy smokers of unfiltered cigarettes than light smokers of filter cigarettes.

(B) More heavy smokers of unfiltered cigarettes die of cancer than light smokers of filter cigarettes.

(C) A heavy smoker of unfiltered cigarettes who has cancer is more likely to die than a light smoker of unfiltered cigarettes.

(D) A heavy smoker of unfiltered cigarettes who has cancer may be more likely to die than a light smoker of unfiltered cigarettes.

(E) A heavy smoker of unfiltered cigarettes who has cancer is more likely to die than a light smoker of filtered cigarettes who has cancer.

Questions 12–13

Archeologists have come to the support of Arctic anthropologists. A small minority of anthropologists assert that Stone-Age tribes of the Arctic domesticated wolves and trained them to haul sleds. Excavations have recently found evidence to support this claim. Archeologists have found wolf bones near the site of a Stone-Age village. They have also found walrus bones that might have been used on primitive sleds. The small minority of anthropologists believe that their theories have been proved.

12. Which one of the following is true of the evidence cited in the paragraph above?

(A) It is not relevant to the anthropologists' conclusions.

(B) It conclusively contradicts the anthropologists' conclusions.

(C) It neither supports nor refutes the anthropologists' conclusions positively.

(D) It supports the anthropologists' conclusions authoritatively.

(E) It conclusively supports only a part of the anthropologists' conclusions.

13. Which one of the following, if true, would best support the theory of the anthropologists?

(A) Wolves are known to have fed upon the garbage of villages in northern Europe.

(B) Wolves as a species are easily domesticated and trained.

(C) Almost all Stone-Age Arctic tools were made of walrus bone.

(D) Stone-Age villages were located on the migration routes of the caribou herds upon which wolves preyed.

(E) The earliest sled part found in the Arctic was made one thousand years after the Stone Age.

5   **5**

Questions 14–15

The following criticism of a self-portrait by Vincent van Gogh appeared in a magazine in 1917:

"Here we have a work of art which is so self-evidently a degenerate work by a degenerate artist that we need not say anything about the inept creation. It is safe to say that if we were to meet in our dreams such a villainous looking jailbird with such a deformed Neanderthal skull, degenerate ears, hobo beard and insane glare, it would certainly give us a nightmare."

14. The author of this passage makes his point by using

   (A) invective
   (B) analogy
   (C) citation of authority
   (D) paradox
   (E) example

15. In relation to the first sentence of the quotation, the second sentence is

   (A) an example of an effect following a cause
   (B) a specific derived from a general principle
   (C) a logical conclusion
   (D) a contradiction
   (E) a personal experience in support of a generalization

16. A company called Popcorn Packaging is promoting the use of popcorn as a cushioning material in packing. Unlike the commonly used Styrofoam beads or chips, popcorn can be recycled as a food for birds or squirrels and can serve as a garden mulch. Used out of doors, popcorn disappears almost overnight, while the Styrofoam beads may be in the environment for centuries. Even before we became ecology conscious, popcorn was used in packing in the 1940s. Since it now costs less to produce than Styrofoam, there is every reason to return to wide-scale use of packaging by popcorn.

   Which one of the following, if true, would most seriously weaken the author's argument?

   (A) A package using popcorn as a cushioning material will weigh less than a package using Styrofoam beads.
   (B) Popcorn may attract rodents and insects.
   (C) A large number of squirrels can damage a garden by consuming flowering bulbs.
   (D) Less than 1 percent of the material now used for package cushioning is recycled.
   (E) Styrofoam replaced popcorn in the early 1950s because it was cheaper to produce.

17. This produce stand sells fruits and vegetables. All fruits are delicious, and all vegetables are rich in vitamins. Every food that is vitamin-rich is delicious, so everything sold at this stand is delicious.

   Which one of the following assumptions is necessary to make the conclusion in the argument above logically correct?

   (A) The stand sells many fruits and vegetables.
   (B) This produce stand sells only fruits and vegetables.
   (C) Something cannot be both vitamin-rich and delicious.
   (D) Some stands sell fruits that are not delicious.
   (E) Some vegetables are delicious.

GO ON TO THE NEXT PAGE ➤

5 **5** **5** **5** **5**

18. Voter turnout in primary elections has declined steadily from 1982 to 1990. In 1990, more than 80 percent of the Americans eligible to vote failed to do so. Only 11.9 percent of the Democrats and 7.7 percent of the Republicans went to the polls. The largest number of voters turned out for elections in the District of Columbia (28 percent) and in Massachusetts, where the 32 percent total was the highest since 1962. In each of the twenty-four other states holding elections, the number of voters was smaller than it had been in 1986 and 1982.

Based on the information in this passage, which one of the following must be true?

(A) The turnout in the District of Columbia was affected by favorable weather conditions.
(B) Fewer than 20 percent of the eligible major-party voters voted in the 24 states other than Massachusetts.
(C) The voter turnout in Massachusetts is always higher than the turnouts in other states.
(D) The voter turnout decline is a signal of a nationwide voter rebellion.
(E) More voters cast their votes in general elections than in primary elections.

19. Each year the number of schools that no longer allow smoking on school property grows larger. Four states, New Jersey, Kansas, Utah, and New Hampshire, now require tobacco-free schools. The Tobacco Institute has fought against regulations restricting smoking everywhere from airlines to restaurants on the grounds that they trample on the rights of smokers, but is conspicuously absent from school board lobbyists. Tobacco industry spokesmen have denounced the rules treating teachers like children, but have said they will not go on record to defend policies that affect children.

Which one of the following, if true, best accounts for the Tobacco Institute's behavior?

(A) The tobacco industry is presently fighting the charge that it attempts to recruit new smokers among minors.
(B) The tobacco industry can depend on continued high profits from overseas operations, where restrictions do not exist.
(C) Most tobacco companies are highly diversified corporations whose profits no longer depend wholly on tobacco products.
(D) The tobacco industry believes the rights of children to be equal to the rights of adults.
(E) The tobacco industry agrees with the schools that have rules against tobacco.

GO ON TO THE NEXT PAGE ➤

Questions 20–21

A number of lawsuits have been brought against popular singing groups charging that suicidal themes in their songs have led to teenage suicides. So far, the courts have found that the lyrics are protected by the First Amendment. But what if this should change, and a court decides that suicidal themes in popular songs are dangerous? In fact, the songs that have been charged so far are antisuicide; they present sardonically the self-destructive behavior of drinking, drugs, and escape by death. They describe a pitiful state of mind, but they do not endorse it.

Blaming suicide on the arts is nothing new. In the late eighteenth century, Goethe's popular novel *Werther* was said to be the cause of a rash of suicides in imitation of the novel's hero. If we begin to hold suicide in books or music responsible for suicides in real life, the operas of Verdi and Puccini will have to go, and *Romeo and Juliet* and *Julius Caesar* will disappear from high school reading lists.

20. The author of this passage argues by

    (A) providing examples to support two opposing positions
    (B) using an observation to undermine a theoretical principle
    (C) disputing an interpretation of evidence cited by those with an opposing view
    (D) predicting personal experience from a general principle
    (E) accusing the opposing side of using inaccurate statistical information

21. Which one of the following is an assumption necessary to the author's argument?

    (A) A lyric presenting suicide in a favorable light should not have First Amendment protection.
    (B) Literature or music cannot directly influence human behavior.
    (C) Many record albums already carry labels warning purchasers of their dangerous contents.
    (D) The audience, not the performer, is responsible for the audience's actions.
    (E) Freedom of speech is the most threatened of our personal freedoms.

---

22. Haven't you at some time had a favorite song or book or film that was not well known but later became popular? And didn't you feel somehow betrayed and resentful when what you had thought was unique became commonplace? On a larger scale, the same thing happens to novelists or film makers who have enjoyed critical esteem without popular success. Let them become public sensations, and the critics who praised their work will attack them virulently.

This paragraph most likely introduces an article on a film maker who has made a

    (A) series of commercially successful films
    (B) series of commercially unsuccessful films
    (C) single film, a commercial success
    (D) single film, a commercial failure
    (E) critical success and a commercial success

GO ON TO THE NEXT PAGE ➤

5 **5** **5** **5** **5**

23. Studies of the effects of drinking four or more cups of coffee per day have shown that coffee consumption increases work efficiency by improving the ability to process information. People who drink two cups of coffee in the morning are more alert and feel better than those who do not. But there are other factors to be considered.

Which one of the following sentences would provide the most logical continuation of this paragraph?

(A) Contrary to popular belief, drinking coffee cannot erase the effect of alcohol.
(B) Some studies suggest that coffee drinking will protect against cancer of the colon.
(C) Combined with the stress of heavy exercise, coffee drinking may be the cause of higher blood pressure.
(D) Drinking two or more cups of coffee per day increases the risk of heart attacks in men.
(E) Many people cannot distinguish between the taste of decaffeinated and that of regular coffee.

24. All of the members of the chorus will sing in the performance of the oratorio *Messiah*. Some of these are highly trained professionals, some are gifted amateurs, and some are singers of mediocre ability.

If the statements above are true, which one of the following must also be true?

(A) *Messiah* will be performed by highly trained professionals, gifted amateurs, and some singers of mediocre ability.
(B) Some of the members of the chorus are not highly trained professionals, gifted amateurs, or singers of mediocre ability.
(C) *Messiah* will be performed by some highly trained professionals, but not all of them are in the chorus.
(D) Not all of those in the chorus who are gifted amateurs will perform in the oratorio.
(E) All of those who will perform *Messiah* are members of the chorus.

25. The passage of laws that limit elected officials to one or two terms in office is an admission that voters are civic fools, unable to tell good lawmakers from bad ones. To ban all the politicians when the real intention is to get rid of the corrupt ones is to burn the house down to get rid of the vermin.

The author of this passage makes his point chiefly by

(A) defining a key term
(B) exposing a self-contradiction
(C) drawing an analogy
(D) questioning the evidence of his opponents
(E) citing an example

STOP

IF YOU FINISH BEFORE THE TIME IS UP, CHECK YOUR WORK ON THIS SECTION OF THE TEST ONLY.
DO NOT GO ON TO THE NEXT SECTION OF THE TEST UNTIL TIME IS UP FOR THIS SECTION.

Writing Sample

<u>Directions:</u> You have 30 minutes to write an essay in response to a given topic. Take a few minutes to plan your work before you begin writing. DO NOT WRITE ON A TOPIC OF YOUR OWN CHOICE. ESSAYS THAT DO NOT ADDRESS THE GIVEN TOPIC ARE UNACCEPTABLE.

The quality of your writing is more important than the length of your response or the content. Pay attention to organization, appropriate diction, and correct usage. You will not be expected to display any specialized knowledge in your response, nor will you be expected to write a "perfect" essay; law schools understand that you are writing under a time constraint, and will allow for the minor lapses in writing ability that might occur under this circumstance.

Only the lined area in your booklet will be reproduced for the law schools, so do not write outside this space. *Do not* skip lines or use wide margins. These precautions, along with careful planning and legible handwriting that is not unduly large, will keep you within the allowed space.

Sample Topic

Read the following descriptions of Jackson and Brown. *Then, in the space provided, write an argument for deciding which of the two should be assigned the responsibility of hiring teachers for the Hapsville School System.* The following criteria are relevant to your decision:

- The taxpayers want educators who can instill in students the desire to learn and an excitement for knowledge, something that has been lacking in their schools.
- A majority of students' parents believe that their children should be equipped, upon graduation, to earn a living, and thus favor a more trade-oriented (rather than academic) approach to schooling.

JACKSON was appointed as Superintendent of Schools by the Hapsville School Board, which was elected by the community's taxpayers. As a 30-year resident of Hapsville (population 45,000), Jackson is unique in that he holds not only a doctorate in administration, but also a master's degree in education. He taught in the Hapsville schools for 16 years until he served on the state Commission on Education. He has always favored a progressive approach to education, although it may not always have been popular with the town's population. Through the years he has brought many fine teachers to the faculty, because of his willingness to encourage new classroom techniques.

BROWN is a 52-year resident of Hapsville, having been born in the same house in which he now lives. He was elected to the School Board 13 years ago, and continues to win nearly unanimous reelection every two years. As the foremost developer in the Four Counties area, Mr. Brown has had the opportunity to build hundreds of new homes in the six housing developments he's planned and actualized, and, in the interim, has employed hundreds of Hapsville residents as carpenters, electricians, plumbers, architects, landscapers, groundskeepers, etc. As such, he is held in high esteem by most of the town, not only for his providing livelihoods for many, but also for his fair and realistic outlook on life. Mr. Brown feels strongly that the key to life is having a marketable skill.

Answer Key

Section I: Reading Comprehension

1. B	6. A	11. E	16. E	21. B	26. B
2. C	7. C	12. C	17. A	22. C	27. A
3. A	8. A	13. D	18. B	23. C	28. E
4. A	9. B	14. A	19. E	24. D	
5. E	10. A	15. C	20. D	25. A	

Section II: Analytical Reasoning

1. C	5. D	9. D	13. A	17. E	21. B
2. A	6. B	10. A	14. C	18. D	22. D
3. E	7. E	11. E	15. A	19. C	23. D
4. C	8. E	12. D	16. D	20. C	24. C

Section III: Logical Reasoning

1. C	6. A	11. E	16. B	21. E	26. B
2. B	7. B	12. C	17. B	22. E	
3. E	8. C	13. B	18. A	23. B	
4. D	9. B	14. C	19. E	24. E	
5. D	10. E	15. E	20. C	25. D	

Section IV: Analytical Reasoning

1. B	5. D	9. A	13. E	17. E	21. B
2. B	6. E	10. E	14. D	18. C	22. E
3. D	7. C	11. E	15. A	19. B	23. C
4. E	8. E	12. B	16. D	20. C	24. B

Section V: Logical Reasoning

1. B	6. E	11. E	16. B	21. D
2. D	7. B	12. C	17. B	22. E
3. C	8. C	13. B	18. B	23. D
4. D	9. D	14. A	19. A	24. A
5. A	10. A	15. D	20. C	25. C

MODEL TEST ANALYSIS

Doing a model exam and understanding the explanations afterwards are of course important in acquainting you with typical LSAT question types and successful approaches to the questions. However, another benefit of carefully analyzing these model tests is to understand the kinds of errors you are making and thus work to minimize them. For instance, if a very high percentage of your incorrect answers is due to "careless error" or "misread problem" then perhaps you are working much too fast and should slow your pace accordingly. If your incorrect answers are due primarily to "lack of knowledge," then a careful rereading and reworking of the appropriate question-type chapter may be in order. Or if you find that you aren't completing a large number of questions because of lack of time, you may need to either increase your speed or learn to use the "one-check, two-check" technique more effectively.

This kind of analysis of the model test will enable you to identify your particular weaknesses and thus remedy them.

Model Test Analysis

Section	Total Number of Questions	Number Correct	Number Incorrect	Number Unanswered*
I. Reading Comprehension	28			
II. Analytical Reasoning	24			
III. Logical Reasoning	26			
IV. Analytical Reasoning	24			
V. Logical Reasoning	25			
TOTALS:	127			

*At this stage in your preparation, you should not be leaving any blank answer spaces. At least fill in a guess, as there is no penalty for a wrong answer.

Reasons for Incorrect Answers

You may wish to evaluate the explanations before completing this chart.

Section	Total Number Incorrect	Lack of Knowledge	Misread Problem	Careless Error	Unanswered or Wrong Guess
I. Reading Comprehension					
II. Analytical Reasoning					
III. Logical Reasoning					
IV. Analytical Reasoning					
V. Logical Reasoning					
TOTALS:					

Explanation of Answers

Section I

Passage 1

1. **B** The first sentence of the passage makes it clear that government workers are forbidden to strike by statutory law.

2. **C** If strikes are a form of symbolic speech, the denial of the right to strike is arguably a denial of free speech. It also can be argued that it denies due process, the right to picket, and the right to avoid abnormally dangerous working conditions.

3. **A** The courts, not the legislative or the executive branches, must determine the "clear and present danger," according to the Supreme Court decision described in the second paragraph.

4. **A** Because the firing of the controllers had the same effect as a strike, it appears that there was no danger to the public.

5. **E** The author points out that workers in government who do that same job as workers in private industry cannot strike. The passage argues that the nature of the service should determine the right to strike, not the employer.

6. **A** It is possible that the "highly qualified" may seek employment outside of government, because of the no-strike clause. Choices (B), (C), (D), (E) are not plausible weaknesses of the no-strike rule.

Passage 2

7. **C** See lines 4–9. Her father also may have influenced her in the ways suggested in (A), (B), (D), and (E), but these answers are not suggested by the passage itself.

8. **A** We can infer from lines 19–24 that this was Woolf's dilemma, particularly because in lines 25–28 we learn that the emphasis in her feminism was self-reform. E is incorrect; "lucid objectivity" is cited as a strength of her novel The Years, not something that needed to be overcome. C is not supported by the passage because there is nothing to suggest that Virginia Woolf wished to pursue "social work." Similarly, (B) and (D) are not supported by any information in the passage.

9. **B** In the passage, the integration of masculine and feminine (the androgynous mind) and the danger of one-sidedness (lines 18–24) describe Woolf's feminism. Although C and D might also characterize her feminism, the passage emphasizes a need for wholeness. A is not supported by the passage. E might be suggested in lines 30–35 and lines 77–80 but it is *not* presented as a characterization of her feminism.

10. **A** Paragraph two is concerned with the superiority of Woolf's novels to her tracts in dealing with her feminist concerns. Paragraph three contrasts a tract and a novel to illustrate this point. Paragraph three doesn't present a contrast to or a subtopic of paragraph one (B, D), nor does it act as a transition (C). (In fact, the passage could move smoothly from paragraph two to paragraph four even if paragraph three were missing. What would be missing would be a concrete example—i.e., answer A.) Paragraph two does not present an exegesis (E).

11. **E** This opposition is at the heart of the passage—see paragraphs two, three, and four. Different types of novels are *not* contrasted (B), nor is Woolf's aesthetic creed contrasted to the aesthetic creed of the Bloomsbury group (A). (A contrast is suggested in lines 4–9, but it is minor, and not explained or developed.) C is incorrect; the passage explicitly addresses Woolf's *avoidance* of such a contrast and her belief in the androgynous mind. D is unclear and inaccurate.

12. **C** See paragraph four. Although the author does say that Woolf's primary emphasis was on self-reform, he does not suggest that her social concerns were trivial (D). Nothing in the passage suggests that the author is criticizing the Bloomsbury aesthetic creed (A). Similarly, although the author finds Woolf's novels more successful than her tracts, it is a giant leap to infer that he dislikes social reform literature in general (E). (B) is clearly incorrect.

13. **D** The passage states this idea in the first line and then continues throughout to develop the subject of the importance of both feminism and art in Woolf's writing. See lines 37–43. (A) is too limited; these two works are used to illustrate the main point of the passage. (B) is broad and imprecise. (C) is also imprecise. (E) is incorrect; opposition of masculine and feminine is not part of the passage.

Passage 3

14. **A** The author is obviously most concerned with the work of historians and the current state of written history, which is what prompts his discussion of fiction in relation to history. See lines 4–7, 17–20, 53–59, 64–70. Literature and literary concerns (answer C) are secondary.

15. **C** See lines 68–69: ". . . their abandonment of the narrative style." A decline in the writing *ability* of historians (E) is not implied. And although the author does mention the movies and television, he does not attribute the growth of fictional history to an increase in their audiences (B).

16. **E** This attitude is clearly stated in lines 49–53. B may seem correct, but the author does not say that fictional history on its own has won the audience away from traditional history. On the contrary, he suggests that professional historians themselves may be partly responsible for the growth of fictional history (lines 64–68).

17. **A** This book would most clearly fit the definition of fictional history given in lines 35–39. According to the author, it is fictional history that causes the greatest confusion (lines 49–53). (B) and (C) would be classified as historical fiction according to the author's definitions, and (D) and (E) as nonfiction.

18. **B** The second paragraph is devoted to defining and contrasting the two terms. (D) might be considered a possible answer but is less clear and specific. The other answers are simply inaccurate.

19. **E** Nothing in the passage suggests a judgment of history taught in the schools. The other statements are all supported in the passage: (A)—lines 17–20; (B)—lines 64–68; (C)—lines 53–59; (D)—lines 12–16.

20. **D** Throughout the passage the author is most concerned with the growth of fictional history and its effects. None of the other answers present his *attitude* as clearly, though (C) does define fictional history.

21. **B** The author is obviously concerned with the "mischief" that the mixture of history with fiction can cause. However, he presents his concern in a moderate fashion. He is not hostile, he does not preach, he is not pedantic, nor does he display irony. (E) suggests an elevated tone not present in the passage

Passage 4

22. **C** (C) is the best answer because the author explains fear conditioning in order to show how it is a good method for studying emotional memory. (A) is incorrect; the passage "proves" nothing. (B) is also incorrect. The fact that the mechanisms in mammals and vertebrates may be similar is not the main point of the passage; also, the passage does not state that the mechanisms are "the same." (D) is only a supporting point—not the main point—of the passage. (E) is incorrect; the way that phobias are initially created in humans is not addressed in the passage.

23. **C** The passage makes this connection in lines 37–43. (A) is incorrect—see lines 27–28. (B) is also incorrect; lines 72–75 specifically state that cues to which subjects respond fearfully are not linked to complicated cognitive processing. (D) is incorrect because the passage states that stress, rather than *weakening* a response, may cause its recurrence. (E) is not the right choice. See lines 27–28. The rat's conditioned response diminishes only when the conditioned stimulus is administered many times without the unconditioned stimulus. As long as the shock and conditioned stimulus are paired, the rat's response to the conditioned stimulus will remain.

24. **D** The passage states than an extinguished fear response can recover spontaneously or can be reinstated by an irrelevant stressful experience (lines 37–41). We can assume that for a rat, introduction of a cat could be an "irrelevant stressful experience." (A) and (B) are incorrect; both are contradicted by information in the passage (lines 28–32 and lines 32–37). (C) and (E) are not supported by information in the passage.

25. **A** This answer is directly supported in lines 70–72. According to lines 27–28, the response is not related to complex cognitive processing. Therefore, (B) is incorrect. (C) and (D) are not supported by any information presented in the passage. (E) is incorrect; in lines 32–37, the brain's control, rather than lack of control, is cited.

26. **B** The author cites the nine animals to show the wide range of animal groups in which fear conditioning occurs. This supports his point that fear conditioning is an ideal starting point for studies of emotional memory. Although fear conditioning occurring in so many animal groups may support (A) (that the fear response is neural), this is not the primary reason for citing them. See lines 48–52. There is no suggestion of a developmental link between the animal groups listed, making (C) an incorrect choice. (D) and (E) are also incorrect; the author's listing of the nine animals is not connected in the passage to the role of the brain, nor is any point made about the emotions of fruit flies, snails, and so on.

27. **A** The last line of the passage states that the object of the research is to examine the "neurological foundations of fear." (B) and (E) are incorrect; the primary object of the research is not "cognition" nor how mammals are similar. (C) is also incorrect; conditioning is the *method* to be used to study the neurological basis of fear, not the object of the research itself. (D) should be ruled out because the effects of acoustic and visual stimuli are a small part of the research, not its main object.

28. **E** The third paragraph is devoted to reasons that fear conditioning is an "ideal starting point" for research of emotional memory, i.e., it occurs in many animal groups, the signals are not the type to which subjects have preexisting strong emotional reactions, and so on. (A) is incorrect because the definition is completed in paragraphs 1 and 2. (B) is incorrect because the author presents no qualifications or reservations about fear conditioning. (C) is not a good choice because the passage adds new information (i.e., reasons or justifications) and does not summarize. Finally, (D) is not correct because the passage does not present any applications other than the study of emotion and memory for the fear conditioning method.

Section II

Answers 1–6

From the information given, you could have made the following diagram:

```
Higher  A   D   E        Pent. 4 ___
        ?   ?   ?   FG         3 ___  ___
                              2 ___  ___
Lower   B   C   C             1 ___  ___
```

1. **C** Since F and G are on the same floor, they can't be on 4. Since B and C are below A or D/E, they can't be on 4; therefore only A, D, or E can be on 4.

2. **A** If F's apartment is on 2, so is G's. For B and C to be below A, D, and E, B and C must be on 1 and A, D, and E on 3 and 4, but we don't know exactly where on 3/4.

3. **E** If D is on 4, G (and F) *can* be on 3, 2, or 1.

```
D       D       D
FG      AE      AE
AE      FG      BC
BC      BC      FG
```

4. **C** If D and E are on the same floor, A must be on 4. All the other answers are possible but *not* certain.

5. **D** If A is on 4 or C on 1, the arrangement must be either

```
A               A
FG      or      DE
DE              FG
BC              BC
```

6. **B** A and E can be on the same floor if D is on 4.

```
D               D
AE      or      AE
FG              BC
BC              FG
```

Answers 7–12

From the information given, you may have constructed a simple grouping display of information similar to this:

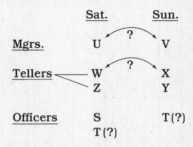

Another possible display might look like this:

```
              Sat.        Sun.
                    ?
Mgrs.          U ‿‿‿ V
                    ?
Tellers ——— W ‿‿‿ X
              Z          Y

Officers       S          T(?)
               T(?)
```

7. **E** From the original information, a manager must be on duty each day and the managers cannot work on the same day. Therefore (A) must be true. (E) does not have to be true, since U's schedule has no bearing on X's schedule. Since W and X will not work on the same day, (B) must also be true. There is no restriction placed on T.

8. **E** V, W, Z, S can work on Saturday without breaking any of the conditions given. Choice (A) is missing a manager. Choice (B) has two managers working on the same day. Choices (C) and (D) have W and X working on the same day.

9. **D** Five employees, U or V, X or W, Z, S, and T are the greatest number to work on Saturday.

10. **A** Since W and X will not work on the same day, (A) must be true. (B) is false since Y must work on Sunday. (C) could be true. Since W's schedule has no effect on Z and U, (D) and (E) may be true or false.

11. **E** Since no employee can work on consecutive days, and there are four tellers, then two must work on Saturday.

12. **D** U, V, W, X, Y, Z, and T have the possibility of working on Sunday; S and Z do not.

Answers 13–19

From the information given, you could have constructed the following simple diagram and display of information:

Clerical – L, J, D, S

Typing – E, G, H   (must use all)

13. **A** From the diagram and information above, if Gene works for Fred, then Lyndia also works for Fred, and Sylvia must work for Cynthia. Since Dennis and Edra will not work together, one of them must work for Cynthia; therefore choice (A) must be false. Jim cannot work for Cynthia.

14. **C** Using the diagram, if Sylvia doesn't work for Cynthia, then Gene must work for Cynthia. If Gene works for Cynthia, then Lyndia must also work for Cynthia, since Gene and Lyndia always work together.

15. **A** If Lyndia and Jim work for Al, then Gene must also work for Al, and Sylvia must work for Cynthia. The diagram would look like this:

First, (A) is true since Gene and Lyndia always work together. Stop there. Go no further. Edra could work for Cynthia or Fred, and also Helen could work for Cynthia or Fred.

16. **D** If Sylvia and Jim work for Al, then Gene and Lyndia must work for Cynthia. Since Dennis and Edra cannot work together, one of them must work for Fred and the other for Al. The diagram would now look like this:

Therefore, only (D) is true.

17. **E** From the diagram, if Lyndia and Sylvia work for Al, then Gene also must work for Al. But either Sylvia or Gene must work for Cynthia. Therefore (E) must be false.

18. **D** From the diagram, if Jim works for Cynthia, then Sylvia must also work for Cynthia, since Gene and Lyndia must work together. Gene and Lyndia cannot work for Fred, because then Dennis and Edra (who cannot work together) would work for Al. Therefore, Lyndia must work for Al. The diagram would look like this:

19. **C** If Al needs only two assistants and Fred needs only one, and if Helen works for Fred, then the diagram would look like this:

Since Gene and Lyndia must work together, they can work for either Al or Cynthia. Since Edra (typist) must work and Dennis and Edra cannot work together, then Dennis doesn't work. Otherwise, Dennis and Edra would work together. Statements A, B, D, and E *could* be true.

Answers 20–24

Drawing a diagram, below, will help answer the questions.

EVENTS

	1	2	3	4	5
RED	G	—	G	—	G
BLUE	—	B/S	—	B/S	—
GREEN					
YELLOW					

Since the red team wins only 3 gold medals, it must win gold medals in events 1, 3, and 5, since no team wins gold medals in consecutive events. Also, note that since blue wins only two medals (neither of them gold), it must have won medals in events 2 and 4, so that it didn't fail to win a medal within two consecutive events. Be aware then that green and yellow, therefore, must each have won medals in all five events.

20. **C** If the green team wins only one gold medal, there remains only one gold medal, which the yellow team must win.

21. **B** Since three medals are given for each event, and, according to our diagram from the facts, red and blue already account for their total awards with one medal in each event, the other two medals in each event must go to yellow and green. Thus, yellow and green will each be awarded five medals.

22. **D** By completing the chart such that the yellow team wins five silver medals, we can see that green must win two gold and three bronze medals.

	1	2	3	4	5
RED	G	—	G	—	G
BLUE	—	B/S	—	B/S	—
GREEN					
YELLOW	S	S	S	S	S

23. **D** We know choices (A) and (B) are both true: both the green and yellow teams each must win five medals. Therefore (E) is also true. Choice (C) is true because three of the gold medals are already won by the red team; since blue doesn't win gold, if green wins one gold, yellow wins the remaining gold medal. Choice (D) is not true: if the green team wins only one silver medal, the yellow team must win at least two silver medals.

24. **C** If a fifth team enters all events and wins only three consecutive silver medals, it must win the silver in events 2, 3, and 4, so that it does not fail to win a medal within two consecutive events. Therefore our diagram would look like this:

	1	2	3	4	5
RED	G	—	G	—	G
BLUE	—	B	—	B	—
GREEN					
YELLOW					
ORANGE	—	S	S	S	—

Therefore, if yellow wins a gold in the 2nd event, green must win a medal in the 3rd event (since no team fails to win a medal within two consecutive events). Thus, green must win a bronze in the 3rd event.

Section III

1. **C** The passage is more restrained in its criticism than (A) or (B), while (D) and (E) are only elements of the paragraph, not its main point.

2. **B** By urging moviegoers to patronize films *in order to* influence academy judges, the author reveals his assumption that the academy will be influenced by the number of people paying to see a movie.

3. **E** Bob's answer shows that he thinks that people other than teachers are mean. His thought was that Andy meant otherwise.

4. **D** The author's concluding contention is that Roosevelt was not only a good marksman, but also an intellectually curious and patient man. If Roosevelt was known to leave safaris which were not immediately productive, this fact would substantially weaken the author's contention about Roosevelt's "patient observation."

5. **D** The words "because of a recent cut in state funding of our program" indicate that another criterion was used in determining entering class size besides candidates' scores and grades, namely, the financial situation of the college. The words *seriously* in choice (B) and *severe* in choice (E) are not necessarily supported by the passage, and thus make those choices incorrect. Since grade point average is only one of several criteria for admission, we cannot deduce (A) with certainty.

6. **A** This sentence not only fits well stylistically but completes the thought of the passage by tying it into the opening statement.

7. **B** The author of this passage actually defines conscience as the ability to sense right and wrong.

8. **C** The main point of the paragraph is the need for campaign reform. Choice (D) supports the argument, while the other three choices are assumptions that might arise, but these are not the main point of the paragraph.

9. **B** This choice offers the most thorough and comprehensive evidence that the viewing of violent television precedes criminal behavior. (A) is not the best choice because it describes viewing habits that follow rather than precede criminal behavior.

10. **E** The use of "overwhelming" leaves the evidence unspecified, thus opening to challenge the extent and nature of the report's data.

11. **E** All of the first four statements can be used to explain the underreporting. In D, for example, if the size of police departments has declined, they would have less manpower available to gather and report information. E is a reason against underreporting rather than an explanation for it.

12. **C** The argument uses the case of the county to call the state figures into question. The underreported figures are "less evidence."

13. **B** If the experiences and lifestyle of the Aryan race are uniquely different from those of other cultures, it would seriously weaken the author's conclusion that studying the Aryan race will be helpful in understanding the experiences and life styles of other races. That its communal arrangements are *unique* would make comparison between the Aryan race and other cultures impossible.

14. **C** The author presents a *contrast* between life and honor: in particular, the final sentence suggests that life and honor have opposite qualities. Of the choices, the only opposite of *transient* is *eternal*.

15. **E** The logic of this statement goes from the general absolute ("all") to the specific ("this animal"), concluding with specific to specific. Symbolically, if P implies Q, then *not Q* implies *not P*. (E) goes from general absolute ("all") to specific ("this liquid"), concluding with specific to specific. Notice how and where the inverse ("not") is inserted. Using symbols, we have that, if P implies Q, then *not Q* implies *not P*.

16. **B** This is a close one. (B) and (D) both weaken the argument by pointing out that all dogs do not always bark, but (B) is absolute. (D) is tentative, since a dog trained not to bark might do so by accident.

17. **B** The apparent discrepancy in the paragraph is why should arrests decline when there are fewer policemen to arrest the criminals? One explanation is that though the number of arrests has declined, the number of crimes has risen, and because there are fewer police officers, more crimes are unsolved.

18. **A** The complaint about ex-employees of the Department of Energy on the board, and the financial tie of the National Academy Board to the Energy Department indicate the officials' belief that the Department of Energy supports the nuclear power industry against the views of environmentalists.

19. **E** Though adding one or two environmentalists might help, they would still be outnumbered by the ten panel members with ties to the Department of Energy. Of the five choices, E offers the best hope of impartiality.

20. **C** (A) contradicts the statement's urging of economy. (B) introduces an irrelevant word, "terminology." (D) and (E) are *absolute* statements about assumptions, but the statement itself is *relative,* urging us only to simplify our assumptions *if one such simplification is possible; in other words, "If an issue is simple, don't complicate it."*

21. **E** The question demonstrates a solution and the fact that an alternative exists.

22. **E** (A) is obviously true. (B) also satisfies the conditions. (C) is correct, since 3.5 was required with a score of 800. (D) is correct, since we do not know anything about numbers of applicants. (E) is inconsistent, since a score of 1200 is required with a GPA of 2.5. (E) specifies a score *less than* 1200. Therefore, a GPA greater than (*not less than*) 2.5 would be required for admittance.

23. **B** To speak in positive terms about the increase in school degrees, the author must assume that the degrees indicate what they are supposed to indicate, that is, well-educated individuals. (A) and (E) are empty statements; (C) and (D) are altogether unsubstantiated by either expressed or implied information.

24. **E** Although the brand name is No-NOCK, the advertisement makes no claim to stop the engine from knocking. All the other claims are contained in the advertisement.

25. **D** The choice repudiates the suggestion that gentleness and graciousness were once part of the American character. (B), another choice worth considering, is not best because it does not address the temperament of tennis players as directly as does (D).

26. **B** By asking Dolores to choose between conventional and nuclear weapons, Fran has concluded that Dolores's statement calls for a decision. (C), worth considering, is not best because Fran supposes that Dolores has *not* made a choice—hence her question.

Section IV

Answers 1–6

From the information given, you should have constructed a diagram similar to this:

1. **B** From the diagram, if the group begins on island W, it could not reach island V in the eight days. Remember three days would have to be spent on W and three on X.

2. **B** From the diagram, if the group stays on island X for three nights, then the group cannot get to island V on the next visit.

3. **D** To answer this question, you must try each answer choice and eliminate the ones that do not connect. From the diagram, the only possible order listed would be U X Z V.

4. **E** From the diagram, if the group visits island W first, it could go to X to Y to Z, back to X, to U back to Y, to V and back to Z. A total of 9 visits. You could work from the choices, but remember to start from the highest number.

5. **D** From the diagram, the group could go from X to W to U to Y to V to Z to Y. This would be 6 different islands.

6. **E** Adding island T to the diagram connected only to U could look like this:

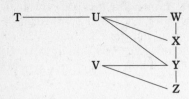

From this revised diagram, only (E) must be true. On the tenth day of a tour starting on Z, the tour group could be on island T. It would go from Z to Y to U to T or Z to X to U to T.

Answers 7–13

From the information given, you could have constructed the following diagram:

Notice the simple markings to show:

There are no ties in the first 3 games.
Team A wins more of the last 3 games than team B.
Team B wins more of the last 5 games than team A.
The last game is a tie.
Games 1 and 3 are won by the same team.

From this information you could deduce that team A wins either game 7 or 8, but not both, and team B cannot win any of the last 3 games. (If team A won both, team B could not win more of the last 5 games.) If team A wins game 7, then 8 is a tie, and if team A wins game 8, then 7 is a tie.

You could also deduce that team B must win games 5 and 6. Your diagram now looks like this:

```
   No Ties            B > A
 ┌──────────┐   ┌─B─ ─B─ ─A─ ─T─ ─T─┐
   1   2   3   4   5   6 │ 7   8   9 │
    \__/__/               └─ ─T─ ─A─ ┘
```

7. **C** From the information given, since games 1 and 3 are won by the same team, then one team wins at least 2 of the first 3 games.

8. **E** From the diagram, game 6 must be won by team B.

9. **A** From the diagram, if game 7 is won by team A, then game 8 must be a tie.

10. **E** From the diagram, you can see that (E) must be true.

11. **E** If team A wins games 1 and 4, then it must also win game 3. This would give team A four wins total, and team B could only win three, therefore team B could not win the series. For this question, the diagram would now look like this:

```
  A      A   A   B   B    A    T
  1   2  3   4   5   6   7  8   9
                          \__/
```

12. **B** If game 4 is won by the winner of game 5, then team B wins game 4. If game 2 is not won by the winner of game 3, then team B wins either game 2 or 3. This gives team B at least four wins and team A only a possible three wins, therefore B is the winner of the series.

13. **E** From the original diagram, team A must win either games 1, 2, and 3, or games 1, 3, and 4 to win the series. [This also eliminates choice (A).] If team B wins exactly one of the first four games [choice (B)], then team B cannot win the series as team A will win at least three games. If team A wins only three of the first seven games [choice (C)], then team A could still lose the series as team B could win games 2, 4, 5, and 6, with team A winning only games 1, 3, and 7. Team B could win the series by winning two of the first four games, eliminating choice (D).

Answers 14–18

Drawing a simple diagram, below, will help answer the questions.

```
                                    TR
                                     *
                              ___ J    FDR
M, A, K, FDR→ ___ ___ _M_ _A_  K – FDR or
                                   FDR – K
```

Note that, once Madison is placed in position 3 on the bottom, Adams must go in position 4 in order to leave spots for Kennedy to be adjacent to Franklin Delano Roosevelt.

14. **D** If Theodore Roosevelt is second from the left (on top), then Franklin Delano Roosevelt must be first on the bottom since one Roosevelt may not be above the other. Therefore, Kennedy must be second on the bottom.

15. **A** Adams must go to the far right on the bottom to allow Kennedy to be adjacent to Franklin Delano Roosevelt.

16. **D** If Washington and Kennedy are both first on their shelves, then Franklin Delano Roosevelt must be second on the lower shelf. Therefore, Theodore Roosevelt cannot be second on the top shelf and therefore must be third. Thus, statement D cannot be true.

17. **E** Since Adams must be on the right in the second row, only (E) is not possible.

18. **C** If Lincoln is next to Jefferson, that leaves Theodore Roosevelt and Washington for the first two positions on the top shelf. All of the choices are therefore true except (C) because that choice would place one Roosevelt above the other, which is not permitted.

Answers 19–24

19. **B** Since lima beans will not go with kidney beans or chili beans, they can go only with wax beans and garbanzos. Therefore, there is only one salad (limas + wax + garbanzos) that contains limas and that may be served at the party.

20. **C** The combinations of salads without chili beans are as follows:

1. garbanzos + wax + limas
2. garbanzos + limas + kidneys
3. garbanzos + wax + kidneys
4. wax + limas + kidneys

But remember that the *servable* salads may not include limas with kidneys or chili beans, thus reducing the number to two: garbanzos + wax + kidneys, and garbanzos + wax + limas.

21. **B** Without any restrictions there are 10 possible ways to choose three ingredients from a total of five:

CGW   GWL   WLK
CGL   GLK
CGK   GWK
CWL
CWK
CLK

However, the imposed restrictions (lima beans do not go with kidney beans or chili beans) narrow the servable salads down to five:

CGW   GWL   ~~WLK~~
~~CGL~~   ~~GLK~~
CGK   GWK
~~CWL~~
CWK
~~CLK~~

22. **E** From the chart above, we can see that garbanzos and wax beans appear more times in the servable salads. The other ingredients do not appear as often.

23. **C** From our chart we can see that having only enough wax beans for two salads will eliminate two of the four wax bean salads. Therefore, instead of five servable salads, there will now be only three.

24. **B** Again from our chart, if we eliminate the servable salads with garbanzos, we are left with only one servable salad: chili + wax + kidneys.

Section V

1. **B** The correct answer must use both premises. The first qualifies the assertion with "normally," so (A) will not follow, but (B) (with the qualifier "may") will. (C) may or may not be true, but it is not a logical conclusion based on the two premises. (D) and (E), like (A), do not use both premises.

2. **D** The question asked concerns the danger to public health, but the reply does not deal with this issue at all. It changes the subject.

3. **C** Reducing coffee consumption in general will not guarantee a healthier population (A) if "heavy" consumers do not reduce their coffee intake. Reducing coffee consumption would make those who drink a morning cup of coffee feel less well (B). (C) is a logical conclusion since heavy consumption increases heart attack risk. There is no information in the passage to justify the assertion about percolated coffee (D). If coffee may protect against colon cancer, (E) is not true.

4. **D** The issue of the danger of pesticides is addressed by (A), (C), and (E), while (B) calls into question the objectivity of the Food and Agriculture Department. But (D) deals with a different issue: air pollution. And if air pollution is a cause of illness, pesticides may be less to blame.

5. **A** The question contains its own prior judgment (underpay, unfair promotion policies) on what it asks, regardless of a "yes" or "no" answer. Similarly, the adjective "excessive" and the adverb "unfairly" prejudge any answer in choice (A).

6. **E** Since fares have risen, the cost of fuel has risen or there are no fare wars. And if there are no fare wars, the number of passengers is larger. Only (E) cannot be true. (B) is possible if fuel costs have risen, and there are fare wars.

7. **B** Though the argument for a decline in fishing off Newfoundland is convincing, the generalization that the "fishing industry in the Americas" will disappear is here based only on information about the Atlantic waters off Canada. It is possible that other areas have not been so affected.

8. **C** The advertisement asserts filter cigarettes cannot have great taste. A reasonable inference is that Gold Star is not a filter cigarette. (A) is contradicted by this ad without visual appeal. (B) is contradicted by this ad, which does not specifically praise a brand. (D) is illogical given the existence of this ad. Nothing in the ad supports (E).

9. **D** Choices (A), (B), and (C) strengthen the case for building the toll road. The environmentalists may be able to make their case for one of the other possible routes that, if less direct, would not disturb the reserve. With the information we have, the value of (E) is indeterminable.

10. **A** There is nothing in the paragraph to support (E), and there are details that contradict (B), (C), and (D). That "sales in the United States continue to increase" supports (A).

11. **E** The passage does not give the information that would lead to the conclusion in (A), (B), or (C). (E) is a better answer than (D), the odds against the heavy smoker being 40 in 100 as opposed to 25 in 100 for the light smoker.

12. **C** The presence of wolf bones and walrus bones near a village is not evidence that wolves were trained to haul sleds; it does not disprove the theory, however.

13. **B** Choices (A), (C), (D), and (E) would undermine the theory. But if wolves were easily domesticated and trained, it would make the theory of their domestication by Stone-Age tribes more plausible.

14. **A** The author makes his point by invective, an abrasive verbal attack.

15. **D** The first sentence asserts the needlessness of commenting on the picture; the second nonetheless makes a detailed criticism.

16. **B** If popcorn attracts rodents and insects, warehouses where packages using popcorn are stored would have vermin problems.

17. **B** Only (B) is a necessary assumption. It must be assumed that no other items (for example dressings, recipes, spices, etc.) are sold at the stand in order to conclude definitively that everything sold there is delicious.

18. **B** Though (E) is probably true, it is not a conclusion based on the information in the passage. But the passage does assert that only 19.67 percent (11.9 plus 7.7) of the eligible voters in the Democratic and Republican parties went to the polls.

19. **A** Choices (B) and (C), although true, are not relevant, while (D) and (E) are probably untrue. That it is only in the schools that the tobacco spokesmen are silent supports the inference of (A).

20. **C** In both paragraphs, the author disputes the interpretations of his opponents.

21. **D** The author assumes that an audience is able to evaluate a work and determine its own course of action.

22. **E** The opening lines describe esteem without popularity, later followed by popular success.

23. **D** The "But" introducing the last sentence suggests that a contrast, a disadvantage of coffee, is to follow. Either (C) or (D) is possible, but since exercise has not been an issue, (D) is the better choice.

24. **A** Only choice (A) must be true. There may be other performers as well as the chorus members (the orchestra, for example) in the performance, so (E) is incorrect.

25. **C** The passage draws an analogy comparing corrupt politicians to vermin.

ANALYZING YOUR LSAT SCORE: A BROAD RANGE SCORE APPROXIMATOR

The chart that follows is designed to give you a *general approximation* of the number of questions you need to get right to fall into a general score range and percentile rank on your LSAT. It should help you see if you are in the "ballpark" of the score you need. This range approximator is *not* designed to give you an exact score or to predict your LSAT score. The actual LSAT will have questions that are similar to the ones encountered in this book, but some questions may be either easier or more difficult. The variance in difficulty levels and testing conditions can affect your score range.

Obtaining Your Approximate Score Range

Although the LSAT uses a very precise formula to convert raw scores to scaled scores, for the purpose of this broad range approximation simply total the number of questions you answered correctly. Next divide the total number of correct answers by the total number of questions on the sample test. This will give you the percent correct. Now look at the following chart to see the approximate percent you need to get right to get into your score range. Remember, on the actual test one of the sections is experimental and, therefore, doesn't count toward your score.

On the actual LSAT, the percent of correct answers to get certain scores will vary slightly from test to test, depending on the number of problems and level of difficulty of that particular exam.

An average score is approximately 151.

If you are not in the range that you wish to achieve, check the approximate percent of correct answers that you need to achieve that range. Carefully analyze the types of errors you are making and continue practicing and analyzing. Remember, in trying to approximate a score range, you must take the complete sample test under strict time and test conditions.

Approximate Scaled Score Range	Approx. % of Correct Answers Necessary	Approx. Score Percentile for Test-takers (Est. % below)
171–180	93% and up	98–99.9
161–170	79%–92%	86–97
151–160	62%–78%	52–83
141–150	44%–61%	17–48
131–140	30%–43%	3–15
121–130	20%–29%	0–2

PART III

Profiles of Law Schools

CHAPTER 12

Overview of ABA-Approved Law Schools

There are currently 182 law schools approved by the American Bar Association (including the U.S. Army Judge Advocate General's School, which is not profiled here). The ABA is the largest organization of lawyers in the world, and its members come from every state in the United States. Because the ABA is a voluntary bar association, its members are not required to join in order to practice law, although nearly 40 percent of all American lawyers are currently members.

The power to grant individuals a license to practice law resides in the highest court of each state; thus, every jurisdiction administers its own bar examination, character and fitness inquiry, and licensing procedures for admission to the bar. The states also administer the disciplinary process for sanctioning lawyers who violate ethics rules of professional conduct. Because each state adopts its own rules establishing who is eligible to take the bar examination, some states require all candidates to be graduates of ABA-approved law schools, while others do not (see Chapter 14 for a discussion of non-ABA-approved law schools).

Authority to approve the right of educational institutions to grant degrees has been delegated by Congress to the U.S. Department of Education, which in turn delegates the responsibility for approving degree programs to designated accrediting agencies. In the case of law schools, the agency that has been given this power is the American Bar Association. Within the ABA, accreditation matters are handled by the Accreditation Committee of the Section of Legal Education and Admissions to the Bar with the support of a Consultant on Legal Education. The standards of approval themselves are promulgated by the ABA's governing body, the House of Delegates, upon recommendation of the Section of Legal Education. The Accreditation Committee is charged with the inspection and evaluation of law schools and law school programs, not only when a school or program is started, but also periodically during the life of the institution. The purpose of the accreditation process is to assure that every law school in the United States meets a common set of quality standards, and that every degree awarded confers the same benefit on recipients as comparable degrees at other ABA-approved law schools.

The imprimatur of the ABA carries great weight with state bar admission authorities, and every state allows graduates of any ABA law school to sit for the bar exam. From an applicant's standpoint, graduating from an ABA-approved law school is like a stamp of approval, a ticket to seek admission to practice law anywhere in the country. From the point of view of a law student, ABA approval is a guarantee that certain basic educational requirements have been met, and that the education they receive will be comparable to the education at any other ABA-approved law school. Additional information on the accreditation process and law schools generally may be obtained by writing the ABA Section of Legal Education and Admissions to the Bar, 750 North Lake Shore Drive, Chicago, IL 60611.

This does not mean that law schools are all the same. As this Guide demonstrates, law schools come in many shapes and sizes. Some are more difficult to get into than others. Some offer special programs that set them apart from other schools. Some serve special audiences that others do not. Some are rated more highly than others. Neither the ABA nor this Guide attempt to rank law schools. The ABA certifies that approved schools meet minimum standards, but encourages them to seek to exceed those standards. Barron's *Guide to Law Schools* provides a wealth of information to help applicants make the difficult decision about which law school is best for them. Implicit in this approach is the notion that different schools are right for different people, and that no single school is best for everyone.

155

The ranking of law schools by some publications may provide interesting reading, and may reflect the relative prestige of law schools as filtered through the eyes of the publication's editors, but the uncritical use of such rankings without looking at the facts and figures behind them can distort the process of selecting a law school. The real question should be: What are the top ten schools for you personally? The question is not: What are the top ten schools for some faceless editor at some magazine or publishing house?

During 1995 and into 1996, the American Bar Association conducted a thorough review of the standards for approval of law school. A revised set of standards was adopted by the ABA House of Delegates in August, 1996. The impetus for this review came in part from criticism of the standards both inside and outside the ABA, as well as recognition by leaders in the Section of Legal Education and Admissions to the Bar that legal education is changing, particularly in the area of skills education, such as teaching students the practice skills they will need to be successful practitioners, not just the legal theory and analysis characteristic of traditional legal education. These changes to the standards will eventually be integrated into the fabric of the law schools that seek ABA accreditation or reaccreditation.

The following table provides information about the tuition, programs, and academic community at the schools that have been approved by the American Bar Association. This is designed to provide a quick overview of the schools, and should be used in conjunction with the detailed profiles of the individual schools that can be found in Chapter 13.

Most of the information on these charts should be self-explanatory. If you are uncertain about the significance of any item, consult the profile of the school for additional information or explanation.

In several sections of the table, a check (√) indicates "yes" and a blank indicates "no." For example, under Calendar, the possibilities are Fall, Winter, Spring, and Summer. At any given school, you can begin your law studies only at those times indicated by a check.

Since most law schools operate on a semester basis, information about credits and required courses is given in terms of semester hours. If a school operates on the quarter system, the abbreviation *qh* is added.

Similarly, tuition is generally given for a full year. When part-time tuition is given per credit, this refers to semester courses unless the abbreviation *qh* is used.

Where a category does not apply to a school or when information was not available, the cell is left blank.

INSTITUTION	Profile Page	Fee	Deadline	Deadline Financial Aid	TUITION In State Full Time (Part Time)	TUITION Out of State Full Time (Part Time)	Fall	Winter	Spring	Summer	Day	Evening	Credits for JD	Required Credits for Courses	Transferable Summer Courses	Joint Degree	Graduate Law Degree	Enrolled Full Time (Part Time)	Average Age First Year	% Women	% Minority	Attrition Rate %	Faculty Full Time (Part Time)	Volumes	Microforms
American University (Washington College of Law) 4801 Massachusetts Avenue, N.W. Washington, DC 20016-8186 202-274-4101 Fax: 202-274-4107 wcladmit@wcl.american.edu	188		March 1	Check	$23,696 ($16,682)	$23,696 ($16,682)	✓				✓	✓	86	34	✓	✓	✓	873 (448)	24	59	24	1	50 (152)	412,309	1,015,769
Arizona State University (College of Law/Armstrong Hall) Box 877906 Tempe, AZ 85287-7906 602-965-1474 Fax: 602-965-5550 wanda.decrow@asu.edu	190		March 1	Check	$4,938	$12,090	✓				✓		87	40	✓	✓		481	27	49	25	11	37 (21)	351,000	465,411
Baylor University (School of Law) P.O. Box 97288 Waco, TX 76798-7288 254-710-1911 Fax: 254-710-2316 becky-beck@baylor.edu	192	$40	March 1	May 1	$14,719	$14,719	✓		✓	✓	✓		126	79	✓	✓	✓	396	24	40	8	5	21 (33)	114,860	67,835
Boston College (Law School) 885 Centre Street Newton, MA 02459 617-552-4351 Fax: 617-552-2917 bclawadm@bc.edu	194	$65	March 1	March 15	$24,480	$24,480	✓				✓		85	38		✓		828	24	51	18	1	52 (56)	393,179	1,031,218
Boston University (School of Law) 765 Commonwealth Avenue Boston, MA 02215 617-353-3100 bulawadm@bu.edu	196	$50	March 1	March 1	$23,770	$23,770	✓				✓	✓	84	33		✓	✓	892	24	49	23	9	57 (74)	317,000	1,299,800
Brigham Young University (J. Reuben Clark Law School) 342 JRCB Brigham Young University Provo, UT 84602 801-378-4277 Fax: 801-378-5897 wilcock@lawgate.byu.edu	198	$30	Feb 1	March 1	$5,330	$8,000	✓				✓		90	36		✓	✓	452 (5)	26	35	15	1	27 (31)	430,431	137,137
Brooklyn Law School 250 Joralemon Street Brooklyn, NY 11201 718-780-7906 Fax: 718-780-0395 admitq@brooklaw.edu	200	$60	April 1	March 1	$23,340 ($16,625)	$23,340 ($16,625)	✓				✓	✓	86	35	✓	✓	✓	991 (509)	25	49	20	3	67 (97)	486,259	1,103,385

INSTITUTION	Profile Page	Fee	Deadline	Deadline Financial Aid	In State Full Time (Part Time)	Out of State Full Time (Part Time)	Fall	Winter	Spring	Summer	Day	Evening	Credits for JD	Required Credits for Courses	Transferable Summer Courses	Joint Degree	Graduate Law Degree	Full Time (Part Time)	Average Age First Year	% Women	% Minority	Attrition Rate %	Full Time (Part Time)	Volumes	Microforms
California Western School of Law 225 Cedar Street San Diego, CA 92101-3046 619-525-1401 Fax: 619-615-1401 rbriscoe@cwsl.edu	202	$45	April 1	March 18	$22,200 ($16,200)	$22,200 ($16,200)	✓		✓		✓		89	43	✓	✓		639 (61)	27	52	26	14	42 (45)	257,781	643,130
Campbell University (Norman Adrian Wiggins School of Law) P.O. Box 158 Buies Creek, NC 27506 910-893-1754 Fax: 910-893-1780 culaw@webster.campbell.edu	204	$40	open	open	$17,500	$17,500	✓				✓	✓	90	73		✓		297		50	6		19 (18)	156,000	56,998
Capital University (Law School) 303 East Broad Street Columbus, OH 43215-3200 614-236-6500 Fax: 614-236-6972 admissions@law.capital.edu	206	$35	April 1	April 1	$15,979 ($9,918)	$15,979 ($9,918)	✓		✓		✓	✓	86 sem.	42	✓	✓	✓	389 (346)	27	45	11	10	30 (56)	239,000	35,979
Case Western Reserve University (School of Law) 11075 East Boulevard Cleveland, OH 44106 216-368-3600 Fax: 216-368-6144 lawadmissions@po.cwru.edu or lawmoney@po.cwru.edu	208	$40	March 1	May 1	$21,300 ($888/hr)	$21,300 ($888/hr)	✓				✓	✓	88	33	✓	✓	✓	620 (12)	25	45	22	3	46 (64)	365,175	419,218
Catholic University of America (Columbus School of Law) Cardinal Station Washington, DC 20064 (202) 319-5151 Fax: (202) 319-6285	210	$55	March 1	March 1	$25,092 ($18,937)	$25,092 ($18,937)	✓				✓	✓	84	33		✓	✓	654 (278)	23	52	22	4	46 (87)	322,816	52,864
Catholic University of Puerto Rico (School of Law) Avenida Las Americas-Station 6 Ponce, PR 00732 809-841-2000	212		Check	Check							✓	✓	94	82		✓	220	(220)	24	50	26	14 11	(18)	135,000	15,000
Chapman University (School of Law) One University Drive Orange, CA 92866 714-628-2500 Fax: 714-628-2501 misles@chapman.edu	214	$40	open	April 1	$21,600 ($14,850)	$21,600 ($14,850)	✓				✓	✓	88	53 to 54	✓	✓		99 (74)	28	49	26	15	20 (9)	225,945	177,876

School	#	App. Fee	Priority/Deadline	Deadline 2	Resident Tuition	Nonresident Tuition			%	Students			Enrollment							Volumes	Volumes
City University of New York at Queens College (School of Law) 65-21 Main Street Flushing, NY 11367-1300 718-340-4210 Fax: 718-340-4372 admissions@maclaw.law.cuny.edu	216	$40	March 15	May 15	$5,700	$8,930	✓	✓	92	70	✓	✓	389	29	59	41	10	38 (12)		250,000	820,000
Cleveland State University (Cleveland-Marshall College of Law) 1801 Euclid Avenue Cleveland, OH 44115 216-687-2304 Fax: 216-687-6881	218	$35	April 1	March 1	$7,826 ($6,020)	$15,522 ($11,940)	✓	✓	87	34 (plus 2)	✓	✓	481 (305)	27	48	14	10	36 (25)		445,908	57,072
College of William and Mary (William and Mary Law School) P.O. Box 8795 Williamsburg, VA 23187-8795 757-221-3785 Fax: 757-221-3261 lawadmin@facstaff.wm.edu	220	$40	March 1	Feb 15	$9,074	$18,200	✓	✓	90	36	✓	✓	538	25	43	17	2	28 (42)		355,000	840,000
Columbia University (School of Law) 435 West 116th Street New York, NY 10027 212-854-2670 Fax: 212-854-1109	222	$65	Feb 15	March 1	$27,940	$27,940	✓	✓	83	35	✓	✓	1167	24	46	33		86		993,606	679,900
Cornell University (Law School) Myron Taylor Hall Ithaca, NY 14853 607-255-5141 Fax: 607-255-7193	224	$65	Feb 1	March 15	$25,500	$25,500	✓	✓	84	36	✓	✓	546	23	47	25	1	45 (11)		473,665	701,091
Creighton University (School of Law) 2500 California Plaza Omaha, NE 68178 402-280-2872 Fax: 402-280-3161 admit@culaw.creighton.edu	226	$40	May 1	July 1	$16,548 ($555/hr)	$16,548 ($555/hr)	✓	✓	94	39	✓	✓	409 (18)	26	44	9		22 (41)		254,585	95,779
De Paul University (College of Law) 25 East Jackson Boulevard Chicago, IL 60604 312-362-6831 lawinfo@wppost.depaul.edu	228	$40	April 1	March 1	$20,700 ($14,000)	$20,700 ($14,000)	✓	✓	86	37	✓	✓	785 (323)	24	54	20	3	50 (73)		346,097	902,637
Drake University (Law School) 2507 University Avenue Des Moines, IA 50311 515-271-1990 lawadmit@drake.edu	230	$40	April 1	March 1	$17,630	$17,630	✓	✓	90	41	✓	✓	338 (18)	26	46	13	6	30 (24)		280,000	90,000
Duke University (School of Law) Science and Towerview Drive, Box 90393 Durham, NC 27708 919-613-7020 Fax: 919-613-7257 admissions@law.duke.edu	232	$65	Jan 1	March 15	$25,500	$25,500	✓	✓	84	30	✓	✓	680	24	46	26	1	36 (42)		535,000	71,000

INSTITUTION	Profile Page	Fee	Deadline	Deadline Financial Aid	Tuition In State Full Time (Part Time)	Tuition Out of State Full Time (Part Time)	Fall	Winter	Spring	Summer	Day	Evening	Credits for JD	Required Credits for Courses	Transferable Summer Courses	Joint Degree	Graduate Law Degree	Enrolled Full Time (Part Time)	Average Age First Year	% Women	% Minority	Attrition Rate %	Faculty Full Time (Part Time)	Volumes	Microforms
Duquesne University (School of Law) 900 Locust Street, Hanley Hall, Pittsburgh, PA 15282, 412-396-6296, campion@duq.edu	234	$50	April 1	May 31	$15,764 ($12,004)	$15,764 ($12,004)	✓				✓		86	33	✓	✓		377 (314)	27	46	6	2	29 (40)	236,000	210,000
Emory University (School of Law) Gambrell Hall, Atlanta, GA 30322, 404-727-6801, Fax: 404-727-2477, jbalej@law.emory.edu	236	$50	March 1	March 1	$23,870	$23,870	✓				✓		88	39		✓	✓	616	24	52	21	3	46 (47)	300,000	71,734
Florida Coastal School of Law 7555 Beach Boulevard, Jacksonville, FL 32216, 904-680-7710, Fax: 904-680-7776, admissions@fcsl.edu	238	$50	open		$17,540 ($14,030)	$17,540 ($14,030)	✓		✓		✓	✓	87	56	✓	✓		237 (246)	28	43	23	8	27 (31)	127,829	421,745
Florida State University (College of Law) 425 W. Jefferson St., Tallahassee, FL 32306-1601, 850-644-3787, Fax: 850-644-7284, admissions@law.fsu.edu	240	$20	Feb 15	April 1	$4,890	$16,162	✓				✓		88	35	✓	✓		683	25	46	22	3	46 (13)	409,603	842,184
Fordham University (School of Law) 140 West 62nd Street, New York, NY 10023, 212-626-6810	242	$60	March 1	May 1	$24,725 ($18,545)	$24,725 ($18,545)	✓				✓	✓	83	39	✓	✓	✓	1088 (349)	24	46	24	2	64 (200)	543,992	1,044,801
Franklin Pierce Law Center 2 White Street, Concord, NH 03301, 603-228-9217, Fax: 603-228-1074, Ladmissions@fplc.edu	244		May 1	open	$17,050		✓				✓	✓	84	39	✓	✓	359		28	36	12	24 10	(37)	126,896	447,501
George Mason University (School of Law) 3401 North Fairfax Drive, Arlington, VA 22201-4498, 703-993-8010, Fax: 703-993-8260, arichar5@gmu.edu	246		March 1	open	$7,784 ($6,116)	$18,228 ($14,322)	✓				✓	✓	90	41	✓			365 (371)	26	38	10	4	24 (68)	359,000	886,000
George Washington University (Law School) 2000 H Street, N.W., Washington, DC 20052, 202-739-0648, jd@main.nlc.gwu.edu	248	$65	March 1	March 1	$25,635 ($902/hr)	$25,635 ($902/hr)	✓				✓	✓	84	34	✓	✓	✓	1215 (239)	24	45	30	2	67 (170)	519,652	1,096,541

No.	School	App. fee	Deadline 1	Deadline 2	Tuition 1	Tuition 2	%	%	Enrollment	(extra)	col	col	col	col	col	col
250	**Georgetown University** (Law Center) 600 New Jersey Avenue, N.W. Washington, DC 20001 202-662-9010 admis@law.georgetown.edu	$65	Feb 1	March 1	$25,705 ($18,000)	$25,705 ($18,000)	83	31	1352 (612)		24	49	26	1	87 (92)	
252	**Georgia State University** (College of Law) P.O. Box 4037 Atlanta, GA 30302-4037 404-651-2096 Fax: 404-651-2096 cjjackson@gsu.edu	$30	March 15	April 1	$3,392 ($142/hr)	$13,568 ($566/hr)	90	43	395 (233)		30	51	15	11	42 (30)	145,617
254	**Golden Gate University** (School of Law) 536 Mission Street San Francisco, CA 94105-2968 415-442-6630	$40	April 15	March 1	$20,880 ($14,400)	$20,880 ($14,400)	88	54	463 (299)		27	55	18	24	33 (117)	109,831
256	**Gonzaga University** (School of Law) Box 3528 Spokane, WA 99220-3528 509-323-5532 Fax: 509-323-5710 admissions@lawschool.gonzaga.edu	$40	April 1	Feb 1	$19,350 ($645/hr)	$19,350 ($645/hr)	90	58	439 (19)		28	39	15	10	34 (24)	253,517
258	**Hamline University** (School of Law) 1536 Hewitt Avenue St. Paul, MN 55104-1284 651-523-2461 Fax: 651-523-3064 lawadm@gw.hamline.edu	$40	May 15		$17,448	$17,448	88	33	442 (46)		27	55	14	3	29 (52)	151,000
260	**Harvard University** (Harvard Law School) Cambridge, MA 02138 617-495-3109 Fax: 617-495-1110 jdadmiss@law.harvard.edu	$40	Feb 1	check	$25,000		82	30		1658	24	42	28	94 / 1	(75)	1,920,648
262	**Hofstra University** (School of Law) 121 Hofstra University Hempstead, NY 11549 516-463-5916 Fax: 516-463-6264 lawpts@hofstra.edu	$60	April 15	June 1	$23,246	$23,246	87	39	900 (2)			46	18	4	39 (35)	487,630
264	**Howard University** (Howard University) 2900 Van Ness Street, N.W. Washington, DC 20008 202-806-8008 Fax: 202-806-8162 admissions@law.howard.edu	$60	March 31	April 1	$13,030		88	n/av	(3)	412	25	60	94	33 / 5	(23)	283,000
266	**Illinois Institute of Technology** (Chicago-Kent College of Law) 565 West Adams Street Chicago, IL 60661 312-906-5020 admit@kentlaw.edu	$45	April 1	April 15	$21,715 ($15,665)	$21,715 ($15,665)	87	42	796 (347)		25	50	16	5	70 (103)	560,000
270	**Indiana University at Bloomington** (School of Law) 211 S. Indiana Avenue Bloomington, IN 47405-1001 812-855-4765 Fax: 812-855-0555 lawadmis@indiana.edu	$35	open	March 1	$6,850	$17,568	86	36	608 (4)		24	43	20	3	38 (16)	591,504

No.	Library volumes
250	2,207,015
252	623,675
254	120,221
256	596,201
258	87,000
260	187,600
262	1,357,850
264	54,000
266	687,941
270	1,138,543

INSTITUTION	Profile Page	APPLICATIONS Fee	Deadline	Financial Aid Deadline	TUITION In State Full Time (Part Time)	Out of State Full Time (Part Time)	CALENDAR Fall	Winter	Spring	Summer	PROGRAMS Day	Evening	Credits for JD	Required Credits for Courses	Transferable Summer Courses	Joint Degree	Graduate Law Degree	ENROLLED STUDENT BODY Full Time (Part Time)	Average Age First Year	% Women	% Minority	Attrition Rate %	FACULTY Full Time (Part Time)	LIBRARY Volumes	Microforms
Indiana University-Purdue University (Indiana University School of Law-Indianapolis) 735 West New York Street Indianapolis, IN 46202-5194 317-274-2459 Fax: 317-274-3955 khmiller@iupui.edu	268	$35	March 1	March 1	$7,083 ($4,570)	$17,205 ($11,100)	✓				✓	✓	90	37	✓	✓	✓	566 (302)	27	45	13	10	42 (37)	491,716	657,798
Inter-American University of Puerto Rico (School of Law) P.O. Box 70351 San Juan, PR 00936-8351 809-751-1912, ext. 2013	272		Check		$3,250 ($2,590)	$3,250 ($2,590)	✓				✓	✓	92	62	✓			335 (310)	24	47		8	20 (16)	160,098	139,963
John Marshall Law School 315 South Plymouth Court Chicago, IL 60604 312-987-1406 Fax: 312-427-5136 admission@jmls.edu	274	$50	March 1	Check	$21,000 ($700/hr)	$700/hr ($700/hr)	✓		✓		✓	✓	90	52	✓	✓	✓	719 (433)	25	43	17	5	56 (138)	353,737	55,710
Lewis and Clark College (Northwestern School of Law) 10015 Southwest Terwilliger Boulevard Portland, OR 97219 503-768-6613 Fax: 503-768-6671 lawadmss@lclark.edu	276	$50	March 15	March 1	$19,180 ($14,386)	$19,180 ($14,386)	✓				✓	✓	86	28-35	✓	✓	✓	491 (181)	25	47	11	14	37 (54)	451,706	254,548
Louisiana State University (Paul M. Hebert Law Center) Baton Rouge, LA 70803 225-388-8646 Fax: 225-388-8647 bloup@lsu.edu	278	$25	Feb 1	April 1	$6,010	$11,851	✓				✓		97	39	✓	✓		644	24	47	11	25	31 (40)	402,195	887,946
Loyola Marymount University (Loyola Law School) 919 S. Albany Street Los Angeles, CA 90015 213-736-1180 admissions@lls.edu	280	$50	Feb 1	March 2	$22,530 ($15,064)	$22,530 ($15,064)	✓				✓	✓	87	49	✓	✓		992 (352)	24	49	38	3	63 (79)	486,509	1,238,076
Loyola University New Orleans (School of Law) 7214 St. Charles Avenue New Orleans, LA 70118 504-861-5575 Fax: 504-861-5772 ladmit@loyno.edu	282		open	Check	$19,685 ($13,335)	✓					✓	90		✓	✓	✓	503 (147)	23	47	23	12	30 (36)	265,089	570,114	

#	School	Fee	Deadline 1	Deadline 2	Tuition	Tuition							Enrollment								
284	Loyola University of Chicago (School of Law) One East Pearson Street Chicago, IL 60611 312-915-7170 Fax: 312-915-7201 law-admissions@luc.edu	$50	April 1	March 1	$22,990 ($17,244)	$22,990 ($17,244)	✓	86	46	✓	✓	✓	520 (190)	25	58	15	5	29 (149)	354,981	942,152
286	Marquette University (Law School) Office of Admissions, Sensenbrenner Hall, P.O. Box 1881 Milwaukee, WI 53201-1881 414-288-6767 Fax: 414-288-0676 law.admission@marquette.edu	$40	April 1	April 1	$19,100 ($790/hr)	$19,100 ($790/hr)	✓	90	34	✓	✓	✓	420 (65)	25	46	8	2	24 (24)		
288	Mercer University (Walter F. George School of Law) 1021 Georgia Ave. Macon, GA 31201 912-301-2605 Fax: 912-301-2989 Sutton_me@mercer.edu	$45	March 15	April 1	$19,250	$19,250	✓	91	65	✓	✓		415	26	49	12	5	27 (27)	292,000	
290	Michigan State University (Detroit College of Law) 316 Law College Bldg. East Lansing, MI 48824-1300 517-432-0222 Fax: 517-432-0098 heatleya@pilot.msu.edu	$50	April 15	July 2	$16,584 ($12,452)	$15,734 ($11,815)	✓	88	56	✓	✓	✓	547 (149)	28	40	14		25 (40)	102,314	117,794
292	Mississippi College (School of Law) 151 E. Griffith Street Jackson, MS 39201 601-925-7150 pevans@mc.edu	$25	May 1		$14,370	$14,370	✓	88	36	✓	✓	✓	372	26	44	9	7	18 (18)	253,000	540,000
294	New England School of Law 154 Stuart Street Boston, MA 02116 617-422-7210 Fax: 617-422-7200 admit@admin.nesl.edu	$50	March 15	April 15	$15,950 ($11,960)	$15,950 ($11,960)	✓	84	43	✓		✓	592 (366)	28	54	17	7	40 (59)	300,000	645,000
296	New York Law School 57 Worth Street New York, NY 10013-2960 212-431-2888 Fax: 212-966-1522 admissions@nyls.edu	$50	April 1	April 15	$23,268 ($16,588)	$23,268 ($16,588)	✓	86	38	✓	✓	✓	920 (476)	27	48	24	3	53 (82)	463,750	981,917
298	New York University (School of Law) 110 West Third Street New York, NY 10012 212-998-6060 Fax: 212-995-4527	$65	Feb 1	March 15	$27,540	$27,540	✓	82		✓	✓	✓	1328		50	23		114 (71)	997,463	19,309
300	North Carolina Central University (School of Law) 1512 S. Alston Avenue Durham, NC 27707 919-560-6333 Fax: 919-560-6339 jfaucett@wpo.nccu.edu	$30	April 15	Feb 1	$2,288 ($2,288)	$11,392 ($11,392)	✓	88	65	✓	✓	✓	255 (107)		56	53		23 (9)	284,115	639,314

Profile Page	Institution	Fee	App. Deadline	Financial Aid Deadline	Tuition In State Full Time (Part Time)	Tuition Out of State Full Time (Part Time)	Calendar Fall	Day	Evening	Credits for JD	Required Credits for Courses	Transferable Summer Courses	Joint Degree	Graduate Law Degree	Enrolled Full Time (Part Time)	Avg Age First Year	% Women	% Minority	Attrition Rate %	Faculty Full Time (Part Time)	Volumes	Microforms
302	Northeastern University (School of Law) 400 Huntington Avenue Boston, MA 02115 617-373-2395 Fax: 617-373-8865 pbauer@slaw.neu.edu	$65	March 1	March 1	$23,620	$23,620	✓	✓		99	49	✓	✓		591	25	60	25	4	29 (25)	293,243	623,096
304	Northern Illinois University (College of Law) Swen Parson Hall De Kalb, IL 60115 815-753-1420 Fax: 815-753-4501 lawadm@niu.edu	$40	May 15	March 1	$5,887	$11,774	✓	✓		90	36		✓		261 (19)	27	40	25	9	27 (10)	210,312	453,961
306	Northern Kentucky University (Salmon P. Chase College of Law) Louie B. Nunn Hall Highland Heights, KY 41099 606-572-6476 Fax: 606-572-6081 brayg@nku.edu	$30	March 1	April 1	$7,380 ($4,920)	$19,110 ($12,740)	✓	✓		90	42	✓	✓	✓	185 (173)	28	45	6	19	25 (42)	242,595	856
308	Northwestern University (School of Law) 357 East Chicago Avenue Chicago, IL 60611 312-503-8465 Fax: 312-503-0178 nubwadm@nwu.edu	$70	Feb 15	March 15	$26,850	$26,850	✓	✓		86	32		✓	✓	650	25	49	29	1	59 (149)	656,775	195,648
310	Nova Southeastern University (Shepard Broad Law Center) 3305 College Avenue Fort Lauderdale, FL 33314-7721 954-262-6117 Fax: 954-262-3844 admission@nsu.law.nova.edu	$50	March 1	March 1	$19,970 ($14,980)	$19,970 ($14,980)	✓	✓	✓	90	44	✓	✓		726 (212)	25	49	29	8	45 (64)	314,036	137,029
312	Ohio Northern University (Claude W. Pettit College of Law) 525 South Main Street Ada, OH 45810 419-772-2211 Fax: 419-772-1487 g-keener@onu.edu			Check	$18,980	$18,980	✓	✓		87	45	✓			283	26	34	18	6	18 (22)	263,747	72,943
314	Ohio State University (College of Law) 55 West 12th Avenue, John Deaver Drinko Hall Columbus, OH 43210-1391 614-292-8810 Fax: 614-292-1383 roboski.1@osu.edu		March 15	Check	$8,424		✓	✓		88	38	✓	✓	638		22	44	16	33 / 1	(30)	653,399	880,049

School	No.	Fee	App. Deadline	Fin. Aid Deadline	Tuition (Resident)	Tuition (Nonresident)															
Oklahoma City University (School of Law) 2501 North Blackwelder Oklahoma City, OK 73106-1493 405-521-5354 Fax: 405-521-5802 lawadmit@okcu.edu	316	$35	Aug 1	March 1	$15,900 ($10,600)	$15,900 ($10,600)	✓				90	46	✓	✓	371 (133)	30	41	15	8	31 (17)	271,739	618,909
Pace University (School of Law) 78 North Broadway White Plains, NY 10603 914-422-4010 Fax: 914-422-4248 adagostino@genesis.law.pace.edu	318	$55	Feb 15	Feb 1	$22,900 ($17,200)	$22,900 ($17,200)	✓				90	40	✓	✓	448 (305)	25	54	19	6	47 (76)	327,913	60,613
Pennsylvania State University (Dickinson School of Law) 150 South College Street Carlisle, PA 17013 717-240-5207 Fax: 717-241-3503 dsladmit@psu.edu	320	$50	March 1	Feb 15	$15,850	$15,850	✓				88	40	✓	✓	536 (1)	25	42	7	7	35 (57)	425,000	1,017,000
Pepperdine University (School of Law) 24255 Pacific Coast Highway Malibu, CA 90263 310-456-4631 Fax: 310-317-7668 soladmis@pepperdine.edu	322		March 1	Check	$23,810		✓				88	57	✓	✓	662	23	45	17	34 / 5		252,000	87,000
Quinnipiac College (School of Law) 275 Mt. Carmel Avenue Hamden, CT 06518-1948 203-287-3400 Fax: 203-287-3339 ladm@quinnipiac.edu	324	$40	open	April 1	$21,200 ($16,150)	$21,200 ($16,150)	✓				86	53	✓	✓	502 (291)	27	47	14	4	38 (25)	344,390	186,502
Regent University 1000 Regent University Drive Virginia Beach, VA 23464-9800 757-226-4584 Fax: 757-226-4139 lawschool@regent.edu	326	$40	June 1	March 1	$16,480 ($515/hr)	$16,480 ($515/hr)	✓				90	66	✓	✓	413 (78)	27	45	18	7	22 (37)	316,000	900,000
Roger Williams University (School of Law) Ten Metacom Avenue Bristol, RI 02809-5171 401-254-4555 Fax: 401-254-4516 admissions@rwulaw.rwu.edu	328	$60	May 15	May 15	$20,100 ($15,410)	$2,010 ($15,410)	✓				90	54	✓	✓	231 (163)	28	49	11	12	25 (25)	250,000	891,546
Rutgers University/Camden (School of Law) Fifth and Penn Streets Camden, NJ 08102 609-225-6102 Fax: 609-225-6537	332	$50	March 1	March 1	$10,106 ($418/hr)	$14,828 ($617/hr)	✓				84	34	✓	✓	604 (145)	26	49	18	4	43 (65)	407,335	630,770
Rutgers University/Newark (School of Law) S.I. Newhouse Center for Law and Justice, 15 Washington St. Newark, NJ 07102 973-353-5557/5554 Fax 973-353-1445	330		March 1	March 1	$9,100 ($355/hr)	$13,500 ($550/hr)	✓				84	31 to 32	✓	✓	515 (230)	28	46	31	5	49 (34)	412,542	144,376

Institution	Profile Page	Fee	Deadline	Financial Aid Deadline	In State Full Time (Part Time)	Out of State Full Time (Part Time)	Fall	Winter	Spring	Summer	Day	Evening	Credits for JD	Required Credits for Courses	Transferable Summer Courses	Joint Degree	Graduate Law Degree	Full Time (Part Time) Enrolled	Average Age First Year	% Women	% Minority	Attrition Rate %	Faculty Full Time (Part Time)	Volumes	Microforms
Saint John's University (School of Law) 8000 Utopia Parkway Jamaica, NY 11439 718-990-6611/6612 Fax: 718-990-2526 rsvp@sjulaw.stjohns.edu	334		March 1		$22,000 ($16,500)	$22,000 ($16,500)	✓		✓		✓	✓	85	61	✓	✓		691 (276)	23	39	25		59 (37)	432,804	1,148,680
Saint Louis University (School of Law) 3700 Lindell Boulevard St. Louis, MO 63108 314-977-2800 admissions@law.slu.edu	336	$55	March 1	April 1	$20,130 ($15,080)	$20,130 ($15,080)	✓				✓	✓	88	36	✓	✓	✓	550 (227)	26	48	13	5	39 (28)	565,677	51,000
Saint Mary's University (School of Law) One Camino Santa Maria San Antonio, TX 78228-8601 210-436-3523 Fax: 210-431-4202	338	$45	March 1	March 31	$17,515	$17,515	✓				✓		90	46	✓	✓	✓	764		47	39	2	34 (28)	320,000	633,117
Samford University (Cumberland School of Law) 800 Lakeshore Drive Birmingham, AL 35229 205-726-2702 Fax: 205-726-2673 lawadmissions@samford.edu	340	$40	Feb 28	March 1	$18,976	$18,976	✓				✓		90	53	✓	✓	✓	586	24	41	7	2	32 (10)	254,346	471,485
Santa Clara University (School of Law) 500 El Camino Real Santa Clara, CA 95053 408-554-4800 Fax: 408-554-7897 lawadmission@scu.edu	342	$50	March 1	Feb 1	$22,000 ($16,000)	$22,000 ($16,000)	✓				✓	✓	86	46	✓	✓	✓	623 (276)	24	51	30	7	34 (26)	262,447	763,854
Seattle University (School of Law) 900 Broadway Seattle, WA 98122-4340 206-398-4200 Fax: 206-398-4058 lawadmis@seattleu.edu	344	$50	April 1	March 1	$19,110 ($15,925)	$19,110 ($15,925)	✓			✓	✓	✓	90	44	✓	✓	✓	698 (185)	26	57	23	9	35 (62)	323,466	924,769
Seton Hall University (School of Law) One Newark Center Newark, NJ 07102-5210 973-642-8747 Fax: 973-642-8876 admitme@shu.edu	346	$50	April 1	April 15	$20,714 ($750)	$20,714 ($750)	✓				✓	✓	85	44	✓	✓	✓	834 (352)	26	46	15	12	58 (106)	400,039	495,570
South Texas College of Law 1303 San Jacinto Street Houston, TX 77002-7000 713-646-1810 Fax: 713-646-2929 acramer@stcl.edu	348	$50	Feb 25	May 1	$15,540 ($10,360)	$15,540 ($10,360)	✓		✓		✓	✓	90	44	✓		✓	850 (370)	27	44	23	12	54 (33)	198,884	1,053,310

This page is a rotated data table (no column headers printed on this page). Each school forms one row; the numeric data columns are reproduced below in reading order from the school-number column outward.

No.	School	App. fee	Deadline	Deadline	Tuition	Tuition	col	col	✓	✓	col	col	col	col	col	col	col	col	col
350	**Southern Illinois University (School of Law)** Lesar Law Building, Mail Code 6804, Carbondale, IL 62901-6804, 618-453-8767, Fax: 618-453-8769, lawadmit@siu.edu	$25	March 1	March 1	$4,800	$14,400	90	46	✓	✓	350	27	37	8	7	23 (6)	354,239	157,847	
352	**Southern Methodist University (School of Law)** Office of Admissions, P.O. Box 750110, Dallas, TX 75275-0110, 214-768-2550, Fax: 214-768-2549	$50	Feb 1	June 1	$23,000	$23,000	90	37	✓	✓	773 (13)	24	38	13	3	42 (100)	480,000	75,217	
354	**Southern University and A & M College (Law Center)** Post Office Box 9294, Baton Rouge, LA 70813, 225-771-5340, Fax: 225-771-2121	$25	March 31	April 15	$3,288	$7,888	96	75	✓	✓	317	27	52	66	10	30 (14)	415,208	7,867	
356	**Southwestern University (School of Law)** 675 South Westmoreland Avenue, Los Angeles, CA 90005-3992, 213-738-6717, Fax: 213-383-1688, admissions@swlaw.edu	$50	June 30	June 1	$21,990 ($13,927)	$21,990 ($13,927)	87	52	✓	✓	605 (262)	27	51	36		50 (37)	404,177	934,164	
358	**St. Thomas University (School of Law)** 16400 N.W. 32nd Avenue, Miami, FL 33054, 305-623-2310, lamy@stu.edu	$40	April 30	April 15	$20,725	$20,725	90	53	✓	✓	487	27	45	48	25	22 (24)	293,927	990,900	
360	**Stanford University (Stanford Law School)** Crown Quadrangle, Stanford, CA 94305-8610, 650-723-4985, Fax: 650-723-0838, law.admissions@forsythe.stanford.edu, law.admissions@forsythe.stanford.edu/	$50	Feb 1		$26,158	$26,158	86	27	✓	✓	545	25	45	32		52	484,858	1,786	
362	**State University at Buffalo (Law School)** O'Brian Hall, Buffalo, NY 14260, 716-645-2907, Fax: 716-645-5940, coxublaw@buffalo.edu	$50	March 15	March 1	$8,450	$14,000	87	35	✓	✓	712	25	48	18	2	56 (102)	301,692	1,983,759	
364	**Stetson University (College of Law)** 1401 61st Street South, St. Petersburg, FL 33707, 727-562-7802, Fax: 727-343-0136, lawadmit@hermes.law.stetson.edu	$50	March 1	March 1	$20,350	$20,350	88	48	✓	✓	645 (12)	23	55	19	4	42 (40)	356,875	769,000	
366	**Suffolk University (Law School)** 120 Tremont Street, Boston, MA 02108-4977, 617-573-8144, Fax: 617-573-1367	$50	March 1	March 3	$21,750 ($16,310)	$21,750 ($16,310)	84	58	✓	✓	997 (711)	26	50	10	8	60 (114)	318,000	801,693	

Institution	Profile Page	Fee	Deadline	Deadline Financial Aid	Tuition In State Full Time (Part Time)	Tuition Out of State Full Time (Part Time)	Fall	Winter	Spring	Summer	Day	Evening	Credits for JD	Required Credits for Courses	Transferable Summer Courses	Joint Degree	Graduate Law Degree	Enrolled Full Time (Part Time)	Average Age First Year	% Women	% Minority	Attrition Rate %	Faculty Full Time (Part Time)	Volumes	Microforms
Syracuse University (College of Law) Office of Admissions and Financial Aid Syracuse, NY 13244-1030 315-443-1962 Fax: 315-443-9568	368	$50	April 1	March 1	$23,140	$23,140	✓				✓		87	40		✓		763 (3)	24	46	23		47 (43)	377,386	
Temple University (James E. Beasley School of Law) 1719 N. Broad Street Philadelphia, PA 19122 215-204-8925 Fax: 215-204-1185 lawadmis@blue.temple.edu	370	$50	March 1	March 1	$9,226 ($7,378)	$15,990 ($12,792)	✓				✓	✓	86	38		✓	✓	789 (319)	26	47	24	4	57 (191)	511,757	671,141
Texas Southern University (Thurgood Marshall School of Law) 3100 Cleburne Avenue Houston, TX 77004 713-313-7114 Fax: 713-313-1049 cgardner@tsulaw.edu	372		April 1	Check	$5,144	$9,024	✓				✓		90	70	✓			632	27	46	80	35	34 (19)	229,464	100,536
Texas Tech University (School of Law) 1802 Hartford Lubbock, TX 79409 806-742-3985 Fax: 806-742-1629 xydaw@ttacs.ttu.edu	374	$50	Feb 1	March	$6,600	$11,666	✓				✓		90	55	✓	✓		597	25	44	14	15	28 (10)	280,153	492,945
Texas Wesleyan University (School of Law) 1515 Commerce Street Fort Worth, TX 76102 817-212-4040 Fax: 817-212-4002 law-admissions@law.txwes.edu	376		open	Check	$7,800 ($5,720)	✓				✓	✓	88	50	✓			262 (190)	32	41	19	15	26 (24)	152,556	441,501
Thomas Jefferson School of Law 2121 San Diego Avenue San Diego, CA 92110 619-297-9700 Fax: 619-294-4713 adm@tjsl.edu	378	$35	open	Feb 14	$19,950 ($12,400)	$19,950 ($12,400)	✓				✓		88	55	✓			382 (202)	26	39	22		29 (20)	221,247	121,154
Thomas M. Cooley Law School 300 South Capitol Avenue Lansing, MI 48901 517-371-5140 Fax: 517-334-5718 admissions@cooley.edu	380		open	check	$16,500 ($13,200)	$16,500 ($13,200)	✓	✓	✓		✓		90	63	✓			323 (1248)	26	39	16	30	60 (129)	361,885	182,620

School	#	App Fee			Tuition		✓	✓	✓				✓	✓		✓							
Touro College (Jacob D. Fuchsberg Law Center) 300 Nassau Road Huntington, NY 11743 631-421-2244 ext. 312 Fax: 631-421-9708 admissions@tourolaw.edu	382	$50	on a roll	June 1	$20,720 ($16,070)	$20,720 ($16,070)	✓	✓				✓	87	55 to 56	✓	✓	384 (300)	29	49	25	5	37 (30)	380,000	
Tulane University (Law School) Weinmann Hall, 6329 Freret Street New Orleans, LA 70118 504-865-5930 Fax: 504-865-6710 admissions@law.tulane.edu	384	$50	May 1	Feb 15	$22,664	$22,664	✓	✓				✓	88	31	✓	✓	965 (5)	24	47	25	5	50 (49)	500,000	
Union University (Albany Law School) 80 New Scotland Avenue Albany, NY 12208 518-445-2326 Fax: 518-445-2369 admissions@mail.als.edu	386	$50	March 15		$19,995 ($14,996)	$19,995 ($14,996)	✓	✓				✓	87	31	✓	✓	646 (42)	26	53	19	10	41 (41)	247,669	1,421,190
University of Akron (School of Law) Corner Wolf Ledges and University Avenue Akron, OH 44325-2901 330-972-7331 Fax: 330-258-2343 lawadmissions@uakron.edu	388	$35	March 1	May 1	$8,400 ($6,572)	$14,176 ($11,084)	✓	✓				✓	88	44	✓	✓	338 (222)	29	49	13	23	27 (37)	261,818	371,921
University of Alabama (School of Law) Box 870382 Tuscaloosa, AL 35487-0382 205-348-5440 Fax: 205-348-3917 admissions@law.ua.edu	390	$25	March 1	March 1	$4,812	$10,156	✓	✓				✓	90	36	✓	✓	544	24	41	12	2	35 (41)	379,165	97,668
University of Arizona (James E. Rogers College of Law) Mountain and Speedway P.O. Box 210176 Tucson, AZ 85721-0176 520-621-3477 Fax: 520-621-9140 admissions@nt.law.arizona.edu	392		March 1	Check	$5,014	$10,712	✓	✓				✓	85	39	✓	✓	465	25	48	24	1	33 (33)	380,000	426,000
University of Arkansas (School of Law) Robert A. Leflar Law Center, Waterman Hall Fayetteville, AR 72701 501-575-3102	394		April 1	April 1	$3,362	$7,779	✓	✓				✓	90	43	✓	✓	372	26	44	10	1	35 (5)	243,962	43,584
University of Arkansas at Little Rock (School of Law) 1201 McAlmont Street Little Rock, AR 72202-5142 501-324-9439 Fax: 501-324-9433	396	$40	May 1	March 1	$4,800 ($2,880)	$10,800 ($6,480)	✓	✓				✓	87	48	✓	✓	247 (155)	28	46	10	1	29 (29)	164,039	528,208
University of Baltimore (School of Law) 1420 North Charles Street Baltimore, MD 21201-5779 410-837-4459 Fax: 410-837-4450 lwadmiss@ubmail.ubalt.edu	398		April 1	Check	$9,027 ($373/hr)	$16,108 ($630/hr)	✓	✓				✓	90	39	✓	✓	602 (302)	28	49	19	2	45 (79)	287,125	561,053

INSTITUTION	Profile Page	Fee	Deadline	Deadline Financial Aid	In State Full Time (Part Time)	Out of State Full Time (Part Time)	Fall	Winter	Spring	Summer	Day	Evening	Credits for JD	Required Credits for Courses	Transferable Summer Courses	Joint Degree	Graduate Law Degree	Enrolled Full Time (Part Time)	Average Age First Year	% Women	% Minority	Attrition Rate %	Faculty Full Time (Part Time)	Volumes	Microforms
University of California (Hastings College of the Law) 200 McAllister Street San Francisco, CA 94102 415-565-4623 Fax: 415-565-4623 admiss@uchastings.edu	400	$40	March 1	March 1	$11,183	$19,953	✓				✓		86	34		✓	✓	1122	25	49	28	5	47 (73)	627,035	1,229,584
University of California at Berkeley (Boalt Hall) 5 Boalt Hall Berkeley, CA 94720 510-642-2274 Fax: 510-643-6222 admissions@law.berkeley.edu	402	$40	Feb 1	March 2	$10,865	$20,669	✓				✓		85	30		✓	✓	845	24	50	31		61 (102)	680,000	660,000
University of California at Davis (School of Law) King Hall - 400 Mrak Hall Drive Davis, CA 95616-5201 530-752-6477 lawadmissions@ucdavis.edu	406	$40	Feb 1	March 2	$10,882	$20,266	✓				✓		88	33		✓	✓	511	25	52	24	6	31 (34)	276,361	617,054
University of California at Los Angeles (School of Law) P.O. Box 951445 Los Angeles, CA 90095-1445 310-825-2080 Fax: 310-825-9450 admissions@law.ucla.edu	404	$40	Jan 15	Check	$11,011	$20,815	✓				✓		87	35	✓	✓	✓	957	24	53	37	5	79 (26)	470,789	319,675
University of Chicago (Law School) 1111 East 60th Street Chicago, IL 60637 773-702-9484 Fax: 773-834-0942 admissions@law.uchicago.edu	408	$60		March 1	$26,406	$26,406	✓				✓		105	40		✓	✓	564	24	41	17	1	54 (60)	640,000	61,756
University of Cincinnati (College of Law) P.O. Box 210040 Cincinnati, OH 45221-0040 513-556-6805 Admissions@law.uc.edu	410	$35	April 1	March 1	$8,104	$15,564	✓				✓		90	35	✓	✓	✓	374	25	52	20	1	26 (58)	385,617	673,095
University of Colorado (School of Law) Campus Box 403 Boulder, CO 80309-0403 303-492-7203	412	$45	Feb 15	March 1	$5,917	$17,863	✓				✓		89	43		✓	✓	491	26	51	17	5	40 (30)	383,000	725,704
University of Connecticut (School of Law) 55 Elizabeth Street Hartford, CT 06105 860-570-5159 Fax: 860-570-5153 admit@law.uconn.edu	414	$30	April 1	April 1	$10,630 ($6,678)	$22,420 ($14,076)	✓				✓	✓	86	36	✓	✓	✓		25	44	18	1	52 (74)	471,556	976,556

University of Dayton (School of Law) 300 College Park Dayton, OH 45469-2760 937-229-3555 Fax: 937-229-4194 lawinfo@udayton.edu	416	$40	May 1	March 1	$19,860	$19,860	✓			87	36	✓	✓	451	26	42	17	6	28 (34)	270,003	640,225
University of Denver (College of Law) 7039 E. 18th Avenue Denver, CO 80220 303-871-6135 Fax: 303-871-6100	418	$45	open	Feb 15	$20,026 ($12,920)	$20,026 ($12,920)	✓			90	44	✓	✓	743 (269)	27	55	9	4	38 (35)	274,284	48,685
University of Detroit Mercy (School of Law) 651 East Jefferson Avenue Detroit, MI 48226 313-596-0264 Fax: 313-596-0280 udmlawao@udmercy.edu	420	$50	April 15	April 1	$17,360 ($12,400)	$17,360 ($12,400)	✓			90	49	✓	✓	220 (144)	27	52	16	10	19 (20)	307,767	94,430
University of Florida (College of Law) 325 Holland Hall P.O. Box 117622 Gainesville, FL 32611-7622 352-392-2087 Fax: 352-392-2087 patrick@law.ufl.edu	422	$20	Feb 1	April 1	$4,836	$16,109	✓			88	34	✓	✓	1145	25	48	26	4	69 (18)	592,000	200,000
University of Georgia (School of Law) Hirsch Hall. 225 Herty Drive Athens, GA 30602-6012 706-542-7060	424	$30	March 1		$4,116	$16,464	✓			88	33	✓	✓	640	24	47	11	5	48 (36)	480,005	490,965
University of Hawaii at Manoa (William S. Richardson School of Law) 2515 Dole Street Honolulu, HI 96822 808-956-7966 Fax: 808-956-3813 lawadm@hawaii.edu	426		Check	Check	$8,520	$14,940	✓			89	42	✓		245	27	52	72	5	19	248,838	875,305
University of Houston (Law Center) Office of Admissions Houston, TX 77204-6391 713-743-1070 Fax: 713-743-2194 admission@www.law.uh.edu	428	$50	Feb 15	April 1	$6,460 ($4,024)	$11,860 ($7,264)	✓			90	35	✓	✓	762 (227)	25	46	20	3	46 (67)	460,569	911,626
University of Idaho (College of Law) P.O. Box 44232 Moscow, ID 83844-2321 208-885-6423 Fax: 208-885-5709 adewitt@uidaho.edu	430	$40	Feb 1	Feb 15	$4,076	$10,076	✓			88	31	✓		295	28	26	4	9	16 (1)	180,892	
University of Illinois (College of Law) 504 East Pennsylvania Avenue Champaign, IL 61820 217-244-6415 Fax: 217-244-1478	432	$40	March 15	March 15	$8,024	$18,884	✓			90	34	✓	✓	617	24	40	28	1	45 (33)	565,660	775,212

Profile Page	Institution	Fee	App Deadline	Fin. Aid Deadline	In State Full Time (Part Time)	Out of State Full Time (Part Time)	Fall	Day	Evening	Summer	Credits for JD	Required Credits for Courses	Transferable Summer Courses	Joint Degree	Graduate Law Degree	Enrolled Full Time (Part Time)	Average Age First Year	% Women	% Minority	Attrition Rate %	Faculty Full Time (Part Time)	Volumes	Microforms
434	University of Iowa (College of Law) 276 Boyd Law Building, Melrose at Byington Street, Iowa City, IA 52242, 319-335-9095 or 319-335-9142, Fax: 319-335-9019, law-admissions@uiowa.edu	$30	March 1	on a	$6,822	$17,384	✓	✓		✓	90	35	✓	✓	✓	664	25	43	19	6	52 (29)	642,872	290,909
436	University of Kansas (School of Law) 205 Green Hall, Lawrence, KS 66045, 785-864-4378, Fax: 785-864-5054, lindeman@law.wpo.ukans.edu	$40	March 15	March 1	$6,937	$14,433	✓	✓		✓	90	43 to 45	✓	✓		543	23	41	10	3	34 (7)	325,000	333,169
438	University of Kentucky (College of Law) 209 Law Building, Lexington, KY 40506-0048, 606-257-7938, dbakert@pop.uky.edu	$25	March 1	April 1	$5,560	$14,930	✓	✓			90	34	✓	✓		402	23	45	6	4	28 (20)	408,276	976,440
440	University of Louisville (Louis D. Brandeis School of Law) University of Louisville Belknap Campus, Wilson W. Wyatt Hall, Louisville, KY 40292, 502-852-6364, Fax: 502-852-0862, charlene.olivia@louisville.edu	$30	March 1	June 1	$5,560 ($4,900)	$14,930 ($13,500)	✓	✓	✓		90	44	✓	✓		278 (105)	24	42	12	5	32 (19)	325,639	403
442	University of Maine (School of Law) 246 Deering Avenue, Portland, ME 04102, 207-780-4341	$25	Feb 15	Feb 1	$9,150 ($325/hr)	$17,340 ($578/hr)	✓	✓			89	40	✓	✓		255 (7)	30	44	5	3	17 (4)	300,000	
444	University of Maryland (School of Law) 515 West Lombard Street, Baltimore, MD 21201, 410-706-3492, Fax: 410-706-4045, admissions@law.umaryland.edu	$50	March 1	March 15	$9,982 ($7,432)	$18,254 ($13,634)	✓				85	35 to 38	✓	✓		617 (266)	26	53	26	68	53 (68)	273,129	442,334
446	University of Memphis (Cecil C. Humphreys School of Law) Campus Box 526513, Memphis, TN 38152-6513, 901-678-2073, Fax: 901-678-5210, uofmlaw@profnet.law.memphis.edu	$15	Feb 15	April 1	$4,114 ($3,252)	$10,292 ($8,076)	✓	✓			90	56	✓	✓		421 (22)	26	44	13	10	21 (35)	267,566	502,848
448	University of Miami (School of Law) P.O. Box 248087, 1311 Miller Drive, Coral Gables, FL 33124-8087, 305-284-2523, admissions@law.miami.edu	$50	March 10	March 1	$22,640 ($16,980)	$22,640 ($16,980)	✓	✓	✓		88	73	✓	✓	✓	988 (176)	26	46	32	5	58 (103)	348,552	775,463

	School	App Fee	Deadline	Deadline	Tuition (res.)	Tuition (nonres.)																		
450	**University of Michigan** (Law School) 625 South State Street Ann Arbor MI 48109-1215 313-764-0537	$70	Feb 15		$18,930	$24,900	✓		✓	✓	83 min.	37			1067	✓	✓	23	43	23	1	74 (49)	845,328	1,142,830
452	**University of Minnesota** (Law School) 229 19th Avenue S., Office of Admissions Minneapolis, MN 55455 612-625-3487 Fax: 612-626-1874	$40	March 1	Feb 1	$9,300	$15,760	✓		✓	✓	88	32			760	✓	✓	25	48	18	4	42	875,000	300,000
454	**University of Mississippi** (School of Law) Lamar Hall Oxford, MS 38677 601-915-6910 Fax: 601-915-1289 bvinson@olemiss.edu	$25	March 1	March 1	$4,081	$8,003	✓	✓	✓	✓	90	54 to 57			475 (4)	✓	✓	24	40	12	9	26 (11)	296,871	846,235
456	**University of Missouri-Columbia** (School of Law) 103 Hulston Hall Columbia, MO 65211 573-882-6042 Fax: 573-882-9625 umclawadmissions@missouri.edu	$40	March 1	March 1	$9,126	$17,664	✓	✓	✓	✓	89	57			534	✓	✓	23	46	13	5	36 (15)	320,000	444,865
458	**University of Missouri-Kansas City** (School of Law) 500 East 52nd Street Kansas City, MO 64110-2499 816-235-1644 Fax: 816-235-5276 klosterman@umkc.edu		open	Check	$9,108 ($355/hr)	$17,645 ($660/hr)	✓	✓	✓	✓	91	52	✓		456 (31)	✓	✓	27	46	7	5	29 (35)	178,058	77,000
460	**University of Montana** (School of Law) Missoula, MT 59812 406-243-2698 lawadmis@selway.umt.edu	$60	March 1	March 1	$6,695	$12,298	✓	✓	✓	✓	90	59			234	✓		27	41	7	1	19 (16)	108,599	57,584
462	**University of Nebraska** (College of Law) P.O. Box 830902 Lincoln, NE 68583-0902 402-472-2161 Fax: 402-472-5185 lawadm@unlinfo.unl.edu	$25	March 1	March 1	$4,086	$10,485	✓	✓	✓	✓	96	45	✓		378 (1)	✓	✓	26	41	8	10	28 (24)	358,016	860,864
464	**University of New Mexico** (School of Law) 1117 Stanford Drive N.E. Albuquerque, NM 87131-1431 505-277-5072 Fax: 505-277-9958		Feb 15	Check	$4,382	$14,672	✓		✓	✓	86	33			120	✓		25	56	46		32 (27)	300,000	
466	**University of North Carolina at Chapel Hill** (School of Law) Campus Box 3380, 101 Van Hecke-Wettach Hall Chapel Hill, NC 27599-3380 919-962-5109 Fax: 919-843-7939 law_admission@unc.edu		Feb 1	Check	$3,602	$15,702	✓	✓	✓	✓	86	33			683	✓	✓	23	49	21	1	44 (35)	447,320	11,302

Institution	Profile Page	Fee	App. Deadline	Fin. Aid Deadline	Tuition In State Full Time (Part Time)	Tuition Out of State Full Time (Part Time)	Calendar	Day	Evening	Credits for JD	Required Credits for Courses	Transferable Summer Courses	Joint Degree	Graduate Law Degree	Enrolled Full Time (Part Time)	Avg Age First Year	% Women	% Minority	Attrition Rate %	Faculty Full Time (Part Time)	Volumes	Microforms
University of North Dakota (School of Law) Box 9003, Grand Forks, ND 58202; 701-777-2104; Fax: 701-777-2217; linda.kohoutek@thor.law.und.nodak.edu	468		April 1	Check	$4,376	$9,220	Fall	✓		90	34	✓	✓		188	26	39	5	6	14 (9)	251,320	129,554
University of Notre Dame (Notre Dame Law School) P.O. Box 959, Notre Dame, IN 46556-0959; 219-631-6626; Fax: 219-631-3980; law.bulletin.1@nd.edu	470	$55	March 1	March 1	$22,630	$22,630	Fall	✓		90	52	✓	✓	✓	550	23	40	18	1	27 (33)	501,071	1,340,615
University of Oklahoma (College of Law) 300 Timberdell Road, Norman, OK 73019; 405-325-4726; 405-325-0502; kmadden@ou.edu	472	$50	March 15	March 1	$4,472	$13,000	Fall	✓		90	42	✓	✓	✓	582	24	43	15	4	33 (20)	302,738	80,603
University of Oregon (School of Law, William W. Knight Law Center) 1515 Agate Street, Eugene, OR 97403-1221; 541-346-1553; Fax: 541-346-3984; bmcolure@law.uoregon.edu	474		April 1	Check	$10,898	$14,894	Fall	✓		85	37	✓	✓		535	25	48	16	2	32 (11)	177,409	169,187
University of Pennsylvania (Law School) 3400 Chestnut Street, Philadelphia, PA 19104-6204; 215-898-7400; admissions@oyez.law.upenn.edu	476	$65	March 1	March 1	$25,380	$25,380	Fall	✓		89	28		✓	✓	754	24	46	22	1	42 (54)	685,675	868,948
University of Pittsburgh (School of Law) 3900 Forbes Avenue, Pittsburgh, PA 15260; 412-648-1412; 412-648-2647; admissions@law.pitt.edu	478	$50	March 1	March 1	$12,388	$19,362	Fall	✓	92	88	34		✓	✓	685	24	44	10	3	42 (38)	375,000	105,202
University of Puerto Rico (School of Law) P.O. Box 23349, UPR Station, Rio Piedras, PR 00931; 787-764-1655; Fax: 787-764-2675	480		Feb 15	April 1	$2,326 ($1,425)	$2,326	Summer	✓		46			✓	(215)	325 (23)	56		5	(29)	35 / 346,360	641,402	
University of Richmond (The T.C. Williams School of Law) University of Richmond, VA 23173; 804-289-8189; admissions@uofrlaw.richmond.edu	482	$35	Jan 15	Feb 25	$19,940 ($995/hr)	$19,940 ($995/hr)	Fall, Summer	✓		86	38	✓	✓		474 (2)	25	46	19	1	26 (40)	279,403	115,790

#	Fee	Deadline 1	Deadline 2	Tuition 1	Tuition 2																			School
484	$40	Feb 1	March 2	$22,130 ($15,710)	$22,130 ($15,710)	✓				48	85	✓	✓	751 (367)	✓	✓	✓	24	44	23	7	61 (56)	453,301	1,415,092	**University of San Diego (School of Law)** 5998 Alcala Park San Diego, CA 92110 619-260-4528 Fax: 619-260-2218 jdinfo@acusd.edu
486	$40	April 1	rolling	$22,194 ($792/hr)	$22,194 ($792/hr)	✓				48	86	✓	✓	499 (115)	✓	✓	✓	25	56	28	9	24 (59)	295,317	161,252	**University of San Francisco (School of Law)** 2130 Fulton Street San Francisco, CA 94117-1080 415-422-6586 Fax: 415-422-6433
488	$25	Feb 15	April 15	$7,548	$15,616	✓				46	90	✓	✓	708	✓	✓		23	44	11	3	43 (26)	330,000	2,718	**University of South Carolina (School of Law)** Main and Greene Streets Columbia, SC 29208 803-777-7751 Fax: 803-777-7751 usclaw@law.law.sc.edu
490	$15	March 1	Check	$3,210	$9,305	✓				43	90	✓	✓	184	✓	✓	✓	27	47	3	7	15 (2)	188,061	11,824	**University of South Dakota (School of Law)** 414 East Clark Street Vermillion, SD 57069-2390 605-677-5443 Fax: 605-677-5417 lawreg@usd.edu
492	$60	Feb 1	Feb 15	$26,092	$26,092	✓				31	88	✓		608	✓	✓	✓	24	48	41	1	46 (40)	366,333	493,817	**University of Southern California (Law School)** Los Angeles, CA 90089-0071 213-740-7331
494	$15	Feb 1	Feb 14	$4,626	$12,932	✓				46	89	✓	✓	484	✓	✓	✓	25	45	13	4	30 (27)	469,108	1,145,172	**University of Tennessee (College of Law)** 1505 W. Cumberland Avenue Knoxville, TN 37996-1810 865-974-4131 Fax: 865-974-1572 lawadmit@libra.law.utk.edu
496	$65	Feb 1	March 31	$4,800	$12,600	✓				39	86	✓	✓	1387	✓	✓	✓	25	47	17		75 (73)	936,000	879,118	**University of Texas at Austin (School of Law)** 727 East Dean Keeton Street Austin, TX 78705 512-232-1200 Fax: 512-471-6988
498	$35	April 1	May 1	$7,000 ($250/hr)	$14,000 ($500/hr)	✓				66	90	✓	✓	168	✓	✓	✓	29	62	79	15	16 (18)	181,000	90	**University of the District of Columbia (David A. Clarke School of Law)** 4200 Connecticut Avenue, N.W. Washington, DC 20008 Null Fax: 202-274-5583 vcanty@law.udc.edu
500	$40	May 15	open	$21,656 ($14,396)	$21,656 ($14,396)	✓				58	88	✓	✓	693 (357)	✓	✓	✓	24	49	24	11	44 (59)	436,384	1,189,824	**University of the Pacific (McGeorge School of Law)** 3200 Fifth Avenue Sacramento, CA 95817 916-739-7105 Fax: 916-739-7134 admissionsmcgeorge@uop.edu
502	$30	June 1	April 1	$6,802 ($5,668)	$14,132 ($11,777)	✓				42	89	✓	✓	374 (147)	✓	✓	✓	26	46	8	8	31 (25)	320,727	117,964	**University of Toledo (College of Law)** 2801 West Bancroft Street Toledo, OH 43606-3390 419-530-4131 Fax: 419-530-4345 law.utoledo.edu

INSTITUTION	Profile Page	Fee	Deadline	Financial Aid Deadline	In State Full Time (Part Time)	Out of State Full Time (Part Time)	Fall	Winter	Spring	Summer	Day	Evening	Credits for JD	Required Credits for Courses	Transferable Summer Courses	Joint Degree	Graduate Law Degree	Enrolled Full Time (Part Time)	Average Age First Year	% Women	% Minority	Attrition Rate %	Faculty Full Time (Part Time)	Volumes	Microforms
University of Tulsa (College of Law) 3120 East Fourth Place Tulsa, OK 74104-2499 918-631-2709 Fax: 918-631-3630	504	$30	open	open	$17,000 ($11,400)	$17,000 ($11,400)	✓		✓		✓	✓	88	42	✓	✓	✓	442 (119)	27	35	13	8	37 (34)	280,000	688,772
University of Utah (College of Law) 332 South 1400 East Front Salt Lake City, UT 84112 801-581-7479 Fax: 801-581-6897 gormleyl@law.utah.edu	506	$40	Feb 1	Feb 15	$5,127	$11,439	✓				✓		88	40	✓	✓	✓	369	26	43	14	3	28 (32)	300,000	98,000
University of Virginia (School of Law) 580 Massie Road Charlottesville, VA 22903-1789 804-924-7351 Fax: 804-982-2128 lawadmit@virginia.edu	508	$65	Jan 15	Feb 15	$14,201	$20,600	✓				✓		86	27	✓	✓	✓	1090	24	43	15	2	64 (63)	794,529	1,150,000
University of Washington (School of Law) 1100 Northeast Campus Parkway Seattle, WA 98105-6617 206-543-4078	510	$50	Jan 15	Feb 28	$5,500	$13,500	✓				✓		135		✓	✓	✓	520	25	52	29	2	43	506,334	152,661
University of Wisconsin-Madison (Law School) 975 Bascom Mall Madison, WI 53706 608-262-5914 Fax: 608-262-5485 Admissions@law.wisc.educ	512		Feb 1	Check	$3,314 ($285/hr)	$14,866 ($767/hr)	✓				✓	✓	90	30 to 31	✓	✓	✓	807 (52)	25	47	23	1	47	475,000	695,000
University of Wyoming (College of Law) P.O. Box 3035 Laramie, WY 82071 307-766-6416 lawadmis@uwyo.edu	514	$35	March 15	Feb 1	$4,424	$9,692	✓				✓		88	52	✓	✓	✓	235	27	43	4	8	14	134,028	453,081
Valparaiso University (School of Law) Wesemann Hall Valparaiso, IN 46383-6493 219-465-7829 Fax: 219-465-7808 heike.spahn@valpo.edu	516	$30	April 15	March	$17,950 ($695)	$17,950 ($695)	✓				✓	✓	90	46	✓	✓	✓	383 (54)	26	47	14	10	27 (37)	283,803	774,186
Vanderbilt University (School of Law) Nashville, TN 37240 615-322-6452	518	$50	March 1	March 1	$24,350	$24,350	✓				✓		88	34		✓		559	24	45	21	2	36 (40)	207,887	417,126

#	School	App Fee	App Deadline	FA/Other Deadline	Tuition (Resident)	Tuition (Nonresident)	✓	A	B	✓	Applicants	(col)	Age	col	col	col (top/bot)	col (top/bot)	Volumes	Titles
520	Vermont Law School			Check	$20,958		✓	84	44	✓	486		26	48	8	36 / 8	(36)	215,000	95,000
522	Villanova University (School of Law)	$75	Feb 1	open	$20,000		✓	87	44	✓	730		24	48	15	44 / 1	(75)	450,304	138,811
524	Wake Forest University (School of Law)	$60	March 1	May 1	$21,250	$21,250	✓	89	41	✓	453	(12)	24	41	9	2	39 / (28)	341,653	800,000
526	Washburn University (School of Law)	$30	March 15	April 1	$7,530 ($251/hr)	$11,340 ($378/hr)	✓	90	37	✓	411		27	42	15	7	29 / (36)	321,470	141,744
528	Washington and Lee University (School of Law)	$40	Feb 1	Feb 15	$17,950	$17,950	✓	85	37	✓	367		25	42	9	1	33 / (18)	372,675	808,493
530	Washington University in St. Louis (School of Law)	$60	March 1	March 1	$24,240	$24,240	✓	85	7	✓	635		24	43	20	7	47 / (65)	563,292	847,000
532	Wayne State University (Law School)	$20	March 15	April 30	$7,560 ($4,032)	$15,690 ($8,368)	✓	86	36	✓	526	(228)	26	48	17	11	35 / (33)	569,165	1,088,291
534	West Virginia University (College of Law)		March 1		$5,100 ($235/hr)	$12,200 ($600/hr)	✓	93	52	✓	430	(20)	26	46	7		26 / (11)	246,532	355,617
536	Western New England College (School of Law)	$45	open	April 1	$19,064 ($14,297)	$19,064 ($14,297)	✓	88	46-47	✓	317	(253)	27	51	10	14	27 / (38)	360,000	169,000

520 Vermont Law School
P.O. Box 96, Chelsea Street
South Royalton, VT 05068-0096
802-763-8303
Fax: 802-763-7071
admiss@vermontlaw.edu

522 Villanova University (School of Law)
Garey Hall
Villanova, PA 19085
610-519-7010

524 Wake Forest University (School of Law)
P.O. Box 7206, Reynolda Station
Winston-Salem, NC 27109
910-758-5437

526 Washburn University (School of Law)
1700 College
Topeka, KS 66621
785-231-1185
Fax: 785-232-8087
admissions@washburnlaw.edu

528 Washington and Lee University (School of Law)
Lewis Hall
Lexington, VA 24450
540-463-8504
Fax: 540-463-8586
lawadm@wlu.edu

530 Washington University in St. Louis (School of Law)
Box 1120, One Brookings Drive
St. Louis, MO 63130
314-935-4525
Fax: 314-935-6959
admiss@walaw.wash.edu

532 Wayne State University (Law School)
468 W. Ferry Mall
Detroit, MI 48202
313-577-3937
Fax: 313-577-6000
linda.sims@wayne.edu

534 West Virginia University (College of Law)
P.O. Box 6130
Morgantown, WV 26506
304-293-5304
Fax: 304-293-6891
lawaply@wvu.edu

536 Western New England College (School of Law)
1215 Wilbraham Road
Springfield, MA 01119
413-782-1406
Fax: 413-796-2067
lawadmis@wnec.edu

INSTITUTION	Profile Page	Fee	Deadline	Deadline Financial Aid	Tuition In State Full Time (Part Time)	Tuition Out of State Full Time (Part Time)	Fall	Winter	Spring	Summer	Day	Evening	Credits for JD	Required Credits for Courses	Transferable Summer Courses	Joint Degree	Graduate Law Degree	Enrolled Full Time (Part Time)	Average Age First Year	% Women	% Minority	Attrition Rate %	Faculty Full Time (Part Time)	Volumes	Microforms
Western State University (College of Law) 1111 North State College Blvd, Fullerton, CA 92831, 714-738-1000, x2909, Fax: 714-526-1062, joel@wsulaw.edu	538	$50	open	open	$26,570 ($17,670)	✓	✓	✓		✓	✓	✓	88 units	58	✓			240 (342)	43	30			19 (21)	370,000	158,966
Whittier College (School of Law) 3333 Harbor Blvd, Costa Mesa, CA 92626, 714-444-4141, ext. 121, Fax: 714-444-0250, info@whittier.edu	540	$60	March 15	Check	$21,934 ($13,174)	$21,934 ($13,174)	✓				✓	✓	87	40	✓			383 (277)	26	50	37	5	28 (32)	297,614	122,633
Widener University (School of Law) 4601 Concord Pike, P.O. Box 7474 and 3800 Vartan Way, Harris Wilmington, DE 19803, 302-477-2162 (DE); 717-541-3903 (HBG), Fax: 302-477-2224 (DE); 717-541-3999 (HBG), law.admissions@law.widener.edu	542	$60	May 15		$19,500 ($14,620)	$19,500 ($14,620)	✓				✓	✓	87	54	✓	✓	✓	870 (578)	25	47	12	8	75 (91)	314,170	296,560
Willamette University (College of Law) 245 Winter Street S.E., Salem, OR 97301, 503-370-6282, Fax: 503-370-6375, law-admission@willamette.edu	544	$50	April 1	Feb 1	$18,300	$18,300	✓				✓		88	39	✓	✓	✓	407 (7)	26	45	10	12	21 (6)	285,351	850,015
William Mitchell College of Law 875 Summit Avenue, St. Paul, MN 55105-3076, 651-290-6476, Fax: 651-290-6414, admissions@wmitchell.edu	546	$45	June 30	March 16	$18,090 ($13,140)	$18,090 ($13,140)	✓				✓	✓	86	46	✓			501 (518)	29	52	11	2	36 (115)	296,813	132,535
Yale University (Yale Law School) P.O. Box 208329, New Haven, CT 06520-8239, 203-432-4995, admissions.law@yale.edu	548	$65	Feb 15	March 15	$26,950		✓				✓		82	19		✓	576 ✓		25	45	30	58	(35)	798,200	2,583
Yeshiva University (Benjamin N. Cardozo School of Law) 55 Fifth Avenue, New York, NY 10003, 212-790-0274, Fax: 212-790-0482, lawinfo@ymail.yu.edu	550	$60	April 1	April 15	$23,936	$23,936	✓		✓	✓	✓		84	38	✓	✓	✓	915	23	48	21	1	46 (92)	440,400	1,095,152

Regional Maps Locating ABA-Approved Law Schools

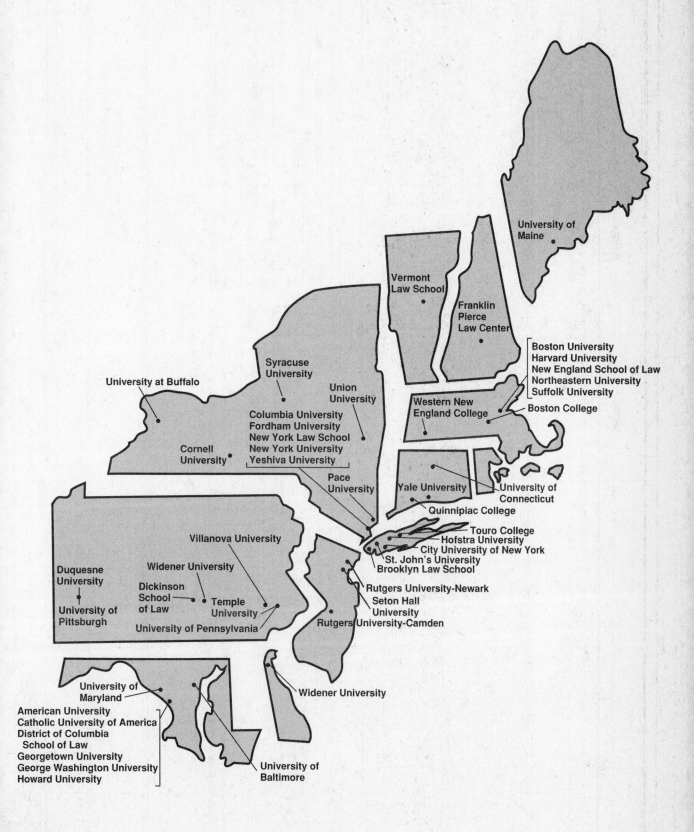

University of Maine

Vermont Law School

Franklin Pierce Law Center

Boston University
Harvard University
New England School of Law
Northeastern University
Suffolk University

Boston College

Syracuse University

Union University

Western New England College

University at Buffalo

Columbia University
Fordham University
New York Law School
New York University
Yeshiva University

Cornell University

Pace University

Yale University

University of Connecticut

Quinnipiac College

Touro College
Hofstra University
City University of New York
St. John's University
Brooklyn Law School

Villanova University

Widener University

Duquesne University

Dickinson School of Law

Temple University

University of Pittsburgh

University of Pennsylvania

Rutgers University-Newark
Seton Hall University
Rutgers University-Camden

Widener University

University of Maryland

American University
Catholic University of America
District of Columbia
   School of Law
Georgetown University
George Washington University
Howard University

University of Baltimore

George Mason University
University of Virginia
Washington and Lee University
College of William & Mary
Regent University
University of Richmond
North Carolina Central University
University of North Carolina at Chapel Hill
Campbell University
Wake Forest University
West Virginia University
Duke University
University of South Carolina
University of Georgia
Georgia State University
Florida Coastal
University of Florida
Nova University
St. Thomas University
University of Miami
Stetson University
Emory University
Mercer University
Florida State University
Northern Kentucky University
University of Kentucky
University of Louisville
University of Tennessee
Vanderbilt University
Memphis State University
Samford University
University of Alabama
University of Mississippi
Mississippi College
Loyola University-New Orleans
Tulane University
University of Arkansas-Fayetteville
University of Arkansas-Little Rock
Southern University
Louisiana State University
Texas Southern University
University of Tulsa
Oklahoma City University
University of Oklahoma
Southern Methodist University
University of Texas at Austin
University of Houston
Texas Tech University
Texas Wesleyan University
Baylor University
St. Mary's University
South Texas College of Law
Catholic University of Puerto Rico
Inter-American University of Puerto Rico
University of Puerto Rico

Profiles of ABA-Approved Law Schools

The school profiles included in Barron's *Guide to Law Schools* comprise the listing of 182 law schools that are fully or provisionally approved by the American Bar Association and grant the J.D. degree. (One ABA-approved law school, the Judge Advocate General's School, located in Charlottesville, Virginia, and associated with the U.S. Army, is not included in our listings because it offers post-J.D. programs only.) The schools are arranged in alphabetical order by the name of the institution to which they are attached or, for independent law schools, by the name of the school. Also included for your convenience is a listing of the law schools by state.

So that you may use the profiles to best advantage, an explanation of the entries follows.

THE HEADING

The first-page heading of each profile presents the official name of the parent college or university (if any) and of the law school and the law school mailing address. The page two heading of each entry contains phone and fax numbers, followed by e-mail and WWW addresses; names and phone numbers of admissions and financial aid contacts; and a map showing the location within the respective state of each school.

THE CAPSULE

The capsule of each profile provides basic information about the law school. Wherever *n/av* is used in the capsule, it means the information was not available. Wherever *none* or *n/app* is used in the capsule, it means the category was not applicable to the law school.

Application filing dates and fees lead off the capsule.

Accrediting agencies, and **degrees granted** fill out this section of the capsule.

Accreditation Every school profiled is fully or provisionally approved by the American Bar Association. This means that the law school has met the educational standards set by the ABA regarding faculty, curricula, facilities, and other matters to qualify its graduates for admission to the Bar. In addition, membership in the Association of American Law Schools (AALS) is also indicated. Schools are not eligible for AALS membership until they have graduated three classes and have been in operation for five years. AALS membership is complementary to, but *not* competitive with, ABA approval.

Degrees Granted Law schools today offer the J.D. (Juris Doctor) degree, rather than the traditional LL.B. This recognizes the fact that virtually all law schools now require a B.A. for admission and that the curriculum of the law school represents graduate-level work. Law schools offering post-law school graduate work leading to such degrees as the LL.M. (Master of Laws), M.C.L. (Master of Comparative Law), and J.S.D. (Doctor of the Science of Law) degrees are noted.

These data are followed by **enrollment** figures for men, women, and minorities, and out-of-state students in the first-year class. Actual figures and percentages are both given.

This section also includes the number of applicants, accepted candidates, and enrolled first-year students.

The current **class profile** includes LSAT scoring and passing-the-bar information.

Finally, **tuition and fees** are graphically displayed for both in- and out-of-state applicants, showing comparisons with average nationwide figures. It is important to remember that tuition costs generally change at least yearly, and that changes can be substantial. Students are therefore urged to contact individual law schools for the most current tuition figures.

Also shown in this section is the percentage of current law students receiving **financial aid.**

Admissions The **admissions** section leads off the law school's descriptive passages, where some of the capsule information is reinforced.

The subsection *Requirements* includes whether a bachelor's degree is an absolute necessity and lists the factors considered in the admissions decision, such as LSAT percentile, GPA, and any nonacademic requirements. Virtually all of the law schools require the LSAT and a bachelor's degree, although some schools admit students without a bachelor's degree in exceptional cases. Very few schools require specific undergraduate courses or degrees or an admissions interview. Although not actual requirements, there are some qualities that schools seek in their applicants, such as preferred LSAT percentiles and GPAs. Where available, these preferred qualities also are given.

The subsection *Procedure* lists the application deadlines for various sessions, when the LSAT should be taken, the application fee, and when students are notified of the admissions decision. If a school makes admissions decisions on a rolling basis, it decides on each application as soon as possible after the file is complete and does not specify a notification deadline. As a general rule, it is best to submit applications as early as possible. Many schools require a tuition deposit to hold a place in the class. In some cases the deposit is refundable; in some, it is partially refundable; and in some, it is nonrefundable. Most schools participate in the Law School Data Assembly Service (LSDAS); if the school uses this application service, it is noted in this section.

The subsection *Special* describes admissions programs and includes information on special recruiting procedures and considerations for minority and disadvantaged students; whether the school's requirements for out-of-state students differ and whether transfer students are admitted. Although requirements for transfer with advanced standing differ from school to school, in general the applicant must have been in good standing at the school he or she is transferring from and must have completed a minimum of one year of law school study. Preadmissions courses offered by the school are also described.

Costs As noted in the explanation for the capsule, costs change from year to year; therefore, students are urged to contact the individual law schools for the most current figures. This section gives costs for tuition, additional fees, room and board, and books and supplies.

Financial Aid This section describes the availability of financial aid. It includes the percentage of students who receive aid; the types and sources of aid available, such as scholarships, grants, loans, part-time jobs, and assistantships; and the criteria for aid awards. The size of the average scholarship or grant is noted. Information on aid application deadlines and notification dates is also provided.

THE GENERAL DESCRIPTION

About the Law School This paragraph indicates, in general, whether the law school is part of a university or college, when it was founded, whether it is public or private, and its religious affiliation, if any. The school's educational philosophy, primary goals, and major characteristics are noted. Because law school programs often make use of law-related institutions, such as courts, jails, and public defenders' offices, the school's proximity to such institutions is noted. There is also information on the law school's facilities: the campus (its size, the type of area in which it is located, and its proximity to a large city); whether housing is available on campus; and whether the housing office helps students find off-campus accommodations. This section also describes the percentage of the campus accessible to physically disabled persons.

Calendar This section describes whether courses are offered for full-time and/or part-time students and whether they are offered during the day and/or evening. It also describes the minimum and maximum lengths of time allowed for completion of the program, when new students may enter the program, the availability of summer sessions, and the availability of transferable summer credits.

Programs Entries list the degrees granted, including graduate law degrees and joint degrees.

The subsection *Required* describes the number of credits needed for the J.D. and the minimum grade point average that must be maintained. The specific mandatory course requirements are listed, as well as any additional requirements for graduation. At some law schools required courses make up a major portion of the curriculum, whereas at others there are fewer required courses, allowing more room for electives. The majority of schools have a fairly even mix of mandatory and elective courses, although in most cases first-year courses are prescribed. Many law schools permit students to take a limited number of relevant graduate courses offered by other schools or departments of the institution.

Special programs are described in the subsection *Electives*. Clinical training programs offer a wide range of activities allied with, but separate from, traditional classroom studies. They cover such areas as working with legal aid societies and antipoverty groups; doing research for consumer-protection agencies; working with public defender programs or as interns in federal, district, or county attorneys' offices; and engaging in a multitude of legal or quasilegal activities. Some law schools offer a variety of programs and special activities, which allow all students to participate in some way. Other law schools have narrow or limited programs, or limit the number of students who may participate. Some schools have special or unusual seminars; some have programs involving study abroad; and some allow students to pursue independent study, usually under the supervision of a member of the law school faculty. Some schools also have tutorial or remedial programs. The most widely taken electives are listed here.

The subsection *Graduation Requirements* describes the minimum grade point average a student must maintain, whether or not there is an upper-division writing requirement, and what other requirements must be fulfilled.

Organizations Virtually all law schools have student-edited law reviews; some law schools publish more than one law review and some publish other types of legal journals and newspapers as well. Students selected to work on these publications gain valuable research, writing, and editing experience. Most schools also have moot court programs and engage in intramural and interschool competitions. Other campus activities and organizations, such as special interest or academic clubs and sororities and fraternities, are also listed in this section.

Library This section lists the resources of the law library, such as the total number of hardcopy volumes, the number of microform volume equivalents, the number of serial publications, and special collections or depositories. Computerized legal-research databases, such as LEXIS and WESTLAW, are noted, as well as the ratio of library volumes to faculty and to students, and the ratio of seats in the library to students. Recent improvements to the library are also described.

Faculty The number of full-time and part-time faculty members is given here. The percentage of full-time faculty members with a graduate law degree is noted. The ratio of full-time students to full-time faculty in an average class and in a clinic are noted here. In addition to regular classroom lectures, those law schools that have a regular program of inviting legal scholars, attorneys, and other notable speakers to campus to lecture on law-related topics are indicated. If the school has a chapter of the Order of the Coif, a national law school honor society, this is also noted here; the number of faculty who are members as well as the number of recent graduates who became members are sometimes given. Only students who are in the top 10 percent of their class are eligible for membership.

Students This paragraph gives an idea of the mix of backgrounds at a school. It includes, where available, data on the geographic distribution of the student body and on how many students enter directly from undergraduate school, have a graduate degree, or have full-time work experience. The average age of entering students is given, as is the age range. The attrition rate and reasons for discontinuing law study are noted.

The **Placement** sidebar is the final section offered for each school entry. Displayed here is information concerning the number of J.D.s awarded the previous academic year, followed by a listing of the placement services and special features available to students. Statistics relating to job interviews and job placement (and average starting salaries) follow. Finally, a breakdown of placement history is presented.

INDEX BY STATE OF ABA-APPROVED LAW SCHOOLS

ALABAMA
Samford University
University of Alabama

ARIZONA
Arizona State University
University of Arizona

ARKANSAS
University of Arkansas
University of Arkansas at Little Rock

CALIFORNIA
California Western School of Law
Chapman University
Golden Gate University
Loyola Marymount University
Pepperdine University
Santa Clara University
Southwestern University
Stanford University
Thomas Jefferson School of Law
University of California
University of California at Berkeley
University of California at Davis
University of California at Los Angeles
University of San Diego
University of San Francisco
University of Southern California
University of the Pacific
Western State University
Whittier College

COLORADO
University of Colorado
University of Denver

CONNECTICUT
Quinnipiac College
University of Connecticut
Yale University

DELAWARE
Widener University

DISTRICT OF COLUMBIA
American University
Catholic University of America
George Washington University
Georgetown University
Howard University
University of the District of Columbia School of
  Law

FLORIDA
Florida Coastal School of Law
Florida State University
Nova Southeastern University
St. Thomas University
Stetson University
University of Florida
University of Miami

GEORGIA
Emory University
Georgia State University
Mercer University
University of Georgia

HAWAII
University of Hawaii at Manoa

IDAHO
University of Idaho

ILLINOIS
De Paul University
Illinois Institute of Technology, Chicago
John Marshall Law School
Loyola University Chicago
Northern Illinois University
Northwestern University
Southern Illinois University
University of Chicago
University of Illinois

INDIANA
Indiana University at Bloomington
Indiana University-Purdue University
University of Notre Dame
Valparaiso University

IOWA
Drake University
University of Iowa

KANSAS
University of Kansas
Washburn University

KENTUCKY
Northern Kentucky University
University of Kentucky
University of Louisville

LOUISIANA
Louisiana State University
Loyola University New Orleans
Southern University and A & M College
Tulane University

MAINE
University of Maine

MARYLAND
University of Baltimore
University of Maryland

MASSACHUSETTS
Boston College
Boston University
Harvard University
New England School of Law
Northeastern University
Suffolk University
Western New England College

MICHIGAN
Michigan State University
Thomas M. Cooley Law School
University of Detroit Mercy
University of Michigan
Wayne State University

MINNESOTA
Hamline University
University of Minnesota
William Mitchell College of Law

MISSISSIPPI
Mississippi College
University of Mississippi

MISSOURI
Saint Louis University
University of Missouri-Columbia
University of Missouri-Kansas City
Washington University in St. Louis

MONTANA
University of Montana

NEBRASKA
Creighton University
University of Nebraska

NEW HAMPSHIRE
Franklin Pierce Law Center

NEW JERSEY
Rutgers University/Camden
Rutgers University/Newark
Seton Hall University

NEW MEXICO
University of New Mexico

NEW YORK
Brooklyn Law School
City University of New York at Queens College
Columbia University
Cornell University
Fordham University
Hofstra University
New York Law School
New York University
Pace University
Saint John's University
State University at Buffalo
Syracuse University
Touro College
Union University, Albany Law School
Yeshiva University

NORTH CAROLINA
Campbell University
Duke University
North Carolina Central University
University of North Carolina at Chapel Hill
Wake Forest University

NORTH DAKOTA
University of North Dakota

OHIO
Capital University
Case Western Reserve University
Cleveland State University
Ohio Northern University
Ohio State University
University of Akron
University of Cincinnati
University of Dayton
University of Toledo

OKLAHOMA
Oklahoma City University
University of Oklahoma
University of Tulsa

OREGON
Lewis and Clark College
University of Oregon
Willamette University

PENNSYLVANIA
Duquesne University
Pennsylvania State University
Temple University
University of Pennsylvania
University of Pittsburgh
Villanova University

PUERTO RICO
Catholic University of Puerto Rico
Inter-American University of Puerto Rico
University of Puerto Rico

RHODE ISLAND
Roger Williams University

SOUTH CAROLINA
University of South Carolina

SOUTH DAKOTA
University of South Dakota

TENNESSEE
University of Memphis
University of Tennessee
Vanderbilt University

TEXAS
Baylor University
Saint Mary's University
South Texas College of Law
Southern Methodist University
Texas Southern University
Texas Tech University
Texas Wesleyan University
University of Houston
University of Texas at Austin

UTAH
Brigham Young University
University of Utah

VERMONT
Vermont Law School

VIRGINIA
College of William and Mary
George Mason University
Regent University
University of Richmond
University of Virginia
Washington and Lee University

WASHINGTON
Gonzaga University
Seattle University
University of Washington

WEST VIRGINIA
West Virginia University

WISCONSIN
Marquette University
University of Wisconsin-Madison

WYOMING
University of Wyoming

Washington College of Law

4801 Massachusetts Avenue, N.W.
Washington, DC 20016-8186

Application Filing	Accreditation
Fall: March 1	ABA, AALS
Spring: n/app	**Degrees Granted**
Fee: n/av	J.D., LL.M.

Enrollment 1998–1999		First-Year Class	
Men:	516 39%	Applied:	5093
Women:	805 59%	Accepted:	2117
Minorities:	317 24%	Enrolled:	523
Out-of-State:	1321 100%		

1998–99 Class Profile

LSAT Percentile: 70%

LSAT Median Score: 156

Percentage passing bar on first try: n/av

Tuition and Fees:

Resident
$24,090

Average (public)
$8,772

Average (private)
$19,562

Nonresident
$24,090

Average (public)
$14,629

Average (private)
$19,562

0 5 10 15 20 25 30

Percentage receiving financial aid: 79%

ADMISSIONS

In the fall 1999 first-year class, 5093 applied, 2117 were accepted, and 523 enrolled. The median LSAT percentile of the most recent first-year class was 70; the median GPA was 3.4 on a scale of 4.0.

Requirements

Applicants must have a bachelor's degree from an accredited institution and take the LSAT. The most important admission factors include GPA, LSAT results, and college attended. No specific undergraduate courses are required. Required undergraduate courses are English, history, and philosophy. Candidates are not interviewed.

Procedure

The application deadline for fall entry is March 1. Applicants should submit an application form, LSAT results, and transcripts, and 2 letters of recommendation and a personal statement are suggested. Check with the school for the current fee. Notification of the admissions decision is approximately 6 weeks after the application is complete. The latest acceptable LSAT test date for fall entry is February. The law school uses the LSDAS.

Special

The law school recruits minority and disadvantaged students through the combined efforts of the Director of Admissions, the Director of Minority Affairs, and the Minority Recruiter, who put together a recruiting plan that focuses on historically black colleges and universities. The Admissions Office then offers programs to encourage minority applications and matriculants. Transfer students must have one year of credit, have attended an ABA-approved law school, and must be in the top 15% of the present law school class.

Costs

Tuition and fees for the 1999-2000 academic year are $24,090 for all full-time students. Tuition for part-time students is $16,932 per year. Books and supplies run $830.

Financial Aid

In a recent year, about 79% of current law students received some form of aid. Awards are based on need. The required financial statement is the FAFSA. Check with the school for current application deadlines. Special funds for minority or disadvantaged students consist of need-based grants. First-year students are notified about their financial aid application approximately 2 weeks after the time of acceptance if the GAPSFAS is filed on time.

About the Law School

American University Washington College of Law was established in 1896 and is a private institution. The campus is in an urban area 3 miles northwest of downtown Washington. The primary mission of the law school is to create a learning atmosphere characterized by cooperation as well as academic rigor, where faculty and students have an opportunity to know each other, and where students know each other as colleagues rather than competitors. Students have access to federal, state, county, city, and local agencies, courts, correctional facilities, law firms, and legal aid organizations in the Washington area. Students also have access to Congress, the Supreme Court, trade associations, and public interest groups resources unique to the nation's capital. Housing for law students is available on campus; the school is located in a residential area of the city where many apartment buildings and rental houses are located. All law school facilities are accessible to the physically disabled.

Calendar

The law school operates on a traditional semester basis. Courses for full-time students are offered both day and evening and must be completed within 3 years. For part-time students, courses are offered both day and evening and must be completed within 4 years. New full- and part-time students are admitted in the fall. There is a 9-week summer session. Transferable summer courses are offered.

Programs

In addition to the J.D., the law school offers the LL.M. Students may take relevant courses in other programs and apply credit toward the J.D.; a maximum of 6 credits may be applied. The following joint degrees may be earned: J.D./M.A. (Juris Doctor/Master of Arts in international affairs), J.D./M.B.A. (Juris Doctor/Master of Business Administration), and J.D./M.S. (Juris Doctor/Master of Science in law, justice, and society).

Phone: 202-274-4101
Fax: 202-274-4107
E-mail: wcladmit@wcl.american.edu
Web: www.wcl.american.edu

Contact

Admissions Office, 202-274-4101 for general inquiries; Financial Aid Office, 202-274-4040 for financial aid information.

DISTRICT OF COLUMBIA

Required

To earn the J.D., candidates must complete 86 total credits, of which 34 are for required courses. They must maintain a minimum GPA of 2.0 in the required courses. The following first-year courses are required of all students: Torts, Contracts, Property I and II, Civil Procedure I and II, Legal Method I and II, Criminal Law, and Constitutional Law. Required upper-level courses consist of Criminal Procedure I and Legal Ethics. The required orientation program for first-year students is 2 days and includes a financial aid entrance interview, registration, dean's and faculty welcome, academic orientation, and school/alumni reception and Student Bar Association social activities.

Electives

The Washington College of Law offers concentrations in corporate law, criminal law, environmental law, family law, international law, juvenile law, litigation, securities law, tax law, and torts and insurance. In addition, clinical experiences offered to students include the Public Interest Clinic for 14 credits, Appellate Advocacy Clinic for 12 credits, and D.C. Litigation Clinic for 7 credits. Internships, available with government agencies and nonprofit entities, are under faculty supervision. The Independent Study Program permits directed research under faculty supervision. The Field Component Program offers field work with the Securities and Exchange Commission and the Commodities Futures Trading Commission. Special lecture series include an extensive series of conferences and speaker series that deal with topics of contemporary interest. In addition, student organizations sponsor lectures and panel discussions on a range of topics. Study abroad consists of summer programs in Chile (study evolving legal structures in Latin America); Paris/Geneva (international business, human rights, and environmental law); a semester exchange: Paris-X Nanterre, France; and the NAFTA County Exchange. Upper-level students counsel other law students in academic subjects and law school adjustment matters in the Peer Counseling Program. The Office of Minority Affairs offers minority programs and advisory services. The most widely taken electives are Evidence, Business Associations, and Administrative Law.

Graduation Requirements

In order to graduate, candidates must have a GPA of 2.0 and have completed the upper-division writing requirement.

Organizations

Students edit the *American University Law Review, Administrative Law Review, American University International Review, American University Journal of Gender and the Law*, and the newspaper *American Jurist*. Intraschool moot court competitions include the Alvina Reckman Myers Competition for first-year students, and the Upper Class Moot Court for second- and third-year students. Annually, teams are sent to many competitions sponsored by other law schools and bar associations, including the Jessup International Law Moot Court and the Inter-American Moot Court Competition. Law student organizations include the ABA-Law School Division, Environmental Law Society, and Equal Justice Foundation. There is a local chapter of National Lawyers Guild, the Federalist society, and Phi Delta Phi.

Library

The law library contains 412,309 hardcopy volumes and 1,015,769 microform volume equivalents, and subscribes to 6019 serial publications. Such on-line databases and networks as LEXIS, DIALOG, WESTLAW, Autocite, NEXIS, VuText, and OCLC are available to law students for research. Special library collections include European Community and U.S. government depositories as well as the Baxter Collection in international law Recently, the law school library moved into a new facility approximately 2½ times the size of the previous facility and seats more than 600 students, with student carrels, student worktables, and research stations, as well as a network of group study rooms. The library was also recently designated as the repository for the National Equal Justice Library, which is an archive of primary and public defender programs. The ratio of library volumes to faculty is 2151 to 1 and to students, 352 to 1. The ratio of seats in the library to students is 1 to 2.

Faculty

The law school has 50 full-time and 152 part-time faculty members, of whom 60 are women. According to AAUP standards for Category I institutions, faculty salaries are above average. About 30% of full-time faculty have a graduate law degree in addition to the J.D.; about 20% of part-time faculty have one. The ratio of full-time students to full-time faculty in an average class is 8 to 1; in a clinic, 10 to 1.

Students

About 59% of the student body are women; 24%, minorities; 8%, African American; 10%, Asian American; 5%, Hispanic; and 1%, Native American. The majority of students come from the Northeast (54%). The average age of entering students is 24; age range is 20 to 45. About 13% of students have a graduate degree. About 1% drop out after the first year for academic or personal reasons; 98% remain to receive a law degree.

College of Law/Armstrong Hall

Box 877906
Tempe, AZ 85287-7906

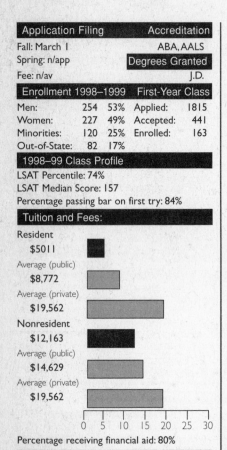

Application Filing		Accreditation	
Fall: March 1		ABA, AALS	
Spring: n/app		**Degrees Granted**	
Fee: n/av		J.D.	
Enrollment 1998–1999		**First-Year Class**	
Men:	254 53%	Applied:	1815
Women:	227 49%	Accepted:	441
Minorities:	120 25%	Enrolled:	163
Out-of-State:	82 17%		

1998–99 Class Profile
LSAT Percentile: 74%
LSAT Median Score: 157
Percentage passing bar on first try: 84%

Tuition and Fees:

Resident
$5011

Average (public)
$8,772

Average (private)
$19,562

Nonresident
$12,163

Average (public)
$14,629

Average (private)
$19,562

0 5 10 15 20 25 30

Percentage receiving financial aid: 80%

ADMISSIONS

In the fall 1999 first-year class, 1815 applied, 441 were accepted, and 163 enrolled. Five transfers enrolled. The median LSAT percentile of the most recent first-year class was 74; the median GPA was 3.37 on a scale of 4.0. The highest LSAT percentile was 99.

Requirements
Applicants must have a bachelor's degree from an accredited institution and take the LSAT. Minimum acceptable GPA is 2.0 on a scale of 4.0. No specific undergraduate courses are required. Candidates are not interviewed.

Procedure
The application deadline for fall entry is March 1. Applicants should submit an application form, LSAT results, transcripts, a nonrefundable application fee, and a personal statement no longer than 3 typed pages. Check with the school for current fee. Notification of the admission decision is mid-April. The latest acceptable LSAT test date for fall entry is February. The law school uses the LSDAS.

Special
The law school recruits minority and disadvantaged students by means of special mailings, personal contact, and the involvement of current students and alumni. Transfer students must have one year of credit, have attended an ABA-approved law school, and in general, be in the top 10% of their law school class.

Costs

Tuition and fees for the 1999-2000 academic year are $5011 for full-time in-state students and $12,163 for out-of-state students. On-campus room and board costs about $7050 annually; and books and supplies run $1000.

Financial Aid

In a recent year, about 80% of current law students received some form of aid. The maximum annual amount of aid from all sources combined, including scholarships, loans, and work contracts, was $29,994. Awards are based on need and merit. The required financial statement is FAFSA. Check with the school for current deadline. Special funds for minority or disadvantaged students consist of Graduate College Mentor Program funds.

About the Law School

Arizona State University College of Law/Armstrong Hall was established in 1967 and is a public institution. The 700-acre campus is in a suburban area 5 miles east of Phoenix, Arizona's capital. The primary mission of the law school is to provide the highest quality professional legal education for its students; to engage in legal research, scholarship and legal education for its students; and to contribute to the local, regional, and national communities through its public service activities. Students have access to federal, state, county, city, and local agencies, courts, correctional facilities, law firms, and legal aid organizations in the Tempe area. Many opportunities, including externships, are available in the capital area. Housing for law students is available on campus and is specifically for graduate and/or law students. Adequate housing is found off campus. All law school facilities are accessible to the physically disabled.

Calendar

The law school operates on a traditional semester basis. Courses for full-time students are offered days only and an occasional evening class and must be completed within 5 years. There is no part-time program. New full-time students are admitted in the fall. There are 2 5-week summer sessions. Transferable summer courses are offered.

Programs

Students may take relevant courses in other programs and apply credit toward the J.D.; a maximum of 6 credits may be applied. The following joint degrees may be earned: J.D./M.B.A. (Juris Doctor/Master of Business Administration), J.D./M.H.S.A. (Juris Doctor/Master of Health Science Services Administration), and J.D./Ph.D. (Juris Doctor/Ph.D. Justice Studies).

Phone: 602-965-1474
Fax: 602-965-5550
E-mail: wanda.decrow@asu.edu
Web: www.law.asu.edu

Contact

Wanda DeCrow, Admissions Officer, 480-965-1474 for general inquiries; Rhonda Sandler, Assistant Dean, 480-965-6925 for financial aid information.

ARIZONA

Required

To earn the J.D., candidates must complete 87 total credits, of which 40 are for required courses. They must maintain a minimum grade average of 70 in the required courses. The following first-year courses are required of all students: Contracts I and II, Criminal Law, Torts I and II, Civil Procedure I and II, Property I and II, Constitutional Law I, and Legal Research and Writing I and II. Required upper-level courses consist of Legal Profession, Constitutional Law II, and Advanced Criminal Procedure. The optional orientation program for first-year students is a 3-day program with an introduction to student services and organizations, a mock substantive class, and a preliminary legal method class.

Electives

There is a Prosecutor Clinic, Law School Clinic, and a Mediation and Arbitration Project, which are generally worth 6 credit hours. There are 10 to 15 seminars per semester worth 2 or 3 credit hours. Final-year students are given preference for clinics and seminars. Externships and field work allow upper-level students to gain up to 12 credits while working at 1 of the 30 participating agencies. There is a Merriam Lecture Series. Study-abroad opportunities are available to upper-level students and consist of a fall semester in London. First-year students designated as "at-risk" may participate in tutorials for all first-year classes. Remedial programs include the Academic Success Program. There are also a Graduate College Mentor program and a Legal Intern Writing program. A special interest group program allows students to participate in information sessions at the Center for Law, Science, and Technology. The most widely taken electives are Evidence, Business Associations, and Federal Courts.

Graduation Requirements

In order to graduate, candidates must have a grade point average of 7, completed the upper-division writing requirement, and completed 87 credit hours including the required courses and the writing requirement.

Organizations

Students edit the *Arizona State Law Journal*, the *Jurimetrics Journal of Law, Science and Technology*, and the newspaper *Devil's Advocate*. The school participates yearly in the National Moot Court Competition, the Environmental Moot Court Competition, and the Jenkes Competition. Student organizations include the Student Bar Association, Women Law Students Association, and the Organization for Public Interest Law and Environmental Law, among others. There are local chapters of Phi Alpha Delta, Phi Delta Phi, and The Federalists. Campus clubs and other organizations include the American Marketing Association, Arizona Horizon Project, and Arnold Air Society, as well as approximately 390 registered clubs and organizations.

Library

The law library contains 351,000 hardcopy volumes and 465,411 microform volume equivalents, and subscribes to 6153 serial publications. Such on-line databases and networks as LEXIS and WESTLAW are available to law students for research. Special library collections include Anglo-American case reports and statutes and special collections of Indian law, Mexican law, and law and technology. Recently, a new library building opened, which provides seating for approximately 490, has 179 study carrels, a 30 station computer laboratory, and LEXIS and WESTLAW rooms containing 10 stations each, and 27 study/meeting rooms. The ratio of library volumes to faculty is 5850 to 1 and to students, 766 to 1. The ratio of seats in the library to students is 1 to 1.

Faculty

The law school has 37 full-time and 21 part-time faculty members, of whom 10 are women. According to AAUP standards for Category I institutions, faculty salaries are average. The ratio of full-time students to full-time faculty in an average class is 12 to 1; in a clinic, 6 to 1. There is a chapter of the Order of the Coif.

Placement

J.D.s awarded:	151
Services available through: a separate law school placement center.	
Full-time job interviews:	50 employers
Summer job interviews:	12 employers
Placement by graduation:	62% of class
Placement within 9 months:	90% of class
Average starting salary:	$34,815 to $52,871
Areas of placement:	
Private practice 2-10 attorneys	22%
Private practice 11-25 attorneys	6%
Private practice 26-50 attorneys	6%
Private practice 51-100 attorneys	15%
Government	17%
Judicial clerkships	16%
unknown	11%
Business/industry	5%
Public interest	1%
Academic	1%

Students

About 49% of the student body are women; 25%, minorities; 4%, African American; 3%, Asian American; 11%, Hispanic; and 6%, Native American. The majority of students come from Arizona (83%). The average age of entering students is 27; age range is 20 to 73. About 11% drop out after the first year for academic or personal reasons; 89% remain to receive a law degree.

BAYLOR UNIVERSITY

School of Law

P.O. Box 97288
Waco, TX 76798-7288

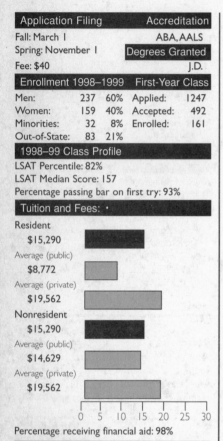

Application Filing		Accreditation
Fall: March 1		ABA, AALS
Spring: November 1		**Degrees Granted**
Fee: $40		J.D.

Enrollment 1998–1999		First-Year Class	
Men:	237 60%	Applied:	1247
Women:	159 40%	Accepted:	492
Minorities:	32 8%	Enrolled:	161
Out-of-State:	83 21%		

1998–99 Class Profile
LSAT Percentile: 82%
LSAT Median Score: 157
Percentage passing bar on first try: 93%

Tuition and Fees: ·

Resident
$15,290
Average (public)
$8,772
Average (private)
$19,562
Nonresident
$15,290
Average (public)
$14,629
Average (private)
$19,562

0 5 10 15 20 25 30

Percentage receiving financial aid: 98%

ADMISSIONS

In the fall 1999 first-year class, 1247 applied, 492 were accepted, and 161 enrolled. Three transfers enrolled. The median LSAT percentile of the most recent first-year class was 81.5; the median GPA was 3.42 on a scale of 4.0. The lowest LSAT percentile accepted was 24; the highest was 98.

Requirements
Applicants must have a bachelor's degree from an accredited institution and take the LSAT. The most important admission factors include LSAT results, GPA, and general background. No specific undergraduate courses are required. Candidates are not interviewed.

Procedure
The application deadline for fall entry is March 1. Applicants should submit an application form, LSAT results, transcripts, LSDAS, a nonrefundable application fee of $40, 2 letters of recommendation, and a personal statement. Notification of the admission decision is 4 to 6 weeks after the application deadline. The latest acceptable LSAT test date for fall entry is December. The law school uses the LSDAS.

Special
The law school recruits minority and disadvantaged students the same as nonminority students. plus targeted mailings. A member of the Law School faculty serves as the Minority Law Student Adviser. Transfer students must have one year of credit, have a minimum GPA of 3.0, and have attended an ABA-approved law school. To be competitive with the applicant pool, the applicants should be in the top 15 to 20% of their class at a comparable law school.

Costs

Tuition and fees for the 1999-2000 academic year are $15,290 for all full-time students. On-campus room and board costs about $8748 annually; books and supplies run $600.

Financial Aid

About 98% of current law students receive some form of aid. The average annual amount of aid from all sources combined, including scholarships, loans, and work contracts, is $21,170. Awards are based on need and merit. The required financial statement is the CSS Profile. The aid application deadline for fall entry is May 1. Special funds for minority or disadvantaged students are available. There are a limited number of scholarships ranging from one-third to one-half of tuition for students who have overcome educational and/or emotional disadvantages or other personal hardship experiences. First-year students are notified about their financial aid application before enrollment.

About the Law School

Baylor University School of Law was established in 1849 and is a private institution. The 432-acre campus is in an urban area 92 miles south of Dallas. The primary mission of the law school is to train students in all facets of the law including theoretical analysis, practical application, legal writing and advocacy, negotiation, and counseling skills to equip them to practice effectively in any area of the law. Students have access to federal, state, county, city, and local agencies, courts, correctional facilities, law firms, and legal aid organizations in the Waco area. A new $30 million, state-of-the-art 125,000 square foot facility is under construction. Housing for law students consists of private and university rental housing, including numerous rooms and condominiums near the Baylor campus and other properties throughout the city of Waco. Families with children may choose to live further away from the campus if they have an automobile.

Calendar

The law school operates on a quarter basis. Courses for full-part-time students are offered days only and must be completed within 5 years. New full-time students are admitted in the fall, spring, and summer. There is an 11-week summer session. Transferable summer courses are offered.

Programs

Students may take relevant courses in other programs and apply credit toward the J.D.; a maximum of 12 credits may be applied. The following joint degrees may be earned: J.D./M.B.A. (Juris Doctor/Master of Business Administration), J.D./M.Tax (Juris Doctor/Master of Taxation), and J.D./M.P.P.A. (Juris Doctor/Master of Public Policy Administration).

Required
To earn the J.D., candidates must complete 126 total credits, of which 79 are for required courses. They must maintain a minimum GPA of 2.0 in the required courses. The following first-year courses are required of all students:

Phone: 254-710-1911
800-BAYLOR
Fax: 254-710-2316
E-mail: becky-beck@baylor.edu
Web: law.baylor.edu

Contact
Becky L. Beck, Admissions Director, 254-710-1911 for general inquiries; Office of Financial Aid, 254-710-2611 for financial aid information.

Legal Analysis, Research, and Communication I, II, and III, Criminal Law, Civil Procedure, Contracts I and II, Property I and II, Torts I and II, and Environmental Legislation and Criminal Procedure. Required upper-level courses consist of Evidence, Constitutional Law, Practice Court I and II, Professional Responsibility, Federal Income Taxation, Business Organization I, Consumer Protection, and Trusts and Estates I. All students must take clinical courses. The required orientation program for first-year students is a 2-day program that covers case analysis, statutory interpretation, and judicial processes.

Electives

The School of Law offers concentrations in criminal law, litigation, and business transactions, administrative law, and estate planning. In addition, a practice court clinic is required in the third year and includes rigorous hands-on training. Students are required to complete at least 3 mini trials and 1 large trial along with several other exercises. There are real-life client opportunities for pro bono divorce cases and other client opportunities for penalty cases. Seminars are available in the area of Supreme Court. Internships are available in the District Attorney's Office, U.S. Attorney's Office, U.S. District Court, U.S. Bankruptcy Court, Texas Attorney General's Office-Child Support Division, Legal Services Office, and others for 2 hours of credit, and the Texas Supreme Court and Court of Criminal Appeals for 5 hours of credit. Independent studies for 1 or 2 hours of credit are available for second- and third-year students under faculty supervision. Field work opportunities are available in a number of offices such as General Counsel for Hillcrest Hospital. Special lecture series include the Frank Wilson Memorial, W.R. White Memorial, R. Matt Dawson Lecture Series, and the John William Minton and Florence Dean Minton Endowed Law School Lecture Series. Students may study in Guadalajara, Mexico and earn up to 5 credits during a 2-week program in August. A faculty-conducted tutorial program is available for students placed on academic probation as well as for other interested students. In addition, there is a designated faculty Minority Student Adviser. The most widely taken electives are Family Law, Alternative Dispute Resolution, Advanced Texas Criminal Procedure, Administration of Estates, Appellate Procedure, and Trusts and Estates II.

Graduation Requirements

In order to graduate, candidates must have a GPA of 2.0.

Organizations
The primary law review is the *Baylor Law Review*. Moot court competitions include the Dawson and Sodd Fall Moot Court and the Strasburger and Price Spring Moot Court. Another intrascholstic competition is the Naman, Howell, Smith and Lee Client Counseling Competition. Other interscholastic competitions available are the National Trial, National Moot Court, National Appellate Advocacy, Texas Young Lawyers Moot Court, National Negotiations, and National Client Counseling. Law student organizations include the Baylor University Student Bar Association, Minority Student Association, and Civil Rights Society. Local chapters of national associations include the R.E.B. Baylor Chapter of Phi Alpha Delta, James P. Alexander Senate of Delta Phi, and the Hemphill Inn Chapter of Phi Delta Phi.

Library
The law library contains 114,860 hardcopy volumes and 67,835 microform volume equivalents, and subscribes to 2153 serial publications. Such on-line databases and networks as LEXIS, DIALOG, WESTLAW, and NEXIS are available to law students for research. Special library collections include the Frank M. Wilson Rare Book Room Collection, which contains first editions and rare printings of legal writings, novels, and research titles relating to law. Recently, the library upgraded both of the computer laboratories, which house IBM-compatible PCs. The ratio of library volumes to faculty is 5489 to 1 and to students, 290 to 1. The ratio of seats in the library to students is 1 to 77.

Faculty
The law school has 21 full-time and 33 part-time faculty members, of whom 9 are women. According to AAUP stan-

Placement

J.D.s awarded:	169

Services available through: separate law school placement center and the university placement center.

Services: resource library; use of telephone/fax/typewriter for job search purposes

Special features: the Direct Contact Program, Resume Collection Program, job search skills programs, mock interviews, guest speaker panel discussions, and participation in various job fairs in Texas as well as out of state.

Full-time job interviews:	31 employers
Summer job interviews:	127 employers
Placement by graduation:	66% of class
Placement within 9 months:	95% of class
Average starting salary:	$36,500 to $65,585

Areas of placement:

Private practice 2-10 attorneys	52%
Private practice 11-25 attorneys	10%
Private practice 26-50 attorneys	4%
Private practice 51-100 attorneys	8%
Government	8%
Business/industry	7%
Judicial clerkships	7%
unknown	3%
Military	1%

dards for Category I institutions, faculty salaries are average. About 25% of full-time faculty have a graduate law degree in addition to the J.D.; about 3% of part-time faculty have one. The ratio of full-time students to full-time faculty in an average class is 25 to 1; in a clinic, 4 to 1. The law school has a regular program of bringing visiting professors and other distinguished lecturers and visitors to campus.

Students
About 40% of the student body are women; 8%, minorities; 1%, African American; 2%, Asian American; and 5%, Hispanic. The majority of students come from Texas (79%). The average age of entering students is 24; age range is 20 to 42. About 80% of students enter directly from undergraduate school, 9% have a graduate degree, and 24% have worked full-time prior to entering law school. About 5% drop out after the first year for academic or personal reasons; 95% remain to receive a law degree.

Law School

885 Centre Street
Newton, MA 02459

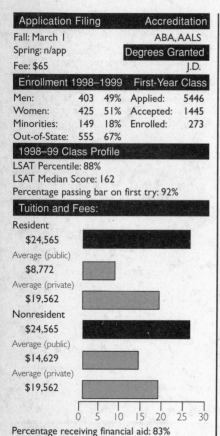

Application Filing		Accreditation
Fall: March 1		ABA, AALS
Spring: n/app		**Degrees Granted**
Fee: $65		J.D.

Enrollment 1998–1999		First-Year Class	
Men:	403 49%	Applied:	5446
Women:	425 51%	Accepted:	1445
Minorities:	149 18%	Enrolled:	273
Out-of-State:	555 67%		

1998–99 Class Profile

LSAT Percentile: 88%
LSAT Median Score: 162
Percentage passing bar on first try: 92%

Tuition and Fees:

Resident
$24,565

Average (public)
$8,772

Average (private)
$19,562

Nonresident
$24,565

Average (public)
$14,629

Average (private)
$19,562

0 5 10 15 20 25 30

Percentage receiving financial aid: 83%

ADMISSIONS

In the fall 1999 first-year class, 5446 applied, 1445 were accepted, and 273 enrolled. Sixteen transfers enrolled. The median LSAT percentile of the most recent first-year class was 88; the median GPA was 3.5 on a scale of 4.0.

Requirements

Applicants must have a bachelor's degree from an accredited institution and take the LSAT. Minimum acceptable GPA is 2.0 on a scale of 4.0. The most important admission factors include academic achievement, character, personality, and undergraduate curriculum. No specific undergraduate courses are required. Candidates are not interviewed.

Procedure

The application deadline for fall entry is March 1. Applicants should submit an application form, LSAT results, a nonrefundable application fee of $65, 2 letters of recommendation, and the LSDAS report. Notification of the admission decision is on a rolling basis. The latest acceptable LSAT test date for fall entry is February. The law school uses the LSDAS.

Special

The law school recruits minority and disadvantaged students through a program of active outreach by the Admissions Committee and minority student organizations. Transfer students must have one year of credit and have attended an ABA-approved law school. Applicants are considered on a space-available basis.

Costs

Tuition and fees for the 1999-2000 academic year are $24,565 for all full-time students. Books and supplies run $800.

Financial Aid

About 83% of current law students receive some form of aid. The average annual amount of aid from all sources combined, including scholarships, loans, and work contracts, is $29,850; maximum, $38,045. Awards are based on need and merit. The required financial statements are the CSS Profile or the FAFSA. The Need Access application may be submitted instead of the CSS Profile. The aid application deadline for fall entry is March 15. Special funds for minority or disadvantaged students consist of additional tuition remission. First-year students are notified about their financial aid application some time before the first deposit is due, if the aid application is timely.

About the Law School

Boston College Law School was established in 1929 and is a private institution. The 40-acre campus is in a suburban area 8 miles west of downtown Boston. The primary mission of the law school is to provide a quality legal education in the Jesuit, Catholic tradition to a highly qualified and diverse group of men and women in order to prepare them to serve their communities and serve as leaders in the profession. Students have access to federal, state, county, city, and local agencies, courts, correctional facilities, law firms, and legal aid organizations in the Newton area. Facilities of special interest to law students include a $16 million library, a $13 million classroom building with state-of-the-art audiovisual and computing capabilities, and a Career Resources Center. Housing for law students is extensive; there is much rental housing in Newton and the surrounding communities, and the College's off-campus Housing Office assists students in finding accommodations. All law school facilities are accessible to the physically disabled.

Calendar

The law school operates on a traditional semester basis. Courses for full-time students are offered days only and must be completed within 4 years. There is no part-time program. New students are admitted in the fall. There is no summer session. Transferable summer courses are not offered.

Programs

Students may take relevant courses in other programs and apply credit toward the J.D.; a maximum of 12 credits may be applied. The following joint degrees may be earned: J.D./M.B.A. (Juris Doctor/Master of Business Administration), J.D./M.S.W. (Juris Doctor/Master of Social Work), J.D./M.Ed. (Juris Doctor/Master of Education), and J.D./M.A. (Juris Doctor/Master of Arts in education).

Phone: 617-552-4351
Fax: 617-552-2917
E-mail: bclawadm@bc.edu
Web: http://www.bc.edu/lawschool

Contact
Elizabeth A. Rosselot, Director of Admissions and Financial Aid, 617-552-4351 for general inquiries and financial aid information.

MASSACHUSETTS ⦿

Required

To earn the J.D., candidates must complete 85 total credits, of which 38 are for required courses. They must maintain a minimum GPA of 2.0 in the required courses. The following first-year courses are required of all students: Torts, Property, Civil Procedure, Contracts, Constitutional Law, Legal Research and Writing, and Introduction to Lawyering and Professional Responsibility. Required upper-level courses consist of Constitutional Law II and Professional Responsibility. The required orientation program for first-year students is a 1 day orientation followed by a 3-day Fundamentals of Legal Process course.

Electives

The Law School offers concentrations in corporate law, criminal law, entertainment, environmental law, family law, international law, juvenile law, litigation, securities law, sports law, tax law, and torts and insurance. In addition, clinics include Civil Litigation Clinic for 7 credits, Women and the Law Clinic for 7 credits, and the Criminal Justice Clinic for 7 credits. Internships include the ULL Externship Program and the Attorney General's Program. A London program is offered to second-and third-year students for 13 credits. Students in the program complete course work in international and comparative law, and serve as legal interns in a range of British organizations. Tutorial programs are available to students who require them. Programming for minority students is sponsored by student groups. Minority students are actively recruited. The most widely taken electives are Taxation, Corporations, and Commercial Law.

Graduation Requirements

In order to graduate, candidates must have a GPA of 2.0.

Organizations

Students edit the *Boston College Law Review, Boston College Environmental Affairs Law Review, Boston College International and Comparative Law Review, Boston College Third World Law Journal,* and the *Uniform Commercial Code Reporter Digest.* Moot court competitions include the Wendell F. Grimes Moot Court, Jessup International Moot Court, and National Moot Court competitions. Other competitions are the Mock Trial, Negotiations, Client Counseling, and Administrative Law Moot Court. Law student organizations include the Law Students Association, Board of Student Advisers, and the Public Interest Law Foundation. There are local chapters of the ABA-Law Student Division, Black Law Students Association, and Latino Law Students Association.

Library

The law library contains 393,179 hardcopy volumes and 1,031,218 microform volume equivalents, and subscribes to 6133 serial publications. Such on-line databases and networks as LEXIS, DIALOG, and WESTLAW are available to law students for research. The ratio of library volumes to faculty is 7709 to 1 and to students, 475 to 1. The ratio of seats in the library to students is 1 to 1.

Faculty

The law school has 52 full-time and 56 part-time faculty members, of whom 38 are women. According to AAUP standards for Category I institutions, faculty salaries are well above average. About 21% of full-time faculty have a graduate law degree in addition to the J.D. The ratio of full-time students to full-time faculty in an average class is 30 to 1; in a clinic, 8 to 1. The law school has a regular program of bringing visiting professors and other distinguished lecturers and visitors to campus. There is a chapter of the Order of the Coif; 22 faculty and 830 graduates are members.

Placement

J.D.s awarded:	272

Services available through: a separate law school placement center.

Special features: extensive skills workshops and career panels featuring alumni and a Career Resource Library that includes books, directories, periodicals, and videotapes. There are on-campus and off-campus recruitment programs.

Full-time job interviews:	288 employers
Summer job interviews:	n/av
Placement by graduation:	n/av
Placement within 9 months:	96% of class

Average starting salary: $18,000 to $106,000

Areas of placement:	
Private practice 2-10 attorneys	11%
Private practice 11-25 attorneys	6%
Private practice 26-50 attorneys	3%
Private practice 51-100 attorneys	43%
Judicial clerkships	18%
Business/industry	11%
Government	6%
Public interest	2%

Students

About 51% of the student body are women; 18%, minorities; 6%, African American; 8%, Asian American; 4%, Hispanic; and 1%, Native American. The majority of students come from Massachusetts (33%). The average age of entering students is 24; age range is 21 to 48. About 40% of students enter directly from undergraduate school, 10% have a graduate degree, and 60% have worked full-time prior to entering law school. About 1% drop out after the first year for academic or personal reasons; 99% remain to receive a law degree.

BOSTON UNIVERSITY

School of Law

765 Commonwealth Avenue
Boston, MA 02215

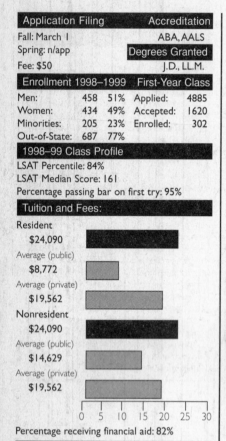

Application Filing	Accreditation
Fall: March 1	ABA, AALS
Spring: n/app	**Degrees Granted**
Fee: $50	J.D., LL.M.

Enrollment 1998–1999		First-Year Class	
Men:	458 51%	Applied:	4885
Women:	434 49%	Accepted:	1620
Minorities:	205 23%	Enrolled:	302
Out-of-State:	687 77%		

1998–99 Class Profile
LSAT Percentile: 84%
LSAT Median Score: 161
Percentage passing bar on first try: 95%

Tuition and Fees:

Resident
$24,090

Average (public)
$8,772

Average (private)
$19,562

Nonresident
$24,090

Average (public)
$14,629

Average (private)
$19,562

0 5 10 15 20 25 30

Percentage receiving financial aid: 82%

ADMISSIONS

In the fall 1999 first-year class, 4885 applied, 1620 were accepted, and 302 enrolled. Five transfers enrolled. The median LSAT percentile of the most recent first-year class was 84.3; the median GPA was 3.39 on a scale of 4.0. The highest LSAT percentile was 99.9.

Requirements
Applicants must have a bachelor's degree from an accredited institution and take the LSAT. The most important admission factors include LSAT results, GPA, and general background. No specific undergraduate courses are required. Candidates are not interviewed.

Procedure
The application deadline for fall entry is March 1. Applicants should submit an application form, LSAT results, transcripts, TOEFL for international students only, a nonrefundable application fee of $50, 2 letters of recommendation, and a dean's letter of certification, and a personal statement. Notification of the admission decision is on a rolling basis. The latest acceptable LSAT test date for

fall entry is February. The law school uses the LSDAS.

Special
The law school recruits minority and disadvantaged students by means of the Candidate Referral Service, LSAC forums, active minority groups on campus, alumni contacts, the Legal Defense Fund Latino Day in New York City, and mailings to HBCU. Transfer students must have one year of credit, have attended an ABA-approved law school, and must submit a regular application, but indicate that it is for a transfer.

Costs

Tuition and fees for the 1999-2000 academic year are $24,090 for all full-time students. On-campus room and board costs about $9350 annually; books and supplies run $997.

Financial Aid

About 82% of current law students receive some form of aid. The average annual amount of aid from all sources combined, including scholarships, loans, and work contracts, is $30,191; maximum, $36,630. Awards are based on need and merit. The required financial statements are CSS Profile or the FAFSA and institutional form. The aid application deadline for fall entry is March 1. Special funds for minority or disadvantaged students consist of Martin Luther King Jr., Whitney Young, Norbert Simmons, and Barbara Jordan fellowships and scholarships. First-year students are notified about their financial aid application within 2 weeks after acceptance.

About the Law School

Boston University School of Law was established in 1872 and is a private institution. The campus is in an urban area in Boston. The primary mission of the law school is to teach its students to understand the nature of the law, to provide them with training in legal principles and professional techniques, and to equip them to succeed in a rapidly changing world. Students have access to federal, state, county, city, and local agencies, courts, correctional facilities, law firms, and legal aid organizations in the Boston area. The school hosts the Center for Law and Health Sciences, the Center for Law and Technology, the Institute of Jewish Law, the Morin Center for Banking Law Studies, and the N. Neal Pike Institute on Law and Disabili-

ty. Facilities of special interest to law students are the Case Center for athletics, the university's Concert Series, the Tsai Performance Center, boating on campus, and all the amenities of Boston, such as the Boston Symphony, opera, theater, and sports. Housing for law students is available as apartment units within walking distance of the school or as suburban accommodations easily reached by mass transportation lines. About 90% of the law school facilities are accessible to the physically disabled.

Calendar

The law school operates on a traditional semester basis. Courses for full-time students are offered days only and must be completed within 3 years. For part-time students, courses are offered both day and evening. New full-and part-time students are admitted in the fall. There is no summer session. Transferable summer courses are not offered.

Programs

In addition to the J.D., the law school offers the LL.M. Students may take relevant courses in other programs and apply credit toward the J.D.; a maximum of 12 credits may be applied. The following joint degrees may be earned: J.D./M.B.A. (Juris Doctor/Master of Business Administration program in law and health care management), J.D./M.S. (Juris Doctor/Master of Science in mass communication), J.D./M.A. (Juris Doctor/Master of Arts in historic preservation studies international relations, and philosophy), J.D./M.P.H. (Juris Doctor/Master of Public Health), and J.D./LL.M. (Juris Doctor/Master of Laws in Taxation).

Required
To earn the J.D., candidates must complete 84 total credits, of which 33 are for required courses. The following first-year courses are required of all students: Contracts, Torts, Civil Procedure, Property, Legal Writing and Research, an elective, and Criminal Law. Required upper-level courses consist of Constitutional Law and Legal Ethics. All students choose from voluntary clinical programs that include a Legal Externship program, Legislative Services, Criminal Trial Advocacy, judicial internships, Legal Aid, and Student Defenders and Prosecutors. The required orientation program for first-year students is 1 1/2 days plus several programs during the first 3 weeks of classes.

Phone: 617-353-3100
E-mail: bulawadm@bu.edu
Web: http://www.bu.edu/LAW

Contact

Barbara J. Selmo, Director of Admissions and Financial Aid, 617-353-3100 for general inquiries; Barbara J. Selmo, Director of Admissions and Financial Aid, 617-353-3160 for financial aid information.

MASSACHUSETTS

Electives

The School of Law offers concentrations in corporate law, environmental law, international law, litigation, health law, and intellectual property. In addition, clinics for upper-level students include Legislative Services, Criminal Trial Advocacy, and Civil Litigation Clinic. Credit varies from 3 to 8 hours. Seminars for varying credit are open to upper-level students. A judicial internship is worth 3 credits and a variety of externships, geared toward individual student interest, are offered for 6 credits. Independent Study (supervised research and writing) is offered to upper-level students for 1 to 3 credits. Special lecture series include the Distinguished Lecture Series, Pappas Distinguished Scholar Program, Esdaile Law Forum, and the Legal History Group Lecture. The school offers 5 overseas study programs: 1 in Lyon, France, 1 in Paris, 1 in Oxford, England, 1 in Leiden, the Netherlands, and 1 in Tel Aviv, Israel. First-year students may take the voluntary First-Year Writing Program tutorial, led by an upper-level qualifying student. The Assistant Dean of Students coordinates a Voluntary Academic Support Program for first-year students whose first-semester grades indicate that they need assistance. The program is offered in the second semester of the first year for no credit. The classes focus on outlining and exam-taking skills. In addition, the Assistant Dean of Students Office, together with minority student organizations, sponsors an orientation program for incoming minority students. A Student Organization Activities Fair, sponsored by the Student Bar Association, introduces students to school organizations and groups. A formal lecture series and other lectures arranged by faculty student organizations, or through a research center, are given regularly by well-known outside speakers throughout the academic year.

Graduation Requirements

In order to graduate, candidates must have a GPA of 2.0, have completed the upper-division writing requirement, and , have researched and written a major paper on a topic of their choice. The paper is faculty supervised and evaluated.

Organizations

Students edit the *Boston University Law Review, American Journal of Law and Medicine, Annual Review of Banking Law, Boston University International Law Journal, Public Interest Law Journal, Journal of Science and Technology Law,* and the newspaper, the *Law Register.* All first-year students participate in the intramural J. Newton Esdaile Moot Court program during the spring semester. Second-year students may participate in the Edward C. Stone Appellate Moot Court Competition in the fall; the top advocates from the Stone Competition advance to the Homer Albers Prize Moot Court Competition during the spring semester of their second year. Teams of third-year students are sent to national competitions such as National Moot Court, National Appellate Advocacy, and Craven Constitutional Law. Students may participate in the ABA-National Trial Competition, the Association of Trial Lawyers of America National Student Trial Advocacy Competition, and the ABA Negotiation and Client Counseling competitions. Student organizations include the Arts Law Association; Civil Liberties Association; and Communications, Entertainment and Sports Law Association. There are local chapters of Federalist Society, Phi Alpha Delta, and Phi Delta Phi.

Library

The law library contains 317,000 hardcopy volumes and 1,299,800 microform volume equivalents, and subscribes to 6432 serial publications. Such on-line databases and networks as LEXIS, DIALOG, WESTLAW, NEXIS, the Internet, CIS, TIARRA (treaty research), and ACCESS UN. are available to law students for research. Special library collections include a U.S. government selected depository, and intellectual property, banking law, tax law, and international law collections. Recently, the library installed a new computer laboratory for students with access to Internet, CD-ROM, computer-assisted legal research, and computer-assisted legal instruction. The ratio of library volumes to faculty is 9960 to 1 and to students, 636 to 1. The ratio of seats in the library to students is 9 to 1.

Faculty

The law school has 57 full-time and 74 part-time faculty members, of whom 48 are women. The ratio of full-time students to full-time faculty in an average clinic is 8 to 1.

Placement

J.D.s awarded:	333

Services available through: separate law school placement center.

Services: extensive off-campus interview programs in 8 cities and numerous specialty job fairs; job search strategy and interview workshops; numerous presentations on areas of practice and law-related careers

Special features: There are 4 staff counselors, 2 of whom are also attorneys. One counselor specializes in public interest and government positions. The school also employs a recruitment and marketing manager, a recruitment coordinator, and a program coordinator. Additionally, there is an extensive internet-based computer database of legal employers, on-line interview selectors and job listings, and numerous publications, directories, manuals, and periodicals on private, public, in-house, judicial clerkships, nontraditional, and academic careers. The school also provides information on domestic and international fellowships. The Career Assistance Program (CAP) matches students with alumni contacts who assist in the job search nationwide.

Full-time job interviews:	374 employers
Summer job interviews:	n/av
Placement by graduation:	75% of class
Placement within 9 months:	75% of class
Average starting salary:	$35,161 to $87,462

Areas of placement:

Private practice 2-10 attorneys	6%
Private practice 11-25 attorneys	9%
Private practice 26-50 attorneys	11%
Private practice 51-100 attorneys	42%
Business/industry	15%
Government	10%
Judicial clerkships	9%
Public interest	2%
Academic	1%

Students

About 49% of the student body are women; 23%, minorities; 3%, African American; 12%, Asian American; 9%, Hispanic; and 1%, Native American. The majority of students come from the Northeast (39%). The average age of entering students is 24; age range is 19 to 43. About 39% of students enter directly from undergraduate school and 12% have a graduate degree. About 9% drop out after the first year for academic or personal reasons; 95% remain to receive a law degree.

BRIGHAM YOUNG UNIVERSITY

J. Reuben Clark Law School

342 JRCB Brigham Young University
Provo, UT 84602

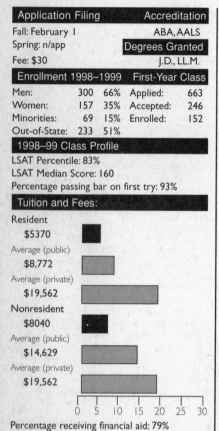

Application Filing		Accreditation
Fall: February 1		ABA, AALS
Spring: n/app		**Degrees Granted**
Fee: $30		J.D., LL.M.

Enrollment 1998–1999		First-Year Class	
Men:	300 66%	Applied:	663
Women:	157 35%	Accepted:	246
Minorities:	69 15%	Enrolled:	152
Out-of-State:	233 51%		

1998–99 Class Profile
LSAT Percentile: 83%
LSAT Median Score: 160
Percentage passing bar on first try: 93%

Tuition and Fees:

Resident
$5370

Average (public)
$8,772

Average (private)
$19,562

Nonresident
$8040

Average (public)
$14,629

Average (private)
$19,562

0 5 10 15 20 25 30

Percentage receiving financial aid: 79%

ADMISSIONS
In the fall 1999 first-year class, 663 applied, 246 were accepted, and 152 enrolled. Five transfers enrolled. The median LSAT percentile of the most recent first-year class was 83; the median GPA was 3.6 on a scale of 4.0. The lowest LSAT percentile accepted was 23; the highest was 99.

Requirements
Applicants must have a bachelor's degree from an accredited institution and take the LSAT. Minimum acceptable LSAT score is 34 and minimum acceptable GPA is 2.5 on a scale of 4.0. The most important admission factors include GPA, LSAT results, and letter of recommendation. No specific undergraduate courses are required. Candidates are interviewed.

Procedure
The application deadline for fall entry is February 1. Applicants should submit an application form, LSAT results, transcripts, a nonrefundable application fee of $30, 3 letters of recommendation, and a personal statement. Notification of the admission decision is March 30. The latest acceptable LSAT test date for fall entry is December. The law school uses the LSDAS.

Special
The law school recruits minority and disadvantaged students by direct mail, law forums, visiting undergraduate institutions, and personal contact from students, alumni, and friends of the law school. The school works closely with the Minority Law Students Association in recruiting minority students. Transfer students must have one year of credit, have attended an ABA-approved law school, and must be in the top third of the class in their prior school.

Costs
Tuition and fees for the 1999-2000 academic year are $5370 for full-time in-state students and $8040 for out-of-state students. On-campus room and board costs about $5860 annually; books and supplies run $1200.

Financial Aid
About 79% of current law students receive some form of aid. The average annual amount of aid from all sources combined, including scholarships, loans, and work contracts, is $10,000; maximum, $17,000. Awards are based on need and merit. The required financial statement are the CSS Profile and the FAFSA. The aid application deadline for fall entry is March 1. Special funds for minority or disadvantaged students are available. First-year students are notified about their financial aid application at time of acceptance.

About the Law School
Brigham Young University J. Reuben Clark Law School was established in 1973 and is a private institution. The 600-acre campus is in a suburban area 50 miles south of Salt Lake City. The primary mission of the law school is to prepare its graduates with the legal skills and ethical strength to make a positive difference for their clients as well as their communities. Students have access to federal, state, county, city, and local agencies, courts, correctional facilities, law firms, and legal aid organizations in the Provo area. Facilities of special interest to law students include a student's own personal study carrel within the law library where books and personal effects may be secured. Housing for law students is available for single and married students within easy access of the school. About 95% of the law school facilities are accessible to the physically disabled.

Calendar
The law school operates on a traditional semester basis. Courses for full-time students are offered days only and must be completed within 3 years. There is no part-time program. New students are admitted in the fall. There is no summer session. Transferable summer courses are not offered.

Programs
In addition to the J.D., the law school offers the LL.M. Students may take relevant courses in other programs and apply credit toward the J.D.; a maximum of 9, credits may be applied if obtaining a master's degree. The following joint degrees may be earned: J.D./M.P.A. (Juris Doctor/Master of Public Administration), J.D./M.B.A. (Juris Doctor/Master of Business Administration), J.D./Ed.D. (Juris Doctor/Doctor of Education), J.D./M.Acc. (Juris Doctor/Master of Accountancy), and J.D./M.Ed. (Juris Doctor/Master of Education).

Required
To earn the J.D., candidates must complete 90 total credits, of which 36 are for required courses. They must maintain a minimum GPA of 2.7 in the required courses. The following first-year courses are required of all students: Torts I and II, Contracts I and II, Civil Procedure I and II, Property I and II, Criminal Law, and Introduction to Advocacy I and II. Required upper-level courses consist of Professional Responsibility and a substantial paper. The required orientation program for first-year students is a 5-day program that includes an introduction to the study of law and legal research.

Phone: 801-378-4277
Fax: 801-378-5897
E-mail: wilcock@lawgate.byu.edu
Web: law.byu.edu

Contact

Lola K. Wilcock, Admissions Director, 801-378-4277 for general inquiries; Douglas Young, 801-378-4104 for financial aid information.

UTAH

Electives

The J. Reuben Clark Law School offers concentrations in corporate law, international law, and tax law. In addition, the law school has several LawHelp seminars in which students are able to provide legal services to clients under the direction of an attorney. Second- and third-year law students may earn up to 10 credits in externships or LawHelp seminars. Each first-year student has one course taught in seminar form; 51 seminars are available for second- and third-year students. Students are allowed up to 6 credit hours for judicial, prosecutorial, governmental, and public interest internships; 2 credit hours for research programs; and 6 for field work. Student organizations sponsor semiweekly lecture series ranging from practical lawyering skills to jurisprudential theory. There are professional seminars for first-year students, and during the winter semester, there are weekly visitors from the practicing bench and bar. Students interested in study abroad programs sponsored by other law schools may transfer credit. Each first-year course has an assigned tutorial. Individual tutors may be requested by professors and will be assigned by the law school. The Assistant Dean meets with students in academic jeopardy and those needing accommodation (ADA) to design study plans (materials, one-on-one peer tutoring, professional consultation). Scholarships are available for minority students; the Minority Law Student Association (MLSA) and the American Indian Law Student Association arrange programs of interest. A joint student/faculty Law School Diversity Committee is geared to expanding the school's diversity. The most widely taken electives are Constitutional Law, Secured Transactions, and Wills and Estates.

Graduation Requirements

In order to graduate, candidates must have a GPA of 2.7, completed the upper-division writing requirement.

Organizations

Students edit the *Brigham Young University Law Review, Journal of Public Law, International and Comparative Law Annual,* and *Journal of Law and Education,* the newspaper *Reuby's Register, The Clark Memorandum,* a semi-annual alumni magazine, and the semi-annual *Alumni News.* The school sends teams to the Jessup International Moot Court Competition (annual, at varied locations); First-Year Moot Court Competition (on-site, winter semester); and five other competitions annually. Other competitions include the John Welch Award for Outstanding Writing, the Founding Fathers Freedom Award, and the Woody Deem Trial Competition. Law student organizations include the Public Interest Law Society, International and Comparative Law Society, and Government and Politics Legal Society. Local chapters of national associations include Phi Alpha Delta, American Inn of Court, and Phi Delta Phi.

Library

The law library contains 430,431 hardcopy volumes and 137,137 microform volume equivalents, and subscribes to 5632 serial publications. Such on-line databases and networks as LEXIS, DIALOG, WESTLAW, and state gateway access to catalogs that are shared databases, LAN access to databases at the main library, and 64 CD-ROM databases are available to law students for research. Special library collections include government documents and Utah State depositories—American Indian Law Collection. Recently, the library upgraded its local area computer network and the NOTIS automated library system. A 38,443-square foot addition in June 1996 doubled the library's size. The ratio of library volumes to faculty is 15,229 to 1 and to students, 717 to 1. The ratio of seats in the library to students is 1 to 1.

Faculty

The law school has 27 full-time and 31 part-time faculty members, of whom 15 are women. According to AAUP standards for Category I institutions, faculty salaries are average. About 4% of full-time faculty have a graduate law degree in addition to the J.D.; about 4% of part-time faculty have one. The ratio of full-time students to full-time faculty in an average class is 16 to 1. The law school has a regular program of bringing visiting professors and other distinguished lecturers and visitors to campus. There is a chapter of the Order of the Coif; 21 faculty and 137 graduates are members.

Placement

J.D.s awarded:	152

Services available through: separate law school placement center.

Services: speaker programs on different areas of practice, resume review service, and workshops

Special features: networking groups, practice areas, tutorials, a legal career planning course, satellite interviewing trips, attorney mock interviewing programs, video interviews, a judicial clerkship handbook, a job hunt handbook, a legal career planning handbook, and alumni receptions.

Full-time job interviews:	62 employers
Summer job interviews:	72 employers
Placement by graduation:	77% of class
Placement within 9 months:	94% of class
Average starting salary:	$22,000 to $90,000

Areas of placement:

Private practice 2-10 attorneys	23%
Private practice 11-25 attorneys	7%
Private practice 26-50 attorneys	6%
Private practice 101+ attorneys	7%
Judicial clerkships	17%
Business/industry	16%
Government	8%
Pursuing full-time degrees	4%
Military	2%
Self-employed	2%

Students

About 35% of the student body are women; 15%, minorities; 1%, African American; 7%, Asian American; 6%, Hispanic; 2%, Native American; and 1%, foreign nationals. The majority of students come from Utah (49%). The average age of entering students is 26; age range is 21 to 46. About 85% of students enter directly from undergraduate school, 5% have a graduate degree, and 10% have worked full-time prior to entering law school. About 1% drop out after the first year for academic or personal reasons; 98% remain to receive a law degree.

BROOKLYN LAW SCHOOL

250 Joralemon Street
Brooklyn, NY 11201

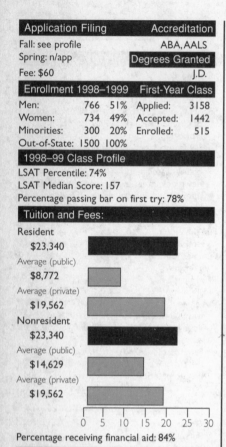

Enrollment 1998–1999   First-Year Class

Men:	766	51%	Applied:	3158
Women:	734	49%	Accepted:	1442
Minorities:	300	20%	Enrolled:	515
Out-of-State:	1500	100%		

1998–99 Class Profile

LSAT Percentile: 74%
LSAT Median Score: 157
Percentage passing bar on first try: 78%

Tuition and Fees:

Resident
$23,340

Average (public)
$8,772

Average (private)
$19,562

Nonresident
$23,340

Average (public)
$14,629

Average (private)
$19,562

0 5 10 15 20 25 30

Percentage receiving financial aid: 84%

ADMISSIONS

In the fall 1999 first-year class, 3158 applied, 1442 were accepted, and 515 enrolled. Eighteen transfers enrolled. The median LSAT percentile of the most recent first-year class was 74; the median GPA was 3.35 on a scale of 4.0. The lowest LSAT percentile accepted was 37; the highest was 97.

Requirements

Applicants must have a bachelor's degree from an accredited institution and take the LSAT. The most important admission factors include LSAT results, GPA, college attended, and academic achievement. No specific undergraduate courses are required. Candidates are not interviewed.

Procedure

The application deadline for fall entry is open, but it is recommended that students apply by April 1. Applicants should submit an application form, LSAT results, transcripts, a nonrefundable application fee of $60, and Dean's Certification Form. Notification of the admission decision is on a rolling basis beginning in December. The latest acceptable

LSAT test date for fall entry is June. The law school uses the LSDAS.

Special

The law school recruits minority and disadvantaged students by means of recruitment visits to historically black colleges and universities; various minority law career days and professional school forums sponsored by colleges and/or national minority student organizations; assistance from school chapters of Asian, black, and Latin American law student associations in recruitment efforts; an annual on-campus Minority Student Recruitment event; the LSDAS Candidate Referral Service (CRS); and a series of orientation programs for prospective students, hosted at the law school. Transfer students must have a minimum GPA of approximately 3.0, have attended an ABA-approved law school, and have a letter of good standing from the dean of the current school. The law school must be a member of AALS; 33 credits are the maximum allowable.

Costs

Tuition and fees for the 1999-2000 academic year are $23,340 for all full-time students. Tuition for part-time students is $16,625 per year. Books and supplies run $1200.

Financial Aid

About 84% of current law students receive some form of aid. The average annual amount of aid from all sources combined, including scholarships, loans, and work contracts, is $24,288. Awards are based on need and merit. The required financial statements are the FAFSA, Need Access Form, and IRS Form 1040's for applicants and their parents. No application is required for merit-based awards. The aid application deadline for fall entry is March 1. Special funds for minority or disadvantaged students include the Geraldo Rivera, MLK, Jr., Judith Bregman, William Randolph Hearst, Edgardo Lopez, and James McClendon, Jr., scholarships. First-year students are notified about their financial aid application at time of acceptance.

About the Law School

Brooklyn Law School was established in 1901. The 1-acre campus is in an urban area in New York City. The primary mission of the law school is not only to train practicing attorneys, but also to help students develop the intellectual capacity required to succeed whether they choose

to practice law or pursue an alternative career with a legal background. Students have access to federal, state, county, city, and local agencies, courts, correctional facilities, law firms, and legal aid organizations in the Brooklyn area. Within walking distance are the U.S. district court, appellate division court, state supreme and family courts, city civil and criminal courts, U.S. attorney's office, King's County district attorney's office, Legal Aid Society, and other city, state, and federal agencies. Facilities of special interest to law students include a technologically advanced library and fully wired classrooms with more than 1400 Internet connections available throughout the facility. Housing for law students is available for nearly 140 students in 7 residence halls located in the landmark Brooklyn Heights Historic District; the Office of Administrative and Student Services publishes current housing information in a weekly newsletter. All law school facilities are accessible to the physically disabled.

Calendar

The law school operates on a traditional semester basis. Courses for full-time students are offered both day and evening and must be completed within 4 years. For part-time students, courses are offered both day and evening and must be completed within 5 years. New full- and part-time students are admitted in the fall. There is a 6-week summer session. Transferable summer courses are offered.

Programs

In addition to the J.D., the law school offers the Foreign Trained Lawyers Certificate Program (20 credits). The following joint degrees may be earned: J.D./M.P.A. (Juris Doctor/Master of Public Administration), J.D./M.B.A. (Juris Doctor/Master of Business Administration), J.D./M.S. (Juris Doctor/Master of Science in planning), J.D./M.U.P. (Juris Doctor/Master of Urban Planning), J.D./M.A. (Juris Doctor/Master of Arts in law and in political science), and J.D./ M.S. (Juris Doctor/Master of Science in library and information science).

Required

To earn the J.D., candidates must complete 86 total credits, of which 35 are for required courses. They must maintain a minimum GPA of 2.0 in the required courses. The following first-year courses are required of all students: Civil Proce-

Phone: 718-780-7906
Fax: 718-780-0395
E-mail: admitq@brooklaw.edu
Web: brooklaw.edu

Contact

Henry W. Haverstick III, Dean of Admissions and Financial Aid, 718-780-7906 for general inquiries; Gerard Anderson, Financial Aid Director, 718-780-7915 for financial aid information.

NEW YORK

dure, Constitutional Law, Contracts, Criminal Law, Legal Process, Legal Writing, Property, and Torts. Required upper-level courses consist of Legal Profession and upper-class writing requirement. The required orientation program for first-year students is an initial week before classes begin and consists of services that are part of the first-year New Student Orientation Program; students receive faculty and student advisers, start the Legal Process course and the First-Year Legal Writing Program, and participate in workshops.

Electives

The Brooklyn Law School offers concentrations in corporate law, criminal law, entertainment, family law, international law, litigation, securities law, sports law, tax law, torts and insurance, intellectual property, international business law, public interest, and international human rights. In addition, any student who has completed the first year of study may take clinics in legal services for the elderly, criminal practice, federal civil litigation, immigration law, mediation, not-for-profit corporations, and bankruptcy. Seminars range from 4 to 6 credits. All students who have completed their first year of study may enroll in internships with judges, criminal justice agencies, and a wide range of organizations in areas such as environmental law, children's rights, business regulation, and arts/entertainment. Up to 3 credits may be earned by any upper-level student who, under the supervision of a faculty member, researches and writes a paper of publishable quality. The Media and Society Lecture Series brings new members from around the country to address current issues involving the media. The Abraham L. Pomerantz lectures focus on corporate or securities law topics and related professional responsibility issues. Summer study sponsored by the Law School in Bologna, Italy, and Beijing is available. Upper-level students may also pursue study abroad through other law schools if they demonstrate, in writing, special needs and obtain the written approval of the Associate Dean for Academic Affairs. First-year students may take advantage of year-long support services offered through the Academic Success Program. A summer legal process course and various tutorial programs specifically target affirmative action students. The most widely taken electives are New York Civil Practice, Commercial

Paper, Criminal Procedure, and Debtor-Creditor Rights.

Graduation Requirements

In order to graduate, candidates must have a GPA of 2.0, have completed the upper-division writing requirement, and have passed the Legal Profession course.

Organizations

Students edit the *Brooklyn Law Review, Brooklyn Journal of International Law,* and *Journal of Law and Public Policy,* and the newspapers *Justinian* and *The Docket.* Moot court teams annually compete in 15 to 18 tournaments including the ABA's National Moot Court Competition; the International Law Students Association's Phillip C. Jessup International Law Competition; and the National First Amendement Competition, co-sponsored by Vanderbilt University and the Freedom Forum. Other competitions include the Texas Young Lawyer's Association National Trial Competition, the College of Trial Lawyers and Bar of City of New York National Moot Court Competition, and Pace University National Environmental Law Competition. Law student organizations include the Student Bar Association and Asian, black, and Latin American law student associations. There are local chapters of the Association of Trial Lawyers of America, the National Lawyers Guild, and Legal Association of Women. Other organizations include the Brooklyn Law Students for the Public Interest; BLS Students Against Domestic Violence; and Entertainment, Arts, and Sports Law.

Library

The law library contains 486,259 hardcopy volumes and 1,103,385 microform volume equivalents, and subscribes to 1000 serial publications. Such on-line databases and networks as LEXIS, DIALOG, WESTLAW, QUICK-LAW, the Internet, OCLC FirstSearch, CIS, Congressional Universe, Legal Trac, Index Master, Law Pro, Nat Law, Web Course in a Box, and Access UN are available to law students for research. Special library collections include a selective U.S. government depository, a selective New York depository, and international law and women in the law collections. Recently, a new library facility was completed. The 78,000 square foot building offers multiple reading rooms, and more than 20 group study and conference rooms. Most

Services available through: a separate law school placement center

Services: on-line job listings and specialized public interest counseling

Special features: a network of 15,000 alumni; and mandatory first-semester individual counseling for first-year students

Full-time job interviews:	53 employers
Summer job interviews:	69 employers
Placement by graduation:	n/av
Placement within 9 months:	95% of class

Average starting salary: $50,000 to $100,000

Areas of placement:

Private practice 2-10 attorneys	21%
Private practice 11-25 attorneys	4%
Private practice 26-50 attorneys	4%
Private practice 51-100 attorneys	3%
Private practice 100+ attorneys	11%
Business/industry	19%
Government	17%
Judicial clerkships	6%
Public interest	4%
Academic	2%

areas of the library have network connections to accommodate student or library-provided laptops. The ratio of seats in the library to students is 1 to 2.

Faculty

The law school has 67 full-time and 97 part-time faculty members, of whom 50 are women. About 25% of full-time faculty have a graduate law degree in addition to the J.D.; about 28% of part-time faculty have one. The ratio of full-time students to full-time faculty in an average class is 16 to 1; in a clinic, 8 to 1. The law school has a regular program of bringing visiting professors and other distinguished lecturers and visitors to campus.

Students

About 49% of the student body are women; 20%, minorities; 6%, African American; 8%, Asian American; and 5%, Hispanic. The average age of entering students is 25; age range is 19 to 56. About 34% of students enter directly from undergraduate school, 8% have a graduate degree, and 66% have worked full-time prior to entering law school. About 3% drop out after the first year for academic or personal reasons; 97% remain to receive a law degree.

CALIFORNIA WESTERN SCHOOL OF LAW

225 Cedar Street
San Diego, CA 92101-3046

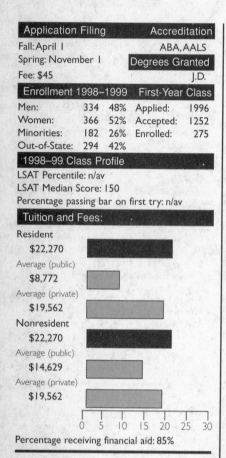

Application Filing	Accreditation
Fall: April 1	ABA, AALS
Spring: November 1	**Degrees Granted**
Fee: $45	J.D.

Enrollment 1998–1999		First-Year Class	
Men:	334 48%	Applied:	1996
Women:	366 52%	Accepted:	1252
Minorities:	182 26%	Enrolled:	275
Out-of-State:	294 42%		

1998–99 Class Profile
LSAT Percentile: n/av
LSAT Median Score: 150
Percentage passing bar on first try: n/av

Tuition and Fees:

Resident
$22,270
Average (public)
$8,772
Average (private)
$19,562
Nonresident
$22,270
Average (public)
$14,629
Average (private)
$19,562

0 5 10 15 20 25 30

Percentage receiving financial aid: 85%

ADMISSIONS
In the fall 1999 first-year class, 1996 applied, 1252 were accepted, and 275 enrolled. The lowest LSAT percentile accepted was 25; the highest was 75.

Requirements
Applicants must have a bachelor's degree from an accredited institution and take the LSAT. The most important admission factors include LSAT results, GPA, academic achievement, and undergraduate curriculum. No specific undergraduate courses are required. Candidates are not interviewed.

Procedure
The application deadline for fall entry is April 1. Applicants should submit an application form, LSAT results, transcripts, a nonrefundable application fee of $45, 2 letters of recommendation, a personal statement, and a resume. Notification of the admission decision is on a rolling basis. The latest acceptable LSAT test date for fall entry is February. The law school uses the LSDAS.

Special
The law school recruits minority and disadvantaged students The Office of Minority Affairs coordinates the ethnic diversity recruitment program and maintains working relationships with law firms, alumni, professional and community organizations, and college administrators who provide valuable resources for minority students. Transfer students must have one year of credit, have attended an ABA-approved law school, submit an official transcript and 2 letters of recommendation, preferably from a law school dean or professors. Preadmissions courses consist of the 6-week Summer Enrichment Program, a 3-credit course, which is an introduction to law school, the tasks of a law student, and the American legal system.

Costs
Tuition and fees for the 1999-2000 academic year are $22,270 for all full-time students. Tuition for all part-time students is $16,270 per year.

Financial Aid
In a recent year, about 85% of law students received some form of aid. The average annual amount of aid from all sources combined, including scholarships, loans, and work contracts, was $28,000; maximum, $32,000. Awards are based on need. The required financial statement is FAFSA. The aid application deadline for fall entry is March 18. Special funds for minority or disadvantaged students consist of scholarships. First-year students are notified about their financial aid application at the time of acceptance.

About the Law School
California Western School of Law was established in 1924. The campus is in an urban area in San Diego. The primary mission of the law school is to emphasize both the academic development of its students and the social and cultural aspects of an attorney's role in society. Students have access to federal, state, county, city, and local agencies, courts, correctional facilities, law firms, and legal aid organizations in the San Diego area. The San Diego Law Library is nearby. Facilities of special interest to law students are within walking distance and include courts, law firms, city, state, and federal agencies, and county law library. Housing for law students is off campus. The school has a housing coordinator to assist students. Most students live within 5 to 10 minutes of school. About 95% of the law school facilities are accessible to the physically disabled.

Calendar
The law school operates on a trimester basis. Courses for full-time students are offered days only and must be completed within 5 years. New full-time students are admitted in the fall and spring. There is a 15-week summer session. Transferable summer courses are offered.

Programs
Students may take relevant courses in other programs and apply credit toward the J.D.; a maximum of 12 credits may be applied. The following joint degrees may be earned: J.D./M.S.W. (Juris Doctor/Master of Social Work) and LL.M./M.C.L. (Master of Laws/Master of Comparative Law).

Phone: 619-525-1401
800-255-4252 out of state 256-4252 x1401
Fax: 619-615-1401
E-mail: rbriscoe@cwsl.edu
Web: cwsl.edu

Contact
Ruth Briscoe, Assistant Director Admissions, 619-625-1402 for general inquiries; Kyle Poston, Executive Director of Financial Aid, 619-525-7060 for financial aid information.

Required
To earn the J.D., candidates must complete 89 total credits, of which 43 are for required courses. They must maintain a minimum grade average of 74 in the required courses. The following first-year courses are required of all students: Legal Skills I and II, Property I and II, Contracts I and II, Torts I, Criminal Law, and Civil Procedure I and II. Required upper-level courses consist of Constitutional Law I, Criminal Procedure, Evidence, Professional Responsibility, Legal Skills III, and Torts II. The required orientation program for first-year students is a mandatory 1-day general orientation. There is also an optional 2-week academic success program for culturally disadvantaged students.

Electives
The California Western School of Law offers concentrations in corporate law, entertainment, environmental law, family law, international law, labor law, litigation, sports law, tax law, real estate law, and telecommunication law. There are a wide variety of specialized seminar courses open to upper-level students. The school has an internship program open to upper-level students; students may take up to 10 credit hours and will receive 1 credit hour for a weekly seminar. Students may assist faculty as research assistants. Special lecture series include the Faculty Speakers Series, the Scholar in Residence Series and S. Houston Lay International Law and Relations Series. Students may participate in any ABA-approved study-abroad program and transfer up to 8 credit hours of work. Tutorial programs include the Academic Success Program. The Office of Minority Affairs administers a 2-week orientation program prior to the fall trimester, coordinates a mentor program for students with local minority lawyers, and sponsors tutorials. The school sponsors more than 30 student organizations that cover a wide range of interests and topics. The most widely taken electives are International Law, Litigation and Advocacy, and Sports and Entertainment.

Graduation Requirements
In order to graduate, candidates must have a grade average of 74, have completed the upper-division writing requirement, and a practicum course.

Organizations
Students edit the *California Western Law Review*, the *California Western International Law Journal*, and the student newspaper the *Commentary*. Moot court competitions include the National Appellate Advocacy, Roger J. Traynor Moot Court, and Phillip C. Jessup International Law. Student organizations include Advocacy Honors Board, Association for Public Interest Law, and Criminal Justice Society. There are local chapters of Delta Theta Phi, Phi Alpha Delta, and Phi Delta Phi.

Library
The law library contains 257,781 hardcopy volumes and 643,130 microform volume equivalents, and subscribes to 3420 serial publications. Such on-line databases and networks as LEXIS, DIALOG, WESTLAW, NEXIS, the Internet, and Legal-Trac are available to law students for research. Special library collections include collections on comparative law, constitutional and human rights law, military law, and international law. There is a partial California Depository Library. Recently, the law school remodeled and refurbished an existing space of the library into a reading room, and upgraded the student computer lab. The ratio of library volumes to faculty is 5189 to 1 and to students, 308 to 1. The ratio of seats in the library to students is 1 to 1.

Faculty
The law school has 42 full-time and 45 part-time faculty members, of whom 34 are women. About 29% of full-time faculty have a graduate law degree in addition to the J.D.; about 14% of part-time faculty have one. The ratio of full-time students to full-time faculty in an average class is 22 to 1; in a clinic, 1 to 1.

Placement
J.D.s awarded:	214

Services available through: A separate law school placement center.
Services: nonlegal career alternatives, judicial clerkships, and decision-making counseling.
Special features: intensive individual planning and counseling, Alumni Career Advisor/mentor program, minority career development program, government legal careers job fair, public interest job fair, 2 career counselors on staff, a Pro Bono Program, and practice area/career option panels.

Full-time job interviews:	19 employers
Summer job interviews:	34 employers
Placement by graduation:	n/av
Placement within 9 months:	78% of class
Average starting salary:	$46,773 to $78,000

Areas of placement:
Private practice 2-10 attorneys	45%
Private practice 11-25 attorneys	15%
Private practice 26-50 attorneys	9%
Private practice 51-100 attorneys	7%
Government	26%
Business/industry	17%
Military	5%
Judicial clerkships	4%
Academic	3%
Public interest	2%

Students
About 52% of the student body are women; 26%, minorities; 3%, African American; 11%, Asian American; 10%, Hispanic; and 1%, Native American. The majority of students come from California (58%). The average age of entering students is 27; age range is 20 to 59. About 4% of students have a graduate degree. About 14% drop out after the first year for academic or personal reasons.

CAMPBELL UNIVERSITY

Norman Adrian Wiggins School of Law

P.O. Box 158
Buies Creek, NC 27506

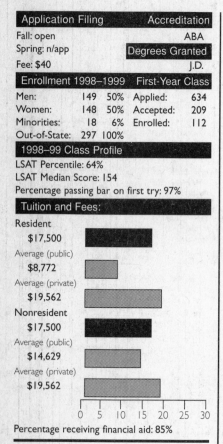

Application Filing	Accreditation
Fall: open	ABA
Spring: n/app	**Degrees Granted**
Fee: $40	J.D.

Enrollment 1998–1999		First-Year Class	
Men:	149 50%	Applied:	634
Women:	148 50%	Accepted:	209
Minorities:	18 6%	Enrolled:	112
Out-of-State:	297 100%		

1998–99 Class Profile
LSAT Percentile: 64%
LSAT Median Score: 154
Percentage passing bar on first try: 97%

Tuition and Fees:

Resident
$17,500

Average (public)
$8,772

Average (private)
$19,562

Nonresident
$17,500

Average (public)
$14,629

Average (private)
$19,562

0 5 10 15 20 25 30

Percentage receiving financial aid: 85%

ADMISSIONS

In the fall 1999 first-year class, 634 applied, 209 were accepted, and 112 enrolled. Two transfers enrolled. The median LSAT percentile of the most recent first-year class was 64; the median GPA was 3.2 on a scale of 4.0.

Requirements

Applicants must have a bachelor's degree from an accredited institution and take the LSAT. The most important admission factors include LSAT results, GPA, and personal interview. No specific undergraduate courses are required. Candidates are interviewed.

Procedure

The application deadline for fall entry is open. Applicants should submit an application form, LSAT results, a nonrefundable application fee of $40, and 2 letters of recommendation. Notification of the admission decision is on a rolling basis. The latest acceptable LSAT test date for fall entry is February. The law school uses the LSDAS.

Special

The law school recruits minority and disadvantaged students by visiting minority schools and through alumni efforts. Transfer students must have one year of credit and have attended an ABA-approved law school.

Costs

Tuition and fees for the 1999-2000 academic year are $17,500 for all full-time students. On-campus room and board costs about $4390 annually, and books and supplies run $750.

Financial Aid

About 85% of current law students receive some form of aid. Awards are based on need and merit. The required financial statement is FAFSA. The aid application deadline for fall entry is open. First-year students are notified about their financial aid application at time of acceptance.

About the Law School

Campbell University Norman Adrian Wiggins School of Law was established in 1976 and is a private institution. The 1450-acre campus is in a rural area 30 miles from both Raleigh and Fayetteville. The primary mission of the law school is to equip men and women for the practice of law, while fostering a sound philosophical and ethical foundation for a legal career, and instill in students a sense of professional responsibility. Students have access to federal, state, county, city, and local agencies, courts, correctional facilities, law firms, and legal aid organizations in the Buies Creek area. The district and superior courts, which are the trial courts of North Carolina, sit in Lillington, approximately 5 miles from the law school. The North Carolina Supreme Court and Court of Appeals and the U.S. District Court for the Eastern District of North Carolina sit in Raleigh, 30 miles away. The Governor's office, the General Assembly, and various executive agencies sit in Raleigh, the state capital. Housing for single law students is available in the dormitories. The University has a limited number of apartments available for married students. Off-campus apartments in the towns surrounding the law school are also available. All law school facilities are accessible to the physically disabled.

Calendar

The law school operates on a traditional semester basis. Courses for full-time students are offered both day and evening and must be completed within 5 years. There is no part-time program. New full-time students are admitted in the fall. There is a 7-week summer session.

Programs

The following joint degrees may be earned: J.D./M.B.A. (Juris Doctor/Master of Business Administration).

Phone: 910-893-1754
800-334-4111, ext. 1754
Fax: 910-893-1780
E-mail: culaw@webster.campbell.edu
Web: webster.campbell.edu/culawsch.htm

Contact

Alan D. Woodlief, Associate Dean for Admissions, 910-893-1753 for general inquiries, or Lou Naylor; Peggy Mason, Director, 910-893-1310 for financial aid information.

NORTH CAROLINA

Required

To earn the J.D., candidates must complete 90 total credits, of which 73 are for required courses. They must maintain a minimum GPA of 70 (on a scale of 100) in the required courses. The following first-year courses are required of all students: Contracts I and II, Civil Procedure I and II, Criminal Law, Legal Method and Research, Appellate Advocacy, Torts I and II, Property I and II, Elementary Jurisprudence, Constitutional Law: Federal Powers and Fourteenth Amendment, Professional Responsibility Lecture Series, and Practical Skills and Values. Required upper-level courses consist of Constitutional Law: First Amendment, Wills and Trusts, Criminal Procedure, Commercial Law I and II, Income Taxation, Evidence, Trial Advocacy, either Pre-Trial Litigation or Advanced Trial Advocacy, Business Associations, Professional Responsibility and Ethics, Alternate Dispute Resolution, Mediation and Conciliation, Law Office Operation and Management, and either Perspectives on Professionalism and Leadership or Perspectives. All students must take clinical courses. The required orientation program for first-year students is a 6-day session that includes both lectures and small group meetings on legal analysis, case analysis and synthesis, and legal research.

Electives

Trial Advocacy is a required "simulated" clinic offering 7 credit hours over 2 semesters. Seminars include Environmental Law, Insurance Law, and Intellectual Property. Public-service internships are available to second- and third-year students with a maximum of 2 hours credit. The Professional Responsibility Lecture Series is required of all first-year students. Special interest group programs include Law Students Civil Rights Research Council. The most widely taken electives are Family Law, Remedies, and Workers' Compensation.

Graduation Requirements

In order to graduate, candidates must have an average of 72 on a scale of 100.

Organizations

Students edit the *Campbell Law Review* and the newspaper *Campbell Law Observer*. Moot court competitions entered by students are the ABA National Appellate Advocacy, National Moot Court, and John Marshall Privacy and International Law Moot Court Competition. Other competitions are the National Trial, American Trial Lawyers Association, National Student Trial Advocacy, ABA Client Counseling, and NITA Tournament of Champions Trial Competition. Law student organizations include the Student Bar Association, ABA-Law Student Division, and Black Law Students Association. Local chapters of national associations include Delta Theta Phi-Bryan Senate and Phi Alpha Delta fraternities.

Library

The law library contains 156,000 hardcopy volumes and 56,998 microform volume equivalents, and subscribes to 650 serial publications. Such on-line databases and networks as LEXIS, DIALOG, WESTLAW, and NEXIS, InfoTrac, Current Index to Legal Periodicals, and CALI are available to law students for research. Special library collections include are in the areas of trial advocacy, ethics and jurisprudence, public interest law, church-state resources, and federal taxation. Recently, the library updated 3 computer laboratories: 1 for teaching, 1 for on-line research, and 1 for research and writing; all have Internet access. The ratio of library volumes to faculty is 4216 to 1 and to students, 525 to 1. The ratio of seats in the library to students is 1 to 1.

Faculty

The law school has 19 full-time and 18 part-time faculty members, of whom 6 are women. About 25% of full-time faculty have a graduate law degree in addition to the J.D.; about 5% of part-time faculty have one. The ratio of full-time students to full-time faculty in an average class is 23 to 1.

Students

About 50% of the student body are women; 6%, minorities; 3%, African American; 1%, Asian American; 1%, Hispanic; and 2%, Native American.

Placement

J.D.s awarded:	107
Services available through: a separate law school placement center.	
Services: in- and out-of-state job fairs	
Special features: targeted mailings sent to regions of North Carolina, press releases issued on student activities, alumni assistance in specific areas of job search, a separate placement resource center and library, a mentor program matching law students with Campbell alumni, and a North Carolina job fair	
Full-time job interviews:	n/av
Summer job interviews:	n/av
Placement by graduation:	68% of class
Placement within 9 months:	99% of class
Average starting salary:	n/av
Areas of placement:	
Private practice 2-100 attorneys	81%
Government	9%
Judicial clerkships	5%
Business/industry	2%
Academic	1%
Public interest	1%
Military	1%

Law School

303 East Broad Street
Columbus, OH 43215-3200

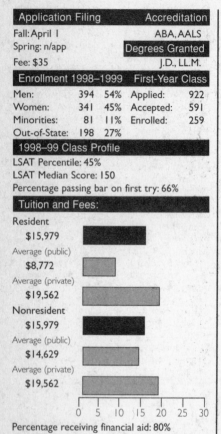

Application Filing		Accreditation
Fall: April 1		ABA, AALS
Spring: n/app		**Degrees Granted**
Fee: $35		J.D., LL.M.

Enrollment 1998–1999		First-Year Class	
Men:	394 54%	Applied:	922
Women:	341 45%	Accepted:	591
Minorities:	81 11%	Enrolled:	259
Out-of-State:	198 27%		

1998–99 Class Profile

LSAT Percentile: 45%
LSAT Median Score: 150
Percentage passing bar on first try: 66%

Tuition and Fees:

Resident
$15,979

Average (public)
$8,772

Average (private)
$19,562

Nonresident
$15,979

Average (public)
$14,629

Average (private)
$19,562

0 5 10 15 20 25 30

Percentage receiving financial aid: 80%

ADMISSIONS

In the fall 1999 first-year class, 922 applied, 591 were accepted, and 259 enrolled. Seven transfers enrolled. The median LSAT percentile of the most recent first-year class was 45; the median GPA was 3.07 on a scale of 4.0. The lowest LSAT percentile accepted was 36; the highest was 99.

Requirements

Applicants must have a bachelor's degree from an accredited institution and take the LSAT. Minimum acceptable GPA is 2.0 on a scale of 4.0. The most important admission factors include academic achievement, LSAT results, and life experience. No specific undergraduate courses are required. Candidates are not interviewed.

Procedure

The application deadline for fall entry is April 1. Applicants should submit an application form, LSAT results, transcripts, a nonrefundable application fee of $35, 2 letters of recommendation, an essay or personal statement, and a $100 tuition deposit for accepted students; a second $100 seat deposit is due by July 6. Notification of the admission decision is on a rolling basis. The latest acceptable LSAT test date for fall entry is February. The law school uses the LSDAS.

Special

The law school recruits minority and disadvantaged students by means of an annual Black Law Students Association open house, targeted mailings, use of minority students, faculty, and alumni in recruitment process, financial assistance programs, and participation in the Academic Success Program. Transfer students must have one year of credit and have attended an ABA-approved law school.

Costs

Tuition and fees for the 1999-2000 academic year are $15,979 for all full-time students. Tuition for part-time students is $9918 annually, or $551 per credit. Books and supplies run $887.

Financial Aid

About 80% of current law students receive some form of aid. The average annual amount of aid from all sources combined, including scholarships, loans, and work contracts, is $16,516; maximum, $28,199. Awards are based on need and merit. The required financial statement is FAFSA. The aid application deadline for fall entry is April 1. Special funds for minority or disadvantaged students include teaching and research assistantships, grants and scholarships, work-study awards, and low-interest student loans. First-year students are notified about their financial aid application at time of acceptance.

About the Law School

Capital University Law School was established in 1903 and is a private institution. The campus is in an urban area in the Discovery District of downtown Columbus. The primary mission of the law school is to develop powers of legal analysis, a critical attitude toward the law, a sense of ethics, and technical skills in legal advocacy, writing, research, and draftsmanship. Students have access to federal, state, county, city, and local agencies, courts, correctional facilities, law firms, and legal aid organizations in the Columbus area. Because Columbus is the state capital, it is the home of the Ohio Supreme Court, the state legislature, and numerous state agencies, including the Ohio Attorney General's Office. In addition to the state's highest court, Ohio is the location of a federal district court and state court of appeals. These courts and major corporate offices are within walking distance. Facilities of special interest to law students include a building containing classrooms, a legal clinic, seminar rooms, a courtroom, a library, an eating area, lounges, meeting rooms, and faculty offices. Housing for law students is available off campus; the university helps students find suitable housing. All law school facilities are accessible to the physically disabled.

Calendar

The law school operates on a traditional semester basis. Courses for full-time and part-time students are offered both day and evening and must be completed within 6 years. New full-time and part-time students are admitted in the fall. There is a 10-week summer session. Transferable summer courses are offered.

Phone: 614-236-6500
Fax: 614-236-6972
E-mail: admissions@law.capital.edu
Web: law.capital.edu

Contact

Linda Mihely, Assistant Dean of Admissions and Financial Aid, 614-236-6310 for general inquiries; Samantha Stalnaker, Assistant Director, 614-236-6350 for financial aid information.

OHIO

Programs

In addition to the J.D., the law school offers the LL.M. Students may take relevant courses in other programs and apply credit toward the J.D.; a maximum of 9 credits may be applied. The following joint degrees may be earned: J.D./M.B.A. (Juris Doctor/Master of Business Administration), J.D./M.S.A. (Juris Doctor/Master of Sports Administration), J.D./LL.M. (Juris Doctor/Master of Laws in taxation), and J.D./M.S.N. (Juris Doctor/Master of Science in Nursing).

Required

To earn the J.D., candidates must complete 86 semester total credits, of which 42 are for required courses. They must maintain a minimum GPA of 2.0 in the required courses. The following first-year courses are required of all students: Contracts I and II, Torts I and II, Property I and II, Constitutional Law I, Legal Writing I and II, Criminal Law, and Civil Prodedure I. Required upper-level courses consist of Evidence, Professional Responsibility, Civil Procedure II, Constitutional Law II, Federal Personal Income Tax, and a writing or research requirement. The required orientation program for first-year students lasts 3 1/2 days and includes 3 mock classroom discussions and meetings with faculty and peer advisers. An extended orientation provides study skills, time and stress management, and exam-taking seminars.

Electives

Students must take 11 credits in their area of concentration. The Law School offers concentrations in environmental law, tax law, and governmental affairs, labor and employment, publicly held companies, small business entities, and alternative dispute resolution. In addition, clinics in general, civil, and criminal litigation are available to students who have qualified as legal interns. Several seminars are offered each year in a variety of subjects. Externships are available through the local, state, and federal courts and through several government agencies and nonprofit organizations. Field work may be done through the Externship Programs, as well as clinics, and the Alternative Dispute Resolution-Night Prosecutor's Program. Special lecture series include the Sullivan Lectures.

There is also a Study-Abroad-at-Home program, the Greece International Law Student Program, and sister-school relationships with law schools in Passau, Germany; Glasgow, Scotland; and Saskatchewan, Canada. Tutorial programs include the Academic Success Programs. The most widely taken electives are Business Associations I and II, Commercial Paper, and Commercial Transactions.

Graduation Requirements

In order to graduate, candidates must have a GPA of 2.0 and have completed the upper-division writing requirement.

Organizations

Students edit *The Capital University Law Review* and the newspaper *Res Ipsa Loquitur*. The Moot Court Board sponsors intrascholastic and interscholastic competitions. Student organizations include the ABA-Law Student Division, Association of Trial Lawyers of America, and Capital Public Interest Law Foundation. There are local chapters of Delta Theta Phi, Phi Delta Phi, and Phi Alpha Delta.

Library

The law library contains 239,000 hardcopy volumes and 35,979 microform volume equivalents, and subscribes to 2385 serial publications. Such on-line databases and networks as LEXIS and WESTLAW are available to law students for research. Recently, the library moved into a new facility, adding seating and more group study rooms, and a computer system, INNOPAC. The ratio of library volumes to faculty is 6387 to 1 and to students, 250 to 1. The ratio of seats in the library to students is 1 to 2.

Faculty

The law school has 30 full-time and 56 part-time faculty members, of whom 14 are women. According to AAUP standards for Category IIA institutions, faculty salaries are average. About 48% of full-time faculty have a graduate law degree in addition to the J.D. The ratio of full-time students to full-time faculty in an average class is 12 to 1.

Placement

J.D.s awarded:	220
Services available through: A separate law school placement center.	
Special features: a career library, recruiting conferences, an alumni network and newsletter, on-campus interviews, and on-line access to postings from 7/9 Ohio law schools	
Full-time job interviews:	8 employers
Summer job interviews:	34 employers
Placement by graduation:	n/av
Placement within 9 months:	90% of class
Average starting salary:	$19,000 to $140,000
Areas of placement:	
Private practice 2-10 attorneys	15%
Private practice 11-25 attorneys	3%
Private practice 26-50 attorneys	2%
Private practice 51-100 attorneys	2%
Private practice 100+ attorneys	9%
Solo practice	4%
Private practice, unknown size	3%
Business/industry	31%
Government	25%
Judicial clerkships	5%
Academic	3%

Students

About 45% of the student body are women; 11%, minorities; 7%, African American; 2%, Asian American; and 2%, Hispanic. The majority of students come from Ohio (73%). The average age of entering students is 27; age range is 22 to 60. About 29% of students enter directly from undergraduate school and 14% have a graduate degree. About 10% drop out after the first year for academic or personal reasons; 98% remain to receive a law degree.

School of Law

11075 East Boulevard
Cleveland, OH 44106

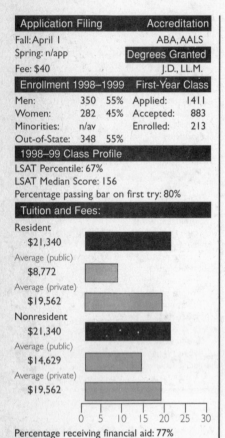

Application Filing		Accreditation
Fall: April 1		ABA, AALS
Spring: n/app		**Degrees Granted**
Fee: $40		J.D., LL.M.

Enrollment 1998–1999			First-Year Class	
Men:	350	55%	Applied:	1411
Women:	282	45%	Accepted:	883
Minorities:	n/av		Enrolled:	213
Out-of-State:	348	55%		

1998–99 Class Profile

LSAT Percentile: 67%
LSAT Median Score: 156
Percentage passing bar on first try: 80%

Tuition and Fees:

Resident
$21,340

Average (public)
$8,772

Average (private)
$19,562

Nonresident
$21,340

Average (public)
$14,629

Average (private)
$19,562

0 5 10 15 20 25 30

Percentage receiving financial aid: 77%

ADMISSIONS

In the fall 1999 first-year class, 1411 applied, 883 were accepted, and 213 enrolled. Seven transfers enrolled. The median LSAT percentile of the most recent first-year class was 67; the median GPA was 3.2 on a scale of 4.0.

Requirements

Applicants must have a bachelor's degree from an accredited institution and take the LSAT. The most important admission factors include writing ability, LSAT results, and academic achievement. No specific undergraduate courses are required. Candidates are not interviewed.

Procedure

The application deadline for fall entry is April 1. Applicants should submit an application form, a nonrefundable application fee of $40, and a personal statement. Notification of the admission decision is between January 1 and May 1. The latest acceptable LSAT test date for

fall entry is February. The law school uses the LSDAS.

Special

The law school recruits minority and disadvantaged students by means of attendance at law school fairs likely to be attended by minority and disadvantaged students, financial assistance, the Pre-Law Conference for People of Color, and co-sponsoring of the Midwest Minority Recruitment Fair. Transfer students must have one year of credit, have attended an ABA-approved law school, and have performed very well at the school from which they are transferring.

Costs

Tuition and fees for the 1999-2000 academic year are $21,340 for all full-time students. Books and supplies run $790.

Financial Aid

About 77% of current law students receive some form of aid. The average annual amount of aid from all sources combined, including scholarships, loans, and work contracts, is $26,700; maximum, $33,060. Awards are based on merit. The required financial statements are FAFSA and and either copies of the student's previous year's federal tax return or a student's statement of income. The aid application deadline for fall entry is May 1. Special funds for minority or disadvantaged students are available. First-year students are notified about their financial aid application approximately 4 weeks after the aid application is complete.

About the Law School

Case Western Reserve University School of Law was established in 1892 and is a private institution. The 128-acre campus is in an urban area 3 miles east of downtown Cleveland. The school has a 450-acre farm in an outlying community. The primary mission of the law school is to prepare leaders in the practice of law, public and community service, and commerce; to provide enlightenment to the legal profession and the larger society; and to foster an accessible, fair, and reliable system of justice. Students have access to federal, state, county, city, and local agencies, courts, correctional facilities, law firms, and legal aid organiza-

tions in the Cleveland area. Home to four of the nation's top 50 law firms, Greater Cleveland ranks fourth in the nation for the number of Fortune 500 company headquarters. Facilities of special interest to law students are the state-of-the-art computer laboratory and moot court room, along with a new legal clinic that operates as a law firm within the law school setting. Most students live in apartments in nearby Cleveland Heights. All law school facilities are accessible to the physically disabled.

Calendar

The law school operates on a traditional semester basis. Courses for full-time students are offered days only and must be completed within 3 years. For part-time students, courses are offered days only and must be completed within 6 years. New full- and part-time students are admitted in the fall. There is a 6-week summer session. Transferable summer courses are offered.

Programs

In addition to the J.D., the law school offers the LL.M. in taxation and in U.S. legal studies. Students may take relevant courses in other programs and apply credit toward the J.D.; a maximum of 9 credits may be applied. The following joint degrees may be earned: J.D./M.B.A. (Juris Doctor/Master of Business Administration), J.D./M.S.S.A. (Juris Doctor/Master of Science in Social Administration), J.D./M.N.O. (Juris Doctor/Master of Nonprofit Management), J.D./M.A. (Juris Doctor/Master of Arts in legal history and bioethics), J.D./M.D. (Juris Doctor/Doctor of Medicine), and J.D./M.P.H. (Juris Doctor/Master of Public Health).

Required

To earn the J.D., candidates must complete 88 total credits, of which 33 are for required courses. They must maintain a minimum GPA of 1.67 in the required courses. The following first-year courses are required of all students: Contracts, Criminal Law, Torts, Research, Analysis, and Writing, Constitutional Law, Civil Procedure, Property, and an elective. Required upper-level courses consist of Professional Responsibility and a substantial research paper. The required orientation program for first-year stu-

Phone: 216-368-3600
800-756-0036
Fax: 216-368-6144
E-mail: lawadmissions@po.cwru.edu or
lawmoney@po.cwru.edu
Web: www.law.cwru.edu

Contact

Barbara Andelman, Assistant Dean for Admissions, 216-368-3600 for general inquiries; Jay Ruffner, Financial Aid Coordinator, 216-368-3602 for financial aid information.

OHIO

dents is 3 days, during which students are welcomed into the law school community, oriented to the facilities and the library, and introduced to ethics and professionalism. They meet often with their first-year writing instructors and become acquainted with school and university administrators.

Electives

The School of Law offers concentrations in corporate law, criminal law, international law, litigation, securities law, tax law, and law and medicine. In addition, clinical courses, offered for either a half-year or full-year, provide students with the opportunity to represent clients in a variety of real-life experiences. Seminars are limited to 12 students and range from Bioethics and Law to Contemporary International Legal Problems. Judicial externships are available to selected students for 3 credits. Supervised research with faculty is worth 2 credit hours, and is offered to second- and third-year students. Field work is not available for credit except through a joint-degree program. Special lecture series include the Sumner Canary Memorial Lectureship, Norman A. Sugarman Tax Lectureship, Oliver C. Schroeder Scholar-in-Residence, Arthur A. Fiske Lectureship, and the Academy. A study-abroad program is created for any student in the country of choice, in addition to the already established programs at the University of Western Ontario and at universities in Mexico and French Canada. Academic exchange arrangements have been made at numerous overseas universities. A Dean's Tutorial Society offers tutorial assistance to first- and second-year students, primarily on exam technique and general writing skills. The school offers an academic assistance program. Moreover, the school is actively involved in the recruitment of students who will enhance the diversity of the student body and legal profession. A Minority Mentor program is offered, as is a tutorial program. An Annual Pre-Law Conference for People of Color is held and the school participates in the annual BLSA Midwest Minority Recruitment Fair. Scholarship opportunities are significant. The most widely taken electives are Evidence, Business Associations and Criminal Procedure, and Wills, Trusts and Future Interests.

Graduation Requirements

In order to graduate, candidates must have a GPA of 2.0 and have completed the upper-division writing requirement.

Organizations

Students edit the Case Western Reserve Law Review, Health Matrix: The Journal of Law-Medicine, Journal of International al Law, Canada-United States Law Journal, and the newspaper The Docket. Students compete in the local Dean Dunmore Moot Court competition; the National Moot Court, held regionally and in New York; J. Braxton Craven, Jr., held at the University of North Carolina; Niagara, Canada-U.S. relations; and the local Jessup competition sponsored by the International Law Society. Other competitions include the Jonathan M. Ault Mock Trial in Houston. Law student organizations include the Student Bar Association and the Student International Law Society. There are local chapters of Phi Delta Phi and Phi Alpha Theta.

Library

The law library contains 365,175 hardcopy volumes and 419,218 microform volume equivalents, and subscribes to 4795 serial publications. Such on-line databases and networks as LEXIS, DIALOG, WESTLAW, and more than 700 electronic services and library catalogs including Q/L, NEWSNET, Ohio Capital Connection, CCH Federal Securities Reporter, Congressional and Statistical Universe. West Ohio CD-ROMS and others are available to law students for research. Special library collections include a U.S. government documents depository and a Canadian government documents depository. Recently, the library implemented a fiber-optic university network and opened the Judge Charles R. Richey Reading Room. The ratio of library volumes to faculty is 7938 to 1 and to students, 577 to 1.

Faculty

The law school has 46 full-time and 64 part-time faculty members, of whom 28 are women. According to AAUP standards for Category I institutions, faculty salaries are well above average. About 15% of full-time faculty have a graduate law degree in addition to the J.D. The ratio of full-time students to full-time faculty in an average class is 15 to 1; in a

Placement

J.D.s awarded:	217

Services available through: a separate law school placement center.
Services: videotaped mock interviews
Special features: speakers, panels, and programs on a wide range of career options. Also, firms, corporations, and agencies are visited and an annual Midwest Minority Recruitment Conference is hosted. The school has an extensive recruitment program that includes both on-campus and out-of-state recruitment programs, as well as Resume Direct and Resume Collect.

Full-time job interviews:	40 employers
Summer job interviews:	61 employers
Placement by graduation:	63% of class
Placement within 9 months:	95% of class
Average starting salary:	$26,000 to $125,000

Areas of placement:
Private practice 2-10 attorneys	25%
Private practice 11-25 attorneys	8%
Private practice 26-50 attorneys	10%
Private practice 51-500+ attorneys	30%
Business/industry	13%
Judicial clerkships	8%
Government	3%
Public interest	2%
Academic	1%

clinic, 8 to 1. The law school has a regular program of bringing visiting professors and other distinguished lecturers and visitors to campus. There is a chapter of the Order of the Coif; 100 faculty and 10 graduates are members.

Students

About 45% of the student body are women; 6%, Asian American; and 2%, Hispanic. The majority of students come from Ohio (45%). The average age of entering students is 25; age range is 20 to 50. About 45% of students enter directly from undergraduate school, 23% have a graduate degree, and 55% have worked full-time prior to entering law school. About 3% drop out after the first year for academic or personal reasons; 90% remain to receive a law degree.

Columbus School of Law

Cardinal Station
Washington, DC 20064

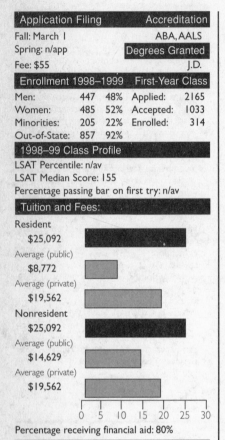

Application Filing		Accreditation
Fall: March 1		ABA, AALS
Spring: n/app		**Degrees Granted**
Fee: $55		J.D.

Enrollment 1998–1999			First-Year Class	
Men:	447	48%	Applied:	2165
Women:	485	52%	Accepted:	1033
Minorities:	205	22%	Enrolled:	314
Out-of-State:	857	92%		

1998–99 Class Profile
LSAT Percentile: n/av
LSAT Median Score: 155
Percentage passing bar on first try: n/av

Tuition and Fees:

Resident
$25,092
Average (public)
$8,772
Average (private)
$19,562
Nonresident
$25,092
Average (public)
$14,629
Average (private)
$19,562

0 5 10 15 20 25 30

Percentage receiving financial aid: 80%

ADMISSIONS

In the fall 1999 first-year class, 2165 applied, 1033 were accepted, and 314 enrolled. Nineteen transfers enrolled. The median GPA of the most recent first-year class was 3.1 on a scale of 4.0. The lowest LSAT percentile accepted was 23; the highest was 99.

Requirements
Applicants must have a bachelor's degree from an accredited institution and take the LSAT. The most important admission factors include LSAT results, GPA, and letter of recommendation. No specific undergraduate courses are required. Candidates are not interviewed.

Procedure
The application deadline for fall entry is March 1. Applicants should submit an application form, LSAT results, transcripts, a nonrefundable application fee of $55, and 2 letters of recommendation. Notification of the admission decision is on a rolling basis. The latest acceptable LSAT test date for fall entry is February. The law school uses the LSDAS.

Special
The law school recruits minority and disadvantaged students by visiting colleges and geographical areas with large minority populations. Minority applicants are encouraged to write brief background statements as part of the admissions process. Transfer students must have one year of credit, have attended an ABA-approved law school, be in good standing, and be competitive in class rank.

Costs

Tuition and fees for the 1999-2000 academic year are $25,092 for all full-time students. Tuition for all part-time students is $18,937 per year, or $880 per credit. On-campus room and board costs about $6772 annually; and books and supplies run $783.

Financial Aid

About 80% of current law students receive some form of aid. The maximum annual amount of aid from all sources combined, including scholarships, loans, and work contracts, is $39,684. Awards are based on need and merit, along with community service in conjunction with other considerations. The required financial statement is FAFSA. The aid application deadline for fall entry is March 1. Special funds for minority or disadvantaged students are available. Scholarships are merit based. First-year students are notified about their financial aid application after acceptance, when the financial aid file is complete, beginning in March.

About the Law School

Catholic University of America Columbus School of Law was established in 1898 and is a private institution. The 154-acre campus is in an urban area in a noncommercial area, accessible by public transportation. The primary mission of the law school is to provide a small, diverse student body with a quality legal education and to prepare students for the ethical practice of law. Students have access to federal, state, county, city, and local agencies, courts, correctional facilities, law firms, and legal aid organizations in the Washington area, including the nearby Library of Congress and the U.S. Supreme Court. Facilities of special interest to law students consist of a law school facility completed in 1994, that houses all components of the school. Law students also have access to the university's athletic complex, including a pool, Nautilus equipment, sauna, tennis courts, and a track. Housing for law students is available in 2 dormitories as single and double rooms. A variety of apartments and private rooms is within easy traveling distance. All law school facilities are accessible to the physically disabled.

Calendar

The law school operates on a traditional semester basis. Courses for full-time students are offered days only and must be completed within 5 years. For part-time students, courses are offered evenings only and must be completed within 6 years. New full-and part-time students are admitted in the fall. There is a 7- to 8-week summer session. Transferable summer courses are offered.

Programs

Students may take relevant courses in other programs and apply credit toward the J.D. If the student is not a joint degree candidate, 3 courses maybe applied. The following joint degrees may be earned: J.D./M.L.S. (Juris Doctor/Master of Library Science), J.D./M.S.W. (Juris Doctor/Master of Social Work), J.D./M.A. (Juris Doctor/Master of Arts in accounting, philosophy, psychol), and J.D./J.C.L. (Juris Doctor/Licentiate of Canon Law).

Contact

George Braxton, Admissions Director, 202-319-5151 for general inquiries; Gretchen Bonfardine, 202-319-5143 for financial aid information.

DISTRICT OF COLUMBIA ®

Required

To earn the J.D., candidates must complete 84 total credits, of which 33 are for required courses. They must maintain a minimum grade coverage of 70 (2.0) in the required courses. The following first-year courses are required of all students: Lawyering Skills, Contracts, Constitutional Law, Property, Criminal Law, Torts, and Civil Procedure. Required upper-level courses consist of Professional Reponsibility. The required orientation program for first-year students occurs during the first week and consists of the beginning of the Lawyering Skills course, a general introduction to the law library and the law school, study skills, and social activities.

Electives

The Columbus School of Law offers concentrations in corporate law, criminal law, family law, international law, labor law, litigation, media law, securities law, tax law, and public policy and law and religion. In addition, 7 clinical programs emphasize client representation. Two others involve legislative, administrative, and policy-making processes. Courses are open to upper-level students and credit varies. Seminars are also open only to upper-level students. Internships are available in a variety of legal settings and are supervised by practicing attorneys. Students may serve as research assistants to law faculty members. Special lecture series are the Pope John XXIII Lectures, the Brendan F. Brown Distinguished Lectures and Scholars-in-Residence, and the Mirror of Justice Lectures. There is a 6-week summer program at the Jagiellonian University in Cracow, Poland. Student groups and individual faculty members conduct informal tutorial sessions. A 2-week early start program is offered to entering students whose numerical credentials indicate that it would be especially beneficial. The most widely taken electives are Evidence, Corporations, and Family Law.

Graduation Requirements

In order to graduate, candidates must have a minimum grade average of 70 (or 2.0) and have completed the upper-division writing requirement.

Organizations

Student-edited publications are *The Catholic University of America Law Review, The Journal of Contemporary Health Law and Policy, CommLaw Conspectus: Journal of Communications Law and Policy,* and the newspaper *Judicial Notice.* Moot Court teams compete in the Wagner Cup in Labor Law, Environmental Law, and Polsky Criminal Law. Student organizations include student divisions of the ABA and the American Society of International Law, Communications Law Students, and Evening Law Students. There is a local chapter of Thurgood Marshall American Inn of Court. Other organizations include the Graduate Student Association.

Library

The law library contains 322,816 hardcopy volumes and 52,864 microform volume equivalents, and subscribes to 5334 serial publications. Such on-line databases and networks as LEXIS, DIALOG, and WESTLAW are available to law students for research. Special library collections include a partial U.S. government depository and United Nations documents, which may be accessed through hard-bound, on-line, and CD-ROM indices or by the Internet. Recently, construction was completed on a law building featuring a 3-level library wing with 3 videotape viewing rooms, spacious tables and computer-equipped carrels with task lights, classic scholar reading rooms, and 2 computer laboratories that also serve as training centers. The ratio of library volumes to faculty is 7173 to 1 and to students, 347 to 1. The ratio of seats in the library to students is 1 to 2.

Faculty

The law school has 46 full-time and 87 part-time faculty members, of whom 34 are women. According to AAUP standards for Category I institutions, faculty salaries are average. About 20% of full-time faculty have a graduate law degree in addition to the J.D. The ratio of full-time students to full-time faculty in an average class is 14 to 1; in a clinic, 8 to 1. The law school has a regular program of bringing visiting professors and other distinguished lecturers and visitors to campus.

Placement

J.D.s awarded:	291

Services available through: a separate law school placement center.

Services:

Special features: individual consultations, on-campus interviewing, consortium interviewing conferences, resume collection service, workshops on planning and executing a job search, writing resumes and cover letters, developing interviewing skills, building legal credentials, understanding the legal job market, and videotapes of alumni discussing specialties

Full-time job interviews:	53 employers
Summer job interviews:	53 employers
Placement by graduation:	89% of class
Placement within 9 months:	100% of class
Average starting salary:	$22,000 to $88,000
Areas of placement:	
Private practice 2-100 attorneys	38%
Government	23%
Judicial clerkships	18%
Business/industry	14%
Unknown	5%
Public interest	2%

Students

About 52% of the student body are women; 22%, minorities; 13%, African American; 4%, Asian American; and 5%, Hispanic. The majority of students come from the Northeast (55%). The average age of entering students is 23; age range is 20 to 51. About 37% of students enter directly from undergraduate school and 7% have a graduate degree. About 4% drop out after the first year for academic or personal reasons; 95% remain to receive a law degree.

School of Law

Avenida Las Americas-Station 6
Ponce, PR 00732

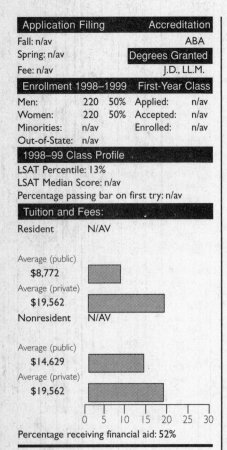

Application Filing	Accreditation
Fall: n/av	ABA
Spring: n/av	**Degrees Granted**
Fee: n/av	J.D., LL.M.

Enrollment 1998–1999		First-Year Class	
Men:	220 50%	Applied:	n/av
Women:	220 50%	Accepted:	n/av
Minorities:	n/av	Enrolled:	n/av
Out-of-State:	n/av		

1998–99 Class Profile
LSAT Percentile: 13%
LSAT Median Score: n/av
Percentage passing bar on first try: n/av

Tuition and Fees:

Resident   N/AV

Average (public)
$8,772

Average (private)
$19,562

Nonresident   N/AV

Average (public)
$14,629

Average (private)
$19,562

0 5 10 15 20 25 30

Percentage receiving financial aid: 52%

ADMISSIONS

Information in the above capsule is approximate. The median LSAT percentile of the most recent first-year class was 13; the median GPA was 2.9 on a scale of 4.0.

Requirements
Applicants must have a bachelor's degree from an accredited institution and take the LSAT. Minimum acceptable GPA is 2.5 on a scale of 4.0. The most important admission factors include GPA, LSAT results, general background, and motivation.

Procedure
Check with the school for current application fee and deadlines. Applicants should submit an application form, transcripts, and PAEG. The latest acceptable LSAT test date for fall entry is June.

Special
Transfer students must have a minimum GPA of 2.0. Preadmissions courses consist of allowing students with an undergraduate GPA of lower than 2.5 or who don't achieve adequate scores on the admissions exam to enroll in special remedial courses and then be admitted conditionally.

Financial Aid

About 52% of current law students received some form of aid in a recent year. The average annual amount of aid from all sources combined, including scholarships, loans, and work contracts, was $2000. Awards are based on need and merit. The required financial statement is GAPSFAS. Check with the school for current application deadlines.

About the Law School

Catholic University of Puerto Rico School of Law was established in 1961 and is a private institution. The 92-acre campus is in an urban area 60 miles from San Juan. The primary mission of the law school is to develop lawyers with a thorough training in the law and a practical mastery of legal techniques within the context of Catholic teachings. Students have access to federal, state, county, city, and local agencies, courts, correctional facilities, law firms, and legal aid organizations in the Ponce area. Housing for law students is available.

Calendar

The law school operates on a traditional semester basis. Courses for full-and part-time students are offered both day and evening. New full-and part-time students are admitted in the fall. There is a summer session.

Programs

In addition to the J.D., the law school offers the LL.M. Students may take relevant courses in other programs and apply credit toward the J.D. The following joint degrees may be earned: J.D./M.B.A. (Juris Doctor/Master of Business Administration).

Contact
Manuel Luciano, Associate Dean, 787-841-2000, ext. 341 for general inquiries; Maria Izquierdo de Whitaker, Director of Student Aid, 787-841-2000 for financial aid information.

PUERTO RICO

Required

To earn the J.D., candidates must complete 94 total credits, of which 82 are for required courses. The following first-year courses are required of all students: Introduction to Law, Legal Bibliography and Writing, Constitutional Law, Property Law, Moral and Dogmatic Theory, Family Law, Criminal Procedure, Obligations, and Logic and Redaction. Required upper-level courses consist of Special Contracts, Civil Procedure I and II, Torts, Corporations, Successions and Donations, Evidence, Notarial Law, Mercantile law, Mortgages, Legal Ethics, Legal Clinics, Administrative Law, Appellate Practice, Negotiable Instruments, Federal Jurisdiction, Special Logical Procedures, and Advanced Logical Analysis.

Electives

Clinical training is provided through the school's downtown Ponce Legal Aid Clinic for indigent clients and through judicial clerkships in superior and federal district courts and placements with district attorneys' offices. The Center for Legal and Social Investigations allows for research under the supervision of a faculty director.

Organizations
The primary law review is the *Revista de Derecho Puertorriqueno*, which is edited by a student board. Law student organizations include the Law Student Division of the American Bar Association, National Law Students of Puerto Rico, and the Women's Rights Organization. Local chapters of national associations are Delta Theta Phi and Phi Alpha Delta.

Library
The law library contains 135,000 hardcopy volumes and 15,000 microform volume equivalents. Special library collections include deposits of U.S. government and United Nations documents.

Faculty
The law school has 14 full-time and 18 part-time faculty members. About 50% of full-time faculty have a graduate law degree in addition to the J.D. The ratio of full-time students to full-time faculty in an average class is 12 to 1.

Students
About 50% of the student body are women. The average age of entering students is 24; age range is 21 to 51. About 50% of students enter directly from undergraduate school. About 11% drop out after the first year for academic or personal reasons.

Placement	
J.D.s awarded:	n/av
Services available through: separate law school placement center	
Full-time job interviews:	n/av
Summer job interviews:	n/av
Placement by graduation:	n/av
Placement within 9 months:	n/av
Average starting salary: (recent year)	$14,000
Areas of placement:	
Unknown	50%
Academic	50%

School of Law

One University Drive
Orange, CA 92866

Application Filing		Accreditation
Fall: open		ABA
Spring: n/app		**Degrees Granted**
Fee: $40		J.D.

Enrollment 1998–1999		First-Year Class	
Men:	89 51%	Applied:	607
Women:	84 49%	Accepted:	266
Minorities:	45 26%	Enrolled:	87
Out-of-State:	21 12%		

1998–99 Class Profile

LSAT Percentile: 64%
LSAT Median Score: 154
Percentage passing bar on first try: n/av

Tuition and Fees:

Resident
$21,650

Average (public)
$8,772

Average (private)
$19,562

Nonresident
$21,650

Average (public)
$14,629

Average (private)
$19,562

0 5 10 15 20 25 30

Percentage receiving financial aid: 94%

ADMISSIONS
In the fall 1999 first-year class, 607 applied, 266 were accepted, and 87 enrolled. Nine transfers enrolled. The median LSAT percentile of the most recent first-year class was 64; the median GPA was 3.0 on a scale of 4.0. The lowest LSAT percentile accepted was 26; the highest was 99.

Requirements
Applicants must have a bachelor's degree from an accredited institution and take the LSAT. Minimum acceptable GPA is 2.0 on a scale of 4.0. The most important admission factors include LSAT results, GPA, and personal interview. No specific undergraduate courses are required. Candidates are not interviewed.

Procedure
The application deadline for fall entry is open. Applicants should submit an application form, LSAT results, TOEFL, where indicated, a nonrefundable application fee of $40, 2 letters of recommendation, and personal statement, LSDAS report, letters of recommendation submitted to LSDAS. Notification of the admission decision is usually within two weeks of file com. The latest acceptable LSAT test date for fall entry is June. The law school uses the LSDAS.

Special
The law school recruits minority and disadvantaged students by recruiting at colleges and universities that have a high percentage of minority students, and by advertising in and supporting publications reaching the various ethnic communities. Transfer students must have one year of credit, have attended an ABA-approved law school, and 2 letters of recommendation (one from a law professor) an official law transcript and letter of good standing, and LSDAS Report.

Costs
Tuition and fees for the 1999-2000 academic year are $21,650 for full-time in-state students and $21,650 for out-of-state students. Tuition for part-time students is $14,900 per credit in-state and $14,900 out-of-state. Books and supplies run $800.

Financial Aid
About 94% of current law students receive some form of aid. The average annual amount of aid from all sources combined, including scholarships, loans, and work contracts, in $23,500; maximum, $36,000. Awards are based on need and merit. The required financial statement is FAFSA. The aid application deadline for fall entry is April 1. First-year students are notified about their financial aid application at Students get an estimate of aid when an offer is made by the committee. Actual financial aid offer is made after the student accepts the admit offer, and makes a deposit.

About the Law School
Chapman University School of Law was established in 1995 and is a private institution. The 52-acre campus is in a suburban area in Orange, California. The primary mission of the law school is to provide personalized education in a challenging academic environment that stimulates intellectual inquiry, embraces diverse ideas and viewpoints, and fosters competent, ethical lawyering that enhances the capacity of legal institutions to provide justice include a students have access to federal, state, county, city, and local agencies, courts, correctional facilities, law firms, and legal aid organizations in the Orange area. Facilities of special interest to law students include a state of the art law building, with drop ports throughout, digital document cameras, touch screen computers at podiums, electronic court rooms, and assisted-listening devices. Limited university-owned housing is available for law school students. Various apartment complexes are within proximity of the law school. All law school facilities are accessible to the physically disabled.

Calendar
The law school operates on a traditional semester basis. Courses for full-time students are offered both day and evening and must be completed within 5 years. For part-time students, courses are offered both day and evening and must be completed within 6 years. New full-time students are admitted in the fall; part-time, fall. There is a 7- week summer session. Transferable summer courses are offered.

Programs
Students may take relevant courses in other programs and apply credit toward the J.D.; a maximum of 6 credits may be applied. The following joint degrees may be earned: J.D.M.B.A. (to be offered in 2001).

Phone: 714-628-2500
877-Chaplaw
Fax: 714-628-2501
E-mail: misles@chapman.edu
Web: chapman.edu/law

Contact

Maryam Isles, Admissions Coordinator, 714-628-2525 for general inquiries; Peggy Crawford, Director of Financial Aid, 714-628-2510 for financial aid information.

CALIFORNIA

Required

To earn the J.D., candidates must complete 88 total credits, of which 53 to 54 are for required courses. They must maintain a minimum GPA of 2.0 in the required courses. The following first-year courses are required of all students: Property I and II, Torts I and II, Contracts I and II, Criminal Law, Civil Procedure, and Legal Research and Writing I and II. Required upper-level courses consist of Constitutional Law I and II, Federal Income Tax, Evidence, writing requirement, Corporations, Lawyering Skills, and Legal Ethics. The required orientation program for first-year students lasts approximately 4 days and includes an introduction to the process of legal education and analysis, professionalism, legal education in practice, as well as informal, social events and information. Sessions on navigating through the Law School experience.

Electives

Students must take 11 to 12 in their area of concentration. The School of Law offers concentrations in corporate law, environmental law, tax law, and land use/ real estate. In addition, A U.S. Tax Court Clinic is available for students who have completed Federal Income Tax, Estate and Gift Tax, and Taxation of Business Organizations with a C+ or better and have an overall GPA of 2.5 or higher. A variety of seminar-type courses are offered, ranging from 2 to 4 credits. Credits vary with a maximum of 8 total. Special lecture series include the Distinguished Jurist in Residence Program, open to all students for no credit. Various externship opportunities are available to students in good standing for 3 units. The Academic Support Program offers lectures and workshops, individualized tutoring for students and referrals to university or outside programs or support services designed to meet identified special student needs. The most widely taken electives are Externship, clinical coursework, Wills and Trusts.

Graduation Requirements

In order to graduate, candidates must have a GPA of 2.0, completed the upper-division writing requirement, and have satisfied ABA residency requirements.

Organizations

Students edit *The Chapman Law Review, Nexus,* and *A Journal of Opinion.* Moot court competitions include Giles Rich Moot Court, Traynor Moot Court, and Jessup International Moot Court. Other competitions include Negotiation Competition, American Trial Lawyers Competition, International Arbitration Competition, Vis International Commercial Competition, Client Counseling Competition, and National Environmental Competition. Student organizations include the Student Bar Association, Honor Council, and Women's Law Forum. There are local chapters of the Public Interest Law Forum (NAPIL), Phi Alpha Delta, and ABA-LSD. Other organizations include the Environmental Law Society, Tax Law Society, and Technology and Intellectual property Law Society.

Library

The law library contains 225,945 hardcopy volumes and 177,876 microform volume equivalents, and subscribes to 577 serial publications. Such on-line databases and networks as LEXIS and WESTLAW are available to law students for research. Special library collections include The library maintains special collections to support the financial aid and placement areas of the law school. Recently, the library Being a young library, the collection has grown to 225,945 volumes and 134,695 titles, plus 4,974 serials subscriptions. The library moved into it's new facility in June of 1999, substantially increasing seating and facility size. The ratio of library volumes to faculty is 10,117 to 1 and to students, 988 to 1.

Faculty

The law school has 20 full-time and 9 part-time faculty members, of whom 9 are women. According to AAUP standards for Category IIA institutions, faculty salaries are well above average. About 33% of full-time faculty have a graduate law degree in addition to the J.D. The ratio of full-time students to full-time faculty in an average class is 9 to 1; in a clinic, 10 to 1. The law school has a regular program of bringing visiting professors and other distinguished lecturers and visitors to campus. There is a chapter of the Order of the Coif; 2 faculty are members.

Placement

J.D.s awarded:	65
Services available through: A separate law school placement center.	
Services: information sessions, panels, law firm nights, mock interviews, and a mentor program	
Special features: a 1 credit elective course on the Business of Practicing Law	
Full-time job interviews:	n/av
Summer job interviews:	n/av
Placement by graduation:	28% of class
Placement within 9 months:	82% of class
Average starting salary:	$31,000 to $60,000
Areas of placement:	
Private practice 2-10 attorneys	34%
Private practice 11-25 attorneys	4%
Private practice 26-50 attorneys	2%
Private practice 51-100 attorneys	2%
Business/industry	24%
Government	16%
Solo practice	8%
Academic	4%
Judicial clerkships	4%
Public interest	2%

Students

About 49% of the student body are women; 26%, minorities; 1%, African American; 11%, Asian American; 13%, Hispanic; and 1%, Native American. The majority of students come from California (88%). The average age of entering students is 28; age range is 20 to 53. About 13% of students have a graduate degree. About 15% drop out after the first year for academic or personal reasons; 80% remain to receive a law degree.

CITY UNIVERSITY OF NEW YORK

City University of New York School of Law at Queens College

65-21 Main Street
Flushing, NY 11367-1300

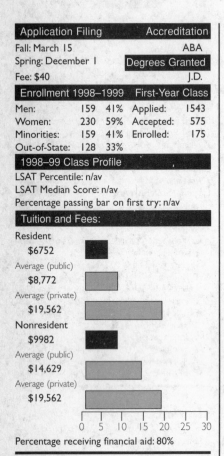

Application Filing			Accreditation
Fall: March 15			ABA
Spring: December 1			**Degrees Granted**
Fee: $40			J.D.

Enrollment 1998–1999			First-Year Class	
Men:	159	41%	Applied:	1543
Women:	230	59%	Accepted:	575
Minorities:	159	41%	Enrolled:	175
Out-of-State:	128	33%		

1998–99 Class Profile
LSAT Percentile: n/av
LSAT Median Score: n/av
Percentage passing bar on first try: n/av

Tuition and Fees:

Resident
$6752

Average (public)
$8,772

Average (private)
$19,562

Nonresident
$9982

Average (public)
$14,629

Average (private)
$19,562

0 5 10 15 20 25 30

Percentage receiving financial aid: 80%

ADMISSIONS

In the fall 1999 first-year class, 1543 applied, 575 were accepted, and 175 enrolled. Three transfers enrolled.

Requirements

Applicants must have a bachelor's degree from an accredited institution and take the LSAT. The most important admission factors include letter of recommendation, writing ability, and academic achievement. No specific undergraduate courses are required. Candidates are not interviewed.

Procedure

The application deadline for fall entry is March 15. Applicants should submit an application form, LSAT results, transcripts, a nonrefundable application fee of $40, 2 letters of recommendation, and a personal statement. Notification of the admission decision is the beginning of January. The latest acceptable LSAT test date for fall entry is February. The law school uses the LSDAS.

Special

The law school recruits minority and disadvantaged students through programs similar to those used by most other law schools. Transfer students must have one year of credit and have attended an ABA-approved law school.

Costs

Tuition, fees, books, and supplies for the 1999-2000 academic year are $6752 for in-state students and $9982 for out-of-state students.

Financial Aid

About 80% of current law students receive some form of aid. The maximum annual amount of aid from all sources combined, including scholarships, loans, and work contracts, is $17,900. Awards are based on need. The required financial statement is the FAFSA. The aid application deadline for fall entry is May 15. Special funds for minority or disadvantaged students include the Professional Opportunity Scholarship, CLEO, and various other scholarships. First-year students are notified about their financial aid application on a rolling basis.

About the Law School

City University of New York School of Law at Queens College was established in 1983 and is a public institution. The campus is in an urban area in the New York City borough of Queens. The primary mission of the law school is to emphasize clinical education, legal theory, and professional responsibility by integrating these elements into the curriculum, and to develop special relationships and work opportunities with the city's courts, agencies, advocacy groups, and law firms. The school aims to prepare students for careers in public service and public interest law. Students have access to federal, state, county, city, and local agencies, courts, correctional facilities, law firms, and legal aid organizations in the Flushing area. There are several notable in-house clinical programs. Facilities of special interest to law students include a 3-story building adjacent to the Queens College campus, which houses classrooms, the library, lounge, administrative offices, a day-care center, and a cafeteria. Housing for law students is available off campus. About 98% of the law school facilities are accessible to the physically disabled.

Calendar

The law school operates on a traditional semester basis. Courses are offered days only and must be completed within 5 years. There is no part-time program. New students are admitted in the fall and spring. There is a 6-week summer session. Transferable summer courses are not offered.

Programs

Joint degrees may be arranged individually according to student interest.

Phone: 718-340-4210
Fax: 718-340-4372
E-mail: admissions@maclaw.law.cuny.edu
Web: www.law.cuny.edu

Contact
William D. Perez, Director of Admissions, 718-340-4210 for general inquiries; Angela Joseph, Director of Financial Aid, 718-340-4292 for financial aid information.

NEW YORK

Required
To earn the J.D., candidates must complete 92 total credits, of which 70 are for required courses. They must maintain a minimum GPA of 2.0 in the required courses. The following first-year courses are required of all students: Law and a Market Economy I and II; Liberty, Equality, and Due Process; Lawyering Seminar: Work of a Lawyer; Responsibility for Injurious Conduct I and II; Civil and Criminal Procedure I;, Law and Family Relations; and Legal Research I and II. Required upper-level courses consist of Lawyering and the Public Interest I and II, Law and a Market Economy III, Civil and Criminal Procedure II, Public Institutions and Law, Constitutional Structures and the Law, and Lawyering Seminar. All students must take clinical courses. The required orientation program for first-year students is a 1-week academic, skills, and social program including court visits.

Electives
The City University of New York School of Law at Queens College offers concentrations in criminal law, environmental law, family law, international law, juvenile law, labor law, litigation, health, mediation, domestic violence, elder law, immigration, human rights, and civil rights. The elective clinic program includes one-half of a student's course load for the entire third year. Recently, Immigrants' Rights, General Law Office, and Battered Women were offered. Additionally, a community development clinic was added in 1995. Each first- and second-year student is affiliated with a lawyering seminar, a group of about 20 students who work together to simulate a small law firm. It provides study facilities, offices for faculty members, videotaping equipment, a library, a secretarial office, and other facilities for simulating interviews, negotiation and counseling sessions, and conferences. Internships are available. A professional skills center is available to students who are encountering academic difficulty. The most widely taken electives are New York Practice and Evidence.

Graduation Requirements
In order to graduate, candidates must have a GPA of 2.0.

Organizations
Students edit the *New York City Law Review* and a student newspaper, *The Brief*, and participate in the annual Jessup International Moot Court Competition. Student organizations include the Black Law Students Association, Women's Coalition, and La Sociedad Estudiantil de Derechos de CUNY. Local chapters of national associations include Phi Delta Phi, the Student Bar Association, and the American Bar Association Law Student Division. Other organizations include the Children's Rights Association, the Haiti Human Rights Delegation, and the Coalition Against Domestic Violence.

Library
The law library contains 250,000 hardcopy volumes and 820,000 microform volume equivalents, and subscribes to 2600 serial publications. Such on-line databases and networks as LEXIS, DIALOG, and WESTLAW are available to law students for research. Special library collections include a U.S. Government Printing Office depository; the school is a member of the New York Joint International Law Program Consortium. The library maintains a large number of student access computer terminals, microform readers, and microform reader-printers. The ratio of library volumes to faculty is 6740 to 1 and to students, 524 to 1. The ratio of seats in the library to students is 1 to 1.

Faculty
The law school has 38 full-time and 12 part-time faculty members, of whom 32 are women. About 20% of full-time faculty have a graduate law degree in addition to the J.D. The ratio of full-time students to full-time faculty in an average class is 13 to 1. The law school has a regular program of bringing visiting professors and other distinguished lecturers and visitors to campus.

Placement

J.D.s awarded:	135

Services available through: a separate law school placement center

Services: counseling, seminars, workshops, and panels with local practitioners, faculty, and alumni

Special features: The Office of the Integration of Practice and Learning is responsibile for helping students find meaningful work. Special focus is placed on public interest careers.

Full-time job interviews:	8 employers
Summer job interviews:	n/av
Placement by graduation:	n/av
Placement within 9 months:	83% of class
Average starting salary:	$22,000 to $42,000

Areas of placement:

Private practice 2-100 attorneys	34%
Government	24%
Public interest	18%
Business/industry	15%
Judicial clerkships	8%
Academic	1%

Students
About 59% of the student body are women; 41%, minorities; 16%, African American; 13%, Asian American; 12%, Hispanic; and 1%, Native American. The majority of students come from New York (67%). The average age of entering students is 29; age range is 20 to 66. About 20% of students enter directly from undergraduate school, 25% have a graduate degree, and 60% have worked full-time prior to entering law school. About 10% drop out after the first year for academic or personal reasons; 85% remain to receive a law degree.

CLEVELAND STATE UNIVERSITY

Cleveland-Marshall College of Law

1801 Euclid Avenue
Cleveland, OH 44115

Application Filing	Accreditation
Fall: April 1	ABA, AALS
Spring: n/app	**Degrees Granted**
Fee: $35	J.D., LL.M.

Enrollment 1998–1999		First-Year Class	
Men:	410 52%	Applied:	1220
Women:	376 48%	Accepted:	617
Minorities:	110 14%	Enrolled:	254
Out-of-State:	94 12%		

1998–99 Class Profile

LSAT Percentile: 50%
LSAT Median Score: 150
Percentage passing bar on first try: 68%

Tuition and Fees:

Resident
$7826

Average (public)
$8,772

Average (private)
$19,562

Nonresident
$15,522

Average (public)
$14,629

Average (private)
$19,562

0 5 10 15 20 25 30

Percentage receiving financial aid: 83%

ADMISSIONS

In the fall 1999 first-year class, 1220 applied, 617 were accepted, and 254 enrolled. Fourteen transfers enrolled. The median LSAT percentile of the most recent first-year class was 50; the median GPA was 3.0 on a scale of 4.0. The lowest LSAT percentile accepted was 5; the highest was 95.

Requirements

Applicants must have a bachelor's degree from an accredited institution and take the LSAT. Minimum acceptable GPA is 2.0 on a scale of 4.0. The most important admission factors include academic achievement, LSAT results, and ethnic background. No specific undergraduate courses are required. Candidates are not interviewed.

Procedure

The application deadline for fall entry is April 1. Applicants should submit an application form, LSAT results, transcripts, a nonrefundable application fee of $35, 2 letters of recommendation, and a personal statement. Notification of the admission decision is on a rolling basis. The latest acceptable LSAT test date for fall entry is February. The law school uses the LSDAS.

Special

The law school recruits minority and disadvantaged students by means of the Legal Career Opportunities Program, a special admissions program for applicants whose background and experience deserve special consideration. The Admissions Committee invites applicants whose test scores or academic records are not strong but whose skills, accomplishments, and other qualifications merit consideration. The Admissions Committee seeks to admit candidates who have encountered adversity but have a record of accomplishment, either academic or professional. LCOP, an evening program, begins in the early part of June and continues through mid-July; students earn 2 or 3 semester credits, depending on the summer course that is offered, and credit is applied to the J.D. degree program. Transfer students must have one year of credit, have a minimum GPA of 3.0, and must have attended an ABA-approved law school.

Costs

Tuition and fees for the 1999-2000 academic year are $7826 for full-time in-state students and $15,522 for out-of-state students. Tuition for part-time students is $6020 per year in-state and $11,940 out-of-state. On-campus room and board costs about $7950 annually; and books and supplies run $700.

Financial Aid

About 83% of current law students receive some form of aid. The average annual amount of aid from all sources combined, including scholarships, loans, and work contracts, is $12,000; maximum, $17,500. Awards are based on need and merit. The required financial statement is FAFSA. The aid application deadline for fall entry is March 1. A variety of funds is available for students of color who are disadvantaged. Students who complete the admissions and financial aid materials are considered for these funds. First-year students are notified about their financial aid application at time of acceptance.

About the Law School

Cleveland State University Cleveland-Marshall College of Law was established in 1897 and is a public institution. The campus is in an urban area in downtown Cleveland. The primary mission of the law school is to prepare students to enter a learned profession and to provide them with an understanding of the legal profession and system and of their responsibility to maintain and improve the legal system in order to serve society. Students have access to federal, state, county, city, and local agencies, courts, correctional facilities, law firms, and legal aid organizations in the Cleveland area. Facilities of special interest to law students are the intramural competition, student health services, library, student social center, Cleveland Public Library, physical education facilities, University Circle Cultural Arts Center, Playhouse Square, and student counseling services. Housing for law students is available in nearby suburbs, many within a 20-minute commuting distance. All law school facilities are accessible to the physically disabled.

Calendar

The law school operates on a traditional semester basis. Courses for full-time students are offered days only and must be completed within 6 years. For part-time students, courses are offered evenings only. First-year part-time students are limited to evenings and must complete all courses within 6 years. New full-time students are admitted in the fall; part-time, fall. There is a 7-week summer session. Transferable summer courses are offered.

Contact
Margaret A. McNally, Assistant Dean for Admissions, 216-687-2304 for general inquiries; Catherine Buzanski, Financial Aid Administrator, 216-687-2317 for financial aid information.

OHIO

Programs

In addition to the J.D., the law school offers the LL.M. Students may take relevant courses in other programs and apply credit toward the J.D.; a maximum of 8 credits may be applied (except for joint-degree candidates). The following joint degrees may be earned: J.D./M.B.A. (Juris Doctor/Master of Business Administration), J.D./M.P.A. (Juris Doctor/Master of Public Administration), and J.D/M.U.P.D.D. (Juris Doctor/Master of Urban Planning, Design and Development).

Required

To earn the J.D., candidates must complete 87 total credits, of which 34 (plus 2 electives in specified areas) are for required courses. They must maintain a minimum GPA of 2.0 in the required courses. The following first-year courses are required of all students: Contracts, Civil Procedure, Criminal Law, Legal Writing, Property, Torts, and a perspective elective. Required upper-level courses consist of Constitutional Law, Evidence, Business Associations, Tax I, and Commercial Law. The required orientation program for first-year students is 3 days long and includes social activities, introductory classes in case briefing, library tours, and peer adviser meetings.

Electives

The Cleveland-Marshall College of Law offers concentrations in corporate law, international law, labor law, litigation, tax law, and public policy, health law, civil advocacy and dispute resolution. In addition, the Employment Law Clinic offers from 6 to 10 credits, the Community Advocacy Clinic offers from 2 to 10 credits, and the Fair Housing Clinic offers from 2 to 8 credits. Upper-level students may take seminars and up to 3 hours of independent research; seminar papers fulfill the upper-level writing requirement. A judicial externship is worth 6 credits; students work 24 hours a week in a federal or state appellate court. A U.S. Attorney externship is worth 7 credits; students are placed in a civil or criminal U.S. Attorney's office. There are independent/public service externships worth 4 to 6 hours. Special lecture series include the Cleveland-Marshall Lecture

Series. Students may participate in study-abroad programs run by ABA/AALS-approved law schools. Cleveland-Marshall also runs a summer program in St. Petersburg, Russia. First-year students admitted to the Legal Career Opportunities Program are offered tutorials. Cleveland-Marshall has a Director of Minority Affairs who oversees minority programs. A variety of special interest group programs is available. The most widely taken electives are Advocacy, Business, and Tax.

Graduation Requirements

In order to graduate, candidates must have a GPA of 2.0, have completed the upper-division writing requirement, and have completed a course with an administrative component of law, evidence, and legal professions.

Organizations

Students edit the *Cleveland State Law Review, Journal of Law and Health*, and the newspaper *The Gavel*. The college sends teams to some 41 competitions, including the National Appellate Advocacy and the National Moot Court. Law student organizations include the Student Bar Association, Women's Legal Caucus, and Lawyers Guild. There are local chapters of the NBA-Law School Division and the ABA-Law School Division.

Library

The law library contains 445,908 hardcopy volumes and 57,072 microform volume equivalents, and subscribes to 3805 serial publications. Such on-line databases and networks as LEXIS, DIALOG, WESTLAW, and Internet, SCHOLAR, VuTExt, Datatimes, BRS, RLIN, Compuserve, Gongwer, EPIC, OCLC, Hannah, and MF-DIS are available to law students for research. Special library collections include federal government documents. Recently, the library added a 4-story structure with 85,000 square feet, including a 50-seat computer laboratory, 207 student carrels, and 17 group-study rooms. The ratio of library volumes to faculty is 7669 to 1 and to students, 393 to 1. The ratio of seats in the library to students is 1 to 2.

Placement

J.D.s awarded:	238

Services available through: a separate law school placement center.
Services: practice interviews, matching students with local attorneys for interest interviews, and career-related workshops.
Special features: There is individualized counseling, cover letter development, a skills bank, first-year orientation program, mock interviews, and references and resources containing more than 1000 employment opportunities annually.

Full-time job interviews:	22 employers
Summer job interviews:	32 employers
Placement by graduation:	n/av
Placement within 9 months:	96% of class
Average starting salary:	$18,000 to $90,000

Areas of placement:

Private practice 2-10 attorneys	41%
Private practice 11-25 attorneys	9%
Private practice 26-50 attorneys	1%
Private practice 51-100 attorneys	5%
Business/industry	16%
Government	15%
Judicial clerkships	4%
Public interest	2%
Academic	2%

Faculty

The law school has 36 full-time and 25 part-time faculty members, of whom 21 are women. According to AAUP standards for Category III institutions, faculty salaries are well above average. About 20% of full-time faculty have a graduate law degree in addition to the J.D. The ratio of full-time students to full-time faculty in an average class is 21 to 1; in a clinic, 4 to 1. The law school has a regular program of bringing visiting professors and other distinguished lecturers and visitors to campus.

Students

About 48% of the student body are women; 14%, minorities; 10%, African American; 3%, Asian American; and 2%, Hispanic. The majority of students come from the Midwest (93%). The average age of entering students is 27; age range is 21 to 64. About 10% of students enter directly from undergraduate school and 12% have a graduate degree. About 10% drop out after the first year for academic or personal reasons.

COLLEGE OF WILLIAM AND MARY

William and Mary Law School

P.O. Box 8795
Williamsburg, VA 23187-8795

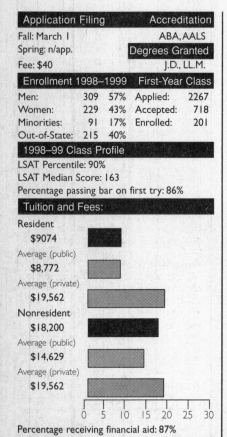

Application Filing		Accreditation	
Fall: March 1		ABA, AALS	
Spring: n/app.		**Degrees Granted**	
Fee: $40		J.D., LL.M.	

Enrollment 1998–1999		First-Year Class	
Men:	309 57%	Applied:	2267
Women:	229 43%	Accepted:	718
Minorities:	91 17%	Enrolled:	201
Out-of-State:	215 40%		

1998–99 Class Profile
LSAT Percentile: 90%
LSAT Median Score: 163
Percentage passing bar on first try: 86%

Tuition and Fees:

Resident
$9074

Average (public)
$8,772

Average (private)
$19,562

Nonresident
$18,200

Average (public)
$14,629

Average (private)
$19,562

0 5 10 15 20 25 30

Percentage receiving financial aid: 87%

ADMISSIONS

In the fall 1999 first-year class, 2267 applied, 718 were accepted, and 201 enrolled. Five transfers enrolled. The median LSAT percentile of the most recent first-year class was 90; the median GPA was 3.36 on a scale of 4.0. The lowest LSAT percentile accepted was 41; the highest was 99.

Requirements
Applicants must have a bachelor's degree from an accredited institution and take the LSAT. All factors in a candidate's background are considered important. No specific undergraduate courses are required. Candidates are interviewed.

Procedure
The application deadline for fall entry is March 1. Applicants should submit an application form, LSAT results, transcripts, a nonrefundable application fee of $40, 2 letters of recommendation, and a personal statement. Notification of the admission decision is in the spring. The

latest acceptable LSAT test date for fall entry is February. The law school uses the LSDAS.

Special
The law school recruits minority and disadvantaged students by means of on- and off-campus recruitment, a brochure, grant proposals, LSDAS Candidate Referral Service, BLSA Program, and financial aid. Transfer students must have attended an ABA-approved law school.

Costs

Tuition and fees for the 1999-2000 academic year are $9074 for full-time in-state students and $18,200 for out-of-state students. On-campus room and board costs about $5583 annually; books and supplies run $1000.

Financial Aid

About 87% of current law students receive some form of aid. The average annual amount of aid from all sources combined, including scholarships, loans, and work contracts, is $18,903; maximum, $31,078. Awards are based on need and merit. The required financial statement is the FAFSA. The aid application deadline for fall entry is February 15. Diversity is considered as a factor in the packaging of aid. First-year students are notified about their financial aid application in late March.

About the Law School

College of William and Mary, William and Mary Law School was established in 1779 and is a public institution. The 1200-acre campus is in a small town 45 miles west of Norfolk, and 45 miles east of Richmond. The primary mission of the law school is to provide students with a superior legal education in a close-knit collegial environment and to offer the opportunity to confront the demands of constructive citizenship and leadership. Students have access to federal, state, county, city, and local agencies, courts, correctional facilities, law firms, and legal aid organizations in the Williamsburg area. The National Center for State Courts and Colonial Williamsburg are also available. In addition to the Law Library, the school includes the Courtroom 21 Project, the world center for

courtroom technology research, and the McGlothlis Courtroom, the world's most technologically advanced courtroom. The project has an extensive student staff, trains all second-year students in hands-on courtroom technology use, and supports the law school activities including a legal technology seminar. Housing for law students is available in graduate apartments located next to the law school building. Commercial apartments, townhouses, and other area housing are available as well. About 90% of the law school facilities are accessible to the physically disabled.

Calendar

The law school operates on a traditional semester basis. Courses for full-time students are offered days only and must be completed within 3 years. there is no part-time program. New full-time students are admitted in the fall. There is a 6-week summer session. Transferable summer courses are offered.

Programs

In addition to the J.D., the law school offers the LL.M. Students may take relevant courses in other programs and apply credit toward the J.D.; a maximum of 6 credits may be applied. The following joint degrees may be earned: J.D./M.B.A. (Juris Doctor/Master of Business Administration), J.D./M.P.P. (Juris Doctor/Master of Public Policy), and J.D./M.A. (Juris Doctor/Master of Arts in American studies).

Required
To earn the J.D., candidates must complete 90 total credits, of which 36 are for required courses. They must maintain a minimum GPA of 2.0 in the required courses. The following first-year courses are required of all students: Civil Procedure, Contracts, Property, Torts, Constitutional Law, Legal Skills I and II, Criminal Law, and a statutory/regulatory course. Required upper-level courses consist of Legal Skills III, IV, and V. All students All student clinics are elective courses that provide students actual contact with legal cases, clients, and/or courts. There are a limited number of places in each clinic and students can enroll in only 1 clinic while at law school. The required orientation program for first-year students is a 1-week program

Phone: 757-221-3785
Fax: 757-221-3261
E-mail: lawadm@facstaff.wm.edu
Web: http://www.wm.edu

Contact

Faye F. Shealy, Associate Dean, 757-221-3785 for general inquiries; Ed Irish, Director of Student Financial Aid, 757-221-2420 for financial aid information.

designed to introduce incoming first-year law students to legal analysis, legal vocabulary, legal teaching methods, legal writing, and the law firm structure of the Legal Skills Program.

Electives

Clinics, worth 3 credits each and limited to third-year students, include Attorney General practice, employee relations, and Virginia Court of Appeals. Seminars, worth 3 credits, are open to both second- and third-year students (size limited to 15 to 25 students) and include civil rights, constitutional decision making, and legal technology. Internships, worth 2 to 3 credits, marry a classroom component with supervised work in an office setting and include domestic violence, legal aid, and environmental law and sciences. Other programs include independent research (1 credit), directed research (3 credits), and tax research (2 credits). open to second- and third-year students. Field work is offered through a clerking program open to second- and third-year students for 1 credit, involving 40 hours with a law firm or judge, writing of a synopsis of work done, and receiving an evaluation letter from the firms or judges. Special lectures include the Institute of Bill of Rights Law, Cutler Lectures, George Wythe Lectures, and Judges Forum. Study abroad is available during the summer in Madrid, Spain, with most classes worth 2 credits and open to any second- or third-year student who applies. Tutorial programs for students experiencing academic difficulties; minority programs arranged by the minority student organizations; and special interest group programs arranged by individual student organizations are available. The most widely taken electives are business, evidence, and corporations.

Graduation Requirements

In order to graduate, candidates must have a GPA of 2.0 and have completed the upper-division writing requirement.

Organizations

Students edit the *William and Mary Law Review, William and Mary Bill of Rights Journal, William and Mary Journal of Women and the Law, William and Mary Environmental Law and Policy Review*, and the newspaper *Amicus Curiae*. Ten teams compete each year at competitions such as the National Tournament, ABA Tournament, and Jessup International Tournament. Each year the school sponsors the National Trial Team competitions and the Bushrod T. Washington Moot Court Tournament, which is open to second-year students only, with the top 32 students earning the right to compete on one of the teams in their third year. The William B. Spong, Jr. Invitational Moot Court Tournament attracts approximately 20 to 22 teams each year. Law student organizations include the Moot Court Board, Federalist Society, and Institute of Bill of Rights-Law Student Division. There are local chapters of ABA-Law Student Division, Phi Alpha Delta, and Phi Delta Phi. Campus clubs and other organizations include Catholic Graduate Student Association, Christian Fellowship, and Balfour-Hillel.

Library

The law library contains 355,000 hardcopy volumes and 840,000 microform volume equivalents, and subscribes to 4750 serial publications. Such on-line databases and networks as LEXIS, DIALOG, WESTLAW, First Search, and VIVA are available to law students for research. Special library collections include a Thomas Jefferson law collection, environmental law, Roman law books, constitutional law, and taxation. Recently, the library installed a new reference desk and 2 computer laboratories with 32 stations. The ratio of library volumes to faculty is 12,000 to 1 and to students, 660 to 1. The ratio of seats in the library to students is 1 to 4.

Faculty

The law school has 28 full-time and 42 part-time faculty members, of whom 20 are women. According to AAUP standards for Category I institutions, faculty salaries are average. About 19% of full-time faculty have a graduate law degree in addition to the J.D.; about 16% of part-time faculty have one. The ratio of full-time students to full-time faculty in an average class is 35 to 1; in a clinic, 4 to 1. The law school has a regular program of bringing visiting professors and other distinguished lecturers and visitors to campus. There is a chapter of the Order of the Coif; 15 faculty and 321 graduates are members.

Placement

J.D.s awarded:	180
Services available through: separate law school placement center.	
Services: career planning/counseling, 7 summer public service funding programs, 14 off-campus job fairs, and assistance with judicial clerkships	
Special features: professional staff includes 2 attorneys who, together, have significant experience in career counseling, practicing law, and lawyer recruiting and hiring. The emphasis is on individualized career planning for students with extensive programs and resources designed to enable them to make informed career choices. Students interested in public service work may utilize funding programs which, during the summer of 1999, provided approximately $100,000 for internships throughout the world.	
Full-time job interviews:	106 employers
Summer job interviews:	178 employers
Placement by graduation:	74% of class
Placement within 9 months:	96% of class
Average starting salary:	$24,000 to $91,000
Areas of placement:	n/av

Students

About 43% of the student body are women; 17%, minorities; 10%, African American; 4%, Asian American; 1%, Hispanic; and 2%, Native American. The majority of students come from Virginia (60%). The average age of entering students is 25; age range is 20 to 47. About 43% of students enter directly from undergraduate school, 15% have a graduate degree, and 57% have worked full-time prior to entering law school. About 2% drop out after the first year for academic or personal reasons; 100% remain to receive a law degree.

School of Law

435 West 116th Street
New York, NY 10027

Application Filing		Accreditation
Fall: February 15		ABA, AALS
Spring: n/app		Degrees Granted
Fee: $65		J.D., LL.M., S.J.D.

Enrollment 1998–1999		First-Year Class	
Men:	633 54%	Applied:	6137
Women:	534 46%	Accepted:	n/av
Minorities:	385 33%	Enrolled:	367
Out-of-State:	875 75%		

1998–99 Class Profile
LSAT Percentile: 98%
LSAT Median Score: 169
Percentage passing bar on first try: 92%

Tuition and Fees:

Resident
$28,574

Average (public)
$8,772

Average (private)
$19,562

Nonresident
$28,574

Average (public)
$14,629

Average (private)
$19,562

0   5   10   15   20   25   30

Percentage receiving financial aid: 75%

ADMISSIONS

In the fall 1999 first-year class, 6137 applied and 367 enrolled. One-hundred-four transfers enrolled. The median LSAT percentile of the most recent first-year class was 98; the median GPA was 3.6 on a scale of 4.0. The highest LSAT percentile was 99.

Requirements
Applicants must have a bachelor's degree from an accredited institution (except in very rare circumstances) and take the LSAT. No specific undergraduate courses are required. Candidates are not interviewed.

Procedure
The application deadline for fall entry is February 15. Applicants should submit an application form, LSAT results, transcripts, a nonrefundable application fee of $65, and 3 letters of recommendation. Accepted students must pay a nonrefundable tuition deposit of $200. Early decision applicants are notified by mid-December. Notification of the admission decision is usually by April for regular applicants. The latest acceptable LSAT test date for fall entry is December. The law school uses the LSDAS.

Special
The law school recruits minority and disadvantaged students through outreach efforts, which include site visits to undergraduate institutions with high representations of minority and economically disadvantaged students counseling initiatives, and national database searches with invitations to apply. Transfer students must have one year of credit, have attended an ABA-approved law school, and have completed the first year with distinction at an ABA-approved law school or at an accredited Canadian law school.

Costs

Tuition and fees for the 1999-2000 academic year are $28,574 for all full-time students. On-campus room and board costs about $11,305 annually; books and supplies run $755.

Financial Aid

About 75% of current law students receive some form of aid. The average annual amount of aid from scholarships, loans, and work contracts is $35,000; maximum, $44,580. Scholarships generally are awarded on the basis of need with a few external awards on a merit basis. The required financial statements are FAFSA and a need-access application. The aid application deadline for fall entry is March 1. First-year students are notified about their financial aid application at time of acceptance.

About the Law School

Columbia University School of Law was established in 1858 and is a private institution. The 36-acre campus is in the Morningside Heights section of northwest Manhattan. The primary mission of the law school is to be one of the world's leading centers of research and scholarship regarding law and its role in our society. Students have access to federal, state, county, city, and local agencies, courts, correctional facilities, law firms, and legal aid organizations in the New York area. The city of New York offers students a broad range of opportunities from which to gain legal experience in a variety of legal and political agencies. Recently, Columbia Law School has seen the construction of 2 new buildings, as well as the top-to-bottom expansion and renovation of its main building, Jerome Greene Hall. In addition to the recently completed 8-story building housing the *Columbia Law Review*, clinical programs, and Center for Public Interest Law, a new building for several state-of-

the-art classrooms and offices for student services and international programs has been opened. The $80 million building project has allowed all 3 buildings to be fully wired, offering students instant access to e-mail, the Internet, and legal research databases. On-campus apartments are available to both single law students and couples; the Central University's Housing Registry helps find off-campus housing. About 98% of the law school facilities are accessible to the physically disabled.

Calendar

The law school operates on a traditional semester basis. Courses for full-time students are offered days only and must be completed within 3 years (4 1/2 year curriculum is possible for students with disabilities or those with parental responsibilties for small children who choose to undertake a reduced course load). There is no part-time program. New full-time students are admitted in the fall. There is no summer session. Transferable summer courses are not offered.

Programs

In addition to the J.D., the law school offers the LL.M and S.J.D. Students may take relevant courses in other programs and apply credit toward the J.D.; a maximum of 10 credits may be applied. The following joint degrees may be earned: J.D./ M.B.A. (Juris Doctor/Master of Business Administration), J.D./M.F.A. (Juris Doctor/Master of Arts in theater arts), J.D./M.S. (Juris Doctor/Master of Science in journalism, urban planning, soccial work), J.D./M.I.A. (Juris Doctor/Master of International Affairs), J.D./M.P.A. (Juris Doctor/Master of Public Affairs (Columbia)), J.D./M.A., M.Phil., or Ph.D. (Juris Doctor/Master of Arts or Doctor of Philosophy in history), and J.D./M.P.A. (Juris Doctor/Master of Public Administration with Princeton's Woodrow Wilson School).

Required
To earn the J.D., candidates must complete 83 total credits, of which 35 are for required courses. The following first-year courses are required of all students: Legal Methods and Legal Writing and Research, Constitutional Law or Property, Contracts, Torts, Civil Procedure, Criminal Law, Foundations of the Regulatory State, Foundation Year Moot Court, and Perspectives on Legal Thought. Required upper-level courses consist of Profession of Law (focusing on professional ethics), a minimum of 2

Phone: 212-854-2670
Fax: 212-854-1109
Web: www.law.columbia.edu

Contact

James Milligan, Dean of Admissions, 212-854-2670 for general inquiries; Alice Rigas, Financial Aid Director, 212-854-7730 for financial aid information.

NEW YORK

writing credits earned during the upper-class years, and a pro bono service requirement (40 hours in second and third years. Clinics are electives. The required 2-day orientation program for first-year students starts before Legal Methods course begins. Social events for students, faculty and alumni take place on campus and around New York City.

Electives

The School of Law offers concentrations in corporate law, criminal law, entertainment law, environmental law, family law, international law, labor law, litigation, media law, securities law, sports law, tax law, torts and insurance, constitutional law, human rights law, labor law, history and philosophy of law, health care and the law, and education law. In addition, clinics such as the Mediation Clinic, Child Advocacy Clinic, and Human Rights Clinic offer field work opportunities to upper-class students for 5 to 7 points. Seminars are offered in such areas as Constitutional Law, Corporate Law, and Human Rights for 2 points (generally). Admission to a seminar is by lottery. Additional training through internships is available through arrangements with city agencies and consumer advocacy groups; clerkships with criminal, appellate, and federal court judges; and the pro bono service requirement. Research may be done as part of the legal writing requirement. Credit may be earned in journal work, independent, or supervised research. Law school lectures regularly bring leading figures from business, politics, entertainment, and areas of the law and judiciary to Columbia. At the Dean's Breakfast Series distinguished alumni meet informally with small groups of students. There is a 4-year double degree program with the University of Paris, giving students a J.D. and Maitrise en Droit, a 4-year program with the University of London, giving students a J.D. and LL.B, and a 3-year program with the University of London where students receive a Columbia J.D. and University of London LL.M. Moreover, there are semester-abroad programs in Amsterdam, Paris, Buenos Aires, Jerusalem, Fukuoka (Japan), and Johannesburg (South Africa). Special interest groups include the Leyden-Amsterdam-Columbia summer program in American law, programs offered through the Parker School of Foreign and Comparative Law, the International Fellows Program, and a Visiting Scholars Pro-

gram and Moscow Exchange (a student-organized spring break exchange program). The most widely taken electives are Corporations, Federal Income Taxation, and Securities.

Graduation Requirements

In order to graduate, candidates must have completed the upper-division writing requirement and satisfied degree requirements (including pro bono service).

Organizations

Students edit the *Columbia Law Review*, *Columbia Journal of Environmental Law*, *Columbia Human Rights Law Review*, *Columbia Journal of Law and Social Problems*, *Columbia Journal of Transnational Law*, *Columbia Journal of Asian Law*, *American Review of International Arbitration*, *Columbia-VLA Journal of Law and the Arts*, *Columbia Business Law Review*, *Columbia Journal of Gender and the Law*, and *Columbia Journal of East European Law*, and Columbia Science and Technology Law Review. As well as the newspaper *Columbia Law School News* and the yearbook *Pegasus*. The Moot Court Committee sponsors the Harlan Fiske Stone Honor Competition and the Jerome Michael Jury Trials. Students also participate, with distinction, in the Jessup International Moot Court Competition. Other competitions include the Frederick Douglass National Competition. Law student organizations include the American Civil Liberites Union, Columbia Society of International Law, and Environmental Law Society. There are local chapters of National Lawyers Guild, Public Interest Law Students Association, and the Federalist Society.

Library

The law library contains 993,606 hard-copy volumes and 679,900 microform volume equivalents, and subscribes to 6860 serial publications. Such on-line databases and networks as LEXIS, DIALOG, WESTLAW, and NEXIS plus full access to the Internet and World Wide Web are available. Special library collections include a notable collection on foreign law, Roman law, and a large rare book collection, Perlin Papers, as well as papers from the Nuremberg Trials. Local Area Network (LAN) connections are available for laptops. $7 million gift for improvements to the law library. Financed a restructured library organi-

Placement

J.D.s awarded:	385
Services available through: separate law school placement center	
Services: extensive judicial clerkship counseling	
Special features: resource library, web-based newsletter, career adviser program, a public interest program, extensive web-based resource database, E-mail of all position listings	
Full-time job interviews:	200 employers
Summer job interviews:	500 employers
Placement by graduation:	97% of class
Placement within 9 months:	n/av
Average starting salary:	$35,000 to $160,000

Areas of placement:

Private practice 26-50 attorneys	1%
Private practice 51-100 attorneys	2%
Private practice 100-251+ attorneys	7%
Private practice 252 + attorneys	6%
Judicial clerkships	19%
Business/industry	3%
Government	2%
Academic	1%
Public interest	1%

zation providing more staff for direct user support.

Faculty

The law school has 86 full-time and 77 part-time faculty members, of whom 40 are women. According to AAUP standards for Category I institutions, faculty salaries are well above average. About 15% of full-time faculty have a graduate law degree in addition to the J.D.; about 10% of part-time faculty have one. The ratio of full-time students to full-time faculty in an average class is 14 to 1; in a clinic, 8 to 1. The law school has a regular program of bringing visiting professors and other distinguished lecturers and visitors to campus.

Students

For the class that entered in August 1999, were about 46% of the student body were women; 33%, minorities; 11%, African American; 15%, Asian American; 7%, Hispanic; and 1%, Native American. The majority of students come from New York (25%). The average age of entering students is 24; age range is 20 to 47. About 33% of students enter directly from undergraduate school and 18% have a graduate degree.

CORNELL UNIVERSITY

Law School

Myron Taylor Hall
Ithaca, NY 14853

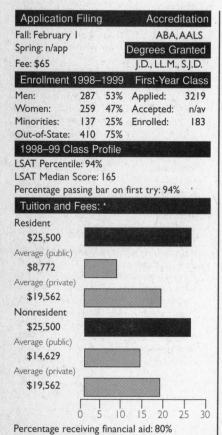

Application Filing			Accreditation
Fall: February 1			ABA, AALS
Spring: n/app			**Degrees Granted**
Fee: $65			J.D., LL.M., S.J.D.

Enrollment 1998–1999		First-Year Class	
Men:	287 53%	Applied:	3219
Women:	259 47%	Accepted:	n/av
Minorities:	137 25%	Enrolled:	183
Out-of-State:	410 75%		

1998–99 Class Profile

LSAT Percentile: 94%
LSAT Median Score: 165
Percentage passing bar on first try: 94%

Tuition and Fees: *

Resident
$25,500

Average (public)
$8,772

Average (private)
$19,562

Nonresident
$25,500

Average (public)
$14,629

Average (private)
$19,562

0   5   10   15   20   25   30

Percentage receiving financial aid: 80%

ADMISSIONS

In the fall 1999 first-year class, 3219 applied and 183 enrolled. Eleven transfers enrolled. The median LSAT percentile of the most recent first-year class was 94; the median GPA was 3.6 on a scale of 4.0.

Requirements

Applicants must have a bachelor's degree from an accredited institution and take the LSAT. No specific undergraduate courses are required. Candidates are not interviewed.

Procedure

The application deadline for fall entry is February 1. Applicants should submit an application form, LSAT results, a nonrefundable application fee of $65, 3 letters of recommendation, and a personal statement. Transcripts must be sent via the LSDAS. Notification of the admission decision is from January through April. The latest acceptable LSAT test date for fall entry is December. The law school uses the LSDAS.

Special

The law school recruits minority and disadvantaged students by aggressively encouraging them to apply. In addition, a student's minority or disadvantaged status is considered to be a positive part of the application; offers of financial aid are also made. Transfer students must have one year of credit, have attended an ABA-approved law school, and must be in the top 10% of the class.

Costs

Tuition and fees for the 1999-2000 academic year are $25,500 for all full-time students. On-campus room and board costs about $7620 annually, and books and supplies run $760.

Financial Aid

About 80% of current law students receive some form of aid. The average annual amount of aid from all sources combined, including scholarships, loans, and work contracts, is $23,000; maximum, $37,950. Awards are based on need and merit. The required financial statements are FAFSA and Need Access. The aid application deadline for fall entry is March 15. Special funds for minority or disadvantaged students consist of need-based enhanced grants. First-year students are notified about their financial aid application at time of acceptance.

About the Law School

Cornell University Law School was established in 1888 and is a private institution. The 745-acre campus is in a small town 250 miles northwest of New York City. The primary mission of the law school is to teach law within the context of humanity. Students have access to federal, state, county, city, and local agencies, courts, correctional facilities, law firms, and legal aid organizations in the Ithaca area. A full range of opportunities consistent with a small city is available to students. Facilities of special interest to law students are the Legal Aid Clinic, international legal studies program, and the Legal Information Institute. Housing for law students is ample both on and off campus. About 90% of the law school facilities are accessible to the physically disabled.

Calendar

The law school operates on a traditional semester basis. Courses for full-time students are offered days only and must be completed within 3 years. There is no part-time program. New full-time students are admitted in the fall. There is a 4-week summer session. Transferable summer courses are offered.

Programs

In addition to the J.D., the law school offers the LL.M and S.J.D. Students may take relevant courses in other programs and apply credit toward the J.D.; a maximum of 12 credits may be applied. The following joint degrees may be earned: J.D./M.B.A. (Juris Doctor/Master of Business Administration), J.D./M.I.L.R. (Juris Doctor/Master of Industrial and Labor Relations), J.D./M.R.P. (Juris Doctor/Master of Regional Planning), J.D./M.A., Ph.D. (Ph.D. Juris Doctor/Master of Arts in Philosophy or Doctor of Philosophy J.D./M.P.A. (Juris Doctor/Master of Public Administration), J.D./LL.M. (in international and comparative law), J.D./Maitrise en Droit (French law degree), and J.D./M.L.L.P. (Juris Doctor/Master of German and European Law and Legal Practice).

Phone: 607-255-5141
Fax: 607-255-7193

Contact

607-255-5141 for general inquiries; Financial Aid Office, 607-255-6292 for financial aid information.

NEW YORK
◉

Required

To earn the J.D., candidates must complete 84 total credits, of which 36 are for required courses. They must maintain a minimum GPA of 2.3 in the required courses. The following first-year courses are required of all students: Civil Procedure, Constitutional Law, Contracts, Legal Methods, Criminal Law, Property, and Torts. Required upper-level courses consist of a writing requirement (2 writing courses) and Professional Responsibility course. The required orientation program for first-year students is a 2-day introduction to the school.

Electives

Students must take 14 credits in their area of concentration. The Law School offers concentrations in advocacy, business law and regulation, general practice, and public law. In addition, clinics, worth 4 to 6 credits, include the Legal Aid clinic, Small Business Clinic, and Youth Law Clinic. Multiple seminars in the upper division are open to a maximum of 16 students per semester. Internships offered include the judicial externship, Neighborhood Legal Services, Criminal Justice, and legislative. Full-term externships are worth 12 credits at approved sites. Special lecture series are the International Lecture Series, the Robert S. Stevens Lecture Series, Henry Korn Lecture Series, Bernard S. Yadowitz Lecture Series, and the Berger Program in International Law. Study abroad may be done through the Paris Institute, exchange programs (Sydney and Humboldt), and individual ABA-approved programs. An academic support coordinator and student tutors are available. A minority orientation program and Minorities-in-the-Law Conference are held. The most widely taken electives are Corporations, Evidence, and Federal Income Taxation.

Graduation Requirements

In order to graduate, candidates must have a GPA of 2.3, completed the upper-division writing requirement, and first-year Legal Methods Writing Program, and Professional Responsibility course.

Organizations

Students edit the *Cornell Law Review, Cornell Journal of Law and Public Policy, Cornell International Law Journal,* LII BUlletin NY, LII Bulletin-Patent, the student newspaper *Tower,* and the *Cornell Law Forum.* A variety of moot court competitions, such as the Cuccia Cup, Jessup, and Niagara CISG, are held, mostly at the school. Law student organizations include the Herbert W. Briggs Society of International Law, Cornell Law Students Association, and Environment Law.

Library

The law library contains 473,665 hardcopy volumes and 701,091 microform volume equivalents, and subscribes to 6314 serial publications. Such on-line databases and networks as LEXIS, DIALOG, WESTLAW, and NEXIS are available to law students for research. Special library collections include international and foreign law, a U.S. government documents depository, the Bennett Collection of Statutory Materials, and rare books. Recently, the library was refurbished and expanded.

Faculty

The law school has 45 full-time and 11 part-time faculty members, of whom 19 are women. According to AAUP standards for Category I institutions, faculty salaries are well above average. About 16% of full-time faculty have a graduate law degree in addition to the J.D.; about 9% of part-time faculty have one. The ratio of full-time students to full-time faculty in an average class is 12 to 1; in a clinic, 8 to 1. The law school has a regular program of bringing visiting professors and other distinguished lecturers and visitors to campus. There is a chapter of the Order of the Coif; 30 faculty and 18 graduates are members.

Students

About 47% of the student body are women; 25%, minorities; 6%, African American; 13%, Asian American; 4%, Hispanic; and 2%, Native American. The majority of students come from the Northeast (45%). The average age of entering students is 23; age range is 20 to 40. Less than 35% of students enter directly from undergraduate school. About 25% of students have a graduate degree and 50% have worked full-time prior to entering law school. About 1% drop out after the first year for academic or personal reasons; 99% remain to receive a law degree.

CREIGHTON UNIVERSITY

School of Law

2500 California Plaza
Omaha, NE 68178

Application Filing		Accreditation
Fall: May 1		ABA, AALS
Spring: n/app		**Degrees Granted**
Fee: $40		J.D.

Enrollment 1998–1999		First-Year Class	
Men:	241 56%	Applied:	718
Women:	186 44%	Accepted:	481
Minorities:	38 9%	Enrolled:	159
Out-of-State:	265 62%		

1998–99 Class Profile

LSAT Percentile: 52%
LSAT Median Score: 151
Percentage passing bar on first try: 88%

Tuition and Fees:

Resident
$17,114

Average (public)
$8,772

Average (private)
$19,562

Nonresident
$17,114

Average (public)
$14,629

Average (private)
$19,562

0 5 10 15 20 25 30

Percentage receiving financial aid: 90%

ADMISSIONS

In the fall 1999 first-year class, 718 applied, 481 were accepted, and 159 enrolled. Five transfers enrolled. The median LSAT percentile of the most recent first-year class was 52; the median GPA was 3.1 on a scale of 4.0. The lowest LSAT percentile accepted was 18; the highest was 96.

Requirements
Applicants must have a bachelor's degree from an accredited institution and take the LSAT. The most important admission factors include LSAT results, GPA, and general background. No specific undergraduate courses are required. Candidates are not interviewed.

Procedure
The application deadline for fall entry is May 1. Applicants should submit an application form, LSAT results, transcripts, a nonrefundable application fee of $40, and 2 letters of recommendation. Notification of the admission decision is on a rolling basis. The latest acceptable LSAT test date for fall entry is February. The law school uses the LSDAS.

Special
The law school recruits minority and disadvantaged students by means of a substantial Minority Scholarship Program. Transfer students must have one year of credit and have attended an ABA-approved law school.

Costs

Tuition and fees for the 1999-2000 academic year are $17,114 for all full-time students. On-campus room and board costs about $9000 annually; books and supplies run $870.

Financial Aid

About 90% of current law students receive some form of aid. The maximum annual amount of aid from all sources combined, including scholarships, loans, and work contracts, is $27,634. Awards are based on need and merit. Loans are need based, whereas scholarships are based on need and merit combined. The required financial statement is FAFSA. The aid application deadline for fall entry is July 1. Special funds for minority or disadvantaged students consist of substantial scholarship grants to Native American, African American, and Hispanic applicants. First-year students are notified about their financial aid application at the time of acceptance.

About the Law School

Creighton University School of Law was established in 1904 and is a private institution. The 93.5-acre campus is in an urban area near downtown Omaha. The primary mission of the law school is to train lawyers to practice in every jurisdiction in the United States and to prepare men and women to render morally responsible services in all phases of the administration of justice. Students have access to federal, state, county, city, and local agencies, courts, correctional facilities, law firms, and legal aid organizations in the Omaha area. The state's capital and legislature are 45 minutes away by car. The law center houses all functions of the law school under one roof. The library recently doubled in size, allowing for more individual and group study spaces. Housing for law students is available in a university-sponsored high-rise apartment complex exclusively for use by professional students. About 98% of the law school facilities are accessible to the physically disabled.

Calendar

The law school operates on a traditional semester basis. Courses for all students are offered both day and evening. Courses for full-time students must be completed within 3 years; courses for part-time students must be completed within 6 years. New students are admitted in the fall. There is a 5- to 6-week summer session. Transferable summer courses are offered.

Programs

Students may take relevant courses in other programs and apply credit toward the J.D.; a maximum of 6 credits may be applied. The following joint degrees may be earned: J.D./M.B.A. (Juris Doctor/Master of Business Administration).

Phone: 402-280-2872
800-282-5835
Fax: 402-280-3161
E-mail: admit@culaw.creighton.edu
Web: http://www.creighton.edu/culaw

Contact

Andrea D. Bashara, Assistant Dean, 402-280-2872 for general inquiries; Dean Obenauer, Associate Director, 402-280-2731 for financial aid information.

NEBRASKA

Required

To earn the J.D., candidates must complete 94 total credits, of which 39 are for required courses. They must maintain a minimum grade average of 57 (on a scale of 50 to 100 in the required courses). The following first-year courses are required of all students: Constitutional Law I and II, Contracts I and II, Torts I and II, Legal Research, Property I and II, Civil Procedure I and II, and Legal Writing I. Required upper-level courses consist of Legal Writing II and Professional Responsibility. The required orientation program for first-year students is 2 days of general orientation, including an introduction to briefing cases and the Socratic method.

Electives

Students must take 24 credits in their area of concentration. The School of Law offers concentrations in corporate law, criminal law, litigation, and tax law. In addition, Milton R. Abrahams Legal Clinic is open to all students who have completed all required courses and are classified as third-year students. The Clinic accepts a variety of civil matters that vary in complexity. Clinic participants earn 4 credit hours. Seminars, worth 2 and 3 credits, include the Securities Practice Seminar, Advanced Writing Seminar, and Mediation Seminar. Many electives have fewer than 20 students and are taught in seminar fashion. Internships are offered to eligible upper-level students in many different city, county, and federal offices and legal aid offices. Participants serve as law clerks to the various attorneys and judges, for 3 nonclassroom hours. Students may select research topics and write papers for credit under the guidance of a faculty member. Special lecture series include the annual TePoel Lecture Series, Civil Rights Lecture Series, and Lane Foundation Lectures. Students may study abroad in ABA-accredited programs and transfer up to 6 credit hours. The Black Law Students Association and Latino Law Students Association offer tutorial programs to minority members. The most widely taken electives are Evidence, Business Associations, and Trusts and Estates I.

Graduation Requirements

In order to graduate, candidates must have a minimum grade average of 65 and have completed the upper-division writing requirement.

Organizations

Students edit the *Creighton Law Review.* The student newspaper is *The Advocate.* Moot Court opportunities include first- and second-year intramural ABA regional, national, and international tournaments plus invitational tournaments. Other competitions include the Negotiation Competition, Client Counseling Competition, Trial Competition, and essay competitions. Student organizations include the Creighton, Domestic and International Moot Court, Student Bar Association, and the Public Interest Law Forum. There are local chapters of Phi Alpha Delta, Phi Delta Phi, and American Trial Lawyers Association.

Library

The law library contains 254,585 hardcopy volumes and 95,779 microform volume equivalents, and subscribes to 898 serial publications. Such on-line databases and networks as LEXIS, WESTLAW, and Legal-Trac, Congressional Universe, FirstSearch, CD-ROM Products, LOIS, RIA Checkpoint are available to law students for research. The Law Library is a selective U.S. government depository consisting of a complete Congressional Information Service Legislative History service from 1970 to the present, Nebraska Appellate and Supreme Court briefs, and a rare book collection containing approximately 750 British and American legal texts from the 15th through the 19th centuries. Recently, the library was remodeled and a new lower level was constructed. This project nearly doubled the size of the library, and added 7 new group study rooms, a 24-station computer classroom, and multiple data lines for network access. The ratio of library volumes to faculty is 11,572 to 1 and to students, 596 to 1. The ratio of seats in the library to students is 1 to 2.

Placement

J.D.s awarded:	140
Services available through: A separate law school placement center.	
Special features: Web page (job postings are password protected)	
Full-time job interviews:	17 employers
Summer job interviews:	n/av
Placement by graduation:	56% of class
Placement within 9 months:	96% of class
Average starting salary:	$22,000 to $65,000
Areas of placement:	
Private practice 2-10 attorneys	48%
Private practice 11-25 attorneys	20%
Private practice 26-50 attorneys	5%
Private practice 51-100 attorneys	8%
Business/industry	21%
Government	18%
Judicial clerkships	8%

Faculty

The law school has 22 full-time and 41 part-time faculty members, of whom 21 are women. According to AAUP standards for Category IIA institutions, faculty salaries are above average. About 41% of full-time faculty have a graduate law degree in addition to the J.D. The ratio of full-time students to full-time faculty in an average class is 19 to 1; in a clinic, 6 to 1. The law school has a regular program of bringing visiting professors and other distinguished lecturers and visitors to campus.

Students

About 44% of the student body are women; 9%, minorities; 2%, African American; 1%, Asian American; 5%, Hispanic; and 1%, Native American. The majority of students come from Nebraska (38%). The average age of entering students is 26; age range is 21 to 44. About 46% of students enter directly from undergraduate school and 8% have a graduate degree.

DE PAUL UNIVERSITY

College of Law

25 East Jackson Boulevard
Chicago, IL 60604

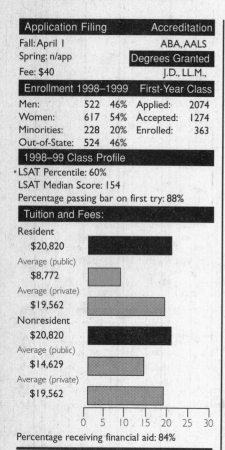

Application Filing	Accreditation
Fall: April 1	ABA, AALS
Spring: n/app	**Degrees Granted**
Fee: $40	J.D., LL.M.,

Enrollment 1998–1999	First-Year Class		
Men:	522 46%	Applied:	2074
Women:	617 54%	Accepted:	1274
Minorities:	228 20%	Enrolled:	363
Out-of-State:	524 46%		

1998–99 Class Profile
- LSAT Percentile: 60%
LSAT Median Score: 154
Percentage passing bar on first try: 88%

Tuition and Fees:

Resident
$20,820

Average (public)
$8,772

Average (private)
$19,562

Nonresident
$20,820

Average (public)
$14,629

Average (private)
$19,562

0 5 10 15 20 25 30

Percentage receiving financial aid: 84%

ADMISSIONS

In the fall 1999 first-year class, 2074 applied, 1274 were accepted, and 363 enrolled. Eight transfers enrolled. The median LSAT percentile of the most recent first-year class was 60; the median GPA was 3.2 on a scale of 4.0. The lowest LSAT percentile accepted was 23; the highest was 98.

Requirements

Applicants must have a bachelor's degree from an accredited institution and take the LSAT. No specific undergraduate courses are required. Candidates are not interviewed.

Procedure

The application deadline for fall entry is April 1. Applicants should submit an application form, LSAT results, transcripts, a nonrefundable application fee of $40, and 1 letter of recommendation. Accepted students must pay $200; another deposit is required upon registration in June. Notification of the admission decision is on a rolling basis. The latest acceptable LSAT test date for fall entry is February. The law school uses the LSDAS.

Special

The law school recruits minority and disadvantaged students through office appointments, direct mail, and a number of on-campus programs. In addition, merit scholarships are awarded. Transfer students must have one year of credit, have attended an ABA-approved law school, and submit their LSDAS reports, law school transcripts, and letters of good standing by August 1.

Costs

Tuition and fees for the 1999-2000 academic year are $20,820 for all full-time students. Tuition for part-time students is $14,120 annually run $900.

Financial Aid

About 84% of current law students receive some form of aid. The average annual amount of aid from all sources combined, including scholarships, loans, and work contracts, is $2500; maximum, $10,000. Awards are based on need and merit. The required financial statement is FAFSA. The aid application deadline for fall entry is March 1. Merit awards are available to minority or disadvantaged students. First-year students are notified about their financial aid application within 4 weeks after their financial aid file is complete.

About the Law School

De Paul University College of Law was established in 1898 and is a private institution. The campus is in an urban area in downtown Chicago. The primary mission of the law school is to train and educate men and women who will ethically and competently represent the legal profession in urban and international settings and in private practice, business, or government. Students have access to federal, state, county, city, and local agencies, courts, correctional facilities, law firms, and legal aid organizations in the Chicago area. Extensive clinical and externship opportunities are available. Facilities of special interest to law students include amphitheater-style video-equipped classrooms, a state-of-the-art moot court room, a legal clinic, and the law library. Housing for law students is available off campus. The Office of Admission assists students in locating apartments and studios. About half of the student body is from out of state. All law school facilities are accessible to the physically disabled.

Calendar

The law school operates on a traditional semester basis. Courses for full-and part-time students are offered both day and evening and must be completed within 5 years. Part-time students may take some upper-level day courses. New full-and part-time students are admitted in the fall. There is a 6-week summer session. Transferable summer courses are offered.

Programs

In addition to the J.D., the law school offers the LL.M in Taxation and in Health Law. Students may take relevant courses in other programs and apply credit toward the J.D. The following joint degrees may be earned: J.D./M.B.A. (Juris Doctor/Master of Business Administration), J.D./M.S. (Juris Doctor/Master of Public Service Management), and J.D./M.A. (Juris Doctor/Master in International Studies).

Required

To earn the J.D., candidates must complete 86 total credits, of which 37 are for required courses. They must maintain a

Phone: 312-362-6831
800-428-7453
E-mail: lawinfo@wppost.depaul.edu
Web: law.depaul.edu

Contact

Priscilla Miller, Assistant Director, 312-362-6831 for general inquiries; Office of Financial Aid, 312-362-8091 for financial aid information.

ILLINOIS

minimum GPA of 2.0 in the required courses. The following first-year courses are required of all students: Civil Procedure, Contracts I and II, Torts, Legal Writing I and II, Constitutional Process I and II, Criminal Law, and Property. Required upper-level courses consist of Criminal Procedure, a senior seminar with a research paper, and Legal Profession. The required orientation program for first-year students is a 3-day program for full-time students and a 4-night program for part-time students.

Electives

The College of Law offers concentrations in corporate law, criminal law, entertainment law, environmental law, family law, international law, juvenile law, labor law, litigation, media law, securities law, sports law, tax law, torts and insurance, health law, and international human rights law. In addition, upper-level students enrolled in the legal clinic handle specific cases from client interviews to court proceedings under direct supervision of staff attorneys. Seminars are 3-credit courses taken during the last year of legal studies. The school also offers internships. Students work with a government agency (such as the State Attorney's Office, the Public Defender's Office, or the judiciary) or other organizations. Students may undertake an independent study project in which they develop an in-depth, publishable research paper under the guidance of a professor. Courses with field work are offered in Health Law, International Human Rights, and Mediation, as well as a legal clinic. An annual Visiting Scholar program is offered. Students may study abroad in an exchange program in conjunction with University College in Dublin, Ireland. An extensive Academic Support Program under the supervision of the Assistant Dean for Educational Services is offered. A wide range of services and activities for minorities are provided by DePaul's Black, Latino, and Asian student associations. Special interest programs include the Women's Law Caucus, Public Interest Law Association, Human Rights Bar Association, Environmental Law Society, Labor Law Society, and International Law Society. The most widely taken electives are Litigation Strategies, Alternate Dispute Resolution, and Corporate Law.

Graduation Requirements

In order to graduate, candidates must have a GPA of 2.0, and have completed the upper-division writing requirement and a required seminar.

Organizations

Students edit the *De Paul Law Review, Journal of Health and Hospital Law, De Paul Business Journal, De Paul/LCA Journal of Arts and Entertainment Law, Environmental Law Digest*, and the *International Law Digest*. The *Cause of Action* is the student newspaper. Students participate in an annual international moot court competition. The Moot Court Society enters national and international competitions. Negotiations, Client Counseling, and Jessup International Moot Court competitions are held annually. Law student organizations include the Women's Law Caucus, the National Lawyers Guild, and Computer Law Society. There are local chapters of the Federalist Society, International Law Society, and Justinian Society of Lawyers. Other organizations include Phi Alpha Delta, Delta Theta Phi, and Brehon Society.

Library

The law library contains 346,097 hardcopy volumes and 902,637 microform volume equivalents, and subscribes to 4926 serial publications. Such on-line databases and networks as LEXIS, WESTLAW, and CALI, plus more than 100 databases through the University Library Web page are available to law students for research. Special library collections include an official U.S. government depository, and tax law, health law, and human rights law collections. Recently, a total renovation of the 3-floor library was completed. The ratio of library volumes to faculty is 2814 to 1 and to students, 346,097 to 1. The ratio of seats in the library to students is 1 to 2.

Faculty

The law school has 50 full-time and 73 part-time faculty members, of whom 45 are women. About 30% of full-time faculty have a graduate law degree in addition to the J.D.; about 10% of part-time faculty have one. The ratio of full-time students to full-time faculty in an aver-

Placement

J.D.s awarded:	308

Services available through: separate law school placement center and the university placement center

Services: career and advisory programs are available as well as an Alumni Job Newsletter, Student Career Bulletin, in-office fax and copier, and Network, Internet, LEXIS, and WESTLAW capabilities

Special features: The De Paul College of Law Alumni Board is very active in career planning and placement programs, and supports a proactive approach to student and alumni career development.

Full-time job interviews:	20 employers
Summer job interviews:	50 employers
Placement by graduation:	48% of class
Placement within 9 months:	90% of class
Average starting salary:	$24,000 to $90,000

Areas of placement:

Private practice 2-10 attorneys	25%
Private practice 11-25 attorneys	11%
Private practice 26-50 attorneys	3%
Private practice 51-100 attorneys	13%
Business/industry	24%
Government	15%
Judicial clerkships	4%
Academic	2%
Public interest	2%
Military	1%

age class is 15 to 1; in a clinic, 6 to 1. The law school has a regular program of bringing visiting professors and other distinguished lecturers and visitors to campus. There is a chapter of the Order of the Coif; 50 faculty and 166 graduates are members.

Students

About 54% of the student body are women; 20%, minorities; 6%, African American; 6%, Asian American; 7%, Hispanic; 1%, Native American; and 1%, foreign nationals. The majority of students come from Illinois (54%). The average age of entering students is 24; age range is 21 to 49. About 44% of students enter directly from undergraduate school, 10% have a graduate degree, and 62% have worked full-time prior to entering law school. About 3% drop out after the first year for academic or personal reasons; 97% remain to receive a law degree.

DRAKE UNIVERSITY

Law School

2507 University Avenue
Des Moines, IA 50311

Application Filing	Accreditation
Fall: April 1	ABA, AALS
Spring: n/app	**Degrees Granted**
Fee: $40	J.D.

Enrollment 1998–1999		First-Year Class	
Men:	191 54%	Applied:	639
Women:	165 46%	Accepted:	428
Minorities:	46 13%	Enrolled:	123
Out-of-State:	160 45%		

1998–99 Class Profile

LSAT Percentile: 52%
LSAT Median Score: 151
Percentage passing bar on first try: n/av

Tuition and Fees:

Resident
$17,630

Average (public)
$8,772

Average (private)
$19,562

Nonresident
$17,630

Average (public)
$14,629

Average (private)
$19,562

0 5 10 15 20 25 30

Percentage receiving financial aid: 90%

ADMISSIONS

In the fall 1999 first-year class, 639 applied, 428 were accepted, and 123 enrolled. Two transfers enrolled. The median LSAT percentile of the most recent first-year class was 52; the median GPA was 3.2 on a scale of 4.0. The lowest LSAT percentile accepted was 8; the highest was 97.

Requirements

Applicants must have a bachelor's degree from an accredited institution and take the LSAT. The most important admission factors include LSAT results, GPA, and undergraduate curriculum. No specific undergraduate courses are required. Candidates are not interviewed.

Procedure

The application deadline for fall entry is April 1. Applicants should submit an application form, LSAT results, transcripts, a nonrefundable application fee of $40, and a personal statement. Notification of the admission decision is within 4 to 6 weeks after the application is complete. The latest acceptable LSAT test date for fall entry is June. The law school uses the LSDAS.

Special

The law school recruits minority and disadvantaged students by means of targeted efforts at nationally identified feeder schools for students of color, the use of the Candidate Referral Service (CRS), and a February recruitment event during National Minority Law School Recruitment Month. Transfer students must have one year of credit, and have attended an ABA-approved law school. Generally, students must rank in the upper half of their current law school class and have certification of good academic standing and eligibility to re-enroll at that school.

Costs

Tuition and fees for the 1999-2000 academic year are $17,630 for all full-time students. On-campus room and board costs about $5900 annually; books and supplies run $900.

Financial Aid

About 90% of current law students receive some form of aid. The average annual amount of aid from all sources combined, including scholarships, loans, and work contracts, is $22,480; maximum, $28,800. Awards are based on need and merit. Loans are offered on the basis of need. The school offers numerous scholarships, some based solely on merit; the majority are awarded on a merit and need combination. Drake also offers public interest scholarships and scholarships for disadvantaged students. The required financial statement is FAFSA. The aid application deadline for fall entry is March 1. Special funds for minority or disadvantaged students consist of the Law Opportunity scholarships, which are awards for entering students from educationally or economically disadvantaged backgrounds who demonstrate need. First-year students are notified about their financial aid application some time after admission and before a seat deposit is required.

About the Law School

Drake University Law School was established in 1865 and is a private institution. The 120-acre campus is in an urban area 5 miles northwest of downtown Des Moines. The primary mission of the law school is to provide students with the opportunities to benefit from hands-on learning experiences and to gain the skills needed to be successful in whatever career path they choose in any geographic location. Students have access to federal, state, county, city, and local agencies, courts, correctional facilities, law firms, and legal aid organizations in the Des Moines area. as well as legal clinics, insurance companies, corporate offices, and internships. Facilities of special interest to law students are the Constitutional Law Resource Center, Agricultural Law Center, Neal and Bea Smith Law Center, the school's legal clinic, and a national training center for public service attorneys. Housing for law students is in university-owned and privately-owned apartments located within walking distance of the campus; housing is also available in city suburbs just 15 minutes from the campus. About 99% of the law school facilities are accessible to the physically disabled.

Calendar

The law school operates on a traditional semester basis. Courses for full-and part-time students are offered days only and must be completed within 6 years. New full-and part-time students are admitted in the fall and summer. There is a 7-week summer session. Transferable summer courses are offered.

Programs

Students may take relevant courses in other programs and apply credit toward the J.D.; a maximum of 6 credits may be applied. The following joint degrees may be earned: J.D./M.B.A. (Juris Doctor/Master of Business Administration), J.D./M.P.A. (Juris Doctor/Master of Public Administration), J.D./M.A. (Juris Doctor/ Master of Arts in mass communications and in political science), J.D./M.S. (Juris Doctor/ Master of Science in agricultural economics), J.D./Pharm.D. (Juris Doctor/ Pharmacy Doctorate), and J.D./M.S.W. (Juris Doctor/Master of Social Work).

Required

To earn the J.D., candidates must complete 90 total credits, of which 41 are for required courses. They must maintain a minimum GPA of 2.0 in the required courses. The following first-year courses are required of all students: Torts, Property, Criminal Law, Civil Procedure I and II, Contracts I and II, Legal Research, Writing, and Appellate Practice, and Constitutional Law I. Required upper-level courses consist of Constitutional Law, Legal Ethics and Professional Responsibility, and Advanced Legal Writing. All students who have completed 45 hours of class may take the clinical

Phone: 515-271-1990
800-44-DRAKE, ext. 2782
E-mail: lawadmit@drake.edu
Web: www.lawdrake.edu

Contact

Kara Blanchard, Office of Admissions, 515-271-2782; 800-44-DRAKE, ext. 2782 for general inquiries; Kara Blanchard, Admissions and Financial Aid, 515-271-2782; 800-44-DRAKE, ext. 2782 for financial aid information.

IOWA

courses as electives. The required orientation program for first-year students is 3 days in length and includes a formal welcome, registration instructions, law school tour, fee payment session, small group meetings, computer training, sessions on professionalism, and the non-credit Introduction to Law course.

Electives

The Law School offers concentrations in corporate law, criminal law, environmental law, family law, international law, labor law, litigation, securities law, tax law, torts and insurance, agricultural law, commercial law, employment law, and constitutional law. In addition, clinical experience is offered through Client Representation and Litigation, which is worth 4 credit hours, and Advanced Client Representation and Litigation Services, worth 2 hours. Students must have completed 45 hours of classroom course work prior to enrolling. To enroll in seminars, students must have completed 30 hours with a 2.0 GPA; to enroll in more than one seminar, a student must have completed 45 hours with a cumulative GPA of 2.5. Generally, 1 to 3 hours of credit may be granted for a seminar course. Internships are available in administrative law, the legislature, the judiciary, insurance, environmental law, securities, probate, and health law. Internships with the prosecutor, the county attorney, the U.S. Attorney's Office, and the Civil Rights Commission are also available. Credit varies from 1 to 4 credit hours and prerequisites vary. Independent research may be undertaken for 1 to 3 credit hours and is graded on a credit/no credit basis. A Public Law Externship worth 10 credit hours is offered. Special lecture series include the Constitutional Law Resource Center Speaker Series and the Dwight D. Opperman Lecture in Constitutional Law. Drake offers a 4-week summer abroad program in Nantes, France worth up to 6 credits; credit may also be accepted from programs offered by other law schools. The Academic Support Program is offered to all students. In addition, the Legal Writing Tutorial Services are led by an English professor and are offered to all students, while second- and third-year students offer tutorial services to all first-year students and to upper-level students in Evidence. Special interest group programs include the Summer Institute in Constitutional Law and the Summer Institute in Agricultural Law. The most widely taken electives are Trial Advocacy, Client Representation and Litigation, and Advanced Client Representation and Litigation.

Graduation Requirements

In order to graduate, candidates must have a GPA of 2.0, have completed the upper-division writing requirement, completed 6 semesters for residence credit and 90 hours for academic credit, and have satisfied the advanced writing requirement through either independent study or course work.

Organizations

Students edit the *Drake Law Review*, the *Journal of World Agricultural Law*, and the student newspaper *The Gavel*. Moot court teams are sent to the C. Edwin Moore Appellate Advocacy, National Moot Court, and National Appellate Advocacy competitions. Other competitions are the National Mock Trial Competition, Client Counseling Competition, and Negotiations Competition. Student organizations include the Student Bar Association, Latino Lawyers Society, and International Law Society. There are local chapters of the Order of Barristers, American Trial Lawyers Association, and Delta Theta Phi.

Library

The law library contains 280,000 hardcopy volumes and 90,000 microform volume equivalents, and subscribes to 3000 serial publications. Such on-line databases and networks as LEXIS, DIALOG, WESTLAW, NEXIS, Legaltrac, CIS Congressional Universe, and RIA Check-Point are available to law students for research. Special library collections include a government depository, and agricultural, tax, computer, and constitutional law collections. Recently, the library completed a new $8.5 million, 70,000 square foot library. In addition to the on-line catalog and automated circulation system, the library provides computer access with several computer laboratories and Ethernet connections throughout the library, at carrels, tables, and study rooms, including Internet access from any student workstation in the library. The ratio of library volumes to faculty is 10,169 to 1 and to students, 833 to 1.

Placement

J.D.s awarded:	150
Services available through: separate law school placement center	
Services: provides seminars	
Special features: a nationwide network of alumni in specific geographic and practice areas that has been developed to assist students with employment opportunities; additionally, students are assisted by 2 full-time staff	
Full-time job interviews:	22 employers
Summer job interviews:	22 employers
Placement by graduation:	56% of class
Placement within 9 months:	91% of class
Average starting salary:	$22,000 to $128,000

Areas of placement:

Private practice 2-10 attorneys	20%
Private practice 11-25 attorneys	9%
Private practice 26-50 attorneys	3%
Private practice 51-100 attorneys	3%
Private practice 100 + attorneys	3%
Solo practice	6%
Business/industry	20%
Government	14%
Judicial Clerkships	12%
Academic	2%

Faculty

The law school has 30 full-time and 24 part-time faculty members, of whom 15 are women. According to AAUP standards for Category IIA institutions, faculty salaries are well above average. About 26% of full-time faculty have a graduate law degree in addition to the J.D. The ratio of full-time students to full-time faculty in an average class is 20 to 1. The law school has a regular program of bringing visiting professors and other distinguished lecturers and visitors to campus. There is a chapter of the Order of the Coif; 12 faculty and 586 graduates are members.

Students

About 46% of the student body are women; 13%, minorities; 5%, African American; 3%, Asian American; 3%, Hispanic; and 1%, foreign nationals. The majority of students come from the Midwest (82%). The average age of entering students is 26; age range is 21 to 53. About 8% of students have a graduate degree. About 6% drop out after the first year for academic or personal reasons; 94% remain to receive a law degree.

School of Law

Science and Towerview Drives
Box 90393
Durham, NC 27708

Application Filing		Accreditation
Fall: January 1		ABA, AALS
Spring: n/app		**Degrees Granted**
Fee: $65		J.D., LL.M., S.J.D., M.L.S.

Enrollment 1998–1999		First-Year Class	
Men:	367 54%	Applied:	3418
Women:	313 46%	Accepted:	n/av
Minorities:	177 26%	Enrolled:	236
Out-of-State:	585 86%		

1998–99 Class Profile
LSAT Percentile: n/av
LSAT Median Score: 165
Percentage passing bar on first try: n/av

Tuition and Fees:

Resident
$26,103

Average (public)
$8,772

Average (private)
$19,562

Nonresident
$26,103

Average (public)
$14,629

Average (private)
$19,562

0 5 10 15 20 25 30

Percentage receiving financial aid: 75%

ADMISSIONS

In the fall 1999 first-year class, 3418 applied and 236 enrolled. Eleven transfers enrolled. The median GPA of the most recent first-year class was 3.5. The highest LSAT percentile was 99.

Requirements
Applicants must have a bachelor's degree from an accredited institution and take the LSAT. No specific undergraduate courses are required. Candidates are not interviewed.

Procedure
The application deadline for fall and summer entry is January 1. Applicants should submit an application form, LSAT results, transcripts, a nonrefundable application fee of $65, 2 academic letters letters of recommendation, and 1 certification from an academic dean. Notification of the admission decision is on a rolling basis. The latest acceptable LSAT test date for fall entry is December. The law school uses the LSDAS.

Special
The law school invites admitted minority applicants to visit the school and meet with faculty and other minority students. Minority student organizations work with the Admissions Office to contact and recruit minority candidates. Transfer students must have one year of credit, have attended an ABA-approved law school, and must be eligible to re-enroll and otherwise be in good standing at the current law school.

Costs

Tuition and fees for the 1999-2000 academic year are $26,103 for all full-time students. There is no part-time program. On-campus room and board costs about $4200 annually; and books and supplies run $1200.

Financial Aid

About 75% of current law students receive some form of aid. The average annual amount of aid from all sources combined, including scholarships, loans, and work contracts, is $21,000; maximum, $39,201. Awards are based on need and merit. The required financial statement is FAFSA. The aid application deadline for fall and summer entry is March 15. Special funds for minority or disadvantaged students consist of a scholarship for minority students established by the national law firm of Baker and McKenzie. First-year students are notified about their financial aid application some time shortly after acceptance.

About the Law School

Duke University School of Law was established in 1930 and is a private institution. The campus is in an urban area in Durham. The primary mission of the law school is to prepare students for responsible and productive lives in the legal profession. The law school also provides leadership at both national and international levels to improve the law and legal institutions through teaching, research, and other forms of public service. Students have access to federal, state, county, city, and local agencies, courts, correctional facilities, law firms, and legal aid organizations in the Durham area. The school is an integral part of Duke University, so students have access to all the resources of a major research university. Facilities of special interest to law students include the Private Adjudication Center; Pro Bono Project; Center for Law, Ethics, and National Security; Center for the Study of Congress; and Center for the Study of Global Information Technologies. Housing for law students is limited on campus, but there are ample rental units in the surrounding area. All law school facilities are accessible to the physically disabled.

Calendar

The law school operates on a traditional semester basis. Courses for full-time students are offered days only and must be completed within 3 years. New full-time students are admitted in the fall and summer. There is a 10-week summer session. Transferable summer courses are not offered.

Programs

In addition to the J.D., the law school offers the LL.M, S.J.D., and M.L.S. Students may take relevant courses in other programs and apply credit toward the J.D.; a maximum of 3 credits may be applied. The following joint degrees may be earned: J.D./M.A. (Juris Doctor/Master of Arts in cultural anthropology, economics, English, environmental studies, history, humanities, mechanical engineering, philosophy, political science, psychology, public policy studies, or romance studies), J.D./LL.M. (Juris Doctor/Master of Laws in comparative and international law), J.D./M.D. (Juris Doc-

Contact

Admissions Staff, 919-613-7020 for general inquiries; Kochie Richardson, Assistant Director of Financial Aid, 919-613-7025 for financial aid information.

NORTH CAROLINA

tor/Master of Medicine), J.D./M.B.A. (Juris Doctor/Master of Business Administration), J.D./Ph.D. (Juris Doctor/Doctor of Philosophy in political science), J.D./M.E.M. (Juris Doctor/Master of Environmental Management), J.D./M.S. (Juris Doctor/Master of Science in mechanical engineering), J.D./M.P.P. (Juris Doctor/Master of Public Policy), and J.D./M.T.S. (Juris Doctor/Master of Theological Studies).

Required

To earn the J.D., candidates must complete 84 total credits, of which 30 are for required courses. They must maintain a minimum GPA of 2.1 in the required courses. The following first-year courses are required of all students: Constitutional Law, Contracts, Civil Procedure, Criminal Law, Professional Responsibility, Legal Research and Writing, Property, and Torts. Clinical courses are available as elective course work for upper-class students. The required orientation program for first-year students lasts 4 days immediately prior to start of classes.

Electives

Students who have met the prerequisites may take clinics. Credit hours are dependent on the particular course. Many students gain clinical experience by providing volunteer legal services in areas of individual interest through pro bono work, which, if taken as independent study, is worth academic credit. Students can take seminars, worth 2 to 3 credit hours each. International law internships are offered to upper-class students for 14 credit hours. One to 3 credit hours may be granted for directed independent research with the permission of supervising faculty. Through the Pro Bono Project, students provide volunteer legal services in areas of individual interest. Special lectures include the Annual Brainerd Currie Memorial Lecture Series. Study abroad is possible through the Summer Institute in Transnational Law in Geneva or Hong Kong. This program is required of J.D./LL.M. students. Up to 6 hours of academic credit is offered and is available to all J.D. students. Tutorial assistance is provided as needed. The most widely taken electives are Business, Evidence, and International Law.

Graduation Requirements

In order to graduate, candidates must have a GPA of 2.1.

Organizations

Students edit the *Duke Law Journal, Law and Contemporary Problems, Alaska Law Review, Duke Journal of Comparative and International Law*, and the newspaper the *Herald*. Other publications include interdisciplinary magazines such as the *Duke Environmental Law and Public Policy Forum* and the *Duke Journal of Gender Law and Policy*. Moot court competitions include the National Moot Court in Richmond, Virginia; Jessup International Law Moot Court; and the J. Braxton Craven, Jr. Memorial Moot Court at the University of North Carolina. Law student organizations include the Duke Bar Association, Moot Court Board, and International Law Society. Local chapters of national associations include the ABA-Law Student Division, Amnesty International, and American Civil Liberties Union.

Library

The law library contains 535,000 hardcopy volumes and 71,000 microform volume equivalents, and subscribes to 6998 serial publications. Such on-line databases and networks as LEXIS, DIALOG, WESTLAW, and First Search, Uncover, NEXIS are available to law students for research. Special library collections include federal government documents, the Christie Collection of jurisprudence, and the Riddick Collection of autographed senatorial papers. Recently, the library completed a major renovation and expansion that enlarged the law library to more than 65,000 net square feet and is designed to accommodate both the traditional and rapidly changing needs of the law school community. The ratio of library volumes to faculty is 6859 to 1 and to students, 787 to 1. The ratio of seats in the library to students is 1 to 4.

Placement

J.D.s awarded:	197

Services available through: A separate law school placement center.

Special features: The staff of the Office of Career Planning and Placement makes a special effort to get to know all the students and to offer personal attention and assistance whenever possible.

Full-time job interviews:	450 employers
Summer job interviews:	n/av
Placement by graduation:	94% of class
Placement within 9 months:	99% of class
Average starting salary:	$35,000 to $95,000

Areas of placement:

Private practice 11-25 attorneys	1%
Private practice 26-50 attorneys	2%
Private practice 51-100 attorneys	72%
Judicial clerkships	17%
Government	2%
Unknown	2%
Military	2%
Academic	1%
Public interest	1%

Faculty

The law school has 36 full-time and 42 part-time faculty members, of whom 22 are women. About 19% of full-time faculty have a graduate law degree in addition to the J.D.; about 4% of part-time faculty have one. The ratio of full-time students to full-time faculty in an average class is 18 to 1; in a clinic, 12 to 1. There is a chapter of the Order of the Coif; 10 graduates are members.

Students

About 46% of the student body are women; 26%, minorities; 12%, African American; 8%, Asian American; 4%, Hispanic; and 1%, Native American. The majority of students come from the Northeast (38%). The average age of entering students is 24; age range is 19 to 36. About 49% of students enter directly from undergraduate school, 10% have a graduate degree, and 48% have worked full-time prior to entering law school. About 1% drop out after the first year for academic or personal reasons; 99% remain to receive a law degree.

School of Law

900 Locust Street, Hanley Hall
Pittsburgh, PA 15282

Application Filing		Accreditation
Fall: April 1		ABA, AALS
Spring: n/app		Degrees Granted
Fee: $50		J.D.

Enrollment 1998–1999		First-Year Class	
Men:	374 54%	Applied:	n/av
Women:	317 46%	Accepted:	n/av
Minorities:	41 6%	Enrolled:	240
Out-of-State:	221 32%		

1998–99 Class Profile
LSAT Percentile: 60%
LSAT Median Score: n/av
Percentage passing bar on first try: 80%

Tuition and Fees:

Resident
$16,424

Average (public)
$8,772

Average (private)
$19,562

Nonresident
$16,424

Average (public)
$14,629

Average (private)
$19,562

0 5 10 15 20 25 30

Percentage receiving financial aid: 80%

ADMISSIONS

In the fall 1999 first-year class, 240 enrolled. The median LSAT percentile of the most recent first-year class was 60; the median GPA was 3.2 on a scale of 4.0.

Requirements
Applicants must have a bachelor's degree from an accredited institution and take the LSAT. The most important admission factors include academic achievement, LSAT results, and life experience. No specific undergraduate courses are required. Candidates are not interviewed.

Procedure
The application deadline for fall entry is April 1. Applicants should submit an application form, LSAT results, transcripts, TOEFL for foreign students, a nonrefundable application fee of $50, and 2 letters of recommendation. Notification of the admission decision is on a rolling basis. The latest acceptable LSAT test date for fall entry is December for day students. The law school uses the LSDAS.

Special
The law school recruits minority and disadvantaged students by means of Candidate Referral Service minority search, law fairs, contact with minority coordinators, and assistance with scholarships and grants. Transfer students must have one year of credit and have attended an ABA-approved law school; admission also depends on space availability.

Costs

Tuition and fees for the 1999-2000 academic year are $16,424 for full-time students. Tuition for part-time students is $12,664. Books and supplies run $800.

Financial Aid

About 80% of current law students receive some form of aid. Awards are based on need and merit, along with minority status. The required financial statements are FFS, CSS Profile, and FAFSA. The aid application deadline for fall entry is May 31. Special funds for minority or disadvantaged students consist of scholarships and grants. First-year students are notified about their financial aid application at the time of acceptance.

About the Law School

Duquesne University School of Law was established in 1911 and is a private institution. The 43-acre campus is in an urban area in Pittsburgh. The primary mission of the law school is to educate students in the fundamental principles of law, to assist students in forming sound judgment, and to develop facility in legal research and writing. Students have access to federal, state, county, city, and local agencies, courts, correctional facilities, law firms, and legal aid organizations in the Pittsburgh area. Varied clinical programs supervised by the school allow students to gain practical experience. Facilities of special interest to law students are the District Attorney's Office Clinical Program, the Department of Environmental Resources Clinical Program, in-house Economic and Community Development Clinic, Neighborhood Legal Services Clinic, and Civil and Family Justice. Housing for law students is available off campus. All law school facilities are accessible to the physically disabled.

Calendar

The law school operates on a traditional semester basis. Courses for full-time students are offered days only and must be completed within 4 years. For part-time students, courses are offered both day and evening and must be completed within 5 years. New students are admitted in the fall. There is a 5-week summer session. Transferable summer courses are offered.

Programs

Students may take relevant courses in other programs and apply credit toward the J.D.; the maximum number that may be applied varies. The following joint degrees may be earned: J.D./M.B.A. (Juris Doctor/Master of Business Administration), J.D./M.Div. (Juris Doctor/Master of Divinity in conjunction with Pittsburgh Theologyical Seminary), J.D./M.S.E.S.M. (Juris Doctor/Master of Science in Environmental Science and Management), and J.D./M.A. (Juris Doctor/Master of Communications).

Phone: 412-396-6296
E-mail: campion@duq.edu
Web: duq.edu/law

Contact
Joseph P. Campion, Jr., Director of Admissions, 412-396-6296 for general inquiries; Frank Dutkovich, Financial Aid Director, 412-396-6607 for financial aid information.

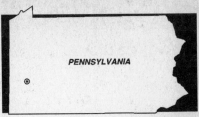

PENNSYLVANIA

Required
To earn the J.D., candidates must complete 86 total credits, of which 33 are for required courses. They must maintain a minimum GPA of 3.0 in the required courses. The following first-year courses are required of all students: Contracts, Torts, Property (second year for evening students), Legal Process and Procedure, Criminal Law and Procedure (second year for evening students), Civil Procedure I, and Legal Research and Writing. Required upper-level courses consist of Professional Responsibility. The required orientation program for first-year students consists of 1-1/2 days of sessions on requirements in the first year and handling stress. The students meet with their faculty adviser and student mentors.

Electives
The School of Law offers concentrations in corporate law, criminal law, environmental law, family law, international law, labor law, litigation, securities law, tax law, and torts and insurance. In addition, clinics, which are all considered upper-division classes worth 3 credits, include the U.S. Attorney's Program, District Attorney's Program, and Pennsylvania Department of Environmental Resources Program. Also open to upper-division students are internships and seminars, both worth 2 to 3 credits. Seminar topics include labor arbitration, collective bargaining, and trial tactics. Upper-division students are eligible to serve as faculty research assistants. Special lectures are given by the guest speakers that visit the school throughout the year. Law students may request permission to participate in study-abroad programs offered by other ABA-approved law schools. There are summer study-abroad programs in China, Ireland, and Russia. The Black Law Students Association sponsors a tutoring program. Special interest programs are offered by the Public Interest Law Association, Health Care Law Association, and Black Law Students Association. The most widely taken electives are Constitutional Law, Taxation, and Evidence.

Graduation Requirements
In order to graduate, candidates must have a GPA of 3.0 and have completed the upper-division writing requirement.

Organizations
Students edit the *Duquesne Law Review*; *Juris*, a news magazine; and the *Duquesne Business Law Journal*. Moot courts include a trial moot court, an appellate moot court, a corporate moot court, and a tax moot court. Law student organizations include the Environmental Law Association, the Federalist Society, and Health Care Law Association. There are local chapters of Phi Alpha Delta, Association of Trial Lawyers of America, and the law student division of the ABA.

Library
The law library contains 236,000 hard-copy volumes and 210,000 microform volume equivalents, and subscribes to 2400 serial publications. Such on-line databases and networks as LEXIS, DIALOG, WESTLAW, and INNOVACQ, and OCLC are available to law students for research. Special library collections include audiovisual tapes and U.S. government documents. Recently, the library installed the INNOVACQ computer system, an audiovisual center, and a West CD-ROM Library. The ratio of library volumes to faculty is 8706 to 1 and to students, 336 to 1. The ratio of seats in the library to students is 1 to 2.

Faculty
The law school has 29 full-time and 40 part-time faculty members, of whom 13 are women. According to AAUP standards for Category IIA institutions, faculty salaries are well above average. About 32% of full-time faculty have a graduate law degree in addition to the J.D.; about 10% of part-time faculty have one. The ratio of full-time students to full-time faculty in an average class is 14 to 1. The law school has a regular program of bringing visiting professors and other distinguished lecturers and visitors to campus.

Placement

J.D.s awarded:	166
Services available through: A separate law school placement center.	
Special features: individual counseling for students, videotaped mock interviews, and focus groups for nontraditional students	
Full-time job interviews:	39 employers
Summer job interviews:	32 employers
Placement by graduation:	50% of class
Placement within 9 months:	91% of class
Average starting salary:	$20,000 to $90,000
Areas of placement:	
Public interest	18%
Business/industry	16%
(unknown)	16%
Private practice 2-10 attorneys	14%
Private practice 11-25 attorneys	5%
Private Practice 26-50 attorneys	5%
Private practice 51-100 attorneys	5%
Government	12%

Students
About 46% of the student body are women; 6%, minorities; 4%, African American; 1%, Asian American; and 1%, Hispanic. The majority of students come from Pennsylvania (68%). The average age of entering students is 27; age range is 21 to 55. About 70% of students have worked full-time prior to entering law school. About 2% drop out after the first year for academic or personal reasons; 95% remain to receive a law degree.

EMORY UNIVERSITY

School of Law

Gambrell Hall
Atlanta, GA 30322

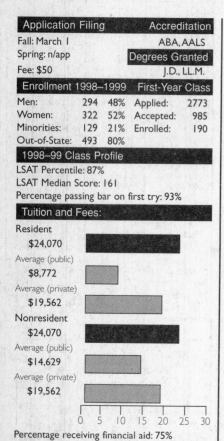

Application Filing	Accreditation
Fall: March 1	ABA, AALS
Spring: n/app	**Degrees Granted**
Fee: $50	J.D., LL.M.

Enrollment 1998–1999		First-Year Class	
Men:	294 48%	Applied:	2773
Women:	322 52%	Accepted:	985
Minorities:	129 21%	Enrolled:	190
Out-of-State:	493 80%		

1998–99 Class Profile

LSAT Percentile: 87%
LSAT Median Score: 161
Percentage passing bar on first try: 93%

Tuition and Fees:

Resident
$24,070

Average (public)
$8,772

Average (private)
$19,562

Nonresident
$24,070

Average (public)
$14,629

Average (private)
$19,562

0 5 10 15 20 25 30

Percentage receiving financial aid: 75%

ADMISSIONS

In the fall 1999 first-year class, 2773 applied, 985 were accepted, and 190 enrolled. Ten transfers enrolled. The median LSAT percentile of the most recent first-year class was 87; the median GPA was 3.4 on a scale of 4.0. The lowest LSAT percentile accepted was 50; the highest was 100.

Requirements

Applicants must have a bachelor's degree from an accredited institution and take the LSAT. The most important admission factors include LSAT results, GPA, and academic achievement. No specific undergraduate courses are required. Candidates are not interviewed.

Procedure

The application deadline for fall entry is March 1. Applicants should submit an application form, LSAT results, transcripts, TOEFL for foreign applicants, a nonrefundable application fee of $50, 2 letters of recommendation, and a personal statement. Notification of the admission decision is from January to May. The latest acceptable LSAT test date for fall entry is February. The law school uses the LSDAS.

Special

The law school recruits minority and disadvantaged students by visiting historically black colleges, attending college law fairs in the fall, sending mailings to minority students, and hosting several special on-site visits throughout the year. Transfer students must have one year of credit, have attended an ABA-approved law school, and have a ranking of at least the top 50% of the class, although the top 20% to 25% is preferred. Preadmissions courses consist of the occasional CLEO summer institutes.

Costs

Tuition and fees for the 1999-2000 academic year are $24,070 for all full-time students. On-campus room and board costs about $10,910 annually; books and supplies run $1514.

Financial Aid

About 75% of current law students receive some form of aid. The average annual amount of aid from all sources combined, including scholarships, loans, and work contracts, is $18,500; maximum, $26,910. Scholarships are based on both merit and need; loans are either need or non-need, depending on the loan. The required financial statements are CSS Profile and FAFSA. The aid application deadline for fall entry is March 1. Special funds for minority or disadvantaged students consist of scholarships based on merit and need. First-year students are notified about their financial aid application at some time shortly after students are accepted but before a tuition deposit is required.

About the Law School

Emory University School of Law was established in 1923 and is a private institution. The 600-acre campus is in an urban area 6 miles northeast of Atlanta. The primary mission of the law school is to educate law students from both a professional and ethical standpoint as they prepare to enter the profession while emphasizing the role of attorney as public servant. Commitment to service underlies both classroom and extracurricular experiences. Students have access to federal, state, county, city, and local agencies, courts, correctional facilities, law firms, and legal aid organizations in the Atlanta area. Students have access to national and regional businesses as well. Facilities of special interest to law students are the more than 40 clinics with federal agencies, judges, public interest offices, and businesses. Housing for law students is available both as university-owned and privately operated housing, both of which are readily available in the immediate area. All law school facilities are accessible to the physically disabled.

Calendar

The law school operates on a traditional semester basis. Courses for full-time students are offered days only and must be completed within 3 years. There is no part-time program. New full-time students are admitted in the fall. There is no summer session. Transferable summer courses are not offered.

Programs

In addition to the J.D., the law school offers the LL.M. Students may take relevant courses in other programs and apply credit toward the J.D.; a maximum of 3 credit hours or 1 class credit may be applied. The following joint degrees may be earned: J.D./M.B.A. (Juris Doctor/Master of Business Administration), J.D./M.Div. (Juris Doctor/Master of Divinity), J.D./M.T.S. (Juris Doctor/Master of Theological Studies), J.D./M.P.H. (Juris Doctor/Master of Public Health), J.D./Ph.D. in religion (Juris Doctor/Doctor of Philosophy in religion), J.D./M.A. (Juris Doctor/Master of Arts in Judaic studies), and J.D./REES (Juris Doctor/Russian East European Studies Certificate).

Phone: 404-727-6801
Fax: 404-727-2477
E-mail: jbalej@law.emory.edu
Web: www.law.emory.edu

Contact
Janet E. Balej, Admission Coordinator, 404-727-6802 for general inquiries; Brenda Hill, Associate Director of Financial Aid, 404-727-6039 for financial aid information.

GEORGIA

Required

To earn the J.D., candidates must complete 88 total credits, of which 39 are for required courses. They must maintain a minimum GPA of 2.25 in the required courses. The following first-year courses are required of all students: Contracts, Torts, Civil Procedure I and II, Criminal Law, Property, Legal Methods, Constitutional Law, and Legal Writing, Research and Appellate Advocacy. Required upper-level courses consist of Evidence, Legal Profession, and Trial Techniques. The required orientation program for first-year students is a 2-day period prior to registration that introduces students to the university and the law school communities. Students also attend a small section class during orientation.

Electives

Clinics are available to second- and third-year students for 2 credits, generally. Seminars are also open to second- or third-year students for 2 hours of academic credit. During the summer, most students have paid internships with firms, businesses, government offices, or public interest agencies. A small number of students may be offered research assistantships. Special lectures in law and public policy and law and medicine are open to the public. A study-abroad exchange program is offered at Leiden University in the Netherlands. Students may also take advantage of other ABA-accredited law school study-abroad programs. Tutorials are offered to all students by professors on an individual basis. Special consideration is given to minority students in the admissions process; scholarships are offered to minority students based on merit and need.

Graduation Requirements

In order to graduate, candidates must have a GPA of 2.25 and have completed the upper-division writing requirement.

Organizations
Student-edited publications are the *Emory Law Journal, Emory International Law Review, Emory Bankruptcy Journal*, and the student-edited newspaper is *Hearsay*. Annually, moot court teams participate in internal competitions and the Georgia Intra-State, National Moot Court, and Jessup Moot Court competitions. Law student organizations include the Student Bar Association, Moot Court Society, and Emory Law Outreach. Local chapters of national associations are Phi Alpha Delta, Black Law Students Association, and Phi Delta Phi. Other on-campus organizations are the Emory Intramural teams and clubs.

Library
The law library contains 300,000 hardcopy volumes and 71,734 microform volume equivalents, and subscribes to 6000 serial publications. Such on-line databases and networks as LEXIS, DIALOG, WESTLAW, NEXIS, OCLC, RUN, and RLIN are available to law students for research. Special library collections include a European Union depository and a federal depository. Recently, the library automated circulation. The ratio of library volumes to faculty is 6521 to 1 and to students, 475 to 1.

Faculty
The law school has 46 full-time and 47 part-time faculty members, of whom 25 are women. According to AAUP standards for Category I institutions, faculty salaries are well above average. About 35% of full-time faculty have a graduate law degree in addition to the J.D. The ratio of full-time students to full-time faculty in an average class is 14 to 1; in a clinic, 2 to 1. There is a chapter of the Order of the Coif; 38 faculty are members.

Placement

J.D.s awarded:	204

Services available through: a separate law school placement center

Special features: personal advising and programming designed to assist students; specific advising in public interest law by the Associate Director of Career Services; and off-campus job fairs in New York and Washington, D.C., among others.

Full-time job interviews:	84 employers
Summer job interviews:	n/av
Placement by graduation:	63% of class
Placement within 9 months:	95% of class
Average starting salary:	$30,750 to $91,395

Areas of placement:

Private practice 2-10 attorneys	27%
Private practice 11-25 attorneys	7%
Private practice 26-50 attorneys	8%
Private practice 51-100 attorneys	5%
Business/industry	24%
Government	14%
Judicial clerkships	13%
Public interest	2%
Academic	1%

Students
About 52% of the student body are women; 21%, minorities; 9%, African American; 6%, Asian American; 4%, Hispanic; and 1%, foreign nationals. The majority of students come from the South (46%). The average age of entering students is 24; age range is 20 to 48. About 45% of students enter directly from undergraduate school, 9% have a graduate degree, and 50% have worked full-time prior to entering law school. About 3% drop out after the first year for academic or personal reasons; 95% remain to receive a law degree.

FLORIDA COASTAL SCHOOL OF LAW

7555 Beach Boulevard
Jacksonville, FL 32216

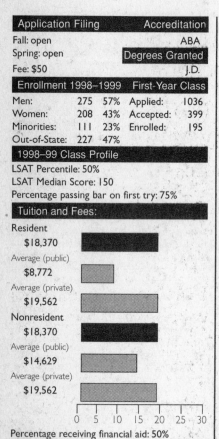

Application Filing	Accreditation
Fall: open	ABA
Spring: open	**Degrees Granted**
Fee: $50	J.D.

Enrollment 1998–1999		First-Year Class	
Men:	275 57%	Applied:	1036
Women:	208 43%	Accepted:	399
Minorities:	111 23%	Enrolled:	195
Out-of-State:	227 47%		

1998–99 Class Profile
LSAT Percentile: 50%
LSAT Median Score: 150
Percentage passing bar on first try: 75%

Tuition and Fees:

Resident
$18,370

Average (public)
$8,772

Average (private)
$19,562

Nonresident
$18,370

Average (public)
$14,629

Average (private)
$19,562

0 5 10 15 20 25 30

Percentage receiving financial aid: 50%

ADMISSIONS
In the fall 1999 first-year class, 1036 applied, 399 were accepted, and 195 enrolled. Fifteen transfers enrolled. The median LSAT percentile of the most recent first-year class was 50; the median GPA was 2.9 on a scale of 4.0. The lowest LSAT percentile accepted was 15; the highest was 93.

Requirements
Applicants must have a bachelor's degree from an accredited institution and take the LSAT. Minimum acceptable GPA is 2.0 on a scale of 4.0. No specific undergraduate courses are required. Candidates are not interviewed.

Procedure
The application deadline for fall entry is open. Applicants should submit an application form, LSAT results, a nonrefundable application fee of $50, and 2 letters of recommendation. Notification of the admission decision is on a rolling basis. The latest acceptable LSAT test date for fall entry is June. The law school uses the LSDAS.

Special
Transfer students must have a minimum GPA of 2.0 and have attended an ABA-approved law school.

Costs
Tuition and fees for the 1999-2000 academic year are $18,370 for all full-time students. Tuition and fees for all part-time students are $14,860. Books and supplies run $800.

Financial Aid
About 50% of current law students receive some form of aid. The average annual amount of aid from all sources combined, including scholarships, loans, and work contracts, is $18,500; maximum, $22,000. Awards are based on need and merit. The required financial statement is FAFSA. The financial aid application deadline is open. First-year students are notified about their financial aid application at the time of acceptance.

About the Law School
Florida Coastal School of Law was established in 1994 and is a private institution. The 5-acre campus is in a suburban area near downtown Jacksonville and the beach. The primary mission of the law school is to distinguish itself as a forward-looking, globally interactive, and culturally diverse institution dedicated to having a positive impact on its students, the community, the legal profession, and the justice system. Students have access to federal, state, county, city, and local agencies, courts, correctional facilities, law firms, and legal aid organizations in the Jacksonville area. Facilities of special interest to law students include the Information Resources and Technology Division; the Center for Strategic Governance and Information Initiatives Island and on-Campus Teen Court. Housing for law students includes a large variety of close and affordable off-campus apartments and houses. All law school facilities are accessible to the physically disabled.

Calendar
The law school operates on a traditional semester basis. Courses for full-time students are offered both day and evening and must be completed within 5 years. For part-time students, courses are offered both day and evening and must be completed within 6 years. New full-time and part-time students are admitted in the fall and spring. There is an 8-week summer session. Transferable summer courses are offered.

Programs
Students may take relevant courses in other programs and apply credit toward the J.D.; a maximum of 6 credits may be applied.

Phone: 904-680-7710
877-210-2591
Fax: 904-680-7776
E-mail: admissions@fcsl.edu
Web: fcsl.edu

Contact

904-680-7710 for general inquiries; Office of Admissions, 904-680-7710 for financial aid information.

Required

To earn the J.D., candidates must complete 87 total credits, of which 56 are for required courses. They must maintain a minimum GPA of 2.0 in the required courses. The following first-year courses are required of all students: Paths of the Law, Civil Dispute Resolution, Lawyering Process I, Contracts I, Torts, Constitutional Law, Criminal Law, Civil Dispute Resolution II, Lawyering Process II, Contracts II, and Property. Required upper-level courses consist of Business Associations, Constitutional Law II, Constitutional Law III, Constitutional Law IV, Evidence, International or Comparitive Law, Lawyers & Society, Legislative Process, Professional Responsibility, and a Regulatory law course. The required orientation program for first-year students is 2 days long and includes interactions with faculty staff, and students; the role of the lawyer and professionalism; the responsibilities of the future lawyer and student ethics; Academic Success programs; and a reception.

Electives

Third-year clinics include Criminal, Municipal, and a Mediation class with a clinic, each worth 6 credit hours. Seminars are available to upper-division students only. These include Sports Law, Appellate Advocacy, and Maritime Law, each worth 3 credit hours. Judicial internships can be taken for 3 or 4 credit hours. However, students must have completed Professional Responsibility and Evidence courses (Constitution Law I, II, and III if working with a federal judge) and have a GPA of 2.0 or above. Advanced Legal Research, worth 2 credit hours, is open to upper-division students. There is also independent study, worth 2 credit hours, for students who have completed 42 credit hours. The School of Law invites practioners, judges, and other public figures to speak on a variety of topics, including legal practice, legal education, and jurisprudence. An Academic

Success Program is aimed at serving three groups of students; (1) incoming students considered at risk because of low LSAT scores or low GPA; (2) or students who are re-entering school after a long absence; and (3) current students who are at risk or on academic probation. The program consists of workshops on a variety of topics, including case briefing, study aids, and exam-taking. In addition, the School of Law has tutors for all first-year classes. Students may also meet with the program director to deal with individual problems and issues.

Graduation Requirements

In order to graduate, candidates must have a GPA of 2.0.

Organizations

Students edit the *Florida Coastal School of Law Review*, the *Weekly Leader*, and the newspaper, *Coastal Tidings*. Moot court competitions include the Robert Orseck Memorial Moot Court and the E. Earl Zehemer Memorial Moot Court. Law student organizations include the Student Bar Association, Black American Law Students Association, and Habitat for Humanity. There is a local chapter of ABA-Law Students Division. Other organizations include the Environmental and Land Use Club, Hispanic American Law Students Association, and Christian Legal Society.

Library

The law library contains 127,829 hardcopy volumes 199,120 volume equivalent, and 421,745 microform volume equivalents, and subscribes to 2047 serial publications. Such on-line databases and networks as LEXIS, WESTLAW, CCH Tax, and Mathew Bender Authority are available to law students for research. Recently, the library networked study carrels. The ratio of library volumes to faculty is 9956 to 1 and to students, 475 to 1. The ratio of seats in the library to students is 1 to 9.

Placement

J.D.s awarded:	106

Services available through: A separate law school placement center.
Special features: extensive programming on a variety of career development topics including practice areas, work environments, alternative careers, and transition from school to the work force.

Full-time job interviews:	n/av
Summer job interviews:	n/av
Placement by graduation:	n/av
Placement within 9 months:	n/av
Average starting salary:	n/av
Areas of placement:	n/av

Faculty

The law school has 27 full-time and 31 part-time faculty members, of whom 15 are women. The ratio of full-time students to full-time faculty in an average class is 20 to 1; in a clinic, 13 to 1. The law school has a regular program of bringing visiting professors and other distinguished lecturers and visitors to campus.

Students

About 43% of the student body are women; 23%, minorities; 12%, African American; 3%, Asian American; 8%, Hispanic; and 1%, Native American. The majority of students come from Florida (53%). The average age of entering students is 28; age range is 21 to 69. About 50% of students enter directly from undergraduate school, 20% have a graduate degree, and 50% have worked full-time prior to entering law school. About 8% drop out after the first year for academic or personal reasons; 92% remain to receive a law degree.

College of Law

425 W. Jefferson St.
Tallahassee, FL 32306-1601

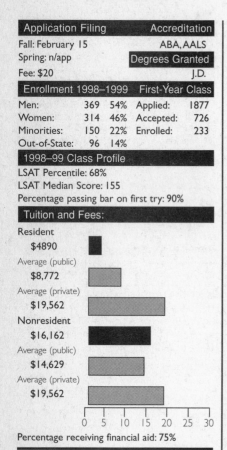

Application Filing		Accreditation
Fall: February 15		ABA, AALS
Spring: n/app		**Degrees Granted**
Fee: $20		J.D.

Enrollment 1998–1999		First-Year Class	
Men:	369 54%	Applied:	1877
Women:	314 46%	Accepted:	726
Minorities:	150 22%	Enrolled:	233
Out-of-State:	96 14%		

1998–99 Class Profile
LSAT Percentile: 68%
LSAT Median Score: 155
Percentage passing bar on first try: 90%

Tuition and Fees:

Resident
$4890

Average (public)
$8,772

Average (private)
$19,562

Nonresident
$16,162

Average (public)
$14,629

Average (private)
$19,562

0 5 10 15 20 25 30

Percentage receiving financial aid: 75%

ADMISSIONS

In the fall 1999 first-year class, 1877 applied, 726 were accepted, and 233 enrolled. Twelve transfers enrolled. The median LSAT percentile of the most recent first-year class was 68; the median GPA was 3.3 on a scale of 4.0. The highest LSAT percentile was 98.

Requirements
Applicants must have a bachelor's degree from an accredited institution and take the LSAT. The most important admission factors include academic achievement and LSAT results. No specific undergraduate courses are required. Candidates are not interviewed.

Procedure
The application deadline for fall entry is February 15. Applicants should submit an application form, LSAT results, transcripts, a nonrefundable application fee of $20, 2 letters of recommendation, and a personal statement. Notification of the admission decision is on a rolling basis. The latest acceptable LSAT test date for fall entry is February. The law school uses the LSDAS.

Special
The law school recruits minority and disadvantaged students through the LSDAS-CRS, by sponsoring special programs throughout the year, and by recruiting at colleges and universities. Requirements are different for out-of-state students in that LSAT scores and GPA requirements are generally higher for nonresidents. Transfer students must have one year of credit and be in the top third of their class.

Costs

Tuition and fees for the 1999-2000 academic year are $4890 for full-time in-state students and $16,162 for out-of-state students. On-campus room and board costs about $9000 annually; books and supplies run $1000.

Financial Aid

About 75% of current law students receive some form of aid. The maximum annual amount of aid from all sources combined, including scholarships, loans, and work contracts, is $18,500. Awards are based on need and merit. Fellowships of up to $10,000 per year also are available. About 1% of the students serve as research assistants to faculty members. The required financial statement is FAFSA. The aid application deadline for fall entry is April 1. Special funds for minority or disadvantaged students include a stipend for attending a summer orientation program. Other scholarships and aid are available. The average amount is $14,500. First-year students are notified about their financial aid application on a rolling basis.

About the Law School

Florida State University College of Law was established in 1966 and is a public institution. The 1200-acre campus is in a suburban area in Tallahassee, the state capital. The primary mission of the law school is to prepare students to practice law in a changing, pluralistic society by offering a curriculum that includes strong internship and joint-degree programs. Students have access to federal, state, county, city, and local agencies, courts, correctional facilities, law firms, and legal aid organizations in the Tallahassee area. The College of Law is located 1 block from the Florida Supreme Court building and within 5 blocks of federal, state, district, county, and bankruptcy courts, the State Legislature, and the State and Supreme Court law libraries. Housing for law students is available in dormitories for single students and apartments for both single and married students. A housing office helps students find off-campus accommodations.

Calendar

The law school operates on a traditional semester basis. Courses for full-time students are offered both day and evening and must be completed within 3 years. There is no part-time program. New full-time students are admitted in the fall. There is a 7-week summer session. Transferable summer courses are offered.

Programs

Students may take relevant courses in other programs and apply credit toward the J.D.; a maximum of 6 credits may be applied. The following joint degrees may be earned: J.D./M.B.A. (Juris Doctor/ Master of Business Administration), J.D./M.P.A. (Juris Doctor/Master of Public Administration), J.D./M.S. (Juris Doctor/Master of Science in economics), J.D./M.S.P. (Juris Doctor/Master of Science in Urban and Regional Planning), J.D./M.S.W. (Juris Doctor/Master of Social Work), and J.D./M.S. (Juris Doctor/Master of Science in international affairs).

Phone: 850-644-3787
Fax: 850-644-7284
E-mail: admissions@law.fsu.edu

Contact

Sharon Booker, Director of Admissions and Records, 850-644-3787 for general inquiries; Joanne Clark, Financial Aid Office, 850-644-5871 for financial aid information.

Required

To earn the J.D., candidates must complete 88 total credits, of which 35 are for required courses. They must maintain a minimum grade average of 67 or better in the required courses. The following first-year courses are required of all students: Civil Procedure, Torts, Contracts I and II, Property I and II, Legal Writing and Research I and II, Criminal Law, and Constitutional Law I. Required upper-level courses consist of Constitutional Law II, Professional Responsibility, and a writing requirement course. All students must complete 20 hours of civil pro bono work. The required orientation program for first-year students is a 3-day program that includes an introduction to legal education, research and writing, and ethics.

Electives

The College of Law offers concentrations in environmental law, international law, and mediation. In addition, the college offers 20 externship programs, either full- or part-time, encompassing 5 judicial placements, several administrative agency placements, and many civil and criminal lawyering programs. A variety of seminars is offered such as insurance, legal ethics, and bankruptcy. There are the Brown Bag Lecture Series and the Mason Ladd Memorial Lectures. Study abroad is available during summer terms at Oxford University in England, University of West Indies in Barbados, and at Charles University in Pragne; the Czech Republic. The Academic Support Program is open to all interested first-year students. The most widely taken electives are Evidence, Business Associations, and Income Tax.

Graduation Requirements

In order to graduate, candidates must have completed the upper-division writing requirement, 20 hours of pro bono work, and the 6-semester residency requirement.

Organizations

The primary law review is the *Florida State University Law Review*. Other law journals are the *Journal of Land Use and Environmental Law*, begun in 1983 and the state's first and only student publication in environmental and land law use. Students also edit the *Journal of Transnational Law and Policy*. The college's moot court team participates in about 10 regional and national competitions each year, including the Florida Bar Robert Orseck Moot Court Competition, and the John Gibbons National Constitutional Criminal Law Moot Court Competition. The college also takes part in 3 mock trial competitions each year. Law student associations include the Student Bar Association and chapters of the American Civil Liberties Union and the American Trial Lawyers Association.

Library

The law library contains 409,603 hard-copy volumes and 842,184 microform volume equivalents, and subscribes to 5248 serial publications. Such on-line databases and networks as LEXIS, WEST-LAW, and more than 100 databases including OCLC First Search are available to law students for research. Special library collections include rare English, American, and Floridian legal materials, including a first edition of Blackstone's Commentaries, and videotapes of oral arguments before the Florida Supreme Court of cases since 1985. Recently, wireless Internet access was added throughout the library. The ratio of library volumes to faculty is 8904 to 1 and to students, 626 to 1. The ratio of seats in the library to students is 1 to 53.

Faculty

The law school has 46 full-time and 13 part-time faculty members, of whom 19 are women. According to AAUP standards for Category I institutions, faculty salaries are average. About 13% of full-time faculty have a graduate law degree in addition to the J.D. The ratio of full-time students to full-time faculty in an average class is 14 to 1; in a clinic, 13 to 1. The law school has a regular program of bringing visiting professors and other distinguished lecturers and visitors to campus. There is a chapter of the Order of the Coif; 36 faculty and 319 graduates are members.

FLORIDA

Placement

J.D.s awarded:	204

Services available through: a separate law school placement center and the university placement center

Services: various workshops/lectures on specific placement topics such as Internet job hunting, and judicial clerkships

Special features: a monthly job notice bulletin for alumni; E-mail notification of job opportunities for students

Full-time job interviews:	36 employers
Summer job interviews:	47 employers
Placement by graduation:	46% of class
Placement within 9 months:	92% of class
Average starting salary:	$24,000 to $86,000

Areas of placement:

Private practice 2-10 attorneys	13%
Private practice 11-25 attorneys	6%
Private practice 26-50 attorneys	3%
Private practice 51-100 attorneys	2%
Unknown	35%
Government	25%
Business/industry	5%
Judicial clerkships	5%
Public interest	3%
Academic	2%
Military	1%

Students

About 46% of the student body are women; 22%, minorities; 10%, African American; 2%, Asian American; 8%, Hispanic; and 1%, Native American. The majority of students come from Florida (86%). The average age of entering students is 25; age range is 20 to 58. About 3% drop out after the first year for academic or personal reasons; 97% remain to receive a law degree.

School of Law

140 West 62nd Street
New York, NY 10023

Application Filing	Accreditation
Fall: March 1	ABA, AALS
Spring: n/app	**Degrees Granted**
Fee: $60	J.D., LL.M.

Enrollment 1998–1999		First-Year Class	
Men:	775 54%	Applied:	4866
Women:	662 46%	Accepted:	1285
Minorities:	345 24%	Enrolled:	463
Out-of-State:	474 33%		

1998–99 Class Profile

LSAT Percentile: 90%
LSAT Median Score: 164
Percentage passing bar on first try: 88%

Tuition and Fees:

Resident
$24,915

Average (public)
$8,772

Average (private)
$19,562

Nonresident
$24,915

Average (public)
$14,629

Average (private)
$19,562

0   5   10   15   20   25   30

Percentage receiving financial aid: 74%

ADMISSIONS

In the fall 1999 first-year class, 4866 applied, 1285 were accepted, and 463 enrolled. Forty-seven transfers enrolled. The median LSAT percentile of the most recent first-year class was 90; the median GPA was 3.4 on a scale of 4.0. The lowest LSAT percentile accepted was 30; the highest was 99.

Requirements

Applicants must have a bachelor's degree from an accredited institution and take the LSAT. The most important admission factors include LSAT results, GPA, and general background. No specific undergraduate courses are required. Candidates are not interviewed.

Procedure

The application deadline for fall entry is March 1. Applicants should submit an application form, LSAT results, transcripts, TOEFL if the student is from a non-English-speaking country, a nonrefundable application fee of $60, and a personal statement. LSAT results, and transcripts are submitted through LSDAS. Notification of the admission decision is 6 to 8 weeks after application is complete. The latest acceptable LSAT test date for fall entry is February. The law school uses the LSDAS.

Special

The law school recruits minority and disadvantaged students by means of attendance at forums and law fairs, LSDAS Candidate Referral Service, alumni assistance, and current minority students contacting accepted minority applicants. Transfer students must have a minimum GPA of 3.0, have attended an ABA-approved law school, and fulfill a 2-year residency requirement at Fordham.

Costs

Tuition and fees for the 1999-2000 academic year are $24,915 for all full-time students. Tuition for all part-time students is $18,685 per year. On-campus room and board costs about $12,620 annually, and books and supplies run $760.

Financial Aid

About 74% of current law students receive some form of aid. The average annual amount of aid from all sources combined, including scholarships, loans, and work contracts, is $25,500; maximum, $39,000. Awards are based on need along with approximately 10% based on merit. The required financial statement is CSS Profile or FAFSA. The aid application deadline for fall entry is May 1. Special funds for minority or disadvantaged students consist of funds contributed by benefactors of the school specifically to assist minority and disadvantaged students. Also, some school funds are specifically allocated to assist minority and disadvantaged students. First-year students are notified about their financial aid application at after acceptance, when their file is complete.

About the Law School

Fordham University School of Law was established in 1905 and is a private institution. The 8-acre campus is in an urban area in the Lincoln Center area of New York City. The primary mission of the law school is to provide students with a comprehensive understanding of legal doctrine and a solid foundation of analytical reasoning, lawyering skills, and professional values that they will be able to use throughout their careers in law practice or law-related professions; to contribute to the development of the law and legal education; and to serve the wider community. Students have access to federal, state, county, city, and local agencies, courts, correctional facilities, law firms, and legal aid organizations in the New York area. Lincoln Center, with its many cultural attractions, is across the street; the midtown area, home of the media, law firms, corporate headquarters, and nonprofit organizations, is a few blocks away; there is also convenient transportation to the courts. Facilities of special interest to law students include the law school and attached buildings, which include a 250-seat amphitheater, 2 cafeterias, student activities center, student journal offices, counseling center, bookstore, 2 computer centers, and a chapel. Housing for law students is available in a 250-bed, 20-story university residence hall connected to the law school. There is some student housing in the neighborhood; many students commute from other parts of the city or the metropolitan area. About 95% of the law school facilities are accessible to the physically disabled.

Calendar

The law school operates on a traditional semester basis. Courses for full-time students are offered both day and evening and must be completed within 3 years. For part-time students, courses are offered both day and evening and must be completed within 4 years. New full- and part-time students are admitted in the fall. There is a 8-week summer session. Transferable summer courses are offered.

Programs

In addition to the J.D., the law school offers the LL.M. Students may take relevant courses in other programs and apply credit toward the J.D.; a maximum of 13 credits may be applied. The following joint degrees may be earned: J.D./M.B.A. (Juris Doctor/Master of Business Administration) and J.D./M.S.W. (Juris Doctor/Master of Social Work).

Required

To earn the J.D., candidates must complete 83 total credits, of which 39 are for required courses. They must maintain a minimum GPA of 1.9 in the required courses. The following first-year courses are required of all students: Contracts, Criminal Justice, Civil Procedure, Property, Torts, Constitutional Law, Legal Process, and Legal Writing and Research. Required upper-level courses consist of Corporations and Partnerships and Professional Responsibility. The required orientation program for first-year students is a 1-day program and a 1-week legal process course. There are separate programs for legal writing, library use, career planning, university resources, and clinical programs.

Contact

Kevin Downey, Assistant Dean, Admissions, 212-636-6810 for general inquiries; James A. McGough, Financial Aid Director, 212-636-6815 for financial aid information.

NEW YORK

Electives

The School of Law offers concentrations in corporate law, criminal law, entertainment, environmental law, family law, international law, labor law, litigation, maritime law, media law, securities law, sports law, tax law, torts and insurance, and European Community law, trial advocacy, public interest law, consumer law, professional responsiblity, antitrust and economic regulation, banking and finance, and commercial law. In addition, clinics, which are open to upper-class students who have satisfied prerequisites, include Litigation Skills, Comprehensive Lawyering Skills, and Mediation. Seminars are also open to upper-class students; they are usually 2 or 3 credits. A selection of recent offerings includes Advanced Bankruptcy, Advanced Copyright Law, and Advanced Evidence. After the first year, students may participate in a broad range of actual practice settings in federal and state courts, administrative agencies, prosecutors' and defenders' offices, and nonprofit agencies. These internships earn 2 credits. Research is done through the Stein Institute of Law and Ethics Research fellowships and the MCI/Fordham Travel Abroad Fellowship. Also, many students serve as research assistants to faculty. Field work may be undertaken in the noncredit Pro Bono program, where students assist in preparing cases under the direction of attorneys from the Legal Aid Society and various public agencies and not-for-project organizations through Fordham's Public Interest Resource Center. Special lecture series include John F. Sonnett Lectures by distinguished judges and litigators; Stein Lectures in ethics and professional responsiblity; Noreen E. McNamara Lectures by outstanding women in the profession; and Robert L. Levine Lectures by distinguished legal scholars. Anyone may study abroad for up to 1 year for up to 24 credits in approved subjects with the MCI/Fordham Travel Abroad Fellowship. The noncredit Academic Enrichment program provides additional training in briefing cases, study strategies, and exam-taking techniques. The school contributes to the CLEO program. Public service programs include a nonlegal community service project; advocacy projects for battered women, low-income tenants, and unemployed individuals; and student-funded fellowships for summer work at public interest organizations. The most widely taken electives are Income Taxation, New York Practice, and Bankruptcy.

Graduation Requirements

In order to graduate, candidates must have a GPA of 1.9 and have completed the upper-division writing requirement.

Organizations

Students edit the *Fordham Law Review, Fordham Urban Law Journal, Fordham International Law Journal, Fordham Environmental Law Journal, Fordham Entertainment, Mass Media, and Intellectual Property Journal*, the newspaper, *Advocate*, and the yearbook *In Summation*. Moot court competitions include the intramural William Hughes Mulligan and the I. Maurice Wormser and the intramural Irving R. Kaufman Securities Law Competition. Teams also compete at the National Moot Court, Jessup International Law, and Craven Constitutional Law, Cardozo Entertainment Law, National Trial Advocacy, National Tax, and National Products Liability competitions. Law student organizations include the Student Bar Association, International Law Society, and Labor Law Club. There are local chapters of the Federalist Society, National Lawyers Guild, and Phi Alpha Delta. Additionally, the university has the largest student-run radio station in the country and more than 100 other organizations for students. There are approximately 40 student-run organizations at the Law School.

Library

The law library contains 543,992 hardcopy volumes and 1,044,801 microform volume equivalents, and subscribes to 5572 serial publications. Such on-line databases and networks as LEXIS, DIALOG, WESTLAW, and NEXIS are available to law students for research. Special library collections include an EEC collection and a federal documents depository. Recently, the library purchased the INNOPACQ on-line catalog system and retroconverted the card catalog to a machine-readable form. Also, an Automated Circulation System was installed, as well as a LAN for student computers and the computer classroom and laboratory. Many new carrels and tables were wired for data use. The ratio of library volumes to faculty is 8500 to 1 and to students, 379 to 1. The ratio of seats in the library to students is 1 to 3.

Placement

J.D.s awarded:	449
Services available through: a separate law school placement center.	
Services: self-assessment seminars, mock interviews, networking/job prospecting workshops, MBTI	
Special features: The school designs its own programs to ensure that students have opportunites to interact with alumni and employers	
Full-time job interviews:	320 employers
Summer job interviews:	n/av
Placement by graduation:	90% of class
Placement within 9 months:	99% of class
Average starting salary:	$40,000 to $140,000
Areas of placement:	
Private practice 2-10 attorneys	7%
Private practice 11-25 attorneys	7%
Private practice 26-50 attorneys	5%
Private practice 51-100 attorneys	48%
Business/industry	13%
Government	11%
Judicial clerkships	6%
Academic	1%
Public interest	1%

Faculty

The law school has 64 full-time and 200 part-time faculty members, of whom 82 are women. According to AAUP standards for Category I institutions, faculty salaries are well above average. About 45% of full-time faculty have a graduate law degree in addition to the J.D.; about 8% of part-time faculty have one. The ratio of full-time students to full-time faculty in an average class is 50 to 1; in a clinic, 8 to 1. The law school has a regular program of bringing visiting professors and other distinguished lecturers and visitors to campus. There is a chapter of the Order of the Coif.

Students

About 46% of the student body are women; 24%, minorities; 8%, African American; 9%, Asian American; and 7%, Hispanic. The majority of students come from the Northeast (85%). The average age of entering students is 24; age range is 20 to 51. About 34% of students enter directly from undergraduate school, 4% have a graduate degree, and 66% have worked full-time prior to entering law school. About 2% drop out after the first year for academic or personal reasons; 98% remain to receive a law degree.

2 White Street
Concord, NH 03301

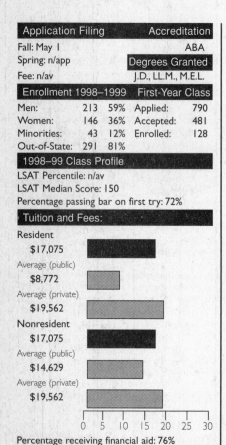

Application Filing		Accreditation
Fall: May 1		ABA
Spring: n/app		**Degrees Granted**
Fee: n/av		J.D., LL.M., M.E.L.

Enrollment 1998–1999		First-Year Class	
Men:	213 59%	Applied:	790
Women:	146 36%	Accepted:	481
Minorities:	43 12%	Enrolled:	128
Out-of-State:	291 81%		

1998–99 Class Profile
LSAT Percentile: n/av
LSAT Median Score: 150
Percentage passing bar on first try: 72%

Tuition and Fees:

Resident
$17,075

Average (public)
$8,772

Average (private)
$19,562

Nonresident
$17,075

Average (public)
$14,629

Average (private)
$19,562

Percentage receiving financial aid: 76%

ADMISSIONS

Information in the above capsule is approximate. In the fall 1999 first-year class, 790 applied, 481 were accepted, and 128 enrolled. Two transfers enrolled. The median GPA of the most recent first-year class was 3.0. The lowest LSAT percentile accepted was 8; the highest was 99.

Requirements

Applicants must have a bachelor's degree from an accredited institution and take the LSAT. The most important admission factors include motivation, academic achievement, and writing ability. No specific undergraduate courses are required. Candidates are interviewed.

Procedure

The application deadline for fall entry is May 1. Applicants should submit an application form, LSAT results, transcripts, 2 letters of recommendation, a nonrefundable application fee, and a personal statement. Notification of the

admission decision is on a rolling basis. The latest acceptable LSAT test date for fall entry is June. The law school uses the LSDAS.

Special

The law school recruits minority and disadvantaged students by inviting applicants who are members of linguistic and/or racial minorities or who are handicapped, to provide a statement addressing nonquantifiable achievements such as overcoming economic, social, and educational obstacles. Transfer students must have one year of credit, have a minimum GPA of 2.0, and have attended an ABA-approved law school.

Costs

Tuition and fees for the 1999-2000 academic year are $17,075 for all full-time students. Books and supplies run $550.

Financial Aid

About 76% of current law students receive some form of aid. The average annual amount of aid from all sources combined, including scholarships, loans, and work contracts, is $2695. Awards are based on need and merit. The required financial statements are GAPSFAS and FAFSA. The aid application deadline for fall entry is open. Special funds for minority or disadvantaged students consist of diversity scholarships that are available to members of groups currently underrepresented in the law center community. They are awarded based on academic and community involvement factors.

About the Law School

Franklin Pierce Law Center was established in 1973 and is a private institution. The 1-acre campus is in a small town 70 miles north of Boston, Massachusetts. The primary mission of the law school is to encourage innovation in legal education. Self-reliant students who know their strengths, objectives, and motivations are able to shape individualized programs from the array of educational opportunities. Students have access to federal, state, county, city, and local agencies, courts, correctional facilities, law firms, and legal aid organizations in the Concord area. Many students find paid employment, work as

volunteers, or have externships in all these facilities, situated in Concord, the state capital. Facilities of special interest to law students consist of the attorney general offices and city, state, and federal court clerkships. Housing for law students is available around the law center's residential setting. About 95% of the law school facilities are accessible to the physically disabled.

Calendar

The law school operates on a traditional semester basis. Courses for full-time students are offered both day and evening and must be completed within 5 years. There is no part-time program. New full-time students are admitted in the fall. There is a 14-week summer session. Transferable summer courses are offered.

Programs

In addition to the J.D., the law school offers the LL.M and M.E.L.(Master of Education Law). Students may take relevant courses in other programs and apply credit toward the J.D.; a maximum of 8 credits may be applied. The following joint degrees may be earned: J.D./M.I.P. (Juris Doctor/Master of Intellectual Property).

Required

To earn the J.D., candidates must complete 84 total credits, of which 39 are for required courses. They must maintain a minimum GPA of 2.0 in the required courses. The following first-year courses are required of all students: Torts, Property, Constitutional Law, Contracts I and II, Civil Procedure, Legal Writing, Legal Research and Writing, and 1 legal perspective course. Required upper-level courses consist of Criminal Procedure I, Administrative Law, and Professional Responsibility. The required 4-day orientation program for first-year students includes an introduction to the Career Services Center and student organizations, a demonstration of briefing cases, service as a juror for a mock trial, and such social events as an evening with a faculty host at their home.

Electives

The Franklin Pierce Law Center offers concentrations in corporate law, criminal

Phone: 603-228-9217
Fax: 603-228-1074
E-mail: L.admissions@fplc.edu
Web: www.fplc.edu

Contact

Lory Attalla, Acting Director for Admissions, 603-228-9217 for general inquiries; Clinton A. Hanson, Director of Financial Aid, 603-228-1541, ext. 104 for financial aid information.

law, environmental law, family law, international law, juvenile law, litigation, tax law, health law, intellectual property, legal services, regulatory and administrative law, and education law. In addition, the Administrative Advocacy clinic is open to 8 second-year students who handle administrative cases for real clients; it is worth 4 credits. The Appellate Defender clinic is open to second- and third-year students who prepare criminal appeals to the New Hampshire Supreme Court; it is worth 3 credits. The Civil Practice Clinic allows second- and third-year students to represent clients in divorce, abuse and neglect, child support, housing or bankruptcy proceedings; it is worth 4 credits. The Criminal Practice clinid is available for students to represent clients charged with misdemeanor or juvenile offenses; it is worth 5 credits. Research seminars are offered in medical decision making, Supreme Court issues, and advanced legal research. Externships are offered to students in their fourth, fifth, or sixth semester, for 5 or 13 credits. There are established ones available every semester, and individually designed ones created by the student. Second- and third-year students may take independent study with a specific faculty member for a maximum of 4 credits. Periodically, speakers are invited to the school to lecture on a wide variety of subjects, including civil rights, health law, patent law, and corporate law. Study abroad is possible through programs provided by ABA-approved schools. Computer tutorial programs are offered to all students. While there is no formal remedial program, faculty will work with individuals on request. Teaching assistants are available for individual consultation. All first-year courses have teaching assistants for discussion and explanation. Minorities and others interested in intellectual property are encouraged to apply for an annual Procter & Gamble scholarship. Various student organizations bring in speakers and special programs and conferences annually. The most widely taken electives are Debtor and Creditor Relations, Evidence, and Personal Income Tax.

Graduation Requirements

In order to graduate, candidates must have a GPA of 2.0, have completed 84 credits, have 6 full-time semesters of residency, offset all credits below C- with an equal number of credits of B- or above, have satisfied any terms of academic probation or financial obligation, and not be the subject of an alleged Honor Code violation.

Organizations

Student-edited publications are *IDEA: The Journal Of Law and Technology* and *RISK: Issues of Health and Safety*. The *Annual Survey of New Hampshire Law*, which publishes articles focusing on recent opinions of the New Hampshire Supreme Court, is a 3-credit course in which 2 second-year students write and a third-year student serves as editor. Moot court competitions include the required appellate argument for second semester first-year students. Students annually enter the Fordham Kaufman Securities Law Competition, Pace University Environmental Law Competition, and Giles Sutherland Rich Intellectual Property Moot Court, among others. Students enter legal essay writing contests on a volunteer basis. Law student organizations include the International Law Society, Environmental Law Society, and Women's Law Caucus. Local chapters of national associations include the American Trial Lawyers Association, Phi Alpha Delta, and National Lawyers Guild.

Library

The law library contains 126,896 hardcopy volumes and 447,501 microform volume equivalents, and subscribes to 1044 serial publications. Such on-line databases and networks as LEXIS, DIALOG, WESTLAW, NEXIS, the Internet, and databases relating to patent searching are available to law students for research. Special library collections include an intellectual property special collection, a repository for the Licensing Executives Society, and a federal GPO selective depository. Recently, the library renovated the main floor to provide new areas for reference, circulation, public services, and technical services. The ratio of library volumes to faculty is 10,203 to 1 and to students, 514 to 1. The ratio of seats in the library to students is 1 to 2.

Faculty

The law school has 24 full-time and 37 part-time faculty members, of whom 16 are women. According to AAUP stan-

Placement

J.D.s awarded:	138

Services available through: separate law school placement center

Services: video interviews and playbacks; workshops on information interviewing; career planning for students interested in intellectual property, business, public interest, and general practice; externships for academic credit

Special features: individual and personal service to its students, with emphasis on helping students network; and nationwide academic externship opportunities

Full-time job interviews:	30 employers
Summer job interviews:	30 employers
Placement by graduation:	57% of class
Placement within 9 months:	91% of class
Average starting salary:	$36,000 to $75,000

Areas of placement:

Private practice 2-10 attorneys	22%
Private practice 11-25 attorneys	10%
Private practice 26-50 attorneys	22%
Private practice 51-100 attorneys	10%
Private practice 100+ attorneys	2%
Business/industry	12%
Government	12%
Judicial clerkships	6%
Public interest	2%
Academic	2%

dards for Category IIA institutions, faculty salaries are well above average. About 17% of full-time faculty have a graduate law degree in addition to the J.D. The ratio of full-time students to full-time faculty in an average class is 16 to 1; in a clinic, 1 to 1.

Students

About 36% of the student body are women; 12%, minorities; 2%, African American; 3%, Asian American; 2%, Hispanic; and 1%, Native American. The majority of students come from the Northeast (42%). The average age of entering students is 28; age range is 20 to 45. About 20% of students enter directly from undergraduate school, 20% have a graduate degree, and 80% have worked full-time prior to entering law school. About 10% drop out after the first year for academic or personal reasons; 90% remain to receive a law degree.

School of Law

3401 North Fairfax Drive
Arlington, VA 22201-4498

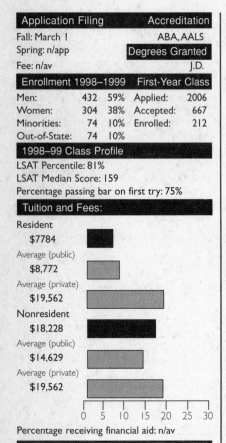

Application Filing	Accreditation
Fall: March 1	ABA, AALS
Spring: n/app	**Degrees Granted**
Fee: n/av	J.D.

Enrollment 1998–1999		First-Year Class	
Men:	432 59%	Applied:	2006
Women:	304 38%	Accepted:	667
Minorities:	74 10%	Enrolled:	212
Out-of-State:	74 10%		

1998–99 Class Profile
LSAT Percentile: 81%
LSAT Median Score: 159
Percentage passing bar on first try: 75%

Tuition and Fees:

Resident
$7784

Average (public)
$8,772

Average (private)
$19,562

Nonresident
$18,228

Average (public)
$14,629

Average (private)
$19,562

0 5 10 15 20 25 30

Percentage receiving financial aid: n/av

ADMISSIONS

In the fall 1999 first-year class, 2006 applied, 667 were accepted, and 212 enrolled. Thirty-five transfers enrolled. The median LSAT percentile of the most recent first-year class was 81; the median GPA was 3.23 on a scale of 4.0.

Requirements

Applicants must have a bachelor's degree from an accredited institution and take the LSAT. The most important admission factors include LSAT results, class rank, and GPA. No specific undergraduate courses are required. Candidates are not interviewed.

Procedure

The application deadline for fall entry is March 1. Applicants should submit an application form, LSAT results, LSDAS Report, 2 letters of recommendation, and a 500-word personal statement. Check wi;th the school for current application fee. Notification of the admission decision is mid-March to end of June. The latest acceptable LSAT test date for fall entry is February. The law school uses the LSDAS.

Special

The law school recruits minority and disadvantaged students through the Law Services' Candidate Referral Service, Law School Forums, regional law fairs, and CLEO. Transfer students must have one year of credit, have a minimum GPA of 3.0, and have attended an ABA-approved law school.

Costs

Tuition and fees for the 1999-2000 academic year are $7784 for full-time in-state students and $18,228 for out-of-state students. Tuition for part-time students is $6116 per year in-state and $14,322 out-of-state.

Financial Aid

Awards are based on need and merit. The required financial statement is the FAFSA. The aid application deadline for fall entry is open. First-year students are notified about their financial aid application between the time of acceptance and the first day of school.

About the Law School

George Mason University School of Law was established in 1979 and is a public institution. The 1-acre campus is in a suburban area 2 miles south of Washington, D.C. The primary mission of the law school is to provide superior legal education programs leading to the first professional degree in law, the Juris Doctor. The school stresses the case method. Students have access to federal, state, county, city, and local agencies, courts, correctional facilities, law firms, and legal aid organizations in the Arlington area. Housing for law students is not available on the metro campus. All law school facilities are accessible to the physically disabled.

Calendar

The law school operates on a traditional semester basis. Courses for full-time students are offered days only and must be completed within 3 years. For part-time students, courses are offered evenings only and must be completed within 4 years. New full-and part-time students are admitted in the fall. There is an 8-week summer session. Transferable summer courses are offered.

Phone: 703-993-8010
Fax: 703-993-8260
E-mail: arichar5@gmu.edu
Web: www.gmu.edu/departments/law

Contact
Anne M. Richard, Director of Admissions, 703-993-8010 for general inquiries; Office of Financial Aid, 703-993-2353 for financial aid information.

VIRGINIA

Programs

Required

To earn the J.D., candidates must complete 90 total credits, of which 41 are for required courses. They must maintain a minimum GPA of 2.0 in the required courses. The following first-year courses are required of all students: Legal Research, Writing, and Analysis I and II, Contracts I and II, Property I and II, Legal and Economic Methods I, Civil Procedure, Criminal Law, Constitutional Law, Torts, and Administrative Law. Required upper-level courses consist of Professional Responsibility, Legal Research, Writing, and Analysis III and IV, and 2 400 series seminars. The optional orientation program for first-year students is presented during the first week of school. The program lasts approximately 4 hours and consists of presentations by the administration, small group meetings with faculty and student advisers, and a reception with representatives of student organizations.

Electives

The School of Law offers concentrations in corporate law, international law, litigation, securities law, patent law, and regulatory law. In addition, clinics are limited to upper-level students, and are worth 2 credits. Two 2-credit seminars or a thesis and 1 seminar are required of all students for graduation. Seminars are taken in the second, third, or fourth year. Internships are limited to upper-level students and are worth 2 to 3 credits, up to a maximum of 4 credits. The Law and Economics Center administers a series of interdisciplinary symposia, lectures, and conferences devoted to current topics in law and economics. The most widely taken electives are Virginia Practice, Domestic Relations, and Business Associations.

Graduation Requirements

In order to graduate, candidates must have a GPA of 2.0 and have completed the upper-division writing requirement.

Organizations
Students edit the *George Mason University Law Review*, the *Civil Rights Law Journal*, the *Journal of International Legal Studies*, and the newspaper *The*

Docket. The school sponsors several in-house competitions each year, and sends teams to numerous national and regional competitions. Law student organizations include the Student Bar Association, Business Law Society, and Association for Public Interest Law. There are local chapters of the ABA-Law Student Division, Phi Delta Phi (Lewis Powell Inn), and Phi Alpha Delta (George Mason Chapter).

Library
The law library contains 359,000 hardcopy volumes and 886,000 microform volume equivalents, and subscribes to 5065 serial publications. Such on-line databases and networks as LEXIS and WESTLAW are available to law students for research. Special library collections include patent law, international law, law and economics, and tax sections. The school is also a participant in the federal government documents depository. Recently, the library added 2 computer laboratories with 15 PCs providing access to the Internet, LEXIS, WESTLAW, and university network facilities. The ratio of library volumes to faculty is 10,000 to 1 and to students, 430 to 1. The ratio of seats in the library to students is 1 to 4.

Faculty
The law school has 24 full-time and 68 part-time faculty members, of whom 14 are women. According to AAUP standards for Category I institutions, faculty salaries are well above average. About 42% of full-time faculty have a graduate law degree in addition to the J.D.; about 3% of part-time faculty have one. The ratio of full-time students to full-time faculty in an average class is 16 to 1.

Students
About 38% of the student body are women; 10%, minorities; 5%, African American; 4%, Asian American; and 2%, Hispanic. The majority of students come from Virginia (90%). The average age of entering students is 26; age range is 20 to 50. About 25% of students enter directly from undergraduate school, 13% have a graduate degree, and 70% have worked full time prior to entering law school. About 4% drop out after the first year for academic or personal reasons; 96% remain to receive a law degree.

Placement	
J.D.s awarded:	226
Services available through: separate law school placement center	
Services: mock interview program, mentoring program	
Special features: participation in the D.C. Public Interest Job Fair, and the BLSA Regional Job Fair.	
Full-time job interviews:	169 employers
Summer job interviews:	n/av
Placement by graduation:	90% of class
Placement within 9 months:	99% of class
Average starting salary:	$16,000 to $240,000
Areas of placement:	
Private practice 2-100 attorneys	44%
Business/industry	21%
Government	17%
Judicial clerkships	10%
Academic	4%
Military	3%
Public interest	1%

Law School

2000 H Street, N.W.
Washington, DC 20052

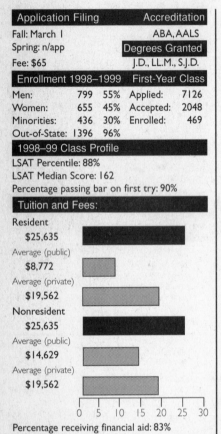

Application Filing	Accreditation
Fall: March 1	ABA, AALS
Spring: n/app	**Degrees Granted**
Fee: $65	J.D., LL.M., S.J.D.

Enrollment 1998–1999		First-Year Class	
Men:	799 55%	Applied:	7126
Women:	655 45%	Accepted:	2048
Minorities:	436 30%	Enrolled:	469
Out-of-State:	1396 96%		

1998–99 Class Profile
LSAT Percentile: 88%
LSAT Median Score: 162
Percentage passing bar on first try: 90%

Tuition and Fees:

Resident
$25,635

Average (public)
$8,772

Average (private)
$19,562

Nonresident
$25,635

Average (public)
$14,629

Average (private)
$19,562

Percentage receiving financial aid: 83%

ADMISSIONS

In the fall 1999 first-year class, 7126 applied, 2048 were accepted, and 469 enrolled. Thirty-four transfers enrolled. The median LSAT percentile of the most recent first-year class was 88; the median GPA was 3.46 on a scale of 4.0. The lowest LSAT percentile accepted was 37; the highest was 100.

Requirements
Applicants must have a bachelor's degree from an accredited institution and take the LSAT. The most important admission factors include academic achievement, LSAT results, and writing ability. No specific undergraduate courses are required. Candidates are not interviewed.

Procedure
The application deadline for fall entry is March 1. Applicants should submit an application form, LSAT results, transcripts, and a nonrefundable application fee of $65. Two letters of recommendation are recommended, but not required. Notification of the admission decision is as soon as a decision is made. The latest acceptable LSAT test date for fall entry is February, but only in certain cases. The law school uses the LSDAS.

Special
The law school recruits minority and disadvantaged students by participating in law forums throughout the country and visiting schools with large minority populations. In addition, each admitted applicant is contacted by a currently enrolled student. Transfer students must have one year of credit and have attended an ABA-approved law school; admissions decisions are based on the applicant's law school record and the amount of space available.

Costs

Tuition and fees for the 1999-2000 academic year are $25,635 for all full-time students. Tuition for part-time students is $902 per credit. Books and supplies run $740.

Financial Aid

About 83% of current law students receive some form of aid. The average annual amount of aid from all sources combined, including scholarships, loans, and work contracts, is $28,867; maximum, $40,122. Awards are based on need and merit. The required financial statements are CSS Profile and FAFSA. The aid application deadline for fall entry is March 1. First-year students are notified about their financial aid application some time after admission, provided all files are complete.

About the Law School

George Washington University Law School was established in 1865 and is a private institution. The campus is in an urban area in downtown Washington, D.C. The primary mission of the law school is to offer students the opportunity to study and observe lawmaking at its source, by combining a wide variety of courses in public law with the traditional fields of law. Students have access to federal, state, county, city, and local agencies, courts, correctional facilities, law firms, and legal aid organizations in the Washington area. Extensive clinical opportunities exist in the nation's capital. Housing for law students consits of a limited number of spaces on campus in efficiency, and 1- and 2-bedroom apartments.

Calendar

The law school operates on a traditional semester basis. Courses for full-time students are offered both day and evening and must be completed within 3 years. For part-time students, courses are offered both day and evening and must be completed within 4 years. New full- and part-time students are admitted in the fall. There is a 7-week summer session. Transferable summer courses are offered.

Programs

In addition to the J.D., the law school offers the LL.M and S.J.D. Students may take relevant courses in other programs and apply credit toward the J.D.; a maximum of 6 credits may be applied. The following joint degrees may be earned: J.D./M.P.A. (Juris Doctor/Master of Public Administration), J.D./M.B.A. (Juris Doctor/Master of Business Administration), J.D./M.A. (Juris Doctor/Master of Arts in international affairs or history), and J.D./M.P.H. (Juris Doctor/Master of Public Health).

Phone: 202-739-0648
E-mail: jd@main.n/c.gwu.edu
Web: www.law.gwu.edu

Contact

Office of Law Admissions, 202-739-0648 for general inquiries; Law Financial Aid Office, 202-739-0641 for financial aid information.

Required

To earn the J.D., candidates must complete 84 total credits, of which 34 are for required courses. They must maintain a minimum GPA of 1.67 in the required courses. The following first-year courses are required of all students in the full-time Day Division: Contracts I and II, Criminal Law, Torts, Civil Procedure I and II, Property, Constitutional Law I, Legal Researching and Writing, and Introduction to Advocacy. Required upper-level courses consist of Professional Responsibility and Ethics. All clinics are optional. The required orientation program for first-year students is a 3-day program that includes registration.

Electives

The Law School offers concentrations in corporate law, criminal law, environmental law, family law, international law, labor law, litigation, securities law, tax law, torts and insurance, government contracts, intellectual property, and constitutional law. In addition, clinics and internships are open to all students; the amount of credit awarded depends on each student's time commitment. Seminars are available to students who have completed all prerequisites, and generally are worth 2 credits. Research programs are open to students through legal writing programs. Credit hours vary according to the paper produced. Field work is offered to students through clinical programs. Credits vary according to each student's time commitment. Through the Enrichment Program, speakers are brought to the law school for lectures and informal seminars that are open to all students. A study-abroad program in international human rights is offered with Oxford University. Tutors can be arranged if needed. Minority programs are sponsored by groups such as the Black Law Students Association, Movimiento Legal Latino, and Asian Law Students Association. Special interest groups include the Law Association for Women, Law Students for the Arts; International Law Society, and politically-oriented groups. The most widely taken electives are Federal Income Taxation, Evidence, and Corporations.

Graduation Requirements

In order to graduate, candidates must have a GPA of 1.67, and have completed the upper-division writing requirement and the required curriculum.

Organizations

Students edit the *George Washington Law Review, Journal of International Law and Economics, Environmental Lawyer,* and the newspaper, *Nota Bene.* The Moot Court Board sponsors the Van Vleck Appellate Moot Court competition, the Jessup Cup competition in international law, and the Giles S. Rich competition in patent law. Teams participate in other moot court competitions around the country. Student organizations include the Student Bar Association, Legal Support Group, and Environmental Law Society. Local chapters of national associations include Phi Alpha Delta, Phi Delta Phi, and the Federalist Society.

Library

The law library contains 519,652 hardcopy volumes and 1,096,541 microform volume equivalents, and subscribes to 5576 serial publications. Such on-line databases and networks as LEXIS, DIALOG, WESTLAW, CIS Congressional Universe, and Legal-Trac are available to law students for research. Special library collections include a government documents collection and an extensive treatise library; particularly strong collections in environmental, intellectual property, international, and government procurement law. Recently, the library renovated the main reading room, and created a rare book room and 2 computer classrooms with Pentium computers. The ratio of library volumes to faculty is 4822 to 1 and to students, 234 to 1. The ratio of seats in the library to students is 1 to 7.

Placement	
J.D.s awarded:	472
Services available through: a separate law school placement center	
Special features: on-line job listings	
Full-time job interviews:	390 employers
Summer job interviews:	n/av
Placement by graduation:	92% of class
Placement within 9 months:	98% of class
Average starting salary:	$67,641
Areas of placement:	
Private practice	62%
Government	13%
Judicial clerkships	9%
Business/industry	6%
Unknown	5%
Public interest	4%
Academic	1%

Faculty

The law school has 67 full-time and 170 part-time faculty members, of whom 64 are women. According to AAUP standards for Category I institutions, faculty salaries are well above average. The ratio of full-time students to full-time faculty in an average class is 15 to 1; in a clinic, 8 to 1. The law school has a regular program of bringing visiting professors and other distinguished lecturers and visitors to campus. There is a chapter of the Order of the Coif.

Students

About 45% of the student body are women; 30%, minorities; 12%, African American; 10%, Asian American; and 8%, Hispanic. The majority of students come from the South (38%). The average age of entering students is 24; age range is 20 to 67. About 36% of students enter directly from undergraduate school, 31% have a graduate degree, and 64% have worked full-time prior to entering law school. About 2% drop out after the first year for academic or personal reasons; 98% remain to receive a law degree.

GEORGETOWN UNIVERSITY

Law Center

600 New Jersey Avenue, N.W.
Washington, DC 20001

Application Filing

Fall: February 1
Spring: n/app
Fee: $65

Accreditation

ABA, AALS

Degrees Granted

J.D., LL.M., S.J.D.

Enrollment 1998–1999 · First-Year Class

Men:	992	51%	Applied:	7873
Women:	972	49%	Accepted:	2383
Minorities:	511	26%	Enrolled:	601
Out-of-State:	1964	100%		

1998–99 Class Profile

LSAT Percentile: 95%
LSAT Median Score: 166
Percentage passing bar on first try: 92%

Tuition and Fees:

Resident
$25,705

Average (public)
$8,772

Average (private)
$19,562

Nonresident
$25,705

Average (public)
$14,629

Average (private)
$19,562

0   5   10   15   20   25   30

Percentage receiving financial aid: 73%

ADMISSIONS

In the fall 1999 first-year class, 7873 applied, 2383 were accepted, and 601 enrolled. Forty-eight transfers enrolled. The median LSAT percentile of the most recent first-year class was 95; the median GPA was 3.6 on a scale of 4.0. The lowest LSAT percentile accepted was 50; the highest was 99.

Requirements

Applicants must have a bachelor's degree from an accredited institution and take the LSAT. Minimum acceptable GPA is 2.0 on a scale of 4.0. The most important admission factors include LSAT results, academic achievement, motivation, and life experience. No specific undergraduate courses are required. Candidates are interviewed for informational purposes only.

Procedure

The application deadline for full-time fall entry is February 1; March 1 for part-time. Applicants should submit an application form, LSAT results, a nonrefundable application fee of $65, and 1 letter of recommendation; transcripts must be received through the LSDAS. Notification of the admission decision is in approximately 6 to 10 weeks. The latest acceptable LSAT test date for fall entry is February. The law school uses the LSDAS.

Special

The law school recruits minority and disadvantaged students by means of an aggressive outreach program that encourages qualified minority and disadvantaged students to apply. Transfer students must have one year of credit and have attended an ABA-approved law school. The Law Center offers, through its ABA/AALS- approved summer programs, a range of courses that students may transfer to their home schools. GULC students may be granted permission to transfer 6 credits from other ABA/AALS summer programs.

Costs

Tuition and fees for the 1999-2000 academic year are $25,705 for all full-time students. Tuition for part-time students is $18,000 annually. On-campus room and board costs about $11,700 annually; books and supplies run $670.

Financial Aid

About 73% of current law students receive some form of aid. The average annual amount of aid from all sources combined, including scholarships, loans, and work contracts, is $29,767; maximum, $40,600. Awards are based on need. The required financial statements are CSS Profile, FAFSA, and Need Access Diskette. The aid application deadline for fall entry is March 1. First-year students are notified about their financial aid application after the student has been accepted for admission and has completed financial aid requirements. Awards are given on a rolling basis.

About the Law School

Georgetown University Law Center was established in 1870 and is a private institution. The 1-acre campus is in an urban area in Washington, D.C. The primary mission of the law school is to prepare graduates to excel in legal careers ranging from private practice to teaching to public service. Students have access to federal, state, county, city, and local agencies, courts, correctional facilities, law firms, and legal aid organizations in the Washington area. Other resources include the U.S. Supreme Court, federal courts, U.S. Congress, and major federal departments and agencies, many of which are within walking distance. Facilities of special interest to law students are the Law Center's 3-building campus, which includes McDonough Hall, with classrooms, cafeteria, pub, administrative and student organization offices and student lounges; Williams Library, a state-of-the-art facility with group study lounges, a computer laboratory, and student journal offices; and the Gewirz Student Center with fitness, child care, and student health facilities. Housing for law students is available in the Gewirz Student Center. Law students are also supported through a variety of other housing programs. About 99% of the law school facilities are accessible to the physically disabled.

Calendar

The law school operates on a traditional semester basis. Courses for full-time students are offered both day and evening and must be completed within 5 years. For part-time students, required courses and electives are offered in the evening only and must be completed within 6 years. New full- and part-time students are admitted in the fall. There is an 8-week summer session. Transferable summer courses are offered.

Programs

In addition to the J.D., the law school offers the LL.M, S.J.D., and LL.M. concentrations in international legal studies, taxation, securities and financial regulation, as well as individual study. A certificate in employee benefits law is also available. Students may take relevant courses in other programs and apply credit toward the J.D.; a maximum of 6 credits may be applied. The following joint degrees may be earned: J.D./M.B.A. (Juris Doctor/Master of Business Administration), J.D./M.S.F.S. (Juris Doctor/Master of Foreign Service), J.D./M.P.H. (Juris Doctor/Master in Public Health), J.D./Phil. (Juris Doctor/Master of Arts or Ph.D. in philosophy), and J.D./Govt. (Juris Doctor/Ph.D. in government).

Required

To earn the J.D., candidates must complete 83 total credits, of which 31 are for required courses. The following first-year courses are required of all students in Curriculum A: Civil Procedure, Constitutional Law I, Contracts, Criminal Justice, Legal Research and Writing, Property, Bargain, Exchange and Liability; in Curriculum B: Democracy and Coercion, Legal Justice Seminar, Government Processes, Legal Practice: Writing and Analysis, and Property in Time. Required upper-level courses consist of Professional Responsibility and a legal

Phone: 202-662-9010
E-mail: admis@law.georgetown.edu
Web: www.law.georgetown.edu

Contact

Cara Woltemate, Office Manager, 202-662-9010 for general inquiries; Ruth Lammert-Reeves, Assistant Dean for Financial Aid, 202-662-9210 for financial aid information.

DISTRICT OF COLUMBIA

writing seminar. The optional orientation program for first-year students is a 4-day program that includes registration, a review of academic services and student activities, an introduction to first-year course work by faculty members, an address by the university president and dean, and the dean's picnic.

Electives

The Law Center offers concentrations in corporate law, criminal law, entertainment law, environmental law, family law, international law, juvenile law, labor law, litigation, maritime law, media law, securities law, sports law, tax law, torts and insurance, commercial law, constitutional law and government, administrative law and government regulation, jurisprudence, public interest law, alternative dispute resolution, negotiations, and trial practice. In addition, the Law Center operates 14 in-house clinical courses in appellate trial legislative and administrative process each year. Clinics, offered to upper-division students for 6 to 12 hours of credit, give students a chance to represent clients in real cases involving criminal, juvenile, environmental, civil rights, spouse abuse, communications, and political asylum issues. More than 150 seminars are offered on such topics as commercial law, constitutional law and government, and corporate law and securities. Supervised research projects may be undertaken for 2 credits under the guidance of a faculty member. Three special lecture series held each academic year bring prominent legal scholars, judges, lawyers, and business executives to the Law Center. There is a 4-week summer study-abroad program in Florence, Italy for up to 6 credits and a 3-week study abroad course in Heidelberg, Germany for up to 4 credits. Although the writing center and tutorials are open to all students for no credit, the tutorial program is primarily designed for first-year students. A diversity clerkship program is offered by the Career Services Office, and other educational programs are sponsored by the Career Services Office and minority student groups. The Public Interest Law Scholars Program provides tuition benefits and funding for 1 summer, and the office of Public Interest and Community Services provides career counseling and pro bono opportunities. For international law, the Global Law Scholars Program prepares students for the changing frontier of international

practice. The most widely taken electives are Constitutional Law, Corporations, and Evidence.

Graduation Requirements

In order to graduate, candidates must have a GPA of 2.0, and have completed the upper-division writing requirement and the Professional Responsibility course.

Organizations

Student-edited publications include the *Georgetown Law Journal, American Criminal Law Review, Gender and the Law, Georgetown Immigration Law Journal, Georgetown International Environmental Law Review, Law and Policy in International Business, Georgetown Journal of Legal Ethics, The Tax Lawyer, The Forum on Fighting Poverty in America*, and the newspaper *Law Weekly.* Moot competitions include a first-year and upper-class appellate moot court competition and a mock trial competition that is open to all students. Georgetown also competes in 12 moot court competitions, including the Jessup International Law, Wagner Labor Law, and Wechsler First Amendment. The law Center sponsors the Beaudry Cup Moot Court (first-year students), Leahy Prize Moot Court (upper-class students), and the William W. Greenhalgh Trial Advocacy competitions. There are 60 student organizations, including the ABA-Law Student Division, American Inn of Court, and Association of Trial Lawyers of America. There are local chapters of Delta Theta Phi, Phi Delta Phi, and Phi Alpha Delta.

Library

The law library contains 456,491 hardcopy volumes (excluding microform) and 960,782 volume and volume equivalents, 2,207,015 microform volume equivalents, and subscribes to 12,441 serial publications. Such on-line databases and networks as LEXIS, DIALOG, WESTLAW, OCLC, and First Search are available to law students for research. Special library collections include rare books as well as international law and tax collections. Recently, the library wired library carrels for network access by student laptops. Numerous print subscriptions are available via the Web to GULC users for access from home. The ratio of library volumes to faculty is 9787 to 1 and to students, 442 to 1.

Faculty

The law school has 87 full-time and 92 part-time faculty members, of whom 41

Placement

J.D.s awarded:	694

Services available through: a separate law school placement center

Services: public interest organizations, small firm job fairs, regional job fairs in cities nationwide, and a large international internship program

Special features: one of the largest fall on-campus recruitment programs in the country; multiple programs for students interested in public service, public policy, international as well as traditional private practice settings; extensive print and database career resource library

Full-time job interviews:	200 employers
Summer job interviews:	600 employers
Placement by graduation:	86% of class
Placement within 9 months:	98% of class
Average starting salary:	$15,800 to $200,000

Areas of placement:

Private practice 26-50 attorneys	4%
Private practice 51-100 attorneys	56%
Judicial clerkships	12%
Government	8%
Business/industry	6%
Public interest	5%
Academic	1%
Military	1%

are women. According to AAUP standards for Category I institutions, faculty salaries are well above average. About 17% of full-time faculty have a graduate law degree in addition to the J.D.; about 10% of part-time faculty have one. The ratio of full-time students to full-time faculty overall is 16 to 1; in a clinic, 7 to 1. The law school has a regular program of bringing visiting professors and other distinguished lecturers and visitors to campus. There is a chapter of the Order of the Coif.

Students

About 49% of the student body are women; 26%, minorities; 11%, African American; 9%, Asian American; 5%, Hispanic; 1%, Native American; and 2%, foreign nationals. The average age of entering students is 24; age range is 20 to 54. About 46% of students enter directly from undergraduate school, 12% have a graduate degree, and 52% have worked full-time prior to entering law school. About 1% drop out after the first year for academic or personal reasons; 97% remain to receive a law degree.

GEORGIA STATE UNIVERSITY

College of Law

P.O. Box 4037
Atlanta, GA 30302-4037

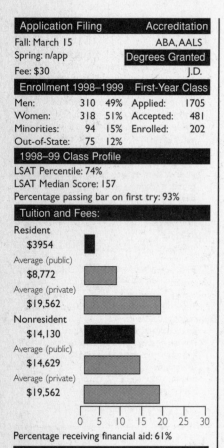

Application Filing	Accreditation
Fall: March 15	ABA, AALS
Spring: n/app	Degrees Granted
Fee: $30	J.D.

Enrollment 1998–1999		First-Year Class	
Men:	310 49%	Applied:	1705
Women:	318 51%	Accepted:	481
Minorities:	94 15%	Enrolled:	202
Out-of-State:	75 12%		

1998–99 Class Profile
LSAT Percentile: 74%
LSAT Median Score: 157
Percentage passing bar on first try: 93%

Tuition and Fees:
Resident
$3954
Average (public)
$8,772
Average (private)
$19,562
Nonresident
$14,130
Average (public)
$14,629
Average (private)
$19,562

Percentage receiving financial aid: 61%

ADMISSIONS
In the fall 1999 first-year class, 1705 applied, 481 were accepted, and 202 enrolled. Nine transfers enrolled. The median LSAT percentile of the most recent first-year class was 74; the median GPA was 3.2 on a scale of 4.0. The lowest LSAT percentile accepted was 33; the highest was 99.

Requirements
Applicants must have a bachelor's degree from an accredited institution and take the LSAT. The most important admission factors include LSAT results, GPA, and academic achievement. No specific undergraduate courses are required. Candidates are not interviewed.

Procedure
The application deadline for fall entry is March 15. Applicants should submit an application form, LSAT results, transcripts, LSDAS report, TOEFL for applicants whose native language is not English, a nonrefundable application fee of $30, 2 letters of recommendation, and a personal statement in support of the applicant's admission. This gives the applicant an opportunity to add information about abilities and interests. Notification of the admission decision begins in January. The latest acceptable LSAT test date for fall entry is February. The law school uses the LSDAS.

Special
The law school recruits minority and disadvantaged students by means of visiting other colleges and universities during graduate and professional program days, speaking to prelaw clubs and classes, and recruiting at schools with large minority student populations. The law school also conducts high school visits. Transfer students must have one year of credit, have attended an ABA-approved law school, and have a letter from the dean of the student's previous law school stating that the student is in good standing and is eligible to return to the school, and stating the student's class ranking.

Costs
Tuition and fees for the 1999-2000 academic year are $3954 for full-time in-state students and $14,130 for out-of-state students. Books and supplies run $1146.

Financial Aid
About 61% of current law students receive some form of aid. The average annual amount of aid from all sources combined, including scholarships, loans, and work contracts, is $2175; maximum, $3500. Awards are based on need and merit. There are also loans that are need- and non-need-based. The required financial statement is FAFSA. The aid application deadline for fall entry is April 1. Special funds for minority or disadvantaged students consist of scholarships. First-year students are notified about their financial aid application at time of acceptance.

About the Law School
Georgia State University College of Law was established in 1982 and is a public institution. The 25-acre campus is in an urban area in the city of Atlanta. The primary mission of the law school is to provide both part- and full-time programs that are designed for students wishing to gain a knowledge of the law, of legal institutions, and of legal processes. The college is equally committed to part- and full-time legal studies. Students have access to federal, state, county, city, and local agencies, courts, correctional facilities, law firms, and legal aid organizations in the Atlanta area. A variety of institutions and law-related agencies are located in the Atlanta area, an economic and government center of the Southeast. Facilities of special interest to law students include the Richard B. Russell Federal Building, Federal Reserve Bank, state capitol building, state legislature, federal, state and local court systems, and offices of the U.S. Attorney, state Attorney General, and county and city District Attorneys. Housing for law students is on a first-come, first-served basis in the Olympic Village, which accommodates 2000 students in modern apartments. All law school facilities are accessible to the physically disabled.

Calendar
The law school operates on a traditional semester basis. Courses for full-and part-time students are offered both day and evening and must be completed within 6 years. New full-and part-time students are admitted in the fall. There is a 7-week summer session. Transferable summer courses are offered.

Programs
Students may take relevant courses in other programs and apply credit toward the J.D.; a maximum of 14 semester hours (J.D./M.B.A., J.D./M.P.A., and JD/M.A. programs may be applied. The following joint degrees may be earned: J.D./M.B.A. (Juris Doctor/Master of Business Administration), J.D./M.P.A. (Juris Doctor/Master of Public Administration), and J.D./M.A. (Juris Doctor/Master of Arts in Philosophy).

Phone: 404-651-2096
Fax: 404-651-2096
E-mail: cjjackson@gsu.edu
Web: law.gsu.edu

Contact
Cheryl Jester Jackson, Director of Admissions, 404-651-2048 for general inquiries; Gwyn Francis, Director of Financial Aid, 404-651-2227 for financial aid information.

GEORGIA

Required
To earn the J.D., candidates must complete 90 total credits, of which 43 are for required courses. They must maintain a minimum grade average of 73 in the required courses. The following first-year courses are required of all students: Civil Procedure I and II, Property I and II, Contracts I and II, Legal Method, Research Writing and Advocacy I and II, Legal Bibliography, Criminal Law, and Torts I and II. Required upper-level courses consist of Constitutional Law, Evidence, Litigation, and Professional Responsibility. The required orientation program for first-year students occurs in the first week of the fall semester and is designed to introduce some of the first-year required courses, college personnel, and facilities, and to familiarize students with procedures.

Electives
Students must take 46 hours in their area of concentration. The College of Law offers concentrations in corporate law, criminal law, environmental law, family law, international law, labor law, litigation, tax law, and torts and insurance. In addition, second- and third-year students may earn 3 or 6 semester hours by enrolling in the Tax Clinic, which permits students to assist individual clients in preparing their cases before the Small Claims Division of the U.S. Tax Court and the administrative appeals offices of the IRS. Seminars are offered to students who have completed the prerequisites and are normally worth 2 semester hours. Internships include working for local district attorneys, solicitors, and defenders; clerking for county, state, and federal judges; and placement in a variety of other governmental or public interest organizations. Independent research for 1 to 2 semester hours credit may be selected by third-year students upon approval by a faculty adviser and the administration. The college does not sponsor a regular study-abroad program, but some elective summer courses are offered that include trips to Europe. The administration offers an academic assistance program for students who need or desire additional help in required courses. Minority and special interest programs are usually sponsored by student organizations and/or faculty members. The most widely taken electives are

Basic Tax; Wills, Trusts, and Estates; and Criminal Procedure.

Graduation Requirements
In order to graduate, candidates must have a grade average of 73 and have completed the upper-division writing requirement.

Organizations
The primary law review is the *Georgia State University Law Review*. Students edit *The Docket, The Black Letter Law*, and *The Federalist*. The Moot Court Society competes 7 or 8 times a year. Other competitions include the National Moot Court competition, sponsored by the Association of the Bar of New York City and the National Appellate Advocacy Competition, sponsored by the ABA. Student organizations include the Christian Legal Society, Lesbian and Gay Law Student Association, and Federalist Society. Local chapters of national associations include the Association of Women Law Students, Black Law Students Association, and Environmental Law Society. Other groups include Delta Theta Phi, Phi Alpha Delta, and Phi Delta Phi law fraternities.

Library
The law library contains 145,617 hardcopy volumes and 623,675 microform volume equivalents, and subscribes to 3504 serial publications. Such on-line databases and networks as LEXIS, DIALOG, and WESTLAW are available to law students for research. Special library collections include a U.S. depository and collections in tax, labor, health law, and international law. Recently, the library upgraded computer systems in the computer laboratory and installed GIL by Endeavor, an automation system; upgraded electric compact shelving; installed wired carrels; and obtained remote storage. The ratio of library volumes to faculty is 3439 to 1 and to students, 229 to 1. The ratio of seats in the library to students is 1 to 2.

Faculty
The law school has 42 full-time and 30 part-time faculty members, of whom 26 are women. According to AAUP standards for Category I institutions, faculty

Placement

J.D.s awarded:	196

Services available through: a separate law school placement center

Services: programming and counseling on career options for lawyers, and participating in national and regional job fairs

Special features: state-of-the-art Internet-based job listings service for students and alumni. Personalized, one-on-one job search planning sessions for first-year, second-year, and third-year students in addition to alumni transitioning into other practice areas and legal-related or alternative careers

Full-time job interviews:	n/av
Summer job interviews:	n/av
Placement by graduation:	n/av
Placement within 9 months:	94% of class
Average starting salary:	$25,000 to $101,000

Areas of placement:

Private practice 2-10 attorneys	25%
Private practice 11-25 attorneys	5%
Private practice 26-50 attorneys	3%
Private practice 51-100 attorneys	6%
Private practice 100+ attorneys	21%
Business/industry	21%
Government	9%
Judicial clerkships	6%
Academic	2%
Public interest	1%
Military	1%

salaries are above average. About 20% of full-time faculty have a graduate law degree in addition to the J.D.; about 7% of part-time faculty have one. The ratio of full-time students to full-time faculty in an average class is 24 to 1. The law school has a regular program of bringing visiting professors and other distinguished lecturers and visitors to campus.

Students
About 51% of the student body are women; 15%, minorities; 11%, African American; 3%, Asian American; 1%, Hispanic; and 7%, multiracial. The majority of students come from Georgia (88%). The average age of entering students is 30; age range is 21 to 61. About 21% of students enter directly from undergraduate school and 19% have a graduate degree. About 11% drop out after the first year for academic or personal reasons; 89% remain to receive a law degree.

School of Law

536 Mission Street
San Francisco, CA 94105-2968

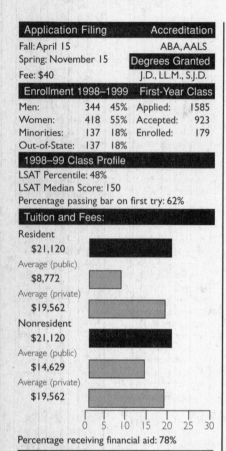

Application Filing	Accreditation
Fall: April 15	ABA, AALS
Spring: November 15	**Degrees Granted**
Fee: $40	J.D., LL.M., S.J.D.

Enrollment 1998–1999		First-Year Class	
Men:	344 45%	Applied:	1585
Women:	418 55%	Accepted:	923
Minorities:	137 18%	Enrolled:	179
Out-of-State:	137 18%		

1998–99 Class Profile
LSAT Percentile: 48%
LSAT Median Score: 150
Percentage passing bar on first try: 62%

Tuition and Fees:

Resident
$21,120

Average (public)
$8,772

Average (private)
$19,562

Nonresident
$21,120

Average (public)
$14,629

Average (private)
$19,562

0 5 10 15 20 25 30

Percentage receiving financial aid: 78%

ADMISSIONS

In the fall 1999 first-year class, 1585 applied, 923 were accepted, and 179 enrolled. Ten transfers enrolled. The median LSAT percentile of the most recent first-year class was 48; the median GPA was 3.07 on a scale of 4.0.

Requirements
Applicants must have a bachelor's degree from an accredited institution and take the LSAT. The most important admission factors include undergraduate curriculum, LSAT results, and general background. No specific undergraduate courses are required. Candidates are not interviewed.

Procedure
The application deadline for fall entry is April 15. Applicants should submit an application form, LSAT results, transcripts, a nonrefundable application fee of $40, 1 letter of recommendation, and a personal statement. Notification of the admissions decision is 4 to 5 weeks after material is submitted. The latest acceptable LSAT test date for fall entry is February. The law school uses the LSDAS.

Special
The law school recruits minority and disadvantaged students by targeting recruiting to under represented communities, supporting the CLEO program, and the law school's minority scholarship program. Transfer students must have one year of credit, and have attended an ABA-approved law school, and are subject to the availability of seats must submit a personal statement, and a competitive review of their academic record from the first year of law school.

Costs

Tuition and fees for the 1999-2000 academic year are $21,120 for all full-time students. Tuition for part-time students is $14,640 per year. Books and supplies run $870.

Financial Aid

About 78% of current law students receive some form of aid. The average annual amount of aid from all sources combined, including scholarships, loans, and work contracts, is $22,000; maximum, $33,000. Awards are based on need and merit. The required financial statement is the FAFSA. The aid application priority deadline for fall entry is March 1. A scholarship fund is reserved for minority students or those from disadvantaged backgrounds. First-year students are notified about their financial aid application at the time of acceptance.

About the Law School

Golden Gate University School of Law was established in 1901 and is a private institution. The campus is in an urban area in the financial district in downtown San Francisco. The primary mission of the law school is to educate lawyers in a humanistic yet rigorous environment through a balance of traditional legal theory courses and clinical experiences. Students have access to federal, state, county, city, and local agencies, courts, correctional facilities, law firms, and legal aid organizations in the San Francisco area. Many internships, externships, and other clinical programs take advantage of government offices, courts, and law firms in the city. Facilities of special interest to law students include the law school, which occupies an architecturally acclaimed building that includes classrooms, a moot court room, student computer laboratories, and a law library. Housing for law students is not available on campus, but the housing office helps students find accommodations off campus. All law school facilities are accessible to the physically disabled.

Calendar

The law school operates on a traditional semester basis. Courses for full-time students are offered days only and must be completed within the 3-year full-time day program. For part-time students, courses are offered evenings only and must be completed within the 4-year part-time evening program. New full- and part-time students are admitted in the fall and spring. There is an 8-week summer session. Transferable summer courses are offered.

Programs

In addition to the J.D., the law school offers the LL.M. and S.J.D. Students may take relevant courses in other programs and apply credit toward the J.D. The following joint degrees may be earned: J.D./M.B.A. (Juris Doctor/Master of Business Administration in law), J.D./M.A. (Juris Doctor/Master of International Studies), and J.D./Ph.D. (J.D./Ph.D. in Clinical Psychology with the Pacific Graduate School of Psychology).

Contact

Admissions Office, 415-442-6630 for general inquiries; Cheryl Barnes, Assistant Dean of Admissions and Financial Aid, 415-442-6635 for financial aid information.

CALIFORNIA

Required

To earn the J.D., candidates must complete 88 total credits, of which 54 are for required courses. They must maintain a minimum GPA of 2.05 in the required courses. The following first-year courses are required of all students: Civil Procedure I and II, Contracts, Property, Torts, Criminal Law, Writing and Research, and Constitutional Law I. Required upper-level courses consist of Appellate Advocacy, Constitutional Law II, Corporations, Criminal Procedure I, Evidence, Solving Legal Problems, Professional Responsibility, and Wills and Trusts. The required orientation program for first-year students is a 4-day program held before classes begin. In addition, enrolled and prospective students may participate in a 3-week Introduction to Law School summer program.

Electives

The School of Law offers concentrations in corporate law, criminal law, environmental law, international law, labor law, litigation, intellectual property law, real estate, and public interest law. In addition, the school offers 8 clinics, worth from 2 to 5 credits. Clinics are Constitutional Law, Criminal Litigation, Environmental Law and Justice, Women's Employment Rights, Civil Practice, and Public Interest/Government. Seminars are worth 2 credits and prerequisites vary. Topics include Asian Pacific Trade, Bankruptcy Litigation, and Disability Rights. Full- and part-time internships with law firms, government agencies, and judges are offered. There is also an Integrated Professional Apprenticeship Curriculum Program (IPAC), which integrates classroom theory, skills, values, and practice. Students may pursue independent research under the direction of faculty members. Study abroad is possible in Bangkok, Thailand and in Istanbul, Turkey. An Academic Assistance Program develops skills in legal analysis and exam writing. Through the Public Interest/Government Clinic, students may work in public interest law firms in preparation to become public interest lawyers. A major part of professional skills training are the Litigation and Advocacy courses, which deal with civil and criminal law, pretrial litigation, mock trial, and other areas. The most widely taken electives are Tax, Remedies, and Entertainment Law.

Graduation Requirements

In order to graduate, candidates must have a GPA of 2.0, have completed the upper-division writing requirement, and have taken writing courses in each of their 3 years in law school.

Organizations

Students edit the *Golden Gate Law Review*, the *Annual Survey of International and Comparative Law*, and the student newspaper *The Caveat*. Teams attend various national and international contests, including the Jessup Moot Court Competition. Other competitions attended are the National Mock Trial Competition, Association of Trial Lawyers of America Competition, and the ABA's Criminal Justice Trial Competition. Law student organizations include the Student Bar Association, Intellectual Property Law Association, and Latino Law Students Association. Local chapters of national associations include the International Law Association, Environmental Law Society, and American Trial Lawyers Association. Other organizations include LEGALS (Lesbian, Gay, Bisexual and Transgender), Black Law Students Association, and Golden Gate Association of International Lawyers.

Library

The law library contains 109,831 hardcopy volumes and 120,221 microform volume equivalents, and subscribes to 3338 serial publications. Such on-line databases and networks as LEXIS, DIALOG, WESTLAW, and CALI are available to law students for research. Special library collections include a depository for both California and federal documents and the archives of the National Educational Foundation. Its collections emphasize taxation, real estate, land use, and individual rights. Recently, the library installed new furniture and computers. The ratio of library volumes to faculty is 6507 to 1 and to students, 350 to 1. The ratio of seats in the library to students is 1 to 2.

Placement

J.D.s awarded:	160
Services available through: separate law school placement center	
Services: encourages private firms and public agencies to list job opportunities, solicits on-campus interviews	
Special features: computer-assisted job search through WESTLAW	
Full-time job interviews:	11 employers
Summer job interviews:	n/av
Placement by graduation:	n/av
Placement within 9 months:	78% of class
Average starting salary:	$44,685
Areas of placement:	
Private practice 2-10 attorneys	32%
Private practice 11-25 attorneys	8%
Private practice 26-50 attorneys	8%
Private practice 51-100 attorneys	14%
Business/industry	19%
Government	10%
Public interest	5%
Academic	2%
Judicial clerkships	2%

Faculty

The law school has 33 full-time and 117 part-time faculty members, of whom 56 are women. About 11% of full-time faculty have a graduate law degree in addition to the J.D.; about 8% of part-time faculty have one. The ratio of full-time students to full-time faculty in an average class is 14 to 1; in a clinic, 5 to 1. The law school has a regular program of bringing visiting professors and other distinguished lecturers and visitors to campus.

Students

About 55% of the student body are women; 18%, minorities; 4%, African American; 8%, Asian American; 6%, Hispanic; and 1%, Native American. The majority of students come from California (82%). The average age of entering students is 27; age range is 20 to 59. About 57% of students enter directly from undergraduate school, 7% have a graduate degree, and 43% have worked full time prior to entering law school. About 24% drop out after the first year for academic or personal reasons; 76% remain to receive a law degree.

School of Law

Box 3528
Spokane, WA 99220-3528

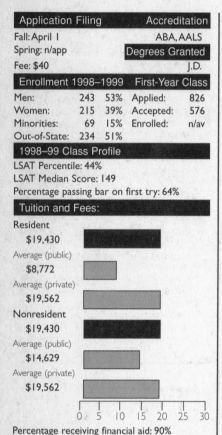

Application Filing		Accreditation
Fall: April 1		ABA, AALS
Spring: n/app		**Degrees Granted**
Fee: $40		J.D.

Enrollment 1998–1999		First-Year Class	
Men:	243 53%	Applied:	826
Women:	215 39%	Accepted:	576
Minorities:	69 15%	Enrolled:	n/av
Out-of-State:	234 51%		

1998–99 Class Profile
LSAT Percentile: 44%
LSAT Median Score: 149
Percentage passing bar on first try: 64%

Tuition and Fees:

Resident
$19,430

Average (public)
$8,772

Average (private)
$19,562

Nonresident
$19,430

Average (public)
$14,629

Average (private)
$19,562

0   5   10   15   20   25   30

Percentage receiving financial aid: 90%

ADMISSIONS

In the fall 1999 first-year class, 826 applied and 576 were accepted. Five transfers enrolled. The median LSAT percentile of the most recent first-year class was 44; the median GPA was 3.2 on a scale of 4.0. The highest LSAT percentile was 92.

Requirements

Applicants must have a bachelor's degree from an accredited institution and take the LSAT. The most important admission factors include LSAT results, GPA, and a personal statement. No specific undergraduate courses are required. Candidates are not interviewed.

Procedure

The application deadline for fall entry is April 1. Applicants should submit an application form and a nonrefundable application fee of $40. Recommendations are not required, but if submitted, there should be no more than 3. A resume and LSDAS report are required. Notification of the admission decision is after January 1- based on when the file is complete. The latest acceptable LSAT test date for fall entry is February. The law school uses the LSDAS.

Special

The law school recruits minority and disadvantaged students by means of CRS mailings, alumni referrals, scholarships, prelaw advisers, campus visits, and law school forums. Transfer students must have one year of credit, have attended an ABA-approved law school, and must be in good standing and eligible to return to their previous law school. They are accepted on a space-available basis.

Costs

Tuition and fees for the 1999-2000 academic year are $19,430 for all full-time students. On-campus room and board costs about $6975 annually; books and supplies run $900.

Financial Aid

About 90% of current law students receive some form of aid. The average annual amount of aid from all sources combined, including scholarships, loans, and work contracts, is $31,550. Awards are based on need and merit. The required financial statement is the FAFSA. The aid application deadline for fall entry is February 1. Special funds for minority or disadvantaged students diversity scholarships. First-year students are notified about their financial aid application within one month of acceptance if the FAFSA is complete.

About the Law School

Gonzaga University School of Law was established in 1912 and is a private institution. The 94-acre campus is in an urban area 1 mile from downtown Spokane. The primary mission of the law school is to preserve and develop a humanistic, Catholic, and Jesuit legal education. Students have access to federal, state, county, city, and local agencies, courts, correctional facilities, law firms, and legal aid organizations in the Spokane area. Facilities of special interest to law students include the law library, the Martin Athletic Center, the Foley Center, and a computer laboratory. Housing for law students is available on campus in graduate student housing. Apartments are also available, often within a 10-block radius of the law school. About 90% of the law school facilities are accessible to the physically disabled.

Calendar

The law school operates on a traditional semester basis. Courses for full-and part-time students are offered days only and must be completed within 5 years. New full-and part-time students are admitted in the fall. There are 2 5-week summer sessions. Transferable summer courses are offered.

Programs

The following joint degrees may be earned: J.D./M.B.A. (Juris Doctor/Master of Business Administration) and J.D./M.Acc. (Juris Doctor/Master of Accounting).

Phone: 509-323-5532
800-793-1710
Fax: 509-323-5710
E-mail: admissions@lawschool.gonzaga.edu
Web: http://www.law.gonzaga.edu

Contact

Tamara Martinez, Assistant Dean for Admissions, 509-323-5532 or 800-793-1710 for general inquiries; Joan Henning, Coordinator of Financial Services, 509-323-3859 for financial aid information.

WASHINGTON

Required

To earn the J.D., candidates must complete 90 total credits, of which 58 are for required courses. They must maintain a minimum GPA of 2.2 in the required courses. The following first-year courses are required of all students: Contracts I and II, Legal Research Writing I and II, Civil Procedure I and II, Property I and II, Torts I and II, Criminal Law, and Constitutional Law I. Required upper-level courses consist of Professional Responsibility, Evidence, Constitutional Law II, Administrative Law, Business Associations, Creditors' Rights, Criminal Procedure, Dispute Resolution or Trial Advocacy, Remedies, Law Office Management workshop, Family Law, a writing requirement, and Legal Writing and Research III and IV. The required orientation program for first-year students consists of 3 days of Introduction to the Legal System and Introduction to the Law.

Electives

The School of Law offers concentrations in corporate law, environmental law, and public interest law. In addition, upper-level students who have completed 60 academic hours may participate in both in-house and outplacement clinics for up to 15 credits. Second-year students may take mini-clinics for 2 credits. Various 2-credit upper-level seminars are offered, including those on the First Amendment, privacy law, and aviation law. Internships are available when 60 academic hours have been completed. Research programs, worth 1 or 2 credits, must be supervised by a faculty member. Special lecture series include the William O. Douglas, Lewis H. Orland, Paul Luvera, Themis Film Series, Public Issues and the Law Forum, and the Dr. Martin Luther King Jr. Committee Series. Tutorial programs are available at a student's request. The Academic Resource Program provides tutorial assistance to paarticipating first-year students. The Student Bar Association sponsors large-group tutorials for all first-year courses. Minority programs are sponsored by the Multicultural Law Caucus, Hawaii Club, JANALA, and BLSA. Special interest group programs include the Public Interest Law Project, Street Law, Property Law Interest Group, and Criminal Defense Law Caucus. The most widely taken electives are Environmental Law, Tax Law, and International Law.

Graduation Requirements

In order to graduate, candidates must have a GPA of 2.2, have completed the upper-division writing requirement, and have 90 credit hours and 90 weeks in residence.

Organizations

Students edit the *Gonzaga Law Review* and the newspaper *Bill of Particulars*. *Across Borders* is a World Wide Web-based journal specializing in international law, business, political and socioeconomic issues. The web site is http://www.law.gonzaga.edu/borders/borders.html. Moot court competitions include the National Appellate Advocacy, Jessup Cup, and National Moot Court. Teams also take part in the Negotiation, National Trial, and Client Counseling competitions. Law student organizations include the Student Bar Association, Public Interest Law Project, and Environmental Law Caucus. There are local chapters of Phi Alpha Delta, Phi Delta Phi, and Alpha Sigma Nu. Campus clubs and other organizations include the Women's Law Caucus, International Law Society, and Christian Legal Society.

Library

The law library contains 253,517 hardcopy volumes and 596,201 microform volume equivalents, and subscribes to 702 serial publications. Such on-line databases and networks as LEXIS, DIALOG, WESTLAW, NEXIS, CARL, OGLC, and the Internet are available to law students for research. Special library collections include Washington State legal materials, legal ethics, Native American law and social issues, legal philosophy, and legal research and writing. Recently, the library has acquired 25 laptop computers that are available for student checkout, and has made substantial investments in audiovisual equipment. There are fast, Pentium-based computers throughout the law school, and the law library's computer laboratories offer free printing to law students. The ratio of library volumes to faculty is 6092 to 1 and to students, 444 to 1. The ratio of seats in the library to students is 1 to 1.

Placement

J.D.s awarded:	147
Services available through: a separate law school placement center	
Services: on-campus interviews, workshops, spring Career Fest, Judicial clerkship Committee Participation, minority Career Fairs	
Special features: counseling on employment and mock videotaped interviews	
Full-time job interviews:	25 employers
Summer job interviews:	30 employers
Placement by graduation:	40% of class
Placement within 9 months:	85% of class
Average starting salary:	$17,880 to $75,800
Areas of placement:	
Private practice 2-10 attorneys	35%
Private practice 11-25 attorneys	6%
Private practice 26-50 attorneys	3%
Private practice 51-100 attorneys	2%
Government	22%
Business/industry	12%
Judicial clerkships	7%
Unknown	6%
Military	3%
Academic	2%
Public interest	2%

Faculty

The law school has 34 full-time and 24 part-time faculty members, of whom 16 are women. According to AAUP standards for Category IIA institutions, faculty salaries are below average. About 17% of full-time faculty have a graduate law degree in addition to the J.D. The ratio of full-time students to full-time faculty in an average class is 27 to 1; in a clinic, 15 to 1.

Students

About 39% of the student body are women; 15%, minorities; 3%, African American; 7%, Asian American; 4%, Hispanic; and 2%, Native American. The majority of students come from Washington (49%). The average age of entering students is 28; age range is 22 to 63. About 85% of students enter directly from undergraduate school, 10% have a graduate degree, and 5% have worked full-time prior to entering law school. About 10% drop out after the first year for academic or personal reasons; 90% remain to receive a law degree.

HAMLINE UNIVERSITY

School of Law

1536 Hewitt Avenue
St. Paul, MN 55104-1284

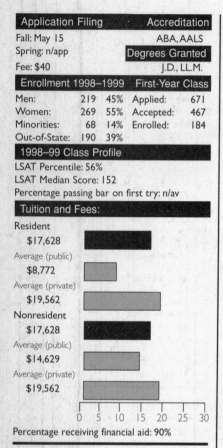

Application Filing		Accreditation
Fall: May 15		ABA, AALS
Spring: n/app		Degrees Granted
Fee: $40		J.D., LL.M.

Enrollment 1998–1999		First-Year Class	
Men:	219 45%	Applied:	671
Women:	269 55%	Accepted:	467
Minorities:	68 14%	Enrolled:	184
Out-of-State:	190 39%		

1998–99 Class Profile

LSAT Percentile: 56%
LSAT Median Score: 152
Percentage passing bar on first try: n/av

Tuition and Fees:

Resident
$17,628
Average (public)
$8,772
Average (private)
$19,562
Nonresident
$17,628
Average (public)
$14,629
Average (private)
$19,562

0 5 10 15 20 25 30

Percentage receiving financial aid: 90%

ADMISSIONS

In the fall 1999 first-year class, 671 applied, 467 were accepted, and 184 enrolled. Four transfers enrolled. The median LSAT percentile of the most recent first-year class was 56; the median GPA was 3.2 on a scale of 4.0. The lowest LSAT percentile accepted was 11; the highest was 96.

Requirements

Applicants must have a bachelor's degree from an accredited institution and take the LSAT. No specific undergraduate courses are required. Candidates are not interviewed.

Procedure

The application deadline for fall entry is May 15. Applicants should submit an application form, LSAT results, transcripts, and a nonrefundable application fee of $40. Two or 3 letters of recommendation are strongly recommended but not required. Notification of the admission decision is 2 to 6 weeks after the file is completed. The latest acceptable LSAT test date for fall entry is February. The law school uses the LSDAS.

Special

The law school recruits minority and disadvantaged students through special consideration in the admissions process and by annually hosting an admissions program geared specifically for minority students. The school also participates in CLEO. Transfer students must have one year of credit, have attended an ABA-approved law school, and submit a letter of good standing and a transcript from the previous institution. Preadmissions courses consist of a summer conditional program, Acceptance by Performance (ABP), in which students selected by the Admissions Committee take 2 courses over a 6-week period. If they pass these courses, they are offered admission.

Costs

Tuition and fees for the 1999-2000 academic year are $17,628 for all full-time students. On-campus room and board costs about $5421 annually, and books and supplies run $500.

Financial Aid

About 90% of current law students receive some form of aid. The average annual amount of aid from all sources combined, including scholarships, loans, and work contracts, is $20,000; maximum, $28,000. Awards are based on need and merit. The required financial statement is FAFSA. Special funds for minority or disadvantaged students include the equivalent of 8 1/2 full-tuition scholarships. First-year students are notified about their financial aid application at the time of acceptance.

About the Law School

Hamline University School of Law was established in 1972 and is a private institution. The 50-acre campus is in a suburban area located between St. Paul and Minneapolis. The primary mission of the law school is to provide socially responsible education with extensive offerings in public law and to integrate analysis, lawyering skills, and ethics. Students have access to federal, state, county, city, and local agencies, courts, correctional facilities, law firms, and legal aid organizations in the St. Paul area. The state capital is minutes away from the campus in St. Paul. Facilities of special interest to law students include an expanded Law Center designed for interaction, with a moot court room as a focal point. The library addition provides increased study space. Housing for law students is readily available, both on and off campus. All law school facilities are accessible to the physically disabled.

Calendar

The law school operates on a traditional semester basis. Courses for full-time students are offered both day and evening and but first-year students attend day only. and must be completed within 5 years. For part-time students, courses are offered both day and evening, but first-year students attend days only. Courses must be completed within 6 years. New full-time students are admitted in the fall; part-time, fall. There is an 8-week summer session. Transferable summer courses are offered.

Programs

In addition to the J.D., the law school offers the LL.M. Students may take relevant courses in other programs and apply credit toward the J.D.; a maximum of 12 credits may be applied. The following joint degrees may be earned: J.D./M.A.P.A. (Juris Doctor/ Master of Arts in Public Administration), J.D./M.B.A. (Juris Doctor/ Master of Business Administration), J.D./A.M.B.A. (Juris Doctor/Accounting Master of Business Administration), J.D./M.A.M. (Juris Doctor/Master of Arts in Management), and J.D./M.A.W.M. (Juris Doctor/Master of Arts in Nonprofit Management).

Phone: 651-523-2461
800-388-3688
Fax: 651-523-3064
E-mail: lawadm@gw.hamline.edu
Web: web.hamline.edu/law

Contact

Office of Admissions, 651-523-2461 800-388-3688 for general inquiries; Lynette Wahl, Associate Director of Financial Aid, 651-523-2280 for financial aid information.

MINNESOTA

Required

To earn the J.D., candidates must complete 88 total credits, of which 33 are for required courses. They must maintain a minimum GPA of 2.0 in the required courses. The following first-year courses are required of all students: Civil Procedure, Contracts, Criminal Law, Torts I, Property I, Legal Research and Writing, and Constitutional Law I. Required upper-level courses consist of Professional Responsibility and seminar course. The required orientation program for first-year students is 1 day long and consists of processing administrative requirements.

Electives

The School of Law offers concentrations in corporate law, criminal law, international law, juvenile law, labor law, and civil dispute resolution; commercial law; government and regulatory affairs; and intellectual property. In addition, 3- or 4-credit clinics provide upper-level students with practical experience in family law and child advocacy, immigration law, public interest law, unemployment compensation law, and alternative dispute resolution. In seminars, 15 upper-level students per semester engage in an in-depth study of a selected topic for 3 credits. Internships for 3 credits offer upper-level students the opportunity to work with expert practitioners in various types of legal practice. Upper-level students may be research assistants for professors. Credit is given only if research assistance is structured as an independent study. Opportunities for study abroad consist of summer programs at the University of Bergen (Norway), Hebrew University (Jerusalem), or the University of Modena (Italy). A legal writing tutorial is available to students with a GPA below 2.0 after the first semester or on the recommendation of the legal writing professors. The Academic Success Program, which includes legal writing tutors and substantive review of courses, is offered to students who need remedial assistance. One of the special minority programs is the Mentoring Program; other offerings include special scholarships and student organizations for minority students. There are a variety of special interest group programs. The most widely taken electives are Alternative Dispute Resolution Family Law, Business Law, and Tax.

Graduation Requirements

In order to graduate, candidates must have a GPA of 2.0 and have completed the upper-division writing requirement and the Professional Responsibility course.

Organizations

Students edit the *Hamline Law Review*, the *Hamline Journal of Public Law and Policy*, and the *Journal of Law and Religion*. There are many moot court competitions, including the National Moot Court, the Frederick Douglas, and the Rich Intellectual Property competition. Law student organizations include the Business Law Association, International Law Society, and Environmental Law Society, and Minnesota Justice Foundation. There are local chapters of Delta Theta Phi, Phi Alpha Delta, and ABA Law School Division.

Library

The law library contains 151,000 hardcopy volumes and 87,000 microform volume equivalents, and subscribes to 900 serial publications. Such on-line databases and networks as LEXIS, DIALOG, WESTLAW, and CD-ROM are available to law students for research. Special library collections include a U.S. government selective depository collection. Recently, the library implemented a computer library expansion and upgrade, CD-ROM facilities, an automated circulation system, new offices, and improved lighting. The ratio of library volumes to faculty is 6040 to 1 and to students, 18 to 1.

Faculty

The law school has 29 full-time and 52 part-time faculty members, of whom 26 are women. According to AAUP standards for Category IIB institutions, faculty salaries are well above average. About 21% of full-time faculty have a graduate law degree in addition to the J.D. The ratio of full-time students to full-time faculty in an average class is 26 to 1; in a clinic, 8 to 1.

Placement

J.D.s awarded:	166

Services available through: a separate law school placement center.
Special features: extensive career programming, an alumni networking program for students, and listings of employers by type, size, and city.

Full-time job interviews:	16 employers
Summer job interviews:	31 employers
Placement by graduation:	57% of class
Placement within 9 months:	96% of class
Average starting salary:	$24,100 to $70,000

Areas of placement:

Private practice 2-10 attorneys	25%
Private practice 11-25 attorneys	5%
Private practice 26-50 attorneys	1%
Private practice 51-100 attorneys	1%
Private practice 100+ attorneys	6%
Business/industry	23%
Judicial clerkships	21%
Government	12%
Public interest	3%
Academic	2%
Military	1%

Students

About 55% of the student body are women; 14%, minorities; 5%, African American; 6%, Asian American; 2%, Hispanic; and 1%, Native American. The majority of students come from the Midwest (90%). The average age of entering students is 27; age range is 20 to 51. About 30% of students enter directly from undergraduate school, 5% have a graduate degree, and 70% have worked full-time prior to entering law school. About 3% drop out after the first year for academic or personal reasons; 95% remain to receive a law degree.

Harvard Law School

Cambridge, MA 02138

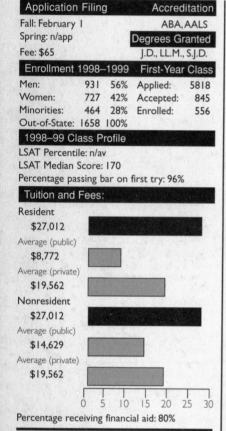

Application Filing		Accreditation
Fall: February 1		ABA, AALS
Spring: n/app		**Degrees Granted**
Fee: $65		J.D., LL.M., S.J.D.

Enrollment 1998–1999		First-Year Class	
Men:	931 56%	Applied:	5818
Women:	727 42%	Accepted:	845
Minorities:	464 28%	Enrolled:	556
Out-of-State: 1658 100%			

1998–99 Class Profile
LSAT Percentile: n/av
LSAT Median Score: 170
Percentage passing bar on first try: 96%

Tuition and Fees:

Resident
$27,012

Average (public)
$8,772

Average (private)
$19,562

Nonresident
$27,012

Average (public)
$14,629

Average (private)
$19,562

0 5 10 15 20 25 30

Percentage receiving financial aid: 80%

ADMISSIONS

In the fall 1999 first-year class, 5818 applied, 845 were accepted, and 556 enrolled. Eleven transfers enrolled. The median GPA of the most recent first-year class was 3.8 on a 4.0 scale.

Requirements

Applicants must have a bachelor's degree from an accredited institution and take the LSAT. No specific undergraduate courses are required. Candidates are not interviewed.

Procedure

The application deadline for fall entry is February 1. Applicants should submit an application form, a non refundable application fee, and 2 letters of recommendation. Students are urged to visit the school. A personal statement and a college certification form are required. Accepted students must make a deposit of $500. Notification of the admission decision is on a rolling basis. The latest acceptable LSAT test date for fall entry is December. The law school uses the LSDAS.

Special

The law school recruits minority and disadvantaged students by encouraging all who would like to study law at Harvard to apply. Transfer students must have one year of credit, have attended an ABA-approved law school, and have outstanding records in college and in the first year of law school.

Costs

Tuition and fees for the 1999-2000 academic year are $27,012 for all full-time students. There is no part-time program. On-campus room and board costs about $9279 annually; and books and supplies run $900.

Financial Aid

About 80% of current law students receive some form of aid. Awards are based on need. The required financial statement is CSS Profile or FAFSA. Check with the school for current application deadlines. First-year students are notified about their financial aid application some time after admission. Assuming a timely aid application, students are not required to submit a deposit to reserve a place in the class until a financial aid decision has been made.

About the Law School

Harvard University Harvard Law School was established in 1817 and is a private institution. The campus is in an urban area within Cambridge. The primary mission of the law school is to stress an understanding of the principles of law and a mastery of such skills as oral advocacy, research, and legal writing, and to educate lawyers to be capable of addressing new legal problems in a changing society. Students have access to federal, state, county, city, and local agencies, courts, correctional facilities, law firms, and legal aid organizations in the Cambridge area. Facilities of special interest to law students are the 21 buildings for classrooms, dormitories, student activities, libraries, and the Hale and Dorr Legal Services Center in Jamaica Plain. Housing for law students consists of law school dormitories, Harvard-affiliated housing, and off-campus housing. There is housing for single and married students. All law school facilities are accessible to the physically disabled.

Calendar

The law school operates on a traditional semester basis. Courses for full-time students are offered days only and must be completed within 3 years. New full-time students are admitted in the fall. There is no summer session. Transferable summer courses are not offered.

Programs

In addition to the J.D., the law school offers the LL.M and S.J.D. Students may take relevant courses in other programs and apply credit toward the J.D.; a maximum of 10 credits through cross-registration credits may be applied. The following joint degrees may be earned: J.D./M.B.A. (Juris Doctor/Master of Business Administration), J.D./M.P.P. (Juris Doctor/Master of Public Policy), J.D./M.A.L.D. (Juris Doctor/Master of Arts in Law and Diplomacy with Tufts'), J.D./Ph.D. (Juris Doctor/Doctor of Philosophy), J.D./M.A. (Juris Doctor/Master of Arts), and J.D./M.P.A. (Juris Doctor/Master of Public Administration).

Phone: 617-495-3109
Fax: 617-495-1110
E-mail: jdadmiss@law.harvard.edu
Web: law.harvard.edu

Contact
617-495-3109, fax 617-436-7290 for general inquiries.

Required

To earn the J.D., candidates must complete 82 total credits, of which 30 are for required courses. The following first-year courses are required of all students: Torts, Contracts, Property, Civil Procedure, Criminal Law, Introduction to Lawyering, and an elective. Required upper-level courses consist of a professional responsibility requirement and a written work requirement. Harvard offers one of the most extensive clinical programs in the country with more than 20 courses offering clinical placements. In addition, several student practice organizations offer clinical placements. The required orientation program for first-year students lasts 2 days and is described as comprehensive.

Electives

Clinical experience is available through the legal services, immigration, and criminal law clinics as well as through student organizations. In addition, more than 17 courses offer clinical field work experience and more than 7 others include simulated exercises. There are many seminars, including those on affirmative action, the federal budgetary process, corporate theory, law and business problems, international law, and law and religion in India. Internships are available but not for credit. Research programs may be conducted with the Center for Criminal Justice, Human Rights Program, East Asian Legal Studies, International Tax Program, Program on International Financial Systems, European Law Research Center, Program in Law and Economics, Program on the Legal Profession, the Program on Negotiation, International and Comparative Legal Studies, International Tax Program, and Islamic Legal Studies. Field work is available in business, civil and criminal, mediation, and environmental law. A number of courses provide students with field work in local courts and government agencies, and others provide instruction in aspects of legal practice through simulated casework and a problem-oriented approach. Lecture series include the BSA Speaker Series, the DSAC Brown-Bag Lunch Discussion Series, East Asian Legal Studies Speaker Program, HLS Forum, Human Rights Program Speakers Series, and Introduction to the World of Law. The most widely taken electives are Constitutional Law, Taxation, and Corporations.

Graduation Requirements

In order to graduate, candidates must have completed the upper-division writing requirement.

Organizations
Students edit the *Harvard Law Review*, *Blackletter Law Journal*, *Civil Rights-Civil Liberties Law Review*, *Human Rights Journal*, *Journal of Law and Public Policy*, *Journal of Law and Technology*, *Journal on Legislation*, *Women's Law Journal*, *International Law Journal*, *Environmental Law Review*, *Latino Law Review*, *Negotiations Journal*, the student newspaper, the *Harvard Law Record*, and a yearbook. Moot court opportunities include the Ames Competition, which offers moot court competitions for first-year and upper-class students. The school also participates in interschool contests, including the Willston Legislative Drafting Competition and the Jessup International Law Moot Court Competition. Students may choose to participate in more than 80 student organizations.

Library
The law library contains 1,920,648 hardcopy volumes and 187,600 microform volume equivalents, and subscribes to 10,000 serial publications. Such on-line databases and networks as LEXIS, DIALOG, WESTLAW, and Harvard On-Line Library Information System (HOLLIS), RUN, Vu/Text, Dow Jones News Retrieval, Legi-Slate are available to law students for research. Special library collections include a comprehensive collection of Anglo American reports and treatises, and a special collection on international law as well as rare books and a 30,000-item art collection. The Law School Library was completely renovated during 1996-1997 to accommodate present and future technology needs of library users.

Faculty
The law school has 94 full-time and 75 part-time faculty members. According to AAUP standards for Category I institutions, faculty salaries are well above average. About 17% of full-time faculty have a graduate law degree in addition to the J.D.

Placement

J.D.s awarded:	553
Services available through: A separate law school placement center.	
Services: on-campus interviews for second- and third-year students	
Full-time job interviews:	n/av
Summer job interviews:	n/av
Placement by graduation:	98% of class
Placement within 9 months:	n/av
Average starting salary:	$32,000 to $72,000
Areas of placement:	
Private practice 2-100 attorneys	61%
Judicial clerkships	24%
Business/industry	8%
Public interest	4%
Government	2%
Academic	1%

Students
About 42% of the student body are women; 28%, minorities; 10%, African American; 12%, Asian American; 5%, Hispanic; and 1%, Native American. The average age of entering students is 24; age range is 19 to 47. About 45% of students enter directly from undergraduate school, 20% have a graduate degree, and 60% have worked full-time prior to entering law school. About 1% drop out after the first year for academic or personal reasons; 99% remain to receive a law degree.

HOFSTRA UNIVERSITY

School of Law

121 Hofstra University
Hempstead, NY 11549

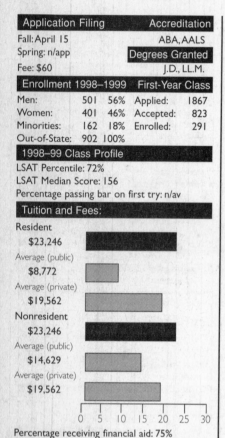

Application Filing		Accreditation
Fall: April 15		ABA, AALS
Spring: n/app		**Degrees Granted**
Fee: $60		J.D., LL.M.

Enrollment 1998–1999			First-Year Class	
Men:	501	56%	Applied:	1867
Women:	401	46%	Accepted:	823
Minorities:	162	18%	Enrolled:	291
Out-of-State:	902	100%		

1998–99 Class Profile

LSAT Percentile: 72%
LSAT Median Score: 156
Percentage passing bar on first try: n/av

Tuition and Fees:

Resident
$23,246
Average (public)
$8,772
Average (private)
$19,562
Nonresident
$23,246
Average (public)
$14,629
Average (private)
$19,562

0 5 10 15 20 25 30

Percentage receiving financial aid: 75%

ADMISSIONS

In the fall 1999 first-year class, 1867 applied, 823 were accepted, and 291 enrolled. Figures in the above capsule are approximate. Five transfers enrolled. The median LSAT percentile of the most recent first-year class was 72; the median GPA was 3.3 on a scale of 4.0. The lowest LSAT percentile accepted was 12; the highest was 98.

Requirements

Applicants must have a bachelor's degree from an accredited institution and take the LSAT. The most important admission factors include academic achievement, GPA, and LSAT results. No specific undergraduate courses are required. Candidates are not interviewed.

Procedure

The application deadline for fall entry is April 15. Applicants should submit an application form, LSAT results, transcripts, a nonrefundable application fee of $60, and 1 letter of recommendation. Notification of the admission decision is

on a rolling basis. The latest acceptable LSAT test date for fall entry is February, generally. The law school uses the LSDAS.

Special

The law school recruits minority and disadvantaged students by means of student, faculty, graduate, and administrator visits to a diverse range of institutions to increase the number of law students from traditionally excluded groups. Transfer students must have one year of credit and have attended an ABA-approved law school.

Costs

Tuition and fees for the 1999-2000 academic year are $23,246 for all full-time students. On-campus room and board costs about $8350 annually; and books and supplies run $900.

Financial Aid

About 75% of current law students receive some form of aid. The average annual amount of aid from all sources combined, including scholarships, loans, and work contracts, is $20,000; maximum, $39,940. Awards are based on need and merit. The required financial statement is FAFSA. The aid application deadline for fall entry is June 1. First-year students are notified about their financial aid application upon acceptance if the financial aid application is complete, or at the time of completion of the financial aid application.

About the Law School

Hofstra University School of Law was established in 1970 and is a private institution. The 240-acre campus is in a suburban area 25 miles east of New York City. The primary mission of the law school is to promote intellectual discussion and debate as faculty and students critically examine the law, the legal profession, and legal education. Students have access to federal, state, county, city, and local agencies, courts, correctional facilities, law firms, and legal aid organizations in the Hempstead area. Students have special access to the federal courthouse located on campus. Facilities of special interest to law students are all university facilities, including the university library center, athletic facilities, cultural programs, and social events. Housing for law students is provided by the university in townhouses and high-

rise residence halls. Many law students rent houses or apartments within a short commuting distance from the university. All law school facilities are accessible to the physically disabled.

Calendar

The law school operates on a traditional semester basis. Courses for full-time students are offered days only and must be completed within 3 years. For part-time students, courses are offered days only and must be completed within 4 years. New full-and part-time students are admitted in the fall. There is a 7-week summer session. Transferable summer courses are offered.

Programs

In addition to the J.D., the law school offers the LL.M. The following joint degrees may be earned: J.D./M.B.A. (Juris Doctor/Master of Business Administration).

Required

To earn the J.D., candidates must complete 87 total credits, of which 39 are for required courses. They must maintain a minimum GPA of 2.0 in the required courses. The following first-year courses are required of all students: Civil Procedure I and II, Contracts I and II, Criminal Law, Lawmaking Institutions, Legal Writing and Research, Property I and II, and Torts I and II. Required upper-level courses consist of Appellate Advocacy, Constitutional Law I and II, Legal Ethics, and Upper-class writing requirements I and II. The required orientation program for first-year students is a 3-day program that includes legal method classes taught by faculty members, general lectures, panels concerning student services, and social activities.

Electives

The School of Law offers concentrations in corporate law, criminal law, environmental law, family law, international law, labor law, litigation, media law, securities law, tax law, torts and insurance, and constitutional law, health law. In addition, students may enroll in the Housing Rights Clinic for 6 credits, the Criminal Justice Clinic for 6 credits, the Environmental Law Clinic for 6 credits, or the Child Advocacy Clinic for 4 to 6 credits. Upper-class students may choose from a large number of 2- to 3-credit seminars. First-year students take one

Contact

516-463-5916 for general inquiries; Nancy Modell, Assistant Dean for Financial Aid, 516-463-5929 for financial aid information.

NEW YORK

required substantive course in a small section of 25 to 30 students. Students may enroll in the Externship Program for 3 credits; they may work for judges or in nonprofit or government agencies, dealing with civil and criminal matters. Faculty-supervised independent study is worth from 2 to 6 credits. The law school offers special problems seminars, in which 3 to 5 students work closely with a professor in a tutorial setting on a topic of current interest. Recent offerings have included: Special Problems in State Constitutional Reform, Special Problems in Tax Ethics, and Special Problems in Reproductive Technology and the Law. In addition, the law school offers an extensive Pro Bono Student Volunteer Program, in which more than 400 students have donated their efforts to assist attorneys and other agencies with cases. Through the Unemployment Action Center, students provide assistance to unemployed persons seeking benefits. A Visiting Scholar Program brings to the law school a distinguished scholar for a visit of 3 to 4 days; the visiting scholar teaches classes, gives a lecture, and meets informally with students and faculty. Annually scheduled lectures involve experts in bankruptcy law, family law, legal ethics, and health law, as well as features by distinguished jurists, scholars, and practitioners. The law school offers a summer program in Nice, France in cooperation with the University of Nice Law School. Incoming students may be selected by the tutorial committee to participate in a voluntary enhancement program taught by faculty. The Director of Multicultural Student Affairs is responsible for minority student affairs, minority recruitment and admissions, the coordination of the law school's Enhancement Program and the coordination of the Dwight L. Greene Scholarship Program. Specific initiatives to support the students of color include: an Open House for minority applicants, Law Day for admitted students of color, a Minority Student Orientation Program for incoming students, a first-year reception, mentoring programs and other programs throughout the year. The most widely taken electives are Business Organizations, Criminal Procedure, and Debtor-Creditor Law.

Graduation Requirements

In order to graduate, candidates must have a GPA of 2.0 and have completed 2 upper-division writing requirements.

Organizations

Students edit the *Hofstra Law Review, Hofstra Labor and Employment Law Journal, Family and Conciliation Courts Review, Hofstra Law and Policy Symposium,* and the newspaper, *Conscience.* Teams compete annually in the National Moot Court, Wagner Moot Court, and a local bar association moot court competition sponsored by the Nassau Academy of Law. Teams are regularly sent to the National Trial Competition (NTC) and the American Trial Lawyers Association (ATLA) competitions. Law student organizations include the Corporate Law Society, Hofstra Law Women, and Environmental Law Society. There are local chapters of Asian-Pacific American Law Student Association, Black American Law Student Association, and LAMBDA Alpha International. Hofstra University supports more than 100 student cultural, media, sports, creative, service, and politically and socially active clubs.

Library

The law library contains 487,630 hardcopy volumes and 1,357,850 microform volume equivalents, and subscribes to 1246 serial publications. Such on-line databases and networks as LEXIS, DIALOG, WESTLAW, and NEXIS, and the Internet are available to law students for research. Special library collections include records and briefs of U.S. Supreme Court cases (1832 to the present) and of the New York Court of Appeals and Appellate Division; federal depository materials; and all U.N. documents (1976 to the present) on microfiche. Additional microfiche holdings are the ABA archival collection (1878 to the present) and the archival collection of the American Law Institute. Recently, the library a new addition with expanded study facilities and a computer research laboratory; added 42 ports for laptop use in the library; installed a Disabled Students Dictation Room, with access to WESTLAW, LEXIS, and the Internet; and increased access to E-mail, word processing, and the Internet. The ratio of library volumes to faculty is 11,083 to 1 and to students, 587 to 1. The ratio of seats in the library to students is 2:3.

Placement

J.D.s awarded:	230

Services available through: A separate law school placement center.

Special features: one-on-one videotaped interview skills training programs, 24-hour resume and cover letter review, computerized employer databases, and Rapid Research program.

Full-time job interviews:	81 employers
Summer job interviews:	10 employers
Placement by graduation:	n/av
Placement within 9 months:	98% of class

Average starting salary: $21,000 to $125,000

Areas of placement:

Private practice 2-10 attorneys	12%
Private practice 11-25 attorneys	3%
Private practice 26-50 attorneys	1%
Private practice 51-100 attorneys	18%
Solo practice	25%
Business/industry	14%
Government	10%
Non-legal	7%
Judicial clerkships	5%
Public interest	3%
Academic	1%

Faculty

The law school has 39 full-time and 35 part-time faculty members, of whom 15 are women. According to AAUP standards for Category I institutions, faculty salaries are well above average. About 31% of full-time faculty have a graduate law degree in addition to the J.D.; about 31% of part-time faculty have one. The ratio of full-time students to full-time faculty in an average class is 24 to 1; in a clinic, 10 to 1. The law school has a regular program of bringing visiting professors and other distinguished lecturers and visitors to campus.

Students

About 46% of the student body are women; 18%, minorities; 7%, African American; 5%, Asian American; and 7%, Hispanic. The age range of entering students is 21 to 54. About 65% of students enter directly from undergraduate school, 10% have a graduate degree, and 33% have worked full-time prior to entering law school. About 4% drop out after the first year for academic or personal reasons; 94% remain to receive a law degree.

HOWARD UNIVERSITY

Howard University

2900 Van Ness Street, N.W.
Washington, DC 20008

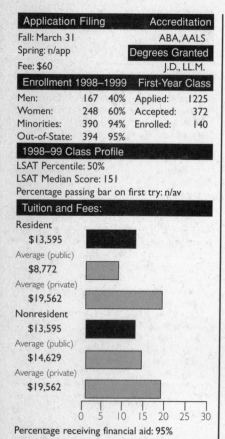

ADMISSIONS

In the fall 1999 first-year class, 1225 applied, 372 were accepted, and 140 enrolled. Ten transfers enrolled. The median LSAT percentile of the most recent first-year class was 50; the median GPA was 2.9 on a scale of 4.0.

Requirements

Applicants must have a bachelor's degree from an accredited institution and take the LSAT. Minimum acceptable LSAT score is 35 and minimum acceptable GPA is 3.0 on a scale of 4.0. The most important admission factors include general background, GPA, and LSAT results. No specific undergraduate courses are required. Candidates are not interviewed.

Procedure

The application deadline for fall entry is March 31. Applicants should submit an application form, LSAT results, transcripts, a nonrefundable application fee of $60, 2 letters of recommendation, a personal statement, and the Dean's survey. Notification of the admission decision is on a rolling basis. The latest acceptable LSAT test date for fall entry is February. The law school uses the LSDAS.

Special

Transfer students must have one year of credit, have attended an ABA-approved law school, and be ranked in the upper one quarter to one third of their class.

Costs

Tuition and fees for the 1999-2000 academic year are $13,595 for all students. On-campus room and board costs about $12,891 annually; books and supplies run $1050.

Financial Aid

About 95% of current law students receive some form of aid. The average annual amount of aid from all sources combined, including scholarships, loans, and work contracts, is $18,000; maximum, $27,536. Awards are based on merit. The required financial statement is FAFSA. The aid application deadline for fall entry is April 1. First-year students are notified about their financial aid application at time of acceptance.

About the Law School

Howard University School of Law was established in 1869 and is a private institution. The 22-acre campus is in an urban area in northwest Washington, D.C. The mission of Howard University School of Law includes the provision of quality education for any student, with emphasis on educational opportunities for those students who may not otherwise have them. Students have access to federal, state, county, city, and local agencies, courts, correctional facilities, law firms, legal aid organizations in the Washington area, and the Washington Consortium of Law Libraries, which offers use of all law libraries in the D.C. metropolitan area. Facilities of special interest to law students include the superior moot court room. Housing for law students is limited on campus; most students live off campus. All law school facilities are accessible to the physically disabled.

Calendar

The law school operates on a traditional semester basis. Courses for full-time students are offered both day and evening and must be completed within 5 years. For part-time students, courses are offered both day and evening. New full-time students are admitted in the fall and spring. There is no summer session. Transferable summer courses are offered.

Programs

In addition to the J.D., the law school offers the LL.M and master's specialization in international law and comparative law. Students may take relevant courses in other programs and apply credit toward the J.D.; a maximum of 30 credits may be applied. The following joint degrees may be earned: J.D./M.B.A. (Juris Doctor/Master of Business Administration).

Phone: 202-806-8008
Fax: 202-806-8162
E-mail: admissions@law.howard.edu
Web: www.law.howard.edu

Contact

Kim Gray, Assistant Director of Admissions, 202-806-8008 for general inquiries; Norman James, Financial Aid Officer, 202-806-8005 for financial aid information.

DISTRICT OF COLUMBIA

Required

To earn the J.D., candidates must complete 88 total credits. They must maintain a minimum grade average of 72 in the required courses. The following first-year courses are required of all students: Torts I & II, Property, Contracts, Civil Procedure, Criminal Law, Legal Method, Legal Research and Writing, and Constitutional Law I. Required upper-level courses consist of Legal Writing II, Constitutional Law II, Professional Responsibility, Evidence, Skills, and Legal Writing III. The required 2-week orientation program for first-year students includes an introduction to legal methods.

Electives

Clinics in a wide range of areas are available to third-year students; 4 to 12 credits are offered for each clinic. Second- and third-year students may take seminars for 3 credits. Internships are available to third-year students for 3 credits. Third-year students may also participate in research for 2 credits. All students may attend tutorials and special lectures for no credit. After the first year of study, students may undertake a study-abroad program. ABA-approved courses worth 2 credits each are offered at HUSL/University of Western Capetown, South Africa. The most widely taken electives are Federal Tax; Wills, Trusts, and Estates; and Administrative Law.

Graduation Requirements

In order to graduate, candidates must have a grade average of 75 on a scale of 100 and have completed the upper-division writing requirement.

Organizations

Students edit the *Howard Law Journal* and the newspaper *Barrister*. Moot court competitions include ABA National Appellate Advocacy-Northeast Regional, Jessup International, and Frederick Douglass National. Law student organizations include the Student Bar Association, International Law Society and Entertainment Law Association. There are local chapters of Black Law Students Association, Public Interest Law Society, and the ABA.

Library

The law library contains 283,000 hardcopy volumes and 54,000 microform volume equivalents, and subscribes to 1643 serial publications. Such on-line databases and networks as LEXIS, DIALOG, WESTLAW, and the Internet are available to law students for research. Special library collections include Fats Waller Litigation Files and a civil rights collection. Recently, the library implemented a Web-based library catalog, developed library home-page research tools, and distributed CD-ROM materials for the library LAN. The ratio of library volumes to faculty is 8333 to 1 and to students, 555 to 1. The ratio of seats in the library to students is 1 to 3.

Faculty

The law school has 33 full-time and 23 part-time faculty members, of whom 19 are women. About 2% of full-time faculty have a graduate law degree in addition to the J.D.; about 4% of part-time faculty have one. The ratio of full-time students to full-time faculty in an average class is 40 to 1; in a clinic, 8 to 1. The law school has a regular program of bringing visiting professors and other distinguished lecturers and visitors to campus.

Students

About 60% of the student body are women; 94%, minorities; 87%, African American; 4%, Asian American; 4%, Hispanic; and 5%, Caucasian. The majority of students come from the Northeast (39%). The average age of entering students is 25; age range is 21 to 48. About 80% of students enter directly from undergraduate school, 7% have a graduate degree, and 20% have worked full-time prior to entering law school. About 5% drop out after the first year for academic or personal reasons; 94% remain to receive a law degree.

Placement

J.D.s awarded:	118
Services available through: a separate law school placement center	
Special features: first-year summer clerkship program (through partnerships with major law firms and corporations) summer associate training program; workshops and seminars on job search skills, legal career settings, practice specialties, and employment trends	
Full-time job interviews:	109 employers
Summer job interviews:	169 employers
Placement by graduation:	60% of class
Placement within 9 months:	91% of class
Average starting salary:	$30,000 to $150,000
Areas of placement:	
Private practice 2-10 attorneys	5%
Private practice 11-25 attorneys	1%
Private practice 26-50 attorneys	3%
Private practice 51-100 attorneys	3%
Government	30%
Business/industry	19%
Judicial clerkships	16%
Public interest	3%
Unknown	1%
Academic	1%

Chicago-Kent College of Law

565 West Adams Street
Chicago, IL 60661

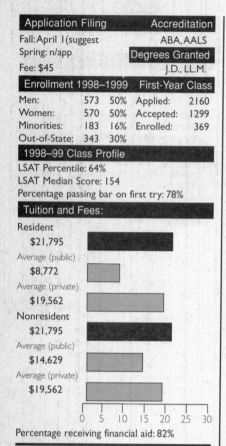

Application Filing	Accreditation
Fall: April 1 (suggest	ABA, AALS
Spring: n/app	**Degrees Granted**
Fee: $45	J.D., LL.M.

Enrollment 1998–1999		First-Year Class	
Men:	573 50%	Applied:	2160
Women:	570 50%	Accepted:	1299
Minorities:	183 16%	Enrolled:	369
Out-of-State:	343 30%		

1998–99 Class Profile

LSAT Percentile: 64%
LSAT Median Score: 154
Percentage passing bar on first try: 78%

Tuition and Fees:

Resident
$21,795

Average (public)
$8,772

Average (private)
$19,562

Nonresident
$21,795

Average (public)
$14,629

Average (private)
$19,562

0 5 10 15 20 25 30

Percentage receiving financial aid: 82%

ADMISSIONS

In the fall 1999 first-year class, 2160 applied, 1299 were accepted, and 369 enrolled. Seven transfers enrolled. The median LSAT percentile of the most recent first-year class was 64; the median GPA was 3.2 on a scale of 4.0. The lowest LSAT percentile accepted was 33; the highest was 98.

Requirements

Applicants must have a bachelor's degree from an accredited institution and take the LSAT. No specific undergraduate courses are required. Candidates are not interviewed.

Procedure

The (suggested) application deadline for fall entry is April 1. Applicants should submit an application form, LSAT results, transcripts, a nonrefundable application fee of $45, 1 letter of recommendation (academic preferred), and a nonrefundable seat deposit, payable in 2 installments in April and June. Notification of the admission decision is on a rolling basis. The latest acceptable LSAT test date for fall entry is June. The law school uses the LSDAS.

Special

The law school recruits minority and disadvantaged students through minority student law days, direct mail, and events sponsored by minority law student groups. Transfer students must have one year of credit, have attended an ABA-approved law school, and submit a letter of good standing from the dean of their law school and 1 letter of recommendation.

Costs

Tuition and fees for the 1999-2000 academic year are $21,795 for all full-time students. Tuition for part-time students is $15,745 annually. On-campus room and board costs about $6400 annually; books and supplies run $610.

Financial Aid

About 82% of current law students receive some form of aid. The average annual amount of aid from all sources combined, including scholarships, loans, and work contracts, is $26,105; maximum, $51,302. Awards are based on need and merit. The required financial statement is FAFSA. The aid application deadline for fall entry is April 15. Special funds for minority or disadvantaged students are available. First-year students are notified about their financial aid application at time of acceptance.

About the Law School

Illinois Institute of Technology Chicago-Kent College of Law was established in 1888 and is a private institution. The campus is in an urban area in downtown Chicago. The primary mission of the law school is to provide students with a solid grounding in legal theory and ethics, along with innovative approaches to teaching and skills training. Students have access to federal, state, county, city, and local agencies, courts, correctional facilities, law firms, and legal aid organizations in the Chicago area. The college is located in the Loop, which is Chicago's central business district, and is within walking distance to county, state, city, and federal agencies, courts, and law firms. Facilities of special interest to law students include a 10-story law building, which houses the law school and the M.B.A., M.P.A., and Master of Science in Environmental Management programs, as well as the Stuart Graduate School of Business. The majority of classrooms and seminar rooms have power and data ports at each seat for connection to the computer network. There is also a modern, state-of-the-art courtroom. Afford-

able housing is available in nearby urban and suburban neighborhoods. The law school is close to all public transportation. All law school facilities are accessible to the physically disabled.

Calendar

The law school operates on a traditional semester basis. Courses for full-time students are offered both day and evening and must be completed within 5 years. For part-time students, courses are offered both day and evening and must be completed within 6 years. New full- and part-time students are admitted in the fall. There is an 8-week summer session. Transferable summer courses are offered.

Programs

In addition to the J.D., the law school offers the LL.M. Students may take relevant courses in other programs and apply credit toward the J.D.; a maximum of 12 credits may be applied. The following joint degrees may be earned: J.D./M.B.A. (Juris Doctor/Master of Business Administration), J.D./LL.M. (Juris Doctor/Master of Laws in taxation or financial services), J.D./M.S. (Juris Doctor/Master of Science in financial markets and trading), J.D./M.P.A. (Juris Doctor/Master of Public Administration), J.D./M.E.M. (Juris Doctor/Master of Science in environmental management), and J.D./M.P.H. (Juris Doctor/Master of Public Health).

Required

To earn the J.D., candidates must complete 87 total credits, of which 42 are for required courses. They must maintain a minimum GPA of 2.1 in the required courses. The following first-year courses are required of all students: Torts, Contracts, Property, Criminal Law, Civil Procedure, Legal Writing I and II, and Justice and the Legal System. Required upper-level courses consist of Professional Responsibility, Constitutional Law, Seminar, Advanced Research, and Legal Drafting. The required orientation program for first-year students is a 1-week program combining introductory programs, library tours, computer training, legal research and writing, and small sessions with current students and faculty.

Electives

Students must take 14 credits in their area of concentration. The Chicago-Kent College of Law offers concentrations in corporate law, criminal law, entertainment law, environmental law, international law, labor law, litigation, securities

Phone: 312-906-5020
E-mail: admit@kentlaw.edu
Web: http://www.kentlaw.edu

Contact

Michael S. Burns, Assistant Dean for Admissions, 312-906-5020 for general inquiries; Ada Chin, Director of Financial Aid, 312-906-5180 for financial aid information.

ILLINOIS

law, tax law, torts and insurance, intellectual property, public interest, real estate, dispute resolution, and litigation. A certificate program for J.D. students in environmental and energy law includes a series of electives in land use, energy, and environmental law as well as interdisciplinary classes in the scientific and economic analysis of environmental problems. There are similar certificate programs in international and comparative law, litigation and alternative dispute resolution, intellectual property law, and labor and employment law. In addition, students may take clinical work in criminal, civil, mediation, health, or tax areas through the Chicago-Kent-law offices. One seminar of 2 hours credit is required of all students. Recently offered seminars include Bioethics and the Law, Race-Conscious Remedies, and Current Energy Issues. An Advanced Externship Program places students with public agencies and teaching attorneys in areas such as environmental, bankruptcy, international, and First Amendment Law. A Judicial Externship program places students in clerkships with federal judges. Students can take Individual Research for 1 credit per semester. Special lecture series include the Morris Lecture in International and Comparative Law, the Piper Lecture in Labor Law, the Green Lecture in Law and Technology, the Institute for Science Law and Technology Conferences, and the Global Law and Policy Initiative Conferences. Study abroad is possible through the London Consortium, and the college accepts credits from most ABA-accredited law school study-abroad programs. The Academic Empowerment Program is offered to students based on factors including LSAT score, undergraduate and graduate GPA, socioeconomic background, years out of school, native language, and disabilities. Student groups, sponsor minority programs. A certificate program for J.D. students in environmental and energy law includes a series of electives in land use, energy, and environmental law as well as interdisciplinary classes in the scientific and economic analysis of environmental problems. There are similar certificate programs in international and comparative law, litigation and alternative dispute resolution, intellectual property law, and labor and employment law. The most widely taken electives are Evidence, Remedies, and Business Organizations.

Graduation Requirements

In order to graduate, candidates must have a GPA of 2.1, and have completed the upper-division writing requirement, required courses, Professional Responsibility, and a seminar. Attendance at Professionalism Day is also required for all students.

Organizations

Students edit the *Chicago-Kent Law Review*, which is published 3 times a year, *The Journal of Intellectual Property*, and the *Employee Rights and Employment Policy Journal*. The student newspaper is the *Kent Commentator*. The Moot Court Honor Society, which enters its members in 10 intercollegiate competitions annually, sponsors the Ilana Diamond Rovner Appellate Advocacy Competition for upper-class students who are members of the Society. First-year students compete in the Charles Evans Hughes Moot Court Competition. The College of Law's 43 law student organizations include the Environmental Law Society, International Law Society, and the Society of Women in Law. There are local chapters of the Asian-American, Black, and Hispanic Law Students associations.

Library

The law library contains 560,000 hardcopy volumes and 687,941 microform volume equivalents, and subscribes to 9012 serial publications. Such on-line databases and networks as LEXIS, DIALOG, WESTLAW, the Internet, EPIC, ProQuest, and Illinet are available to law students. Special library collections include a depository of federal documents, a special collection on law and the aging, Illinois Supreme Court records, Illinois Pollution Control Board records, as well as international organization documents. The Information Center consists of the Chicago-Kent Law Library, the Library of International Relations, and the Stuart Business Library. Users have access to a database of more than 3 million imaged pages and network access to numerous CD-ROMs. The ratio of library volumes to faculty is 8000 to 1 and to students, 490 to 1. The ratio of seats in the library to students is 1 to 2.

Faculty

The law school has 70 full-time and 103 part-time faculty members, of whom 54 are women. According to AAUP standards for Category I institutions, faculty

Placement

J.D.s awarded:	332
Services available through: separate law school placement center	
Special features: 7 full-time plus 2 part-time staff members, including 4 counselors; a resource center with reference materials and computers for resume printing and database searches, participation in 5 minority job fairs, 2 public interest career conferences, the Patent Law Interview Program, and 4 additional job fairs (LLM, MAP, International, and SciLaw)	
Full-time job interviews:	34 employers
Summer job interviews:	45 employers
Placement by graduation:	n/av
Placement within 9 months:	95% of class
Average starting salary:	$12,000 to $160,000
Areas of placement:	
Private practice 2-10 attorneys	19%
Private practice 11-25 attorneys	7%
Private practice 26-50 attorneys	5%
Private practice 51-100 attorneys	5%
Private practice 100 + attorneys	15%
Private practice firm size unknown	3%
Business/industry	19%
Government	17%
Judicial clerkships	5%
Public interest	2%
Academic	1%

salaries are average. About 40% of full-time faculty have a graduate law degree in addition to the J.D.; about 27% of part-time faculty have one. The ratio of full-time students to full-time faculty in an average class is 38 to 1; in a clinic, 9 to 1. The law school has a regular program of bringing visiting professors and other distinguished lecturers and visitors to campus. There is a chapter of the Order of the Coif; 70 faculty and 101 graduates (over the last 3 years) are members.

Students

About 50% of the student body are women; 16%, minorities; 5%, African American; 6%, Asian American; and 4%, Hispanic. The majority of students come from the Midwest (83%). The average age of entering students is 25; age range is 20 to 46. About 46% of students enter directly from undergraduate school, 6% have a graduate degree, and 54% have worked full-time prior to entering law school. About 5% drop out after the first year for academic or personal reasons; 95% remain to receive a law degree.

Indiana University School of Law-Indianapolis

735 West New York Street
Indianapolis, IN 46202-5194

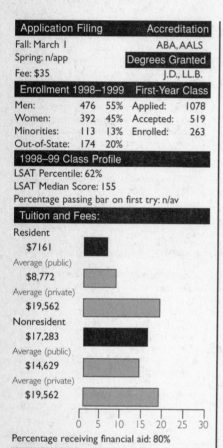

Application Filing	Accreditation
Fall: March 1	ABA, AALS
Spring: n/app	Degrees Granted
Fee: $35	J.D., LL.B.

Enrollment 1998–1999		First-Year Class	
Men:	476 55%	Applied:	1078
Women:	392 45%	Accepted:	519
Minorities:	113 13%	Enrolled:	263
Out-of-State:	174 20%		

1998–99 Class Profile
LSAT Percentile: 62%
LSAT Median Score: 155
Percentage passing bar on first try: n/av

Tuition and Fees:

Resident
$7161

Average (public)
$8,772

Average (private)
$19,562

Nonresident
$17,283

Average (public)
$14,629

Average (private)
$19,562

0 5 10 15 20 25 30

Percentage receiving financial aid: 80%

ADMISSIONS

In the fall 1999 first-year class, 1078 applied, 519 were accepted, and 263 enrolled. Twenty-one transfers enrolled. The median LSAT percentile of the most recent first-year class was 62; the median GPA was 3.2 on a scale of 4.0. The lowest LSAT percentile accepted was 6; the highest was 99.

Requirements
Applicants must have a bachelor's degree from an accredited institution and take the LSAT. Minimum acceptable LSAT percentile is 20 and minimum acceptable GPA is 2.5 on a scale of 4.0. The most important admission factors include LSAT results, GPA, and academic achievement. No specific undergraduate courses are required. Candidates are not interviewed.

Procedure
The application deadline for fall entry is March 1. Applicants should submit an application form, LSAT results, transcripts, a nonrefundable application fee of $35, and a personal statement. Notification of the admissions decision is on a rolling basis. The latest acceptable LSAT test date for fall entry is February. The law school uses the LSDAS.

Special
The law school recruits minority and disadvantaged students by means of Minority Law Day visits to historically black colleges and universities, CLEO, and LSASS candidate referral search. Transfer students must have one year of credit, have a minimum GPA of 3.0, and have attended an ABA-approved law school. Acceptance also depends on space availability.

Costs

Tuition and fees for the 1999-2000 academic year are $7161 for full-time in-state students and $17,283 for out-of-state students. Tuition for part-time students is $4648 per year in-state and $11,178 out-of-state. On-campus room and board costs about $8000 annually; and books and supplies run $500.

Financial Aid

About 80% of current law students receive some form of aid. The average annual amount of aid from all sources combined, including scholarships, loans, and work contracts, is $11,000; maximum, $18,500. Awards are based on need and merit, but if awards are from a private donor, requirements may differ. The required financial statements are CSS Profile and the law school's financial aid application. The aid application deadline for fall entry is March 1. Special funds for minority or disadvantaged students consist of awards from private donors and the National Labor Relations Board, Region 25, as well as Indiana CLEO for under represented groups in the legal field. First-year students are notified about their financial aid application at time of acceptance.

About the Law School

Indiana University-Purdue University's Indiana University School of Law-Indianapolis was established in 1895 and is a public institution. The campus is in an urban area in Indianapolis. The primary mission of the law school is to provide a legal education that will equip graduates with highly refined analytical and problem-solving skills, compassion, and ethics. Students have access to federal, state, county, city, and local agencies, courts, correctional facilities, law firms, and legal aid organizations in the Indianapolis area. Facilities of special interest to law students include the Municipal Court House, where some classes are held, and the National Institute of Fitness and Sports. Housing for law students is available for single and married students in university-owned housing, but is in short supply. Most students live in off-campus apartments.

Calendar

The law school operates on a traditional semester basis. Courses for full-time students are offered days only and must be completed within 66 months. For part-time students, courses are offered evenings only and must be completed within 66 months. New full-time students are admitted in the fall; part-time, fall. There is an 8-week summer session. Transferable summer courses are offered.

Programs

In addition to the J.D., the law school offers the LL.B. The following joint degrees may be earned: J.D./M.B.A. (Juris Doctor/Master of Business Administration), J.D./M.P.A. (Juris Doctor/Master of Public Affairs), J.D./M.H.A. (Juris Doctor/Master of Health Administration), and J.D./M.P.H. (Juris Doctor/Master of Public Health).

Phone: 317-274-2459
Fax: 317-274-3955
E-mail: khmiller@iupui.edu
Web: iulaw.indy.indiana.edu

Contact

Karen Miller, Admissions Coordinator, 317-274-2459 for general inquiries; Jim Schutter, Graduate School, 317-278-4723 for financial aid information.

INDIANA

Required

To earn the J.D., candidates must complete 90 total credits, of which 37 are for required courses. They must maintain a minimum GPA of 2.3 in the required courses. The following first-year courses are required of all students: Civil Procedure I and II, Contracts I and II, Legal Writing I and II, Property I and II, Torts I and II, and Criminal Law. Required upper-level courses consist of Constitutional Law I and Professional Responsibility. The required orientation program for first-year students is 2 days in the fall, which covers case briefing, outlining, library use, and basic computer use.

Electives

The Indiana University School of Law-Indianapolis offers concentrations in corporate law, criminal law, international law, litigation, and tax law. Halfway through their studies, students may take clinics in Civil Practice, Disability, and Criminal Defense. Clients are represented by students under the supervision of faculty. Seminars are available for 2 credits in areas such as evidence, agricultural law, and American legal history. Internships for students are offered in banking (trust division); commercial, environmental, immigration, international, and local government law; with the federal court; with the Indiana Civil Liberties Union; with a public defender; and for noncredit opportunities. Credit varies from none to 2 hours. A special lecture series is active at the law school with various speakers and topics of interest. Study abroad is available through the Annual Summer China and France programs as well as the International Human Rights program. Tutorial assistance is offered through the Dean's Tutorial Society, led by students, and the Tutorial Study group, led by a faculty member. There is a summer program for first-year students prior to fall classes. A Minority Law Day is held for prospective students. Indiana CLEO is available for under represented groups in the legal profession. Special interest group programs are Law and Medicine and the Colloquium on Environmental Law. The most widely taken electives are Environmental Law and Family Law.

Graduation Requirements

In order to graduate, candidates must have a GPA of 2.3 and have completed the upper-division writing requirement.

Organizations

Students edit the *Indiana Law Review*, the *Indiana International and Comparative Law Review*, and the student newspaper, *The Dictum*. Moot court teams are sent annually to the ABA-National Appellate Advocacy Competition, the Privacy Competition in Chicago, Illinois, and the Philip C. Jessup Internaional Law Competition. Teams also compete in the Client Counseling Competition. Law student organizations include the Black Law Students Association, Women's Caucus, and Phi Alpha Delta. Other organizations include the Health Law Society, the Law and Technology Association, and the Wendell Wilkie International Law Society.

Library

The law library contains 491,716 hardcopy volumes and 657,798 microform volume equivalents, and subscribes to 6994 serial publications. Such on-line databases and networks as LEXIS and WESTLAW are available to law students for research. Special library collections include United States government and United Nations publications. The ratio of library volumes to faculty is 9756 to 1 and to students, 500 to 1. The ratio of seats in the library to students is 1 to 1.

Faculty

The law school has 42 full-time and 37 part-time faculty members, of whom 25 are women. According to AAUP standards for Category IIA institutions, faculty salaries are above average. About 39% of full-time faculty have a graduate law degree in addition to the J.D.; about 16% of part-time faculty have one. The ratio of full-time students to full-time faculty in an average class is 16 to 1; in a clinic, 10 to 1. The law school has a regular program of bringing visiting professors and other distinguished lecturers and visitors to campus.

Placement

J.D.s awarded:	243
Services available through: separate law school placement center	
Services: mock interviews and a 24-hour resume service	
Special features: panel discussions on alternative and nontraditional careers. The "A Day in the Life" series highlights the judiciary, corporate law, clerkships, and public interest careers, among others.	
Full-time job interviews:	44 employers
Summer job interviews:	n/av
Placement by graduation:	65% of class
Placement within 9 months:	92% of class
Average starting salary:	$24,000 to $60,000
Areas of placement:	
unknown	63%
Business/industry	16%
Government	12%
Judicial Clerkships	4%
Public Interest	3%
Academic	2%

Students

About 45% of the student body are women; 13%, minorities; 4%, African American; 1%, Asian American; 1%, Hispanic; and 1%, Native American. The majority of students come from Indiana (80%). The average age of entering students is 27; age range is 21 to 53. About 25% of students enter directly from undergraduate school, 14% have a graduate degree, and 74% have worked full-time prior to entering law school. About 10% drop out after the first year for academic or personal reasons; 90% remain to receive a law degree.

INDIANA UNIVERSITY/BLOOMINGTON

School of Law

211 S. Indiana Avenue
Bloomington, IN 47405-1001

Application Filing		Accreditation
Fall: open		ABA, AALS
Spring: n/app		**Degrees Granted**
Fee: $35		J.D., LL.M., M.C.L., S.J.D.

Enrollment 1998–1999		First-Year Class	
Men:	388 63%	Applied:	1493
Women:	224 43%	Accepted:	692
Minorities:	122 20%	Enrolled:	203
Out-of-State:	269 44%		

1998–99 Class Profile
LSAT Percentile: 84%
LSAT Median Score: 160
Percentage passing bar on first try: 91%

Tuition and Fees:

Resident
$7210

Average (public)
$8,772

Average (private)
$19,562

Nonresident
$17,928

Average (public)
$14,629

Average (private)
$19,562

Percentage receiving financial aid: 40%

ADMISSIONS

In the fall 1999 first-year class, 1493 applied, 692 were accepted, and 203 enrolled. Nineteen transfers enrolled. The median LSAT percentile of the most recent first-year class was 84; the median GPA was 3.4 on a scale of 4.0. The highest LSAT percentile was 99.

Requirements
Applicants must have a bachelor's degree from an accredited institution and take the LSAT. The most important admission factors include academic achievement, GPA, and undergraduate curriculum. No specific undergraduate courses are required. Candidates are not interviewed.

Procedure
The application deadline for fall entry is open. Applicants should submit an application form, LSAT results, transcripts, a nonrefundable application fee of $35, and a personal statement (recommended). Notification of the admission decision is beginning of December, prior to matriculation. The latest acceptable LSAT test

date for fall entry is February; June also acceptable. The law school uses the LSDAS.

Special
The law school recruits minority and disadvantaged students by recruiting at minority colleges and universities in major urban areas; by hosting a Minority Law Day for interested students and prelaw advisers, and by providing fellowships. Transfer students must have one year of credit, have attended an ABA-approved law school, have a superior law school record, have credentials comparable to the class into which they wish to transfer (in terms of LSAT score and GPA), and provide reasons for transfer. Space availabilty is also a factor in the acceptance decision.

Costs

Tuition and fees for the 1999-2000 academic year are $7210 for full-time in-state students and $17,928 for out-of-state students. On-campus room and board costs about $6150 annually; and books and supplies run $1045.

Financial Aid

In a recent year, about 40% of law students received some form of aid. The average annual amount of aid from all sources combined, including scholarships, loans, and work contracts, was $17,453; maximum, $30,926. Awards are based on need and merit. The required financial statement is FAFSA. Check with the school for the current aid application deadline. Special funds for minority or disadvantaged students include Education Opportunity Fellowships and Graduate Minority Fellowships (through the University's Research and Graduate School). First-year students are notified about their financial aid application beginning mid-March for scholarships; summer for loan packages.

About the Law School

Indiana University/Bloomington School of Law was established in 1842 and is a public institution. The 1855-acre campus is in a small town 50 miles south of Indianapolis. The primary mission of the law school is to prepare graduates for the many roles lawyers may play throughout the world; to stress the development and discipline of analytical reasoning, clear writing skills, and a deep understanding

of the basic principles of a variety of substantive areas of the law; to prepare global professionals for leadership roles in the 21st century. Students have access to federal, state, county, city, and local agencies, courts, correctional facilities, law firms, and legal aid organizations in the Bloomington area. The school has been completely remodeled, including classrooms; trial and appellate courtrooms; a new student lounge and canteen; offices for student groups; and a computer center and laptop room, both of which are located in the law library. On-campus graduate student housing is available in several units (total: approximately 395,338 square feet); off-campus housing options include apartments, condominiums, and houses for rent throughout the community. All law school facilities are accessible to the physically disabled.

Calendar

The law school operates on a traditional semester basis. Courses for full-time students are offered days only and must be completed within 3 years. There is no part-time program. New full-time students are admitted in the fall and summer. There are several summer sessions. Transferable summer courses are offered.

Programs

In addition to the J.D., the law school offers the LL.M, M.C.L., and S.J.D. Students may take relevant courses in other programs and apply credit toward the J.D.; a maximum of 6 credits may be applied. The following joint degrees may be earned: J.D./M.B.A. (Juris Doctor/Master of Business Administration), J.D./M.P.A. (Juris Doctor/Master of Public Affairs), J.D./M.S.E.S. (Juris Doctor/Master of Science in Enviromental Science), J.D./M.L.S. (Juris Doctor/Master of Library Science), and J.D./M.A. or J.D./M.S. (Juris Doctor/Master of Arts or Juris Doctor/Master of Science in telecommunications).

Required
To earn the J.D., candidates must complete 86 total credits, of which 36 are for required courses. They must maintain a minimum GPA of 2.3 in the required courses. The following first-year courses are required of all students: Criminal Law, Civil Procedure I and II, Contracts I and II, Torts, Property, Constitutional

Phone: 812-855-4765
Fax: 812-855-0555
E-mail: lawadmis@indiana.edu
Web: www.law.indiana.edu

Contact
Patricia Clark, Director of Admissions, 812-855-4765 for general inquiries; Patricia S. Clark, Admissions Coordinator, 812-855-2704 for financial aid information.

Law I, and Legal Research and Writing I and II. Students are not required to take clinical courses at this time. The school holds a required 2-day orientation program immediately preceding the beginning of classes. Law School policies and procedures, academic regulations, course requirements, and special services (career planning, educational assistance) are discussed.

Electives
The School of Law offers concentrations in corporate law, criminal law, entertainment, environmental law, family law, international law, juvenile law, labor law, litigation, maritime law, media law, securities law, sports law, tax law, torts and insurance, communications law, and law and society. Clinics include the Community Legal Clinic, which assists area residents with family law issues; the Child Advocacy Clinic, which provides students with for-credit legal experiences in pending custody, visitation, and guardianship cases; and the Federal Courts Clinic, in which students work with a federal judge in Indianapolis for one day each week and receive academic credit. Each year the school offers 10 to 14 seminars that involve intensive analysis of one or more legal issues and submission of a substantive research paper. Internships are available in all 3 years of law study with a variety of public agencies, non-profit organizations, and public interest groups, and may be arranged for credit. Students must demonstrate proficiency in legal research and writing by the execution of a complex research project involving problem definition, research, and completion of a substantial written product. Credit ranges from 1 to 3 credits. Second- and third-year students may arrange supervised clinical projects under the direction of a faculty member who specializes in the relevant area of law. A number of prominent judges and lawyers visit the school each year, including Chief Justice Rehnquist and Judge Ginsberg. The School participates in a consortium that holds a semester-long program in London each spring. All first-year students take small group instruction in a year-long course designed to teach students to research and write about legal issues. Remedial programs include a voluntary Educational Assistance Program. The school hosts a Minority Law Day each year for prospective students and prelaw advisers and participates in the state bar Minority

Clerkship Program and in the state-run Legal Education Opportunities Program. Special interest group programs include the Jurist-in-Residence and Practitioner-in-Residence programs. The most widely taken electives are Business, communications/intellectual property, and environmental law.

Graduation Requirements
In order to graduate, candidates must have a GPA of 2.3 and have completed the upper-division writing requirement. Students must be in residence in an approved law school for 6 semesters of full-time study.

Organizations
Students edit the *Indiana Law Journal*, *Federal Communications Law Journal*, and the *Indiana Journal of Global Legal Studies*. Annual competitions include the ABA National Appellate Advocacy Competition, Jessup International Competition, the Trial Practice Competition, and the Negotiations Competition. The school hosts its own internal Sherman Minton Moot Court Competition. Law student organizations include the Moot Court Board, Black Law Students Association, and Christian Legal Society. There are local chapters of Delta Theta Phi, Phi Alpha Delta, and Phi Delta Phi.

Library
The law library contains 591,504 hardcopy volumes and 1,138,543 microform volume equivalents, and subscribes to 7584 serial publications. Such on-line databases and networks as LEXIS, DIALOG, WESTLAW, and NEXIS, OCLC, GPO Access, and the Internet are available to law students for research. The law library is a depository for records and briefs of the U.S. Supreme Court, Indiana Court of Appeals, Indiana Supreme Court, and Seventh Circuit Court of Appeals; a selective depository for U.S. government publications; and houses a rare books and archives collection. The library recently added a laptop room where students can bring their own laptops and connect to the university's network. Network cards may be checked out for students who need them. The ratio of library volumes to faculty is 18,485 to 1 and to students, 911 to 1. The ratio of seats in the library to students is 1 to 1.

Placement

J.D.s awarded:	215

Services available through: A separate law school placement center.
Services: job fairs and career planning seminars, videotaped mock interview program, minority clerkship program
Special features: office staffed by two experienced attorneys; extensive resource collection and handout series on career options and job search strategies; an alumni career network; weekly career seminars; and an employer visitation program

Full-time job interviews:	n/av
Summer job interviews:	117 employers
Placement by graduation:	65% of class
Placement within 9 months:	96% of class
Average starting salary:	$19,000 to $185,000

Areas of placement:
Private practice 2-10 attorneys	19%
Private practice 11-25 attorneys	5%
Private practice 26-50 attorneys	9%
Private practice 51-100 attorneys	9%
Private practice 101-250 attorneys	6%
Government	12%
Unknown	12%
Business/industry	11%
Judicial clerkships	9%
Public interest	5%
Academic	3%

Faculty
The law school has 38 full-time and 16 part-time faculty members, of whom 17 are women. According to AAUP standards for Category I institutions, faculty salaries are average. About 41% of full-time faculty have a graduate law degree in addition to the J.D.; about 13% of part-time faculty have one. The ratio of full-time students to full-time faculty in an average class is 18 to 1; in a clinic, 5 to 1. There is a chapter of the Order of the Coif; 16 faculty are members.

Students
About 43% of the student body are women; 20%, minorities; 8%, African American; 5%, Asian American; and 4%, Hispanic. The majority of students come from Indiana (56%). The average age of entering students is 24; age range is 18 to 52. About 50% of students enter directly from undergraduate school, 10% have a graduate degree, and 50% have worked full-time prior to entering law school. About 3% drop out after the first year for academic or personal reasons; 97% remain to receive a law degree.

INTER-AMERICAN UNIVERSITY OF PUERTO RICO

School of Law

P.O. Box 70351
San Juan, PR 00936-8351

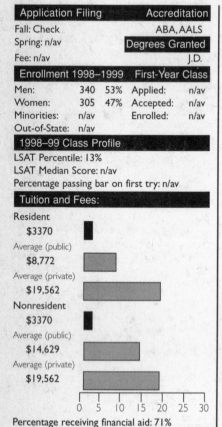

Application Filing	Accreditation
Fall: Check	ABA, AALS
Spring: n/av	**Degrees Granted**
Fee: n/av	J.D.

Enrollment 1998–1999		First-Year Class	
Men:	340 53%	Applied:	n/av
Women:	305 47%	Accepted:	n/av
Minorities:	n/av	Enrolled:	n/av
Out-of-State:	n/av		

1998–99 Class Profile
LSAT Percentile: 13%
LSAT Median Score: n/av
Percentage passing bar on first try: n/av

Tuition and Fees:

Resident
$3370

Average (public)
$8,772

Average (private)
$19,562

Nonresident
$3370

Average (public)
$14,629

Average (private)
$19,562

0   5   10   15   20   25   30

Percentage receiving financial aid: 71%

ADMISSIONS

Information in the above capsule is approximate. Twelve transfers enrolled in a recent year. The median LSAT percentile of the most recent first-year class was 13; the median GPA was 3.1 on a scale of 4.0. The lowest LSAT percentile accepted was 2; the highest was 86.

Requirements

Applicants must have a bachelor's degree from an accredited institution and take the LSAT. Minimum acceptable LSAT score is 130 and minimum acceptable GPA is 2.5 on a scale of 4.0. No specific undergraduate courses are required.

Procedure

Check with the school for current application deadlines and fees. Applicants should submit an application form, LSAT results, transcripts, PAEG scores, and have a proficiency in Spanish. Accepted students must pay a $25 seat deposit. Notification of the admission decision is by May 20. The latest acceptable LSAT test date for fall entry is February.

Special

Requirements are different for out-of-state students in that foreign students are required to submit evidence of their authorization to study in Puerto Rico, as well as the documents required by the Immigration and Naturalization Office of the U.S. Department of Justice. Transfer students must have a minimum GPA of 2.5, and have attended an ABA-approved law school. They are admitted for fall, spring, or summer session. The school offers a compulsory 3-week summer preparation course for students admitted to the J.D. program.

Costs

Tuition and fees for the 1999-2000 academic year are $3370 for all full-time students. Tuition for part-time students is $2710 annually. Books and supplies run $600.

Financial Aid

About 71% of current law students received some form of aid in a recent y[ear. The average annual amount of aid from all sources combined, including scholarships, loans, and work contracts, was $8466. Awards are based on need and merit. The required financial statement is FAFSA. First-year students are notified about their financial aid application at the time of acceptance.

About the Law School

Inter-American University of Puerto Rico School of Law was established in 1961 and is a private institution. The campus is in an urban area in metropolitan San Juan. The primary mission of the law school is to train professionals competent for public and private practice through a broad background in the history and development of the law, particularly how it affects contemporary Puerto Rican legal issues and institutions; and also to promote legal research and continued legal education of its alumni and others in the legal profession. Students have access to federal, state, county, city, and local agencies, courts, correctional facilities, law firms, and legal aid organizations in the San Juan area. The school's location grants students access to additional resources such as the University of Puerto Rico Law School and the Puerto Rico Bar Association. Facilities of special interest to law students are the moot court room and law library. Housing for law students is available in the neighborhood for those students who reside outside the metropolitan area. The school does not provide housing facilities.

Calendar

The law school operates on a traditional semester basis. Courses for full-time students are offered both day and evening and must be completed within 3 to 6 years. For part-time students, courses are offered both day and evening and must be completed within 4 to 8 years. New full-and part-time students are admitted in the fall. There is a summer session.

Phone: 809-751-1912, ext. 2013

Contact

Lilia Oquendo, Esq. Dean of Students, 787-751-1912, ext. 2011 for general inquiries; Aida M. Gonzalez Veve, Director of Financial Aid, 787- 751-1912, ext. 2014 for financial aid information.

PUERTO RICO

Programs

Required

To earn the J.D., candidates must complete 92 total credits, of which 62 are for required courses. They must maintain a minimum GPA of 2.0 in the required courses. The following first-year courses are required of all students: Introduction to Law, Research Analysis and Writing, Family Law, Criminal Law, Property Law, Constitutional Law I, General Theory of Obligations and Contracts, and Criminal Procedure. Required upper-level courses consist of Constitutional Law II, History of Puerto Rican Law, Administrative Law, Civil Procedure - Successions, Evidence, Torts, Ethics of the Legal Professional, Mortgage Law, and Litigation: Theory, Doctrine, and Practice. All students must take clinical courses. The required orientation program for first-year students is a summer introductory course and a program during the week preceding the fall semester.

Electives

The Legal Aid Clinic involves students in offering legal advice, handling cases before courts and administrative agencies, and drafting legal documents for 4 credits. Seminars provide in-depth study in various areas of law and are worth 3 credits each. The most widely taken electives are Labor Law, Employment Law, Commercial Law, Corporate Law, Federal Jurisdiction, and Notarial Practice.

Graduation Requirements

In order to graduate, candidates must have a GPA of 2.0 and have completed the upper-division writing requirement.

Organizations

The primary law review is the *Revista Juridica de la Universidad Interamerica de Puerto Rico*, which is edited by students, professors, and scholars. The student newspaper is the *Student Council Bulletin*. Other publications include *AD REM*. Student council members serve on law school committees. There are local chapters of the ABA-Law Student Division, National Law Students Association, Phi Alpha Delta-Luis Munoz Morales chapter, and the National Hispanic Bar Association - Law Student Division. Other organizations include the Students' Cooperative Bookstore.

Library

The law library contains 160,098 hardcopy volumes and 139,963 microform volume equivalents, and subscribes to 2329 serial publications. Such on-line databases and networks as LEXIS the Internet, LIBIS (the university's library), and MICROJURIS (Puerto Rican Law Data Base) are available to law students for research. Special library collections include Domingo Toledo Alamo, Jose Ramon Velez Torres, and Hipolito Marcano. Also, 3 private collections of civil law books include rare books. Recently, the library had main library services that were fully computerized (circulation, acquisition, and an on-line catalog with bilingual subject headings—English and Spanish) and a new building was constructed. The ratio of library volumes to faculty is 4447 to 1 and to students, 270 to 1. The ratio of seats in the library to students is 1 to 2.

Faculty

The law school has 20 full-time and 16 part-time faculty members, of whom 11 are women. About 70% of full-time faculty have a graduate law degree in addition to the J.D.; about 37% of part-time faculty have one. The ratio of full-time students to full-time faculty in an average class is 13 to 1; in a clinic, 4 to 1.

Students

About 47% of the student body are women. The average age of entering students is 24; age range is 21 to 50. About 90% of students enter directly from undergraduate school and 10% have a graduate degree. About 8% drop out after the first year for academic or personal reasons; 92% remain to receive a law degree.

Placement	
J.D.s awarded:	n/av
Services available through:	Office of the Dean of Students
Full-time job interviews:	n/av
Summer job interviews:	n/av
Placement by graduation:	n/av
Placement within 9 months:	n/av
Average starting salary:	n/av
Areas of placement:	n/av

Inter-American University of Puerto Rico   **273**

JOHN MARSHALL LAW SCHOOL

315 South Plymouth Court
Chicago, IL 60604

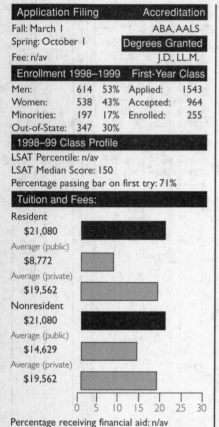

Application Filing	Accreditation
Fall: March 1	ABA, AALS
Spring: October 1	**Degrees Granted**
Fee: n/av	J.D., LL.M.

Enrollment 1998–1999		First-Year Class	
Men:	614 53%	Applied:	1543
Women:	538 43%	Accepted:	964
Minorities:	197 17%	Enrolled:	255
Out-of-State:	347 30%		

1998–99 Class Profile
LSAT Percentile: n/av
LSAT Median Score: 150
Percentage passing bar on first try: 71%

Tuition and Fees:

Resident
$21,080

Average (public)
$8,772

Average (private)
$19,562

Nonresident
$21,080

Average (public)
$14,629

Average (private)
$19,562

0 5 10 15 20 25 30

Percentage receiving financial aid: n/av

ADMISSIONS

In the fall 1999 first-year class, 1543 applied, 964 were accepted, and 255 enrolled. Fifteen transfers enrolled. The median GPA of the most recent first-year class was 3.4 on a scale of 4.0.

Requirements

Applicants must have a bachelor's degree from an accredited institution and take the LSAT. The most important admission factors include character, personality, GPA, and LSAT results. No specific undergraduate courses are required. Candidates are not interviewed.

Procedure

The application deadline for fall entry is March 1. Applicants should submit an application form, TOEFL or TWE if applicable, a nonrefundable application fee, 2 to 3 letters of recommendation, and LSDAS report. Notification of the admission decision is 2 to 5 weeks after the file is complete. The latest acceptable LSAT test date for fall entry is June. The law school uses the LSDAS.

Special

Transfer students must have a minimum GPA of 2.5 and have attended an ABA-approved law school.

Costs

Tuition and fees for the 1999-2000 academic year are $21,080 for all full-time students. Tuition for all part-time students is $700 per credit. Books and supplies run $770.

Financial Aid

In a recent year, The maximum annual amount of aid from all sources combined, including scholarships, loans, and work contracts, was $31,338. Awards are based on need and merit. The required financial statement is FAFSA. Check with the school for current application deadline. First-year students are notified about their financial aid application at the time of acceptance.

About the Law School

John Marshall Law School was established in 1899. The campus is in an urban area in Chicago. The primary mission of the law school is to provide students with an intellectually challenging foundation in legal principles and a rigorous background in lawyering skills. Students have access to federal, state, county, city, and local agencies, courts, correctional facilities, law firms, and legal aid organizations in the Chicago area. Housing for law students is readily available and assistance is provided through the admissions office. All law school facilities are accessible to the physically disabled.

Calendar

The law school operates on a traditional semester basis. Courses for full-time students are offered both day and evening and must be completed within 5 years. For part-time students, courses are offered both day and evening and Saturdays and must be completed within 6 years. New full-and part-time students are admitted in the fall and spring. There is an 8-week summer session. Transferable summer courses are offered.

Programs

In addition to the J.D., the law school offers the LL.M and LL.M. in intellectual property, taxation, and real estate. The following joint degrees may be earned: J.D./M.B.A. (Juris Doctor/Master of Business Administration).

Phone: 312-987-1406
537-4280
Fax: 312-427-5136
E-mail: admission@jmls.edu
Web: www.jmls.edu

Contact
Admissions and Student Affairs, 312-987-1406 for general inquiries; Susan Bogart, Assistant Director, 312-427-2737, ext. 510 for financial aid information.

ILLINOIS

Required
To earn the J.D., candidates must complete 90 total credits, of which 52 are for required courses. They must maintain a minimum GPA of 2.0 in the required courses. The following first-year courses are required of all students: Contracts I and II, Property I and II, Criminal Law, Torts I and II, Civil Procedure I and II, Lawyering Skills I and II, and Constitutional Law I and II. Required upper-level courses consist of Evidence, Trial Advocacy, and Lawyering Skills III and IV. All students must take clinical courses. The required orientation program for first-year students is 1 day for day students and 2 evenings for evening students entering with the August class, and 2 evenings for day and evening students entering with the January class.

Electives
The John Marshall Law School offers concentrations in international law, tax law, and advocacy and dispute resolution, business, estate planning, general practice, informatics, intellectual property, and real estate. In addition, clinics are open to students with at least 53 hours and prior approval. Clinics offer from 1 to 3 credits and are with the Chicago Corporation Counsel, Fair Housing, Legal Aid Bureau, Illinois Attorney General, intellectual property law, judicial and legislative clerkships, Legal Aid Bureau, Public Defender, State's Attorney of Cook County, Travelers and Immigrants Aid, and the U.S. Attorney, Northern District of Illinois. Seminars are worth 2 to 3 credits, and are in the areas of banking, business planning, computers, constitutional law, counseling and negotiating, estate planning, information law, rights of prisoners, scientific evidence, intellectual property, taxation, and trial advocacy. Research programs, worth 1 to 2 credits, are open to students who have at least 59 hours. A scholarly paper must be produced from research supervised by a faculty member. Special interest groups are the Center for Informatics Law, Center for Intellectual Property Law, Center for Forensic Science, Fair Housing Legal Support Center, and the International Law Program. The most widely taken electives are Corporations, Remedies, and Negotiable Instruments.

Graduation Requirements
In order to graduate, candidates must have a GPA of 2.0, completed the upper-division writing requirement, and have completed 4 semesters of Lawyering Skills.

Organizations
Student-edited publications are *The John Marshall Law Review*, the *Journal of Computer and Informtion Law*, and the student newspaper *Decisive Utterance*. Teams are sent annually to more than 20 interscholastic moot court competitions. Law student organizations include the Student Bar Association, Illinois State Bar Association-Law Student Division, and ABA-Law Student Division.

Library
The law library contains 353,737 hardcopy volumes and 55,710 microform volume equivalents, and subscribes to 5011 serial publications. Such on-line databases and networks as LEXIS, DIALOG, WESTLAW, and NEXIS, CCALI, InfoTrac, Wilsondisc, OCLC, and DOLLY, the school's on-line catalog are available to law students for research. Special library collections include a U.S. goverment documents depository. The ratio of library volumes to faculty is 6317 to 1 and to students, 326 to 1. The ratio of seats in the library to students is 1 to 2.

Faculty
The law school has 56 full-time and 138 part-time faculty members, of whom 43 are women. About 25% of full-time faculty have a graduate law degree in addition to the J.D. The ratio of full-time students to full-time faculty in an average class is 23 to 1.

Students
About 43% of the student body are women; 17%, minorities; 6%, African American; 5%, Asian American; 5%, Hispanic; and 1%, Native American. The majority of students come from Illinois (70%). The average age of entering students is 25; age range is 20 to 69. About 14% of students have a graduate degree and 40% have worked full-time prior to entering law school. About 5% drop out after the first year for academic or personal reasons.

Placement	
J.D.s awarded:	313
Services available through: a separate law school placement center.	
Services:	
Special features: the Law Practice Management Program, an 8-week course offered free to recent graduates interested in starting their own practice	
Full-time job interviews:	35 employers
Summer job interviews:	35 employers
Placement by graduation:	52% of class
Placement within 9 months:	90% of class
Average starting salary:	$48,900
Areas of placement:	
Private practice 2-10 attorneys	23%
Private practice 11-25 attorneys	7%
Private practice 26-50 attorneys	6%
Private practice 51-100 attorneys	4%
Private practice 100+ attorneys; 6%	
unknown	6%
Business/industry	21%
Government	12%
Judicial clerkships	4%
Public interest	1%

LEWIS AND CLARK COLLEGE

Northwestern School of Law

10015 Southwest Terwilliger Boulevard
Portland, OR 97219

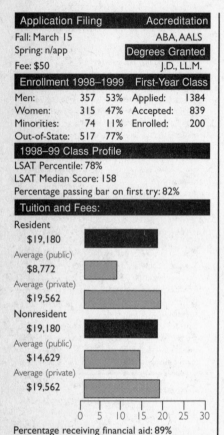

Application Filing	Accreditation
Fall: March 15	ABA, AALS
Spring: n/app	**Degrees Granted**
Fee: $50	J.D., LL.M.

Enrollment 1998–1999		First-Year Class	
Men:	357 53%	Applied:	1384
Women:	315 47%	Accepted:	839
Minorities:	74 11%	Enrolled:	200
Out-of-State:	517 77%		

1998–99 Class Profile
LSAT Percentile: 78%
LSAT Median Score: 158
Percentage passing bar on first try: 82%

Tuition and Fees:

Resident
$19,180

Average (public)
$8,772

Average (private)
$19,562

Nonresident
$19,180

Average (public)
$14,629

Average (private)
$19,562

0 5 10 15 20 25 30

Percentage receiving financial aid: 89%

ADMISSIONS

In the fall 1999 first-year class, 1384 applied, 839 were accepted, and 200 enrolled. Ten transfers enrolled. The median LSAT percentile of the most recent first-year class was 78; the median GPA was 3.2 on a scale of 4.0. The lowest LSAT percentile accepted was 21; the highest was 99.

Requirements

Applicants must have a bachelor's degree from an accredited institution and take the LSAT. The most important admission factors include LSAT results, GPA, and writing ability. No specific undergraduate courses are required. Candidates are not interviewed.

Procedure

The application deadline for fall entry is March 15. Applicants should submit an application form, LSAT results, transcripts, a nonrefundable application fee of $50, 1 or 2 letters of recommendation, an essay, an LSDAS report of undergrad-

uate work, and optional statements on extracurricular activities or special circumstances the committee might want to consider in evaluating the candidate. Notification of the admission decision is on a rolling basis. The latest acceptable LSAT test date for fall entry is June. The law school uses the LSDAS.

Special

The law school recruits minority and disadvantaged students by having law school representatives visit undergraduate institutions with significant ethnic enrollment, by offering special scholarships, and by inviting prelaw advisers from undergraduate schools with large ethnic minority populations to visit the campus. Transfer students must have one year of credit, have attended an ABA-approved law school, and have achieved strong academic standing at the school from which the student is transferring, and present a compelling reason for wishing to transfer to Lewis and Clark.

Costs

Tuition and fees for the 1999-2000 academic year are $19,180 for all full-time students. Tuition for part-time students is $14,386 per year. Books and supplies run $800.

Financial Aid

About 89% of current law students receive some form of aid. The average annual amount of aid from all sources combined, including scholarships, loans, and work contracts, is $22,590; maximum, $31,845. Awards are based on need and merit. The required financial statement is the FAFSA. The aid application deadline for fall entry is March 1. Special funds for minority or disadvantaged students consist of scholarship monies from the school, Oregon State Bar funds for ethnic minorities, scholarships funded by the Oregon Law Foundation, and a special Native American Scholarship funded by the Quinnault tribe. First-year students are notified about their financial aid application at time of acceptance.

About the Law School

Lewis and Clark College Northwestern School of Law was established in 1884

and is a private institution. The 31-acre campus is in a suburban area within Portland. The primary mission of the law school is to train and educate about the law and about being ethical, well-rounded professionals. The school also strives to advance the knowledge, skills, and professionalism of legal practitioners. Students have access to federal, state, county, city, and local agencies, courts, correctional facilities, law firms, and legal aid organizations in the Portland area. The American Inns of Court, clinical internship seminars, externships, and the Oregon student appearance rule, which allows students to appear in court, are available to students. Facilities of special interest to law students include a 600-acre wilderness park, which borders the campus, and the undergraduate school, which has indoor and outdoor pools, a gymnasium, tennis and racquetball courts, and weight-lifting equipment. Housing for law students consists of a wide variety of off-campus apartments and houses that students share at reasonable rents. All law school facilities are accessible to the physically disabled.

Calendar

The law school operates on a traditional semester basis. Courses for full-time students are offered both day and evening and must be completed within 5 years. For part-time students, courses are offered both day and evening and must be completed within 6 years. New full- and part-time students are admitted in the fall. There are two 5-week summer sessions.

Programs

In addition to the J.D., the law school offers the LL.M.

Required

To earn the J.D., candidates must complete 86 total credits, of which 28 to 35 are for required courses. They must maintain a minimum GPA of 1.7 in first-year courses. The following first-year courses are required of all students: Criminal Law (full-time students), Civil Procedure, Contracts, Property, Torts, Legal Analysis and Writing, and Constitutional Law I. Required upper-level courses consist of Constitutional Law II, Seminar, Professionalism, and Criminal

Phone: 503-768-6613
800-303-4860
Fax: 503-768-6671
E-mail: lawadmss@lclark.edu
Web: http://www.lclark.edu/law

Contact

Emily Allen, Director of Admissions, 503-768-6613 for general inquiries; Marsha Webber, Assistant Director of Financial Services, 503-768-7097 for financial aid information.

OREGON

Law (part-time students). All students must take clinical courses. The required orientation program for first-year students is a two-day program consisting of student registration on the first day and legal analysis introduction on the second day.

Electives

The Northwestern School of Law offers concentrations in corporate law, criminal law, environmental law, family law, international law, labor law, litigation, tax law, torts and insurance, intellectual property, and employment law. In addition, the law school operates a clinic in downtown Portland. The clinic serves indigent clients and performs civil work. It is available to all upper-division students; qualified students may make court appearances. Seminars are available in a variety of subjects, ranging from environmental crimes to sex and the law. Seminars are limited to 20 students and usually require a paper. Each upper-division student must take 1 seminar to graduate. A 3-hour seminar is offered in conjunction with a 10-hour per week placement in the areas of criminal law, natural resources, and legal services for the disabled. The school also offers full-semester externships, which require a substantial paper in addition to working full time in an approved placement with significant faculty supervision. Students may work as research assistants to faculty members, write for the law review, and perform independent research projects for credit with faculty. Full-semester externships around the country and abroad are also available to students. One summer program includes a course taught at a wildlife refuge. The Higgins Visitor consists of a 2-week long visit from a distinguished attorney or professor who lectures in classes and to the school at large, and who meets with students in small groups. The school also invites a distinguished visitor in the area of natural resources. There are also faculty colloquia and speakers invited by various student groups. An academic support program that focuses on study skills and group support is available to first-year ethnic minority students and to any upper-division student in academic difficulty. The school actively recruits ethnic minority candidates. An academic support program offers students the opportunity to begin the first year of school 1

week early, take a miniclass, and learn about exams and study skills. This is followed by seminars and workshops during the academic year. The most widely taken electives are environmental, intellectual property, and business/corporate law.

Graduation Requirements

In order to graduate, candidates must have a GPA of 2.0 in upper-division courses and have completed the upper-division writing requirement.

Organizations

The primary law review is *Environmental Law*. Other student-edited publications include the *Journal of Small and Emerging Business Law, International Legal Perspectives*, and *Animal Law*. Moot court competitions consist of appellate advocacy, regional appellate advocacy, and client counseling. A writing competition for the best paper in the area of international law is sponsored by the law firm of Ragen, Davis, and Wright. Law student organizations include Student Bar Association, Environmental Law Caucus, and National Lawyers Guild. There are local chapters of ABA-Law Student Division, Phi Delta Phi, and International Law Society. The Softball Commission and various intramural sports are among the campus clubs and organizations.

Library

The law library contains 451,706 hardcopy volumes and 254,548 microform volume equivalents, and subscribes to 4873 serial publications. Such on-line databases and networks as LEXIS, WESTLAW, First Search, the Internet, Congressional Universe Innovative, CCH Online, Quicklaw LegalTrac, and BNA Environment Library are available to law students for research. Special library collections include the Milton Pearl Environmental Law Collection, the Tax/Estate Planning Collection, the Federal Patent and Trademark Depository Library, and the Samuel Johnson Public Land Law Review collection. Recently, the library added 76 networked study seats. The ratio of library volumes to faculty is 11,568 to 1 and to students, 580 to 1. The ratio of seats in the library to students is 1 to 3.

Placement

J.D.s awarded:	217

Services available through: a separate law school placement center

Services: extensive resource library, 2 mentor programs, a video mock interview program, a monthly jobs newsletter, a comprehensive web site with links, an on-campus interview program, and a public interest/pro bono honors program

Special features: information panels given by alumni and other Portland practitioners, a public-interest career information fair, monthly breakfasts with attorneys, clerking opportunities available throughout the year in Portland, an alumni network around the country, and law firm receptions for first-year students

Full-time job interviews:	15 employers
Summer job interviews:	37 employers
Placement by graduation:	40% of class
Placement within 9 months:	91% of class
Average starting salary:	$35,000 to $50,000

Areas of placement:

Private practice 2-10 attorneys	18%
Private practice 11-25 attorneys	6%
Private practice 26-50 attorneys	3%
Private practice 51-100 attorneys	3%
Business/industry	20%
Government	17%
Judicial clerkships	12%
Public interest	5%
Academic	2%

Faculty

The law school has 37 full-time and 54 part-time faculty members, of whom 27 are women. According to AAUP standards for Category IIB institutions, faculty salaries are well above average. About 26% of full-time faculty have a graduate law degree in addition to the J.D. The ratio of full-time students to full-time faculty in an average class is 14 to 1; in a clinic, 10 to 1.

Students

About 47% of the student body are women; 11%, minorities; 1%, African American; 5%, Asian American; 3%, Hispanic; 2%, Native American; and 4%, international students. The average age of entering students is 25; age range is 20 to 55. About 14% drop out after the first year for academic or personal reasons; 86% remain to receive a law degree.

Paul M. Hebert Law Center

Baton Rouge, LA 70803

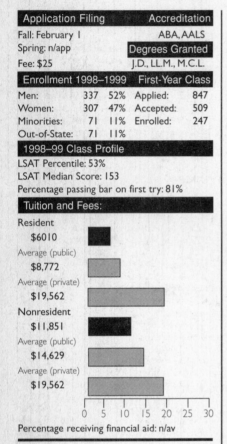

Application Filing	Accreditation
Fall: February 1	ABA, AALS
Spring: n/app	**Degrees Granted**
Fee: $25	J.D., LL.M., M.C.L.

Enrollment 1998–1999			First-Year Class	
Men:	337	52%	Applied:	847
Women:	307	47%	Accepted:	509
Minorities:	71	11%	Enrolled:	247
Out-of-State:	71	11%		

1998–99 Class Profile
LSAT Percentile: 53%
LSAT Median Score: 153
Percentage passing bar on first try: 81%

Tuition and Fees:

Resident
$6010

Average (public)
$8,772

Average (private)
$19,562

Nonresident
$11,851

Average (public)
$14,629

Average (private)
$19,562

0 5 10 15 20 25 30

Percentage receiving financial aid: n/av

ADMISSIONS

In the fall 1999 first-year class, 847 applied, 509 were accepted, and 247 enrolled. One transfer enrolled. The median LSAT percentile of the most recent first-year class was 53; the median GPA was 3.3 on a scale of 4.0. The lowest LSAT percentile accepted was 6; the highest was 98.

Requirements
Applicants must have a bachelor's degree from an accredited institution and take the LSAT. The most important admission factors include academic achievement and LSAT results. No specific undergraduate courses are required. Candidates are not interviewed.

Procedure
The application deadline for fall entry is February 1. Applicants should submit an application form, LSAT results, transcripts, a nonrefundable application fee of $25, and a $500 seat deposit credited toward tuition. Notification of the admission decision is on a rolling basis. The latest acceptable LSAT test date for fall entry is February. The law school uses the LSDAS.

Special
The law school recruits minority and disadvantaged students by means of an active recruiting program that identifies students through test scores and information received through the Law Services Candidate Referral Program. Requirements are different for out-of-state students in that credentials are usually higher than for in-state applicants, due to a 10% limit on out-of-state students. Transfer students must have one year of credit, have attended an ABA-approved law school, and have reasons for seeking a transfer, and provide information on their overall first-year academic performance.

Costs

Tuition and fees for the 1999-2000 academic year are $6010 for full-time in-state students and $11,851 for out-of-state students. On-campus room and board costs about $5500 annually and books and supplies run $500.

Financial Aid

The required financial statement is FFS. The aid application deadline for fall entry is April 1. First-year students are notified about their financial aid application shortly after applying.

About the Law School

Louisiana State University Paul M. Hebert Law Center was established in 1906 and is a public institution. The campus is in an urban area in Baton Rouge. The primary mission of the law school is to develop to the highest level the intellectual and professional capabilities of Louisiana citizens through resident instruction while enriching instruction and establishing new frontiers of knowledge through research and scholarly activity. Students have access to federal, state, county, city, and local agencies, courts, correctional facilities, law firms, and legal aid organizations in the Baton Rouge area. Legislative and executive branches of state government are also accessible to students. Housing for law students is available in residence hall accommodations, as well as rooms and apartments in privately-owned facilities and university facilities.

Calendar

The law school operates on a traditional semester basis. Courses for full-time students are offered days only and must be completed within 4 years. There is no part-time program. New full-time students are admitted in the fall. There is a 7-week summer session. Transferable summer courses are offered.

Programs

In addition to the J.D., the law school offers the LL.M and M.C.L. Students may take relevant courses in other programs and apply credit toward the J.D.; a maximum of 9 hours of credit may be applied. The following joint degree may be earned: M.P.A./J.D. (Master of Public Administration/Juris Doctor).

Phone: 225-388-8646
Fax: 225-388-8647
E-mail: bloup@lsu.edu
Web: law.lsu.edu

Contact

Associate Director of Admissions, 225-388-8646 for general inquiries; Kathy Sciacchetano, Director, 225-388-3103 for financial aid information.

LOUISIANA

Required

To earn the J.D., candidates must complete 97 total credits, of which 39 are for required courses. They must have a minimum of 55 course credits in the required courses. The following first-year courses are required of all students: Administration of Criminal Justice I, Civil Law Property, Contracts, Louisiana Civil Law System, Basic Civil Procedure I, Constitutional Law I, Criminal Law, Legal Writing and Research, Torts, Obligations, and Basic Civil Procedure II. Required upper-level courses consist of Legal Professions, Evidence, Appellate Advocacy, and Trial Advocacy. All students must take clinical courses. The required orientation program for first-year students provides some 2 hours with students and about 1 hour with faculty.

Electives

The Paul M. Hebert Law Center offers concentrations in corporate law, criminal law, environmental law, family law, international law, juvenile law, labor law, litigation, maritime law, media law, securities law, tax law, and torts and insurance. In addition, third-year students may take clinical courses in preparing for trials and oral arguments, generally worth 2 credits. Seminars are offered for 2 hours of credit. Special lecture series are the Edward Douglass White Lectures, the James J. Bailey Lectures, and the John H. Tucker, Jr. Lectures. Students may study for 6 weeks during the summer in Aix-en-Provence, France. Freshman tutorial programs are available. Minority students may take advantage of the summer conditional admit program. Students must pass the program to enroll in the fall semester.

Graduation Requirements

In order to graduate, candidates must have an average of 68 and complete the upper-division writing requirement by taking a seminar in which they must submit a paper.

Organizations

Students edit the *Louisiana Law Review* and the student newspaper *Civilian*. Moot court competitions include the Tullis Moot Court at the law center and at the regional and national Jessup Moot Court and National Moot Court competitions. Teams also participate in the F. Lee Bailey, Frederick Douglass, and Entertainment Law moot courts, and the American Trial Lawyers and Louisiana State Bar Association, Young Lawyers Division, Mock Trial competitions. Law student organizations include the Student Bar Association, Flory Trial Club, and the Moot Court Board.

Library

The law library contains 402,195 hardcopy volumes and 887,946 microform volume equivalents, and subscribes to 3001 serial publications. Such on-line databases and networks as LEXIS, DIALOG, WESTLAW, and NEXIS, OCLC, ONLINE public access catalog, and the Internet are available to law students for research. Special library collections include a U.S. government document depository, a depository for Louisiana Supreme Court and Court of Appeals briefs and records, and international, comparative, and foreign law collections, which include Roman law. Recently, the library updated 3 computer laboratories. The ratio of library volumes to faculty is 12,974 to 1 and to students, 629 to 1. The ratio of seats in the library to students is 1 to 1.

Faculty

The law school has 31 full-time and 40 part-time faculty members, of whom 7 are women. About 29% of full-time faculty have a graduate law degree in addition to the J.D.; about 28% of part-time faculty have one. The ratio of full-time students to full-time faculty in an average class is 60 to 1; in a clinic, 20 to 1. There is a chapter of the Order of the Coif.

Placement

J.D.s awarded:	172
Services available through: a separate law school placement center.	
Special features: resume quick check, mock interviews for students, individual counseling, guest speakers, and special programs.	
Full-time job interviews:	43 employers
Summer job interviews:	65 employers
Placement by graduation:	69% of class
Placement within 9 months:	85% of class
Average starting salary: $23,000 to $100,000	
Areas of placement:	
Private practice 2-10 attorneys	24%
Private pracice 11-25 attorneys	20%
Private practice 26-50 attorneys	7%
Private practice 51-100 attorneys	7%
Private practice 101-500 attorneys	5%
Private Practice - solo	2%
Judicial clerkships	23%
Government	7%
Business/industry	3%
Academic	1%
Military	1%

Students

About 47% of the student body are women; 11%, minorities; 9%, African American; 1%, Asian American; and 1%, Hispanic. The majority of students come from Louisiana (89%). The average age of entering students is 24; age range is 20 to 50. About 25% drop out after the first year for academic or personal reasons; 75% remain to receive a law degree.

Loyola Law School

919 S. Albany Street
Los Angeles, CA 90015

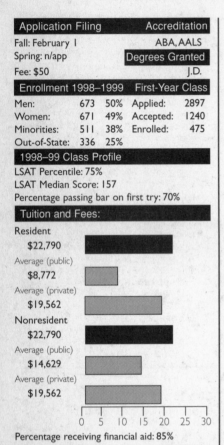

Application Filing		Accreditation
Fall: February 1		ABA, AALS
Spring: n/app		Degrees Granted
Fee: $50		J.D.

Enrollment 1998–1999		First-Year Class	
Men:	673 50%	Applied:	2897
Women:	671 49%	Accepted:	1240
Minorities:	511 38%	Enrolled:	475
Out-of-State:	336 25%		

1998–99 Class Profile

LSAT Percentile: 75%
LSAT Median Score: 157
Percentage passing bar on first try: 70%

Tuition and Fees:

Resident
$22,790

Average (public)
$8,772

Average (private)
$19,562

Nonresident
$22,790

Average (public)
$14,629

Average (private)
$19,562

0 5 10 15 20 25 30

Percentage receiving financial aid: 85%

ADMISSIONS

In the fall 1999 first-year class, 2897 applied, 1240 were accepted, and 475 enrolled. Twenty-one transfers enrolled. The median LSAT percentile of the most recent first-year class was 75; the median GPA was 3.28 on a scale of 4.0. The lowest LSAT percentile accepted was 30; the highest was 99.

Requirements
Applicants must have a bachelor's degree from an accredited institution and take the LSAT. The most important admission factors include academic achievement, LSAT results, and general background. No specific undergraduate courses are required. Candidates are not interviewed.

Procedure
The application deadline for fall entry is February 1. Applicants should submit an application form, TOEFL (where applicable), a nonrefundable application fee of $50, 1 letter of recommendation, and a personal statement. Notification of the admission decision is December through June. The latest acceptable LSAT test date for fall entry is February. The law school uses the LSDAS.

Special
The law school recruits minority and disadvantaged students with programs such as the Open House, campus visits by faculty, and financial support for outstanding minority applicants. Additionally, there is a Summer Institute program for students who need additional preparation prior to law school. Transfer students must have one year of credit, have attended an ABA-approved law school, and have above average performance at the prior law school.

Costs

Tuition and fees for the 1999-2000 academic year are $22,790 for all full-time students. Tuition for all part-time students is $15,250 per year. Books and supplies run $620.

Financial Aid

About 85% of current law students receive some form of aid. The average annual amount of aid from all sources combined, including scholarships, loans, and work contracts, is $27,860; maximum, $36,235. Awards are based on need and merit. The required financial statement is FAFSA. The aid application deadline for fall entry is March 2. Special funds for minority or disadvantaged students consist of scholarships. First-year students are notified about their financial aid application at time of acceptance.

About the Law School

Loyola Marymount University Loyola Law School was established in 1920 and is a private institution. The 2.5-acre campus is in an urban area ½ mile west

of downtown Los Angeles. The primary mission of the law school is to educate men and women who will be leaders of both the legal profession and society, demonstrating in their practice of law and public service the highest standards of personal integrity, professional ethics, and a deep concern for social justice in the Jesuit Marymount tradition. Students have access to federal, state, county, city, and local agencies, courts, correctional facilities, law firms, and legal aid organizations in the Los Angeles area. Facilities of special interest to law students are the federal and municipal courts that are the regional head offices of major law firms and companies that comprise the financial center of the Pacific Rim countries. Housing for law students is not available on campus, but there is a housing referral service. All law school facilities are accessible to the physically disabled.

Calendar

The law school operates on a traditional semester basis. Courses for full- and part-time students are offered both day and evening and must be completed within 5 years. New full- and part-time students are admitted in the fall. There is a 7-week summer session. Transferable summer courses are offered.

Programs

Students may take relevant courses in other programs and apply credit toward the J.D.; a maximum of 6 credits may be applied. The following joint degrees may be earned: J.D./M.B.A. (Juris Doctor/Master of Business Administration).

Required
To earn the J.D., candidates must complete 87 total credits, of which 49 are for required courses. They must maintain a minimum grade average of 60 in the required courses. The following first-year courses are required of all students: Criminal Law, Civil Procedure, Constitutional Law I, Contracts, Legal Research and Writing, Property, and Torts. Required upper-level courses consist of Constitutional Law II, Ethical Lawyering, Evidence, and a writing course. The required orientation program for first-year students is 3 to 4 days.

Phone: 213-736-1180
E-mail: admissions@lls.edu
Web: www.lls.edu

Contact

Carmen Ramirez, Associate Director for Admissions, 213-736-1180 for general inquiries; John Hoyt, Director of Financial Aid, 212-736-1140 for financial aid information.

CALIFORNIA

Placement

J.D.s awarded:	405

Services available through: a separate law school placement center.

Services: information on practice areas, computer-assisted job search, and on-campus interview programs

Special features: numerous workshops and panel discussions, an extensive resource library, special programs for students interested in pursuing government or public interest careers, and programs promoting issues of diversity and minority recruitment and hiring.

Full-time job interviews:	67 employers
Summer job interviews:	74 employers
Placement by graduation:	62% of class
Placement within 9 months:	91% of class
Average starting salary:	$40,000 to $83,000

Areas of placement:

Private practice 2-10 attorneys	14%
Private practice 11-25 attorneys	9%
Private practice 26-50 attorneys	12%
Private practice 51-100	15%
Business/industry	22%
Government	10%
Unknown	8%
Academic	4%
Judicial clerkships	3%
Public interest	3%

Electives

The Loyola Law School offers concentrations in corporate law, criminal law, entertainment, environmental law, family law, international law, juvenile law, labor law, litigation, maritime law, media law, securities law, sports law, tax law, and torts and insurance. In addition, clinics are open to advanced students in good academic standing for a maximum of 14 clinical credits. Seminars and research programs are open to advanced students; these students are also eligible for internships, field work, and study-abroad programs. Seminars are generally worth 2 units each. The Fritz B. Burns Lecture Series brings nationally known legal scholars to the law school for debate and discourse. The law school offers 3 study abroad programs: Costa Rica (worth 4 units); Bologna, Italy (worth 2 to 4 units); and Beijing China (worth 3 units). Tutorials are available to students with academic need. The most widely taken electives are Copyright Law, Sports Law, and Marital Property.

Graduation Requirements

In order to graduate, candidates must have a grade average of 74.5, have completed the upper-division writing requirement, and 58 resident credits in addition to 40 hours of community service work.

Organizations

The primary student-edited law review is *Loyola of Los Angeles Law Review*. Other student-edited law reviews are the *Loyola of Los Angeles International and Comparative Law Review*, the *Loyola Entertainment Law Review*, and the student newspaper *The Loyola Reporter*. Annual moot court competitions include the Jessup, National, and Traynor competitions. Other competitions include the Byrne Trial Advocacy Competition, which includes on- and off-campus competitions in the fall and spring, the Black Law Students Association (BLSA) Moot Court Competition, the Hispanic National Bar Association (HWBA) Moot Court Competition, the White Collar Crime Competition, and the Patent Law Competition. Law student organizations include the Entertainment and Sports Law Society, the Criminal Law Society, and the St. Thomas Moore Honor Society. Local

chapters of national associations include Amnesty International, National Lawyers Guild, and Public Interest Law Association. Campus clubs and other organizations include the women's Law Association, the Asian Pacific American Law Students Association (APALSA), and the Corporate and Business Law Association.

Library

The law library contains 486,509 hardcopy volumes and 1,238,076 microform volume equivalents, and subscribes to 6992 serial publications. Such on-line databases and networks as LEXIS, WESTLAW, and Congressional Masterfile I and II, Congressional Universe, Dow Jones, State Net, RLIN, ORION, CALI, and LUCY (the library's on-line catalog) are available to law students for research. Special library collections include federal and state depositories and foreign collections of selected European, Latin American, and Pacific Rim countries. A complete U.S. legislative history from 1970 to the present includes all available records and briefs of the U.S. Supreme Court. There is also a complete collection of United Nations documents, law and popular culture, and a CBS News O.J. Simpson archive. Recently, the library was renovated and expanded. The renovated library features generous study carrels with electrical outlets, comfortable lounge seating, 24 group study rooms and 6 multi-media rooms. The library's Computer Resource Center offers 89 workstations and 461 Internet accessible ports throughout the library for laptop computer connections. The ratio of library volumes to faculty is 6482 to 1 and to students, 341 to 1. The ratio of seats in the library to students is 1 to 2.

Faculty

The law school has 63 full-time and 79 part-time faculty members, of whom 51 are women. According to AAUP standards for Category IIA institutions, faculty salaries are well above average. About 10% of full-time faculty have a graduate law degree in addition to the J.D.; about 1% of part-time faculty have one. The ratio of full-time students to full-time faculty in an average class is 21

to 1; in a clinic, 7 to 1. The law school has a regular program of bringing visiting professors and other distinguished lecturers and visitors to campus. There is a chapter of the Order of the Coif; 32 faculty and 420 graduates are members.

Students

About 49% of the student body are women; 38%, minorities; 4%, African American; 21%, Asian American; 12%, Hispanic; and 1%, Native American. The majority of students come from the West (75%). The average age of entering students is 24; age range is 20 to 55. About 50% of students enter directly from undergraduate school, 15% have a graduate degree, and 30% have worked full-time prior to entering law school. About 3% drop out after the first year for academic or personal reasons; 97% remain to receive a law degree.

School of Law

7214 St. Charles Avenue
New Orleans, LA 70118

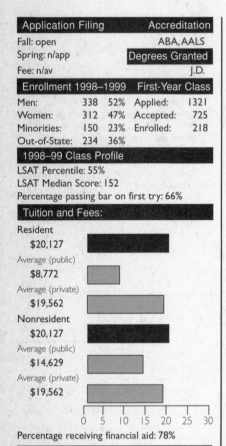

Application Filing		Accreditation
Fall: open		ABA, AALS
Spring: n/app		Degrees Granted
Fee: n/av		J.D.

Enrollment 1998–1999		First-Year Class	
Men:	338 52%	Applied:	1321
Women:	312 47%	Accepted:	725
Minorities:	150 23%	Enrolled:	218
Out-of-State:	234 36%		

1998–99 Class Profile

LSAT Percentile: 55%
LSAT Median Score: 152
Percentage passing bar on first try: 66%

Tuition and Fees:

Resident
$20,127

Average (public)
$8,772

Average (private)
$19,562

Nonresident
$20,127

Average (public)
$14,629

Average (private)
$19,562

0 5 10 15 20 25 30

Percentage receiving financial aid: 78%

ADMISSIONS

In the fall 1999 first-year class, 1321 applied, 725 were accepted, and 218 enrolled. Fifteen transfers enrolled. The median LSAT percentile of the most recent first-year class was 55; the median GPA was 2.95 on a scale of 4.0. The lowest LSAT percentile accepted was 15; the highest was 94.

Requirements

Applicants must take the LSAT. The most important admission factors include LSAT results, academic achievement, and GPA. No specific undergraduate courses are required. Candidates are interviewed.

Procedure

The application deadline for fall entry is open. Check with the school for current fee. Applicants should submit an application form, LSAT results, transcripts, LSDAS report, a non-refundable application fee, 3 letters of recommendation (suggested, but not required), and a per-

sonal statement (suggested, but not required). Notification of the admission decision is 4 to 6 weeks after the file is completed. The latest acceptable LSAT test date for fall entry is generally February. The law school uses the LSDAS.

Special

The law school recruits minority and disadvantaged students through alumni involvement, recruitment at institutions with traditionally minority-dominated enrollment, the use of CLEO, and the Black Law Students Association and Spanish-American Law Student Association. Transfer students must have one year of credit, have attended an ABA-approved law school, and have entering LSAT and undergraduate GPA eligible for acceptance at Loyola and above average law school GPA.

Costs

Tuition and fees for the 1999-2000 academic year are $20,127 for all full-time students. Tuition for all part-time students is $13,777 per year or $635 per credit. On-campus room and board costs about $8325 annually; and books and supplies run $800.

Financial Aid

In a recent year, about 78% of current law students received some form of aid. The average annual amount of aid from all sources combined, including scholarships, loans, and work contracts, was $19,833; maximum, $29,200. Awards are based on need and merit. The required financial statement is FAFSA. Check with the school for current application deadlines. Special funds for minority or disadvantaged students consist of scholarships and grants based on academic merit alone. First-year students are notified about their financial aid application at time of acceptance.

About the Law School

Loyola University - New Orleans School of Law was established in 1914 and is a private institution. The 4.2-acre campus is in an urban area. The primary mission of the law school is to educate future members of the bar to be skilled advocates and sensitive counselors-at-law committed to ethical standards in pursuit of human dignity for all. Students have access to federal, state, county, city,

and local agencies, courts, correctional facilities, law firms, and legal aid organizations in the New Orleans area. Facilities of special interest to law students include the U.S. Court of Appeals for the Fifth Circuit, the Supreme Court of the State of Louisiana, and the U.S. Court for the Eastern District of Louisiana. Housing for law students is available in a dorm located directly across the street from the law school building; there is no married student housing on campus. All law school facilities are accessible to the physically disabled.

Calendar

The law school operates on a traditional semester basis. Required courses for full-time students are offered day only; electives, day and evening and must be completed within 5 years. For part-time students, required courses are offered, evening only; electives, day and evening and must be completed within 5 years. New full-and part-time students are admitted in the fall. There is an 8- week summer session. Transferable summer courses are offered.

Programs

Students may take relevant courses in other programs and apply credit toward the J.D.; a maximum of 9 credits may be applied. The following joint degrees may be earned: J.D./M.A. (Juris Doctor/Master of Arts in communications), J.D./M.A. (Juris Doctor/Master of Arts in religious studies), J.D./M.P.A. (Juris Doctor/Master of Public Administration), J.D./M.B.A. (Juris Doctor/Master of Business Administration), and J.D./M.U.R.P. (Juris Doctor/Master of Urban and Regional Planning).

Required

To earn the J.D., candidates must complete 90 total credits. They must maintain a minimum GPA of 2.0 in the required courses. The following first-year courses are required of all students: Contracts I, Civil Procedure I and II, Civil Law of Persons or Common Law Property I, Moot Court, Legal Profession, Conventional Obligations or Contracts II, Torts I and II, Criminal Law, Legal Research and Writing, and Civil Law Property or Common Law Property II. Required upper-level courses consist of Constitutional Law I and II, Successions or Trusts and Estates, Evidence,

Phone: 504-861-5575
Fax: 504-861-5772
E-mail: ladmit@loyno.edu
Web: www.loyno.edu

Contact

K. Michele Allison-Davis, Assistant Dean of Admissions, 504-861-5575 for general inquiries; Wally Boudet, Director of Financial Aid, 504-865-3231 for financial aid information.

LOUISIANA

Business Organizations I and II, Administration of Criminal Justice I, Donations (civil law students only), Sales and Leases or Commercial Transactions, Taxation I, Secured Transactions, Community Property (civil law students only), Law and Poverty, Security Rights or Secured Transactions, and Louisiana Code of Civil Procedure (civil law students only). All students must take clinical courses. The required orientation program for first-year students is held for 2 days prior to the beginning of classes. Students complete requirements for registration, receive welcoming remarks from university officials, meet professors, and meet with upper-level students.

Electives

The School of Law offers concentrations in corporate law, criminal law, family law, international law, litigation, maritime law, tax law, torts and insurance, and civil law, and public interest law. In addition, there are 2 clinics for third-year students who may earn a total of 9 credit hours for 3 semesters (including the summer semester). At the Public Law Center, students participate in legislative and administrative advocacy, and at the Loyola Law Clinic, students participate in a clinical setting, working on both civil and criminal cases. Seminars are offered as part of the regular curriculum. Credit is usually 2 hours. Second- and third-year law students in the upper third of their class may participate in internship programs. Students devote at least 12 hours a week to various assignments for a total of 4 credits earned over 2 semesters. Independent research projects may be undertaken under the supervision of a professor for 1 or 2 credit hours, depending on the project. A Street Law course also is available. Loyola offers several lecture series that promote the legal professions. No credit is given and attendance is voluntary. There are study-abroad programs in Cuernavaca, Mexico; Brazil or Costa Rica; Moscow and St. Petersburg, Russia; Budapest, Hungary; Vienna, Austria; Cape Town, South Africa; and Kyoto, Japan. All programs are open to second- and third-year students who may earn a total of 6 to 8 credits. Second- and third-year students may tutor underclassmen in the Legal Research and Writing and Moot Court programs. The Academic Success Program is maintained for first-year stu-

dents who need assistance with organizing and preparing for classes and exams. Minority grants based on merit are available. The most widely taken electives are Admiralty, Maritime Personal Injury, and Negotiable Instruments.

Graduation Requirements

In order to graduate, candidates must have a GPA of 2.0, have completed the upper-division writing requirement, and have fulfilled the reading requirement by taking 1 of 3 courses that give a philosophical and historical perspective on law.

Organizations

Students edit the *Loyola Law Review*, the *Poverty Law Journal*, and the *Loyola Intellectual Property and High Technology Law Quarterly*. Moot court competitions include the National Moot Court Competition, the William B. Spong Competition at William and Mary Law School, and the Tulane Moot Court Competition at Tulane Law School. Other competitions include the Frederick Douglass Moot Court Competition (participation by the Black Law Students Association) and the Thomas Tang Competition (participation by the Asian Pacific American Law Student Association). Student organizations include the Student Bar Association, Black Law Students Association, and Spanish-American Law Students Association. Delta Theta Phi, Phi Delta Phi, and National Lawyers Guild have local chapters. Other organizations include Communications Law Society, JD/MBA Society, and Loyola Environmental Law Society.

Library

The law library contains 265,089 hardcopy volumes and 570,114 microform volume equivalents, and subscribes to 2543 serial publications. Such on-line databases and networks as LEXIS, DIALOG, WESTLAW, and NEXIS are available to law students for research. Special library collections include French, Quebec, and Scottish law; U.S. government documents and Louisiana state documents; and GATT depository. Recently, the library added CD-ROM to computers. The ratio of library volumes to faculty is 4017 to 1 and to students, 394 to 1. The ratio of seats in the library to students is 1 to 1.

Placement

J.D.s awarded:	194
Services available through: a separate law school placement center and the university placement center.	
Services: such as coordination of speakers for various employment opportunities, a student news and job information monthly newsletter, and a resume bank.	
Full-time job interviews:	70 employers
Summer job interviews:	n/av
Placement by graduation:	94% of class
Placement within 9 months:	93% of class
Average starting salary:	$42,000 to $60,000
Areas of placement:	
Private practice 2-100 attorneys	50%
Judicial clerkships	12%
Unknown	12%
Business/industry	10%
Government	8%
Public interest	7%
Academic	1%

Faculty

The law school has 30 full-time and 36 part-time faculty members, of whom 14 are women. According to AAUP standards for Category IIA institutions, faculty salaries are well above average. About 37% of full-time faculty have a graduate law degree in addition to the J.D.; about 19% of part-time faculty have one. The ratio of full-time students to full-time faculty in an average class is 17 to 1; in a clinic, 10 to 1.

Students

About 47% of the student body are women; 23%, minorities; 11%, African American; 3%, Asian American; 8%, Hispanic; and 1%, Native American. The majority of students come from Louisiana (64%). The average age of entering students is 23; age range is 21 to 55. About 12% drop out after the first year for academic or personal reasons; 88% remain to receive a law degree.

School of Law

One East Pearson Street
Chicago, IL 60611

Application Filing	Accreditation
Fall: April 1	ABA, AALS
Spring: n/app	**Degrees Granted**
Fee: $50	J.D., LL.M., S.J.D., M.J.

Enrollment 1998–1999		First-Year Class	
Men:	300 42%	Applied:	2164
Women:	410 58%	Accepted:	924
Minorities:	107 15%	Enrolled:	231
Out-of-State:	270 38%		

1998–99 Class Profile
LSAT Percentile: 78%
LSAT Median Score: 158
Percentage passing bar on first try: 85%

Tuition and Fees:

Resident
$23,100
Average (public)
$8,772
Average (private)
$19,562
Nonresident
$23,100
Average (public)
$14,629
Average (private)
$19,562

0 5 10 15 20 25 30

Percentage receiving financial aid: 85%

ADMISSIONS

In the fall 1999 first-year class, 2164 applied, 924 were accepted, and 231 enrolled. Four transfers enrolled. The median LSAT percentile of the most recent first-year class was 78; the median GPA was 3.3 on a scale of 4.0. The lowest LSAT percentile accepted was 40; the highest was 98.

Requirements

Applicants must have a bachelor's degree from an accredited institution and take the LSAT. The most important admission factors include academic achievement, GPA, and LSAT results. No specific undergraduate courses are required. Candidates are not interviewed.

Procedure

The application deadline for fall entry is April 1. Applicants should submit an application form, LSAT results, transcripts, a nonrefundable application fee of $50, and 2 academic letters of recommendation. Notification of the admission decision is within 4 weeks. The latest acceptable LSAT test date for fall entry is February. The law school uses the LSDAS.

Special

The law school recruits minority and disadvantaged students national law forums, university-sponsored law days. Transfer students must have one year of credit, have a minimum GPA of 3.0, and have attended an ABA-approved law school.

Costs

Tuition and fees for the 1999-2000 academic year are $23,100 for all full-time students. Tuition for all part-time students is $17,354 annually, or $766 per credit. Books and supplies run $900.

Financial Aid

About 85% of current law students receive some form of aid. The average annual amount of aid from all sources combined, including scholarships, loans, and work contracts, is $25,000; maximum, $37,240. Awards are based on need and merit. The required financial statement is FAFSA. The aid application deadline for fall entry is March 1. Special funds for minority or disadvantaged students consist of 2 renewable full-tuition scholarships and 2 partial tuition scholarships. First-year students are notified about their financial aid application at the time of acceptance. After the March 1 deadline, admitted students are notified of an award 2 to 3 weeks after the school receives results of the FAFSA.

About the Law School

Loyola University Chicago School of Law was established in 1908 and is a private institution. The campus is in an urban area in Chicago. The primary mission of the law school is to encourage the development of a sense of professional responsibility and respect for the judicial process, and an understanding of the social, moral, and ethical values inherent in the practice of law. Students have access to federal, state, county, city, and local agencies, courts, correctional facilities, law firms, and legal aid organizations in the Chicago area. Facilities of special interest to law students consist of the Water Tower campus housing a gymnasium, a cafeteria, coffee shop, and bookstore. Loyola also has a campus in Rome, Italy. The law school is in the heart of Chicago's North Michigan Avenue shopping/tourist district, within blocks of Lake Michigan and cultural attractions including the Museum of Contemporary Art. Apartments are available within walking distance of the

law school and in various Chicago neighborhoods; university apartments are available at the Lake Shore campus. All law school facilities are accessible to the physically disabled.

Calendar

The law school operates on a traditional semester basis. Courses for full-time students are offered both day and evening and must be completed within 4 years. For part-time students, courses are offered both day and evening and must be completed within 6 years. New full- and part-time students are admitted in the fall. There is a summer session. Transferable summer courses are offered.

Programs

In addition to the J.D., the law school offers the LL.M, S.J.D., and M.J. (Master of Jurisprudence in health law, child law, and business law). Students may take relevant courses in other programs and apply credit toward the J.D.; a maximum of 9 credits may be applied. The following joint degrees may be earned: J.D./M.B.A. (Juris Doctor/ Master of Business Administration), J.D./M.S.W. (Juris Doctor/ Master of Social Work), J.D./M.A. (Juris Doctor/ Master of Arts in political science), and JD/M.S.I.R. (Juris Doctor/ Master of Human Resources and Industrial Relations).

Required

To earn the J.D., candidates must complete 86 total credits, of which 46 are for required courses. They must maintain a minimum GPA of 2.0 in the required courses. The following first-year courses are required of all students: Civil Procedure I and II, Contracts, Criminal Law, Constitutional Law I and II, Property I and II, Torts, Legal Research, and Legal Writing I and II. Required upper-level courses consist of Federal Income Tax, Professional Responsibility, Advocacy, and Business Organizations. The required orientation program for first-year students is a 2- to 3-day program that acquaints students with school regulations, facilities, and program requirements; during orientation, a writing evaluation is conducted.

Electives

The School of Law offers concentrations in corporate law, criminal law, family law, international law, juvenile law, labor law, litigation, tax law, and health law, and public interest law. With the exceptions of health law, child law, and tax law, none of

Phone: 312-915-7170
800-545-5744
Fax: 312-915-7201
E-mail: law-admissions@luc.edu
Web: www.luc.edu/schools/law

Contact

Law Admission and Financial Assistance, 312-915-7170 for general inquiries; Michael Minnice, Assistant Director of Financial Assistance, 312-915-7170 for financial aid information.

ILLINOIS

the concentrations is formalized. In addition, clinical legal experience is gained through the Loyola University Community Law Center, where students provide legal assistance to area residents who cannot afford private legal representation. The Federal Tax Clinic is staffed by law students who are trained in tax law and handle a wide range of legal matters related to federal income tax law before the IRS and the Tax Court. The Child Law Clinic has been established for students interested in representing abused or neglected children. Moreover, the Business Law Clinic offers legal representation at low cost to small businesses and community-based organizations. Seminars, of which there are a variety, are offered for 2 to 3 credit hours. Second- and third-year law students receive 3 hours credit for teaching a course called Street Law in Chicago-area high schools. Law students attend weekly seminars in which they study Illinois law and educational methodology. Externships are available every semester; supervised experience is offered in judicial, criminal, corporate, health law, child law, and or government for 2 or 3 credit hours. Individualized research projects, under the supervision of a faculty member, are available every semester for 1 to 2 hours credit. Special lecture series include the Baker McKenzie Lecture on professionalism, the Wing-Tat Lee Lecture on international and comparative law, the Dooley Lecture on the judiciary, and the Law and Literature Lecture. Study-abroad programs include the Rome Program and the Oxford Program. Rome and Oxford are each 5-week summer programs offering 4 or 5 elective courses for 2 credits each. Loyola's Academic Enhancement Program is conducted during the spring semester. The voluntary program provides extensive tutoring and faculty mentors to students who fall within the lower 20% of the first-year class. The Law Enrichment Program for Minority High School Students allows law students to receive credit for working with high school students with a view to increasing minority enrollment in law schools. The Child Advocacy Program utilizes interdisciplinary instruction and field experience to train students to become child advocates. The Public Interest Law Program provides law students with opportunities to explore public interest law through the legal clinic. The most

widely taken electives are Evidence, Sales, and Secured Transactions.

Graduation Requirements

In order to graduate, candidates must have a GPA of 2.0, have completed the upper-division writing requirement, and 86 hours that fulfill all required courses.

Organizations

Student-edited publications include the *Loyola Law Journal, Loyola Consumer Law Review, Annals of Health Law, Public Interest Law Reporter, Children's Legal Rights Journal, the International Forum,* the newspaper, *Blackacre,* and a weekly SBA newsletter. A bi-weekly newsletter, *The Bulletin,* is published by the law school administration with student assistance. Moot Court competitions include the National Moot Court, Jessup Competition, and Wagner (labor law). Other competitions include the National Mock Trial Competition and the Client Counseling Competition and Negotiations Competition, both sponsored by the ABA. Loyola also participates annually in the Intra-school Moot Court Competition, Chicago Bar, Illinois Bar, Niagara, Sutherland Rich (intellectual property), National Juvenile Law, National Health Law, ABA, Hispanic Bar, Frederick Douglass, and Thomas Tang. Student organizations include the Student Bar Association, Decalogue Society, and National Lawyers Guild. There are local chapters of the Black Law Students Association, American Society of International Law, and Latin American Law Student Association. Other organizations include Health Law Society, Child Law Society, and Phi Alpha Delta Legal Fraternity.

Library

The law library contains 354,981 hardcopy volumes and 942,152 microform volume equivalents, and subscribes to 3389 serial publications. Such on-line databases and networks as LEXIS, DIALOG, and WESTLAW are available to law students for research. Special library collections include a G.P.O. depository, an Illinois depository, and a collection on medical jurisprudence. The ratio of library volumes to faculty is 10,757 to 1 and to students, 502 to 1. The ratio of seats in the library to students is 1 to 2.

Faculty

The law school has 29 full-time and 149 part-time faculty members, of whom 62

Placement

J.D.s awarded:	202

Services available through: a separate law school placement center.

Services: alumni may be contacted through research conducted on Martindale-Hubbell, LEXIS, and WESTLAW.

Special features: mock interviews, minority job fairs, the Patent Law Interview Program, the Midwest Public Interest Law Career Conference, biweekly student newsletter, 3 computer terminals and printer for resume and cover letter production and career research, a Public Service Law Center, and the Public Service Law Network Worldwide Internet database.

Full-time job interviews:	100 employers
Summer job interviews:	200 employers
Placement by graduation:	82% of class
Placement within 9 months:	96% of class
Average starting salary:	$20,000 to $101,000

Areas of placement:

Private practice 2-10 attorneys	10%
Private practice 11-25 attorneys	5%
Private practice 26-50 attorneys	3%
Private practice 51-100 attorneys	2%
Private practice 100+ attorneys	40%
Solo practice	6%
Government	19%
Business/industry	18%
Judicial clerkships	3%
Public interest	2%
Military	1%

are women. According to AAUP standards for Category I institutions, faculty salaries are above average. About 27% of full-time faculty have a graduate law degree in addition to the J.D. The ratio of full-time students to full-time faculty in an average class is 18 to 1; in a clinic, 9 to 1. The law school has a regular program of bringing visiting professors and other distinguished lecturers and visitors to campus.

Students

About 58% of the student body are women; 15%, minorities; 5%, African American; 7%, Asian American; 5%, Hispanic; and 3%, foreign national. The majority of students come from Illinois (62%). The average age of entering students is 25; age range is 22 to 53. About 55% of students enter directly from undergraduate school. About 5% drop out after the first year for academic or personal reasons; 90% remain to receive a law degree.

Law School

Office of Admissions,
Sensenbrenner Hall, P.O. Box 1881
Milwaukee, WI 53201-1881

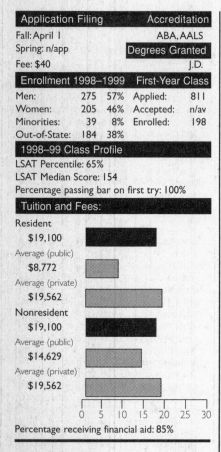

Application Filing		Accreditation	
Fall: April 1		ABA, AALS	
Spring: n/app		**Degrees Granted**	
Fee: $40			J.D.

Enrollment 1998–1999			First-Year Class	
Men:	275	57%	Applied:	811
Women:	205	46%	Accepted:	n/av
Minorities:	39	8%	Enrolled:	198
Out-of-State:	184	38%		

1998–99 Class Profile

LSAT Percentile: 65%

LSAT Median Score: 154

Percentage passing bar on first try: 100%

Tuition and Fees:

Resident
$19,100

Average (public)
$8,772

Average (private)
$19,562

Nonresident
$19,100

Average (public)
$14,629

Average (private)
$19,562

0 5 10 15 20 25 30

Percentage receiving financial aid: 85%

ADMISSIONS

In the fall 1999 first-year class, 811 applied and 198 enrolled. Fifteen transfers enrolled. The median LSAT percentile of the most recent first-year class was 65; the median GPA was 3.1 on a scale of 4.0.

Requirements

Applicants must have a bachelor's degree from an accredited institution and take the LSAT. The most important admission factors include character, personality, GPA, and LSAT results. No specific undergraduate courses are required. Candidates are not interviewed.

Procedure

The application deadline for fall entry is April 1. Applicants should submit an application form, LSAT results, transcripts, TOEFL for students from non-English speaking countries, a nonrefundable application fee of $40, and 1 letter of recommendation. Accepted students must pay a nonrefundable $250 first tuition deposit and a $250 second tuition deposit in June; both are applied to the first semester tuition. Notification of the admission decision is on a rolling basis. The latest acceptable LSAT test date for fall entry is February. The law school uses the LSDAS.

Special

Transfer students must have one year of credit, have attended an ABA-approved law school, and must complete a minimum number of credits at Marquette.

Costs

Tuition and fees for the 1999-2000 academic year are $19,100 for all full-time students. On-campus room and board costs about $7560 annually; and books and supplies run $800.

Financial Aid

About 85% of current law students receive some form of aid. Awards are based on need and merit. The required financial statement is the FAFSA. The aid application deadline for fall entry is April 1. Special funds for minority or disadvantaged students are available. First-year students are notified about their financial aid application at after acceptance but prior to enrollment if financial aid forms were filed in a timely fashion.

About the Law School

Marquette University Law School was established in 1892 and is a private institution. The 80-acre campus is in an urban area adjacent to downtown Milwaukee. The primary mission of the law school is to offer a balanced curriculum noted for its comprehensive teaching of both the theory and practice of law and to instill in students a sense of professional responsibility. (Marquette graduates are admitted to the Wisconsin bar without taking the bar exam.) Students have access to federal, state, county, city, and local agencies, courts, correctional facilities, law firms, and legal aid organizations in the Milwaukee area. The courthouse is 2 blocks away; municipal courts are located 2½ blocks from the school. Facilities of special interest to law students are the Legal Research Center, Sensenbrenner Hall, and fitness and recreation centers. Housing for law students consists of on-campus and campus area apartments; the Office of Residence Life assists students with off-campus accommodations. About 99% of the law school facilities are accessible to the physically disabled.

Calendar

The law school operates on a traditional semester basis. Courses for full-time students are offered both day and evening and must be completed within 5 years. For part-time students, courses are offered both day and evening and must be completed within 6 years. New full- and part-time students are admitted in the fall. There is a summer session. Transferable summer courses are offered.

Programs

Students may take relevant courses in other programs and apply credit toward the J.D. The following joint degrees may be earned: J.D./M.B.A. (Juris Doctor/ Master of Business Administration), J.D./M.A. (Juris Doctor/Master of Arts in political science), J.D./M.A. (Juris Doctor/Master of Arts in international affairs and bioethics).

Contact

Director of Admissions, 414-288-6767 for general inquiries; Office of Student Financial Aid, 414-288-7390 for financial aid information.

WISCONSIN

Required

To earn the J.D., candidates must complete 90 total credits, of which 34 are for required courses. They must maintain a minimum GPA of 2.0 in the required courses. The following first-year courses are required of all students: The Civil Process, Contracts, Property, Torts, Legal Writing, Legal Communication, Constitutional Law, Criminal Law, The Lawyer in American Society, and Process Elective (choice of Administrative Law, Alternative Dispute Resoulution, or Criminal Process). Required upper-level courses consist of a perspectives course, advanced legal communication, a workshop course, and Law and the Ethics of Lawyering. The required orientation program for first-year students is 1 week prior to the start of the semester and includes all aspects of law school. Students meet with professors in small groups; discussions include classes in The Lawyer in American Society.

Electives

The Law School offers concentrations in corporate law, criminal law, environmental law, family law, international law, juvenile law, labor law, litigation, sports law, tax law, torts and insurance, constitutional law, and intellectual property. In addition clinical training is available through the Prosecutor Clinic, Defender Clinic, and Legal Aid Society. Small enrollment courses provide students with an opportunity to work intensely under faculty supervision and are generally worth 2 credits. Internships are available in both appellate and trial courts, including the Wisconsin Supreme Court and the U.S. Court of Appeals for the Seventh Circuit, and with the Municipal Ordinance Defense Clinics. Research programs provide students with an appreciation of the relationship of law to other disciplines and an understanding of the process through which legal doctrine is formed, as well as comparisons of the American legal system with other legal systems. A supervised field-work program provides students with the opportunity to intern with a variety of governmental and public service agencies such as the Equal Employment Opportunity Commission, Internal Revenue Service, Centro Legal, Juvenile Law-Children's Court, and the U.S. Attorney's Office. Study abroad is available through the T.C. Beirne School of Law, the University of Queensland, and the Brisbane (Australia) Program in International, Comparative, and Foreign Law. There is an Academic Support Program for first-year students. The school actively recruits minority students. The most widely taken electives are Trial Advocacy, Criminal Procedure, and Sports Law courses.

Graduation Requirements

In order to graduate, candidates must have a GPA of 2.0 and have completed the upper-division writing requirement.

Organizations

Students edit the *Marquette Law Review, Marquette Sports Law Journal, Marquette Intellectual Property Law Review*, and the *Federation of Insurance and Corporate Counsel Quarterly*. Moot court competitions include patent law, sports law, and intellectual property competitions. National competitions include the National Moot Court, Philip C. Jessup International, Giles Rich Intellectual Property, and Sports Law Moot Court. Law student organizations include the Student Bar Association, Health Law Society, and Environmental Law Society. There are local chapters of Delta Theta Phi, Phi Alpha Delta, and Phi Delta Phi.

Library

The law library subscribes to 3108 serial publications. Such on-line databases and networks as LEXIS, DIALOG, WEST-LAW, and Legal Trac, Marcat, Wiscat, NEXIS, and InfoTrac are available to law students for research. Special library collections include a federal depository. Recently, the library upgraded the computer laboratory. The ratio of library volumes to faculty is 10,273 to 1 and to students, 543 to 1. The ratio of seats in the library to students is 1 to 5.

Placement

J.D.s awarded:	153

Services available through: separate law school placement center.

Services: mock interviews

Special features: personal counseling with students access to a computer and a laser printer in the office to prepare resumes and cover letters, and access to an on-line WESTLAW database of lawyers and judicial clerkships

Full-time job interviews:	n/av
Summer job interviews:	n/av
Placement by graduation:	n/av
Placement within 9 months:	93% of class
Average starting salary:	$25,500 to $90,000

Areas of placement:

Private practice 2-10 attorneys	24%
Private practice 11-25 attorneys	11%
Private practice 26-50 attorneys	7%
Private practice 51-100 attorneys	3%
unknown	23%
Judicial clerkships	10%
Business/industry	10%
Government	8%
Public interest	3%
Academic	1%

Faculty

The law school has 24 full-time and 24 part-time faculty members, of whom 12 are women. According to AAUP standards for Category I institutions, faculty salaries are below average. About 2% of full-time faculty have a graduate law degree in addition to the J.D. The ratio of full-time students to full-time faculty in an average class is 15 to 1. The law school has a regular program of bringing visiting professors and other distinguished lecturers and visitors to campus.

Students

About 46% of the student body are women; 8%, minorities; 3%, African American; 3%, Asian American; and 3%, Hispanic. The majority of students come from Wisconsin (62%). The average age of entering students is 25; age range is 21 to 63. About 62% of students enter directly from undergraduate school, 10% have a graduate degree, and 27% have worked full-time prior to entering law school. About 2% drop out after the first year for academic or personal reasons.

MERCER UNIVERSITY

Walter F. George School of Law

1021 Georgia Ave.
Macon, GA 31201

Application Filing	Accreditation
Fall: March 15	ABA, AALS
Spring: n/app	**Degrees Granted**
Fee: $45	J.D.

Enrollment 1998–1999		First-Year Class	
Men:	214 52%	Applied:	958
Women:	201 49%	Accepted:	470
Minorities:	50 12%	Enrolled:	154
Out-of-State:	208 50%		

1998–99 Class Profile

LSAT Percentile: n/av
LSAT Median Score: 152
Percentage passing bar on first try: 85%

Tuition and Fees:

Resident
$19,250

Average (public)
$8,772

Average (private)
$19,562

Nonresident
$19,250

Average (public)
$14,629

Average (private)
$19,562

0 5 10 15 20 25 30

Percentage receiving financial aid: 85%

ADMISSIONS

In the fall 1999 first-year class, 958 applied, 470 were accepted, and 154 enrolled. Ten transfers enrolled. The median GPA of the most recent first-year class was 3.2. The lowest LSAT percentile accepted was 25; the highest was 75.

Requirements
Applicants must have a bachelor's degree from an accredited institution and take the LSAT. The most important admission factors include LSAT results, academic achievement, and GPA. No specific undergraduate courses are required. Candidates are not interviewed.

Procedure
The application deadline for fall entry is March 15. Applicants should submit an application form, LSAT results, transcripts, a nonrefundable application fee of $45, 2 letters of recommendation, and a personal statement to be used as a writing sample. Notification of the admission decision is on the day of the decision. The latest acceptable LSAT test date for fall entry is February. The law school uses the LSDAS.

Special
The law school recruits minority and disadvantaged students by visiting colleges that are traditionally minority schools and by using the Candidate Referral Service of Law Services to identify qualified minority students. Transfer students must have one year of credit, have attended an ABA-approved law school, be in the top 50% of their class, submit a letter of good standing from their Dean, have 2 letters of recommendation from their professors, subscribe to LSDAS, and submit a current transcript of all law schools atended to Mercer.

Costs

Tuition and fees for the 1999-2000 academic year are $19,250 for all full-time students. On-campus room and board costs about $11,900 annually; books and supplies run $600.

Financial Aid

About 85% of current law students receive some form of aid. The average annual amount of aid from all sources combined, including scholarships, loans, and work contracts, is $28,500; maximum, $31,750. Students are awarded merit scholarships and need- and non-need-based loans. The required financial statements are FAFSA and an institutional application. The aid application deadline for fall entry is April 1. First-year students are notified about their financial aid application at the time of application to law school.

About the Law School

Mercer University Walter F. George School of Law was established in 1873 and is a private institution. The 130-acre campus is in an urban area 80 miles south of Atlanta, Georgia. The educational program is based on a commitment to preparing students for high-quality general practice of law, and to do so in a learning environment that is strongly supportive and consistently professional. Mercer seeks to produce genuinely good lawyers in an ethical as well as a pragmatic sense. Students have access to federal, state, county, city, and local agencies, courts, correctional facilities, law firms, and legal aid organizations in the Macon area. Facilities of special interest to law students include the law school's facility in one of Macon's 6 historical districts. The 3-story building overlooks downtown Macon and was built as a partial replica of Philadelphia's Independence Hall. Housing for law students is available as privately-owned and university-owned apartments within walking distance of the school and multiple apartment complexes throughout the city. All law school facilities are accessible to the physically disabled.

Calendar

The law school operates on a traditional semester basis. Courses for full-time students are offered days only and must be completed within 3 years. For part-time students, courses are offered days only and must be completed within 5 years. New full-and part-time students are admitted in the fall. There is a 7-week summer session. Transferable summer courses are offered.

Programs

The following joint degrees may be earned: J.D./M.B.A. (Juris Doctor/Master of Business Administration).

Phone: 912-301-2605
800-637-2378
Fax: 912-301-2989
E-mail: Sutton_me@mercer.edu
Web: www.Law.Mercer.edu

Contact

Marilyn E. Sutton, Assistant Dean of Admissions and Financial Aid, 912-301-2605 for general inquiries; S. Leigh Love, Director of Financial Aid, 912-301-2064 for financial aid information.

GEORGIA

Required

To earn the J.D., candidates must complete 91 total credits, of which 65 are for required courses. They must maintain a minimum grade average of 76 in the required courses. The following first-year courses are required of all students: Contracts, Criminal Law, Property, Torts, American Constitutional System, Jurisdiction and Judgments, Sales, Statutory Law and Analysis, Legal Writing, and Introduction to Legal Research. Required upper-level courses consist of Civil Lawsuits, Legal Writing II, Income Taxation, Evidence, Remedies, and Law of Lawyering. All students must take clinical courses. The required orientation program for first-year students is a 1-week course, Introduction to Law Study, taught before the start of regular first-year courses. It carries 1 hour of credit, has an exam, and is graded. Additional information is offered in a 2-day session before the start of classes.

Electives

The Walter F. George School of Law offers concentrations in corporate law, criminal law, environmental law, family law, international law, juvenile law, labor law, litigation, media law, securities law, sports law, tax law, and torts and insurance. No concentrations are formally recognized; all areas are offered as electives. In addition, all students must elect at least 1 advanced skills course that simulates law practice tasks. Most students enroll in a trial practice course. Each student must also elect at least 1 seminar in the third year. Approximately 12 seminars are offered each year on a range of subjects from legal ethics to sports law. Supervised internships may be arranged under the Public Interest Practicum Program. Three lecture series bring speakers to the school annually. A limited number of students are selected annually to voluntarily tutor deserving first-year students. A Writing Skills Laboratory, staffed by an attorney with a degree in English, is available to all students on a voluntary basis. Minority programs include a local BLSA chapter and a local Hispanic Students Association. The most widely taken electives are Business Associations, Criminal Procedure, and Decedents' Estates and Trusts.

Graduation Requirements

In order to graduate, candidates must have a grade average of 76 and have completed the upper-division writing requirement.

Organizations

Students edit the *Mercer Law Review*, and the student newspaper, *The Janus Chronicle*. Additional editorial experience may be gained with the *Journal of Southern Legal History*, published by the law school. Competitions include the national Moot Court Competition, Gabrielli National Family Law Competition, and Gibbons National Criminal Procedure Competition. Other competitions include Florida Workers Compensation, Georgian Intrastate Competition, Vale National Corporate Law Competition, National Negotiation Competition, and National Client Counseling Competition. Law student organizations include the ABA-Law Student Division, Association of Women Law Students, and Black Law Students Association. There are local chapters of Phi Alpha Delta and Phi Delta Phi. Other clubs and organizations include Public Interest Law Society, Student Bar Association, and Christian Legal Society.

Library

The law library contains 292,000 hardcopy volumes, and subscribes to 1050 serial publications. Such on-line databases and networks as LEXIS, WESTLAW, NEXIS, CCH Online Tax Service, Congressional Universe, Galileo, and Shepards are available to law students for research. Special library collections include Georgia legal research materials. Recently, the library renovated with new carpeting and paint, and new wiring for laptop computers. The ratio of library volumes to faculty is 8342 to 1 and to students, 720 to 1. The ratio of seats in the library to students is 1 to 1.

Placement

J.D.s awarded:	134
Services available through: a separate law school placement center	
Special features: videotaped practice interviews and critiques, job fairs and consortia, and seminars and educational panels on types of practice and interviewing	
Full-time job interviews:	22 employers
Summer job interviews:	42 employers
Placement by graduation:	52% of class
Placement within 9 months:	90% of class
Average starting salary:	$24,000 to $78,000
Areas of placement:	
Private practice 2-10 attorneys	30%
Private practice 11-25 attorneys	5%
Private practice 26-50 atorneys	5%
Private practice 51-100 attorneys	3%
Private practice 251-500 attorneys	2%
Solo practice	3%
Judicial clerkships	18%
Government	9%
Business/industry	4%
Public interest	3%
Academic	2%

Faculty

The law school has 27 full-time and 27 part-time faculty members, of whom 10 are women. According to AAUP standards for Category IIA institutions, faculty salaries are below average. About 22% of full-time faculty have a graduate law degree in addition to the J.D.; about 18% of part-time faculty have one. The ratio of full-time students to full-time faculty in an average class is 15 to 1. The law school has a regular program of bringing visiting professors and other distinguished lecturers and visitors to campus.

Students

About 49% of the student body are women; 12%, minorities; 7%, African American; 2%, Asian American; 1%, Hispanic; and 1%, Native American. The majority of students come from the South (93%). The average age of entering students is 26; age range is 20 to 50. About 5% drop out after the first year for academic or personal reasons; 95% remain to receive a law degree.

Detroit College of Law

316 Law College Bldg.
East Lansing, MI 48824-1300

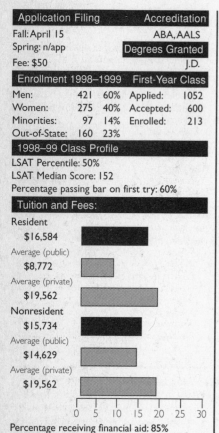

Application Filing	Accreditation
Fall: April 15	ABA, AALS
Spring: n/app	**Degrees Granted**
Fee: $50	J.D.

Enrollment 1998–1999		First-Year Class	
Men:	421 60%	Applied:	1052
Women:	275 40%	Accepted:	600
Minorities:	97 14%	Enrolled:	213
Out-of-State:	160 23%		

1998–99 Class Profile

LSAT Percentile: 50%
LSAT Median Score: 152
Percentage passing bar on first try: 60%

Tuition and Fees:

Resident
$16,584

Average (public)
$8,772

Average (private)
$19,562

Nonresident
$15,734

Average (public)
$14,629

Average (private)
$19,562

Percentage receiving financial aid: 85%

ADMISSIONS

In the fall 1999 first-year class, 1052 applied, 600 were accepted, and 213 enrolled. Thirty-five transfers enrolled. The median LSAT percentile of the most recent first-year class was 50; the median GPA was 3.1 on a scale of 4.0. The lowest LSAT percentile accepted was 20; the highest was 95.

Requirements

Applicants must have a bachelor's degree from an accredited institution and take the LSAT. The most important admission factors include LSAT results, GPA, and academic achievement. No specific undergraduate courses are required. Candidates are interviewed.

Procedure

The application deadline for fall entry is April 15. Applicants should submit an application form, LSAT, ACT, SAT I, GRE, and GMAT scores, and a nonrefundable application fee of $50. Letters of recommendation are recommended but

not required. Accepted students must submit a nonrefundable tuition deposit of $200, which is credited toward tuition. Notification of the admission decision is on a rolling basis, as early as possible after the file is completed. The latest acceptable LSAT test date for fall entry is February. The law school uses the LSDAS.

Special

The law school recruits minority and disadvantaged students by means of conducting special interviews for acceptance purposes, awarding half- and full-tuition scholarships, and sponsoring an annual Minority Recruitment Conference and an Enhance Your Future Conference. Transfer students must have one year of credit, have a minimum GPA of 3.0, have attended an ABA-approved law school, be in good academic standing, and be eligible to return to the law school they currently attend.

Costs

Tuition and fees for the 1999-2000 academic year are $16,584 for new full-time students and $15,734 for returning students. Tuition for new part-time students is $12,452 per academic year and $11,815 for returning students. On-campus room and board costs about $6364 annually; books and supplies run $872.

Financial Aid

About 85% of current law students receive some form of aid. The average annual amount of aid from all sources combined, including scholarships, loans, and work contracts, is $17,433; maximum, $27,160. Awards are based on need and merit. The required financial statement is FAFSA. The aid application deadline for fall entry is July 2. Special funds for minority or disadvantaged students are available on the basis of academic promise as evidenced by LSAT scores and undergraduate curriculum and performance. First-year students are notified about their financial aid application at the time of the application's submission.

About the Law School

Michigan State University Detroit College of Law was established in 1891 and is a private institution. The 5000+ acre

campus is in a suburban area just outside the state capital. The primary mission of the law school is to provide outstanding educational training and opportunities for qualified applicants seeking to enter the legal profession. Students have access to federal, state, county, city, and local agencies, courts, correctional facilities, law firms, and legal aid organizations in the East Lansing area. Through the externship programs, a number of local courts are used officially as training forums for students. Facilities of special interest to law students include the college's expanded operations and law library, classrooms, offices for faculty, administrators and student organizations, study and lounge facilities, the Moot Court, the expanded computer laboratory, and the Career Services Office. Housing for law students is available both on and off campus. On-campus housing includes both residence halls and apartments. All law school facilities are accessible to the physically disabled.

Calendar

The law school operates on a traditional semester basis. Courses for full-time students are offered primarily days and must be completed within 3 years. For part-time students, courses are offered primarily evenings and must be completed within 4 years. New students are admitted in the fall; There is an 8-week summer session. Transferable summer courses are offered.

Programs

Students may take relevant courses in other programs and apply credit toward the J.D.; a maximum of 5 credits may be applied. The following joint degrees may be earned: J.D./M.B.A. (Juris Doctor/Master of Business Administration), J.D./M.P.A. (Juris Doctor/Master of Public Administration), J.D./M.L.R.H.R. (Juris Doctor/Master of Labor Relations & Human Resources), J.D./M.A. (Juris Doctor/Master of Arts), and J.D./M.S. (Juris Doctor/Master of Science).

Required

To earn the J.D., candidates must complete 88 total credits, of which 56 are for required courses. They must maintain a minimum GPA of 2.0 in the required

Phone: 517-432-0222
844-9352
Fax: 517-432-0098
E-mail: heatleya@pilot.msu.edu
Web: www.dcl.edu

Contact

Lorae Hamilton, Assistant Director of Admissions, 517-432-0222 for general inquiries; financial aid officers, 517-432-6810 for financial aid information.

courses. The following first-year courses are required of all students: Contracts I and II, Property, Civil Procedure I and II, Torts, Research, Writing, and Advocacy I and II, Constitutional Law I, and . Required upper-level courses consist of Basic Income Taxation, Decendents' Estates and Trusts, Criminal Law, Constitutional Law II, Corporations, Agency and Partnership, Commercial Transactions, Secured Transactions, Small Business Enterprises, Evidence, and Legal Profession. Clinical courses are electives. The required orientation program for first-year students consists of a social event and 3 days of intensive study in research and writing. Students are taught research skills, use of library techniques, how to brief a case, and how to write an exam. Students receive a reading assignment prior to entry and are expected to be prepared at orientation.

Electives

Students must take 14 in their area of concentration. The Detroit College of Law offers concentrations in international law and tax law. In addition, clinical programs and externships offer students practical experience in criminal and civil law in work environments including the Women's Justice Center, Misdemeanor Defender's Clinic, and Landlord-Tenant Clinic, Wayne County Circuit Court, Juvenile Defender's Office, and federal and local prosecutors' offices. Students may intern as judicial clerks in the federal courts. The Centre for Canadian-United States Law offers courses on Canadian law and Canadian-American relations and sponsors summer internships in Ottawa and Montreal. In the Legal Drafting Program, students prepare legislative documents and develop explanations of their applications. Students combine class participation (civil law topics such as landlord/tenant, housing law, family law, and rights and liberties and consumer law) with performance in local high schools in a course entitled Street Law. There are student-, faculty-, and alumni-sponsored lecture series featuring experts on current matters of law. Students participate in internships in the Houses of Parliament in Ottawa and Montreal and in Cluj, Romania. Students, with permission, are allowed to study abroad through other ABA-

approved law programs. Minorities are active in the Wolverine Student Bar Association and sponsor tutorial programs in regular courses as well as exam-writing techniques. The most widely taken electives are Environmental Law, Immigration Law, and Sports Law.

Graduation Requirements

In order to graduate, candidates must have a GPA of 2.0 and have completed the upper-division writing requirement.

Organizations

Students edit the *Detroit College of Law Review*, the *Journal of International Law and Practice*, the *Entertainment and Sports Law Journal*, and *The Journal of Medicine and Law*. Other student publications are a Sixth Circuit Survey publication and an issue publishing the results of the National Labor Law Writing Competition. The student newspapers are *The Brief Case*, *Eco-Voice on Environmental Law*, and *Res Ipsa Loquitur*. A Moot Court Board offers intramural competitions. The college participates in regional, national, and international moot court competitions, including the National Moot Court, William F. Starr Insurance Law, and Chicago Bar Association Moot Court. Student organizations include the Detroit College of Law Student International Law Society, Environmental Law Society, and Medical-Legal Society.

Library

The law library contains 102,314 hardcopy volumes and 117,794 microform volume equivalents, and subscribes to 2398 serial publications. Such on-line databases and networks as LEXIS, WESTLAW, and the Internet are available to law students for research. Special library collections include international, labor, and taxation; there is a Government Printing Office depository. Recently, the library installed a 24-station computer laboratory on Novell providing access to the Internet, word processing, and other networks, and provided laptop access throughout a brand new law library and building. The ratio of library volumes to faculty is 8127 to 1 and to students, 294 to 1. The ratio of seats in the library to students is 1 to 3.

Placement

J.D.s awarded:	182
Services available through: A separate law school placement center.	
Special features: On-line job listing service, J.D. JobNet	
Full-time job interviews:	13 employers
Summer job interviews:	21 employers
Placement by graduation:	n/av
Placement within 9 months:	86% of class
Average starting salary:	$30,000 to $64,000
Areas of placement:	
Private practice 2-10 attorneys	28%
Private practice 11-25 attorneys	6%
Private practice 26-50 attorneys	2%
Private practice 51-100 attorneys	3%
Private practice 101-500 attorneys	3%
Solo practice	4%
Business/industry	16%
Judicial clerkships	12%
Government	10%
Unknown	10%

Faculty

The law school has 25 full-time and 40 part-time faculty members, of whom 20 are women. According to AAUP standards for Category I institutions, faculty salaries are above average. About 28% of full-time faculty have a graduate law degree in addition to the J.D.; about 20% of part-time faculty have one. The ratio of full-time students to full-time faculty in an average class is 22 to 1.

Students

About 40% of the student body are women; 14%, minorities; 7%, African American; 3%, Asian American; 2%, Hispanic; and 1%, Native American. The majority of students come from Michigan (77%). The average age of entering students is 28; age range is 22 to 51. About 5% of students have a graduate degree.

MISSISSIPPI COLLEGE

School of Law

151 E. Griffith Street
Jackson, MS 39201

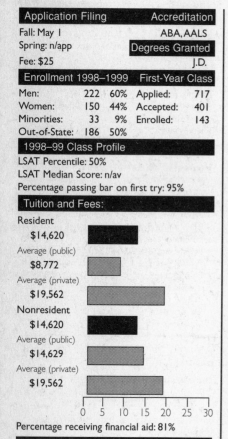

Application Filing		Accreditation
Fall: May 1		ABA, AALS
Spring: n/app		**Degrees Granted**
Fee: $25		J.D.

Enrollment 1998–1999		First-Year Class
Men:	222 60%	Applied: 717
Women:	150 44%	Accepted: 401
Minorities:	33 9%	Enrolled: 143
Out-of-State:	186 50%	

1998–99 Class Profile
LSAT Percentile: 50%
LSAT Median Score: n/av
Percentage passing bar on first try: 95%

Tuition and Fees:

Resident
$14,620
Average (public)
$8,772
Average (private)
$19,562
Nonresident
$14,620
Average (public)
$14,629
Average (private)
$19,562

0   5   10   15   20   25   30

Percentage receiving financial aid: 81%

ADMISSIONS

In the fall 1999 first-year class, 717 applied, 401 were accepted, and 143 enrolled. Two transfers enrolled. The median LSAT percentile of the most recent first-year class was 50; the median GPA was 3.0 on a scale of 4.0. The highest LSAT percentile was 93.

Requirements

Applicants must have a bachelor's degree from an accredited institution and take the LSAT. Minimum acceptable LSAT percentile is 38. The most important admission factors include LSAT results, GPA, and academic achievement. No specific undergraduate courses are required. Candidates are not interviewed.

Procedure

The application deadline for fall entry is May 1. Applicants should submit an application form, LSAT results, transcripts, and a nonrefundable application fee of $25. Notification of the admission decision is on a rolling basis. The latest acceptable LSAT test date for fall entry is February. The law school uses the LSDAS.

Special

The law school recruits minority and disadvantaged students at historically black institutions. Scholarship and stipends are designated for tuition for minority students. Transfer students must have one year of credit, have a minimum GPA of 2.0, have attended an ABA-approved law school, submit an LSDAS report and 2 letters of recommendation from their current law faculty, as well as a letter of good standing from their current law school dean.

Costs

Tuition and fees for the 1999-2000 academic year are $14,620 for all students. Books and supplies run $850.

Financial Aid

About 81% of current law students receive some form of aid. The average annual amount of aid from all sources combined, including scholarships, loans, and work contracts, is $16,000; maximum, $20,938. Awards are based on merit. The required financial statements are GAPSFAS and the college's own. Special funds for minority or disadvantaged students consist of minority scholarships. First-year students are notified about their financial aid application at time of acceptance.

About the Law School

Mississippi College School of Law was established in 1975 and is a private institution. The campus is in an urban area in Jackson. The primary mission of the law school is to impart to its students quality education within the context of a Christian institution and to instill in them the highest degree of professional proficiency and integrity. Students have access to federal, state, county, city, and local agencies, courts, correctional facilities, law firms, and legal aid organizations in the Jackson area. Housing for law students is available off campus. Some on-campus housing at the Clinton campus may be available. All law school facilities are accessible to the physically disabled.

Calendar

The law school operates on a traditional semester basis. Courses for full-time students are offered days only and must be completed within 3 years. There is no part-time program. New full-time students are admitted in the fall. There is a 9-week summer session. Transferable summer courses are offered.

Programs

The following joint degrees may be earned: J.D./M.B.A. (Juris Doctor/Master of Business Administration).

Phone: 601-925-7150
800-738-1236
E-mail: pevans@mc.edu
Web: http:\\www.mc.edu\~ladwww

Contact

Patricia H. Evans, Director of Admissions, 601-925-7150 for general inquiries; Cathy Nash, 601-925-7110 for financial aid information.

MISSISSIPPI

Required

To earn the J.D., candidates must complete 88 total credits, of which 36 are for required courses. They must maintain a minimum GPA of 2.0 in the required courses. The following first-year courses are required of all students: Torts, Contracts I and II, Property I and II, Civil Procedure I and II, Criminal Law, Legal Process, Constitutional Law, and Introduction to Litigation Skills. Required upper-level courses consist of Professional Responsibility and Ethics and a writing requirement. The required orientation program for first-year students is a 3-day program that includes how to brief a case, an introduction to basic legal methods, and the development of the Anglo-American legal system.

Electives

The School of Law offers concentrations in corporate law, litigation, and general and government related areas. In addition, seminars are open to all upper-class students and are usually worth 2 credit hours. The externship program is a small, select program that provides closely supervised externships with legal/judicial offices and governmental agencies; 2 credit hours are generally given. Legal research and writing programs provide an opportunity to work directly with a faculty member on a topic of the student's choice for 2 credit hours. Field work is possible through the extern program, which is open to upper-class students. Placement is with government and nonprofit entities for 1 to 3 hours during a semester to provide hands-on training. A remedial writing workshop is offered to first-year students exhibiting need based upon a written submission; no credit is offered. A 3 credit-hour special interest program, Comparative Legal Systems: Civil Law and Common Law, is offered to students interested in Louisiana law. The most widely taken electives are Trial Practice, Pretrial Practice, and Counseling and Negotiations.

Graduation Requirements

In order to graduate, candidates must have a GPA of 2.0 and have completed the upper-division writing requirement.

Organizations

Students edit the *Mississippi College Law Review* and the student paper, *Legal Eye*. The Moot Court board conducts the Copeland, Cook, and Taylor Moot Court competitions. In spring, the board advises students in Appellate Advocacy I for first-year students. Law student organizations include the Law Student Association, Women's Student Bar Association, and Environmental Club. There are local chapters of Phi Alpha Delta, Delta Theta Phi, and Phi Delta Phi.

Library

The law library contains 253,000 hard-copy volumes and 540,000 microform volume equivalents, and subscribes to 3100 serial publications. Such on-line databases and networks as LEXIS, DIALOG, and WESTLAW are available to law students for research. Special library collections include a partial government printing office depository for U.S. government documents. Recently, the library became a member of CALI and the computer laboratory was made available to students. The ratio of library volumes to faculty is 12,000 to 1 and to students, 513 to 1. The ratio of seats in the library to students is 1 to 1.

Faculty

The law school has 18 full-time and 18 part-time faculty members, of whom 8 are women. About 38% of full-time faculty have a graduate law degree in addition to the J.D. The ratio of full-time students to full-time faculty in an average class is 24 to 1; in a clinic, 24 to 1. The law school has a regular program of bringing visiting professors and other distinguished lecturers and visitors to campus. There is a chapter of the Order of the Coif; 6 faculty are members.

Students

About 44% of the student body are women; 9%, minorities; 9%, African American; 1%, Asian American; and 1%, Hispanic. The majority of students come from Mississippi (50%). The average age of entering students is 26; age range is 21 to 53. About 70% of students enter directly from undergraduate school, 10% have a graduate degree, and 20% have worked full-time prior to entering law school. About 7% drop out after the first year for academic or personal reasons; 93% remain to receive a law degree.

Placement	
J.D.s awarded:	105
Services available through: A separate law school placement center.	
Full-time job interviews:	32 employers
Summer job interviews:	32 employers
Placement by graduation:	63% of class
Placement within 9 months:	90% of class
Average starting salary:	$35,000 to $48,000
Areas of placement:	
Private practice 2-10 attorneys	30%
Private practice 11-25 attorneys	25%
Private practice 26-50 attorneys	10%
Judicial clerkships	20%
Government	10%
Business/industry	2%
Military	1%

NEW ENGLAND SCHOOL OF LAW

154 Stuart Street
Boston, MA 02116

Application Filing		Accreditation
Fall: March 15		ABA, AALS
Spring: n/app		**Degrees Granted**
Fee: $50		J.D.

Enrollment 1998–1999			First-Year Class	
Men:	443	46%	Applied:	2097
Women:	518	54%	Accepted:	1521
Minorities:	163	17%	Enrolled:	337
Out-of-State:	481	50%		

1998–99 Class Profile
LSAT Percentile: n/av
LSAT Median Score: n/av
Percentage passing bar on first try: n/av

Tuition and Fees:

Resident
$16,100

Average (public)
$8,772

Average (private)
$19,562

Nonresident
$16,100

Average (public)
$14,629

Average (private)
$19,562

0 5 10 15 20 25 30

Percentage receiving financial aid: 82%

ADMISSIONS
In the fall 1999 first-year class, 2097 applied, 1521 were accepted, and 337 enrolled. Twenty-six transfers enrolled.

Requirements
Applicants must have a bachelor's degree from an accredited institution and take the LSAT. The most important admission factors include LSAT results, GPA, and motivation. No specific undergraduate courses are required. Candidates are not interviewed.

Procedure
The application deadline for fall entry is March 15. Applicants should submit an application form, LSAT results, transcripts, a nonrefundable application fee of $50, 2 letters of recommendation, a personal statement, and the LSDAS Report. Notification of the admission decision is on a rolling basis. The latest acceptable LSAT test date for fall entry is February. The law school uses the LSDAS.

Special
The law school recruits minority and disadvantaged students by means of attendance at minority recruitment fairs, a Minority Outreach Recruitment Program geared toward institutions with large minority populations, and participation in CLEO and CRS searches. Transfer students must have one year of credit, have a minimum average of C+, and have a dean's letter of good standing.

Costs
Tuition and fees for the 1999-2000 academic year are $16,100 for all full-time students. Tuition for all part-time students is $12,110 per year, or $650 per credit. Books and supplies run $900.

Financial Aid
About 82% of current law students receive some form of aid. The average annual amount of aid from all sources combined, including scholarships, loans, and work contracts, is $23,406; maximum, $31,340. Awards are based on need and merit. The required financial statements are FAFSA, the institutional application, and federal tax returns. The aid application deadline for fall entry is April 15. Special funds for minority or disadvantaged students consist of the Maclean Grant for disadvantaged students and the Jacqueline Lloyd Grant for minority students. First-year students are notified about their financial aid application at time of acceptance.

About the Law School
New England School of Law was established in 1908 and is a private institution. The campus is in an urban area in Boston. The primary mission of the law school is to provide the opportunity for quality legal education and ethical training to men and women, especially those who might otherwise not have that opportunity. Students have access to federal, state, county, city, and local agencies, courts, correctional facilities, law firms, and legal aid organizations in the Boston area. Boston is the state capital, and as such offers many opportunities to law students. Facilities of special interest to law students are the Clinical Law Office, a school-sponsored neighborhood law office that provides clinical training and assists low-income litigants, and other clinical programs with the attorney general, Massachusetts Revenue Department, and other agencies. Housing for law students is not available on campus; however, assistance is provided for finding housing and roommates. About 98% of law school facilities are accessible to the physically disabled.

Calendar
The law school operates on a traditional semester basis. Courses for full-time students are offered both day and evening and must be completed within 5 years. For part-time students, courses are offered both day and evening and must be completed within 6 years. New full-time and part-time students are admitted in the fall. There is an 8-week summer session. Transferable summer courses are offered.

Programs
Students may take relevant courses in other programs and apply credit toward the J.D.; a maximum of 6 credits may be applied.

Phone: 617-422-7210
Fax: 617-422-7200
E-mail: admit@admin.nesi.edu
Web: www.nesi.edu

Contact

617-422-7210 for general inquiries; Douglas Leman, Director of Financial Aid, 617-451-0010, ext. 298 for financial aid information.

MASSACHUSETTS

Required

To earn the J.D., candidates must complete 84 total credits, of which 43 are for required courses. They must maintain a minimum GPA of 2.0 in the required courses. The following first-year courses are required of all students: Civil Procedure, Constitutional Law, Contracts, Property, Torts, and Legal Methods. Required upper-level courses consist of Criminal Law, Evidence, Criminal Procedure I, and Law and Ethics of Lawyering. The required orientation program for first-year students is a 1-week program with panel discussions on legal issues and lectures on the legal process, how to brief a case, and the procedures of a civil case.

Electives

The New England School of Law offers concentrations in corporate law, criminal law, environmental law, family law, international law, litigation, and tax law. In addition, clinics are available to second- and third-year day division students and third- and fourth-year evening division students for 2 to 6 credits. All upper-class students may take electives for 2 to 3 credits. Final-year students may undertake research programs for a 2 credit maximum per year. Special lecture series are available to all students for no credit. Up to 6 credits may be transferred from another school's ABA-approved study abroad program. In addition, the law school offers The Practice of Law in England and the European Community in London, England. Two courses are offered in each 2-week session. Participants may enroll in 1 2-credit course each session. A noncredit remedial research and writing program is open to first-year students. Noncredit minority programs are open to all students. The most widely taken electives are Wills, Estates and Trusts, and Business Organization.

Graduation Requirements

In order to graduate, candidates must have a GPA of 2.0 and have completed the upper-division writing requirement.

Organizations

Students edit the *New England Law Review*, the *New England Journal on Criminal and Civil Confinement*, and the student newspaper, *Due Process*. Other publications include the *International and Comparative Law Annual*. Students participate in an annual in-house Honors Moot Court Competition and Trial Competition. Other competitions include the National Moot Court Competition, National Trial Competition, National Tax Moot Court, Jessup International Moot Court, and occasionally the ABA Appellate Advocacy Competition. Student organizations include the Student Bar Association, International Law Society, and Environmental Law Society. There are local chapters of the ABA-Law Student Division and Phi Alpha Delta law fraternity.

Library

The law library contains 300,000 hardcopy volumes and 645,000 microform volume equivalents, and subscribes to 3100 serial publications. Such on-line databases and networks as LEXIS, DIALOG, WESTLAW, and OCLC, RLIN, DOW JONES, NEXIS, CD-ROMs, the Internet, World Wide Web, New England Law Library Consortium, and the Boston Regional Library System are available to law students for research. Special library collections include women and the law, Portia Law School archives, a Massachusetts continuing legal education depository, Massachusetts and New England-area publications, and media. Recently, the library added the INNOPAC On-line Catalog, 3 Windows '98 student computer laboratories for desktop Web access for faculty and students, desktop access to a networked CD-ROM collection, several multimedia workstations, a digitized database of exams, and school archives. The ratio of library volumes to faculty is 3030 to 1 and to students, 357 to 1. The ratio of seats in the library to students is 1 to 2.

Placement

J.D.s awarded:	261
Services available through: A separate law school placement center.	
Services: computerized job search resources and assistance with judicial clerkships	
Special features: individual and group counseling services as well as strong alumni contacts.	
Full-time job interviews:	16 employers
Summer job interviews:	16 employers
Placement by graduation:	41% of class
Placement within 9 months:	87% of class
Average starting salary:	$27,000 to $95,000
Areas of placement:	
Private practice 2-10 attorneys	31%
Private practice 11-25 attorneys	4%
Private practice 26-50 attorneys	3%
Private practice 51-100 attorneys	6%
Business/industry	26%
Government	13%
Judicial clerkships	9%
Public interest	3%
Academic	2%
Unknown	2%
Military	1%

Faculty

The law school has 40 full-time and 59 part-time faculty members, of whom 25 are women. According to AAUP standards for Category IIA institutions, faculty salaries are well above average. About 22% of full-time faculty have a graduate law degree in addition to the J.D.; about 23% of part-time faculty have one. The ratio of full-time students to full-time faculty in an average class is 26 to 1; in a clinic, 10 to 1. The law school has a regular program of bringing visiting professors and other distinguished lecturers and visitors to campus.

Students

About 54% of the student body are women; 17%, minorities; 6%, African American; 5%, Asian American; 5%, Hispanic; and 1%, Native American. The majority of students come from Massachusetts (50%). The average age of entering students is 28; age range is 19 to 57. About 7% drop out after the first year for academic or personal reasons; 93% remain to receive a law degree.

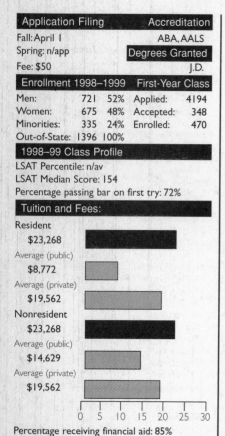

NEW YORK LAW SCHOOL

57 Worth Street
New York, NY 10013-2960

Application Filing	Accreditation
Fall: April 1	ABA, AALS
Spring: n/app	**Degrees Granted**
Fee: $50	J.D.

Enrollment 1998–1999		First-Year Class	
Men:	721 52%	Applied:	4194
Women:	675 48%	Accepted:	348
Minorities:	335 24%	Enrolled:	470
Out-of-State:	1396 100%		

1998–99 Class Profile
LSAT Percentile: n/av
LSAT Median Score: 154
Percentage passing bar on first try: 72%

Tuition and Fees:

Resident
$23,268

Average (public)
$8,772

Average (private)
$19,562

Nonresident
$23,268

Average (public)
$14,629

Average (private)
$19,562

0 5 10 15 20 25 30

Percentage receiving financial aid: 85%

ADMISSIONS

In the fall 1999 first-year class, 4194 applied, 348 were accepted, and 470 enrolled. Nineteen transfers enrolled. The median GPA of the most recent first-year class was 3.12.

Requirements

Applicants must have a bachelor's degree from an accredited institution and take the LSAT. Minimum acceptable GPA is 2.0 on a scale of 4.0. No specific undergraduate courses are required. Candidates are not interviewed.

Procedure

The application deadline for fall entry is April 1. Applicants should submit an application form, LSAT results, 2nd a nonrefundable application fee of $50. Accepted students must submit a $250 deposit by April 1, which is applied toward tuition upon registration, and submit a $500 deposit by June 1. Notification of the admission decision is on a rolling basis. The latest acceptable LSAT test date for fall entry is February. The law school uses the LSDAS.

Special

The law school recruits minority and disadvantaged students through diversity recruitment efforts initiated by the minority recruitment coordinator in the Admissions Office. Transfer students must have one year of credit, have a minimum GPA of 3.0, have attended an ABA-approved law school, and have a bachelor's degree from an accredited college or university.

Costs

Tuition and fees for the 1999-2000 academic year are $23,268 for all full-time students. Tuition for all part-time students is $16,588. On-campus room and board costs about $9945 annually; books and supplies run $800.

Financial Aid

About 85% of current law students receive some form of aid. The average annual amount of aid from all sources combined, including scholarships, loans, and work contracts, in $18,500; maximum, $33,975. Scholarships are awarded on the basis of merit. NYLS need-based grants are awarded on the basis of financial need. The required financial statement is FAFSA. The aid application deadline for fall entry is April 15. Special funds for minority or disadvantaged students are available through scholarship funds. First-year students are notified about their financial aid application contingent upon its completion.

About the Law School

New York Law School was established in 1891. The campus is in an urban area in the TriBeCa section of New York City. The primary mission of the law school is to deliver a sense of public service in law students, melding the theoretical and the practical to provide a strong foundation of legal knowledge as well as diverse perspectives. Students have access to federal, state, county, city, and local agencies, courts, correctional facilities, law firms, and legal aid organizations in the New York area. Facilities of special interest to law students include the Communications Media Center, which promotes learning about mass communications law; the Center for New York City Law, which focuses on urban governmental and legal processes; and the Center for International Law, which supports teaching and research in that field. Housing for law students consists of dormitory rooms in a newly renovated facility 15 minutes from the school. Additional apartments and roommate referrals are available through the Housing Office. All law school facilities are accessible to the physically disabled.

Calendar

The law school operates on a traditional semester basis. Courses for full-time students are offered both day and evening and must be completed within 3 years. For part-time students, courses are offered both day and evening and must be completed within 4 years. New full-time and part-time students are admitted in the fall. There is an 8-week summer session. Transferable summer courses are not offered.

Programs

Students may take relevant courses in other programs and apply credit toward the J.D.; a maximum of 10 credits from the New School for Social Research may be applied. The following joint degrees may be earned: J.D./M.B.A. (Juris Doctor/Master of Business Administration) (in association with Baruch College).

Required

To earn the J.D., candidates must complete 86 total credits, of which 38 are for required courses. They must maintain a minimum GPA of 2.0 in the required courses. The following first-year courses are required of all students: Civil Procedure, Contracts I and II, Lawyering, Legal Reasoning, Writing and Research, Torts, Criminal Law, Property, Written and Oral Advocacy, and Evidence. Required upper-level courses consist of Constitutional Law I and II, The Legal Profession, and Writing Requirement. Clinical programs are included in the Lawyering Skills program, where faculty-supervised students represent clients with current legal matters pending before various federal and state courts and administrative agencies. The required orientation program for first-year students is a week-long and is designed to ease the anxieties of incoming students by having them meet infor-

Phone: 212-431-2888
877-YES-NYLS
Fax: 212-966-1522
E-mail: admissions@nyls.edu
Web: www.nyls.edu

Contact

Office of Admissions, 212-431-2888 for general inquiries; Eileen Doyle, Director of Financial Aid, 212-431-2828 for financial aid information.

NEW YORK

mally with professors and fellow students at planned social events as well as introducing them to the rigors of law studies.

Electives

The New York Law School offers concentrations in corporate law, criminal law, entertainment, environmental law, family law, international law, labor law, litigation, media law, securities law, tax law, torts and insurance, and business and commercial law, constitutional law, procedure and evidence, property and real estate, public interest law, administrative law and practice, and immigration law. In addition, students in the Civil and Human Rights Clinic have assisted with racial discrimination cases in federal court as well as housing cases and related banking and discrimination matters, social security cases, and nonlitigation representation and counseling of not-for-profit corporations. Students gain additional legal practice experience through workshop courses. These courses link a seminar in a specialized body of law to field placements in offices and agencies practicing in that area of the law. Externships and judicial internships provide opportunities to do actual legal work, in private or public law offices or in judges' chambers, while being supervised by a practitioner at the placement site and meeting with a faculty member at the school. Special lecture series include the Steifel Symposium, Fall Executive Speakers Series, New York City Law Breakfasts, Solomon Lecture, Professional Development Seminar, Faculty Lecture Series, Dean's Roundtable, and Spotlight on Women. Independent study programs are available. The Academic Support Program consists of a condensed introductory course in legal methods in the summer followed by weekly tutorial meetings with second- and third-year teaching fellows through the first academic year. The Admissions Office has an Assistant Director with specific responsibility for minority recruitment and enrollment initiatives. In conjunction with the Office of Student Life, the Asian American Law Students Association, Black Law Students Association, and the Latino Law Students Association offer support to minority students. Special

interest group programs include Media Law Project, Domestic Violence Project, and New York Law School Civil Liberties Union. The most widely taken electives are Commercial Transactions, Corporations, and Wills, Trusts, and Future Interests.

Graduation Requirements

In order to graduate, candidates must have a GPA of 2.0 and have completed the upper-division writing requirement.

Organizations

Students edit the *New York Law School Law Review, New York Law School Journal of Human Rights, New York Law School Journal of International and Comparative Law*, and the newspaper *The L.* Students may participate in the Froessel Moot Court intramural competition. Students become members of the Moot Court Association by invitation and may represent the school in intramural competitions held at law schools nationwide. The Robert F. Wagner National Labor Law Moot Court competition is hosted by the school each spring. There are local chapters of Phi Alpha Delta and Phi Delta Phi.

Library

The law library contains 463,750 hardcopy volumes and 981,917 microform volume equivalents, and subscribes to 4485 serial publications. Such on-line databases and networks as LEXIS, DIALOG, WESTLAW, Legal-Trac, WILSON DISC, CIS Masterfile I and II and CD-ROM, NEXIS, OCLC, Wilsonline, Law Schools On-line, Index to UN Documents, and 25 other CD-ROM databases are available to law students for research. Special library collections include the U.S. government documents depository and special collections in communications rights law, alternative dispute resolution, and labor law. Recently, the library added the INNOPAC On-line Catalog, with dial-in access to the library's holdings and electronic access to the Index of Legal Periodicals. A CD-ROM tower workstation is available. The ratio of library volumes to faculty is 2885 to 1 and to students, 298 to 1. The ratio of seats in the library to students is 1 to 1.

Placement

J.D.s awarded:	403

Services available through: A separate law school placement center.

Services: more than 200 law firms participated in the 1999 recruitment programs

Special features: a resource library, which contains a collection of job search and career planning materials, information on law firms, corporations, government agencies, the judiciary, public interest organizations, a computerized database, and an alumni network

Full-time job interviews:	n/av
Summer job interviews:	n/av
Placement by graduation:	n/av
Placement within 9 months:	93% of class
Average starting salary:	$39,500 to $62,500

Areas of placement:

Private practice	45%
Government	20%
Business/industry	16%
Unknown	8%
Judicial clerkships	6%
Public interest	3%
Academic	2%

Faculty

The law school has 53 full-time and 82 part-time faculty members, of whom 42 are women. About 36% of full-time faculty have a graduate law degree in addition to the J.D.; about 19% of part-time faculty have one. The ratio of full-time students to full-time faculty in an average class is 22 to 1; in a clinic, 6 to 1. The law school has a regular program of bringing visiting professors and other distinguished lecturers and visitors to campus. There is a chapter of the Order of the Coif.

Students

About 48% of the student body are women; 24%, minorities; 8%, African American; 7%, Asian American; 6%, Hispanic; and 3%, mixed race/ethnicity. The average age of entering students is 27; age range is 21 to 58. About 3% drop out after the first year for academic or personal reasons; 85% remain to receive a law degree.

NEW YORK UNIVERSITY

School of Law

110 West Third Street
New York, NY 10012

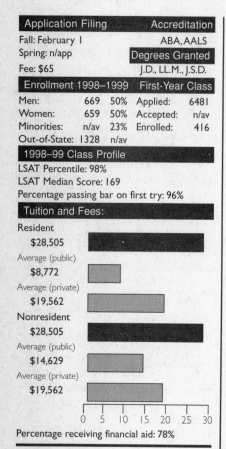

Application Filing	Accreditation
Fall: February 1	ABA, AALS
Spring: n/app	**Degrees Granted**
Fee: $65	J.D., LL.M., J.S.D.

Enrollment 1998–1999		First-Year Class	
Men:	669 50%	Applied:	6481
Women:	659 50%	Accepted:	n/av
Minorities:	n/av 23%	Enrolled:	416
Out-of-State:	1328 n/av		

1998–99 Class Profile

LSAT Percentile: 98%
LSAT Median Score: 169
Percentage passing bar on first try: 96%

Tuition and Fees:

Resident
$28,505

Average (public)
$8,772

Average (private)
$19,562

Nonresident
$28,505

Average (public)
$14,629

Average (private)
$19,562

0 5 10 15 20 25 30

Percentage receiving financial aid: 78%

ADMISSIONS

In the fall 1999 first-year class, 6481 applied and 416 enrolled. Forty-five transfers enrolled. The median LSAT percentile of the most recent first-year class was 98; the median GPA was 3.65 on a scale of 4.0.

Requirements

Applicants must have a bachelor's degree from an accredited institution and take the LSAT. No specific undergraduate courses are required. Candidates are not interviewed.

Procedure

The application deadline for fall entry is February 1. Applicants should submit an application form, LSAT results, transcripts, a nonrefundable application fee of $65, 1 letter of recommendation, and a personal statement. Notification of the admission decision is by mid-April. The latest acceptable LSAT test date for fall entry is December. The law school uses the LSDAS.

Special

The law school recruits minority and disadvantaged students by paying special attention to application information other than the GPA and LSAT results. Transfer students must have one year of credit, have attended an ABA-approved law school, and must submit all college and law school transcripts, LSAT scores, a letter of recommendation from a law school professor, and a statement of good standing from a dean. The school attended must be a member of the AALS or be approved by the Section on Legal Education of the ABA.

Costs

Tuition and fees for the 1999-2000 academic year are $28,505 for all students. On-campus room and board costs about $16,805 annually; books and supplies run $650.

Financial Aid

About 78% of current law students receive some form of aid. Awards are based on need and merit. The required financial statement is the FAFSA. The aid application deadline for fall entry is March 15. First-year students are notified about their financial aid application at the time of acceptance.

About the Law School

New York University School of Law was established in 1835 and is a private institution. The campus is in an urban area in New York City. The primary mission of the law school is to produce men and women who are leaders of the bar, public and private, in a world that operates across national boundaries. Students have access to federal, state, county, city, and local agencies, courts, correctional facilities, law firms, and legal aid organizations in the New York area. In addition, the many and varied resources of New York City are available. Facilities of special interest to law students include Vanderbilt Hall, which contains classrooms, faculty and administrative offices, and the library; Fuchsberg Hall, which houses the clinical programs, and D'Agostino and Mercer Student residences, with meeting rooms, student journal offices, and a conference center. Housing for law students is available for virtually all who request it, including couples and families; 2 law-school-owned apartment buildings are within 4 blocks of the campus. About 95% of the law school facilities are accessible to the physically disabled.

Calendar

The law school operates on a traditional semester basis. Courses are offered both day and evening, but classes are primarily during the day and must be completed within 6 years. There is no part-time program. New students are admitted in the fall. There is a summer session. Transferrable summer courses are offered.

Programs

In addition to the J.D., the law school offers the LL.M. and J.S.D. Students may take relevant courses in other programs and apply credit toward the J.D.; a maximum of 10 credits may be applied. The following joint degrees may be earned: J.D./LL.M. (Juris Doctor/Master of Laws in taxation), J.D./M.B.A. (Juris Doctor/Master of Business Administration), J.D./M.P.A. (Juris Doctor/Master of International and Public Affairs), J.D./M.U.P. (Juris Doctor/Master of Urban Planning), J.D./M.P.A. (Juris Doctor/Master of Public Administration), J.D./M.S.W. (Juris Doctor/Master of Social Work), and J.D./M.A. (Juris Doctor/ Master of Arts).

Phone: 212-998-6060
Fax: 212-995-4527
E-mail: law.jdadmissions@nyu.edu
Web: http://www.law.nyu.edu

Contact

Kenneth Kleinrock, Assistant Dean for Admissions, 212-998-6060 for general inquiries; Stephen Brown, Director, 212-998-6050 for financial aid information.

NEW YORK

Required

To earn the J.D., candidates must complete 82 total credits. The following first-year courses are required of all students: Contracts I and II, Criminal Law, Civil Procedure I and II, Property, Torts, and Lawyering. Required upper-level courses consist of Constitutional Law, Professional Responsibility, the Legal Institutions requirement, and 2 upper-level writing requirements. The required orientation program for first-year students is a 2-day academic and social orientation period before the start of classes, followed by a series of optional weekly programs during the first term.

Electives

The School of Law offers concentrations in corporate law, criminal law, entertainment, environmental law, family law, international law, juvenile law, labor law, litigation, securities law, and tax law. In addition, clinics provide simulated and actual trial experience; clinics include the Capital Defender Clinic, Civil Rights Clinic, and International Human Rights clinic. Seminars are offered in areas such as constitutional law, corporate and commercial law, and criminal justice. The school provides financial assistance for summer internships for 175 first- and second-year students committed to public interest law. These summer internships are with public interest organizations worldwide. Additionally, Root-Tilden-Kern Scholars participate in a 10-week internship in public interest law. Students may arrange with faculty to conduct research; the Directed Writing Project requires a substantial paper that may fulfill part of the upper-level writing requirement. Research is also part of the Hays Civil Liberties Program, open to selected third-year students, the Boudin and Blaustein Fellowships in human rights, and junior fellowships in international legal studies. Among others, special lecture series include the Root-Tilden-Kern Speakers Program, the Program for the Study of Law, Philosophy and Social Theory, the Program on Philanthropy and the Law, and the Legal History Colloquium. Study abroad is possible through a one-semester exchange program with universities in several countries. The most widely taken electives are colloquia (faculty-student discussions), all 16 clinical program and advocacy courses, and seminars.

Graduation Requirements

In order to graduate, candidates must have completed the upper-division writing requirement and have attended 6 semesters of classes.

Organizations

Students edit the *New York University Law Review*, Annual Survey of American Law, *Journal of International Law and Politics*, *Environmental Law Journal*, *Review of Law and Social Change*, *Journal of Legislation and Public Policy*, *Tax Law Review*, *Clinical Law Review*, *Eastern European Constitutional Review*, the newspaper, *The Commentator*, and the *Moot Court Board Casebook*. Members of the Moot Court Board enter intraschool and national competitions. There are more than 40 funded law student groups on campus, including the Student Bar Association. For a full listing of student organizations, please refer to the school's web site at www.law.nyu.edu/studentlife/.

Library

The law library contains 997,463 hardcopy volumes and 19,309 microform volume equivalents, and subscribes to 6918 serial publications. Such on-line databases and networks as LEXIS, DIALOG, WESTLAW, CIS, CCH, and many foreign and international Internet databases are available to law students for research. Special library collections include Anglo-American materials, international law, Jewish law, tax law, patent, trademark, and copyright law, and securities and finance law. The library's seating capacity is 897. Recently, the library has been wired for approximately 100 public access terminals connected to the Internet, as well as plug-in capacity for student laptops. Concurrently, students have access to electronic sources from a hard-wired Resnet in the 2 law school dorms. The Global Law Program and a $500,000 grant from the Starr Foundation have increased the library's focus on foreign, comparative, and international law. The ratio of library volumes to faculty is 9975 to 1 and to students, 570 to 1. The ratio of seats in the library to students is 1 to 1.3.

Placement

J.D.s awarded:	434
Services available through: a separate law school placement center	
Services: hosting 35 legal career panel discussions with 150 lawyers each year, and sending judicial clerkship letters of recommendation	
Special features: Early Interview Week each August, public interest and government and international job fairs, and off-campus recruitment programs in Washington, D.C., Chicago, Los Angeles, and San Francisco	
Full-time job interviews:	450
Summer job interviews:	n/av
Placement by graduation:	97% of class
Placement within 9 months:	100% of class
Average starting salary:	$37,500 public; $90,600 private

Areas of placement:

Private practice 2-10 attorneys	1%
Private practice 11-25 attorneys	1%
Private practice 26-50 attorneys	5%
Private practice 51-100 attorneys	11%
Private practice 101 attorneys	46%
Judicial clerkships	16%
Public interest	9%
Business/industry	4%
Government	3%
Academic	1%

Faculty

The law school has 114 full-time and 71 part-time faculty members, of whom 61 are women. According to AAUP standards for Category I institutions, faculty salaries are well above average. The ratio of full-time students to full-time faculty in an average class is 13 to 1; in a clinic, 8 to 1. The law school has a regular program of bringing visiting professors and other distinguished lecturers and visitors to campus. There is a chapter of the Order of the Coif.

Students

About 50% of the student body are women; 23%, minorities; 6%, African American; 10%, Asian American; and 7%, Hispanic. About 38% of students enter directly from undergraduate school and 11% have a graduate degree.

School of Law

1512 S. Alston Avenue
Durham, NC 27707

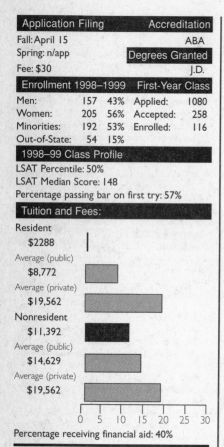

Application Filing		Accreditation
Fall: April 15		ABA
Spring: n/app		**Degrees Granted**
Fee: $30		J.D.

Enrollment 1998–1999		First-Year Class	
Men:	157 43%	Applied:	1080
Women:	205 56%	Accepted:	258
Minorities:	192 53%	Enrolled:	116
Out-of-State:	54 15%		

1998–99 Class Profile
LSAT Percentile: 50%
LSAT Median Score: 148
Percentage passing bar on first try: 57%

Tuition and Fees:

Resident
$2288

Average (public)
$8,772

Average (private)
$19,562

Nonresident
$11,392

Average (public)
$14,629

Average (private)
$19,562

0   5   10   15   20   25   30

Percentage receiving financial aid: 40%

ADMISSIONS

In the fall 1999 first-year class, 1080 applied, 258 were accepted, and 116 enrolled. One transfer enrolled. The median LSAT percentile of the most recent first-year class was 50; the median GPA was 3.15 on a scale of 4.0. The lowest LSAT score accepted was 143 (149 part-time); the highest was 152 (162 part-time).

Requirements
Applicants must have a bachelor's degree from an accredited institution and take the LSAT. No specific undergraduate courses are required. Candidates are not interviewed.

Procedure
The application deadline for fall entry is April 15. Applicants should submit an application form, LSAT results, transcripts, a nonrefundable application fee of $30, and 2 letters of recommendation. Accepted students who intend to enroll must submit a nonrefundable $100 tuition deposit, which is applied to the student's first tuition payment. Notification of the admissions decision is on a rolling basis. The latest acceptable LSAT test date for fall entry is February. The law school uses the LSDAS.

Special
The law school recruits minority and disadvantaged students by means of the Performance-Based Admissions Program, which is designed to identify applicants who have the potential to succeed in law school but whose undergraduate transcripts and LSAT scores do not meet traditional standards. Transfer students must have a minimum GPA of 2.0, have attended an ABA-approved law school, and be in good standing with the previous law school. One year of residence at the School of Law is required.

Costs

Tuition and fees for the 1999-2000 academic year are $2288 for full-time in-state students and $11,392 for out-of-state students. Tuition for part-time students is $2288 per year in-state and $11,392 out-of-state. On-campus room and board costs about $4213 annually.

Financial Aid

About 40% of current law students receive some form of aid. The average annual amount of aid from all sources combined, including scholarships, loans, and work contracts, is $400. Awards are based on need and merit. The required financial statement is the FAFSA. The aid application deadline for fall entry is February 1. Special funds for minority or disadvantaged students are available through fellowships and national associations. The Council on Legal Education Opportunity (CLEO) is a federally funded program for disadvantaged students.

About the Law School

North Carolina Central University School of Law was established in 1939 and is a public institution. The 105-acre campus is in an urban area 20 miles from Raleigh, and 5 miles from Research Triangle Park. The primary mission of the law school is to provide a challenging and broad-based educational program designed to stimulate intellectual inquiry, and foster in each student a sense of community service, professional responsibility, and personal integrity. The law school student body is diverse in terms of gender, ethnicity, and economic and experiential backgrounds. Students have access to federal, state, county, city, and local agencies, courts, correctional facilities, law firms, and legal aid organizations in the Durham area. Facilities of special interest to law students are a modern law library, computer laboratory, academic support programs, and individual offices for student organizations. Some on-campus housing is available for single students, but married students must live off campus. About 90% of the law school facilities are accessible to the physically disabled.

Calendar

The law school operates on a traditional semester basis. Courses for full-time students are offered days only (some special elective classes may meet in the evening and must be completed within 3 years.) For part-time students, courses are offered evenings only and must be completed within 4 years. New full- and part-time students are admitted in the fall. There are two 5 1/2-week summer sessions. Transferable summer courses are offered.

Programs

Students may take relevant courses in other programs and apply credit toward the J.D.; a maximum of 6 credits may be applied. The following joint degrees may be earned: J.D./M.L.S. (Juris Doctor/Master of Library and Information Services) and J.D./M.B.A. (Juris Doctor/Master of Business Administration).

Phone: 919-560-6333
Fax: 919-560-6339
E-mail: jfaucett@wpo.nccu.edu
Web: www.nccu.edu/law

Contact
Jacqueline P. Faucett, Admissions Coordinator, 919-530-5243 for general inquiries; Assistant Dean Douglas, Office of Scholarships and Student Aid, 919-560-6202 or 919-530-6365 for financial aid information.

NORTH CAROLINA

Required
To earn the J.D., candidates must complete 88 total credits, of which 65 (63 part-time) are for required courses. They must maintain a minimum GPA of 2.0 in the required courses. The following first-year courses are required of all students: Contracts I, Civil Procedure I, Property I, Legal Method I, Torts I, Legal Bibliography, Contracts II, Civil Procedure II, Property II, Legal Method II, and Criminal Law. Required upper-level courses consist of Advanced Legal Writing I and II or Senior Writing (Evening Program), Appellate Advocacy I, Business Associations or Corporations (evening program), Constitutional Law I and II, Decedents' Estates and Trusts I, Evidence, Professional Responsibility, Sales and Secured Transactions, Statutory Interpretation, and Taxation. Although not required, students are encouraged to enroll in the clinical program. There is a new model law office that houses clinical facilities. The required orientation program for first-year students lasts 2 days and includes preenrollment seminars.

Electives
The Clinical Experience Program consists of preliminary courses in the rules of evidence and trial practice with mock trials and oral arguments. Students work with law enforcement officials, legal services agencies, and attorneys in North Carolina. Seminars include the Land Loss Prevention Project (LLPP), which assists limited-resource landholders to preserve their lands and livelihoods; the Civil Rights Project, an in-depth study of special problems involved in litigating federal civil rights actions; and Women in the Law. The school is a member of an interinstitutional enrollment program that includes Duke University School of Law and University of North Carolina School of Law. An academic support program is available to students for assistance with specific academic needs, problems, and adjustment expectations. Tutorials in each first-year substantive course and selected upper-level courses are open to all interested students. In addition,

the school offers a noncredit writing laboratory for 1 hour every week in the fall and spring semesters. The Pro Bono Clinic offers many opportunities for second- and third-year students to volunteer in local special interest agencies and organizations. The most widely taken electives are the Clinical Program, Criminal Procedure, and Trial Practice.

Graduation Requirements
In order to graduate, candidates must have a GPA of 2.0 and have completed the upper-division writing requirement.

Organizations
Students edit the *North Carolina Central Law Journal* and the newspaper *The Barrister*. Moot Court competitions include the J. Braxton Craven, Jr. Memorial Moot Court Competition; Saul Lefkowitz Moot Court Competition; and Ernest B. Fullwood Moost Court Competition. Other competitions include Trial Advocacy Competition, National Trial Competition, and Association of Trial Lawyers of America (ATLA) Trial Competition. Law student organizations include the Student Bar Association, Intellectual Property Society, and Entertainment and Sports Law Association. There are local chapters of Phi Alpha Delta, Phi Delta Phi, and Delta Theta Phi. Other organizations include Alpha Kappa Alpha Sorority, Delta Sigma Theta Sorority, and Omega Psi Phi Fraternity.

Library
The law library contains 284,115 hard-copy volumes and 639,314 microform volume equivalents, and subscribes to 2370 serial publications. Such on-line databases and networks as LEXIS, DIALOG, and WESTLAW are available to law students for research. Special library collections include a depository for U.S. government documents. The ratio of library volumes to faculty is 4420 to 1 and to students, 363 to 1. The ratio of seats in the library to students is 1 to 1.

Placement

J.D.s awarded:	95

Services available through: a separate law school placement center.

Services: workshop sessions on various practice areas; mock interviews and participation in job fairs

Special features: placement programs that bring in recruiters from government, private firms, legal services, and corporations

Full-time job interviews:	7 employers
Summer job interviews:	18 employers
Placement by graduation:	49% of class
Placement within 9 months:	89% of class
Average starting salary:	$25,000 to $101,000

Areas of placement:

Private practice 2-100 attorneys	43%
Government	18%
Public interest	6%
Judicial clerkships	5%
Business/industry	5%
Military	2%
Academic	2%

Faculty
The law school has 23 full-time and 9 part-time faculty members, of whom 15 are women. According to AAUP standards for Category IIA institutions, faculty salaries are above average. About 49% of full-time faculty have a graduate law degree in addition to the J.D.; about 5% of part-time faculty have one. The ratio of full-time students to full-time faculty in an average class is 15 to 1. The law school has a regular program of bringing visiting professors and other distinguished lecturers and visitors to campus.

Students
About 56% of the student body are women; 53%, minorities; 49%, African American; 1%, Asian American; 2%, Hispanic; and 1%, Native American. The majority of students come from North Carolina (85%).

School of Law

400 Huntington Avenue
Boston, MA 02115

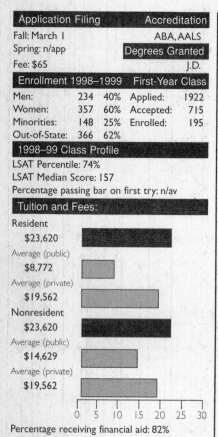

Application Filing		Accreditation
Fall: March 1		ABA, AALS
Spring: n/app		**Degrees Granted**
Fee: $65		J.D.

Enrollment 1998–1999			First-Year Class	
Men:	234	40%	Applied:	1922
Women:	357	60%	Accepted:	715
Minorities:	148	25%	Enrolled:	195
Out-of-State:	366	62%		

1998–99 Class Profile

LSAT Percentile: 74%

LSAT Median Score: 157

Percentage passing bar on first try: n/av

Tuition and Fees:

Resident
$23,620

Average (public)
$8,772

Average (private)
$19,562

Nonresident
$23,620

Average (public)
$14,629

Average (private)
$19,562

0 5 10 15 20 25 30

Percentage receiving financial aid: 82%

ADMISSIONS

In the fall 1999 first-year class, 1922 applied, 715 were accepted, and 195 enrolled. Two transfers enrolled. The median LSAT percentile of the most recent first-year class was 74; the median GPA was 3.2 on a scale of 4.0. The lowest LSAT percentile accepted was 10; the highest was 97.

Requirements

Applicants must have a bachelor's degree from an accredited institution and take the LSAT. The most important admission factors include academic achievement, work experience, and LSAT results. No specific undergraduate courses are required. Candidates are interviewed.

Procedure

The application deadline for fall entry is March 1. Applicants should submit an application form, LSAT results, transcripts, TOEFL if indicated, a nonrefundable application fee of $65, 2 letters of recommendation, and a personal statement. Notification of the admission decision is made on February 1, March 15, and April 15. The latest acceptable LSAT test dates for fall entry are October, December, and February. The law school uses the LSDAS.

Special

The law school recruits minority and disadvantaged students by targeting historically black colleges and universities, providing scholarships, and being a member of CLEO. Transfer students must have one year of credit, have attended an ABA-approved law school, and must submit 1 recommendation from the dean of their current law school attesting to their good standing and eligibility, and at least 1 letter from a first-year law professor.

Costs

Tuition and fees for the 1999-2000 academic year are $23,620 for all full-time students. On-campus room and board costs about $11,700 annually; and books, supplies and loan fees run $1740.

Financial Aid

About 82% of current law students receive some form of aid. The average annual amount of aid from all sources combined, including scholarships, loans, and work contracts, is $23,821; maximum, $39,800. Awards are based on need and merit. The required financial statement is FAFSA. The aid application deadline for fall entry is March 1. Special funds for minority or disadvantaged students consist of full or partial tuition scholarships. First-year students are notified about their financial aid application at the time of acceptance.

About the Law School

Northeastern University School of Law was established in 1898 and is a private institution. The 5556-acre campus is in an urban area in Boston. The primary mission of the law school is to fuse theory and practice with ethical and social justice ideals so that students understand what it is that lawyers do, how they do it, and the difference they can make in the life of others. Students have access to federal, state, county, city, and local agencies, courts, correctional facilities, law firms, and legal aid organizations in the Boston area. Housing for law students is available in on-campus housing. All law school facilities are accessible to the physically disabled.

Calendar

The law school operates on a quarter basis. Courses for full-time students are offered days only and must be completed within 3 years. There is no part-time program. New full-time students are admitted in the fall. There is a 12-week summer session that is part of the required curriculum. Transferable summer courses are offered.

Programs

Students may take relevant courses in other programs and apply credit toward the J.D.; a maximum of 6 credits may be applied. The following joint degrees may be earned: J.D./M.B.A. (Juris Doctor/Master of Business Administration) and J.D./M.S. (Juris Doctor/Master of Science in accounting).

Required

To earn the J.D., candidates must complete 99 total credits, of which 49 are for required courses. The following first-year courses are required of all students: Torts, Property, Contracts, Constitutional Issues, Criminal Justice, Civil Procedure, Legal Practice, and Law, Culture, and Difference. Required upper-level courses consist of Professional Responsibility. All students are required to complete 4 supervised legal internships under the school's Program of Cooperative Legal Education. In the second and third years of school, students alternate every 3 months between full-time class work and full-time co-op work. The school also offers traditional clinical courses as electives for upper-level students. The required orientation program for first-year students is 1 to 2 days and introduces students to the first-year curriculum, faculty, law school, and university services.

Phone: 617-373-2395
Fax: 617-373-8865
E-mail: pbauer@slaw.neu.edu
Web: www.slaw.neu.edu

Contact

617-373-2395 for general inquiries; Marilyn Molnar, Associate Director, Graduate/Law, Financial Aid, 617-373-5899 for financial aid information.

MASSACHUSETTS

Electives

The School of Law offers concentrations in corporate law, criminal law, environmental law, family law, international law, labor law, and public interest, and advocacy. In addition, clinical courses include Certiorari Clinic/Criminal Appeals for 3 credits, Criminal Advocacy for 7 credits, and Domestic Violence: Abuse Prevention and Criminal Intervention for 6 credits. Seminars include an Advanced Writing Seminar, Health Law Seminar, and Racism and American Law Seminar. Research assistantships are available with individual professors. For field work, students are required to complete 4 distinct cooperative legal education quarters during the second and third year of school, alternating every 3 months between full-time classes and full-time work. Study abroad is possible through international co-ops available on a limited basis. There are many academic support programs, including the Legal Writing Workshop, Legal Analysis Workshop, and Analytical Skills Workshop. Upper-level courses include Advanced Writing, Legal Reasoning, Advanced Legal Research, and a not-for-credit Bar preparation course. Minority students may take advantage of the Legal Analysis Workshop and tutorial programs, which are targeted to students of color. Special interest groups include the Environmental Law Forum, Tobacco Products Liability Project, and Center for Artificial Intelligence and Law. The most widely taken electives are Evidence, Corporations, and Trusts and Estates.

Graduation Requirements

In order to graduate, candidates must have completed the cooperative education requirement, and a public interest requirement.

Organizations

Students frequently participate in moot court competitions nationwide. Student organizations include the National Lawyers Guild, Queer Caucus, and Jewish Law Students Association. There are local chapters of the Black Law Students Association, Asian Pacific Law Students Association, and LaTinola Law Students Association. Other organizations include Environmental Law Forum, International Law Society, and National Lawyers Guild.

Library

The law library contains 293,243 hardcopy volumes and 623,096 microform volume equivalents, and subscribes to 3345 serial publications. Such on-line databases and networks as LEXIS, DIALOG, WESTLAW, and OCLC/FirstSearch, Internet, CIS Congressional Universe CIS Statistical Universe, Legal Trac, LOIS, and Social Law Library's on-line databases are available to law students for research. Special library collections include the Sara Ehrmann Collection on the death penalty and the Pappas Public Interest Law Collection. Recently, the library upgraded the law library's computer network and network intrastructure. Many additional network parts were added throughout the library for laptop connectivity. The ratio of library volumes to faculty is 8378 to 1 and to students, 476 to 1. The ratio of seats in the library to students is 1 to 1.

Faculty

The law school has 29 full-time and 25 part-time faculty members, of whom 27 are women. According to AAUP standards for Category I institutions, faculty salaries are above average. About 17% of full-time faculty have a graduate law degree in addition to the J.D. The ratio of full-time students to full-time faculty in an average class is 21 to 1; in a clinic, 9 to 1. The law school has a regular program of bringing visiting professors and other distinguished lecturers and visitors to campus.

Placement

J.D.s awarded:	196
Services available through: A separate law school placement center.	
Services: career development and self-assessment workshops and counseling, a Career Resource Library, materials prepared by the Office of Career Services or Self-Assessment, interviewing skills, resume writing, networking, job search strategies, and judicial clerkships.	
Special features: The director of the office is an attorney and the associate director has a master's degree in management.	
Full-time job interviews:	26 employers
Summer job interviews:	36 employers
Placement by graduation:	n/av
Placement within 9 months:	94% of class
Average starting salary:	$23,000 to $94,000
Areas of placement:	
Private practice 2-10 attorneys	12%
Private practice 11-25 attorneys	4%
Private practice 26-50 attorneys	5%
Private practice 51-100 attorneys	16%
Judicial clerkships	23%
Public interest	18%
Government	8%
Non-legal government, public interest, business	7%
Business/industry	6%

Students

About 60% of the student body are women; 25%, minorities; 9%, African American; 9%, Asian American; 7%, Hispanic; and 2%, International Students. The majority of students come from Massachusetts (38%). The average age of entering students is 25; age range is 20 to 60. About 28% of students enter directly from undergraduate school, 15% have a graduate degree, and 72% have worked full-time prior to entering law school. About 4% drop out after the first year for academic or personal reasons; 97% remain to receive a law degree.

College of Law

Swen Parson Hall
De Kalb, IL 60115

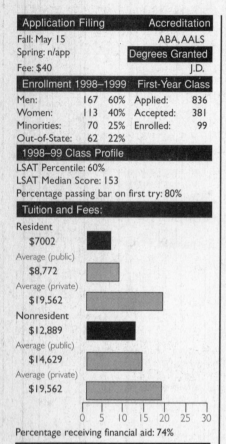

Application Filing	Accreditation
Fall: May 15	ABA, AALS
Spring: n/app	**Degrees Granted**
Fee: $40	J.D.

Enrollment 1998–1999		First-Year Class	
Men:	167 60%	Applied:	836
Women:	113 40%	Accepted:	381
Minorities:	70 25%	Enrolled:	99
Out-of-State:	62 22%		

1998–99 Class Profile
LSAT Percentile: 60%
LSAT Median Score: 153
Percentage passing bar on first try: 80%

Tuition and Fees:

Resident
$7002

Average (public)
$8,772

Average (private)
$19,562

Nonresident
$12,889

Average (public)
$14,629

Average (private)
$19,562

0 5 10 15 20 25 30

Percentage receiving financial aid: 74%

ADMISSIONS

In the fall 1999 first-year class, 836 applied, 381 were accepted, and 99 enrolled. Six transfers enrolled. The median LSAT percentile of the most recent first-year class was 60; the median GPA was 3.0 on a scale of 4.0. The highest LSAT percentile was 93.

Requirements
Applicants must have a bachelor's degree from an accredited institution and take the LSAT. The most important admission factors include academic achievement, LSAT results, and GPA. No specific undergraduate courses are required. Candidates are not interviewed.

Procedure
The application deadline for fall entry is May 15. Applicants should submit an application form, LSAT results, a nonrefundable application fee of $40, 2 letters of recommendation, a personal statement, and the LSDAS report. Notification of the admission decision is as early as possible, on a rolling basis. The latest acceptable LSAT test date for fall entry is June. The law school uses the LSDAS.

Special
The law school recruits minority and disadvantaged students by encouraging all in;dividuals who are underrepresented ethnically, and culturally or who are financially disadvantaged to apply. The BLSA, HLSA, ALSN, and the Women's Law Caucus work closely with the Admissions Office to increase the student body's diversity. Transfer students must have one year of credit and have attended an ABA-approved law school.

Costs

Tuition and fees for the 1999-2000 academic year are $7002 for full-time in-state students and $12,889 for out-of-state students. On-campus room and board costs about $4744 annually; books and supplies run $1400.

Financial Aid

About 74% of current law students receive some form of aid. The average annual amount of aid from all sources combined, including scholarships, loans, and work contracts, is $14,000; maximum, $15,460. Awards are based on need and merit. The required financial statement is FAFSA. The aid application deadline for fall entry is March 1. Special funds for minority or disadvantaged students consist of scholarships for partial- or full-tuition waivers (some with stipends) available to culturally and/or financially disadvantaged individuals. First-year students are notified about their financial aid application upon receipt of application.

About the Law School

Northern Illinois University College of Law was established in 1974 and is a public institution. The 755-acre campus is in a small town 65 miles west of Chicago. The primary mission of the law school is to prepare its graduates not only for the traditional role of lawyers, but for the nontraditional tasks that may be assumed by the law-trained. Students have access to federal, state, county, city, and local agencies, courts, correctional facilities, law firms, and legal aid organizations in the De Kalb area. Facilities of special interest to law students include a full service law library, which is adjacent to the main university library; a computer laboratory for law students as well as other laboratories on campus; and a moot court room equipped with voice-activated cameras as well as a movable wall to create classroom space. Neptune Hall, 1 block away from the law school, has the first floor designated for law students. There are also affordable apartment options surrounding the campus. All law school facilities are accessible to the physically disabled.

Calendar

The law school operates on a traditional semester basis. Courses for full-time students are offered days only and must be completed within 3 years. For part-time students, courses are offered days only and must be completed within 5 years. New full-and part-time students are admitted in the fall. There is no summer session. Transferable summer courses are not offered.

Programs

Students may take relevant courses in other programs and apply credit toward the J.D.; a maximum of 6 credits may be applied. The following joint degrees may be earned: J.D./M.B.A. (Juris Doctor/Master of Business Administration).

Phone: 815-753-1420
800-892-3050 (in-state)
Fax: 815-753-4501
E-mail: lawadm@niu.edu
Web: niu.edu/col

Contact

Special Assistant to the Director of Admissions, 815-753-8559 for general inquiries; Assistant to the Director of Admission and Financial Aid, 815-753-9485 for financial aid information.

ILLINOIS

Required

To earn the J.D., candidates must complete 90 total credits, of which 36 are for required courses. They must maintain a minimum GPA of 2.0 in the required courses. The following first-year courses are required of all students: Legal Research, Writing, and Advocacy I and II, Criminal Law, Torts I and II, Civil Procedure, Property, Contract I and II, and Constitutional Law I. Required upper-level courses consist of Constitutional Law II and Professional Responsibility. The required orientation program for first-year students is a 1-day introduction to the university and law school.

Electives

The College of Law offers concentrations in corporate law, criminal law, environmental law, family law, international law, juvenile law, labor law, litigation, maritime law, tax law, torts and insurance, and public interest. There is an Appellate Defender Clinical program for 3 credit hours for students who want to do clinic work under the supervision of a staff attorney at the Illinois Appellate Defender Office. All students must complete a 3-hour seminar in their fourth or fifth semester. Externships are offered in the Judicial Externship Program, which places students with state and federal judges; externships are also available with state criminal prosecutors, public defenders, and civil legal services for the needy. There is a Riley Lecture Series on Professionalism. Study abroad in Agen, France is available for law students as well as other options through the International Program Office. Tutors are available to first-year students upon request. The Academic Support Program is available by invitation for students who the committee feels may need additional support during the first year of law school. Peer and faculty support programs are available for minorities. Speakers on a variety of topics are sponsored by the Women's Law Caucus, International Law Society, HLSA, and BLSA. The most widely taken electives are Evidence, and Trust and Estates.

Graduation Requirements

In order to graduate, candidates must have a GPA of 2.0.

Organizations

The *Northern Illinois University Law Review* and *The Advocate* are student-edited publications. Teams compete at the National Moot Court, the Chicago Area Moot Court, and the Illinois State Bar Association Moot Court competitions. Other competitions include the ABA Client Counseling and the ABA Negotiation competitions. Student organizations include the International Law Society, Women's Law Caucus, and the Public Interest Law Society. There are local chapters of Phi Alpha Delta, Delta Theta Phi, and the American Civil Liberties Union. Other organizations include the Organization of Latin American Students, Minority Graduate Students Association, and the Gay/Lesbian Union.

Library

The law library contains 210,312 hard-copy volumes and 453,961 microform volume equivalents, and subscribes to 3200 serial publications. Such on-line databases and networks as LEXIS, DIALOG, WESTLAW, LIS, OCLC, Illinet Online, and the Internet are available to law students for research. Special library collections include a federal document selective depository. Recently, the library was expanded by 5000 square feet for additional volumes, study area, and a larger computer laboratory. The ratio of library volumes to faculty is 13,145 to 1 and to students, 751 to 1.

Faculty

The law school has 27 full-time and 10 part-time faculty members, of whom 11 are women. According to AAUP standards for Category I institutions, faculty salaries are below average. About 36% of full-time faculty have a graduate law degree in addition to the J.D.; about 15% of part-time faculty have one. The ratio of full-time students to full-time faculty in an average class is 16 to 1.

Placement

J.D.s awarded:	102

Services available through: separate law school placement center and the university placement center

Services: participation in regional and national job fairs

Special features: individual career counseling for students and alumni about traditional and nontraditional jobs for law graduates

Full-time job interviews:	10 employers
Summer job interviews:	10 employers
Placement by graduation:	38% of class
Placement within 9 months:	90% of class
Average starting salary:	$27,000 to $70,000

Areas of placement:

Private practice 2-10 attorneys	20%
Private practice 11-25 attorneys	6%
Private practice 26-50 attorneys	13%
Private practice 51-100 attorneys	6%
Government	19%
Public interest	16%
Business/industry	10%
Solo practice	4%
Judicial clerkships	4%
Military	1%
Academic	1%

Students

About 40% of the student body are women; 25%, minorities; 7%, African American; 8%, Asian American; 8%, Hispanic; and 1%, Native American. The majority of students come from Illinois (78%). The average age of entering students is 27; age range is 22 to 58. About 9% drop out after the first year for academic or personal reasons.

Salmon P. Chase College of Law

Louie B. Nunn Hall
Highland Heights, KY 41099

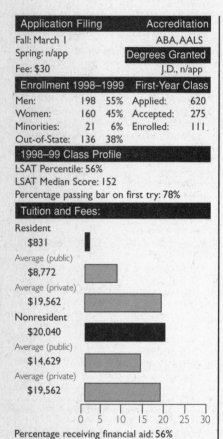

Application Filing	Accreditation
Fall: March 1	ABA, AALS
Spring: n/app	**Degrees Granted**
Fee: $30	J.D., n/app

Enrollment 1998–1999		First-Year Class	
Men:	198 55%	Applied:	620
Women:	160 45%	Accepted:	275
Minorities:	21 6%	Enrolled:	111
Out-of-State:	136 38%		

1998–99 Class Profile
LSAT Percentile: 56%
LSAT Median Score: 152
Percentage passing bar on first try: 78%

Tuition and Fees:

Resident
$831

Average (public)
$8,772

Average (private)
$19,562

Nonresident
$20,040

Average (public)
$14,629

Average (private)
$19,562

0 5 10 15 20 25 30

Percentage receiving financial aid: 56%

ADMISSIONS

In the fall 1999 first-year class, 620 applied, 275 were accepted, and 111 enrolled. Twelve transfers enrolled. The median LSAT percentile of the most recent first-year class was 56; the median GPA was 3.1 on a scale of 4.0. The lowest LSAT percentile accepted was 18; the highest was 98.

Requirements
Applicants must have a bachelor's degree from an accredited institution and take the LSAT. The most important admission factors include LSAT results, GPA, and writing ability. No specific undergraduate courses are required. Candidates are not interviewed.

Procedure
The application deadline for fall entry is March 1. Applicants should submit an application form, LSAT results, transcripts, a nonrefundable application fee of $30, 2 letters of recommendation, and a personal statement. Transcripts must

be submitted through the LSDAS. A $150 acceptance deposit must be submitted to reserve a place after an offer is made, and a $300 registration deposit is required preceding enrollment. Notification of the admission decision is on a rolling basis. The latest acceptable LSAT test date for fall entry is February.

Special
The law school recruits minority and disadvantaged students through minority career days, contacts with members of the school's Black American Law Students Association and through the Law Services CRS search. Requirements are different for out-of-state students in that admissions are more selective. Transfer students must have a minimum GPA of 3.0, have attended an ABA-approved law school, must be in good standing and eligible to continue study, and must provide an official transcript documenting acceptably high-quality performance.

Costs

Tuition and fees for the 1999-2000 academic year are $831 for full-time in-state students and $20,040 for out-of-state students. Tuition for part-time students is $5602 per year in-state and $13,422 out-of-state. On-campus room and board costs about $2587 annually; and books and supplies run $500.

Financial Aid

About 56% of current law students receive some form of aid. The average annual amount of aid from all sources combined, including scholarships, loans, and work contracts, is $16,888; maximum, $18,500. Awards are based on need and merit. The required financial statement is the FAFSA. The aid application deadline for fall entry is April 1. Special funds for minority or disadvantaged students include scholarships. First-year students are notified about their financial aid application at time of acceptance.

About the Law School

Northern Kentucky University Salmon P. Chase College of Law was established in 1893 and is a public institution. The 300-acre campus is in a suburban area 7 miles southeast of Cincinnati. The primary mission of the law school is to train competent lawyers and to enable students to gain proficiency in specific areas

of law. Students have access to federal, state, county, city, and local agencies, courts, correctional facilities, law firms, and legal aid organizations in the Highland Heights area. The school is located in a major metropolitan area that provides a wide variety of opportunities for law students. Housing for law students is available on campus in the Residential Village. Both suites and apartments are offered, along with computer rooms, a store, and a dining hall. Dormitories are also available, and numerous apartments are located close to campus. About 95% of the law school facilities are accessible to the physically disabled.

Calendar

The law school operates on a traditional semester basis. Courses for full-time students are offered days only and with some electives being offered on Saturdays and in the evening, and must be completed within 3 ½ years. For part-time students, courses are offered evenings and Saturdays and must be completed within 4 ½ years. New full-time students are admitted in the fall; part-time, fall. There is a 7-week summer session. Transferable summer courses are offered.

Programs

In addition to the J.D., the following joint degree may be earned: J.D./M.B.A. (Juris Doctor/Master of Business Administration).

Required
To earn the J.D., candidates must complete 90 total credits, of which 42 are for required courses. They must maintain a minimum GPA of 2.15 in the required courses. The following first-year courses are required of all students: Civil Procedure I and II, Contracts I and II, Torts I and II, Property I and II, Introduction to Legal Studies, and Basic Legal Skills I and II. Required upper-level courses consist of Constitutional Law I and II, Criminal Law, Criminal Procedure, Evidence, Federal Taxation 1A, and Professional Responsibility. All students are allowed to use a maximum of 12 nonclassroom hours of credit toward graduation. The required orientation program for first-year students consists of an extensive combination of voluntary and required orientation programs: a voluntary half-

Phone: 606-572-6476
Fax: 606-572-6081
E-mail: brayg@nku.edu
Web: www.nku.edu/~@chase

Contact

Gina Bray, Admissions Specialist, 606-572-5384 for general inquiries; Bob Sprauge, Director, Financial Aid Office, 606-572-6437 for financial aid information.

KENTUCKY

day program in May focusing on what entering students can do over the summer to prepare; a voluntary 2-week program offered at no charge twice during July, focusing on developing essential case-reading skills; a required half-day orientation in August to the programs and services available at the College of Law and the University; a required 2-week, 1-credit-hour course in August designed especially to introduce students to their first year of legal studies; and a required half-day program presented in conjunction with the Kentucky Bar Association to sensitize students to ethical concerns.

Electives

Clinics offered include the in-house Local Government Law Center Clinic and specialized clinical externships with federal trial judges, the Children's Law Center, the IRS tax center, and state and local government agencies, as well as a wide variety of more general clinical externships. All clinical opportunities are 2 or 3 credits per semester. Seminars include Business, Technology and Regulation, Constitutional Law, and Criminal Law/Justice. Chase has IOLTA Public Interest Fellowships that provide financial remuneration (rather than credit) to students interning part time during the academic year and full time in the summer with public interest organizations in the Commonwealth. An active supervised independent research program is offered Public policy research opportunities are available through the in-house Local Government Law Center and in conjunction with the Children's Law Center. The *Law Review* sponsors a major national symposium annually. Special tutorial programs (all at no cost) for first-year students include a 2-week Summer Program in Legal Analysis in July before entry; Academic Development program workshops and tutorials on Saturdays in the fall sememter; an exam writing seminar and follow-up tutorials on Saturdays in the spring semester; and additional individual tutoring help available through the Chase Academic Learning and Development Center. Special "early bird" bar preparation programs are provided for graduating students, again at no cost. All first-year students are given small-section experience in substantive courses. In addition, those first-year students with less-developed writing skills are placed in

small, specially enriched legal writing sections. For second-year students in difficulty, special tutorials are available in conjunction with the required Criminal Law course and additional remedial writing instruction is available in conjunction with the Legal Drafting course. Professional and social activities, as well as special tutorial assistance, are available in conjunction with the Black Lawyers Association of Cincinnati (BLAC) and the Cincinnati Bar Association/BLAC Lawyers Association Roundtable. A variety of programs throughout the year is sponsored by the Appalachian Law Society, Environmental Law Organization, International Law Society, Women's Law Caucus, and several law fraternities. Chase offers a wide range of both required and optional academic support programs to help its students prepare for law school. Chase also offers a wide range of legal skills offerings writing, counseling, negotiating, litigating, and oral advocacy courses to help students prepare for legal practice. The most widely taken electives are Wills and Trusts, Corporations, and Trial Advocacy.

Graduation Requirements

In order to graduate, candidates must have a GPA of 2.0 and have completed the upper-division writing requirement.

Organizations

Students edit the *Northern Kentucky Law Review*. Students participate in a variety of moot court competitions at numerous locations. Law student organizations include the Chase Association of Trial Lawyers, Christian Law Students, Environmental Law Society, International Law Society, Legal Volunteers Society, and local chapters of the Young Democrats, Young Republicans, and ABA-Law Student Division.

Library

The law library contains 242,595 hardcopy volumes and 856 microform volume equivalents, and subscribes to 2138 serial publications. Such on-line databases and networks as LEXIS, DIALOG, WESTLAW, and NEXIS are available to law students for research. Special library collections include U.S. Supreme Court records and briefs on microfiche. Recently, the library added a self-service reserve room, a small video viewing

Placement

J.D.s awarded:	112

Services available through: separate law school placement center and the university placement center

Special features: workshops and job fairs, including the Minority Access Program at the University of Cincinnati, Federal Job Options Program, Local Government/Public Interest Job Fair, Alumni Legal Career Options Day, and Bridge the Gap Program

Full-time job interviews:	14 employers
Summer job interviews:	20 employers
Placement by graduation:	50% of class
Placement within 9 months:	94% of class
Average starting salary:	$20,000 to $100,000

Areas of placement:

Private practice 2-10 attorneys	33%
Private practice 11-25 attorneys	5%
Private practice 26-50 attorneys	1%
Private practice 101-250 attorneys	1%
Private practice 250+ attorneys	1%
Business/industry	26%
Government	18%
Judicial clerkships	8%
Academic	1%
Public interest	1%
solo practice	5%

room, and a state-of-the-art computer lab. The ratio of library volumes to faculty is 9087 to 1 and to students, 609 to 1.

Faculty

The law school has 25 full-time and 42 part-time faculty members, of whom 19 are women. According to AAUP standards for Category IIA institutions, faculty salaries are below average. About 28% of full-time faculty have a graduate law degree in addition to the J.D. The ratio of full-time students to full-time faculty in an average class is 7 to 1.

Students

About 45% of the student body are women; 6%, minorities; 4%, African American; 1%, Asian American; 1%, Hispanic; and 1%, Native American. The majority of students come from Kentucky (62%). The average age of entering students is 28; age range is 21 to 65. About 14% of students have a graduate degree. About 19% drop out after the first year for academic or personal reasons.

School of Law

357 East Chicago Avenue
Chicago, IL 60611

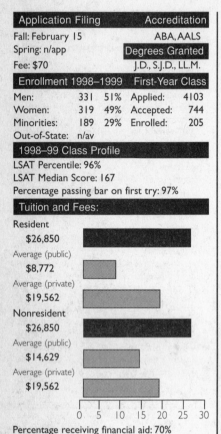

Application Filing	Accreditation
Fall: February 15	ABA, AALS
Spring: n/app	Degrees Granted
Fee: $70	J.D., S.J.D., LL.M.

Enrollment 1998–1999		First-Year Class	
Men:	331 51%	Applied:	4103
Women:	319 49%	Accepted:	744
Minorities:	189 29%	Enrolled:	205
Out-of-State:	n/av		

1998–99 Class Profile
LSAT Percentile: 96%
LSAT Median Score: 167
Percentage passing bar on first try: 97%

Tuition and Fees:

Resident
$26,850
Average (public)
$8,772
Average (private)
$19,562
Nonresident
$26,850
Average (public)
$14,629
Average (private)
$19,562

0 5 10 15 20 25 30

Percentage receiving financial aid: 70%

ADMISSIONS

In the fall 1999 first-year class, 4103 applied, 744 were accepted, and 205 enrolled. Twenty-five transfers enrolled. The median LSAT percentile of the most recent first-year class was 96; the median GPA was 3.5 on a scale of 4.0. The lowest LSAT percentile accepted was 45; the highest was 99.

Requirements

Applicants must have a bachelor's degree from an accredited institution and take the LSAT. The most important admission factors include character, personality, life experience, and academic achievement. No specific undergraduate courses are required. Candidates are interviewed.

Procedure

The application deadline for fall entry is February 15. Applicants should submit an application form, LSAT results, transcripts, a nonrefundable application fee of $70, 2 letters of recommendation, a personal statement, and resume. Regis-

tration with LSDAS is required. Interviews are strongly encouraged. Notification of the admission decision is by May 1. The latest acceptable LSAT test date for fall entry is February. The law school uses the LSDAS.

Special

The law school recruits minority and disadvantaged students through the efforts of the Director of Minority Affairs. Transfer students must have one year of credit, have attended an ABA-approved law school, and have earned a minimum of 30 credit hours.

Costs

Tuition and fees for the 1999-2000 academic year are $26,850 for all full-time students. On-campus room and board costs about $10,214 annually; books and supplies run $1200.

Financial Aid

About 70% of current law students receive some form of aid. Awards are based on need and merit. The required financial statements are FAFSA and the Institutional Financial Aid Application Form. The aid application deadline for fall entry is March 15. Special funds for minority or disadvantaged students consist of the Ronald E. Kennedy Scholarship, awarded on the basis of merit and financial need. First-year students are notified about their financial aid application before May 1 if all required documents are received by the Office of Admission and Financial Aid before the March 15 deadline.

About the Law School

Northwestern University School of Law was established in 1859 and is a private institution. The 20-acre campus is in an urban area in Chicago. The primary mission of the law school is to advance the understanding of law and legal institutions and to produce graduates who are prepared to lead and succeed in a rapidly changing world. Students have access to federal, state, county, city, and local agencies, courts, correctional facilities, law firms, and legal aid organizations in the Chicago area. The Arthur Rubloff Building, an addition to the school, houses the national headquarters of the American Bar Association, American Bar Foundation, and American Bar Endow-

ment. Facilities of special interest to law students consist of 2 fully equipped, modern courtrooms. Computer terminals are available for use in the library and a computer laboratory provides computers and printers for word processing. Housing for law students is available in 2 residence buildings located within 1 block of the school. They have more than 750 rooms, including some 1-bedroom and efficiency apartments for married students. About 90% of the law school facilities are accessible to the physically disabled.

Calendar

The law school operates on a traditional semester basis. Courses for full-time students are offered days only and must be completed within 3 years. There is no part-time program. New full-time students are admitted in the fall. There is no summer session. Transferable summer courses are not offered.

Programs

In addition to the J.D., the law school offers the S.J.D. and LL.M. with a certificate in management. Students may take relevant courses in other programs and apply credit toward the J.D.; a maximum of 6 credits may be applied. The following joint degrees may be earned: J.D./M.M. (Juris Doctor/Master of Management) and J.D./Ph.D. (Juris Doctor/Doctor of Philosophy).

Required

To earn the J.D., candidates must complete 86 total credits, of which 32 are for required courses. They must maintain a minimum GPA of 2.25 in the required courses. The following first-year courses are required of all students: Contracts, Torts, Civil Procedure, Legal Writing, Criminal Law, Property, and Constitutional Law. Required upper-level courses consist of Legal Ethics and a writing requirement that may be fulfilled with either, journal work; a 2-semester Senior Research project, or several upper-level electives with significant writing requirements. The required orientation program for first-year students takes place 2 days before classes begin. First-year students register and receive class assignments, meet with their faculty advisers, tour the school, and attend social functions.

Phone: 312-503-8465
Fax: 312-503-0178
E-mail: nubwadm@nwu.edu
Web: www.law.nwu.edu

ILLINOIS

Contact

Donald Rebstock, Assistant dean of Admissions and Financial Aid, 312-503-8465 for general inquiries; and financial aid information.

Electives

The School of Law offers concentrations in corporate law, international law, litigation, health law, and dispute resolution. In addition, clinics are open to second- and third-year students. A sequence of simulation-based courses offered in the second year include, Clinical Trial Advocacy and Pre-Trial Litigation, as well as case-based instruction. Students also take clinically based Evidence, which presents the principles of evidence in the context of simulated cases. Course credits vary between 3 to 4 hours. Students can represent clients through the Children's and Family Justice Center, Small Business Opportunity Clinic, and Center for International Human Rights. Seminars are offered in legal history, civil law, civil rights litigation, arbitration, race relations, computers and the law, non-profit organizations, criminal evidence, entertainment law, jurisprudence, health law, and other areas. A third-year student may earn up to 14 credits for advanced research under the personal supervision of one or more faculty members. Completion of this project fulfills the writing requirement. Professional Responsibility Practicums consist of a 10 to 12 hours per week field work component, and a weekly 2-hour seminar. Annually, the Rosenthal Lecture Series brings preeminent figures in law and related fields to the school. The Pope and John Lecture on Professionalism deals with ethics and professional responsibility. The Howard J. Trienens Visiting Judicial Scholar Program brings leading jurists to the school to lecture on legal issues and to meet informally with students. Study abroad opportunities include Catholic University of Leuven, Belgium; Free University of Amsterdam, The Netherlands; Tel Aviv University, Israel; and Bond University, Australia. Tutorial programs are offered through the Dean of Students on an individual basis. The Director of Minority Affairs provides academic admission, placement counseling, and other supportive services. The most widely taken electives are Real Estate, Commercial Transactions, and International Law.

Graduation Requirements

In order to graduate, candidates must have a GPA of 2.2 and have completed the upper-division writing requirement.

Organizations

Student-edited publications include the *Northwestern University Law Review*, *The Journal of Criminal Law and Criminology*, *The Northwestern Journal of International Law and Business*, and the newspaper Hoops. Annual moot court competitions are the Arlyn Miner First-Year Moot Court Program, the Julius H. Miner Moot Court, and the Philip C. Jessup International Law Moot Court. Other competitions are the John Paul Stevens Prize for academic excellence, Lowden-Wigmore Prizes for best contributions to journals and best Julius Miner Moot Court performances, Barnet and Scott Hodes Prize for best student paper in international law, Arlyn Miner Book Award for the best brief by a first-year student, Harold D. Shapiro Prize for best student in an international economics relations class, the West Publishing Company Awards for scholastic achievement, and the Nathan Burkhan Memorial Competition for best paper on copyright law. Student organizations include Amnesty International, Feminists for Social Change, and Northwestern Law Students for the Homeless. There are local chapters of the National Lawyers Guild, The Federalist Society, and the ABA-Law Student Division. Other organizations are the Cabrini Green Youth Program, HORIZONS, and Wigmore Folfes, an annual student-run variety show.

Library

The law library contains 656,775 hardcopy volumes and 195,648 microform volume equivalents, and subscribes to 8258 serial publications. Such on-line databases and networks as LEXIS, DIALOG, WESTLAW, CCH Access, and NEXIS are available to law students for research. Special library collections include a large international collection and the Hodes Rare Book Room. The ratio of library volumes to faculty is 11,745 to 1 and to students, 1000 to 1. The ratio of seats in the library to students is 1 to 1.

Placement	
J.D.s awarded:	221
Services available through: separate law school placement center	
Services: arrangement of job fairs for off-campus interviews	
Full-time job interviews:	300 employers
Summer job interviews:	300 employers
Placement by graduation:	96% of class
Placement within 9 months:	99% of class
Average starting salary:	$34,200 to $125,000
Areas of placement:	
Private practice 2-10 attorneys	74%
Judicial clerkships	11%
Government	6%
Academic	2%

Faculty

The law school has 59 full-time and 149 part-time faculty members, of whom 51 are women. According to AAUP standards for Category I institutions, faculty salaries are well above average. About 99% of full-time faculty have a graduate law degree in addition to the J.D.; all part-time faculty have one. The ratio of full-time students to full-time faculty in an average class is 12 to 1; in a clinic, 8 to 1. The law school has a regular program of bringing visiting professors and other distinguished lecturers and visitors to campus. There is a chapter of the Order of the Coif; 40 faculty and 20 graduates are members.

Students

About 49% of the student body are women; 29%, minorities; 8%, African American; 13%, Asian American; and 7%, Hispanic. The majority of students come from the Midwest (38%). The average age of entering students is 25; age range is 21 to 44. About 24% of students enter directly from undergraduate school, 8% have a graduate degree, and 76% have worked full-time prior to entering law school. About 1% drop out after the first year for academic or personal reasons; 99% remain to receive a law degree.

Shepard Broad Law Center

3305 College Avenue
Fort Lauderdale, FL 33314-7721

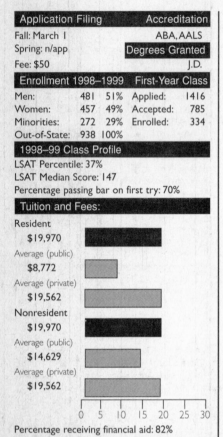

Application Filing		Accreditation
Fall: March 1		ABA, AALS
Spring: n/app		**Degrees Granted**
Fee: $50		J.D.

Enrollment 1998–1999		First-Year Class	
Men:	481 51%	Applied:	1416
Women:	457 49%	Accepted:	785
Minorities:	272 29%	Enrolled:	334
Out-of-State:	938 100%		

1998–99 Class Profile

LSAT Percentile: 37%
LSAT Median Score: 147
Percentage passing bar on first try: 70%

Tuition and Fees:

Resident
$19,970

Average (public)
$8,772

Average (private)
$19,562

Nonresident
$19,970

Average (public)
$14,629

Average (private)
$19,562

0 5 10 15 20 25 30

Percentage receiving financial aid: 82%

ADMISSIONS

In the fall 1999 first-year class, 1416 applied, 785 were accepted, and 334 enrolled. Twenty-three transfers enrolled. The median LSAT percentile of the most recent first-year class was 37; the median GPA was 2.88 on a scale of 4.0. The lowest LSAT percentile accepted was 3; the highest was 99.

Requirements

Applicants must have a bachelor's degree from an accredited institution and take the LSAT. The most important admission factors include undergraduate curriculum, life experience, and academic achievement. No specific undergraduate courses are required. Candidates are not interviewed.

Procedure

The application deadline for fall entry is March 1. Applicants should submit an application form, LSAT results, transcripts, a nonrefundable application fee of $50, and 2 letters of recommendation are suggested. Notification of the admission decision is on a rolling basis. The latest acceptable LSAT test date for fall entry is February (June for part-time students). The law school uses the LSDAS.

Special

The law school recruits minority and disadvantaged students by means of on-campus minority programs, attendance at historically black college fairs, and participation in and maintenance of a good relationship with the CLEO program. Transfer students must have one year of credit, have attended an ABA-approved law school, have no grade below C in required courses, and provide a letter of good standing from the current dean. Foreign attorneys are also admitted. Preadmissions courses consist of summer conditional admissions programs where students must earn at least a C+ average for 2 courses.

Costs

Tuition and fees for the 1999-2000 academic year are $19,970 for all full-time students. Tuition for all part-time students is $14,980 annually. On-campus room and board costs about $6677 annually; and books and supplies run $1450.

Financial Aid

About 82% of current law students receive some form of aid. The maximum annual amount of aid from all sources combined, including scholarships, loans, and work contracts, is $35,515. Awards are based on need and merit. Loans are need-based; most scholarships are merit-based; some scholarships are need- and merit-based. The required financial statements are FAFSA and no statements are required for merit-based aid. The aid application deadline for fall entry is March 1. Special funds for minority or disadvantaged students are scholarship funds. First-year students are notified about their financial aid application when application for aid is complete.

About the Law School

Nova Southeastern University Shepard Broad Law Center was established in 1974 and is a private institution. The 232-acre campus is in a suburban area 3 miles west of Fort Lauderdale, Florida. The primary mission of the law school is to allow students to reach their potential as ethical, competent, and caring advocates in a supportive environment stressing lawyering skills and values. Students have access to federal, state, county, city, and local agencies, courts, correctional facilities, law firms, and legal aid organizations in the Fort Lauderdale area. Facilities of special interest to law students is the Leo C. Goodwin, Sr., Hall. All students can access computing facilities from anywhere in the building using wireless technology. Housing for law students is in 4 university-owned apartment buildings; there are also numerous apartments available near the campus. All law school facilities are accessible to the physically disabled.

Calendar

The law school operates on a traditional semester basis. Courses for full-time students are offered both day and evening and must be completed within 5 years. For part-time students, courses are offered evenings only with some day classes available, and must be completed within 6 years. New full-and part-time students are admitted in the fall. There is a 7-week summer session. Transferable summer courses are offered.

Programs

Students may take relevant courses in other programs and apply credit toward the J.D.; a maximum of 4 (8 in joint-degree programs) credits may be applied. The following joint degrees may be earned: J.D./M.B.A. (Juris Doctor/Master of Business Administration), J.D./M.S. (Juris Doctor/Master of Science in psychology), J.D./M.S. (Juris Doctor/Master of Science in dispute resolution), and J.D./M.U.R.P. (Juris Doctor/Master of Urban and Regional Planning).

Phone: 954-262-6117
800-986-6529
Fax: 954-262-3844
E-mail: admission@nsu.law.nova.edu
Web: http://www.nsu.law.nova.edu

Contact

Nancy Kelly Sanguigni, Director, 954-262-6117 for general inquiries; Lynn Acosta, Counselor, Financial Aid Office, 800-522-3243 for financial aid information.

Required

To earn the J.D., candidates must complete 90 total credits, of which 44 are for required courses. The following first-year courses are required of all students: Contracts, Torts, Criminal Law, Property, Civil Procedure, Constitutional Law I, and Lawyering Skills and Values I and II. Required upper-level courses consist of Professional Responsibility, an upper class writing requirement, Constitutional Law II, Evidence or Corporations, and Lawyering Skills and Values III and IV. All students are guaranteed a clinical semester. The required orientation program for first-year students includes an introduction to the law school experience before classes begin; other sessions are held during the semester.

Electives

The Shepard Broad Law Center offers concentrations in corporate law, criminal law, environmental law, international law, torts and insurance, and children and family. In addition, the clinics offer 12 credits to students who work with families and children, an environmental group, an international agency, a prosecutor or public defender, a corporation or business firm, a personal injury firm, or a mediation program. The mediation program is worth 8 credits. Upper-level students may take seminars for 2 to 3 credits. As interns, students earn 2 credits researching for a judge or serving as a guardian ad litem. The Career Development Office sponsors lecture series on various types of law practices. The office also offers lawyering skills courses in its Career Development Academy. ABA-approved summer programs in Caracas, Venezuela, and Cambridge, England are available. The Law Center is seeking ABA acquiescence for programs in Costa Rica and Israel. Tutorial programs consist of the Academic Resource Program, including a writing program taught by an English professor who holds a J.D. Special interest group programs are the Individuals with Disabilities Project and Guardian ad Litem. Both offer credit for working to protect the rights of the disabled and children. The most widely taken electives are Family Law, Evidence, and Wills and Trusts.

Graduation Requirements

In order to graduate, candidates must have a GPA of 2.0, have completed the upper-division writing requirement, and passed all required courses.

Organizations

Students edit the *Nova Law Review*, the *Journal of International and Comparative Law*, and the newspaper, *Broadly Speaking*. Intramural moot court competitions are held in the fall for upper-class students and in the winter for first-year students; the Round Robin Moot Court Competition is hosted by NSU each February. A team competes in the American Trial Lawyers Association trial competition as well as other trial and moot court competitions. Law student organizations include the International Law Society, Entertainment and Sports Law Society, and the Student Bar Association. Local chapters of national associations include the ABA-Law Student Division, Phi Alpha Delta, and Phi Delta Phi. Campus clubs and other organizations include Yearbook, Young Democrats, and Young Republicans.

Library

The law library contains 314,036 hardcopy volumes and 137,029 microform volume equivalents, and subscribes to 1213 serial publications. Such on-line databases and networks as LEXIS, DIALOG, WESTLAW, and Wilsonline, NEXIS, OCLC, Seflink, and First Search are available to law students for research. Special library collections include state, federal, and United Nations depositories and collections in tax, criminal law, international law, children/family, jurisprudence, admiralty, trial practice, and law and popular culture. Recently, the library expanded the computer laboratory and permanent learning center facilities, including interactive video, CD-ROM, and computer-assisted instruction stations. The ratio of library volumes to faculty is 6976 to 1 and to students, 334 to 1. The ratio of seats in the library to students is 1 to 6.

Placement

J.D.s awarded:	290

Services available through: a separate law school placement center.
Services: Southeast Minority Job Fair, Mid-Florida Job Fair
Special features: the Alumni Job-Line, and a monthly alumni job bulletin

Full-time job interviews:	22 employers
Summer job interviews:	25 employers
Placement by graduation:	n/av
Placement within 9 months:	86% of class
Average starting salary:	$29,914 to $38,747

Areas of placement:

Private practice 2-10 attorneys	28%
Private practice 11-25 attorneys	12%
Private practice 26-50 attorneys	4%
Private practice 51-100 attorneys	4%
Government	22%
Business/industry	15%
Unknown	8%
Judicial clerkships	3%
Public interest	1%
Military	1%
Academic	1%

Faculty

The law school has 45 full-time and 64 part-time faculty members, of whom 38 are women. About 40% of full-time faculty have a graduate law degree in addition to the J.D.; about 14% of part-time faculty have one. The ratio of full-time students to full-time faculty in an average class is 50 to 1; in a clinic, 20 to 1. The law school has a regular program of bringing visiting professors and other distinguished lecturers and visitors to campus. There is a chapter of the Order of the Coif; 5 faculty are members.

Students

About 49% of the student body are women; 29%, minorities; 8%, African American; 2%, Asian American; and 19%, Hispanic. The age range of entering students is 22 to 85. About 8% drop out after the first year for academic or personal reasons; 83% remain to receive a law degree.

Claude W. Pettit College of Law

525 South Main Street
Ada, OH 45810

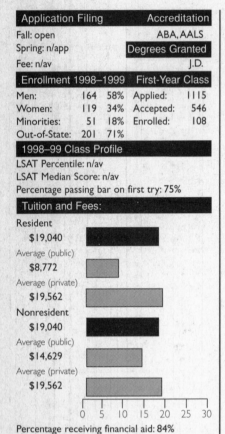

Application Filing	Accreditation
Fall: open	ABA, AALS
Spring: n/app	**Degrees Granted**
Fee: n/av	J.D.

Enrollment 1998–1999		First-Year Class	
Men:	164 58%	Applied:	1115
Women:	119 34%	Accepted:	546
Minorities:	51 18%	Enrolled:	108
Out-of-State:	201 71%		

1998–99 Class Profile
LSAT Percentile: n/av
LSAT Median Score: n/av
Percentage passing bar on first try: 75%

Tuition and Fees:

Resident
$19,040
Average (public)
$8,772
Average (private)
$19,562
Nonresident
$19,040
Average (public)
$14,629
Average (private)
$19,562

0 5 10 15 20 25 30

Percentage receiving financial aid: 84%

ADMISSIONS

In the fall 1999 first-year class, 1115 applied, 546 were accepted, and 108 enrolled. Eight transfers enrolled. The median GPA of the most recent first-year class was about 2.95 on a scale of 4.0. The lowest LSAT percentile accepted was 8; the highest was 99.

Requirements

Applicants must have a bachelor's degree from an accredited institution and take the LSAT. Minimum acceptable GPA is 2.0 on a scale of 4.0. The most important admission factors include LSAT results, GPA, and college attended. No specific undergraduate courses are required. Candidates are not interviewed.

Procedure

Applicants should submit an application form, transcripts, a nonrefundable application fee, and the LSDAS report. Check with the school for current fee. Notification of the admission decision is on a rolling basis. The latest acceptable LSAT test date for fall entry is June. The law school uses the LSDAS.

Special

The law school recruits minority and disadvantaged students by means of on-site college recruitment, CLEO, CRS mailings, and campus visit days. Transfer students must have attended an ABA-approved law school and provide a letter of good standing, a transcript of law school work, undergraduate transcripts, and the LSDAS report.

Costs

Tuition and fees for the 1999-2000 academic year are $19,040 for all full-time students. On-campus room and board costs about $5860 annually; and books and supplies run $700.

Financial Aid

In a recent year, about 84% of current law students receive some form of aid. The average annual amount of aid from all sources combined, including scholarships, loans, and work contracts, was $24,300; maximum, $30,180. Awards are based on need and merit. The required financial statements are FAFSA and the school's financial aid application. Check with the school for current deadline. There are special funds for students to enhance cultural and ethnic diversity. First-year students are notified about their financial aid application at the time of acceptance.

About the Law School

Ohio Northern University Claude W. Pettit College of Law was established in 1885 and is a private institution. The 280-acre campus is in a small town 70 miles south of Toledo, Ohio. The primary mission of the law school is to educate and train students from diverse backgrounds to become responsible and successful practitioners capable of exemplary legal service in roles throughout society. Students have access to federal, state, county, city, and local agencies, courts, correctional facilities, law firms, and legal aid organizations in the Ada area. Housing for law students is available on campus and reasonable off-campus housing is also available. About 90% of the law school facilities are accessible to the physically disabled.

Calendar

The law school operates on a traditional semester basis. Courses for full-time students are offered days only and must be completed within 5 years. There is no part-time program. New full-time students are admitted in the fall. There is an 8-week summer session. Transferable summer courses are offered.

Programs

Required

To earn the J.D., candidates must complete 87 total credits, of which 45 are for required courses. The following first-year courses are required of all students: Contracts I and II, Torts I and II, Property I and II, Civil Procedure I and II, Criminal Law, and Legal Research and Writing I and II. Required upper-level

Phone: 419-772-2211
Fax: 419-772-1487
E-mail: g-keener@onu.edu
Web: http://www.law.onu.edu

Contact

Grant Keener Assistant Admissions Director, 419-772-2211 for general inquiries; Financial Aid Director, 419-772-2272 for financial aid information.

OHIO

courses consist of Evidence, Federal Income Tax, Business Organizations I, Constitutional Law I, Legal Profession, and writing seminar. All students must take clinical courses. The required orientation program for first-year students comprises a 2-day introduction to university and law school procedures and the instructional approach followed by 4 special continuing orientation programs.

Electives

The Claude W. Pettit College of Law offers concentrations in environmental law, international law, and tax law. In addition, after students fulfill prerequisite course work, they may receive up to 6 hours of credit for participating in the Senior Citizens Clinic. Seminars are open to second- and third-year students and include Criminal Law, International Legal Issues, and Environmental Law. There is a Civil Internship Program. Field work includes judicial externships with state and federal courts, criminal externships, and governmental-legislative externships. The Annual Kormendy Lecture Series sponsors prominent national legal figures. Recent lecturers have included Justice Clarence Thomas and Professor Deborah Rhode, Stanford School of Law. The college will give credit for ABA-approved law schools' study-abroad programs with prior approval. There is an Icelandic Study Exchange Program. First-year students are assisted by volunteer tutors. Minority students benefit from the Black Law Students Association-sponsored study groups and the EXCEL-Academic Success Program. The Asian-Pacific-American Law Student Association also sponsors special programs. Special interest groups include International Law Society, Legal Association of Women, and Environmental Law Society. The most widely taken electives are Criminal Procedure, Domestic Relations, and Decendents' Estates and Trusts.

Graduation Requirements

In order to graduate, candidates must have a GPA of 2.0 and have completed the upper-division writing requirement.

Organizations

Students edit the *Ohio Northern University Law Review, Women's Law Journal,* and the *Environmental Law Journal.* Teams compete in the New York Bar Association's Annual National Moot Court, ABA Negotiations, and Jessup International Law competitions. Law student organizations include the Student Bar Association, Legal Association of Women, and Black Law Students Association. There are local chapters of Environmental Law Society, International Law Society, and Delta Theta Phi. A campus organization is Habitat for Humanity.

Library

The law library contains 263,747 hardcopy volumes and 72,943 microform volume equivalents, and subscribes to 950 serial publications. Such on-line databases and networks as LEXIS, DIALOG, WESTLAW, and Hannah are available to law students for research. Special library collections include a federal government depository. The ratio of library volumes to faculty is 14,653 to 1 and to students, 809 to 1. The ratio of seats in the library to students is 1 to 3.

Faculty

The law school has 18 full-time and 22 part-time faculty members, of whom 9 are women. According to AAUP standards for Category IIB institutions, faculty salaries are well above average. About 39% of full-time faculty have a graduate law degree in addition to the J.D.; about 9% of part-time faculty have one. The ratio of full-time students to full-time faculty in an average class is 20 to 1; in a clinic, 10 to 1.

Students

About 34% of the student body are women; 18%, minorities; 9%, African American; 3%, Asian American; 2%, Hispanic; and 1%, Native American. The majority of students come from Ohio (29%). The average age of entering students is 26; age range is 21 to 60. About 6% drop out after the first year for academic or personal reasons; 94% remain to receive a law degree.

Placement

J.D.s awarded:	97

Services available through: a separate law school placement center.

Services: Spring Recruiting Conference and Spring Public Interest Career Fair

Special features: An active membership in NALP and the Ohio Law Placement Consortium (OLPC), through which the college participates in a variety of joint recruiting projects throughout the year.

Full-time job interviews:	6 employers
Summer job interviews:	9 employers
Placement by graduation:	45% of class
Placement within 9 months:	50% of class
Average starting salary:	$23,300 to $77,000

Areas of placement:

Private practice 2-10 attorneys	34%
Private practice 11-25 attorneys	2%
Private practice 26-50 attorneys	2%
Private practice 51-100	4%
Government	16%
Business/industry	15%
Judicial clerkships	11%
Public interest	9%
Legal publishing	4%
Military	2%
Academic	2%

College of Law

55 West 12th Avenue,
John Deaver Drinko Hall
Columbus, OH 43210-1391

Application Filing / Accreditation

Application Filing	Accreditation
Fall: March 15	ABA, AALS
Spring: n/app	**Degrees Granted**
Fee: n/av	J.D.

Enrollment 1998–1999   First-Year Class

Men:	337	53%	Applied:	1482
Women:	301	44%	Accepted:	585
Minorities:	102	16%	Enrolled:	214
Out-of-State:	166	26%		

1998–99 Class Profile

LSAT Percentile: 74%
LSAT Median Score: 157
Percentage passing bar on first try: 85%

Tuition and Fees:

Resident
$8,424

Average (public)
$8,772

Average (private)
$19,562

Nonresident
$15,968

Average (public)
$14,629

Average (private)
$19,562

0   5   10   15   20   25   30

Percentage receiving financial aid: 70%

ADMISSIONS

In the fall 1999 first-year class, 1482 applied, 585 were accepted, and 214 enrolled. Ten transfers enrolled. The median LSAT percentile of the most recent first-year class was 74; the median GPA was 3.6 on a scale of 4.0. The highest LSAT percentile was 99.

Requirements
Applicants must have a bachelor's degree from an accredited institution and take the LSAT. The most important admission factors include academic achievement, undergraduate curriculum, and life experience. No specific undergraduate courses are required. Candidates are not interviewed.

Procedure
The application deadline for fall entry is March 15. Applicants should submit an application form, LSAT results, transcripts, 2 letters of recommendation, and the Academic Records Office Evaluation from undergraduate school. There is a non-refundable application fee. Notification of the admission decision is on a rolling basis. The latest acceptable LSAT test date for fall entry is February. The law school uses the LSDAS.

Special
The law school recruits minority and disadvantaged students through participation in CLEO and as a part of the overall recruitment program. Transfer students must have one year of credit and have attended an ABA-approved law school.

Costs

Tuition and fees for the 1999-2000 academic year are $8424 for full-time in-state students and $15,968 for out-of-state students. On-campus room and board costs about $5247 annually; books and supplies run $1588.

Financial Aid

About 70% of current law students receive some form of aid. The average annual amount of aid from all sources combined, including scholarships, loans, and work contracts, is $16,929; maximum, $26,259. Awards are based on need and merit. The required financial statement is the FAFSA. Check with the school for cu;rrent application deadlines. There are special funds for minority or disadvantaged students including CLEO participation. First-year students are notified about their financial aid application shortly after acceptance.

About the Law School

Ohio State University College of Law was established in 1891 and is a public institution. The 3200-acre campus is in an urban area 2 miles north of downtown Columbus. The primary mission of the law school is to produce lawyers from a base of scholarship, education, and service; the approach is broad-based and academically oriented. Students have access to federal, state, county, city, and local agencies, courts, correctional facilities, law firms, and legal aid organizations in the Columbus area. As Columbus is Ohio's capital, students frequently work part time for a number of state agencies during their second and third years of law school. Facilities of special interest to law students are the state legislature and state supreme court. Housing for law students is available in 3 campus dormitories reserved for graduate and professional students; there are plenty of off-campus housing facilities sufficient for all students. All law school facilities are accessible to the physically disabled.

Calendar

The law school operates on a traditional semester basis. Courses for full-time students are offered days only and must be completed within 5 years. There is no part-time program. New students are admitted in the fall. There is an 8-week summer session. Transferable summer courses are offered.

Programs

Students may take relevant courses in other programs and apply credit toward the J.D.; a maximum of 5 credits may be applied. The following joint degrees may be earned: J.D./M.B.A. (Juris Doctor/Master of Business Administration), J.D./M.H.A. (Juris Doctor/Master of Health and Hospital Administration), J.D./M.P.A. (Juris Doctor/Master of Public Administration). Individually designed programs with all graduate departments are offered.

Contact

Charles W. Roboski, Assistant Dean, 614-292-8810 for general inquiries; and financial aid information.

OHIO

Required

To earn the J.D., candidates must complete 88 total credits, of which 38 are for required courses. They must maintain a minimum GPA of 2.0 in the required courses. The following first-year courses are required of all students: Contracts, Torts, Property, Civil Procedure, Constitutional Law, Legal Research, Legislation, Writing and Analysis, and Criminal Law. Required upper-level courses consist of Professional Responsibility, 2 courses with a writing component, and Appellate Practice. The required orientation program for first-year students is 1 day and covers case briefing, professional responsibility, and college policies and offices.

Electives

The College of Law offers concentrations in corporate law, criminal law, entertainment, environmental law, family law, international law, juvenile law, labor law, litigation, media law, securities law, sports law, tax law, torts and insurance, and alternative dispute resolution. In addition, second- and third-year students may take clinics. Second-year students take simulation clinics such as pretrial litigation, negotiation, and client counseling. Third-year students may act as legal interns representing clients under faculty supervision. At least one seminar must be taken by second- or third-year students; seminars range from creative and constitutional aspects of law to those devoted to a student's research of a specific legal area. Internships are available with certain federal and state judges. Research programs include opportunities for independent study. There are field work opportunities in the public and private sector and opportunities to do volunteer work, such as the Volunteer Income Tax Assistance (VITA) program. Special lectures are supported by the Ohio State Law Forum, which invites distinguished academicians, jurists, and practitioners; speakers are also invited by faculty and student groups. Study abroad is possible through the Oxford Summer Program and is open to students from the college and all other accredited law schools. Students can earn 3 or 6 hours of credit during the summer. A legal methods program, designed to help certain first-year students who may need more time and attention adapting to law school, is available. The Black Law Students Associa-

tion, Hispanic Law Students Association, and Asian Law Students Association sponsor various events and programs. Special interest groups include the sports and entertainment law society, pro bono research group, public interest law forum, women's law caucus, and health law society. The most widely taken electives are those that are directly bar-related (Evidence, Corporations), international law offerings, and alternative dispute resolution offerings.

Graduation Requirements

In order to graduate, candidates must have a GPA of 2.0, have completed the upper-division writing requirement, and have taken an ethics course.

Organizations

Students edit the *Ohio State Law Journal, Journal on Dispute Resolution*, and the newspaper *Hearsay*. Appellate Practice is the first moot court experience required of all students. The college has 12 separate moot court teams. There are also several national trial competition teams and 2 negotiation teams. There are also intraschool Moot Court, Negotiation, and Trial Competitions. Law student organizations include the Student Bar Association, the Pro Bono Research Group, and International Law Society. There are local chapters of legal fraternities, as well as a student section of the American Bar Association. Other organizations include Hillel, Ski Club, and the Ballroom Dance Association.

Library

The law library contains 653,399 hardcopy volumes and 880,049 microform volume equivalents, and subscribes to 7722 serial publications. Such on-line databases and networks as LEXIS, DIALOG, WESTLAW, LCS, and OCLC are available to law students for research. Special library collections include a government depository, a large foreign law collection, and materials on dispute resolution. Recently, the library added 64,000 square feet to the existing library space, including 12 study rooms, and added 300 carrels and 40 word processors. The ratio of library volumes to faculty is 19,799 to 1 and to students, 972 to 1. The ratio of seats in the library to students is 1 to 1.

Placement

J.D.s awarded:	221
Services available through: A separate law school placement center.	
Services: practice interviews with local attorneys and job search workshops	
Special features: encouragement to do judicial clerkships	
Full-time job interviews:	52 employers
Summer job interviews:	89 employers
Placement by graduation:	88% of class
Placement within 9 months:	93% of class
Average starting salary:	$28,413 to $55,268
Areas of placement:	
Private practice 2-10 attorneys	52%
Government	14%
Business/industry	13%
Judicial clerkships	10%
Military	4%
Public interest	3%
unknown	2%
Academic	2%

Faculty

The law school has 33 full-time and 30 part-time faculty members, of whom 16 are women. According to AAUP standards for Category I institutions, faculty salaries are above average. The ratio of full-time students to full-time faculty in an average class is 20 to 1; in a clinic, 15 to 1. There is a chapter of the Order of the Coif.

Students

About 44% of the student body are women; 16%, minorities; 7%, African American; 6%, Asian American; and 2%, Hispanic. The majority of students come from Ohio (74%). The average age of entering students is 22; age range is 21 to 47. About 12% of students have a graduate degree. About 1% drop out after the first year for academic or personal reasons; 99% remain to receive a law degree.

School of Law

2501 North Blackwelder
Oklahoma City, OK 73106-1493

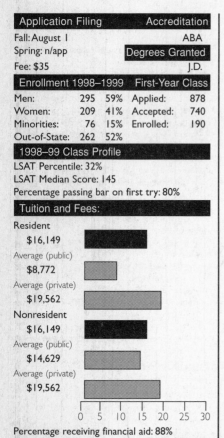

Application Filing	Accreditation
Fall: August 1	ABA
Spring: n/app	**Degrees Granted**
Fee: $35	J.D.

Enrollment 1998–1999		First-Year Class	
Men:	295 59%	Applied:	878
Women:	209 41%	Accepted:	740
Minorities:	76 15%	Enrolled:	190
Out-of-State:	262 52%		

1998–99 Class Profile
LSAT Percentile: 32%
LSAT Median Score: 145
Percentage passing bar on first try: 80%

Tuition and Fees:

Resident
$16,149

Average (public)
$8,772

Average (private)
$19,562

Nonresident
$16,149

Average (public)
$14,629

Average (private)
$19,562

Percentage receiving financial aid: 88%

ADMISSIONS
In the fall 1999 first-year class, 878 applied, 740 were accepted, and 190 enrolled. Six transfers enrolled. The median LSAT percentile of the most recent first-year class was 32; the median GPA was 2.94 on a scale of 4.0. The lowest LSAT percentile accepted was 10; the highest was 92.

Requirements
Applicants must have a bachelor's degree from an accredited institution and take the LSAT. Minimum acceptable GPA is 2.0 on a scale of 4.0. The most important admission factors include LSAT results, GPA, and undergraduate curriculum. No specific undergraduate courses are required. Candidates are not interviewed.

Procedure
The application deadline for fall entry is August 1. Applicants should submit an application form, LSAT results, a nonrefundable application fee of $35, and 2 letters of recommendation. Notification of the admissions decision is as soon as a decision has been made. The latest acceptable LSAT test date for fall entry is June. The law school uses the LSDAS.

Special
The law school recruits minority and disadvantaged students through the Alternate Summer Admissions Program, which is designed for applicants from disadvantaged backgrounds whose LSAT scores and GPAs do not qualify them for regular admission. Transfer students must have attended an ABA-approved law school, be in good standing from their law school, and submit a letter from the dean along with official transcripts. They must complete their last 45 hours at the school.

Costs
Tuition and fees for the 1999-2000 academic year are $16,149 for all full-time students. Tuition for part-time students is $10,845 per year. On-campus room and board costs about $4200 annually; and books and supplies run $750.

Financial Aid
About 88% of current law students receive some form of aid. The average annual amount of aid from all sources combined, including scholarships, loans, and work contracts, is $20,968; maximum, $32,500. Awards are based on need and merit. The required financial statement is the FAFSA. The aid application deadline for fall entry is March 1. First-year students are notified about their financial aid application approximately 2 to 6 weeks after their financial file is completed.

About the Law School
Oklahoma City University School of Law was established in 1907 and is a private institution. The 68-acre campus is in an urban area in Oklahoma City, approximately 3 miles from the state capitol. The primary mission of the law school is to prepare students to become responsible professionals in the legal and leadership roles assumed by lawyers today and that may be assumed in the future. Students have access to federal, state, county, city, and local agencies, courts, correctional facilities, law firms, and legal aid organizations in the Oklahoma City area. Oklahoma City, as the state capital, is a major center for law, business, and banking in the region. Facilities of special interest to law students include the state capitol complex, which contains the Supreme Court, the Court of Criminal Appeals, the Court of Appeals, the state legislature, and various state administrative and regulatory agencies. It is also near the U.S. District Court and numerous other federal and state entities, law firms, and business institutions. Housing for law students is in on-campus dormitories and an on-campus apartment complex. No on-campus housing is available for married students but many private apartments are available in the metro area. All law school facilities are accessible to the physically disabled.

Calendar
The law school operates on a traditional semester basis. Courses for full-time students are offered during the day the first year and both day and evening after, and must be completed within 4 years. For part-time students, required courses are offered during the evening and other courses both day and evenings, and must be completed within 5 years. New full- and part-time students are admitted in the fall. There is a 7-week summer session. Transferable summer courses are offered.

Programs
The following joint degrees may be earned: J.D./M.B.A. (Juris Doctor/Master of Business Administration) and J.D./M.Div. (Juris Doctor/Master of Divinity).

Required
To earn the J.D., candidates must complete 90 total credits, of which 46 are for required courses. They must maintain a minimum GPA of 4.5 on a scale of 12 in the required courses. The following first-year courses are required of all students: Civil Procedure I and II, Contracts I and II, Criminal Law, Legal Research and Writing I and II, Property I, Torts I and II, and Legal Analysis. Required upper-level courses consist of Constitutional Law I, Criminal Procedure I, Evidence, Legal Profession, and Property II. The required orientation program for first-year students consists of both large-

Phone: 405-521-5354
800-633-7242
Fax: 405-521-5802
E-mail: lawadmit@okcu.edu
Web: www.okcu.edu

Contact

Peter Storandt, Director of Admissions, 405-521-5354 or 800-633-7242 for general inquiries; Fran Strange, Director, 405-521-5211 or 800-633-7242 for financial aid information.

group presentations and smaller "breakout" sessions in which students discuss with professors issues such as studying, exams, and stress management.

Electives

There is a 2-credit Native American Legal Assistance Clinic available to 15 students each semester. They work 7 hours a week and meet 1 hour a week in class, under the direction of the clinic's director and supervising attorneys. An externship in criminal law is available for 2 credits, and a federal court externship is available for 1 credit hour. Six to eight 2-hour seminars are offered each semester on selected advanced topics. Recent seminars include Bioethics, Native American Economic Development, and selected topics in Oil and Gas. As part of an internship, students who meet requirements and have a sponsoring attorney may appear in court alone in certain matters. With a supervising attorney present, they may handle any court proceeding. Students may conduct research through seminars, advanced reading courses, supervised papers, or directed research projects. They may also assist faculty as research assistants. The annual Quinlan Lecture series presents a nationally preeminent legal scholar or jurist. The annual Brennan Lecture series presents a nationally prominent scholar or jurist in the field of state constitutional law. An academic support program is available for first-year students and for second-year students on academic probation. Students with writing problems may seek help at the University Writing Center. The academic support program offers tutoring by upper-level students. Minority programs include the Native American Legal Resource Center. The most widely taken electives are Wills and Estates, Bankruptcy, and Corporations.

Graduation Requirements

In order to graduate, candidates must have a GPA of 4.5 on a scale of 12, have completed the upper-division writing requirement, and have 6 or 8 residency semesters, depending on whether the student is enrolled full- or part-time, respectively.

Organizations

The Oklahoma City University Law Review publishes 3 issues annually. The Board of Governors publishes *The Verdict*, a monthly newsletter. The law school has an annual Intramural Moot Court Competition. It also fields teams for the ABA Moot Court and the Jessup International Law Moot Court. There is also an Energy Law Writing Competition. Law student organizations include Law Partners, Environmental Law Association, and Federalist Society. There are local chapters of Hand Inn (Phi Delta Phi) and the Vaught Chapter (Phi Alpha Delta). In addition, two Inns of Court (William J. Holloway, Jr. Inn and Ruth Bader Ginsburg Inn) are affiliated with the school.

Library

The law library contains 271,739 hardcopy volumes and 618,909 microform volume equivalents, and subscribes to 3972 serial publications. Such on-line databases and networks as LEXIS, DIALOG, WESTLAW, Index Manager, Legal-Trac, First-Search, the Internet, and CALI Library Exercises are available to law students for research. Special library collections include Native American collections and the Real Property Title Standards Collection. Recently, the library gained a 25-workstation computer lab that also has Macs. A 12-workstation lab, with a screen and whiteboard, is used for teaching small groups. Each law student has an E-mail address. Students have home access through the Web to CALI, a collection of more than 90 interactive computer exercises covering 22 legal education subjects. The law school and library web pages provide links to career services, current job information, course descriptions, admissions information, web subscriptions such as the Matthew Bender Authority and CIS Congressional Universe, and the university and law library on-line catalog (OLIB). Study rooms and carrels on the lower level are wired to the law library and campus networks, while on-line workstations are available on all floors. The ratio of library volumes to faculty is 8472 to 1 and to students, 592 to 1. The ratio of seats in the library to students is 1 to 2.

Placement

J.D.s awarded:	142
Services available through: a separate law school placement center	
Services: Sunbelt Minority Job Fair, Patent Job Fair, Chicago, Illinois, and Southeastern Minority Job Fair, National Association Public Interest law in Washington, D.C.	
Special features: 2 full-time career services personnel who help students find employment; resource center materials, including monthly employment listings in a publication exchanged with approximately 85 ABA-approved law schools nationwide; and a Graduate Mentor Program	
Full-time job interviews:	9 employers
Summer job interviews:	9 employers
Placement by graduation:	n/av
Placement within 9 months:	78% of class
Average starting salary:	$27,500 to $42,000
Areas of placement:	
Private practice 2-10 attorneys	27%
Private practice 11-25 attorneys	7%
Private practice 26-50 attorneys	4%
Private practice 51-100 attorneys	1%
Private practice 250+ attorneys	1%
Solo practice	5%
Business/industry	12%
Judicial clerkships	6%
Academic	4%
Public interest	2%

Faculty

The law school has 31 full-time and 17 part-time faculty members, of whom 15 are women. About 29% of full-time faculty have a graduate law degree in addition to the J.D. The ratio of full-time students to full-time faculty in an average class is 19 to 1; in a clinic, 10 to 1. The law school has a regular program of bringing visiting professors and other distinguished lecturers and visitors to campus.

Students

About 41% of the student body are women; 15%, minorities; 6%, African American; 4%, Asian American; 5%, Native American; 4%, Hispanic American. The majority of students come from Oklahoma (48%). The average age of entering students is 30; age range is 21 to 56. About 8% drop out after the first year for academic or personal reasons; 92% remain to receive a law degree.

PACE UNIVERSITY

School of Law

78 North Broadway
White Plains, NY 10603

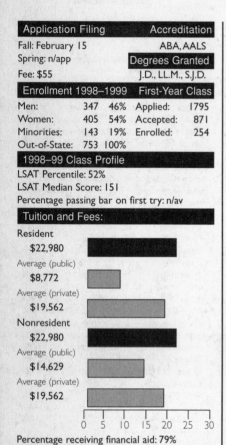

Application Filing		Accreditation
Fall: February 15		ABA, AALS
Spring: n/app		**Degrees Granted**
Fee: $55		J.D., LL.M., S.J.D.

Enrollment 1998–1999		First-Year Class	
Men:	347 46%	Applied:	1795
Women:	405 54%	Accepted:	871
Minorities:	143 19%	Enrolled:	254
Out-of-State:	753 100%		

1998–99 Class Profile

LSAT Percentile: 52%

LSAT Median Score: 151

Percentage passing bar on first try: n/av

Tuition and Fees:

Resident
$22,980

Average (public)
$8,772

Average (private)
$19,562

Nonresident
$22,980

Average (public)
$14,629

Average (private)
$19,562

Percentage receiving financial aid: 79%

ADMISSIONS

In the fall 1999 first-year class, 1795 applied, 871 were accepted, and 254 enrolled. The median LSAT percentile of the most recent first-year class was 52; the median GPA was 3.2 on a scale of 4.0. The lowest LSAT percentile accepted was 21; the highest was 96.

Requirements

Applicants must have a bachelor's degree from an accredited institution and take the LSAT. Minimum acceptable LSAT score is 21 and minimum acceptable GPA is 2.0 on a scale of 4.0. The most important admission factors include LSAT results, GPA, and letters of recommendation. No specific undergraduate courses are required. Candidates are not interviewed.

Procedure

The application deadline for fall entry is February 15. Applicants should submit an application form, LSAT results, transcripts, a nonrefundable application fee of $55, 2 letters of recommendation, a personal statement, and TOEFL or TWE test scores if applicable. Notification of the admission decision is on a rolling basis. The latest acceptable LSAT test date for fall entry is February. The law school uses the LSDAS.

Special

The law school recruits minority and disadvantaged students by hosting a Law Day for minority students each year and visiting historically black colleges. In 1999, Pace hosted the Puerto Rican Legal Defense and Education Fund Program. Transfer students must have one year of credit, have attended an ABA-approved law school, and have a maximum of 30 transfer credits from state approved law schools. Students eligible for admittance under the Conditional Admission Program (those with either GPA or LSAT scores lower than average but who have potential) can attend a 6-week summer program to earn admittance.

Costs

Tuition and fees for the 1999-2000 academic year are $22,980 for all full-time students. Tuition for all part-time students is $17,260 per year or $768 per credit. On-campus room and board costs about $8000 annually, and books and supplies run $1000.

Financial Aid

About 79% of current law students receive some form of aid. The average annual amount of aid from all sources combined, including scholarships, loans, and work contracts, is $22,233; maximum, $37,000. Awards are based on need and merit. The required financial statement is FAFSA. The aid application deadline for fall entry is February 1. First-year students are notified about their financial aid application at time of acceptance.

About the Law School

Pace University School of Law was established in 1976 and is a private institution. The 12-acre campus is in a suburban area in White Plains. The primary mission of the law school is to permit students the flexibility to build their own program of legal study on the foundation of basic legal principles and skills. Students have access to federal, state, county, city, and local agencies, courts, correctional facilities, law firms, and legal aid organizations in and around White Plains, which is the Westchester county seat. Legal institutions in New York City are also accessible. Facilities of special interest to law students include a 12-acre campus with a $10 million classroom building that joins 4 other buildings, including the library, cafeteria and faculty offices. Housing for law students consists of an on-campus residence hall, providing single rooms. The university also assists students in locating off-campus accommodations in close proximity to campus. All law school facilities are accessible to the physically disabled.

Calendar

The law school operates on a traditional semester basis. Courses for full-time students are offered days only and may be completed within a minimum of 3 years. For part-time students, courses are offered evenings only and may be completed within a minimum of 4 years. New full- and part-time students are admitted in the fall. There is a 7-week summer session. Transferable summer courses are offered.

Programs

In addition to the J.D., the law school offers the S.J.D., and the LL.M in environmental law/ and comparative law. Students may take relevant courses in other programs and apply credit toward the J.D.; a maximum of 10 credits may be applied. The following joint degrees may be earned: J.D./M.B.A. (Juris Doctor/Master of Business Administration) and J.D./M.P.A. (Juris Doctor/Master of Public Administration with a concentration in government, not-for-profit, and health care administration).

Phone: 914-422-4010
Fax: 914-422-4248
E-mail: adagostino@genesis.law.pace.edu

Contact

Office of Admissions, 914-422-4210 for general inquiries; Richard Hendrickson, Associate Director, Financial Aid, 914-422-4050 for financial aid information.

NEW YORK

Required

To earn the J.D., candidates must complete 90 total credits, of which 40 are for required courses. They must maintain a minimum GPA of 2.0 in the required courses. The following first-year courses are required of all students: Civil Procedure I and II, Contract I and II, Property I and II, and Legal Analysis and Writing I and II (combined with Criminal Law, Torts I and II, and Constitutional Law I. Required upper-level courses consist of Constitutional Law II, Federal Income Tax I, Professional Responsibility, a writing requirement, and electives from 18 course programs comprising more than 70 courses. Students can register for a maximum of 13 clinical credit hours if they wish to test for the New York bar exam. The required orientation program for first-year students consists of a full week prior to the beginning of classes, with substantive law courses that emphasize briefing techniques and lectures.

Electives

Students must take 12 credits for environmental and international law and 15 credits for health law. The School of Law offers concentrations in corporate law, criminal law, environmental law, family law, and international law. In addition, seminars include advanced Administrative Law, Censorship, and Comparative Environmental Law Tutorial. Students may work as interns in prosecutors' or public defenders' offices or municipal attorney's offices, or may help income taxpayers in cases involving the Internal Revenue Service. A Judicial Administration Internship course allows students to do field research on problems in the criminal justice system. Outstanding third-year students may be eligible for clerkships with federal and state judges. Research assistant positions are available for students to work with faculty members. The school hosts 3 academic lectures each year: Dyson Lecture, the Garrison Lecture in Environmental law, and the Blank Lecture on Ethics. A semester at the University of London's Faculty of Laws is available each spring for second- and third-year students as well as visiting students from other ABA accredited institutions. Tutorial programs include the Academic Support Program and the Dean's Scholar Program. Special programs focus on environmental concerns and the legal issues surround-

ing them. In addition, the Social Justice Center and Women's Justice Center provide legal training in the area of public interest. The most widely taken electives are Family Law, Environmental Law, and International Law.

Graduation Requirements

In order to graduate, candidates must have a GPA of 2.0.

Organizations

Students edit the *Pace Law Review*, the *Pace Environmental Law Review*, the *Pace Yearbook of International Law*, and the student newspaper *Hearsay*. The Moot Court Committee sponsors a required competition for first-year students and an advanced competition for second- and third-year students, and sends teams to national and international competitions. Internal competitions include the National Environmental Moot Court and Jessup International Moot Court competitions. Other competitions include Client Counseling, sponsored by the American Bar Association, Environmental Law National Moot Court, and Unified Moot Court competition. Student organizations include the Student Bar Association, Women's Association of Law Students, and the Environmental Law Society. Phi Alpha Delta has a local chapter.

Library

The law library contains 327,913 hardcopy volumes and 60,613 microform volume equivalents, and subscribes to 1168 serial publications. Such on-line databases and networks as LEXIS, DIALOG, WESTLAW, and NEXIS, the Internet, and the OCLC Web page are available to law students for research. Special library collections include collections on environmental law, international law with an emphasis on international trade and business law, and a selective U.S. government depository. Recently, the library improved seating, upgraded computers, wired carrels for laptop access, and enhanced access to audiovisual materials. The ratio of library volumes to faculty is 6734 to 1 and to students, 394 to 1. The ratio of seats in the library to students is 1 to 8.

Placement

J.D.s awarded:	243

Services available through: a separate law school placement center.
Services: seminars and workshops, on-line job listings for students and alumni
Special features: videotaped mock interviews, Alumni Adviser and Westchester Bar Association Mentor programs, the Alumni Mentor Program for first years, a career newsletter, and annual bulletin of career information

Full-time job interviews:	39 employers
Summer job interviews:	29 employers
Placement by graduation:	55% of class
Placement within 9 months:	86% of class
Average starting salary:	$38,000 to $65,500

Areas of placement:

Private practice 2-10 attorneys	20%
Private practice 11-25 attorneys	9%
Private practice 26-50 attorneys	3%
Private practice 51-100 attorneys	4%
Business/industry	18%
Government	16%
Judicial clerkships	3
Public interest	3%
Academic	2%

Faculty

The law school has 47 full-time and 76 part-time faculty members, of whom 39 are women. According to AAUP standards for Category I institutions, faculty salaries are well above average. About 28% of full-time faculty have a graduate law degree in addition to the J.D.; about 16% of part-time faculty have one. The ratio of full-time students to full-time faculty in an average class is 15 to 1; in a clinic, 12 to 1. The law school has a regular program of bringing visiting professors and other distinguished lecturers and visitors to campus.

Students

About 54% of the student body are women; 19%, minorities; 7%, African American; 5%, Asian American; 8%, Hispanic; and 1%, Native American. The average age of entering students is 25; age range is 21 to 60. About 28% of students enter directly from undergraduate school, 16% have a graduate degree, and 60% have worked full-time prior to entering law school. About 6% drop out after the first year for academic or personal reasons; 84% remain to receive a law degree.

Dickinson School of Law

150 South College Street
Carlisle, PA 17013

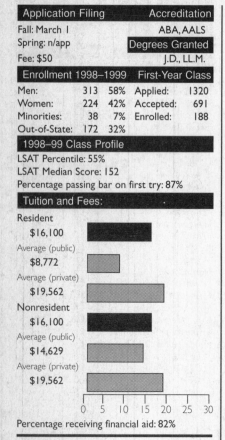

Application Filing	Accreditation
Fall: March 1	ABA, AALS
Spring: n/app	Degrees Granted
Fee: $50	J.D., LL.M.

Enrollment 1998–1999		First-Year Class	
Men:	313 58%	Applied:	1320
Women:	224 42%	Accepted:	691
Minorities:	38 7%	Enrolled:	188
Out-of-State:	172 32%		

1998–99 Class Profile
LSAT Percentile: 55%
LSAT Median Score: 152
Percentage passing bar on first try: 87%

Tuition and Fees:

Resident
$16,100
Average (public)
$8,772
Average (private)
$19,562
Nonresident
$16,100
Average (public)
$14,629
Average (private)
$19,562

0 5 10 15 20 25 30

Percentage receiving financial aid: 82%

ADMISSIONS
In the fall 1999 first-year class, 1320 applied, 691 were accepted, and 188 enrolled. The median LSAT percentile of the most recent first-year class was 55; the median GPA was 3.2 on a scale of 4.0. The lowest LSAT percentile accepted was 17; the highest was 95.

Requirements
Applicants must have a bachelor's degree from an accredited institution and take the LSAT. The most important admission factors include LSAT results, GPA, and academic achievement. No specific undergraduate courses are required. Candidates are not interviewed.

Procedure
The application deadline for fall entry is March 1. Applicants should submit an application form, LSAT results, transcripts, a nonrefundable application fee of $50, 2 (preferably academic) letters of recommendation, a record of work experience, and a 1-page personal statement. Notification of the admission decision is on a rolling basis. The latest acceptable LSAT test date for fall entry is February. The law school uses the LSDAS.

Special
The law school recruits minority and disadvantaged students by means of minority forums such as the LSAT Candidate Referral Service, Minority Students Visitation Weekends, and outreach by current minority students and minority alumni. Transfer students must have one year of credit, have attended an ABA-approved law school, and be in the top 25% of the previous law school in order to be competitive for available space.

Costs
Tuition and fees for the 1999-2000 academic year are $16,100 for all full-time students. On-campus room and board costs about $6200 annually; and books and supplies run $800.

Financial Aid
About 82% of current law students receive some form of aid. The average annual amount of aid from all sources combined, including scholarships, loans, and work contracts, is $23,101; maximum, $29,075. Awards are based on need and merit. The required financial statements are the FAFSA and Access diskette. The aid application deadline for fall entry is February 15. First-year students are notified about their financial aid application at the time of acceptance.

About the Law School
Pennsylvania State University Dickinson School of Law was established in 1834 and is a public institution. The 5-acre campus is in a small town 18 miles west of Harrisburg. (The school has 11 additional acres at another location.) The primary mission of the law school is to offer a balanced program of study that lays the foundation for careers in leadership positions as lawyers, judges, legislators, public officials, and community leaders by fostering development of sound analytical skills, judgment, and communication skills. Students have access to federal, state, county, city, and local agencies, courts, correctional facilities, law firms, and legal aid organizations in the Carlisle area. Facilities of special interest to law students include the Dale F. Shughart Community Law Center, located a few blocks from the Law School. It houses the Family and Disability law clinics. The building's law library and proximity to county courts and offices create an environment identical to that of many private law offices. The Levinson Curtilage provides single

dormitory rooms for some 14% of the students. There is also affordable housing within walking distance. About 95% of the law school facilities are accessible to the physically disabled.

Calendar
The law school operates on a traditional semester basis. Courses for full-time students are offered days only and must be completed within 4 years. For part-time students, courses are offered days only and must be completed within 5 years. New full-and part-time students are admitted in the fall. There are two 4-week summer sessions abroad. Transferable summer courses are offered.

Programs
In addition to the J.D., the law school offers the LL.M and LL.M. in comparative law for foreign lawyers. Students may take relevant courses in other programs and apply credit toward the J.D.; a maximum of 6 credits may be applied (unless students are enrolled in a joint degree program). The following joint degrees may be earned: J.D./M.P.A. (Juris Doctor/Master of Public Administration), J.D./M.E.P.C. (Juris Doctor/Master of Environmental Pollution Control), J.D./M.S.E.P.C. (Juris Doctor/Master of Science in environmental pollution control), J.D./M.B.A. (Juris Doctor/Master of Business Administration), and J.D./M.Eng. (Juris Doctor/Master of Engineering in environmental pollution control).

Required
To earn the J.D., candidates must complete 88 total credits, of which 40 are for required courses. They must maintain a minimum grade average of 70 in the required courses. The following first-year courses are required of all students: Civil Procedure, Contracts, Property, Torts, Lawyering Skills I and II, Criminal Procedure, Criminal Law, Constitutional Law, and Legislative and Administrative Interpretation and Process. Required upper-level courses consist of Appellate Practice, Basic Federal Income Tax, Evidence, Professional Responsibility,and one of the following: Sales, Secured Transactions, or Negotiable Instruments and Payment Law. The required orientation program for first-year students is a 2-day process during which students are introduced to faculty and staff of the law school as well as the structure of the court system, the anatomy of a case, and basic case briefing.

Phone: 717-240-5207
800-840-1122
Fax: 717-241-3503
E-mail: dsladmit@psu.edu
Web: www.dsl.edu

Contact

Barbara A. Guillaume, Director of Admissions Services, 717-240-5207 for general inquiries; Joyce James, Financial Aid Director, 717-240-5256 for financial aid information.

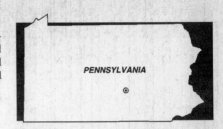

PENNSYLVANIA

Electives

The Dickinson School of Law offers concentrations in corporate law, criminal law, entertainment, environmental law, family law, international law, labor law, litigation, tax law, and torts and insurance. In-house clinics include Family Law, Art, Sports, and Entertainment Law and Disability Law for second- and third-year students. Enrollment in any clinic is limited to 2 semesters. A student may earn up to 9 credits for clinics, but may not enroll in more than 1 clinic concurrently. Seminars include Elder Law, Comparative Law, Race, Racism and American Law, Education Law, and Anglo-American Legal History. Seminars are designed to develop and test students' research and writing skills. A small number of students can earn up to 3 credits during a summer, working without compensation in a government or public setting, similar to the field-placement clinic settings. These students also attend an orientation meeting before beginning their service and a review session at the end of the summer. Research programs (independent study) may be arranged with full-time professors. Any second- or third-year student may elect one independent study for 2 credits. More than one third of the Law School's students obtain clinical credit in either an in-house clinic or field-placement clinic. Field-placement settings include several state agencies and the FCC, state and federal judges, local government offices, public prosecutor and public defender offices at the state and federal levels, and legal services offices. Students earn up to 6 credits for 2 semesters' work. Special lecture series include the Dean's Forum Polisher Lecture, Senior Speakers' Dinner, Speakers Trust Fund, and Faculty Development Committee Series. Study abroad consists of two 4-week summer credit programs: 1 in Florence, Italy, the other in Vienna, Austria; Strasbourg, France; and Brussels, Belgium, in the areas of international law and comparative legal systems. Student-to-student tutoring is provided when requested by individual students, particularly those experiencing academic difficulty. Students who do not perform well after first-semester, first-year examinations are offered the opportunity to receive one-on-one assistance from a full-time faculty member as part of the school's Academic Support Program. In addition, the Director of the Academic Support program reviews these students' performanc-

es. First-year students who do not perform well in their Lawyering Skills class are offered the opportunity to receive one-on-one assistance from the writing specialists. All first-year students who are members of the Minority Law Students Association may participate in a voluntary tutoring program. The most widely taken electives are Advocacy I, Sales, and Trusts and Estates.

Graduation Requirements

In order to graduate, candidates must have an average of 70 and have completed the upper-division writing requirement a seminar, and the Appellate Practice course, which requires preparation of an appellate brief.

Organizations

The primary law review is the *Dickinson Law Review*. Others include the *Dickinson Journal of International Law* and the *Dickinson Journal of Environmental Law and Policy*. *Res Ipsa Loquitur* is the student yearbook. The school generally fields as many as 10 teams in various interscholastic competitions. The competitions include Jessup International, National Appellate, National Trial, an ABA client counseling competition, an environmental law competition, and a labor law competition. Law student organizations include PILF, International Law Society, and Federalist Society. There are local chapters of ABA Law Student Division, Amnesty International, and Association of Trial Lawyers of America. Campus organizations include Corpus Juris Society, Women's Law Caucus, and Dickinson Lesbian and Gay Law Association.

Library

The law library contains 425,000 hardcopy volumes and 1,017,000 microform volume equivalents, and subscribes to 1200 serial publications. Such on-line databases and networks as LEXIS, DIALOG, WESTLAW, and LIAS are available to law students for research. Special library collections include a U.S. government depository, European Community and United Nations documents, and Pennsylvania briefs and records. Recently, the library opened 3 new computer classrooms with 72 desktop computers. The ratio of library volumes to faculty is 12,115 to 1 and to students, 809 to 1. The ratio of seats in the library to students is 1 to 1.

Placement

J.D.s awarded:	168
Services available through: separate law school placement center	
Services: videotaped practice interviews	
Special features: a very personalized emphasis, which is available due to limited enrollment.	
Full-time job interviews:	36 employers
Summer job interviews:	45 employers
Placement by graduation:	53% of class
Placement within 9 months:	94% of class
Average starting salary:	$25,000 to $80,000
Areas of placement:	
Private practice 2-10 attorneys	18%
Private practice 11-25 attorneys	8%
Private practice 26-50 attorneys	3%
Private practice 51-100 attorneys	14%
Judicial clerkships	33%
Government	11%
Business/industry	6%
Public interest	2%
Military	2%
Academic	1%

Faculty

The law school has 35 full-time and 57 part-time faculty members, of whom 21 are women. According to AAUP standards for Category IIB institutions, faculty salaries are well above average. About 43% of full-time faculty have a graduate law degree in addition to the J.D.; about 14% of part-time faculty have one. The ratio of full-time students to full-time faculty in an average class is 21 to 1; in a clinic, 4 to 1. The law school has a regular program of bringing visiting professors and other distinguished lecturers and visitors to campus.

Students

About 42% of the student body are women; 7%, minorities; 2%, African American; 2%, Asian American; 2%, Hispanic; and 1%, Native American. The majority of students come from Pennsylvania (68%). The average age of entering students is 25; age range is 20 to 48. About 31% of students have worked full-time prior to entering law school. About 7% drop out after the first year for academic or personal reasons.

PEPPERDINE UNIVERSITY

School of Law

24255 Pacific Coast Highway
Malibu, CA 90263

Application Filing	Accreditation
Fall: March 1	ABA, AALS
Spring: n/app	**Degrees Granted**
Fee: $50	J.D., M.D.R.

Enrollment 1998–1999	First-Year Class

Men:	364	55%	Applied:	2520
Women:	298	45%	Accepted:	1200
Minorities:	113	17%	Enrolled:	234
Out-of-State:	298	45%		

1998–99 Class Profile

LSAT Percentile: 71%
LSAT Median Score: 156
Percentage passing bar on first try: 62%

Tuition and Fees:

Resident
$23,835

Average (public)
$8,772

Average (private)
$19,562

Nonresident
$23,835

Average (public)
$14,629

Average (private)
$19,562

0 5 10 15 20 25 30

Percentage receiving financial aid: 85%

ADMISSIONS

In the fall 1999 first-year class, 2520 applied, 1200 were accepted, and 234 enrolled. Fifteen transfers enrolled. The median LSAT percentile of the most recent first-year class was 71; the median GPA was 3.3 on a scale of 4.0.

Requirements

Applicants must have a bachelor's degree from an accredited institution and take the LSAT. No specific undergraduate courses are required. Candidates are not interviewed.

Procedure

The application deadline for fall entry is March 1. Applicants should submit an application form, a nonrefundable application fee, 2 letters of recommendation, a photograph, and a $200 deposit. Check with the school for current fee. Notification of the admission decision is on a rolling basis. The latest acceptable LSAT test date for fall entry is February. The law school uses the LSDAS.

Special

The law school recruits minority and disadvantaged students by actively encouraging applications from ethnic minorities. Transfer students must have one year of credit, have attended an ABA-approved law school, submit an official law school transcript, a letter from the dean indicating the student's eligibility to continue his or her studies and indicating the student's class rank, and supply a photocopy of the current school's LSDAS report. The student must rank in the top 15% of the first-year law class.

Costs

Tuition and fees for the 1999-2000 academic year are $23,835 for all full-time students. On-campus room and board costs about $10,004 annually; and books and supplies run $700.

Financial Aid

In a recent year, about 85% of current law students received some form of aid. The maximum annual amount of aid from all sources combined, including scholarships, loans, and work contracts, was $37,084. Awards are based on need and merit. Need-based financial aid awards are generally a combination of grants, loans, and work-study employment. The required financial statement is FAFSA. Check with the school for current application deadline. Special funds for minority or disadvantaged students consist of the Diversity Scholarship, based on academic and personal achievement. First-year students are notified about their financial aid application 2 weeks after acceptance notification, if completed.

About the Law School

Pepperdine University School of Law was established in 1969 and is a private institution. The 830-acre campus is in a small town 30 miles north of Los Angeles, California. The primary mission of the law school is to provide highly qualified students with a distinctive and superior legal education. The school maintains a Christian emphasis. Students have access to federal, state, county, city, and local agencies, courts, correctional facilities, law firms, and legal aid organizations in the Malibu area. Facilities of special interest to law students include the Odell McConnell Law Center, which overlooks the Pacific Ocean; the facility contains an auditorium-classroom, law library, classrooms, an atrium, an appellate courtroom, a trial courtroom, cafeteria, lounges, and student services offices. Housing for law students is limited on campus; on-campus apartments house 4 students in each of the 36 apartments. All law school facilities are accessible to the physically disabled.

Calendar

The law school operates on a traditional semester basis. Courses for full-time students are offered days only. There is no part-time program. New full-time students are admitted in the fall. There is a 7 1/2-week summer session. Transferable summer courses are offered.

Phone: 310-456-4631
Fax: 310-317-7668
E-mail: soladmis@pepperdine.edu
Web: http://law.pepperdine.edu

Contact

Shannon Phillips, Director of Admissions and Records, 310-456-4631 for general inquiries; Janet Lockhart, Director of Financial Aid, 310-456-4633 for financial aid information.

Programs

In addition to the J.D., the law school offers the M.D.R. (Master of Dispute Resolution). The following joint degrees may be earned: J.D./M.B.A. (Juris Doctor/Master of Business Administration) and J.D./M.D.R. (Juris Doctor/Master of Dispute Resolution).

Required

To earn the J.D., candidates must complete 88 total credits, of which 57 are for required courses. They must maintain a minimum grade average of 72 in the required courses. The following first-year courses are required of all students: Civil Pleadings and Procedure I and II, Contracts I and II, Criminal Law, Legal Research and Writing I and II, Real Property I and II, Torts I and II, and Criminal Procedure. Required upper-level courses consist of Constitutional Law I and II, Corporations, Evidence, Federal Income Taxation, Professional Responsibility, Remedies, and Wills and Trusts. The required orientation program for first-year students is 2 days.

Electives

The School of Law offers concentrations in corporate law, criminal law, entertainment, environmental law, family law, international law, labor law, tax law, and tort law, property law, intellectual property law, advocacy and dispute resolution, public interest, and constitutional law. In addition, clinical opportunities are available with the District Attorney's Office of Los Angeles and Ventura counties, and with state and federal court judges in Los Angeles and Ventura counties. Also, smaller programs offer training in corporate and securities law, tax law, juvenile law, domestic arbitration, labor law, consumer protection, trade regulation, and with various media industries. Second- and third-year students may study in the London Law Program fall, spring, and summer semesters. Courses are taught by British and American faculty. Students can attend 1 or 2 semesters; if 2 semesters, it must be summer/fall or spring/summer. An academic support program begins 1 week prior to the start of school. The most widely taken electives are the London Law Program, clinics, and entertainment and sports law courses.

Graduation Requirements

To graduate students must have a minimum grade average of 72.

Organizations

Students edit the *Pepperdine Law Review*. First-year students participate in an appellate advocacy experience. Upper-level students compete for places on teams that attend the National Moot Court and other competitions. Each spring there is the Dalsimer Moot Court intraschool competition. Law student organizations are the Student Bar Association, Asian Pacific American Law Students Association, and Black Law Students Association. There are local chapters of Delta Theta Phi, Phi Alpha Delta, and Phi Delta Phi.

Library

The law library contains 252,000 hardcopy volumes and 87,000 microform volume equivalents, and subscribes to 1300 serial publications. Such on-line databases and networks as LEXIS, DIALOG, and WESTLAW are available to law students for research. The ratio of library volumes to faculty is 504 to 1 and to students, 36 to 1. The ratio of seats in the library to students is 1 to 7.

Faculty

The law school has 34 full-time faculty members, of whom 5 are women. According to AAUP standards for Category IIA institutions, faculty salaries are well above average.

Students

About 45% of the student body are women; 17%, minorities; 5%, African American; 7%, Asian American; 4%, Hispanic; and 1%, Native American. The majority of students come from California (55%). The average age of entering students is 23; age range is 20 to 55. About 6% of students have a graduate degree. About 5% drop out after the first year for academic or personal reasons.

Placement

J.D.s awarded:	256
Services available through:	
Services: co-sponsor workshops on practice specialties	
Special features: seminars to assist students in preparing resumes and improving job search and interviewing skills, counseling expertise in practice areas and alternative careers	
Full-time job interviews:	220 employers
Summer job interviews:	n/av
Placement by graduation:	65% of class
Placement within 9 months:	92% of class
Average starting salary:	n/av
Areas of placement:	n/av

QUINNIPIAC COLLEGE

School of Law

275 Mt. Carmel Avenue
Hamden, CT 06518-1948

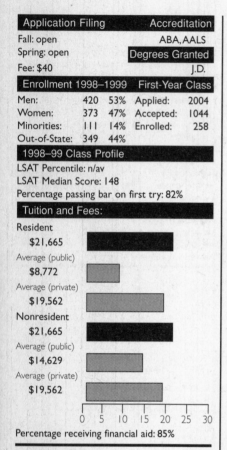

Application Filing			Accreditation
Fall: open			ABA, AALS
Spring: open			**Degrees Granted**
Fee: $40			J.D.

Enrollment 1998–1999			First-Year Class
Men:	420	53%	Applied: 2004
Women:	373	47%	Accepted: 1044
Minorities:	111	14%	Enrolled: 258
Out-of-State:	349	44%	

1998–99 Class Profile

LSAT Percentile: n/av

LSAT Median Score: 148

Percentage passing bar on first try: 82%

Tuition and Fees:

Resident
$21,665

Average (public)
$8,772

Average (private)
$19,562

Nonresident
$21,665

Average (public)
$14,629

Average (private)
$19,562

0 5 10 15 20 25 30

Percentage receiving financial aid: 85%

ADMISSIONS

In the fall 1999 first-year class, 2004 applied, 1044 were accepted, and 258 enrolled. Three transfers enrolled. The median GPA of the most recent first-year class was 2.95 on a 4.0 scale. The lowest LSAT percentile accepted was 9; the highest was 97.

Requirements

Applicants must have a bachelor's degree from an accredited institution and take the LSAT. The most important admission factors include LSAT results, GPA, and academic achievement. No specific undergraduate courses are required. Candidates are interviewed.

Procedure

The application deadline for fall entry is open. Applicants should submit an application form, LSAT results, transcripts, a nonrefundable application fee of $40, 2 letters of recommendation, and an admissions essay. Notification of the admission decision is on a rolling basis so decisions are continously rendered as files are completed. The latest acceptable LSAT test date for fall entry is June. The law school uses the LSDAS.

Special

The law school recruits minority and disadvantaged students by means of student search, community outreach programs, the CLEO program, minority days on campus, and attendance at various minority programs. Transfer students must have one year of credit, have attended an ABA-approved law school, and a letter of good standing from the dean of the law school from which the student is transferring. A 7-week summer conditional acceptance program is taught by a full professor. Upon successful completion, the student is admitted into the part-time evening program in the fall. The law faculty decides each April if the program is to be offered that summer.

Costs

Tuition and fees for the 1999-2000 academic year are $21,665 for all full-time students. Tuition for all part-time students is $16,615 annually or $850 per credit. Books and supplies run $1000.

Financial Aid

About 85% of current law students receive some form of aid. The average annual amount of aid from all sources combined, including scholarships, loans, and work contracts, is $18,915; maximum, $35,360. Awards are based on need and merit. The required financial statement is FAFSA. The priority aid application deadline for fall entry is April 1. The priority deadline for spring is December 1. Special funds for minority or disadvantaged students consist of a diversity scholarship and grant program. First-year students are notified about their financial aid application at the time of acceptance.

About the Law School

Quinnipiac College School of Law was established in 1978 and is a private institution. The 300-acre campus is in a suburban area 90 miles north of New York City. The primary mission of the law school is to provide an education in the nature and the function of law and the skills of legal practice. Students have access to federal, state, county, city, and local agencies, courts, correctional facilities, law firms, and legal aid organizations in the Hamden area. Facilities of special interest to law students are the School of Law Library, Student Activities Center and Grand Courtroom. Housing for law students is available off-campus in the area; the Office of Residential Life and Admissions Office assists students with housing opportunities. All law school facilities are accessible to the physically disabled.

Calendar

The law school operates on a traditional semester basis. Courses for full-and part-time students are offered both day and evening and must be completed within 6 years. New full-time students are admitted in the fall; part-time, fall and spring. There is a 7-week summer session. Transferable summer courses are offered.

Programs

The following joint degrees may be earned: J.D./M.B.A. (Juris Doctor/Master of Business Administration) and J.D./M.H.A. (Juris Doctor/Master of Health Administration).

Phone: 203-287-3400
Fax: 203-287-3339
E-mail: ladm@quinnipiac.edu
Web:
http://www.quinnipiac.edu/academics/law.asp

Contact

John J. Noonan, Dean of Admissions, 203-287-3400 for general inquiries; Anne Traverso, Director of Financial Aid, 203-287-3405 for financial aid information.

CONNECTICUT

Required

To earn the J.D., candidates must complete 86 total credits, of which 53 are for required courses. They must maintain a minimum GPA of 2.0 in the required courses. The following first-year courses are required of all students: Legal Skills I and II, Criminal Law, Civil Procedure I and II, Contracts I and II, Property, Constitutional Law, and Torts. Required upper-level courses consist of Federal Income Tax, Business Organizations, Evidence, Commercial Law, Trusts and Estates, Administrative Law, and Lawyer's Professional Responsibility. The required orientation program for first-year students is a 1-day general introductory program to the school, the faculty, the administration, and the students. There is also a continuing program in the first semester covering professional responsibility and ethics.

Electives

The School of Law offers concentrations in corporate law, criminal law, environmental law, family law, international law, labor law, litigation, tax law, and health law. Students may participate in a Civil Clinic for 8 credits, a Criminal Justice Clinic for 7 credits, and a Tax Clinic for 8 credits. Seminars are varied. The internship program includes 5 courses, and students receive variable credits for the internship. Areas are public interest, corporate counsel, judicial, legislative, and municipal counsel. Research programs are varied. A summer program in Ireland with Trinity College (Dublin), as well as independent study-abroad programs are available. An academic support program and writing program are available to students at the law school. A bar review class is taught by a law professor. There is a special minority recruitment and information day at the school, with the Thurgood Marshall Awards Dinner in the evening recognizing individual achievement and service to the school. The most widely taken electives are Criminal Procedure, Family Law, and Advanced Constitutional Law.

Graduation Requirements

In order to graduate, candidates must have a GPA of 2.0 and have completed the upper-division writing requirement.

Organizations

Students edit the *Quinnipiac College Law Review*, *Quinnipiac Probate Law Journal*, Quinnipiac Health Law Journal, and the student newspaper, *The Quinnipiac Legal Times*. Moot court competitions are the National Appellate Advocacy Competition, Albert Mugel Tax Moot Court Competition, and Dean Jerome Prince Evidence Competition. The Mock Trial Society competes in American Trial Lawyers Competition, Texas Young Lawyers Association Competition, and the American Bar Association Competition. Student organizations include the Student Bar Association, Women's Law Association, and the Black Law Students Association. There are local chapters of Phi Alpha Delta and Phi Delta Phi on campus.

Library

The law library contains 344,390 hardcopy volumes and 186,502 microform volume equivalents, and subscribes to 2793 serial publications. Such on-line databases and networks as LEXIS, DIALOG, WESTLAW, and NEXIS are available to law students for research. Special library collections include a government depository library and a tax collection. The facility was completed in May 1995. The ratio of library volumes to faculty is 9063 to 1 and to students, 434 to 1. The ratio of seats in the library to students is 1 to 1.

Faculty

The law school has 38 full-time and 25 part-time faculty members, of whom 17 are women. About 50% of full-time faculty have a graduate law degree in addition to the J.D. The ratio of full-time students to full-time faculty in an average class is 20 to 1; in a clinic, 8 to 1. The law school has a regular program of bringing visiting professors and other distinguished lecturers and visitors to campus.

Placement

J.D.s awarded:	221

Services available through: A separate law school placement center.

Services: counseling on cover letter preparation, mock interviews, educational and informational programs, and membership in law placement consortia.

Special features: staff members with J.D. degrees counsel students and develop employment opportunities for students and graduates.

Full-time job interviews:	n/av
Summer job interviews:	30+
Placement by graduation:	n/av
Placement within 9 months:	94% of class
Average starting salary:	$34,000 to $38,000

Areas of placement:

Private practice 2-10 attorneys	42%
Private practice 11-25 attorneys	42%
Private practice 26-50 attorneys	42%
Private practice 51-100 attorneys	42%
Business/industry	22%
Government	16%
Unknown	9%
Judicial clerkships	6%
Public interest	4%
Academic	1%

Students

About 47% of the student body are women; 14%, minorities; 6%, African American; 2%, Asian American; 5%, Hispanic; and 1%, Native American. The majority of students come from Connecticut (56%). The average age of entering students is 27; age range is 20 to 64. About 22% of students enter directly from undergraduate school and 9% have a graduate degree. About 4% drop out after the first year for academic or personal reasons; 96% remain to receive a law degree.

REGENT UNIVERSITY

School of Law

1000 Regent University Drive
Virginia Beach, VA 23464-9800

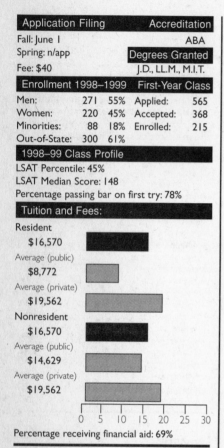

Application Filing		Accreditation
Fall: June 1		ABA
Spring: n/app		Degrees Granted
Fee: $40		J.D., LL.M., M.I.T.

Enrollment 1998–1999		First-Year Class	
Men:	271 55%	Applied:	565
Women:	220 45%	Accepted:	368
Minorities:	88 18%	Enrolled:	215
Out-of-State:	300 61%		

1998–99 Class Profile

LSAT Percentile: 45%
LSAT Median Score: 148
Percentage passing bar on first try: 78%

Tuition and Fees:

Resident
$16,570

Average (public)
$8,772

Average (private)
$19,562

Nonresident
$16,570

Average (public)
$14,629

Average (private)
$19,562

0   5   10   15   20   25   30

Percentage receiving financial aid: 69%

ADMISSIONS

In the fall 1999 first-year class, 565 applied, 368 were accepted, and 215 enrolled. Thirteen transfers enrolled. The median LSAT percentile of the most recent first-year class was 45; the median GPA was 3.1 on a scale of 4.0. The lowest LSAT percentile accepted was 18; the highest was 97.

Requirements
Applicants must have a bachelor's degree from an accredited institution and take the LSAT. Minimum acceptable GPA is 2.0 on a scale of 4.0. The most important admission factors include academic achievement, character, personality, and general background. No specific undergraduate courses are required. Candidates are not interviewed.

Procedure
The application deadline for fall entry is June 1. Applicants should submit an application form, LSAT results, transcripts, a nonrefundable application fee of $40, and 3 letters of recommendation. Notification of the admission decision is on a rolling basis. The latest acceptable LSAT test date for fall entry is June. The law school uses the LSDAS.

Special
The law school recruits minority and disadvantaged students through recruitment travel, referrals, CRS mailings, and special scholarships. Transfer students must have 1 year of credit, have a minimum GPA of 2.0, and have attended an ABA-approved law school.

Costs

Tuition and fees for the 1999-2000 academic year are $16,570 for all full-time students. On-campus room and board costs about $6150 annually; books and supplies run $1000.

Financial Aid

About 69% of current law students receive some form of aid. The average annual amount of aid from all sources combined, including scholarships, loans, and work contracts, is $3250; maximum, $15,345. Awards are based on need and merit, along with leadership and public interest. The required financial statement is FAFSA. The aid application deadline for fall entry is March 1. Special funds for minority or disadvantaged students include 2 scholarship categories for individuals called to serve the minority community. First-year students are notified about their financial aid application at the time of acceptance.

About the Law School

Regent University School of Law was established in 1986 and is a private institution. The 80-acre campus is in a suburban area 7 miles southeast of Norfolk, Virginia. The primary mission of the law school is to train lawyers to participate effectively and professionally in the private and public sectors of this nation while affirming their understanding of the relationship between Christian principles and the practice of law. Students have access to federal, state, county, city, and local agencies, courts, correctional facilities, law firms, and legal aid organizations in the Virginia Beach area. Facilities of special interest to law students include a 134,000-square foot law center equipped with the latest technology in audiovisual equipment, such as cameras for simultaneous broadcasting. There is also a 350-seat moot court/city council chamber. Housing for law students consists of university-owned and operated two- and three-bedroom apartments (224 units). All law school facilities are accessible to the physically disabled.

Calendar

The law school operates on a traditional semester basis. Courses for full-time students are offered both day and evening and must be completed within 5 years. For part-time students, courses are offered evenings only and Saturday. New full- and part-time students are admitted in the fall. There is a 9-week summer session. Transferable summer courses are not offered.

Programs

In addition to the J.D., the law school offers the LL.M and M.I.T. (Master of International Taxation). Students may take relevant courses in other programs and apply credit toward the J.D.; a maximum of 6 credits may be applied. The following joint degrees may be earned: J.D./M.B.A. (Juris Doctor/Master of Business Administration) and J.D./M.A. (Juris Doctor/Master of Arts in government, management, and communications).

Phone: 757-226-4584
Fax: 757-226-4139
E-mail: lawschool@regent.edu
Web: www.regent.edu/law/admissions

Contact

Charles W. Roboski, Director of Law Admissions, 757-226-4584 for general inquiries; Bonnie Creef, 757-226-4584 for financial aid information.

VIRGINIA

Required

To earn the J.D., candidates must complete 90 total credits, of which 66 are for required courses. They must maintain a minimum GPA of 2.0 in the required courses. The following first-year courses are required of all students: Common Law, Contracts I and II, Criminal Law, Torts I and II, Civil Procedure I and II, Legal Research and Writing I and II, and Property I and II. Required upper-level courses consist of Constitutional Law, Evidence, Individual Federal Income Taxation, and Law and Professional Responsibility. The optional orientation program for first-year students is a 2-day program including a legal study skills workshop covering preparation for class, case briefing, outlining, and study skills. There is also an orientation for electronic legal education using a laptop computer.

Electives

The School of Law offers concentrations in family law and litigation. In addition, seminars include Human Life and Death, Crime and Punishment, Inalienable Rights, Environmental Law, Charitable Trusts, Constitutional Litigation, Jurisprudence, Legal History, and Advanced Family Law. Internships are available as research assistants or law clerks for a public interest law firm. Research programs include Advanced Legal Research, a special project, and Independent Studies, which may be undertaken for 1 to 3 hours of credit each. Practical experience may also be gained through externships (up to a maximum of 4 hours of credit) in an approved study program with a practicing attorney or judicial officer, or with a federal/state prosecutor or defender. Study abroad includes a summer session in Strasbourg, France that emphasizes international human rights and jurisprudence. A mandatory summer assistance program is offered to select admits. Part of the program is for credit and part is not. The most widely taken electives are Remedies, Bankruptcy, and Drafting of Contracts.

Graduation Requirements

In order to graduate, candidates must have a GPA of 2.0 and have completed the upper-division writing requirement.

Organizations

Students edit the *Regent University Law Review* and the student newspaper *Class Action*. Moot court competitions for students include the Jessup International, sponsored by the Grotius International Law Society; National Juvenile Law Competition; and Spong Cup Moot Court. Other competitions include the ABA Negotiation, sponsored by the ABA-Law Student Division, and the Robert Merhige, Jr. National Environmental Law, sponsored by the University of Richmond. Student organizations include the Student Bar Association, Moot Court Board, and Alternative Dispute and Client Counseling Board. There are local chapters of the Christian Legal Society, Federalist Society, and The American Inns of Court. Other organizations include Regent Students for Life, Catholic Law Student Organization, and Sports and Entertainment Law Society.

Library

The law library contains 316,000 hardcopy volumes and 900,000 microform volume equivalents, and subscribes to 920 serial publications. Such on-line databases and networks as LEXIS, DIALOG, WESTLAW, Legal-Trac, NEXIS, and First-Search are available to law students for research. Special library collections include an essentially complete set of CIS microfiche and the Transylvania Collection from former Transylvania University Law School (Kentucky) with materials dating from the 1700's. Recently, the library was remodeled and has expanded to about 35,000 feet. The ratio of library volumes to faculty is 12,153 to 1 and to students, 638 to 1. The ratio of seats in the library to students is 1 to 2.

Faculty

The law school has 22 full-time and 37 part-time faculty members, of whom 9 are women. About 23% of full-time faculty have a graduate law degree in addition to the J.D.; about 16% of part-time faculty have one. The ratio of full-time students to full-time faculty in an average class is 17 to 1.

Placement

J.D.s awarded:	130

Services available through: a separate law school placement center.

Services:

Special features: extensive career planning and professional development seminars, participation in career planning programs, panel discussions and mock interviews, as well as one-to-one counseling of law students with the director. Examples of fall programs include topics such as Interview Skills Workshop, Resume Preparation, Focusing on a Litigation Career, Solo Practice, and What Being a Lawyer is Really Like.

Full-time job interviews:	14 employers
Summer job interviews:	n/av
Placement by graduation:	n/av
Placement within 9 months:	79% of class
Average starting salary:	n/av
Areas of placement:	
Private practice 2-10 attorneys	44%
Private practice 11-25 attorneys	6%
Private practice 26-50 attorneys	2%
Unknown	6%
Business/industry	14%
Government	10%
Academic	8%
Public interest	6%
Military	3%
Judicial clerkships	1%

Students

About 45% of the student body are women; 18%, minorities; 4%, African American; 1%, Asian American; 2%, Hispanic; and 2%, foreign national. The majority of students come from Virginia (39%). The average age of entering students is 27; age range is 50 to 20. About 28% of students enter directly from undergraduate school, 6% have a graduate degree, and 72% have worked full-time prior to entering law school. About 7% drop out after the first year for academic or personal reasons; 91% remain to receive a law degree.

ROGER WILLIAMS UNIVERSITY

School of Law

Ten Metacom Avenue
Bristol, RI 02809-5171

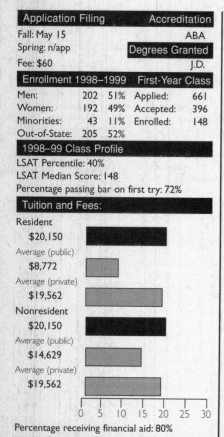

Application Filing	Accreditation
Fall: May 15	ABA
Spring: n/app	**Degrees Granted**
Fee: $60	J.D.

Enrollment 1998–1999   First-Year Class

Men:	202	51%	Applied:	661
Women:	192	49%	Accepted:	396
Minorities:	43	11%	Enrolled:	148
Out-of-State:	205	52%		

1998–99 Class Profile

LSAT Percentile: 40%
LSAT Median Score: 148
Percentage passing bar on first try: 72%

Tuition and Fees:

Resident
$20,150

Average (public)
$8,772

Average (private)
$19,562

Nonresident
$20,150

Average (public)
$14,629

Average (private)
$19,562

0   5   10   15   20   25   30

Percentage receiving financial aid: 80%

ADMISSIONS

In the fall 1999 first-year class, 661 applied, 396 were accepted, and 148 enrolled. Seven transfers enrolled. The median LSAT percentile of the most recent first-year class was 40; the median GPA was 3.0 on a scale of 4.0. The lowest LSAT percentile accepted was 8; the highest was 96.

Requirements

Applicants must have a bachelor's degree from an accredited institution and take the LSAT. Minimum acceptable GPA is 2.0 on a scale of 4.0. The most important admission factors include LSAT results, GPA, and academic achievement. No specific undergraduate courses are required. Candidates are interviewed.

Procedure

The application deadline for fall entry is May 15. Applicants should submit an application form, LSAT results, transcripts, TOEFL for students who are citizens of a foreign country and whose native language is not English, a nonrefundable application fee of $60, and a personal statement. Notification of the admission decision is on a rolling basis. The latest acceptable LSAT test date for fall entry is June. The law school uses the LSDAS.

Special

The law school recruits minority and disadvantaged students by visiting historically black and Hispanic colleges and universities. Transfer students must have a minimum GPA of 2.0, have attended an ABA-approved law school, and a letter of good standing from their prior law school.

Costs

Tuition and fees for the 1999-2000 academic year are $20,150 for all full-time students. Tuition for all part-time students is $15,460 annually, or $670 per credit. Books and supplies run $1000.

Financial Aid

About 80% of current law students receive some form of aid. The average annual amount of aid from all sources combined, including scholarships, loans, and work contracts, is $25,000; maximum, $34,690. Awards are based on need and merit. The required financial statement is FAFSA. The aid application deadline for fall entry is May 15. First-year students are notified about their financial aid application at the time of acceptance.

About the Law School

Roger Williams University School of Law was established in 1992 and is a private institution. The 140-acre campus is in a small town on a peninsula in the historic seacoast town of Bristol. The primary mission of the law school is to prepare students for the competent and ethical practice of law. Students have access to federal, state, county, city, and local agencies, courts, correctional facilities, law firms, and legal aid organizations in the Bristol area, as well state library archives, university libraries at Brown University, University of Rhode Island, Providence College, and Rhode Island Historical Society. Facilities of special interest to law students include the Criminal Defense and Family Law clinics located in Providence. Housing for law students is available in 1-bedroom apartments and townhouses 2 miles from campus. The neighboring towns of Bristol and Warren also have numerous apartments available in private homes and apartment complexes. All law school facilities are accessible to the physically disabled.

Calendar

The law school operates on a traditional semester basis. Courses for full-time students are offered both day and evening and must be completed within 3 years. For part-time students, courses are offered both day and evening and must be completed within 4 years. New full- and part-time students are admitted in the fall. There is a 7-week summer session. Transferable summer courses are offered.

Programs

The following joint degrees may be earned: J.D./M.C.P. (Juris Doctor/Master of Community Planning) and J.D./M.M.A. (Juris Doctor/Master of Marine Affairs).

Phone: 401-254-4555
633-2727
Fax: 401-254-4516
E-mail: admissions@rwulaw.rwu.edu
Web: http:\\law.rwu.edu

Contact

Nanci Tessier, Director of Admissions, 401-254-4555 for general inquiries; Chris Earnshaw, Assistant Director, Financial Planning, 401-254-4510 for financial aid information.

RHODE ISLAND

Required

To earn the J.D., candidates must complete 90 total credits, of which 54 are for required courses. They must maintain a minimum GPA of 2.0 in the required courses. The following first-year courses are required of all students: Contracts I and II, Civil Procedure I and II, Torts, Property, Criminal Law, Legal Methods I and II, and Criminal Procedure. Required upper-level courses consist of Legal Methods III and IV, Professional Responsibility, Constitutional Law, Evidence, Federal Income Tax, Administrative Law, Business Organizations, and Commerical Law. All students must take clinical courses. The required orientation program for first-year students is held 3 1/2 days prior to the first day of classes, includes an introduction to the judicial system and the study of law, case briefing, exam-taking techniques, professionalism, meetings with academic advisers, student services introduction, and social events.

Electives

Third-year students participate in the Criminal Defense Clinic and the Family Law Clinic for 6 credits. Seminars, available to second- and third-year students, include White Collar Crime, Marine Pollution, Ocean and Coastal Law, and Judicial Process. They are worth 2 credits each. Internships for third-year students consist of judicial clerkships worth 3 credits and clerkships with the Rhode Island Attorney General's Office, Public Defenders Office, and Legal Services for 3 credits. There is faculty-supervised directed research for 1 or 2 credits, a faculty development speakers program, multicultural law student program, Faculty Mentor/Adviser program, and a writing program taught by the Dean of Students. Study abroad is available through the London Summer Institute in conjunction with Inns of Court School of Law and in Lisbon, Portugal. There are workshops on studying, briefing, course outlining, and exam taking. The most widely taken electives are Wills and Trusts, Constitutional Law II, and Family Law.

Graduation Requirements

In order to graduate, candidates must have a GPA of 2.0 and have completed the upper-division writing requirement.

Organizations

Students edit the *Roger Williams University Law Review* and the newspaper *The Docket*. Moot court competitions include the Roger Williams University School of Law Moot Court, the National Moot Court Competition, and the John R. Brown Admiralty Moot Court Competition. Law student organizations include the Marine Affairs Society, Student Bar Association, and Environmental Law Society. Local chapters of national organizations include the American Trial Lawyers Association and ABA. Other cliubs include the Multiculutral Law Students Association, the Women's Law Caucus, and the Justinian Law Society.

Library

The law library contains 250,000 hardcopy volumes and 891,546 microform volume equivalents, and subscribes to 3288 serial publications. Such on-line databases and networks as LEXIS, DIALOG, WESTLAW, and Ocean State FREENET, New England Law Library Consortium, and Consortium of Rhode Island Academic and Research Libraries are available to law students for research. Special library collections include Rhode Island law, the State Justice Institute depository, and Maritime Law. Recently, the library redesigned and updated the Law Library web site, established a web-based public on-line catalog, installed a proxy server to allow home access to library web-based subscription services, and upgraded computers in the main computer laboratory. The ratio of library volumes to faculty is 9416 to 1 and to students, 621 to 1. The ratio of seats in the library to students is 1 to 1.

Faculty

The law school has 25 full-time and 25 part-time faculty members, of whom 12 are women. According to AAUP standards for Category IIB institutions, faculty salaries are well above average. About 33% of full-time faculty have a graduate law degree in addition to the J.D.; about 8% of part-time faculty have one. The ratio of full-time students to full-time faculty in an average class is 27 to 1; in a clinic, 10 to 1. The law school has a regular program of bringing visiting professors and other distinguished lecturers and visitors to campus.

Placement

J.D.s awarded:	101
Services available through: A separate law school placement center.	
Services:	
Special features: extensive one-on-one counseling sessions, symposiums, and coordinated programs with the Rhode Island Bar Association, and a student research pool for project-based assignments with local attorneys.	
Full-time job interviews:	7 employers
Summer job interviews:	7 employers
Placement by graduation:	n/av
Placement within 9 months:	92% of class
Average starting salary:	$25,000 to $105,000
Areas of placement:	
Private practice 2-10 attorneys	44%
Private practice 11-25 attorneys	2%
Private practive 26-50 attorneys	2%
Private practice 51-100 attorneys	2%
Business/industry	28%
Government	9%
Judicial clerkships	8%
Public interest	4%
Academic	1%

Students

About 49% of the student body are women; 11%, minorities; 5%, African American; 2%, Asian American; and 3%, Hispanic. The majority of students come from the Northeast (86%). The average age of entering students is 28; age range is 20 to 64. About 22% of students enter directly from undergraduate school, 8% have a graduate degree, and 31% have worked full-time prior to entering law school. About 12% drop out after the first year for academic or personal reasons; 86% remain to receive a law degree.

School of Law

S.I. Newhouse Center for Law and Justice,
15 Washington St.
Newark, NJ 07102

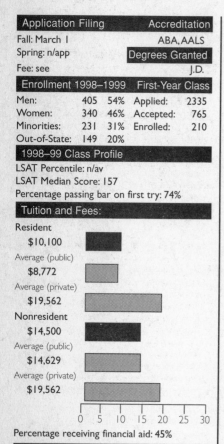

Application Filing		Accreditation
Fall: March 1		ABA, AALS
Spring: n/app		Degrees Granted
Fee: see		J.D.

Enrollment 1998–1999		First-Year Class	
Men:	405 54%	Applied:	2335
Women:	340 46%	Accepted:	765
Minorities:	231 31%	Enrolled:	210
Out-of-State:	149 20%		

1998–99 Class Profile
LSAT Percentile: n/av
LSAT Median Score: 157
Percentage passing bar on first try: 74%

Tuition and Fees:

Resident
$10,100

Average (public)
$8,772

Average (private)
$19,562

Nonresident
$14,500

Average (public)
$14,629

Average (private)
$19,562

0 5 10 15 20 25 30

Percentage receiving financial aid: 45%

ADMISSIONS

In the fall 1999 first-year class, 2335 applied, 765 were accepted, and 210 enrolled. Information in the above capsule is approximate. Thirteen transfers enrolled. The median GPA of the most recent first-year class was 3.3. The highest LSAT percentile was 99.

Requirements
Applicants must have a bachelor's degree from an accredited institution and take the LSAT. However, applicants may be considered with three-quarters of their undergraduate work completed. The most important admission factors include academic achievement, LSAT results, and GPA. No specific undergraduate courses are required. Candidates are not interviewed.

Procedure
The application deadline for fall entry is March 1. Applicants should submit an application form, LSAT results, transcripts, a nonrefu;ndable application fee, TOEFL, if applicable, 1 letter of recom-

mendation, and LSAT results and transcripts are sent through the LSDAS. Notification of the admission decision is on a rolling basis from March. The latest acceptable LSAT test date for fall entry is February. The law school uses the LSDAS.

Special
The law school recruits minority and disadvantaged students through participation in LSAC forums, participation in Puerto Rican Legal Defense Fund Law Day, visits to historically black colleges, black, Latino, and Asian law days, and contact with high school and college students. The Minority Student Program is open to disadvantaged students of all races. Transfer students must have one year of credit, have a minimum GPA of 3.0, have attended an ABA-approved law school, and a letter of good standing.

Costs

Tuition and fees for the 1999-2000 academic year are $10,100 for full-time in-state students and $14,500 for out-of-state students. Tuition for part-time studetns is $355 per credit in-state, and $550 per credit out-of-state. On-campus room and board costs about $7400 annually; and books and supplies run $1000.

Financial Aid

In a recent year, about 45% of current law students received some form of aid. The average annual amount of aid from all sources combined, including scholarships, loans, and work contracts, was $15,000; maximum, $22,000. Awards are based on need and merit, though most financial aid and scholarships are awarded on the basis of need. Limited merit scholarships and a number of need and merit scholarships are also available. The required financial statement is FAFSA. The aid application deadline for fall entry is March 1. Special funds for minority or disadvantaged students consist of the Ralph Bunche Fellowships, which yield tuition remission and a $12,000 stipend; the C. Clyde Ferguson Scholarships, which yield full in-state tuition and housing for New Jersey residents; Marie Slocum Scholarship; Judge Herbert Tate, Sr. Scholarship; Judge John Dios Scholarship; and a Special Minority Student Scholarship. First-year students are notified about their financial aid application at several weeks after an offer of admission.

About the Law School

Rutgers University/Newark School of Law was established in 1908 and is a public institution. The 11-acre campus is in an urban area in the city of Newark, 8 miles southwest of New York. The primary mission of the law school is to prepare students for professional practice by offering high-quality education in all fields of law, as well as to preserve and expand knowledge as part of a national community of legal scholars, and to serve the public by working to achieve social justice through law. Students have access to federal, state, county, city, and local agencies, courts, correctional facilities, law firms, and legal aid organizations in the Newark area. Also nearby are the American Civil Liberties Union and public interest organizations. Facilities of special interest to law students are the federal courts and county and state court complexes, which are located in downtown Newark, the Newark Museum and Public Library, which are located within one block of the Law School, and the New Jersey Performing Arts Center, which is located just a few blocks away. Housing for law students is available on campus—a third of students live on campus. Most students live in nearby communities, however. All law school facilities are accessible to the physically disabled.

Calendar

The law school operates on a traditional semester basis. Courses for full-time students are offered both day and evening and must be completed within 3 1/2 years. For part-time students, courses are offered both day and evening and must be completed within 4 1/2 years. New full-and part time students are admitted in the fall. There is a 7-week summer session. Transferable summer courses are offered.

Programs

Students may take relevant courses in other programs and apply credit toward the J.D.; a maximum of 12 credits in joint degree programs and 9 in dual degree credits may be applied. The following joint degrees may be earned: J.D./M.A. (Juris Doctor/Master of Arts in criminal justice, political science), J.D./M.C.R.P. (Juris Doctor/Master in City and Regional Planning), and J.D./M.B.A. (Juris Doctor/Master of Business Administration).

Phone: 973-353-5557/5554
Fax: 973-353-1445
Web: .rutgers.edu

Contact
Olga Hunczak, Director of Admissions, 973-353-5557/5554 for general inquiries; Marcia Brown, Assistant Dean/Director Minority Services, 973-353-5644 for financial aid information.

Placement

J.D.s awarded:	212

Services available through: A separate law school placement center.

Services: extensive on-campus interviewing program as well as co-sponsorship of off-campus job fairs; career panels on specific practice areas, judicial clerkships, networking and job search skills

Special features: with stress placed on individual counseling, the alumni/ae job hotline, updated daily, and videotaped mock interviews.

Full-time job interviews:	59 employers
Summer job interviews:	68 employers
Placement by graduation:	n/av
Placement within 9 months:	92% of class
Average starting salary:	$25,000 to $85,000

Areas of placement:

Unknown	40%
Judicial Clerkships	24%
Business/Industry	20%
Government	9%
Public Interest	5%
Academic	2%

Required

To earn the J.D., candidates must complete 84 total credits, of which 31 to 32 are for required courses. They must maintain a minimum GPA of 1.67 in the required courses. The following first-year courses are required of all students: Contracts, Torts, Property, Criminal Law, Constitutional Law, Civil Procedure, Legal Research and Writing I and II, and a required freshman elective. All students All students may elect to choose among extensive in-house clinical programming. The required orientation program for first-year students is 2 days and covers registration, student services, health and safety issues, an Introduction to Legal Research course, and provides opportunities to meet upper-class students and all student organization representatives.

Electives

The School of Law offers concentrations in corporate law, criminal law, entertainment, environmental law, family law, international law, juvenile law, labor law, litigation, media law, securities law, sports law, tax law, torts and insurance, and constitutional law, health law, and intellectual property. In addition, students can earn up to 8 credits per semester for clinics. Clinics are open only to upper-level students, and some require the student to be in their final year. Clinics are Constitutional Rights, Women's Rights, Environmental, Animal Rights, Urban Legal, Special Education, and Federal Tax Law. Some 20 seminars are offered each semester. They are open to all upper-level students and offer the opportunity to write a substantial legal paper that meets the writing requirement. Each seminar carries 2 credits. Students may engage in internships with state or federal magistrates, justices, or judges. These carry 3 credits and are open to all upper-level students with grades of B- or better and are supported by a weekly in-house seminar. Students may assist full-time faculty members in their research for 2 or 3 credits. Independent research may be undertaken by upper-level students for 2 or 3 credits with faculty permission. Special lecture series include Pfizer, Stoffer, and Weintraub lectureships, which are given annually. Students may enroll for up to 6 credits in an ABA/AALS- sponsored summer-abroad program. Approximately 25 students engage in this study every summer, from China to Greece and in U of Leiden-Holland. First-year students are tutored by upper-level students with good grades; tutors may earn 2 credits. The Minority Student Program is dependent on socio-economic status, regardless of race. The school also has programs on behalf of women, minority groups, and gay and lesbian groups. The most widely taken electives are Fundamentals of Estate Planning, Evidence, and Commercial Law I and II.

Graduation Requirements

In order to graduate, candidates must have a GPA of 2.0 and have completed the upper-division writing requirement.

Organizations

Students edit the *The Rutgers Law Review, Computer and Technology Law Journal, Women's Rights Law Reporter, and Race and the Law Review*, and *The Rutgers Law Record*. Students compete in the Nathan Baker Mock Trial, David Cohn Moot Court, and the ABA Negotiations competitions. Students are also invited to participate in approximately 25 to 30 writing competitions, among them the Nathan Burkan Copyright Competition. Law student organizations include Student Bar Association, Public Interest Law Foundation, and Federalist Society. There are local chapters of Student Lawyers Guild, Jackson chapter of Phi Alpha Delta, and ABA-Law Students Division. Other campus groups include Medicine and Health Law Society, Women's Law Forum, and International Students Society.

Library

The law library contains 412,542 hardcopy volumes and 144,376 microform volume equivalents, and subscribes to 3073 serial publications. Such on-line databases and networks as LEXIS, DIALOG, and WESTLAW are available to law students for research. Special library collections include depositories for U.S. and New Jersey documents. Recently, the library installed INNOPAC, an automated serials and acquisition system and on-line public access catalog. The ratio of library volumes to faculty is 4309 to 1 and to students, 512 to 1. The ratio of seats in the library to students is 1 to 2.

Faculty

The law school has 49 full-time and 34 part-time faculty members, of whom 24 are women. According to AAUP standards for Category IIA institutions, faculty salaries are well above average. About 6% of full-time faculty have a graduate law degree in addition to the J.D. The ratio of full-time students to full-time faculty in an average class is 29 to 1; in a clinic, 8 to 1. There is a chapter of the Order of the Coif; 35 faculty and 123 graduates are members.

Students

About 46% of the student body are women; 31%, minorities; 13%, African American; 8%, Asian American; and 10%, Hispanic. The majority of students come from the Northeast (91%). The average age of entering students is 28; age range is 20 to 50. About 40% of students enter directly from undergraduate school, 21% have a graduate degree, and 34% have worked full-time prior to entering law school. About 5% drop out after the first year for academic or personal reasons; 95% remain to receive a law degree.

RUTGERS, THE STATE UNIVERSITY OF NEW JERSEY

School of Law-Camden

Fifth and Penn Streets
Camden, NJ 08102

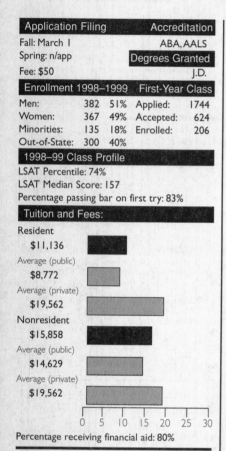

Application Filing		Accreditation
Fall: March 1		ABA, AALS
Spring: n/app		**Degrees Granted**
Fee: $50		J.D.

Enrollment 1998–1999		First-Year Class	
Men:	382 51%	Applied:	1744
Women:	367 49%	Accepted:	624
Minorities:	135 18%	Enrolled:	206
Out-of-State:	300 40%		

1998–99 Class Profile

LSAT Percentile: 74%
LSAT Median Score: 157
Percentage passing bar on first try: 83%

Tuition and Fees:

Resident
$11,136
Average (public)
$8,772
Average (private)
$19,562
Nonresident
$15,858
Average (public)
$14,629
Average (private)
$19,562

0 5 10 15 20 25 30

Percentage receiving financial aid: 80%

ADMISSIONS

In the fall 1999 first-year class, 1744 applied, 624 were accepted, and 206 enrolled. Fifty-one transfers enrolled. The median LSAT percentile of the most recent first-year class was 74; the median GPA was 3.2 on a scale of 4.0. The lowest LSAT percentile accepted was 41; the highest was 98.

Requirements

Applicants must have a bachelor's degree from an accredited institution and take the LSAT. The most important admission factors include LSAT results, academic achievement, and general background. No specific undergraduate courses are required.

Procedure

The application deadline for fall entry is March 1. Applicants should submit an application form, LSAT results, transcripts, a nonrefundable application fee of $50, and 2 letters of recommendation. Notification of the admission decision is on a rolling basis. The latest acceptable LSAT test date for fall entry is February, occasionally June. The law school uses the LSDAS.

Special

The law school recruits minority and disadvantaged students by means of mail, student organizations, interviews, campus visits, and law forums. Transfer students must have one year of credit and have attended an ABA-approved law school.

Costs

Tuition and fees for the 1999-2000 academic year are $11,136 for full-time in-state students and $15,858 for out-of-state students. Tuition for part-time in-state students is $418 per credit and $617 per credit for out-of-state students. On-campus room and board costs about $5168 annually; and books and supplies run $1000.

Financial Aid

About 80% of current law students receive some form of aid. The average annual amount of aid from all sources combined, including scholarships, loans, and work contracts, is $16,800. Awards are based on need and merit. The required financial statement is FAFSA. The aid application deadline for fall entry is on a rolling basis beginning March 1. Special funds for minority or disadvantaged students consist of funds that are available from state, university, and school programs. First-year students are notified about their financial aid application at the time of acceptance.

About the Law School

Rutgers, The State University of New Jersey School of Law-Camden was established in 1926 and is a public institution. The 25-acre campus is in an urban area adjacent to Center City district of Philadelphia. The primary mission of the law school is to provide a dynamic program of professional training, distinguished legal scholarship, and service to the bar and community. Students have access to federal, state, county, city, and local agencies, courts, correctional facilities, law firms, and legal aid organizations in the Camden area. Facilities of special interest to law students include computer laboratories, E-mail accounts, Internet connections, and on-line legal research. Housing for law students is available in a 6-story apartment complex that houses 248 students in 62 graduate apartments. About 90% of the law school facilities are accessible to the physically disabled.

Calendar

The law school operates on a traditional semester basis. Courses for full-and part-time students are offered both day and evening and must be completed within 5 years. New full-and part-time students are admitted in the fall. There is a 7-week summer session. Transferable summer courses are offered.

Programs

Students may take relevant courses in other programs and apply credit toward the J.D.; a maximum of 6 credits may be applied. The following joint degrees may be earned: J.D./M.S. (Juris Doctor/Master of Science in public policy), J.D./M.C.R.P. (Juris Doctor/Master of City and Regional Planning), J.D./M.P.A. (Juris Doctor/Master of Public Administration in health care ma), J.D./M.B.A. (Juris Doctor/Master of Business Administration), J.D./M.D. (Juris Doctor/Doctor of Medicine), J.D./M.S.W. (Juris Doctor/Master of Social Work), and J.D./M.P.A. (Juris Doctor/Master of Public Administration).

Required

To earn the J.D., candidates must complete 84 total credits, of which 34 are for required courses. They must maintain a minimum GPA of 2.0 in the required courses. The following first-year courses are required of all students: Civil Procedure, Contracts, Torts, Legal Research

Phone: 609-225-6102
800-466-7561
Fax: 609-225-6537

Contact

Maureen B. O'Boyle, Associate Director of Admiss, 609-225-6102 for general inquiries; Richard Woodland, Financial Aid Director, 609-225-6039 for financial aid information.

and Writing, Constitutional Law, Criminal Law, Property, and Moot Court I. Required upper-level courses consist of Professional Responsibility, elective courses with writing components, and Introduction to Federal Income Taxation. The required orientation program for first-year students is 3 days prior to the start of classes; there is a briefing on reading and analyzing cases, library usage, legal writing, Professional responsibility, and general study techniques, as well as an introduction to computer usage and student organizations and social events.

Electives

The School of Law-Camden offers concentrations in corporate law, criminal law, environmental law, family law, international law, labor law, litigation, tax law, and health law, public interest law. Clinics include a Small Business Counseling Clinic, worth 3 credits and a Civil Practice Clinic, worth 4 credits. The Pro Bono/Public Interest program enables students to represent clients, under the supervision of attorneys, in domestic violence, immigration, and bankruptcy cases, and to conduct mediations in local courts. All students take at least 1 course each semester with a significant writing component to complete the advanced writing requirement. The school conducts an extensive externship program, worth 6 credits, for third-year students in good academic standing. Third-year students may take independent study for 1 to 2 credits, under the supervision of a faculty member. The annual state Constitution Law Lecture and Corman Distinguished Lecture bring nationally known scholars and jurists to the law school. Students can also attend other law schools' study-abroad programs. No-credit tutorial programs are offered on an individual basis for students in need. Workshops on study techniques, test taking, and individual subject review are available for all students. An extensive Academic Success Program is also available. Programming for minority students is sponsored by student groups and supported by the administration and faculty. The most widely taken electives are Evidence, Commercial Law, and Business Organizations.

Graduation Requirements

In order to graduate, candidates must have a GPA of 2.0 and have completed the upper-division writing requirement.

Organizations

Students edit the *Rutgers Law Journal* and the *Rutgers Journal of Law and Religion*. A highlight of the upper-level curriculum is the Judge James A. Hunter III Advanced Moot Court Program. Other moot court competitions include the National Moot Court Competition, the Jessup International Moot Court Competition, the Gibbons National Criminal Procedure Moot Court Competition, Admiralty Moot Court Competition, National Black Law Students Association Frederick Douglass Competition, National Latino Law Students Association Moot Court Competition, and the Environmental Moot Court Competition. Law student organizations include the Student Bar Association, Association for Public Interest Law, and the Francis Deak International Law Society. There are local chapters and clubs of all major national law student organizations, including Phi Alpha Delta law fraternity, Women's Law Caucus, Black Law Student Association, Hispanic Students Association, and Asian/Pacific American Student Association.

Library

The law library contains 407,335 hardcopy volumes and 630,770 microform volume equivalents (plus 2,241 microfilm), and subscribes to 1360 serial publications. Such on-line databases and networks as LEXIS, WESTLAW, and RLIN are available to law students for research. Special library collections include a historical collection of Soviet and Eastern European legal matters and a U.S. government depository library. Recently, the library added a computer room and court web sites (the only access in New Jersey for New Jersey administrative court cases). The ratio of library volumes to faculty is 9473 to 1 and to students, 544 to 1. The ratio of seats in the library to students is 1 to 2.

Faculty

The law school has 43 full-time and 65 part-time faculty members, of whom 31 are women. According to AAUP standards for Category IIA institutions, faculty salaries are well above average. About 39% of full-time faculty have a graduate law degree in addition to the J.D.; about 28% of part-time faculty have one. The ratio of full-time students to full-time faculty in an average class is 20 to 1; in a clinic, 8 to 1. The law school has

Placement

J.D.s awarded:	210

Services available through: A separate law school placement center.

Services: assistance with LEXIS, WESTLAW, and the Internet career searches; fall and spring on-campus interview programs

Special features: interview workshops, on-campus interview programs, career forums, resource library, and participation in a consortium with the law schools of the University of Pennsylvania, Temple, and Villanova; full service Career Services Office with 3 full-time professional career services staff members in addition to 1 full-time pro bono coordinator and public interest adviser; videotaped mock interviews, individualized and small group career workshops, career panels, and several alumni and attorney mentoring programs.

Full-time job interviews:	150 employers
Summer job interviews:	150 employers
Placement by graduation:	84% of class
Placement within 9 months:	95% of class
Average starting salary:	$30,000 to $105,000

Areas of placement:

Private practice 2-10 attorneys	5%
Private practice 11-25 attorneys	4%
Private practice 26-50 attorneys	4%
Private practice 51-100 attorneys	14%
Private practice firm size unknown	3%
Judicial clerkships	41%
Business/industry	16%
Government	7%
Military	3%
Public interest	2%
Academic	1%

a regular program of bringing visiting professors and other distinguished lecturers and visitors to campus.

Students

About 49% of the student body are women; 18%, minorities; 7%, African American; 6%, Asian American; 3%, Hispanic; 1%, Native American; and 1%, foreign. The majority of students come from New Jersey (60%). The average age of entering students is 26; age range is 20 to 70. About 42% of students enter directly from undergraduate school, 8% have a graduate degree, and 56% have worked full-time prior to entering law school. About 4% drop out after the first year for academic or personal reasons; 91% remain to receive a law degree.

SAINT JOHN'S UNIVERSITY

School of Law

8000 Utopia Parkway
Jamaica, NY 11439

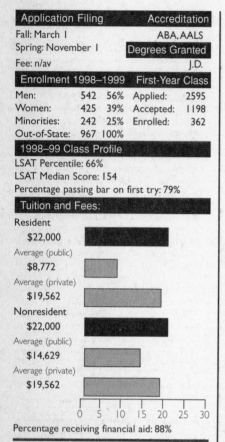

Application Filing	Accreditation
Fall: March 1	ABA, AALS
Spring: November 1	Degrees Granted
Fee: n/av	J.D.

Enrollment 1998–1999		First-Year Class	
Men:	542 56%	Applied:	2595
Women:	425 39%	Accepted:	1198
Minorities:	242 25%	Enrolled:	362
Out-of-State:	967 100%		

1998–99 Class Profile
LSAT Percentile: 66%
LSAT Median Score: 154
Percentage passing bar on first try: 79%

Tuition and Fees:

Resident
$22,000

Average (public)
$8,772

Average (private)
$19,562

Nonresident
$22,000

Average (public)
$14,629

Average (private)
$19,562

0   5   10   15   20   25   30

Percentage receiving financial aid: 88%

ADMISSIONS

In the fall 1999 first-year class, 2595 applied, 1198 were accepted, and 362 enrolled. Thirteen transfers enrolled. The median LSAT percentile of the most recent first-year class was 66.6; the median GPA was 3.05 on a scale of 4.0.

Requirements
Applicants must have a bachelor's degree from an accredited institution and take the LSAT. No specific undergraduate courses are required. Candidates are not interviewed.

Procedure
The application deadline for fall entry is March 1. Applicants should submit an application form, LSAT results, transcripts, and a personal statement. Check with the school for the current fee. Notification of the admissions decision is as soon as the application is complete. The latest acceptable LSAT test date for fall entry is February. The law school uses the LSDAS.

Special
The law school recruits minority and disadvantaged students through a Special Diversity Admissions Program, which consists of a substantive course taught and graded according to the same standard applied to all students in first-year courses. There is also a B.A./J.D. joint degree program with member schools of the United Negro College Fund, which includes scholarship funding and living expenses for participating students. Transfer students must have one year of credit, have attended an ABA-approved law school, and have a letter of good standing from the dean of the present law school, have a copy of the LSDAS report, and have an official transcript from the present law school.

Costs

Tuition and fees for the 1999-2000 academic year are $22,000 for all full-time students. Tuition for part-time students is $16,500, per year. On-campus room and board costs about $8550 annually; and books and supplies run $1000.

Financial Aid

In a recent year, about 88% of current law students received some form of aid. The average annual amount of aid from all sources combined, including scholarships, loans, and work contracts, was $18,227; maximum, $36,000. Awards are based on need and merit. The required financial statement is the FAFSA. Check with the school for current deadlines. Special funds for minority or disadvantaged students are available. First-year students are notified about their financial aid application at the time of acceptance.

About the Law School

Saint John's University School of Law was established in 1925 and is a private institution. The 100-acre campus is in a suburban area 15 miles east of New York City. The primary mission of the law school is to impart training and competency in the basic skills and techniques of the legal profession, a grasp of the history and system of the common law, and a familiarity with important statutes and decisions in federal and state jurisdictions, including the state of New York. Students have access to federal, state, county, city, and local agencies, courts, correctional facilities, law firms, and legal aid organizations in the Jamaica area. Facilities of special interest to law students consist of the recently expanded and renovated law school with unique architecture, featuring a full service dining room and a library incorporating the most recent advances in library science and research technology. Housing for law students is available on campus and the school's Admissions Office also provides a housing network and information on housing available in the surrounding area. All law school facilities are accessible to the physically disabled.

Calendar

The law school operates on a traditional semester basis. Courses for full-time students are offered both day and evening and must be completed within 3 years. For part-time students, courses are offered evenings only and must be completed within 4 years. New full-time students are admitted in the fall and spring; part-time, fall. There is an 8-week summer session. Transferable summer courses are offered.

Programs

The following joint degrees may be earned: J.D./B.A.-B.S. (Juris Doctor/Bachelor of Arts and/or Bachelor of Science), J.D./M.A. (Juris Doctor/Master of Arts in government and politics), and J.D./M.B.A. (Juris Doctor/Master of Business Administration).

Phone: 718-990-6611/6612
Fax: 718-990-2526
E-mail: rsvp@sjulaw.stjohns.edu
Web: stjohns.edu/law

Contact
Admissions Office, 718-990-6611 for general inquiries; Jorge Rodriguez, Financial Aid Director, 718-990-2000 for financial aid information.

NEW YORK

Required
To earn the J.D., candidates must complete 85 total credits, of which 61 are for required courses. They must maintain a minimum GPA of 2.0 in the required courses. The following first-year courses are required of all students: Contracts I and II, Property I and II, Torts I and II, Introduction to Civil Procedure, Legal Method, Criminal Law, and Legal Research and Writing. Required upper-level courses consist of Evidence I and II, Business Organizations I and II, Basic Income Tax, Constitutional Law, Commercial Transactions, Professional Responsibility, and Trusts and Estates. The required orientation program for first-year students is a 2-week program describing the program of study, rules and regulations of the law school, support services, tutorial programs, and career development.

Electives
The School of Law offers concentrations in criminal law, environmental law, family law, labor law, litigation, securities law, and tax law. In the Civil Clinical Seminar, students work in a legal services office that provides representation to the poor or in a public service or governmental agency. In the Criminal Clinical Seminar, students work in a district attorney's office, a Legal Aid office, or in the law department of the state Supreme Court or Criminal Court. In the Judicial Clinical Seminar, students work in the federal, state, or city court system. Research may be undertaken through the St. Thomas More Institute for Legal Research, which publishes the *St. John's Law Review* and *The Catholic Lawyer*. Candidates for membership must have at least a B cumulative average and must participate in a writing competition. Through the Street Law Program, students join teams that inform neighborhood residents about their legal rights, or speak to interested high school students about legal careers. Each year, the school hosts guest speakers, Judge-in-Residence and Scholar-in-Residence programs, and various other symposia. The school offers an expanded tutorial program. Minority and disadvantaged students may take part in the scholarship program. The most widely taken electives are New York Practice I, Criminal Procedure I, and Family Law.

Graduation Requirements
In order to graduate, candidates must have a GPA of 2.0 and have completed the upper-division writing requirement.

Organizations
The primary law review is the *St. John's Law Review*. Other law reviews include the *Journal of Legal Commentary, The Catholic Lawyer, International Law Review of the New York State Bar Association*, and *American Bankruptcy Institute Law Review*. The student newspaper is *The Forum* and the yearbook is *Res Gestae*. Internally, students compete in the Preliminary Argument of the National Moot Court Competition. Externally, teams are sent to the National Moot Court and the John Marshall (Benton) National competitions. Other competitions include the Criminal Law Institute and the Civil Trial Institute. Law student organizations include the Student Bar Association, Admiralty Law Society, and American Law Students Association. Local chapters of national associations include Delta Theta Phi, Phi Alpha Delta, and Phi Delta Phi.

Library
The law library contains 432,804 hardcopy volumes and 1,148,680 microform volume equivalents, and subscribes to 5500 serial publications. Such on-line databases and networks as LEXIS, DIALOG, WESTLAW, NEXIS, SUNY/OCLC are available to law students for research. Special library collections include the St. Thomas More Collection and a U.S. government documents depository. Recently, the library expanded shelf space and renovated the facility, added a 22-terminal computer classroom, and expanded the computer laboratory. The ratio of library volumes to faculty is 9618 to 1 and to students, 393 to 1. The ratio of seats in the library to students is 1 to 2.

Placement

J.D.s awarded:	373
Services available through: separate law school placement center	
Services: information and workshop presentations on applying for federal judicial clerkships; career and job search panels	
Special features: extended hours 4 days a week to accommodate both day and evening students, Saturday hours once a month; a newsletter for students; and a newsletter, job binders, and telephone hotline for alumni.	
Full-time job interviews:	45 employers
Summer job interviews:	53 employers
Placement by graduation:	64% of class
Placement within 9 months:	95% of class
Average starting salary:	$24,000 to $165,000
Areas of placement:	
Private practice 2-10 attorneys	21%
Private practice 11-25 attorneys	9%
private practice 26-50 attorneys	9%
Private practice 51-100 attorneys	8%
Government	20%
Business/industry	12%
Judicial clerkships	11%
Academic	7%
Military	2%
Public interest	1%

Faculty
The law school has 59 full-time and 37 part-time faculty members, of whom 26 are women. According to AAUP standards for Category I institutions, faculty salaries are well above average. About 59% of full-time faculty have a graduate law degree in addition to the J.D.; about 15% of part-time faculty have one. The ratio of full-time students to full-time faculty in an average class is 14 to 1; in a clinic, 8 to 1.

Students
About 39% of the student body are women; 25%, minorities; 7%, African American; 8%, Asian American; 9%, Hispanic; and 1%, Native American. The average age of entering students is 23; age range is 20 to 49.

SAINT LOUIS UNIVERSITY

School of Law

3700 Lindell Boulevard
St. Louis, MO 63108

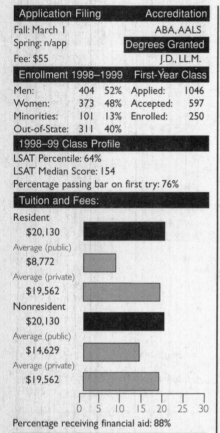

Application Filing	Accreditation
Fall: March 1	ABA, AALS
Spring: n/app	**Degrees Granted**
Fee: $55	J.D., LL.M.

Enrollment 1998–1999		First-Year Class	
Men:	404 52%	Applied:	1046
Women:	373 48%	Accepted:	597
Minorities:	101 13%	Enrolled:	250
Out-of-State:	311 40%		

1998–99 Class Profile
LSAT Percentile: 64%
LSAT Median Score: 154
Percentage passing bar on first try: 76%

Tuition and Fees:

Resident
$20,130

Average (public)
$8,772

Average (private)
$19,562

Nonresident
$20,130

Average (public)
$14,629

Average (private)
$19,562

0 5 10 15 20 25 30

Percentage receiving financial aid: 88%

ADMISSIONS

In the fall 1999 first-year class, 1046 applied, 597 were accepted, and 250 enrolled. Four transfers enrolled. The median LSAT percentile of the most recent first-year class was 64; the median GPA was 3.3 on a scale of 4.0. The lowest LSAT percentile accepted was 11; the highest was 99.

Requirements
Applicants must have a bachelor's degree from an accredited institution and take the LSAT. The most important admission factors include LSAT results and GPA. No specific undergraduate courses are required. Candidates are not interviewed.

Procedure
The application deadline for fall entry is March 1. Applicants should submit an application form, TOEFL where applicable, a nonrefundable application fee of $55, and 2 letters of recommendation. Accepted students must pay a $100 deposit to reserve a place and a $200 final deposit to confirm attendance. Notification of the admission decision is on a rolling basis. The latest acceptable LSAT test date for fall entry is February. The law school uses the LSDAS.

Special
The law school actively recruits minority and disadvantaged students through the Special Admission Summer Institute, scholarships for diversity, active BLSA and Latin American Society, and the Minority Clerkship Program, and by recruiting at colleges and universities throughout the United States. Transfer students must have one year of credit, have attended an ABA-approved law school, and rank in the top quarter of the law class.

Costs

Tuition and fees for the 1999-2000 academic year are $20,130 for all full-time students. Tuition for all part-time students is $15,080 annually or $830 per credit. Books and supplies run $600.

Financial Aid

About 88% of current law students receive some form of aid. The average annual amount of aid from all sources combined, including scholarships, loans, and work contracts, is $20,000; maximum, $32,000. Awards are based on need and merit. The required financial statement is FAFSA. The aid application deadline for fall entry is April 1. Special funds for minority or disadvantaged students consist of scholarships and grants up to full tuition. Awards are based on merit, and the average award is $8000. First-year students are notified about their financial aid application some time after acceptance.

About the Law School

Saint Louis University School of Law was established in 1843 and is a private institution. The 50-acre campus is in an urban area within St. Louis. The primary mission of the law school is consistent with the Jesuit nature of the institution; academic excellence and freedom of inquiry, a genuine concern for the development of each student as a person, and an effort to sensitize students to the moral and ethical dimensions of law and lawyering. Students have access to federal, state, county, city, and local agencies, courts, correctional facilities, law firms, and legal aid organizations in the St. Louis area. Housing for law students consists of off-campus housing, which is readily available and affordable. All law school facilities are accessible to the physically disabled.

Calendar

The law school operates on a traditional semester basis. Courses for full-time students are offered both day and evening and must be completed within 3 years. For part-time students, courses are offered both day and evening and must be completed within 5 years (4 years including summers). New full-and part-time students are admitted in the fall. There is an 8-week summer session. Transferable summer courses are offered.

Programs

In addition to the J.D., the law school offers the LL.M. Students may take relevant courses in other programs and apply credit toward the J.D.; a maximum of 6 credits may be applied. The following joint degrees may be earned: J.D./M.B.A. (Juris Doctor/Master of Business Administration), J.D./M.H.A. (Juris Doctor/Master of Health Care Administration), J.D./M.A. (Juris Doctor/Master of Arts in urban affairs), J.D./M.A. (Juris Doctor/Master of Arts in public administration), J.D./M.S.W. (Juris Doctor/Master of Social Work), and J.D./M.P.H. (Juris Doctor/Master of Public Health).

Phone: 314-977-2800
E-mail: admissions@law.slu.edu
Web: www.law.slu.edu

Contact

Assistant Dean and Director of Admissions, 314-977-2800 for general inquiries; Hal Deuser, Director of Financial Aid, 314-977-2350 for financial aid information.

MISSOURI

Required

To earn the J.D., candidates must complete 88 total credits, of which 36 are for required courses. They must maintain a minimum GPA of 2.0 in the required courses. The following first-year courses are required of all students: Contracts I and II, Torts, Property, Civil Procedure I and II, Legal Research and Writing I and II, Taxation, and Constitutional Law I. Required upper-level courses consist of Legal Profession (Professional Ethics), a seminar, and a humanistic requirement. The required orientation program for first-year students is 3 days.

Electives

The School of Law offers concentrations in international law, labor law, and health law. In addition, clinical training includes the Civil Clinic, Criminal Clinic, Judicial Process Clinic, and the Corporate General Counsel Externship Program. An average of 10 seminars are offered each semester. Internships are available through clinical programs. Special lecture series include the Melvin Dubinsky Visiting Lecture, the Richard Childress Memorial Lecture Series, the Terence K. McCormack Memorial Lecture, the Sanford Sarasohn Memorial Lecture, and the James Millstone Lecture. Summer study abroad is available in Brussels, Belgium and at Ruhr University in Bochum, Germany. Beginning the summer of 2001, the School of Law will annually have a summer study abroad program in Madrid. All students are offered an academic support adviser. The Summer Institute includes students with some educational disadvantage, such as students with English as a second language or those with a learning disability. There is also a Minority Clerkship Program. Special interest group programs include the William C. Wefel Center for Employment Law, the Center for Health Law Studies, and the Center for International and Comparative Law. The most widely taken electives are Health Law, Employment Law/Business, and International Law.

Graduation Requirements

In order to graduate, candidates must have a GPA of 2.0.

Organizations

Students edit the *Saint Louis University Law Journal*, *Public Law Review*, *Saint Louis-Warsaw Transatlantic Law Journal*, *Fidelity and Suretyship Newsletter*, and *Journal of Health Law*. Students may participate in the Jessup International Moot Court Program, numerous writing competitions, and a client counseling competition. Student organizations include the Student Bar Association, ABA-Law Student Division, the Health Law Association, the International Law Society, and the Women's Law Student Association. There are local chapters of Phi Alpha Delta, Delta Theta Phi, and Phi Delta Phi.

Library

The law library contains 565,677 hardcopy volumes and 51,000 microform volume equivalents, and subscribes to 6400 serial publications. Such on-line databases and networks as LEXIS, DIALOG, WESTLAW, and Medline, OCLC, and Internet are available to law students for research. Special library collections include the Leonor K. Sullivan Congressional Papers, the Leo C. Brown Arbitration Papers, the Irish Law Collection, the Jewish Law Collection, and the Polish Law Collection. Recently, the library installed a specially equipped PC for those with reading disabilties. The ratio of library volumes to faculty is 8443 to 1 and to students, 728 to 1. The ratio of seats in the library to students is 1 to 2.

Faculty

The law school has 39 full-time and 28 part-time faculty members, of whom 21 are women. According to AAUP standards for Category I institutions, faculty salaries are average. About 51% of full-time faculty have a graduate law degree in addition to the J.D. The ratio of full-time students to full-time faculty in an average class is 20 to 1; in a clinic, 3 to 1. The law school has a regular program of bringing visiting professors and other distinguished lecturers and visitors to campus.

Placement

J.D.s awarded:	244

Services available through: A separate law school placement center.

Services: special programs on various areas of practice, such as health law, international, corporate, government, public interest, and judicial clerkships.

Special features: an extensive career library with a computer search service

Full-time job interviews:	40 employers
Summer job interviews:	55 employers
Placement by graduation:	60% of class
Placement within 9 months:	95% of class
Average starting salary:	$33,000 to $66,000

Areas of placement:

Private practice 2-10 attorneys	20%
Private practice 11-25 attorneys	2%
Private practice 26-50 attorneys	6%
Private practice 51-100 attorneys	8%
Private practice 100+ attorneys	18%
Unknown	4%
Business/industry	21%
Government	10%
Judicial clerkships	9%
Public interest	1%
Academic	1%

Students

About 48% of the student body are women; 13%, minorities; 6%, African American; 3%, Asian American; 3%, Hispanic; and 1%, Native American. The majority of students come from the Midwest (70%). The average age of entering students is 26; age range is 20 to 54. About 42% of students enter directly from undergraduate school, 13% have a graduate degree, and 58% have worked full-time prior to entering law school. About 5% drop out after the first year for academic or personal reasons; 90% remain to receive a law degree.

School of Law

One Camino Santa Maria
San Antonio, TX 78228-8601

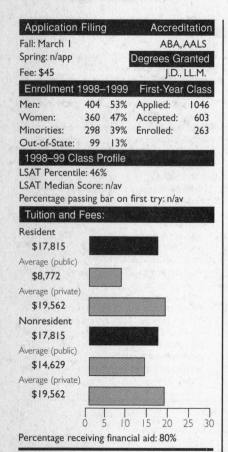

Application Filing	Accreditation
Fall: March 1	ABA, AALS
Spring: n/app	**Degrees Granted**
Fee: $45	J.D., LL.M.

Enrollment 1998–1999		First-Year Class	
Men:	404 53%	Applied:	1046
Women:	360 47%	Accepted:	603
Minorities:	298 39%	Enrolled:	263
Out-of-State:	99 13%		

1998–99 Class Profile

LSAT Percentile: 46%
LSAT Median Score: n/av
Percentage passing bar on first try: n/av

Tuition and Fees:

Resident
$17,815

Average (public)
$8,772

Average (private)
$19,562

Nonresident
$17,815

Average (public)
$14,629

Average (private)
$19,562

0   5   10   15   20   25   30

Percentage receiving financial aid: 80%

ADMISSIONS

In the fall 1999 first-year class, 1046 applied, 603 were accepted, and 263 enrolled. Four transfers enrolled. The median LSAT percentile of the most recent first-year class was 46; the median GPA was 3.0 on a scale of 4.0. The lowest LSAT percentile accepted was 25; the highest was 75.

Requirements

Applicants must have a bachelor's degree from an accredited institution and take the LSAT. Minimum acceptable GPA is 2.0 on a scale of 4.0. No specific undergraduate courses are required. Candidates are not interviewed.

Procedure

The application deadline for fall entry is March 1. Applicants should submit an application form, a nonrefundable application fee of $45, and as many as 5 letters of recommendation may be accepted. Notification of the admission decision is after May 1. The latest acceptable LSAT test date for fall entry is February. The law school uses the LSDAS.

Special

Transfer students must have one year of credit, have a minimum GPA of 2.5, and have attended an ABA-approved law school.

Costs

Tuition and fees for the 1999-2000 academic year are $17,815 for all full-time students. On-campus room and board costs about $2223 annually; books and supplies run $1100.

Financial Aid

About 80% of current law students receive some form of aid. The average annual amount of aid from all sources combined, including scholarships, loans, and work contracts, is $18,500; maximum, $20,000. Awards are based on need. The required financial statement is the FAFSA. The aid application deadline for fall entry is March 31. Special funds for minority or disadvantaged students are available based on need. First-year students are notified about their financial aid application at time of acceptance.

About the Law School

Saint Mary's University School of Law was established in 1948 and is a private institution. The 132-acre campus is in a suburban area in San Antonio, Texas. The primary mission of the law school is to offer a solid curriculum of traditional legal studies and to teach students the practical skills and habits necessary to practice effective public service advocacy. Students have access to federal, state, county, city, and local agencies, courts, correctional facilities, law firms, and legal aid organizations in the San Antonio area. A joint program with the Universidad de Monterrey (Mexico) allows attorneys to represent clients with business in Mexico. St. Mary's has an exchange program with the Universidad

Autonoma de Coahuila (Mexico). The Center for Conciliation and Arbitration facilitates commercial dispute resolutions through means other than litigation. Housing for law students is available in on-campus resident dormitory facilities for single students only. Information and application forms may be obtained from the Director of Housing. All law school facilities are accessible to the physically disabled.

Calendar

The law school operates on a traditional semester basis. Courses for full-time students are offered days only and must be completed within 5 years. There is no part-time program. New students are admitted in the fall. There is a 5 1/2-week summer session. Transferable summer courses are offered.

Programs

In addition to the J.D., the law school offers the LL.M. The following joint degrees may be earned: J.D./M.B.A. (Juris Doctor/Master of Business Administration), J.D./M.P.A. (Juris Doctor/Master of Public Administration), J.D./M.Econ (Juris Doctor/Master of Economics), J.D./M.A. (Juris Doctor/Master of Arts in theology and in international relations), and J.D./M.S. (Juris Doctor/Master of Science in engineering).

Required

To earn the J.D., candidates must complete 90 total credits, of which 46 are for required courses. They must maintain a minimum GPA of 2.0 in the required courses. The following first-year courses are required of all students: Constitutional Law, Legal Research and Writing, Contracts I and II, Legal Methods, Criminal Law, Procedure I, Property I and II, and Torts I and II. Required upper-level courses consist of Professional Responsibility, Evidence I and II, Texas Civil Procedure, a perspective course, and a research paper that fulfills the writing requirement. Although not required, law students are urged to participate in clinics for credit in the third year or as volunteers in the first and second years. The required orientation program for first-year students consists of a 2-day orientation session during which first-year law students discuss their expectations regarding law school and the law profession.

Contact
Catherine L. Mery, Admissions Officer, 210-436-3523 for general inquiries; Diana Perez, 210-431-6743 for financial aid information.

Electives
The School of Law offers concentrations in corporate law, criminal law, environmental law, family law, international law, juvenile law, labor law, litigation, maritime law, securities law, tax law, and torts and insurance. In addition, four clinics—Civil Justice Clinic, Criminal Justice Clinic, Immigration and Human Rights Clinic, and Community Development Clinic—are open to second- and third-year students. Limited to an enrollment of 12 students, seminars include Natural Resource Protection Law; Doing Business with Mexico; and International Law. Two judicial internships, with the Texas Supreme Court and with the Court of Appeals, Third District of Texas, both located in Austin, Texas, are offered. Students earn 4 hours of credit for the internship and may enroll at the University of Texas Law School for additional credits. Students are required to do field work in the clinical programs. Students in the judicial internships spend a semester at the court, and students may seek independent study credit for worthwhile projects taken with the approval and supervision of a faculty member. St. Mary's sponsors conferences and symposia on such diverse topics as United Nations Law and Legal Research, Human Rights in the Americas, and Legal Aspects of Doing Business with Mexico. The school also presents lectures by renowned legal scholars. Beginning in the second semester of the first year, students who scored poorly in their first-semester examinations are required to attend small-group tutorials. The tutorials are conducted by upper-class students under professional supervision. Each year, 20 students are accepted into the Law Skills Enhancement Program, a 5-week summer program that provides intensive writing instruction and instruction on how to read, analyze, and brief cases. The Minority Law Students Association, the Black Allied Law Students Association, and the Asian-Pacific American Law Students Association offer tutorials to first-year students who are members. Special-interest groups include the Society of Legal Entrepreneurs, Education Law Association, Environmental Law Society, Criminal Law Association, and Family Law Association. Several student groups, including the Environmental Law Society, the Women's Bar Association, and the Minority Law Students

Association, have developed mentor relationships with local bar associations. The most widely taken electives are Wills and Estates, Trusts, and Business Associations.

Graduation Requirements
In order to graduate, candidates must have a GPA of 2.0 and have completed the upper-division writing requirement.

Organizations
Students edit the *St. Mary's University School of Law Law Journal* and the *Hispanic Law Review*. Moot court competitions include the Norvell Moot Court Competition, involving all Texas schools, and the Walker Moot Court, held on campus. Other competitions include the Shannon Thurmond Giltner Novice Mock Trial, National Mock Trial, and the ABA Client-Counseling. Law student organizations are the Student Bar Association, Family Law Association, and William Sessions American Inn of Court. Local chapters of national associations are Delta Theta Phi, Delta Alpha Delta, and Harlan Society. Campus clubs and other organizations include the Student Aggie Bar Association and the Longhorn Bar Association.

Library
The law library contains 320,000 hardcopy volumes and 633,117 microform volume equivalents, and subscribes to 3804 serial publications. Such on-line databases and networks as LEXIS, DIALOG, and WESTLAW are available to law students for research. Special library collections include Mexican legal materials, microtext of records and briefs of the United States Supreme Court, and legal documents from the United Nations and from American, British, Canadian, and international law. The library is a depository for U.S. government documents. The ratio of library volumes to faculty is 8362 to 1 and to students, 373 to 1. The ratio of seats in the library to students is 1 to 3.

Faculty
The law school has 34 full-time and 28 part-time faculty members, of whom 19 are women. About 30% of full-time faculty have a graduate law degree in addition to the J.D. The ratio of full-time students to full-time faculty in an average

Placement	
J.D.s awarded:	242

Services available through: separate law school placement center.
Services: individual strategy sessions and a weekly job newsletter.
Special features: The Office of Career Counseling and Services arranges seminars throughout the year to assist students in career planning and job searches. Alumni mentors are available, and a new Student Resource Center has been established.

Full-time job interviews:	35 employers
Summer job interviews:	n/av
Placement by graduation:	68% of class
Placement within 9 months:	92% of class
Average starting salary:	$24,000 to $55,000

Areas of placement:

Private practice 2-10 attorneys	29%
Private practice 11-25 attorneys	2%
Private practice 26-50 attorneys	2%
Private practice 51-100 attorneys	7%
Government	10%
Self-employed	9%
Judicial clerkships	7%
Business/industry	4%
Academic	2%
Public interest	1%
Military	1%
Unknown	26%

class is 26 to 1; in a clinic, 4 to 1. The law school has a regular program of bringing visiting professors and other distinguished lecturers and visitors to campus.

Students
About 47% of the student body are women; 39%, minorities; 5%, African American; 4%, Asian American; and 29%, Hispanic. The majority of students come from Texas (87%). The age range of entering students is 23 to 65. About 2% drop out after the first year for academic or personal reasons; 88% remain to receive a law degree.

Cumberland School of Law

800 Lakeshore Drive
Birmingham, AL 35229

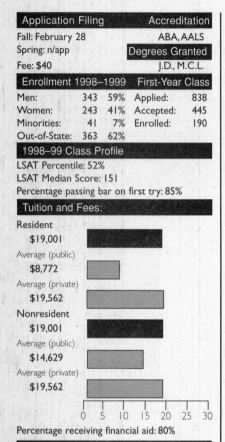

Application Filing	Accreditation
Fall: February 28	ABA, AALS
Spring: n/app	**Degrees Granted**
Fee: $40	J.D., M.C.L.

Enrollment 1998–1999			First-Year Class	
Men:	343	59%	Applied:	838
Women:	243	41%	Accepted:	445
Minorities:	41	7%	Enrolled:	190
Out-of-State:	363	62%		

1998–99 Class Profile

LSAT Percentile: 52%

LSAT Median Score: 151

Percentage passing bar on first try: 85%

Tuition and Fees:

Resident
$19,001

Average (public)
$8,772

Average (private)
$19,562

Nonresident
$19,001

Average (public)
$14,629

Average (private)
$19,562

0 5 10 15 20 25 30

Percentage receiving financial aid: 80%

ADMISSIONS

In the fall 1999 first-year class, 838 applied, 445 were accepted, and 190 enrolled. Four transfers enrolled. The median LSAT percentile of the most recent first-year class was 52; the median GPA was 3.0 on a scale of 4.0. The lowest LSAT percentile accepted was 17.4; the highest was 99.1.

Requirements

Applicants must have a bachelor's degree from an accredited institution and take the LSAT. The most important admission factors include LSAT results, GPA, and academic achievement. No specific undergraduate courses are required. Candidates are not interviewed.

Procedure

The application deadline for fall entry is February 28. Applicants should submit an application form, a nonrefundable application fee of $40, and 2 letters of recommendation. LSAT results and transcripts must come from LSDAS. Notification of the admission decision is on a rolling basis. The latest acceptable LSAT test date for fall entry is February. The law school uses the LSDAS.

Special

The law school recruits minority and disadvantaged students by means of recruiting at historically black colleges and universities. The Black Law Students Association is active in on-campus recruiting and has special events for minority students during the school's Pre-Law Day. Transfer students must have one year of credit, have a minimum GPA of 3.0, have attended an AALS- and ABA-approved school, and have a letter of good standing from the dean of the former law school.

Costs

Tuition and fees for the 1999-2000 academic year are $19,001 for all full-time students. Books and supplies run $1074.

Financial Aid

About 80% of current law students receive some form of aid. The average annual amount of aid from all sources combined, including scholarships, loans, and work contracts, is $22,000; maximum, $29,000. Awards are based on need and merit. The required financial statement is FAFSA. The aid application deadline for fall entry is March 1. Special funds for minority or disadvantaged students consist of full or partial tuition scholarships. First-year students are notified about their financial aid application at time of acceptance.

About the Law School

Samford University Cumberland School of Law was established in 1847 and is a private institution. The 300-acre campus is in a suburban area 6 miles from downtown Birmingham. The primary mission of the law school is to educate students to be responsible lawyers, trained to exercise their professional skills competently with sensitivity to the needs and concerns of their clients, and to act in strict accord with the highest ethical standards. Students have access to federal, state, county, city, and local agencies, courts, correctional facilities, law firms, and legal aid organizations in the Birmingham area. Facilities of special interest to law students include an $8.4 million, 61,000-square-foot freestanding library connected to the Law School building by a covered breezeway on the second floor, easily accessible to physically disabled students. Housing for law students is available off campus in any number of nearby neighborhoods. Assistance in obtaining apartment rental information is provided by the Student Bar Association, which also provides a roommate referral service. About 95% of the law school facilities are accessible to the physically disabled.

Calendar

The law school operates on a traditional semester basis. Courses for full-time students are offered days only and must be completed within 4 years. There is no part-time program. New full-time students are admitted in the fall. There is a 9-week summer session. Transferable summer courses are offered.

Programs

In addition to the J.D., the law school offers the M.C.L. Students may take relevant courses in other programs and apply credit toward the J.D.; a maximum of 12 credits may be applied. The following joint degrees may be earned: J.D./M.B.A. (Juris Doctor/Master of Business Administration), J.D./M.P.H. (Juris Doctor/Master of Public Health), J.D./M.Acc. (Juris Doctor/Master of Accounting), J.D./M.Div. (Juris Doctor/Master of Divinity), J.D./M.P.A. (Juris Doctor/Master of Public Administration), and J.D./M.S. (Juris Doctor/Master of Science in environmental management).

Phone: 205-726-2702
800-888-7213
Fax: 205-726-2673
E-mail: lawadmissions@samford.edu
Web: http://www.samford.edu/schools/law.html

Contact
Mitzi S. Davis, Assistant Dean, 800-888-7213 for general inquiries; David Long, Assistant Director of Financial Aid, 800-888-7245 for financial aid information.

ALABAMA

Required
To earn the J.D., candidates must complete 90 total credits, of which 53 are for required courses. They must maintain a minimum GPA of 2.0 in the required courses. The following first-year courses are required of all students: Tort I and II, Contracts I and II, Property I and II, Criminal Law, Civil Procedure I and II, Legal Research and Writing I, Evidence, and Legal Research and Writing II. Required upper-level courses consist of Constitutional Law I and II, Business Organizations, Basic Federal Income Tax, Decedents' Estates and Trusts, Professional Responsibility, and Commercial Transactions I and II. The required orientation program for first-year students is designed to introduce new students to the school, the faculty, and the curriculum. Entering students participate in an intensive 1-week introduction to legal research and writing prior to the beginning of classes.

Electives
The Center for Advocacy and Clinical Education offers upper-level students clinical courses for 1 to 2 credit hours and internships for 2 to 3 credit hours. Seminars are offered for 2 credit hours. Research programs are directed by individual professors and are aimed at upper-level students. Field work placement is available with government agencies, judges, and legal services. Special lecture series include the Cordell Hull Speakers Forum, a student-run organization; the Ray Rushton Distinguished Lecturer Series; the Cumberland Colloquium on Law, Religion, and Culture, a faculty-run organization; the Thurgood Marshall Speakers' Forum, a student-sponsored event; and a faculty colloquium on American Regal History. Study-abroad programs include international and comparative law at the University of Durham in Durham, England; the University of Victoria in Victoria, British Columbia and at the faculdade de Direito da Universidade de Soto Paulo, The Sao Paulo University Law School. Legal Research and Writing Teaching Fellows conduct writing laboratories. The Black Law Students' Association sponsors a tutorial program, a mentor program, a speakers forum and special recognition events. The most widely taken electives are Domestic Relations, Bankruptcy, and Real Estate Transactions.

Graduation Requirements
In order to graduate, candidates must have a GPA of 2.0 and have completed the upper-division writing requirement.

Organizations
Students edit the *Cumberland Law Review*, the *American Journal of Trial Advocacy*, and the newspaper *Pro Confesso*. Moot court competitions include the Justice Janie Shores Moot Court; Gordon T. Saad, which is held in conjunction with the Appellate Advocacy course; and the Robert Donworth Freshman. Other competitions are Mock Trial, Herbert W. Peterson Senior, Judge James O. Haley Federal Court, Parham H. Williams Freshman Mock Trial, Albert P. Brewer Client Counseling, and Negotiation. Student organizations include the Association of Trial Lawyers of America, ABA-Student Division, and Federalist Society. Local chapters of national organizations include Delta Theta Phi, Phi Alpha Delta, and Phi Delta Phi. Other organizations include the State Student Bar Associations of Alabama, Florida, Georgia, Mississippi, North Carolina, South Carolina, Tennessee, and Virginia.

Library
The law library contains 254,346 hardcopy volumes and 471,485 microform volume equivalents, and subscribes to 2848 serial publications. Such on-line databases and networks as LEXIS and WESTLAW are available to law students for research. Special library collections include the Brantley collection. Recently, the library added the Lucille Stewart Beeson Law Library. The ratio of library volumes to faculty is 7283 to 1 and to students, 391 to 1. The ratio of seats in the library to students is 1 to 1.

Faculty
The law school has 32 full-time and 10 part-time faculty members, of whom 10 are women. According to AAUP standards for Category IIA institutions, faculty salaries are well above average. About 21% of full-time faculty have a graduate law degree in addition to the J.D.; about 13% of part-time faculty have one. The ratio of full-time students to full-time faculty in an average class is 19 to 1; in a clinic, 10 to 1.

Placement
J.D.s awarded:	204

Services available through: a separate law school placement center.
Services: national and regional law fairs
Special features: interviewing and job search skills workshops, pictorial directory, alumni job placement newsletter, and speakers' forum on legal career specialties

Full-time job interviews:	18 employers
Summer job interviews:	56 employers
Placement by graduation:	45% of class
Placement within 9 months:	92% of class
Average starting salary:	$24,600 to $100,000

Areas of placement:
Private practice 2-10 attorneys	45%
Private practice 11-25 attorneys	17%
Private practice 26-50 attorneys	4%
Private practice 51-100 attorneys	3%
Business/industry	10%
Government	10%
Judicial clerkships	9%
Military	3%
Academic	2%
Public interest	2%

Students
About 41% of the student body are women; 7%, minorities; 5%, African American; 1%, Asian American; and 1%, Hispanic. The majority of students come from Alabama (38%). The average age of entering students is 24; age range is 20 to 48. About 2% drop out after the first year for academic or personal reasons; 91% remain to receive a law degree.

School of Law

500 El Camino Real
Santa Clara, CA 95053

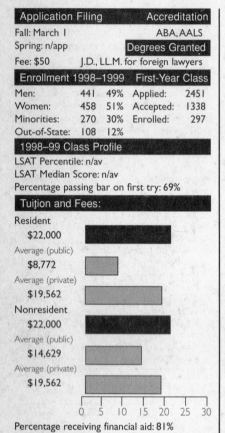

Application Filing	Accreditation
Fall: March 1	ABA, AALS
Spring: n/app	**Degrees Granted**
Fee: $50	J.D., LL.M. for foreign lawyers

Enrollment 1998–1999		First-Year Class	
Men:	441 49%	Applied:	2451
Women:	458 51%	Accepted:	1338
Minorities:	270 30%	Enrolled:	297
Out-of-State:	108 12%		

1998–99 Class Profile
LSAT Percentile: n/av
LSAT Median Score: n/av
Percentage passing bar on first try: 69%

Tuition and Fees:

Resident
$22,000

Average (public)
$8,772

Average (private)
$19,562

Nonresident
$22,000

Average (public)
$14,629

Average (private)
$19,562

0 5 10 15 20 25 30

Percentage receiving financial aid: 81%

ADMISSIONS

In the fall 1999 first-year class, 2451 applied, 1338 were accepted, and 297 enrolled. Forty-four transfers enrolled. The 75th LSAT percentile of the most recent first-year class was 158; the 75th percentile GPA was 3.48 on a scale of 4.0.

Requirements
Applicants must have a bachelor's degree from an accredited institution and take the LSAT. The most important admission factors include LSAT results, undergraduate curriculum, and GPA. No specific undergraduate courses are required. Candidates are not interviewed.

Procedure
The application deadline for fall entry is March 1. Applicants should submit an application form, LSAT results, transcripts, a nonrefundable application fee of $50; letters of recommendation are optional. Notification of the admission decision is January through May. The latest acceptable LSAT test date for fall entry is February. The law school uses the LSDAS.

Special
The law school recruits minority and disadvantaged students by means of ethnic student organizations that advise the faculty admissions committee and by providing substantial financial assistance. Transfer students must have one year of credit, have attended an ABA-approved law school, and have a letter of good standing from their prior school.

Costs

Tuition and fees for the 1999-2000 academic year are $22,000 for all full-time students. Tuition for all part-time students is $16,000 annually or $760 per credit. Books and supplies run $904.

Financial Aid

About 81% of current law students receive some form of aid. The average annual amount of aid from all sources combined, including scholarships, loans, and work contracts, is $23,733; maximum, $35,154. Awards are based on need and merit. The required financial statement is FAFSA. The aid application deadline for fall entry is February 1. Special funds for minority or disadvantaged students consist of the Law Faculty Scholarship. First-year students are notified about their financial aid application at the time of acceptance for scholarships; other aid decisions are made known upon completion of financial aid applications.

About the Law School

Santa Clara University School of Law was established in 1912 and is a private institution. The 104-acre campus is in a suburban area less than 1 mile west of San Jose and 45 miles south of San Francisco. The primary mission of the law school is wholly consistent with the Jesuit purpose in professional education: to train men and women of competence,

conscience, and compassion. Students have access to federal, state, county, city, and local agencies, courts, correctional facilities, law firms, and legal aid organizations in the Santa Clara area. The area is widely known as Silicon Valley. Local law firms have specialties that serve the needs of the high-tech industry and advise the school. Facilities of special interest to law students are Heafey Law Library, Bergin Hall, the faculty office building, Law Clinic, Law House and Bannan Hall, which houses classrooms and the law student lounge; law review offices at Benton street; and the East San Jose Community Law Center. Housing for law students is limited on campus to 20 2- or 3-person apartments; housing of all types is readily available off campus. About 97% of law school facilities are accessible to the physically disabled.

Calendar

The law school operates on a traditional semester basis. Courses for full-time students are offered both day and evening and must be completed within 5 years. For part-time students, courses are offered both day and evening and must be completed within 5 years. New full-time students are admitted in the fall; part-time, fall. There is a 7 1/2- week summer session. Transferable summer courses are offered.

Programs

In addition to the J.D., the law school offers the LL.M and a degree for foreign lawyers. Students may take relevant courses in other programs and apply credit toward the J.D.; a maximum of 12 credits may be applied. The following joint degrees may be earned: J.D./M.B.A. (Juris Doctor/Master of Business Administration).

Required
To earn the J.D., candidates must complete 86 total credits, of which 46 are for required courses. They must maintain a minimum GPA of 2.3 in the required courses. The following first-year courses are required of all students: Legal Research and Writing, Torts, Contracts, Property, Criminal Law, and Pleading and Civil Procedure. Required upper-level courses consist of Constitutional Law I and II, Business Organizations, Evidence, and The Legal Profession. The

Phone: 408-554-4800
Fax: 408-554-7897
E-mail: lawadmission@scu.edu
Web: scu.edu/law

Contact

Jeanette Leach, Associate Director, 408-554-4800 for general inquiries; Bryan Hinkle, Financial Aid Counselor, 408-554-4800 for financial aid information.

required orientation program for first-year students is a 3-day introduction to the legal system and the study of law.

Electives

The School of Law offers concentrations in corporate law, criminal law, environmental law, family law, international law, labor law, litigation, tax law, high tech law, and public interest law. In addition, through the on-campus Law Clinic Office, upper-division students practice law under the supervision of faculty. Students participate in all phases of a case, from the initial client interview through trial and may receive 3 to 6 units. Fifteen to 20 seminars are offered each year in areas such as sports law, drug abuse law, and computer law. Internships are in civil practice and the criminal justice system. Judicial externships are offered with the California Supreme Court and other state and federal courts. Faculty members engage students as research assistants for a variety of projects. During the academic year, students have access to the courts and legal community of the San Francisco Bay Area. The voluntary Pro Bono Project matches students and alumni for work on pro bono cases. The school hosts lectures on topics ranging from intellectual property issues to current events in international law. The Institute of International and Comparative Law sponsors Summer Law study-abroad programs in Strasbourg, France; Budapest, Hungary; Geneva, Switzerland; Oxford, England; Hong Kong; Singapore; Seoul, Korea; Bangkok, Thailand; Tokyo, Japan; Beijing, P.R.C; Ho Chi Minh City, Vietnam; Kuala Lumpur, Malaysia; and Munich, Germany. The Academic Success Program offers personal and tutorial support to minority students, students identified through the admission process as needing academic support, and students recommended by their first-year instructors. Tutorial support emphasizes legal analysis and uses the writing of briefs, outlines, and exams to develop this skill. Students may earn a certificate in public interest law by taking 14 units, plus a unit of Public Interest Seminar, and completing a practicum. Certificates are also offered in international law and high-technology law with varying requirements. The most widely taken electives are Community Property, Wills and Trusts, and Remedies.

Graduation Requirements

In order to graduate, candidates must have a GPA of 2.3 on a 4.3 scale, completed the upper-division writing requirement, and have fulfilled a residency requirement of 3 academic years in the full-time division or 4 academic years in the part-time division.

Organizations

Students edit the *Santa Clara Law Review* and the *Computer and High Technology Law Journal*. The student newspaper is *The Advocate*. Moot court competitions include the Jessup International Moot Court, Traynor Moot Court, and the Giles Rich Moot Court. Other competitions include ABA Client Counseling Competition, ABA National Trial Competition, and the Negotiation Competition. Student organizations include Intellectual Property Association, Public Interest Coalition, and the International Law Society. Phi Alpha Delta has a local chapter. Other campus organizations include the Student Bar Association, BALSA, and Women in Law.

Library

The law library contains 262,447 hardcopy volumes and 763,854 microform volume equivalents, and subscribes to 3544 serial publications. Such on-line databases and networks as LEXIS, DIALOG, WESTLAW, and RELIN are available to law students for research. Special library collections include the proceedings of the House Judiciary Committee on the Watergate Hearings. Recently, the library installed an integrated library automation system, beginning with OPAC; upgraded student computer laboratories with Pentiums; networked some carrels; and remodeled the reference area. The ratio of library volumes to faculty is 7498 to 1 and to students, 282 to 1. The ratio of seats in the library to students is 1 to 2.

Placement

J.D.s awarded:	279
Services available through: a separate law school placement center.	
Services:	
Special features: fall and spring on-campus interview programs, career-oriented workshops and events, web site with current listings and job search tips, extensive resource library, and reciprocity with other Bay Area and ABA-accredited law schools.	
Full-time job interviews:	24 employers
Summer job interviews:	60 employers
Placement by graduation:	n/av
Placement within 9 months:	90% of class
Average starting salary:	$65,000
Areas of placement:	
Business/industry	21%
Private practice 2-10 attorneys	17%
Private practice 11-25 attorneys	9%
Private practice 26-50 attorneys	2%
Private practice 51-100 attorneys	7%
Private practice 101+ attorneys	24%
Solo practice	2%
Government	6%
Judicial clerkships	4%
Public interest	1%

Faculty

The law school has 34 full-time and 26 part-time faculty members, of whom 21 are women. According to AAUP standards for Category IIA institutions, faculty salaries are well above average. The ratio of full-time students to full-time faculty in an average class is 30 to 1; in a clinic, 12 to 1. The law school has a regular program of bringing visiting professors and other distinguished lecturers and visitors to campus.

Students

About 51% of the student body are women; 30%, minorities; 3%, African American; 19%, Asian American; 7%, Hispanic; and 1%, Native American. The majority of students come from California (88%). The average age of entering students is 24; age range is 21 to 47. About 35% of students enter directly from undergraduate school and 13% have a graduate degree. About 7% drop out after the first year for academic or personal reasons; 99% remain to receive a law degree.

SEATTLE UNIVERSITY

School of Law

900 Broadway
Seattle, WA 98122-4340

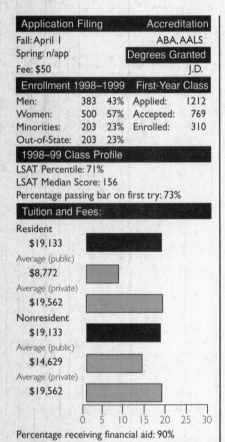

Application Filing	Accreditation
Fall: April 1	ABA, AALS
Spring: n/app	**Degrees Granted**
Fee: $50	J.D.

Enrollment 1998–1999		First-Year Class	
Men:	383 43%	Applied:	1212
Women:	500 57%	Accepted:	769
Minorities:	203 23%	Enrolled:	310
Out-of-State:	203 23%		

1998–99 Class Profile
LSAT Percentile: 71%
LSAT Median Score: 156
Percentage passing bar on first try: 73%

Tuition and Fees:

Resident
$19,133

Average (public)
$8,772

Average (private)
$19,562

Nonresident
$19,133

Average (public)
$14,629

Average (private)
$19,562

0 5 10 15 20 25 30

Percentage receiving financial aid: 90%

ADMISSIONS

In the fall 1999 first-year class, 1212 applied, 769 were accepted, and 310 enrolled. Fifteen transfers enrolled. The median LSAT percentile of the most recent first-year class was 71; the median GPA was 3.2 on a scale of 4.0. The lowest LSAT percentile accepted was 15; the highest was 97.

Requirements
Applicants must have a bachelor's degree from an accredited institution and take the LSAT. The most important admission factors include GPA, LSAT results, character, and personality. No specific undergraduate courses are required. Candidates are not interviewed.

Procedure
The application deadline for fall entry is April 1. Applicants should submit an application form, LSAT results, transcripts, a nonrefundable application fee of $50, 2 letters of recommendation, a personal statement (required), and a resume (optional). Notification of the

admission decision is February 1 to May 1. The latest acceptable LSAT test date for fall entry is June on a limited basis. The law school uses the LSDAS.

Special
The law school recruits minority and disadvantaged students through admission officer visits, minority community service organizations, minority prelaw and bar associations, candidate referral services, prelaw adviser mailings, and a fee waiver program. Transfer students must have one year of credit, have attended an ABA-approved law school, and be in good academic standing and in the top half of their class.

Costs

Tuition and fees for the 1999-2000 academic year are $19,133 for all full-time students. Tuition for all part-time students is $637 per credit. Books and supplies run $625.

Financial Aid

About 90% of current law students receive some form of aid. The average annual amount of aid from all sources combined, including scholarships, loans, and work contracts, is $26,500; maximum, $32,371. Awards are based on need and merit. The required financial statement is the FAFSA. The aid application deadline for fall entry is March 1. Special funds for minority or disadvantaged students range from $2500 to $11,000 and may be renewable, with conditions, for the full term of legal studies. First-year students are notified about their financial aid application at time of acceptance.

About the Law School

Seattle University School of Law was established in 1972 and is a private institution. The 56-acre campus is in an urban area on Seattle's First Hill. The primary mission of the law school is to prepare students to practice law with competence and honor. Students have access to federal, state, county, city, and local agencies, courts, correctional facilities, law firms, and legal aid organizations in the Seattle area. Appellate Court, U.S. District Court, and Superior Court as well as several law firms are located within a 1-block radius of the school. Facilities of special interest to law students include Sullivan Hall, which contains classrooms and seminar

spaces equipped with data ports for each seat and desk space large enough to accommodate a laptop computer for every student. The entire building is wired for the use of on-line legal research services such as Westlaw and other Internet uses. There is also an on-line electronic teaching laboratory. The Archbishop Thomas Murphy Apartments are designed for single students seeking an environment conducive to academic pursuits. They include furnished private studios, private and shared 1-bedrooms, shared 2-bedroom townhouses, and shared 4-bedroom apartments. All apartments feature controlled access, appliances, and microwaves. Rents range fom $485 to $700 per month. All law school facilities are accessible to the physically disabled.

Calendar

The law school operates on a traditional semester basis. Courses for full-time students are offered both day and evening and must be completed within 5 years. For part-time students, courses are offered both day and evening and must be completed within 6 years. New full- and part-time students are admitted in the fall and summer. There is a 6- to 8-week summer session. Transferable summer courses are offered.

Programs

Students may take relevant courses in the business school and apply credit toward the J.D.; a maximum of 4 credits may be applied. The following joint degrees may be earned: J.D./M.B.A. (Juris Doctor/Master of Business Administration), J.D./M.S. (Juris Doctor/Master of Science in finance), J.D./M.A. (Juris Doctor/Master of Arts in applied economics), and J.D./M.I.B (Juris Doctor/Master of International Business).

Required
To earn the J.D., candidates must complete 90 total credits, of which 44 are for required courses. They must maintain a minimum GPA of 2.0 in the required courses. The following first-year courses are required of all students: Criminal Law, Civil Procedure, Contracts, Property, Torts, and Legal Writing. Required upper-level courses consist of Constitutional Law, Legal Writing II, Evidence, and Professional Responsibility. The required orientation program for first-

Phone: 206-398-4200
Fax: 206-398-4058
E-mail: lawadmis@seattleu.edu
Web: http://www.law.seattleu.edu

Contact

Carol Cochran, Associate Director of Admission, 206-398-4200 for general inquiries; Kathleen Koch, Director of Financial Aid, 206-398-4250 for financial aid information.

year students consists of a 2 day series of workshops and, throughout the year, seminars on both academic and non-academic issues.

Electives

The School of Law offers concentrations in corporate law, criminal law, environmental law, international law, labor law, litigation, securities law, tax law, torts and insurance, health and medicine, commercial law, estate planning, intellectual property and law, property law, and real estate. In addition, clinics include Law Practice, a 4- to 6-credit course in which 30 third-year students, supervised by faculty members, represent clients in civil cases and the state in criminal misdemeanor cases. Seminars are available in 15 limited-enrollment advanced classes, worth 2 to 4 credits, with subjects ranging from Constitutional Adjudication and Corporate Finance to Human Rights. Part-time externships, worth 3 to 4 credits, are available for students in the judiciary and with several preapproved agencies and governmental organizations. Full-time judical clerkships, worth 15 credits, are also available. Research programs include work with faculty members conducting research in subjects such as involuntary commitment of mentally ill, and freedom of the press and the First Amendment; independent study on topics of student interest are also encouraged. More than 80% of students are employed in law-related field work positions each year with corporate firms; partnerships; federal, state, and local public agencies; and nonprofit associations. The Alumni/ae Lecture Series brings distinguished scholars, jurists, and practitioners to campus to comment on compelling legal issues. Students may participate in study-abroad programs sponsored by other ABA law schools and receive up to 6 credits. The Academic Resource Center, staffed by a full-time J.D. alumna, offers tutorial services as well as group workshops and seminars. The Alternative Admission Program, designed for historically disadvantaged, physically challenged, and older applicants (limited to 30 students a year) is an intensive program integrating first-year classes with group instruction. Minority programs are conducted through the Black Law Student Association, Latino Law Student Society, and Asian/Pacific Islander Law Student Association. Special interest

group programs include activities by the Environmental Law Society, International Law Society, and Entertainment/Sports Law Society. The most widely taken electives are Administrative Law, UCC Sales, and Secured Transactions.

Graduation Requirements

In order to graduate, candidates must have a GPA of 2.0 and have completed the upper-division writing requirement.

Organizations

Students edit the *Seattle University Law Review; Environmental Law Society* newsletter; *Women's Voice,* a Women's Law Caucus newsletter; and the newspaper *Prolific Reporter.* Moot court competitions include Jessup International Law, Giles S. Rich Patent Law, and Frederick Douglass. Other competitions include National Mock Trial, Association of Trial Lawyers of America, Client Counseling, and Alternative Dispute Resolution. Law student organizations include the Student Bar Association, Public Interest Law Foundation, and St. Thomas More Society. There are local chapters of American Trial Lawyers Association, Phi Alpha Delta, and Phi Delta Phi.

Library

The law library contains 323,466 hard-copy volumes and 924,769 microform volume equivalents, and subscribes to 4169 serial publications. Such on-line databases and networks as LEXIS, DIALOG, WESTLAW, and various topical CD-ROMs are available to law students for research. Special library collections include U.S. government documents depository. Virtually every library carrel, table, and study area provides Internet access. Extensive compact shelving ensures onsite access to all library materials. A Document Delivery Center offers students printing and photocopying services. The ratio of library volumes to faculty is 3334 to 1 and to students, 361 to 1. The ratio of seats in the library to students is 1 to 2.

Faculty

The law school has 35 full-time and 62 part-time faculty members, of whom 34 are women. According to AAUP standards for Category IIA institutions, faculty salaries are well above average. About 15% of full-time faculty have a graduate law degree in addition to the J.D.; about

Placement

J.D.s awarded:	254

Services available through: a separate law school placement center.

Services: comprehensive lists of judges, courts, and application requirements for judicial clerkships.

Special features: daily postings of student and alumni job openings; jobs posted on a website; a "Job Board" newsletter sent to all graduates for free for 1 year; a "Hotline" available 24 hours daily for weekly listing of jobs; and videotaped workshops so evening students and others can have access to information on interviewing techniques, resume writing, and job search strategies. Printed material is also available.

Full-time job interviews:	14 employers
Summer job interviews:	44 employers
Placement by graduation:	57% of class
Placement within 9 months:	90% of class
Average starting salary:	$26,000 to $75,000

Areas of placement:

Private practice 2-10 attorneys	36%
Private practice 11-25 attorneys	5%
Private practice 26-50 attorneys	3%
Private practice 51-100 attorneys	12%
Business/industry	15%
Government	15%
Judicial clerkships	7%
Public interest	3%
Unknown	2%
Military	1%
Academic	1%

15% of part-time faculty have one. The ratio of full-time students to full-time faculty in an average class is 20 to 1; in a clinic, 10 to 1. The law school has a regular program of bringing visiting professors and other distinguished lecturers and visitors to campus.

Students

About 57% of the student body are women; 23%, minorities; 6%, African American; 11%, Asian American; 3%, Hispanic; 1%, Native American; and 2%, Multi-cultural. The majority of students come from Washington (77%). The average age of entering students is 26; age range is 21 to 58. About 20% of students enter directly from undergraduate school; 12% have a graduate degree, and 80% have worked full-time prior to entering law school. About 9% drop out after the first year for academic or personal reasons; 86% remain to receive a law degree.

School of Law

One Newark Center
Newark, NJ 07102-5210

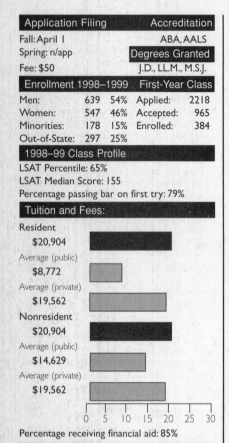

Application Filing		Accreditation
Fall: April 1		ABA, AALS
Spring: n/app		**Degrees Granted**
Fee: $50		J.D., LL.M., M.S.J.

Enrollment 1998–1999		First-Year Class	
Men:	639 54%	Applied:	2218
Women:	547 46%	Accepted:	965
Minorities:	178 15%	Enrolled:	384
Out-of-State:	297 25%		

1998–99 Class Profile
LSAT Percentile: 65%
LSAT Median Score: 155
Percentage passing bar on first try: 79%

Tuition and Fees:

Resident
$20,904

Average (public)
$8,772

Average (private)
$19,562

Nonresident
$20,904

Average (public)
$14,629

Average (private)
$19,562

0   5   10   15   20   25   30

Percentage receiving financial aid: 85%

ADMISSIONS

In the fall 1999 first-year class, 2218 applied, 965 were accepted, and 384 enrolled. Ten transfers enrolled. The median LSAT percentile of the most recent first-year class was 65; the median GPA was 3.2 on a scale of 4.0. The lowest LSAT percentile accepted was 152; the highest was 158.

Requirements

Applicants must have a bachelor's degree from an accredited institution and take the LSAT. Minimum acceptable GPA is 2.5 on a scale of 4.0. The most important admission factors include LSAT results, GPA, and college attended. No specific undergraduate courses are required. Candidates are not interviewed.

Procedure

The application deadline for fall entry is April 1. Applicants should submit an application form, LSAT results, transcripts, TOEFL for non-English-speaking applicants, a nonrefundable application fee of $50, 2 letters of recommendation, and a personal statement. Notification of the admission decision is on a rolling basis beginning in January. The latest acceptable LSAT test date for fall entry is February. The law school uses the LSDAS.

Special

The law school recruits minority and disadvantaged students through Legal Education Opportunities for educationally disadvantaged applicants, Minority Law Day, the Pre-Legal Institute, and the Mentor Program. Transfer students must have one year of credit, have attended an ABA-approved law school, and be in the top 15% of the law class. Preadmissions courses consist of the Pre-Legal Institute, the Mentor Program, and the Legal Education Opportunities program for admission to law school for the educationally disadvantaged.

Costs

Tuition and fees for the 1999-2000 academic year are $20,904 for all full-time students. Tuition and fees for part-time students is $14,840 annually, or $733 per credit. Books and supplies run $850.

Financial Aid

About 85% of current law students receive some form of aid. Awards are based on need and merit. The required financial statement is FAFSA. The aid application deadline for fall entry is April 15. Special funds for minority or disadvantaged students are set aside from overall aid funds. First-year students are notified about their financial aid application at the time of acceptance.

About the Law School

Seton Hall University School of Law was established in 1951 and is a private institution. The 2-acre campus is in an urban area in Newark. The primary mission of the law school is to synthesize a strong traditional approach to legal training with a commitment to community involvement. Students are encouraged to excel and to appreciate key values: integrity, responsibility, ethics, and service. Students have access to federal, state, county, city, and local agencies, courts, correctional facilities, law firms, and legal aid organizations in the Newark area. All legal resources are blocks away from the school. The resources of New York City are 20 minutes away. Facilities of special interest to law students include a modern 200,000 square-foot law center with state-of-the-art computers, library, classrooms, and moot courts. Housing for law students is available as rental housing in the vicinity and university housing on the South Orange campus, 5 miles away. All law school facilities are accessible to the physically disabled.

Calendar

The law school operates on a traditional semester basis. Courses for full- and part-time students are offered both day and evening and must be completed within 6 years. New full- and part-time students are admitted in the fall. There is a 6- to 8-week summer session. Transferable summer courses are offered.

Programs

In addition to the J.D., the law school offers the LL.M and M.S.J. The following joint degree may be earned: J.D./M.B.A. (Juris Doctor/Master of Business Administration).

Phone: 973-642-8747
888-415-7271
Fax: 973-642-8876
E-mail: admitme@shu.edu
Web: www.shu.edu/law

Contact

Kenneth Stevenson, Dean of Admissions and Financial Resource Manager, 973-642-8747 or 888-415-7271, for general inquiries; Sharon Williams, Director of Financial Aid, 973-642-8744 for financial aid information.

NEW JERSEY

Required

To earn the J.D., candidates must complete 85 total credits, of which 44 are for required courses. The following first-year courses are required of all students: Civil Procedure, Constitutional Law, Contracts, Criminal Law, Torts, Property, and Legal Research and Legal Writing. Required upper-level courses consist of Business Associations, Appellate Advocacy, Evidence, Professional Responsibility, and Federal Income Taxation. All students must take clinical courses. The required orientation program for first-year students is a day-long program commencing immediately before the start of classes with activities continuing into the first week of classes.

Electives

The School of Law offers concentrations in corporate law, criminal law, entertainment, environmental law, family law, international law, juvenile law, labor law, litigation, tax law, and health law, property and estates, and public law. In addition, all clinics are live client clinics and include Preventive Law, a voluntary pro bono proram with juvenile counseling, 5 community service placements, and Legal Services. Seminars are offered in all major areas for upper-level students. Internships include Judicial, U.S. Bankruptcy Trustee, and Environmental Protection Administration. Research opportunities include an independent research course, many seminars, and the opportunity to serve as a faculty research assistant. There are lectures in sports law, environmental law, legislative topics, health law, and from nearly all student organizations. There are summer study-abroad programs in Parma and Milan, Italy as well as Cairo, Egypt. Tutorial assistance is available for all first-year courses. Special programs for minority students are the Mentor Program for high school students and the Legal Education Opportunities Admissions program. Special interest group programs are available through various religious and ethnic- based organizations. The most widely taken electives are Criminal Procedure, Decedents' Estates and Trusts, and Remedies.

Graduation Requirements

In order to graduate, candidates must have a GPA of 2.0, have completed the upper-division writing requirement, and have no more than 10 credits of D or D+ and no more than 95 credits.

Organizations

Students edit the *Seton Hall Law Review, Legislative Journal, Sports Law Journal, Constitutional Law Journal,* and the newspaper *Res Ipsa Loquitur.* Second-year students compete in the Appellate Advocacy Moot Court competition; teams are selected from intraschool competitions held for credit during the fall semester. Teams also compete in the National Moot Court Competition and competitions in corporate, constitutional, and family law. Law student organizations include the Health Society, Environmental Law Society, and Women's Law Forum. There are local chapters of Phi Alpha Delta and Black Law Students Association.

Library

The law library contains 400,039 hardcopy volumes and 495,570 microform volume equivalents, and subscribes to 6614 serial publications. Such on-line databases and networks as LEXIS, DIALOG, WESTLAW, and NEXIS, and the Internet are available to law students for research. Special library collections include the Rodino Papers and depositories for federal and New Jersey state documents. Recently, the library completed a new 65,000 square-foot, 3-level facility with electronic classroom and 235 computer workstations. The ratio of library volumes to faculty is 4830 to 1 and to students, 200 to 1. The ratio of seats in the library to students is 1 to 2.

Faculty

The law school has 58 full-time and 106 part-time faculty members, of whom 48 are women. About 25% of full-time faculty have a graduate law degree in addition to the J.D.; about 10% of part-time faculty have one. The ratio of full-time students to full-time faculty in an average class is 24 to 1; in a clinic, 6 to 1. The law school has a regular program of bringing visiting professors and other distinguished lecturers and visitors to campus. There is a chapter of the Order of the Coif.

Placement	
J.D.s awarded:	369
Services available through: A separate law school placement center.	
Services: mentor programs, attorney writing sample review	
Special features: an evening placement counselor, on-site meeting rooms, newsletters, on-line services, extensive placement library.	
Full-time job interviews:	100 employers
Summer job interviews:	100 employers
Placement by graduation:	96% of class
Placement within 9 months:	96% of class
Average starting salary:	n/av
Areas of placement:	n/av

Students

About 46% of the student body are women; 15%, minorities; 5%, African American; 5%, Asian American; and 4%, Hispanic. The majority of students come from New Jersey (75%). The average age of entering students is 26; age range is 21 to 52. About 39% of students enter directly from undergraduate school. About 12% drop out after the first year for academic or personal reasons; 88% remain to receive a law degree.

1303 San Jacinto Street
Houston, TX 77002-7000

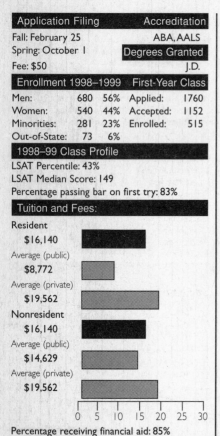

Application Filing	Accreditation
Fall: February 25	ABA, AALS
Spring: October 1	**Degrees Granted**
Fee: $50	J.D.

Enrollment 1998–1999		First-Year Class	
Men:	680 56%	Applied:	1760
Women:	540 44%	Accepted:	1152
Minorities:	281 23%	Enrolled:	515
Out-of-State:	73 6%		

1998–99 Class Profile
LSAT Percentile: 43%
LSAT Median Score: 149
Percentage passing bar on first try: 83%

Tuition and Fees:

Resident
$16,140

Average (public)
$8,772

Average (private)
$19,562

Nonresident
$16,140

Average (public)
$14,629

Average (private)
$19,562

0   5   10   15   20   25   30

Percentage receiving financial aid: 85%

ADMISSIONS
In the fall 1999 first-year class, 1760 applied, 1152 were accepted, and 515 enrolled. Four transfers enrolled. The median LSAT percentile of the most recent first-year class was 43; the median GPA was 2.94 on a scale of 4.0. The lowest LSAT percentile accepted was 15; the highest was 96.

Requirements
Applicants must have a bachelor's degree from an accredited institution and take the LSAT. Minimum acceptable LSAT score is 43 and minimum acceptable GPA is 2.9 on a scale of 4.0. The most important admission factors include LSAT results, GPA, and life experience. No specific undergraduate courses are required. Candidates are not interviewed.

Procedure
The application deadline for fall entry is February 25. Applicants should submit an application form, a nonrefundable application fee of $50, 2 required letters of recommendation, a personal statement, and a resume. Notification of the admission decision is 60 days following the admission deadline. The latest acceptable LSAT test date for fall entry is February. The law school uses the LSDAS.

Special
The law school recruits minority and disadvantaged students by offering application-fee waivers for those with documented need. South Texas considers ethnicity and disadvantaged backgrounds in the admissions process and offers scholarships to those who qualify. Transfer students must have one year of credit, have attended an ABA-approved law school, be ranked in the upper 10% of the current law school class, and be able to provide a letter of good standing.

Costs
Tuition and fees for the 1999-2000 academic year are $16,140 for all full-time students. Tuition for all part-time students is $518 per credit. Books and supplies run $880.

Financial Aid
About 85% of current law students receive some form of aid. The average annual amount of aid from all sources combined, including scholarships, loans, and work contracts, is $25,500; maximum, $37,409. Awards are based on need and merit. The required financial statement is the FAFSA. The aid application deadline for fall entry is May 1. Special funds for minority or disadvantaged students are available through Dean's Fel-

lowship scholarships for new admits and Enhancement Scholarships for continuing students. First-year students are notified about their financial aid application at time of acceptance.

About the Law School
South Texas College of Law was established in 1923 and is a private institution. The full city block campus is in an urban area in downtown Houston. The primary mission of the law school is to develop highly ethical lawyers from all segments of society who are committed to promoting equal and accessible justice for all. Students have access to federal, state, county, city, and local agencies, courts, correctional facilities, law firms, and legal aid organizations in the Houston area. The First and Fourteenth Courts of Appeals for the State of Texas are located on the premises, and the college's Continuing Legal Education courses offered by various sponsors are taught at the law school. Students are within walking distance of many law firms as well as the civil and criminal courts. The law Institute for Medical Studies is a forum for interdiciplinary dialogue and education on health care topics with special legal concerns. The Center for Legal Responsibility involves students in managing conflict, resolving disputes, and devising settlement strategies. Both institutes are actively involved in community outreach and publication. On-campus housing is not available. However, high-rise apartments are within walking distance of the campus. Apartment locators are available, usually at no cost. All law school facilities are accessible to the physically disabled.

Calendar
The law school operates on a traditional semester basis. Courses for full-and part-time students are offered both day and evening and must be completed within 6 years. New full-and part-time students are admitted in the fall. There is an 8-week summer session. Transferable summer courses are offered.

Required
To earn the J.D., candidates must complete 90 total credits, of which 44 are for required courses. They must maintain a minimum GPA of 2.0 in the required courses. The following first-year courses

Phone: 713-646-1810
Fax: 713-646-2929
E-mail: acramer@stcl.edu
Web: http://www.stcl.edu

Contact

Alicia Cramer, Director of Admissions, 713-646-1810 for general inquiries; Jennifer Pham, Director of Financial Aid, 713-646-1820 for financial aid information.

TEXAS

are required of all students: Torts I and II, Contracts I and II, Property I, Civil Procedure, Legal Research and Writing I and II, Criminal Law, and Constitutional Law. Required upper-level courses consist of Property II, Federal Income Tax, Evidence, and Professional Responsibility, and a substantial research paper. The required orientation program for first-year students is generally scheduled the week prior to the beginning of classes, with 3 days dedicated to the full-time students and 3 evenings and a Saturday devoted to part-time students. The program is primarily academic in focus but also includes information from administrators regarding registration, co-curricular programs, and financial aid.

Electives

The South Texas College of Law offers concentrations in environmental law, international law, advocacy, health law, and alternative dispute resolution. In addition, through the General Civil Clinic and under the direct supervision of a faculty member, upper-level students can earn between 3 and 4 credit hours by representing clients in a wide variety of cases in state and federal courts and administrative agencies. To qualify for enrollment in a seminar, a student must have completed 45 hours and usually a required paper. A limit of 3 seminar courses may be applied toward graduation. Seminars are offered for 2 hours credit. Externships are normally offered during the fall, spring, and summer and are limited to a maximum of 6 credit hours. After completion of certain prerequisites, upper-level students are eligible to enroll in the Criminal Process Clinic, Judicial Process Clinic, Public and Governmental Interest Clinic, or the Hospital Law Externship Program. South Texas co-sponsors a number of ABA-approved summer abroad programs, as well as 1 cooperative semester abroad program. Students with the approval of the college, may apply to study abroad as transient students. Approved credit hours earned will be applied toward graduation. South Texas also administers an academic assistance program to help students achieve their scholastic endeavors. The program includes individual counseling and study skills seminars on the outlining process, as well as preparing for and taking exams. The program also provides eligible students with weekly group sessions focusing on study skills and legal analysis. The college is committed to affirmative action programs. The most widely taken electives are Marital Property, Family Law, and Texas Pretrial Procedure.

Graduation Requirements

In order to graduate, candidates must have a GPA of 2.0 and have completed the upper-division writing requirement.

Organizations

Students edit the *South Texas Law Review, Corporate Counsel Review, Currents*, Currents: *International Trade Law Journal*, and the newspaper, *Annotations*. Students enrolled in the Moot Court Competition course are selected to participate among the 24 national moot court and mock trial competitons held annually. Students with 20 or more semester hours are eligible to compete in the college's annual intramural competitions. South Texas has over 23 registered organizations in which students can participate. There are local chapters of Phi Delta Phi, Phi Alpha Delta, and Delta Theta Phi. Campus clubs and other organizations include the Student Bar Association, the Order of the Lytae, and the Order of Barristers.

Library

The law library contains 198,884 hardcopy volumes and 1,053,310 microform volume equivalents, and subscribes to 4204 serial publications. Such on-line databases and networks as LEXIS, DIALOG, WESTLAW, NEXIS, Epic, Internet, First Search, Legal Trac/Infotrac, LOIS, Pro Docs, Mathew Bender Authority, and CALI are available to law students for research. Special library collections include a U.S. government selective depository and a rare books collection, college archives, and various manuscript collections. Recently, the library upgraded the computer laboratory, installed ARIEL (Rapid Document Delivery Via Computer), and Acquired Z39.50 (seamless interface to catalogs of participating schools). The ratio of library volumes to faculty is 3683 to 1 and to students, 196 to 1. The ratio of seats in the library to students is 1 to 6.

Placement

J.D.s awarded:	359

Services available through: separate law school placement center.

Services:

Special features: seminars and speaker programs, skills training workshops, alumni mentor program, tours and visits to local and out-of-city courts, area corporations and law firms, networking breakfasts, 6 to 8 job fairs each year, and coordination of campus interviews.

Full-time job interviews:	22 employers
Summer job interviews:	42 employers
Placement by graduation:	n/av
Placement within 9 months:	82% of class
Average starting salary:	$36,000 to $56,000

Areas of placement:

Private practice 2-10 attorneys	31%
Private practice 11-25 attorneys	6%
Private practice 26-50 attorneys	6%
Private practice 51-100 attorneys	6%
Private practice, size of firm unknown	6%
Business/industry	17%
Government	11%
Judicial clerkships	6%
Public interest	1%
Self-employed	5%
Graduate students	2%
unknown	3%

Faculty

The law school has 54 full-time and 33 part-time faculty members, of whom 21 are women. About 28% of full-time faculty have a graduate law degree in addition to the J.D. The law school has a regular program of bringing visiting professors and other distinguished lecturers and visitors to campus.

Students

About 44% of the student body are women; 23%, minorities; 5%, African American; 5%, Asian American; 12%, Hispanic; 1%, Native American; and 77%, White. The majority of students come from Texas (94%). The average age of entering students is 27; age range is 20 to 54. About 12% drop out after the first year for academic or personal reasons; 88% remain to receive a law degree.

SOUTHERN ILLINOIS UNIVERSITY

School of Law

Lesar Law Building, Mail Code 6804
Carbondale, IL 62901-6804

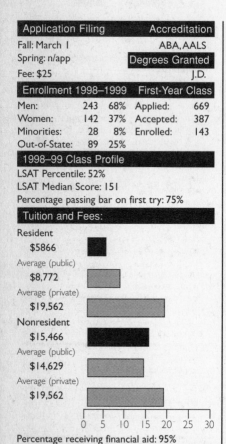

Application Filing	Accreditation
Fall: March 1	ABA, AALS
Spring: n/app	**Degrees Granted**
Fee: $25	J.D.

Enrollment 1998–1999		First-Year Class	
Men:	243 68%	Applied:	669
Women:	142 37%	Accepted:	387
Minorities:	28 8%	Enrolled:	143
Out-of-State:	89 25%		

1998–99 Class Profile
LSAT Percentile: 52%
LSAT Median Score: 151
Percentage passing bar on first try: 75%

Tuition and Fees:

Resident
$5866

Average (public)
$8,772

Average (private)
$19,562

Nonresident
$15,466

Average (public)
$14,629

Average (private)
$19,562

0 5 10 15 20 25 30

Percentage receiving financial aid: 95%

ADMISSIONS
In the fall 1999 first-year class, 669 applied, 387 were accepted, and 143 enrolled. Eleven transfers enrolled. The median LSAT percentile of the most recent first-year class was 52; the median GPA was 3.3 on a scale of 4.0. The lowest LSAT percentile accepted was 26; the highest was 96.

Requirements
Applicants must have a bachelor's degree from an accredited institution and take the LSAT. The most important admission factors include LSAT results, GPA, and writing ability. No specific undergraduate courses are required. Candidates are not interviewed.

Procedure
The application deadline for fall entry is March 1. Applicants should submit an application form, LSAT results, transcripts, a nonrefundable application fee of $25, 2 recommended letters of recommendation, and a personal statement. Notification of the admissions decision is as early as possible. The latest acceptable LSAT test date for fall entry is February. The law school uses the LSDAS.

Special
The law school recruits minority and disadvantaged students by means of the Candidate Referral Service; special programs at the School of Law, including an Open House for admitted minority applicants; networking; and contacting institutions that serve minority and disadvantaged students. Transfer students must have one year of credit and have attended an ABA-approved law school. Applicants may be admitted if it appears likely that they will successfully complete the School of Law curriculum. Factors considered include, among other things, the applicant's law school record, class rank, law school attended, LSAT, and GPA.

Costs
Tuition and fees for the 1999-2000 academic year are $5866 for in-state students and $15,466 for out-of-state students. On-campus room and board costs about $5000 annually; and books and supplies run $810.

Financial Aid
About 95% of current law students receive some form of aid. The average annual amount of aid from all sources combined, including scholarships, loans, and work contracts, is $14,240; maximum, $18,500. Awards are based on need and merit. The required financial statement is the FAFSA. The aid application deadline for fall entry is March 1. Special funds for minority or disadvantaged students include scholarships. First-year students are notified about their financial aid application at time of acceptance.

About the Law School
Southern Illinois University School of Law was established in 1973 and is a public institution. The 3290-acre campus is in a rural area 110 miles southeast of St. Louis, Missouri. The primary mission of the law school is to train lawyers who will be competent to practice law now and in the future, exhibit leadership, and adhere to the ethical standards of the legal profession. Students have access to federal, state, county, city, and local agencies, courts, correctional facilities, law firms, and legal aid organizations in the Carbondale area. Facilities of special interest to law students There are the numerous law firms, state, local, (and federal law offices, non-profit organizations), and courts in southern Illinois where students can get legal experience and training. On-campus housing is available in dorms across the street from the law school. There is also plenty of off-campus housing available within 10 minutes of the law school. All law school facilities are accessible to the physically disabled.

Calendar
The law school operates on a traditional semester basis. Courses for full-time students are offered days only and must be completed within 5 years. There is no part-time program. New full-time students are admitted in the fall. There is an 8-week summer session. Transferable summer courses are offered.

Programs
Students may take relevant courses in other programs and apply credit toward the J.D.; a maximum of 6 credits may be applied. The following joint degrees may be earned: J.D./M.D. (Juris Doctor/Doctor of Medicine), J.D./M.B.A. (Juris Doctor/Master of Business Administration), J.D./M.P.A. (Juris Doctor/Master of Public Administration), J.D./M. Acct. (Juris Doctor/Master of Accounting), J.D./M.S.W. (Juris Doctor/Master of Social Work), and J.D./Ph.D. (Juris Doctor/Doctor of Philosophy in political science).

Phone: 618-453-8767
800-739-9187
Fax: 618-453-8769
E-mail: lawadmit@siu.edu
Web: http://www.siu.edu/~lawsch/

Contact

Assistant Dean for Admissions and Student Affairs, 618-453-8768 for general inquiries; Financial Aid Office Coordinator (Rick Steudel), 618-453-4334 for financial aid information.

ILLINOIS

Required

To earn the J.D., candidates must complete 90 total credits, of which 46 are for required courses. They must maintain a minimum GPA of 2.0 in the required courses. The following first-year courses are required of all students: Torts, Contracts I and II, Property I and II, Lawyering Skills I and II, Legislative and Administrative Process, Civil Procedure I, Criminal Law, and Legal Argumentation. Required upper-level courses consist of Civil Procedure II, Constitutional Law I and II, Evidence, and Legal Profession. The required orientation program for first-year students extends over a 3-day period and consists of small group discussions, tours, a mock class, an ethics lecture, and a full day of academic content.

Electives

The School of Law offers concentrations in international law, litigation, tax law, and health law. In addition, 4 clinics are offered to senior law students for up to 6 hours of credit: the elder law clinic, the alternative dispute resolution clinic, the domestic violence clinic, and the extern clinic. Third-year students, except editors of the *Southern Illinois University Law Journal*, are required to take a senior writing seminar for 3 credit hours. Senior law students may enroll for up to 6 hours in externships; credit is earned by working in a public interest or legal services agency for local prosecutors and public defenders, for local judges, or for local and state agencies. Independent research and writing credit is allowed under certain conditions. Each spring the law school hosts the Lester Lecture Series and a presentation by the Grayson Distinguished Visitors Health Law Professor. A voluntary tutorial program is available for first-year students. An academic enhancement course is available to students who need extra assistance during their first year. The school makes individual accommodations to the needs of its disabled students. The most widely taken electives are Criminal Procedure, Health Law, and Legal Clinic.

Graduation Requirements

In order to graduate, candidates must have a GPA of 2.0, have completed the upper-division writing requirement, and must maintain a 2.0 GPA for courses taken during the third year of law school.

Organizations

Students edit the *Southern Illinois University Law Journal*, and the *Journal of Legal Medicine*. The Moot Court Board sends teams to numerous competitions, including the ABA Appellate Advocacy Competition, Jessup International Moot Court Competition, and Illinois Moot Court Competition. The student division of the ABA holds annual intraschool Client Interviewing and Counseling, and Negotiation competitions. Student organizations include the Student Bar Association, Illinois State Bar Association, and ABA/Law School Division. There are local chapters of the Black Law Students Association, Lesbian and Gay Law Students Association, and Women's Law Forum. Other organizations include the Environmental Law Society, Christian Legal Society, and Amnesty International.

Library

The law library contains 354,239 hardcopy volumes and 157,847 microform volume equivalents, and subscribes to 3923 serial publications. Such on-line databases and networks as LEXIS, WESTLAW, and LCS DIALOG, a statewide library catalog, OCLC, and Legal Trac are available to law students for research. Special library collections include a federal government selective depository library and Illinois state comprehensive document depository. Recently, the library upgraded the computer laboratory and multiple public workstations. The ratio of library volumes to faculty is 16,102 to 1 and to students, 920 to 1. The ratio of seats in the library to students is 1 to 1.

Placement

Placement	
J.D.s awarded:	124
Services available through: a separate law school placement center	
Services:	
Special features:	
Full-time job interviews:	21 employers
Summer job interviews:	21 employers
Placement by graduation:	n/av
Placement within 9 months:	95% of class
Average starting salary:	$25,000 to $90,000
Areas of placement:	
Private practice 2-10 attorneys	27%
Private practice 11-25 attorneys	12%
Private practice 26-50 attorneys	4%
Private practice 51-100 attorneys	5%
Government	26%
Business/industry	8%
Judicial clerkships	5%
Military	3%
Public interest	2%
Academic	1%

Faculty

The law school has 23 full-time and 6 part-time faculty members, of whom 12 are women. According to AAUP standards for Category I institutions, faculty salaries are well below average. About 39% of full-time faculty have a graduate law degree in addition to the J.D. The ratio of full-time students to full-time faculty in an average class is 15 to 1; in a clinic, 8 to 1. The law school has a regular program of bringing visiting professors and other distinguished lecturers and visitors to campus.

Students

About 37% of the student body are women; 8%, minorities; 3%, African American; 2%, Asian American; and 2%, Hispanic. The majority of students come from Illinois (75%). The average age of entering students is 27; age range is 20 to 58. About 7% drop out after the first year for academic or personal reasons; 92% remain to receive a law degree.

SOUTHERN METHODIST UNIVERSITY

School of Law

Office of Admissions, P.O. Box 750110
Dallas, TX 75275-0110

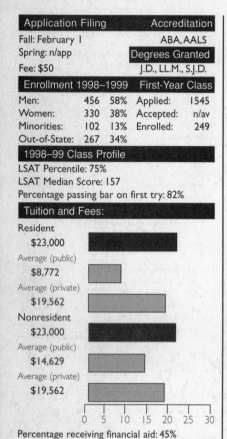

Application Filing	Accreditation
Fall: February 1	ABA, AALS
Spring: n/app	**Degrees Granted**
Fee: $50	J.D., LL.M., S.J.D.

Enrollment 1998–1999		First-Year Class	
Men:	456 58%	Applied:	1545
Women:	330 38%	Accepted:	n/av
Minorities:	102 13%	Enrolled:	249
Out-of-State:	267 34%		

1998–99 Class Profile
LSAT Percentile: 75%
LSAT Median Score: 157
Percentage passing bar on first try: 82%

Tuition and Fees:

Resident
$23,000
Average (public)
$8,772
Average (private)
$19,562
Nonresident
$23,000
Average (public)
$14,629
Average (private)
$19,562

0 5 10 15 20 25 30

Percentage receiving financial aid: 45%

ADMISSIONS

In the fall 1999 first-year class, 1545 applied and 249 enrolled. Seventeen transfers enrolled. The median LSAT percentile of the most recent first-year class was 75; the median GPA was 3.3 on a scale of 4.0. The highest LSAT percentile was 99.

Requirements
Applicants must have a bachelor's degree from an accredited institution and take the LSAT. Minimum acceptable GPA is 2.0 on a scale of 4.0. The most important admission factors include academic achievement, LSAT results, and writing ability. No specific undergraduate courses are required. Candidates are not interviewed.

Procedure
The application deadline for fall entry is February 1. Applicants should submit an application form, LSAT results, a nonrefundable application fee of $50, 2 letters of recommendation, a personal statement, and a resume. Notification of the admission decision is rolling, beginning December 15. The latest acceptable LSAT test date for fall entry is February. The law school uses the LSDAS.

Special
The law school recruits minority and disadvantaged students by means of school visitations and special mailings and telethons. Transfer students must have one year of credit and have attended an ABA-approved law school. Admission for transfers is described as highly competitive and very restrictive.

Costs

Tuition and fees for the 1999-2000 academic year are $23,000 for all full-time students. On-campus room and board costs about $8398 annually; books and supplies run $1290.

Financial Aid

About 45% of current law students receive some form of aid. The average annual amount of aid from all sources combined, including scholarships, loans, and work contracts, is $6000; maximum, $24,744. Awards are based on need and merit. The required financial statements are the FAFSA and others, depending on the type of scholarship being sought. The aid application deadline for fall entry is June 1. Special funds for minority or disadvantaged students are provided through scholarships, which are available on a need and merit basis and are designed to promote the diversity of the student body and the legal profession and to assist those who have had fewer academic opportunities. First-year students are notified about their financial aid application at the time of acceptance.

About the Law School

Southern Methodist University School of Law was established in 1925 and is a private institution. The campus is in a suburban area 5 miles north of downtown Dallas. The primary mission of the law school is to prepare students for the competent and ethical practice of law through a curriculum that combines training in the science and method of law, knowledge of the substance and procedure of law, understanding of the role of law in an international society, and practical experience in handling professional problems. Students have access to federal, state, county, city, and local agencies, courts, correctional facilities, law firms, and legal aid organizations in the Dallas area. Facilities of special interest to law students are the fully computerized Underwood Law Library, built in 1972, and Collins Hall, remodeled and reopened in the fall of 1994, which houses expanded Admissions and Career Services offices, a large Career Services resource center, student lounges, and state-of-the art seminar rooms. Housing for law students, consisting of both single- and married-student housing, is available on campus on a first-come, first-served basis.

Calendar

The law school operates on a traditional semester basis. Courses for full-time students are offered days, with a few evening courses, and must be completed within 5 years. There is no part-time program. New students are admitted in the fall. There is an 8-week summer session.

Programs

In addition to the J.D., the law school offers the LL.M and S.J.D. Students may take relevant courses in other programs and apply credit toward the J.D.; a maximum of 6 credits may be applied. The following joint degrees may be earned: J.D./M.B.A. (Juris Doctor/Master of Business Administration) and J.D./M.A. (Juris Doctor/Master of Arts in applied economics).

Phone: 214-768-2550
Fax: 214-768-2549
Web: law.smu.edu

Contact
214-768-2550 for general inquiries; Financial Aid Counselor, 214-768-3417 for financial aid information.

TEXAS

Required
To earn the J.D., candidates must complete 90 total credits, of which 37 are for required courses. They must maintain a minimum GPA of 2.0 in the required courses. The following first-year courses are required of all students: Contracts, Property, Torts, Civil Procedure, Criminal Law and Procedure, Legal Research, Analysis, and Writing, Lawyering, and Constitutional Law. Required upper-level courses consist of a writing requirement, an edited writing seminar, and Professional Responsibility. The required orientation program for first-year students consists of a 2-day introduction to the study of law.

Electives
The School of Law offers concentrations in corporate law, criminal law, environmental law, family law, international law, litigation, securities law, and tax law. In addition, Civil, Criminal, and Tax clinics may be taken by second- or third-year students who meet prerequisites. Seminars include such topics as Advanced Commercial Law, Antitrust, and Civil Rights. Directed Research is worth a maximum of 3 hours. Field work may be done through Directed Studies, and is worth 1 to 2 hours. A mandatory 30 hours of pro bono work is required for graduation. Special lecture series includes the Murrah Lecture and the Tate Lecture. A summer program at Oxford University is provided for students who wish to study abroad. The Academic Support Tutorial program is available by invitation only. The non-credit Student Tutorial program is available for all first-year law students. Minority programs include Minority Law Day, the Diversity Clerkship Program, Southeastern Minority Job Fair, Sunbelt Minority Job Fair, and the Black/Hispanic/Asian Law Students Associations. Special interest group programs include the Board of Advocates and law student groups.

Graduation Requirements
In order to graduate, candidates must have a GPA of 2.0 and have completed the upper-division writing requirement and a 30-hour pro bono work requirement.

Organizations
Students edit the *SMU Law Review, Journal of Air Law and Commerce, The International Lawyer, Computer Section Reporter, NAFTA: Law and Business Review of the Americas*, and the newspaper *Advocate*. Moot court competitions include the Jackson and Walker, National Frederick Douglass, and Jessup Moot Court competitions. Other competitions include the Client Counseling, ABA Mock Trial, ATLA Mock Trial, and the Geary, Glast, and Middleton Mock Trial. Law student organizations include Barristers, LEGALS, and Student Bar Association. Local chapters of national associations include Delta Theta Phi, Phi Alpha Delta, and Phi Delta Phi.

Library
The law library contains 480,000 hardcopy volumes and 75,217 microform volume equivalents, and subscribes to 2000 serial publications. Such on-line databases and networks as LEXIS, DIALOG, WESTLAW, and NEXIS are available to law students for research. Special library collections include a rare book room. Recently, the library was refurbished with new chairs, tables, carpet, and paint. The ratio of library volumes to faculty is 9792 to 1 and to students, 500 to 1. The ratio of seats in the library to students is 1 to 1.

Faculty
The law school has 42 full-time and 100 part-time faculty members, of whom 13 are women. According to AAUP standards for Category I institutions, faculty salaries are above average. About 40% of full-time faculty have a graduate law degree in addition to the J.D. The ratio of full-time students to full-time faculty in an average class is 20 to 1; in a clinic, 8 to 1. The law school has a regular program of bringing visiting professors and other distinguished lecturers and visitors to campus. There is a chapter of the Order of the Coif; 5 faculty and 10 graduates are members.

Placement
J.D.s awarded:	n/av
Services available through: a separate law school placement center.	
Services: n/av	
Special features: n/av	
Full-time job interviews:	n/av
Summer job interviews:	n/av
Placement by graduation:	68% of class
Placement within 9 months:	95% of class
Average starting salary:	$66,000
Areas of placement:	
Private practice 51-100 attorneys	69%
Business/industry	15%
Government	8%
Unknown	5%
Judicial clerkships	3%
Public interest	1%

Students
About 38% of the student body are women; 13%, minorities. The majority of students come from Texas (66%). The average age of entering students is 24; age range is 20 to 51. About 3% drop out after the first year for academic or personal reasons; 90% remain to receive a law degree.

SOUTHERN UNIVERSITY AND A & M COLLEGE

Law Center

Post Office Box 9294
Baton Rouge, LA 70813

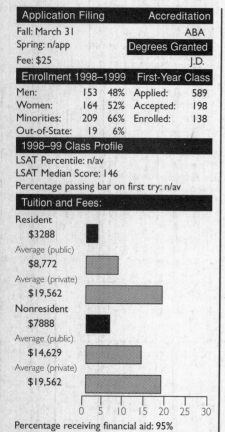

Application Filing	Accreditation
Fall: March 31	ABA
Spring: n/app	**Degrees Granted**
Fee: $25	J.D.

Enrollment 1998–1999		First-Year Class	
Men:	153 48%	Applied:	589
Women:	164 52%	Accepted:	198
Minorities:	209 66%	Enrolled:	138
Out-of-State:	19 6%		

1998–99 Class Profile
LSAT Percentile: n/av
LSAT Median Score: 146
Percentage passing bar on first try: n/av

Tuition and Fees:

Resident
$3288

Average (public)
$8,772

Average (private)
$19,562

Nonresident
$7888

Average (public)
$14,629

Average (private)
$19,562

0 5 10 15 20 25 30

Percentage receiving financial aid: 95%

ADMISSIONS

In the fall 1999 first-year class, 589 applied, 198 were accepted, and 138 enrolled. The median GPA of the most recent first-year class was 2.6.

Requirements

Applicants must have a bachelor's degree from an accredited institution and take the LSAT. Minimum acceptable GPA is 2.0 on a scale of 4.0. The most important admission factors include LSAT results, GPA, and academic achievement. No specific undergraduate courses are required. Candidates are not interviewed.

Procedure

The application deadline for fall entry is March 31. Applicants should submit an application form, LSAT results, transcripts, a nonrefundable application fee of $25, 2 letters of recommendation, and a personal statement. Notification of the admission decision is from April 15 to July 30. The latest acceptable LSAT test date for fall entry is February. The law school uses the LSDAS.

Special

The law school recruits minority and disadvantaged students by means of participation in various programs at minority feeder schools. Transfer students must have one year of credit, have a minimum GPA of 2.5, have attended an ABA-approved law school, and matriculate at least 1 year at the law center if transferring from a Louisiana law school, and 2 if from others.

Costs

Tuition and fees for the 1999-2000 academic year are $3288 for full-time in-state students and $7888 for out-of-state students. On-campus room and board costs about $5375 annually; books and supplies run $1800.

Financial Aid

About 95% of current law students receive some form of aid. The average annual amount of aid from all sources combined, including scholarships, loans, and work contracts, is $13,618; maximum, $18,218. Awards are based on need and merit. The required financial statement is the FFS. The aid application deadline for fall entry is April 15. First-year students are notified about their financial aid application at the time of application to law school.

About the Law School

Southern University and A & M College Law Center was established in 1947 and is a public institution. The campus is in an urban area in Baton Rouge. The primary mission of the law school is to prepare students for the practice of law with specific emphasis upon minorities and the disadvantaged; the program of study is designed to give students a comprehensive knowledge of both the civil law and common law and knowledge of a lawyer's ethics and responsibility to society. Students have access to federal, state, county, city, and local agencies, courts, correctional facilities, law firms, and legal aid organizations in the Baton Rouge area. Facilities of special interest to law students are the Westlaw and LEXIS Laboratory, the Law Review, and the computer laboratory. Housing for law students is convenient and ample. About 90% of the law school facilities are accessible to the physically disabled.

Calendar

The law school operates on a traditional semester basis. Courses for full-time students are offered days only and must be completed within 5 years. There is no part-time program. New full-time students are admitted in the fall. There is a 6-week summer session. Transferable summer courses are offered.

Phone: 225-771-5340
800-537-1135
Fax: 225-771-2121
Web: sus.edu/su/c

Contact

Velma Wilkerson, Admissions Coordinator, 504-771-5340 for general inquiries; Jerome Harris, Director of Financial Aid, 504-771-2141 for financial aid information.

Programs

Required

To earn the J.D., candidates must complete 96 total credits, of which 75 are for required courses. They must maintain a minimum GPA of 2.0 in the required courses. The following first-year courses are required of all students: Basic Civil Procedure, Legal Writing I and II, Legal Research, Torts I and II, Contracts, Civil Law Property, Constitutional Law I, Obligations, Family Law, and Criminal Law. Required upper-level courses consist of Constitutional Law II, Evidence, Civil Procedure I and II, Sales and Leases, Criminal Procedure, Trial Advocacy, Agency and Partnership, Corporations, Successions and Donations, Federal Jurisdiction and Procedure, Commercial Papers, Professional Responsibility, Conflict of Laws, Security Devices, and Advanced Legal Writing I and II. The required orientation program for first-year students is a 1- or 2-day program, with emphasis on analysis, reading comprehension, case briefing, and communication skills.

Electives

Administrative Law, Juvenile, Criminal, and Elderly Law clinics are limited to third-year students who may earn 6 credit hours. Seminars are available in various subject areas for second- and third-year students. Individual student research projects are available for 1 credit hour under the supervision of a professor. Nationally recognized legal scholars are invited each semester to lecture on current issues. At least 3 lectures are scheduled during the school year. Freshman students are required to participate in tutorial programs 2 times a week and 1 monthly session. The most widely taken electives are Civil Rights, Law Office Practice, and Workers Compensation.

Graduation Requirements

In order to graduate, candidates must have a GPA of 2.0.

Organizations

Students edit the *Southern University Law Review* and the student newspaper, *The Public Defender*. Moot court competitions include the annual National Moot Court, the In-House Round Robin, and the Thurgood Marshall competitions. Student organizations include the Student Bar Association, Black Law Students Association, and Student Trial Lawyers Association. Local chapters of national associations include Phi Alpha Delta, Delta Theta Phi, and ABA-Law Student Division. Other organizattions include the Environmental Law Society, Women in Law, and Sports and Entertainment Legal Association.

Library

The law library contains 415,208 hardcopy volumes and 7867 microform volume equivalents, and subscribes to 670 serial publications. Such on-line databases and networks as LEXIS, DIALOG, WESTLAW, NEXIS, and Legal-Trac are available to law students for research. Special library collections include civil rights and civil law collections, and state and federal depositories. Recently, the library added a computer laboratory with 25 terminals and on-line terminals for federal documents. The ratio of library volumes to faculty is 10,226 to 1 and to students, 1310 to 1. The ratio of seats in the library to students is 1 to 89.

Faculty

The law school has 30 full-time and 14 part-time faculty members, of whom 11 are women. According to AAUP standards for Category IIA institutions, faculty salaries are below average. About 20% of full-time faculty have a graduate law degree in addition to the J.D.; about 15% of part-time faculty have one. The ratio of full-time students to full-time faculty in an average class is 12 to 1; in a clinic, 11 to 1. The law school has a regular program of bringing visiting professors and other distinguished lecturers and visitors to campus.

Students

About 52% of the student body are women; 66%, minorities; 66%, African American; 1%, Hispanic; and 33%, Caucasian. The majority of students come from the South (96%). The average age of entering students is 27; age range is 21 to 58. About 50% of students enter directly from undergraduate school, 10% have a graduate degree, and 40% have worked full-time prior to entering law school. About 10% drop out after the first year for academic or personal reasons; 90% remain to receive a law degree.

Placement	
J.D.s awarded:	99
Services available through: a separate law school placement center.	
Special features: Website information on job opportunities and newsletters from other campuses.	
Full-time job interviews:	15 employers
Summer job interviews:	18 employers
Placement by graduation:	90% of class
Placement within 9 months:	10% of class
Average starting salary:	$28,000 to $53,000
Areas of placement:	
Private practice 2-10 attorneys	31%
Private practice 11-25 attorneys	1%
Private practice 26-50 attorneys	1%
Private practice 51-100 attorneys	1%
Government	32%
Judicial clerkships	12%
Unknown	6%
Business/industry	4%
Military	4%
Public interest	2%

LOUISIANA

School of Law

675 South Westmoreland Avenue
Los Angeles, CA 90005-3992

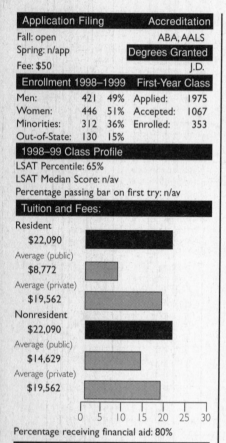

Application Filing	Accreditation
Fall: open	ABA, AALS
Spring: n/app	**Degrees Granted**
Fee: $50	J.D.

Enrollment 1998–1999		First-Year Class	
Men:	421 49%	Applied:	1975
Women:	446 51%	Accepted:	1067
Minorities:	312 36%	Enrolled:	353
Out-of-State:	130 15%		

1998–99 Class Profile
LSAT Percentile: 65%
LSAT Median Score: n/av
Percentage passing bar on first try: n/av

Tuition and Fees:

Resident
$22,090

Average (public)
$8,772

Average (private)
$19,562

Nonresident
$22,090

Average (public)
$14,629

Average (private)
$19,562

0 5 10 15 20 25 30

Percentage receiving financial aid: 80%

ADMISSIONS

In the fall 1999 first-year class, 1975 applied, 1067 were accepted, and 353 enrolled. Eighteen transfers enrolled. The median LSAT percentile of the most recent first-year class was 65; the median GPA was 3.2 on a scale of 4.0. The lowest LSAT percentile accepted was 29; the highest was 97.

Requirements
Applicants must have a bachelor's degree from an accredited institution and take the LSAT. The most important admission factors include LSAT results, GPA, and academic achievement. No specific undergraduate courses are required. Candidates are not interviewed.

Procedure
The application deadline for fall entry is June 30. Applicants should submit an application form, LSAT results, transcripts, a nonrefundable application fee of $50, and a personal statement; up to 3 letters of recommendation are strongly recommended. Notification of the admis-

sion decision is on a rolling basis. The latest acceptable LSAT test date for fall entry is February, although June may be acceptable for some candidates. The law school uses the LSDAS.

Special
The law school recruits minority and disadvantaged students by means of participation by admissions staff in minority recruitment programs at undergraduate campuses around the country, a Law Day program held at the law school for minority junior college and university students, admissions receptions on campus, public service announcements in print and broadcast media, scholarship programs, and programs for prospective students sponsored by minority student organizations at the law school. Transfer students must have one year of credit, a minimum GPA of 2.0, and a maximum of 43 transferable semester units; they must also have attended an ABA-approved law school and submit a letter of good standing from that school's dean. Preadmissions courses consist of Introduction to Legal Writing: a Seminar for Pre-Law Students, a 4-week, noncredit course that provides a foundation in specialized legal writing skills. An academic support program is also offered for 2 weeks before the start of school.

Costs

Tuition and fees for the 1999-2000 academic year are $22,090 for all full-time students. Tuition for all part-time students is $14,027 per year. Books and supplies run $620.

Financial Aid

About 80% of current law students receive some form of aid. The average annual amount of aid from all sources combined, including scholarships, loans, and work contracts, is $20,000; maximum, $35,000. Awards are based on need and merit. The aid application deadline for fall entry is June 1. Special funds for minority or disadvantaged students consist of approximately a dozen different scholarship funds, the most significant of which is the John J. Schumacher Minority Leadership Scholarship Program for outstanding academic and leadership potential. First-year students are notified about their financial aid application within 2 weeks of acceptance.

About the Law School

Southwestern University School of Law was established in 1911 and is a private institution. The 2-acre campus is in an urban area in Los Angeles. The primary mission of the law school is to offer, through an excellent and committed faculty, full-time, part-time, traditional, and nontraditional Juris Doctorate programs that prepare students with diverse backgrounds and interests to assume positions of responsiblity and trust within the legal profession and the greater community. Students have access to federal, state, county, city, and local agencies, courts, correctional facilities, law firms, and legal aid organizations in the Los Angeles area. Facilities of special interest to law students include the renovated historic Bullocks Wilshire building which accommodates the Law Library and features state-of-the-art computer laboratories, research training classrooms, and study rooms. Ample parking for students is available on campus. Housing for law students is not available on campus; however, apartments and homes are located nearby. About 99% of the law school facilities are accessible to the physically disabled.

Calendar

The law school operates on a traditional semester basis. Courses for full-time students are offered days only with some evening electives available and must be completed within 5 years. For part-time students, courses are offered both day and evening and must be completed within 5 years. New full-and part-time students are admitted in the fall. There is an 8-week summer session. Transferable summer courses are offered.

Programs

Required
To earn the J.D., candidates must complete 87 total credits, of which 52 are for required courses. They must maintain a GPA of 2.0 in the required courses. The following first-year courses are required of all students: Civil Procedure I and II, Contracts I and II, Criminal Law, Legal Process, Legal Profession, Legal Research and Writing I and II, Property I and II, and Torts I and II. Required upper-level courses consist of Business Associations, Constitutional Criminal Procedure, Constitutional Law I and II,

Phone: 213-738-6717
Fax: 213-383-1688
E-mail: admissions@swlaw.edu

Contact

Anne Wilson, Admissions Director, 213-738-6717 for general inquiries; Wayne Mahoney, Financial Aid Director, 213-738-6719 for financial aid information.

Evidence, Remedies, and a seminar that satisfies a writing requirement. Simulation training is part of required courses such as Legal Research and Writing and electives such as Civil Pre-Trial Practice; Interviewing, Counseling and Negotiating; and Trial Advocacy. The required orientation program for first-year students is a 3-day program.

Electives

The School of Law offers concentrations in corporate law, criminal law, entertainment, environmental law, family law, international law, litigation, media law, tax law, and health law. In addition, simulated clinical experience is available through courses such as Legal Research and Writing; Interviewing, Counseling, and Negotiating; and Trial Advocacy. Seminars offered for 2 units require in-depth research, analysis, and writing. Titles encompass many areas of the law, including intellectual property, international law, and private and public sector administrative issues. Practical experience may be gained through more than 100 part- and full-time externships available in the judiciary; public interest law firms; federal, state, and local government offices; and entertainment industry settings. Two to ten units per externship placement may be earned on a credit/no credit basis. A limited number of judicial externships in Argentine courts is also available through the Summer Program in Buenos Aires. Paid faculty research assistant positions are available. Special lecture series include the Law Review Distinguished Lecture Series, Faculty Speakers Committee Lecture Series, Alumni Judges Lecture Series, Career Development Panels, and a variety of speakers. The law review and law journal also sponsor scholarly symposia. Study-abroad programs featuring international and comparative law courses taught by school faculty and other international legal experts are offered in Vancouver, B.C., Canada, Buenos Aires, Argentina, and Guanajuato, Mexico. Formal tutorial programs for first-year students and all students on academic probation are offered. Student organizations and faculty members sponsor research and exam-writing tutorials, and librarians conduct tutorials for new law clerks. The Academic Support Program is available for a selected number of entering students. Programs offered especially for minority students include a Minority Career Development seminar, other panel presentations by minority attorneys and judges, and job search skills reviews sponsored by the Placement Office in conjunction with minority bar and law student associations. A Diversity Day for prospective students provides information on admissions and financial aid processes. The most widely taken electives are Administrative Law, Community Property, and Federal Courts.

Graduation Requirements

In order to graduate, candidates must have a GPA of 2.0 and have completed the upper-division writing requirement.

Organizations

Students edit the *Southwestern University Law Review*, the *Southwestern Journal of Law and Trade in the Americas*, a law journal devoted to the legal and economic issues of North, Central, and South America, and the newspaper *The Commentator*. The annual moot court competition for first-year students consists of successive rounds held on campus, at the Los Angeles Superior Court, and the U.S. Court of Appeals. Moot Court Honors Program members compete in 12 to 15 regional and national interscholastic competitions annually. A formal Interscholastic Trial Advocacy Program fields several teams at competitions around the country. Teams also compete in the Interscholastic Client Counseling and the Interscholastic Negotiation competitions. Law Student organizations include the ABA-Law Student Division, Criminal Law Society, and Entertainment and Sports Law Society. There are local chapters of American Society of International Law, Association of Trial Lawyers of America, and the Federalist Society. Graduate student organizations include the Alumni Association, Friends of the Library, and the Dean's Circle.

Library

The law library contains 404,177 hardcopy volumes and 934,164 microform volume equivalents, and subscribes to 4574 serial publications. LEXIS, DIALOG, WESTLAW, NEXIS, Wilsonline (ILP) and the Innopac automated cataloging system are available. Special library collections include U.S. and California depositories, a trial practice collection, and collections in taxation, constitutional law,

Placement

J.D.s awarded:	335
Services available through: n/av	
Services: videotaped mock interviews conducted by alumni practitioners	
Special features: career seminars, panel presentations on various areas of law practice, workshops on job search techniques and interview strategies, joint Career Day and interview programs with other law schools, a comprehensive career resource library, and on-campus interview programs in the fall and spring.	
Full-time job interviews:	n/av
Summer job interviews:	n/av
Placement by graduation:	50% of class
Placement within 9 months:	87% of class
Average starting salary:	$52,000
Areas of placement:	
Private practice 2-10 attorneys	28%
Private practice 11-25 attorneys	13%
Private practice 26-50 attorneys	5%
Private practice 51-100 attorneys	9%
Solo practice	10%
Business/industry	16%
Government	12%
Judicial clerkships	4%
Public interest	1%
Academic	1%

and entertainment law. The ratio of seats in the library to students is 1 to 2.

Faculty

The law school has 50 full-time and 37 part-time faculty members, of whom 31 are women. According to AAUP standards for Category IIA institutions, faculty salaries are well above average. About 20% of full-time faculty have a graduate law degree in addition to the J.D. The ratio of full-time students to full-time faculty in an average class is 17 to 1; in a clinic, 17 to 1.

Students

About 51% of the student body are women; 36%, minorities; 7%, African American; 16%, Asian American; 11%, Hispanic; and 1%, Native American. Most students come from California (85%). The average age of entering students is 27; age range is 20 to 60. About 30% of students enter directly from undergraduate school, 15% have a graduate degree, and 30% have worked full time prior to entering law school.

ST. THOMAS UNIVERSITY

School of Law

16400 N.W. 32nd Avenue
Miami, FL 33054

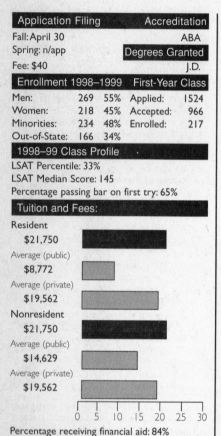

Application Filing		Accreditation
Fall: April 30		ABA
Spring: n/app		**Degrees Granted**
Fee: $40		J.D.

Enrollment 1998–1999		First-Year Class	
Men:	269 55%	Applied:	1524
Women:	218 45%	Accepted:	966
Minorities:	234 48%	Enrolled:	217
Out-of-State:	166 34%		

1998–99 Class Profile
LSAT Percentile: 33%
LSAT Median Score: 145
Percentage passing bar on first try: 65%

Tuition and Fees:

Resident
$21,750

Average (public)
$8,772

Average (private)
$19,562

Nonresident
$21,750

Average (public)
$14,629

Average (private)
$19,562

0 5 10 15 20 25 30

Percentage receiving financial aid: 84%

ADMISSIONS

In the fall 1999 first-year class, 1524 applied, 966 were accepted, and 217 enrolled. Four transfers enrolled. The median LSAT percentile of the most recent first-year class was 33; the median GPA was 2.7 on a scale of 4.0. The lowest LSAT percentile accepted was 15; the highest was 97.

Requirements
Applicants must have a bachelor's degree from an accredited institution and take the LSAT. Minimum acceptable GPA is 2.0 on a scale of 4.0. The most important admission factors include LSAT results, academic achievement, and general background. No specific undergraduate courses are required. Candidates are interviewed.

Procedure
The application deadline for fall entry is April 30. Applicants should submit an application form, LSAT results, transcripts, a nonrefundable application fee of $40, 1 letter of recommendation, and a personal statement. Notification of the admission decision is on a rolling basis. The latest acceptable LSAT test date for fall entry is June. The law school uses the LSDAS.

Special
The law school recruits minority and disadvantaged students by means of recruiting at various historically black colleges and universities, and direct mail to target population using Candidate Referral Service (CRS). Transfer students must have one year of credit, have a minimum GPA of 2.7, have attended an ABA-approved law school, and have a letter of good standing.

Costs

Tuition and fees for the 1999-2000 academic year are $21,750 for all full-time students. On-campus room and board costs about $7900 annually; books and supplies run $800.

Financial Aid

About 84% of current law students receive some form of aid. The average annual amount of aid from all sources combined, including scholarships, loans, and work contracts, is $18,500; maximum, $36,700. Awards are based on need. The required financial statement is FAFSA. The aid application deadline for fall entry is April 15. Special funds for minority or disadvantaged students include scholarships from the Florida Bar Foundation. First-year students are notified about their financial aid application at time of acceptance.

About the Law School

St. Thomas University School of Law was established in 1984 and is a private institution. The campus is in a suburban area 15 miles northwest of downtown Miami. The primary mission of the law school is to provide a personalized, value-oriented legal education to a diverse student body, including those from groups traditionally underrepresented by and within the legal profession. Students have access to federal, state, county, city, and local agencies, courts, correctional facilities, law firms, and legal aid organizations in the Miami area. Housing for law students include on-campus dormitories and a variety of off-campus housing, located within a few miles of the campus. All law school facilities are accessible to the physically disabled.

Calendar

The law school operates on a traditional semester basis. Courses for full-time students are offered both day and evening and must be completed within 5 years. There is no part-time program. New full-time students are admitted in the fall. There is an 8-week summer session. Transferable summer courses are offered.

Programs

Required
To earn the J.D., candidates must complete 90 total credits, of which 53 are for required courses. They must maintain a minimum GPA of 2.0 in the required courses. The following first-year courses are required of all students: Civil Procedure I and II, Contracts I and II, Torts I and II, Criminal Law, Property I, Legal Analysis, Writing, and Research, Appellate Advocacy, and Perspectives on Legal Thought. Required upper-level courses consist of Property I and II, Constitutional Law II, Advanced Legal Research and Writing, Evidence, Criminal Procedure I, Professional Responsibility, and Senior Writing Requirement. The required orientation program for first-year students is a 2-day program during which students register, are introduced to legal research and writing, hear remarks by the Executive Director of the

Phone: 305-623-2310
800-245-4569
E-mail: lamy@stu.edu

Contact

Lydia Amy, Director of Enrollment Services, 305-623-2384 for general inquiries; Office of Financial Aid, 305-628-6547 for financial aid information.

Florida Board of Bar Examiners, meet faculty, administration, and staff, and learn about student organizations.

Electives

The law school sponsors an immigration clinic, appellate clinic, and a family court clinic. Clinics are 4 credits per semester. A wide range of 2-credit seminars are available to upper-class students, including, for example, Church and State, AIDS and the Law, and Equal Protection. Independent research projects may be undertaken by upper-class students for 2 credits. An 8-credit, year-long clinical field placement program is available to upper-class students and features placement in civil and criminal government agencies. A separate summer clinic may be taken for 4 credits. A lecture series every fall offers presentations primarily geared to first-year students on effective note taking, time management and study strategies, stress management, the importance of writing well, and effective exam preparation. St. Thomas sponsors a month-long summer-abroad program in Spain. In addition, upper-class students may take up to 7 credits in an ABA-accredited summer-abroad program sponsored by law schools other than St. Thomas. Students are provided with a high-ranking upper-class tutor upon request. Second- and third-year black students serve as mentors for first-year black law students in a Big Brother/Big Sister program. Legal fraternities and other student organizations offer lecture series, mentoring programs, and other projects. The most widely taken electives are Family Law, Corporations, and Federal Income Tax.

Graduation Requirements

In order to graduate, candidates must have a GPA of 2.0, have completed the upper-division writing requirement, study law in residence for 96 weeks, and pursue the entire study of law as a full-time student for 6 semesters or the equivalent, the last 2 of which must be at St. Thomas.

Organizations

Students edit the *St. Thomas Law Review* and the newspaper *Opinio Juris*. Moot court competitions include the F. Lee Bailey Moot Court, National Environmental Law Moot Court, and Robert Orseck Moot Court. Other competitions include the American Bar Association National Trial Tournament, The American Trial Lawyers Association National Trial Tournament, the Chester Bedell Memorial Trial Tournament, the Florida Academy of Trial Lawyers Trial Tournament, and the National Appellate Advocacy Competition. Organizations for law students include the Student Bar Association, the Florida Association for Women Lawyers, and the Entertainment and Sports Law Society. Local chapters of national organizations include the ABA-Law Student Division, American Trial Lawyers Association, and Phi Delta Phi-Spellman Inn.

Library

The law library contains 293,927 hardcopy volumes and 990,900 microform volume equivalents, and subscribes to 1774 serial publications. Such on-line databases and networks as LEXIS, DIALOG, WESTLAW, and NEXIS are available to law students for research. Recently, the library made available a law library network on reference terminals on both levels of the library and in a computer laboratory. The network provides access to more than 25 CD-ROM titles for students' use. OCLC and Seflink access is provided to the staff. The ratio of library volumes to faculty is 13,360 to 1 and to students, 603 to 1. The ratio of seats in the library to students is 1 to 1.

Faculty

The law school has 22 full-time and 24 part-time faculty members, of whom 17 are women. About 27% of full-time faculty have a graduate law degree in addition to the J.D.; about 13% of part-time faculty have one. The ratio of full-time students to full-time faculty in an average class is 22 to 1; in a clinic, 16 to 1. The law school has a regular program of bringing visiting professors and other distinguished lecturers and visitors to campus.

Placement

J.D.s awarded:	169

Services available through: a separate law school placement center

Services: providing monthly newsletter for students, monthly job listings for alumni, and written guides on aspects of job search and career planning, conducting workshops and seminars, participating in southeastern job fairs, sponsoring guest speakers on areas of legal practice, judicial clerkships, and alternative careers, participating in minority opportunity programs and mentoring programs with alumni and the Florida Bar Association and the Broward and Dade County Bar Associations.

Special features: individualized attention for all students. The Office conducts mandatory individual meetings with first-year students and sets aside 4 hours daily for appointments with advanced students.

Full-time job interviews:	18 employers
Summer job interviews:	18 employers
Placement by graduation:	39% of class
Placement within 9 months:	90% of class
Average starting salary:	$37,212 to $38,559

Areas of placement:

Private practice 2-10 attorneys	33%
Private practice 11-25 attorneys	5%
Private pracice 26-50 attorneys	2%
Private practice 51-100 attorneys	1%
Solo practice	9%
Government	18%
Business/industry	14%
Full-time degree programs	10%
Public interest	2%
Judicial clerkships	2%
Academic	1%

Students

About 45% of the student body are women; 48%, minorities; 13%, African American; 3%, Asian American; and 30%, Hispanic. The majority of students come from Florida (66%). The average age of entering students is 27; age range is 21 to 53. About 90% of students enter directly from undergraduate school, 10% have a graduate degree, and 5% have worked full-time prior to entering law school. About 25% drop out after the first year for academic or personal reasons; 75% remain to receive a law degree.

Stanford Law School

Crown Quadrangle
Stanford, CA 94305-8610

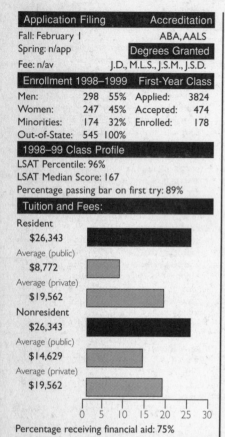

Application Filing		Accreditation
Fall: February 1		ABA, AALS
Spring: n/app		Degrees Granted
Fee: n/av		J.D., M.L.S., J.S.M., J.S.D.

Enrollment 1998–1999		First-Year Class	
Men:	298 55%	Applied:	3824
Women:	247 45%	Accepted:	474
Minorities:	174 32%	Enrolled:	178
Out-of-State:	545 100%		

1998–99 Class Profile
LSAT Percentile: 96%
LSAT Median Score: 167
Percentage passing bar on first try: 89%

Tuition and Fees:

Resident
$26,343

Average (public)
$8,772

Average (private)
$19,562

Nonresident
$26,343

Average (public)
$14,629

Average (private)
$19,562

0   5   10   15   20   25   30

Percentage receiving financial aid: 75%

ADMISSIONS

In the fall 1999 first-year class, 3824 applied, 474 were accepted, and 178 enrolled. Eighteen transfers enrolled. The median LSAT percentile of the most recent first-year class was 96; the median GPA was 3.7 on a scale of 4.0.

Requirements

Applicants must have a bachelor's degree from an accredited institution and take the LSAT. No specific undergraduate courses are required. Candidates are not interviewed.

Procedure

The application deadline for fall entry is February 1. Applicants should submit an application form, LSAT results, transcripts, 2 letters of recommendation, and a statement of good standing from the undergraduate dean. Check with the school for the current fee. Notification of the admissions decision is on a rolling basis. The latest acceptable LSAT test date for fall entry is December. The law school uses the LSDAS.

Special

The law school recruits minority and disadvantaged students by means of attending law forums and Law Days, and making individual school visits. Transfer students must have one year of credit and have attended an ABA-approved law school.

Costs

Tuition and fees for the 1999-2000 academic year are $26,343 for all students. On-campus room and board costs about $10,322 annually; and books and supplies run $1254.

Financial Aid

In a recent year, about 75% of current law students received some form of aid. Awards are based on need. The required financial statements are the FAFSA and Need Access Form. Check with the school for current application deadlines. First-year students are notified about their financial aid application upon receipt of the Need Access Form and FAFSA analysis.

About the Law School

Stanford University Stanford Law School was established in 1893 and is a private institution. The 6109-acre campus is in a suburban area 35 miles south of San Francisco. The primary mission of the law school is to be a national and world leader in the education of lawyers and in the expansion of legal knowledge through research with the ultimate aim of improving the legal orders of the domestic and global communities. Students have access to federal, state, county, city, and local agencies, courts, correctional facilities, law firms, and legal aid organizations in the Stanford area. Housing for law students is guaranteed to all new students who apply for housing by a specified date and are willing to live anywhere on campus. Law students are given priority for Crothers Hall. All law school facilities are accessible to the physically disabled.

Calendar

The law school operates on a traditional semester basis. Courses are offered days only and must be completed within 7 semesters. There is no part-time program. New students are admitted in the fall. There is no summer session. Transferable summer courses are not offered.

Programs

In addition to the J.D., the law school offers the M.L.S., J.S.M., and J.S.D. Students may take relevant courses in other programs and apply credit toward the J.D.; a maximum of 11 credits may be applied. The following joint degrees may be earned: J.D./A.M. (Juris Doctor/Master of Arts in history, economics, political science), J.D./Ph.D. (Juris Doctor/Doctor of Philosophy in economics), J.D./M.P.A. (Juris Doctor/Master of Public Administration with Princeton University), J.D./M.A. (Juris Doctor/Master of Arts in international relations/studies, with Johns Hopkins University), and J.D./M.A. (Juris Doctor/Master of Arts in international policy studies).

Phone: 650-723-4985
Fax: 650-723-0838
E-mail: law.admissions@forsythe.stanford.edu/

Contact
Office of Admissions, 650-723-4985 for general inquiries; Office of Financial Aid, 650-723-9247 for financial aid information.

CALIFORNIA

Required
To earn the J.D., candidates must complete 86 total credits, of which 27 are for required courses. The following first-year courses are required of all students: Civil Procedure, Contracts, Criminal Law, Torts, Research and Legal Writing, Constitutional Law, Property, and Orientation. Required upper-level courses consist of - 1 advanced course that contains at least 1 unit of ethics instruction. The required orientation program for first-year students is a week-long program that includes an introduction to legal institutions and work on case briefings.

Electives
The law school offers courses with clinical components in a variety of areas, including training at the East Palo Alto Community Law Project. Study is integrated with assisting clients in low-income communities. A variety of seminars, worth 2 to 3 units, is offered to upper-level students each year. Externships, from 2 to 8 units of upgraded credit, are offered, typically in the Bay Area. A wide variety of lecture series is sponsored by the law school and student organizations.

Graduation Requirements
In order to graduate, candidates must have completed the upper-division writing requirement and at least one course that offers an intensive consideration of the American legal system from an interdisciplinary perspective of one or more foreign legal systems.

Organizations
Students edit the *Stanford Law Review*, *Environmental Law Journal*, *Stanford Journal of International Law*, *Stanford Law and Policy Review*, *Stanford Journal of Law, Business and Finance*, and the newspaper *Stanford Law Journal*. The Kirkwood Moot Court Competition is held in May each year. All first-year students participate in a non-competitive moot court program in the spring semester as part of their mandatory legal research and writing course. The law school also offers a variety of writing competitions. Student organizations include Asian and Pacific Islander Law Students Association, Black Law Students Association, and Chinese Legal Studies Group. There are local chapters of the Federalist Society, National Lawyers Guild, and Civil Liberties Union.

Library
The law library contains 484,858 hardcopy volumes and 1786 microform volume equivalents, and subscribes to 7619 serial publications. Such on-line databases and networks as LEXIS, DIALOG, WESTLAW, and NEXIS, plus extensive other sources via local and national networks, are available to law students for research. Special library collections include U.S. government documents and California state documents. Recently, the library added additional computer facilities, systems, and databases. The ratio of library volumes to faculty is 9324 to 1 and to students, 890 to 1. The ratio of seats in the library to students is 1 to 1.

Faculty
The law school has 52 full-time faculty members, of whom 11 are women. According to AAUP standards for Category I institutions, faculty salaries are well above average. About 11% of full-time faculty have a graduate law degree in addition to the J.D. The ratio of full-time students to full-time faculty in an average class is 15 to 1. The law school has a regular program of bringing visiting professors and other distinguished lecturers and visitors to campus. There is a chapter of the Order of the Coif.

Students
About 45% of the student body are women; 32%, minorities; 8%, African American; 10%, Asian American; 12%, Hispanic; and 2%, Native American. The average age of entering students is 25; age range is 21 to 37. About 18% of students enter directly from undergraduate school and 31% have a graduate degree.

Placement	
J.D.s awarded:	179
Services available through: separate law school placement center	
Services: Externships are coordinated through the Director of Public Interest Programs.	
Special features: counseling and advising students regarding job search, career decisions, and public service	
Full-time job interviews:	n/av
Summer job interviews:	n/av
Placement by graduation:	n/av
Placement within 9 months:	99% of class
Average starting salary:	n/av
Areas of placement:	
Private practice 2-10 attorneys	2%
Private practice 11-25 attorneys	2%
Private practice 26-50 attorney	3%
Private practice 51-100 attorneys	5%
Private practice 100 + attorneys	47%
Jucicial clerkships	25%
Business/industry	12%
Academic	2%
Public interest	2%

Stanford University **361**

University at Buffalo Law School

O'Brian Hall
Buffalo, NY 14260

Application Filing	Accreditation
Fall: March 15	ABA, AALS
Spring: n/app	**Degrees Granted**
Fee: $50	J.D., LL.M.

Enrollment 1998–1999		First-Year Class	
Men:	370 52%	Applied:	844
Women:	342 48%	Accepted:	510
Minorities:	128 18%	Enrolled:	232
Out-of-State:	64 9%		

1998–99 Class Profile
LSAT Percentile: 60%
LSAT Median Score: 153
Percentage passing bar on first try: 73%

Tuition and Fees:

Resident
$9400

Average (public)
$8,772

Average (private)
$19,562

Nonresident
$14,950

Average (public)
$14,629

Average (private)
$19,562

0   5   10   15   20   25   30

Percentage receiving financial aid: 85%

ADMISSIONS

In the fall 1999 first-year class, 844 applied, 510 were accepted, and 232 enrolled. Thirteen transfers enrolled. The median LSAT percentile of the most recent first-year class was 60; the median GPA was 3.18 on a scale of 4.0. The lowest LSAT percentile accepted was 6; the highest was 98.

Requirements

Applicants must have a bachelor's degree from an accredited institution and take the LSAT. Minimum acceptable LSAT score is 15 and minimum acceptable GPA is 2.0 on a scale of 4.0. The most important admission factors include academic achievement, LSAT results, and writing ability. No specific undergraduate courses are required. Candidates are not interviewed.

Procedure

The application deadline for fall entry is March 15. Applicants should submit an application form, LSAT results, transcripts, a nonrefundable application fee of $50, and 2 letters of recommendation. Notification of the admission decision is as early as February. The latest acceptable LSAT test date for fall entry is February. The law school uses the LSDAS.

Special

The law school recruits minority and disadvantaged students through targeted recruitment efforts at colleges with significant minority student populations and participation in a tuition waiver program for EOP, HEOP, and SEEK students. Transfer students must have one year of credit, have attended an ABA-approved law school, and and submit 2 letters of reference a letter of good standing from the initial law school, the first page of the LSDAS report, and the $50 application fee.

Costs

Tuition and fees for the 1999-2000 academic year are $9400 for full-time in-state students and $14,950 for out-of-state students. On-campus room and board costs about $7200 annually; and books and supplies run $1323.

Financial Aid

About 85% of current law students receive some form of aid. The average annual amount of aid from all sources combined, including scholarships, loans, and work contracts, is $12,757; maximum, $18,500. Awards are based on need. The required financial statement is FAFSA. The aid application deadline for fall entry is March 1. Special funds for minority or disadvantaged students consist of state and federal tuition fellowship programs. First-year students are notified about their financial aid application at the time of acceptance.

About the Law School

State University of New York at Buffalo, University at Buffalo Law School was established in 1887 and is a public institution. The 154 acre campus is in a suburban area 3 miles north of Buffalo in Amherst, NY. The primary mission of the law school is to provide an excellent professional education while emphasizing the role of law and lawyers within the broader context of American society. Students have access to federal, state, county, city, and local agencies, courts, correctional facilities, law firms, and legal aid organizations in the Buffalo area. The University at Buffalo undergraduate and graduate schools and libraries are also available to students. Housing for law students is available both on and off campus, with town home-style residences available on the north campus. About 90% of the law school facilities are accessible to the physically disabled.

Calendar

The law school operates on a traditional semester, 4-1-4 modified semester, and 3-1-3 basis. Check with the school for further information. Courses for full-time students are offered during the day with occasional evening classes and must be completed within 3 to 4 years. There is no part-time program. New full-time students are admitted in the fall. There is a 7-week summer session. Transferable summer courses are offered.

Programs

In addition to the J.D., the law school offers the LL.M in criminal law. Students may take relevant courses in other programs and apply credit toward the J.D.; a maximum of 9 credits may be applied. The following joint degrees may be earned: J.D./M.B.A. (Juris Doctor/Master of Business Administration), J.D./M.S.W. (Juris Doctor/Master of Social Work), and J.D./Ph.D. (Juris Doctor/Doctor of Philosophy in sociology, anthropology, political science, philosophy, environmental studies, and other fields).

Phone: 716-645-2907
Fax: 716-645-5940
E-mail: coxublaw@buffalo.edu
Web: http://www.buffalo.edu/law

Contact

716-645-6233 for general inquiries; Brezetta Stevenson, Financial Aid/Scheduling Coordinator, 716-645-7324 for financial aid information.

NEW YORK

Required

To earn the J.D., candidates must complete 87 total credits, of which 35 are for required courses. The following first-year courses are required of all students: Civil Procedure, Constitutional Law, Contracts, Criminal law, Research and Writing (2 semesters), Property, Torts, Intensive bridge course (taught during the month of January), and Legal Profession and Ethics. Required upper-level courses consist of Federal Tax I and seminar. The required orientation program for first-year students lasts 1 week and includes an introduction to faculty, administrators, and student organizations, as well as an introductory course on legal methods, reasoning, and argument.

Electives

The University at Buffalo Law School offers concentrations in criminal law, environmental law, family law, international law, litigation, tax law, and health law; state and local government; law and social justice, affordable housing development; and community economic and finance transactions. In addition, upper-division students may take clinics for 3 to 4 credit hours each. Topics include affordable housing, education law, and federal criminal practice. They may also take seminars for 3 credit hours. At least 1 seminar is required for each student. There are public interest externships and Geneva internships. Upper-division students may take independent research for 3 to 6 credit hours. Externships are offered in public interest, governmental, and international settings. Special lecture series include the Mitchell and Baldy Center Lecture Series and the Baldy Center "short courses." There are summer internships abroad with leading human rights organizations through the Buffalo Human Rights Center. The Legal Methods program is for first-year students who are educationally disadvantaged. Special interest group programs include the Buffalo Public Interest Law Program, Domestic Violence Task Force, and Prison Task Force. The most widely taken electives are Gratuitous Transfers, Sales-Secured Transactions, and Commercial Paper.

Graduation Requirements

In order to graduate, candidates must have completed the upper-division writing requirement and 89 credit hours. Grades of "H" or "Q" must be earned in at least 74 hours. A seminar is also required.

Organizations

Students edit the *Buffalo Law Review, Buffalo Environmental Law Journal, Buffalo Criminal Law Review*, and the newspaper, *The Opinion*. Other publications include the *Buffalo Journal of Public Interest Law, The ABA Journal of Affordable Housing and Community Development Law,* and *The Buffalo Women's Law Journal*. Moot court competitions include the Desmond Intramural held in November, the National Mugel Tax held in the spring, and the Herbert Wechsler Criminal Moot Court. Law student organizations include the Entertainment and Sport Law Society, Buffalo Environmental Law Society, and the Labor and Employment Law Association. There are local chapters of the Association of Trial Lawyers of America, National Lawyers Guild, and Phi Alpha Delta. Other law student organizations include the Asian American Law Students Association, Black Law Students Association, and the Latin American Law Students Association.

Library

The law library contains 301,692 hardcopy volumes and 1,983,759 microform volume equivalents, and subscribes to 964 serial publications. Such on-line databases and networks as LEXIS, DIALOG, WESTLAW, NEXIS, QL (Canadian Law), LRS (New York Legislation), RLIN, OCLC, First Search, and 100 web-based databases accessible on library network are available to law students for research. Special library collections include a U.S. government document depository; the Morris L. Cohen Rare Book collection; the papers of John Lord O'Brian; Berman Human Rights Collections, and a substantial United Nations documents collection. Recently, the library added a CD-ROM network, 75 Internet ports, and an electronic classroom. The ratio of library volumes to faculty is 5692 to 1 and to students, 444 to 1. The ratio of seats in the library to students is 1 to 2.

Placement

J.D.s awarded:	220
Services available through: A separate law school placement center.	
Services: alumni mentoring program and alumni career panels.	
Special features: an employment bulletin that is sent free for 18 months.	
Full-time job interviews:	19 employers
Summer job interviews:	23 employers
Placement by graduation:	52% of class
Placement within 9 months:	97% of class
Average starting salary:	$31,080 to $60,250
Areas of placement:	
Private practice 2-10 attorneys	25%
Private practice 11-25 attorneys	6%
Private practice 26-50 attorneys	3%
Private practice 51-100 attorneys	6%
Private practice 101+ attorneys	14%
Government	11%
Academic	9%
Business/industry	15%
Public interest	5%
Judicial clerkships	6%

Faculty

The law school has 56 full-time and 102 part-time faculty members, of whom 49 are women. According to AAUP standards for Category I institutions, faculty salaries are above average. About 36% of full-time faculty have a graduate law degree in addition to the J.D.; about 8% of part-time faculty have one. The ratio of full-time students to full-time faculty in an average class is 34 to 1; in a clinic, 10 to 1. The law school has a regular program of bringing visiting professors and other distinguished lecturers and visitors to campus.

Students

About 48% of the student body are women; 18%, minorities; 7%, African American; 5%, Asian American; 6%, Hispanic; and 1%, Native American. The majority of students come from New York (91%). The average age of entering students is 25; age range is 19 to 64. About 35% of students enter directly from undergraduate school, 11% have a graduate degree, and 30% have worked full-time prior to entering law school. About 2% drop out after the first year for academic or personal reasons; 96% remain to receive a law degree.

STETSON UNIVERSITY

College of Law

1401 61st Street South
St. Petersburg, FL 33707

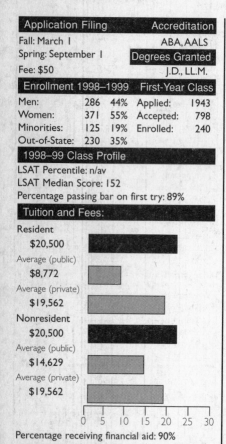

Application Filing		Accreditation
Fall: March 1		ABA, AALS
Spring: September 1		**Degrees Granted**
Fee: $50		J.D., LL.M.

Enrollment 1998–1999		First-Year Class	
Men:	286 44%	Applied:	1943
Women:	371 55%	Accepted:	798
Minorities:	125 19%	Enrolled:	240
Out-of-State:	230 35%		

1998–99 Class Profile
LSAT Percentile: n/av
LSAT Median Score: 152
Percentage passing bar on first try: 89%

Tuition and Fees:

Resident
$20,500
Average (public)
$8,772
Average (private)
$19,562
Nonresident
$20,500
Average (public)
$14,629
Average (private)
$19,562

0 5 10 15 20 25 30

Percentage receiving financial aid: 90%

ADMISSIONS

In the fall 1999 first-year class, 1943 applied, 798 were accepted, and 240 enrolled. Ten transfers enrolled. The median GPA of the most recent first-year class was 3.4 on a scale of 4.0.

Requirements

Applicants must have a bachelor's degree from an accredited institution and take the LSAT. The most important admission factors include LSAT results, GPA, and work experience. No specific undergraduate courses are required. Candidates are interviewed.

Procedure

The application deadline for fall entry is March 1. Applicants should submit an application form, a nonrefundable application fee of $50, a personal statement, and the college questionnaire. Three letters of recommendation are suggested. Notification of the admission decision is on a rolling basis. The latest acceptable LSAT test date for fall entry is December. The law school uses the LSDAS.

Special

The law school recruits minority and disadvantaged students by means of CRS mailings, CLEO, law school forums, and college campus visits. Transfer students must have one year of credit, have attended an ABA-approved law school, and must be ranked in the top 20% of their first-year class.

Costs

Tuition and fees for the 1999-2000 academic year are $20,500 for all full-time students. On-campus room and board costs about $6630 annually; books and supplies run $1000.

Financial Aid

About 90% of current law students receive some form of aid. The average annual amount of aid from all sources combined, including scholarships, loans, and work contracts, is $21,000; maximum, $32,350. Awards are based on need and merit. The required financial statements are FAFSA, supplemental application for Stetson grant, and a copy of an income tax return. The aid application deadline for fall entry is March 1. Special funds for minority or disadvantaged students include the Florida Minority Participation in Legal Education Scholarships program, minority scholarships through the Florida Bar Foundation, and special consideration for the Stetson grant program. First-year students are notified about their financial aid application between the time of acceptance and the due date of the confirmation deposit.

About the Law School

Stetson University College of Law was established in 1900 and is a private institution. The 21-acre campus is in a suburban area 20 miles southwest of Tampa. The primary mission of the law school is to educate men and women who will ethically and competently serve the state, the region, and the nation as members of the legal profession in private practice, business, and government. Students have access to federal, state, county, city, and local agencies, courts, correctional facilities, law firms, and legal aid organizations in the St. Petersburg area. Facilities of special interest to law students include 4 on-campus courtrooms available for skills training. Housing for law students is available in residence halls, 2-bedroom apartments, and school-owned houses for single and married students; also, housing options are available in the community. All law school facilities are accessible to the physically disabled.

Calendar

The law school operates on a traditional semester basis. Courses for full-time students are offered days only and must be completed within 2 1/2 to 3 years. There is no part-time program. New full-time students are admitted in the fall, spring, and summer. There is an 8-week summer session. Transferable summer courses are offered.

Phone: 727-562-7802
Fax: 727-343-0136
E-mail: lawadmit@hermes.law.stetson.edu
Web: http://www.law.stetson.edu

Contact

Director of Admissions, 727-562-7802 for general inquiries; Assistant Director of Financial Aid, 727-562-7813 for financial aid information.

Programs

In addition to the J.D., the law school offers the LL.M. Students may take relevant courses in other programs and apply credit toward the J.D.; a maximum of 12 credits may be applied. The following joint degrees may be earned: J.D./M.B.A. (Juris Doctor/Master of Business Administration).

Required

To earn the J.D., candidates must complete 88 total credits, of which 48 are for required courses. They must maintain a minimum GPA of 2.0 in the required courses. The following first-year courses are required of all students: Civil Procedure I and II, Contracts I and II, Criminal Law, Real Property I and II, Research and Writing I and II, and Torts I and II. Required upper-level courses consist of Business Associations, Constitutional Law, Evidence, Federal Income Taxation, and Professional Responsibility. The required orientation program for first-year students is a 2-day program that consists of general orientation and small groups with faculty mentors that discuss study skills, stress reduction, professionalism, and other topics.

Electives

The College of Law offers concentrations in corporate law, criminal law, environmental law, family law, international law, labor law, litigation, tax law, and torts and insurance. In addition, clinic programs are available to third-year students in civil government, elder law, and labor law. Many seminars for second- and third-year students are offered each year. Externships with state and federal judges are available for third-year students. Inns of Court programs are held every semester with prominent speakers. Other programs are also sponsored by faculty and student organizations of the law school. Second- and third-year students participate in study-abroad programs offered through other law schools and transfer credits back to the law school. Individual tutorial programs are available for all first-year students. The most widely taken electives are clinics and trial practice courses.

Graduation Requirements

In order to graduate, candidates must have a GPA of 2.0, and have completed the upper-division writing requirement, and 20 hours of public service.

Organizations

Students edit the *Stetson Law Review*. Annually, students compete in many competitions, including the National Moot Court, National Appellate Advocacy, and the Orseck Memorial Moot Court competitions. Other competitions include regional, and national client counseling competitions, and state, regional and national Tournament of Champions Mock Trial competitions. Law student organizations include the Student Bar Association; ABA-Law Student Division; and Entertainment, Art, and Sports Law Society. Local chapters of national associations include Delta Theta Phi, Phi Alpha Delta, and Phi Delta Phi.

Library

The law library contains 356,875 hardcopy volumes and 769,000 microform volume equivalents, and subscribes to 5086 serial publications. Such on-line databases and networks as LEXIS, DIALOG, and WESTLAW are available to law students for research. Recently, a new library opened. The ratio of seats in the library to students is 2 to 3.

Faculty

The law school has 42 full-time and 40 part-time faculty members, of whom 17 are women. According to AAUP standards for Category IIA institutions, faculty salaries are above average. About 50% of full-time faculty have a graduate law degree in addition to the J.D.; about 7% of part-time faculty have one. The ratio of full-time students to full-time faculty in an average class is 19 to 1; in a clinic, 10 to 1. The law school has a regular program of bringing visiting professors and other distinguished lecturers and visitors to campus.

Students

About 55% of the student body are women; 19%, minorities; 7%, African American; 2%, Asian American; 9%, Hispanic; and 1%, Native American. The majority of students come from Florida (65%). The average age of entering students is 23; age range is 20 to 51. About 50% of students enter directly from undergraduate school and 50% have worked full-time prior to entering law school. About 4% drop out after the first year for academic or personal reasons; 96% remain to receive a law degree.

Placement

J.D.s awarded:	215
Services available through: a separate law school placement center	
Services: on-campus interviewing programs in the fall and spring semesters	
Special features: office equipment for student use, including computers for job searches on LEXIS and WESTLAW, a fax machine, and a laser printer for resume and cover letter production.	
Full-time job interviews:	33 employers
Summer job interviews:	31 employers
Placement by graduation:	n/av
Placement within 9 months:	93% of class
Average starting salary:	$30,000 to $67,500
Areas of placement:	
Private practice 2-10 attorneys	26%
Private practice 11-25 attorneys	8%
Private practice 26-50 attorneys	2%
Private practice 51-100 attorneys	5%
Government	29%
Unknown	12%
Business/industry	5%
Academic	5%
Judicial clerkships	5%
Public interest	2%
Military	1%

SUFFOLK UNIVERSITY

Law School

120 Tremont Street
Boston, MA 02108-4977

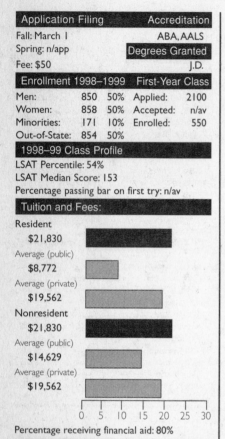

Application Filing	Accreditation
Fall: March 1	ABA, AALS
Spring: n/app	**Degrees Granted**
Fee: $50	J.D.

Enrollment 1998–1999		First-Year Class	
Men:	850 50%	Applied:	2100
Women:	858 50%	Accepted:	n/av
Minorities:	171 10%	Enrolled:	550
Out-of-State:	854 50%		

1998–99 Class Profile

LSAT Percentile: 54%
LSAT Median Score: 153
Percentage passing bar on first try: n/av

Tuition and Fees:

Resident
$21,830

Average (public)
$8,772

Average (private)
$19,562

Nonresident
$21,830

Average (public)
$14,629

Average (private)
$19,562

0 5 10 15 20 25 30

Percentage receiving financial aid: 80%

ADMISSIONS

In the fall 1999 first-year class, 2100 applied and 550 enrolled. Ten transfers enrolled. The median LSAT percentile of the most recent first-year class was 54; the median GPA was 3.2 on a scale of 4.0. The lowest LSAT percentile accepted was 32; the highest was 98.

Requirements

Applicants must have a bachelor's degree from an accredited institution and take the LSAT. Minimum acceptable GPA is 3.0 on a scale of 4.0. The most important admission factors include academic achievement, GPA, and LSAT results. No specific undergraduate courses are required. Candidates are interviewed.

Procedure

The application deadline for fall entry is March 1. Applicants should submit an application form, TOEFL score if applicable, a nonrefundable application fee of $50, undergraduate letters of recommendation, and supplementary personal information for those wishing to emphasize unusual circumstances in their background. Accepted

students must pay a $200 tuition deposit by April 1; a second deposit of $300 is due June 1. Notification of the admissions decision is on a rolling basis. The latest acceptable LSAT test date for fall entry is February. The law school uses the LSDAS.

Special

The law school recruits minority and disadvantaged students by means of an admissions committee, which gives consideration to students who have overcome economic and social disadvantages. Transfer students must have attended an ABA-approved law school and be in good academic standing. The application must be completed by early June. The dean of each previous law school must provide a letter of good standing and a final transcript.

Costs

Tuition and fees for the 1999-2000 academic year are $21,830 for all full-time students. Tuition for part-time students is $16,370 per year. Books and supplies run $1035.

Financial Aid

About 80% of current law students receive some form of aid. The average annual amount of aid from all sources combined, including scholarships, loans, and work contracts, is $22,500; maximum, $38,000. Awards are based on need and merit. The required financial statements are the CSS Profile, Suffolk University financial aid forms and a federal income tax return. The aid application deadline for fall entry is March 3. Special funds for minority or disadvantaged students are available through a number of financial assistance programs. First-year students are notified about their financial aid application at time of acceptance.

About the Law School

Suffolk University Law School was established in 1906 and is a private institution. The campus is in an urban area in downtown Boston on the Freedom Trail. The primary mission of the law school is to produce highly skilled, ethical lawyers with a commitment to public service. In the twenty-first century, the school will connect its past strengths with its vision for the future to provide a relevant, rigorous education in contemporary legal issues combined with solid practical experience. Students have access to federal, state, county, city, and local agencies, courts, correctional facilities, law firms, and legal aid organizations

in the Boston area. The Center for Continuing Professional Development serves the practicing lawyer for the purpose of continuing the legal education. There is also the Battered Women's Advocacy Project, Academic Support Program and Strive Program. Facilities of special interest to law students include Greater Boston Legal Services, SU Clinical Legal in Chelsea, Center for Juvenile Justice, and International Human Rights Project. Housing for law students is not available on campus, but assistance for obtaining housing in the area is available. All law school facilities are accessible to the physically disabled.

Calendar

The law school operates on a traditional semester basis. Courses for full-time students are offered days only and must be completed within 3 years. For part-time students, courses are offered evenings only and must be completed within 4 years. New full-time students are admitted in the fall; part-time, fall. There is a 10-week summer session. Transferable summer courses are offered.

Programs

The following joint degrees may be earned: J.D./M.P.A. (Juris Doctor/Master of Public Administration), J.D./M.B.A. (Juris Doctor/Master of Business Administration), J.D./M.S.I.E. (Juris Doctor/Master of Science in International Economics), J.D./M.S.F. (Juris Doctor/Master of Science in Finance), and J.D./M.S.C.J. (Juris Doctor/Master of Criminal Justice).

Required

To earn the J.D., candidates must complete 84 total credits, of which 58 are for required courses. They must maintain a minimum GPA of 2.0 in the required courses. The following first-year courses are required of all students: Contracts, Torts, Property, Civil Procedure, Criminal Law, Legal Practice Skills, and Constitutional Law. Required upper-level courses consist of Fiduciary Relations, Evidence, and Professional Responsibility. Clinical courses are not required, but are strongly recommended. The required orientation program for first-year students includes the Strive Program, a preorientation program that helps students prepare for the first year of law school. During orientation, students are instructed in the use of the law library and legal research tools (LEXIS, NEXIS, and WESTLAW), practice in issue analysis

Contact

Gail Ellis, Dean of Admissions, 617-573-8144 for general inquiries; Jocelyn Allen, Director of Financial Aid, 617-573-8147 for financial aid information.

MASSACHUSETTS

and writing of legal memoranda, preparation of trial brief and oral arguments, an introduction to computerized legal research systems, and presentation of law school examination study and answer techniques.

Electives

The Law School offers concentrations in corporate law, criminal law, entertainment, environmental law, family law, international law, juvenile law, labor law, litigation, media law, securities law, sports law, tax law, torts and insurance, commercial law, constitutional law, practice, property law, government regulation, trial advocacy, and the legal profession, as well as specialized concentrations in high technology, intellectual property, tax law, health care and biotechnology, civil litigation, and financial services. In addition, clinical programs, usually 3 credits, include the Suffolk Voluntary Defenders, the Prosecutor Program, and the Suffolk University Legal Assistance Bureau. Seminars are available in such areas as Advanced Contracts, Advanced Entertainment Law, and Advanced Juvenile Law. The Legal Internship Program allows students to gain 2 credits per semester for supervised legal work performed for a government or non-profit agency. Many students act as research assistants for individual faculty members on a specific project of mutual interest. Work-study programs are available. The Donahue Lecture Series presents 3 to 4 different national scholars who lecture on various topics in legal education and on the Suffolk Law Forum. Study-abroad programs are offered in conjunction with law schools in Europe, Canada, South America, and Mexico. A summer study-abroad program is available at the University of Lund, Lund, Sweden. Tutorial programs are available through the Legal Practical Skills programs, Academic Support Program, and Academic Scholars Program. Minority programs include the Strive Program and the Academic Resource Center. There are multicultural groups such as the Black Law Students Association, the Asian Law Students Association, and the Hispanic Law Students Association. There are 30 special interest student groups. The most widely taken electives are Trial Advocacy, High Technology, and International Law.

Graduation Requirements

In order to graduate, candidates must have a GPA of 2.0 and have completed the upper-division writing requirement.

Organizations

The primary law review is the *Suffolk University Law Review*. Other law reviews include the *Suffolk Transnational Law Review* and *The Advocate*, a periodical publication. The student newspaper is the *Dicta*. The Moot Court Board runs 5 annual intraschool programs, 7 appellate advocacy teams, and 3 trial teams. Suffolk competes in the National Trial Competition. The school is home for the National Board of Trial Advocacy, which certifies experienced trial lawyers as civil or criminal trial advocacy specialists. Other competitions include the Justice Tom C. Clark Competition, First Year Moot Court Program, Walter H. McLaughlin First Year Oral Advocacy Competition, Mock Trial Competition, and Second Year Trial Program. The appellate advocacy teams include the Constitutional Law Team, Patent Team, International Law Team, National Team, Securities Team, and Tax Team. Student organizations include the American Trial Lawyers Association, Environmental Law Society, and Student Bar Association. There are local chapters of Phi Delta Phi, National Lawyers Guild/Lawyers Guild Convocation, and the Student Bar Association. Other organizations include Shelter Legal Services.

Library

The law library contains 318,000 hardcopy volumes and 801,693 microform volume equivalents, and subscribes to 5904 serial publications. Such on-line databases and networks as LEXIS, DIALOG, WESTLAW, and NEXIS, and membership in the New England Law Library Consortium are available to law students for research. Special library collections include a collection of biographical material on lawyers and judges, famous trials, law and literature, environmental law, criminal law, intellectual property law, biomedical law, and trial pratice materials. Recently, the library moved into a new building with specially designed study carrels and tables. All study seats have electrical and data hookups to the Internet. The ratio of library volumes to faculty is 5000 to 1 and to students, 200 to 1. The ratio of seats in the library to students is 1 to 1.

Faculty

The law school has 60 full-time and 114 part-time faculty members, of whom 38 are women. According to AAUP standards for Category IIA institutions, faculty salaries

Placement

J.D.s awarded:	496

Services available through: a separate law school placement center

Services: professional directories, notices of employment, judicial clerkship information, library facilities for employment information, and panel discussions

Special features: the fall on-campus Recruitment Program, to which the Career Services Office invites law firms, corporations, legal services offices, and state and federal agencies to interview students for employment. The school is also a member of the Massachusetts Law School Consortium, which sponsors other recruitment and career-related programs.

Full-time job interviews:	90 employers
Summer job interviews:	65 employers
Placement by graduation:	60% of class
Placement within 9 months:	94% of class
Average starting salary:	$22,000 to $60,000

Areas of placement:

Private practice 2-10 attorneys	12%
Private practice 11-25 attorneys	15%
Private practice 26-50 attorneys	10%
Private practice 51-100 attorneys	3%
Business/industry	28%
Government	17%
Judicial clerkships	9%
Academic	3%
Unknown	1%
Military	1%

are well above average. About 38% of full-time faculty have a graduate law degree in addition to the J.D.; about 20% of part-time faculty have one. The ratio of full-time students to full-time faculty in an average class is 17 to 1; in a clinic, 10 to 1. The law school has a regular program of bringing visiting professors and other distinguished lecturers and visitors to campus.

Students

About 50% of the student body are women; 10%, minorities; 4%, African American; 4%, Asian American; and 3%, Hispanic. The majority of students come from Massachusetts (50%). The average age of entering students is 26; age range is 20 to 55. About 26% of students enter directly from undergraduate school and 13% have a graduate degree. About 8% drop out after the first year for academic or personal reasons; 92% remain to receive a law degree.

SYRACUSE UNIVERSITY

College of Law

Office of Admissions and Financial Aid
Syracuse, NY 13244-1030

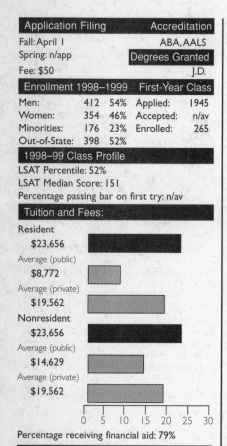

Application Filing		Accreditation
Fall: April 1		ABA, AALS
Spring: n/app		**Degrees Granted**
Fee: $50		J.D.

Enrollment 1998–1999		First-Year Class
Men:	412 54%	Applied: 1945
Women:	354 46%	Accepted: n/av
Minorities:	176 23%	Enrolled: 265
Out-of-State:	398 52%	

1998–99 Class Profile
LSAT Percentile: 52%
LSAT Median Score: 151
Percentage passing bar on first try: n/av

Tuition and Fees:

Resident
$23,656

Average (public)
$8,772

Average (private)
$19,562

Nonresident
$23,656

Average (public)
$14,629

Average (private)
$19,562

0 5 10 15 20 25 30

Percentage receiving financial aid: 79%

ADMISSIONS

In the fall 1999 first-year class, 1945 applied and 265 enrolled. Four transfers enrolled. The median LSAT percentile of the most recent first-year class was 52; the median GPA was 3.3 on a scale of 4.0. The highest LSAT percentile was 99.

Requirements
Applicants must have a bachelor's degree from an accredited institution and take the LSAT. The most important admission factors include GPA, academic achievement, and LSAT results. No specific undergraduate courses are required. Candidates are not interviewed.

Procedure
The application deadline for fall entry is April 1. Applicants should submit an application form, LSAT results, transcripts, a nonrefundable application fee of $50, 3 letters of recommendation, and a personal statement. Notification of the admission decision is on a rolling basis from January to May. The latest acceptable LSAT test date for fall entry is February. The law school uses the LSDAS.

Special
The law school recruits minority and disadvantaged students by means of an in-house Legal Education Opportunity Program, students of color law forums, the CLEO program, and by application review. Transfer students must have one year of credit, have a minimum GPA of 2.5, and have attended an ABA-approved law school.

Costs

Tuition and fees for the 1999-2000 academic year are $23,656 for all full-time students. Tuition for all part-time students is $1012 per credit. On-campus room and board costs about $9214 annually; books and supplies run $1100.

Financial Aid

About 79% of current law students receive some form of aid. Awards are based on need and merit. The required financial statements are FAFSA and the College of Law application form. The aid application deadline for fall entry is March 1. First-year students are notified about their financial aid application at time of acceptance.

About the Law School

Syracuse University College of Law was established in 1895 and is a private institution. The campus is in an urban area 3 miles east of Syracuse. The primary mission of the law school is guided by the philosophy that the best way to train lawyers is to teach them to apply what they learn in the classroom to real legal issues, problems, and clients. The Syracuse Applied Learning Program creates opportunities for students to acquire an understanding of legal theory and doctrine, develop professional skills, and get exposure to the values and ethics of the legal profession. Students have access to federal, state, county, city, and local agencies, courts, correctional facilities, law firms, and legal aid organizations in the Syracuse area. Housing for law students is available both on and off campus. On-campus housing options include a designated law student single-room residence hall, apartment complexes for law and graduate students, and a single-room residence hall for law and graduate students. About 90% of the law school facilities are accessible to the physically disabled.

Calendar

The law school operates on a traditional semester basis. Courses for full-time and part-time students are offered days only and must be completed within 4½ years. New full and part-time students are admitted in the fall; part-time, fall. There is a 7-week summer session. Transferable summer courses are offered.

Programs

Students may take relevant courses in other programs and apply credit toward the J.D.; a maximum of 6 credits may be applied. The following joint degrees may be earned: J.D./M.B.A. (Juris Doctor/Master of Business Administration), J.D./M.P.A. (Juris Doctor/Master of Public Administration), and J.D./M.S. (Juris Doctor/Master of Science in communications, environmental law, engineering, and computer science).

Contact

Admissions Office, 315-443-1962 for general inquiries; Director of Financial Aid, 315-443-1963 for financial aid information.

NEW YORK

Required

To earn the J.D., candidates must complete 87 total credits, of which 40 are for required courses. They must maintain a minimum GPA of 2.0 in the required courses. The following first-year courses are required of all students: Civil Procedure, Constitutional Law I, Contracts, Law Firm, Property, Public Law Processes, Torts, and Criminal Law. Required upper-level courses consist of Professional Responsibility, a writing requirement, and Constitutional Law II. All students are strongly encouraged to take at least 1 clinical course. The required orientation program for first-year students is 2 days long and includes academic programs, the first Law Firm class, and social activities.

Electives

The College of Law offers concentrations in corporate law, criminal law, environmental law, family law, international law, labor law, litigation, media law, securities law, tax law, torts and insurance, and law, technology, and management; law and economics. In addition, second- and third-year students may take clinics for 6 credits in Housing and Finance Law, Public Interest Law Firm, and Children's Rights and Family Law. Second- and third-year students may also earn 1 to 2 credits per semester for seminars. Study-abroad summer programs are available in London and Zimbabwe. Tutorial programs are offered for all students. Minority programs include the Legal Education Opportunity Program. The most widely taken electives are international law, trial practice, and corporations.

Graduation Requirements

In order to graduate, candidates must have a GPA of 2.0 and have completed the upper-division writing requirement.

Organizations

Law students edit the *Syracuse Law Review, Journal of International Law and Commerce, The Labor Lawyer,* and *The Digest.* Annually, students compete in the Edmund H. Lewis Appellate, Lionel O. Grossman Trial, and Jessup Moot Court competitions. Law student organizations include the Law Student Senate, Business Law Society, and International Law Society. There are local chapters of the ABA-Law Student Division, New York State Bar Association, and the Justinian Honor Law Society.

Library

The law library contains 377,386 hardcopy volumes, and subscribes to 5721 serial publications. Such on-line databases and networks as LEXIS, DIALOG, and WESTLAW are available to law students for research. Special library collections include legal history; law, management, and technology; legal practice skills; New York state law; tax and tax policy; and a selected government depository. Recently, the library adopted the NOTIS integrated system which puts OPAC, circulation, and acquisitions on-line; it added 18 WESTLAW with DIALOG stations, 10 LEXIS with NEXIS stations, and integrated on-line legal databases throughout the collection. It also added a student computer cluster containing 30 IBM PCs and an educational training laboratory containing 11 IBM PCs. The ratio of library volumes to faculty is 7904 to 1 and to students, 361 to 1. The ratio of seats in the library to students is 1 to 1.

Faculty

The law school has 47 full-time and 43 part-time faculty members, of whom 27 are women. According to AAUP standards for Category I institutions, faculty salaries are average. About 48% of full-time faculty have a graduate law degree in addition to the J.D. The ratio of full-time students to full-time faculty in an average class is 21 to 1; in a clinic, 10 to 1. The law school has a regular program of bringing visiting professors and other distinguished lecturers and visitors to campus. There is a chapter of the Order of the Coif.

Placement

J.D.s awarded:	214
Services available through: A separate law school placement center.	
Services: workshop on networking, career speaker series, identifying clerkship opportunities.	
Special features: individual counseling for law students	
Full-time job interviews:	n/av
Summer job interviews:	n/av
Placement by graduation:	n/av
Placement within 9 months:	88% of class
Average starting salary:	$20,800 to $101,000
Areas of placement:	
Private practice 2-10 attorneys	8%
Private practice 11-25 attorneys	4%
Private practice 26-50 attorneys	5%
Private practice 51-100 attorneys	3%
firm size unknown	27%
Business/industry	18%
Government	14%
Judicial clerkships	8%
Unknown	7%
Academic	3%
Public interest	3%
Academic	1%

Students

About 46% of the student body are women; 23%, minorities; 7%, African American; 8%, Asian American; 4%, Hispanic; and 1%, foreign nationals. The largest group of students come from New York (48%). The average age of entering students is 24; age range is 20 to 52. About 10% of students have a graduate degree.

James E. Beasley School of Law

1719 N. Broad Street
Philadelphia, PA 19122

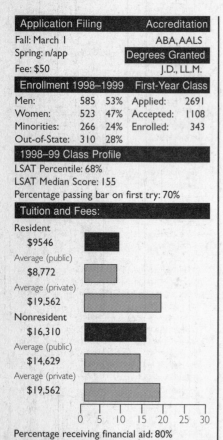

Application Filing	Accreditation
Fall: March 1	ABA, AALS
Spring: n/app	**Degrees Granted**
Fee: $50	J.D., LL.M.

Enrollment 1998–1999			First-Year Class	
Men:	585	53%	Applied:	2691
Women:	523	47%	Accepted:	1108
Minorities:	266	24%	Enrolled:	343
Out-of-State:	310	28%		

1998–99 Class Profile
LSAT Percentile: 68%
LSAT Median Score: 155
Percentage passing bar on first try: 70%

Tuition and Fees:

Resident
$9546

Average (public)
$8,772

Average (private)
$19,562

Nonresident
$16,310

Average (public)
$14,629

Average (private)
$19,562

0 5 10 15 20 25 30

Percentage receiving financial aid: 80%

ADMISSIONS

In the fall 1999 first-year class, 2691 applied, 1108 were accepted, and 343 enrolled. Four transfers enrolled. The median LSAT percentile of the most recent first-year class was 68; the median GPA was 3.24 on a scale of 4.0. The lowest LSAT percentile accepted was 21; the highest was 99.

Requirements
Applicants must have a bachelor's degree from an accredited institution and take the LSAT. Minimum acceptable LSAT score is 20 and minimum acceptable GPA is 2.35 on a scale of 4.0. No specific undergraduate courses are required. Candidates are interviewed.

Procedure
The application deadline for fall entry is March 1. Applicants should submit an application form, LSAT results, transcripts, TOEFL (when English is not a student's primary language), a nonrefundable application fee of $50, and a personal statement. Notification of the admission

decision is 10 to 12 weeks after the file is completed. The latest acceptable LSAT test date for fall entry is February. The law school uses the LSDAS.

Special
The law school recruits minority and disadvantaged students through visits to colleges and cities with large minority populations; faculty and student contact with minority applicants; special programs at the Law School Annual Open House; LSDAS's Candidate Referral Service; and contact with college prelaw advisers. The Sp.A.C.E. program, the law school's disretionary admissions process, seeks to identify applicants whose GPA and LSAT scores may not fully represent their abilities and potential, including minority applicants and economically disadvantaged applicants. Transfer students must have one year of credit, and have attended an ABA-approved and AALS- member law school. They must rank in the top 20% of their class after completion of one year. Availability of seats is also a factor in admission.

Costs

Tuition and fees for the 1999-2000 academic year are $9546 for full-time in-state students and $16,310 for out-of-state students. Tuition for part-time students is $7698 per year in-state and $13,112 out-of-state. On-campus room and board costs about $6246 annually; and books and supplies run $1200.

Financial Aid

About 80% of current law students receive some form of aid. The average annual amount of aid from all sources combined, including scholarships, loans, and work contracts, is $18,301; maximum, $30,854. Awards may be based on merit only, need only, or a combination of need and merit. The required financial statement is the FAFSA. The aid application deadline for fall entry is March 1. Special funds for minority or disadvantaged students consist of a limited number of partial tuition scholarships that are awarded to students admitted through the Sp.A.C.E. program (the discretionary admissions process) who have outstanding performance records and demonstrated financial need. First-year students are notified about their financial aid application after admission, and when their financial aid forms are received and processed.

About the Law School

Temple University James E. Beasley School of Law was established in 1895 and is a public institution. The 95-acre campus is in an urban area 2 miles north of downtown Philadelphia. The law school is committed to the philosophy that legal education must provide both practical and theoretical knowledge. Students have access to federal, state, county, city, and local agencies, courts, correctional facilities, law firms, and legal aid organizations in the Philadelphia area. The Temple Legal Aid Office is housed in the law school's main building. Facilities of special interest to law students include large moot court room; 2 trial courtrooms; an 11-level open-stack law library with 2 multilevel reading rooms; 750 study carrels and table seats; a new legal conference center; and a planned expansion of the law school facilities into Barrack Hall, a state-of-the-art educational environment in an architecturally significant building. Housing for law students on campus is apartment - style; many students choose off-campus housing since the law school is accessible by car and public transportation. In addition, the Admissions Office maintains updated information on housing prospects and a list of other students looking for roommates. All law school facilities are accessible to the physically disabled.

Calendar

The law school operates on a traditional semester basis. Courses for full-time students are offered days only and must be completed within 3 years. For part-time students, courses are offered both day and evening and must be completed within 4 years. New full and part-time students are admitted in the fall. There is an 8-week summer session. Transferable summer courses are not offered.

Programs

In addition to the J.D., the law school offers the LL.M. Students may take relevant courses in other programs and apply credit toward the J.D./M.C.A. a maximum of 12 credits may be applied; other joint degrees are condiered on a case-by-case basis. The following joint degrees may be earned: J.D./M.B.A. (Juris Doctor/ Master of Business Administration), J.D./LL.M. (Juris Doctor/Master of Laws in taxation), and J.D./LL.M. (Juris Doctor/Master of Laws in transnational law).

Phone: 215-204-8925
800-560-1428
Fax: 215-204-1185
E-mail: lawadmis@blue.temple.edu
Web: http://www.temple.edu/lawschool

Contact

Admissions Staff, 215-204-8925 or 800-560-1428 for general inquiries; Financial Aid Office, 215-204-8943 for financial aid information.

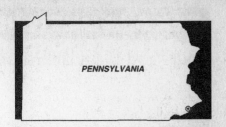

PENNSYLVANIA

Required

To earn the J.D., candidates must complete 86 total credits, of which 38 are for required courses. They must maintain a minimum GPA of 2.0 in the required courses. The following first-year courses are required of all students: Civil Procedure I, Constitutional Law, Contracts I and II, Criminal Law I, Legal Writing and Research, Property, Torts, and Legal Decision Making. Required upper-level courses consist of Professional Responsibility and 2 writing requirements. The school offers, but does not require, participation in an extensive selection of clinical opportunities. The required orientation program for first-year students consists of a 5-day program that provides an overview of academic requirements, faculty regulations, university and law school services, financial aid, general placement information, and social activities.

Electives

The James E. Beasley School of Law offers concentrations in corporate law, criminal law, environmental law, family law, international law, juvenile law, litigation, securities law, tax law, torts and insurance, public interest law, technology law, intellectual property law, constitutional and civil rights law, health care law, administrative and government law, and jurisprudence. In addition, extensive clinics are offered to third-and fourth-year students in the areas of litigation, mediation, and transactional work. There is an extensive number of writing seminar courses, each of which is worth 3 credits per semester. Special lecture series include the Fogel and Meyers lecture series, the Business Law Forum, and numerous other lectures offered by faculty members and guests of the law school. Summer sessions, worth from 2 to 6 credits, are available in Rome, Italy; Athens, Greece; and Tel Aviv, Israel. A full semester abroad is offered in Tokyo, Japan, for up to 18 credits. All these sessions are open to students after their first year. Some faculty conduct guided research in a tutorial format, which is worth a maximum of 3 credits per semester. There is a faculty mentoring program for students who are having academic difficulty. The most widely taken electives are Evidence, Business Associations, and Criminal Procedure.

Graduation Requirements

In order to graduate, candidates must have a GPA of 2.0 and have completed the upper-division writing requirement.

Organizations

Students edit the *Temple Law Review, Temple International and Comparative Law Journal, Temple Environmental Law and Technology Journal, Temple Political and Civil Rights Law Review*, and the newspaper *Class Action*. Moot court competitions are the I. Herman Stern and Samuel J. Polsky Moot Court competitions held annually at the school; students also attend other competitions throughout the country. Outside competitions include the Jessup International, ABA National Negotiation, National Invitational Tournament of Champions, National Trial, National Association of Criminal Defense Lawyers, and American Trial Lawyers Association competitions. More than 30 different student organizations flourish at the law school. The Student Bar Association acts as the students' representative in the law school administration, and is the umbrella organization that oversees the many diverse student activities and organizations. There are local chapters of the Black Law Students Association, Moot Court, and National Lawyers Guild.

Library

The law library contains 511,757 hardcopy volumes and 671,141 microform volume equivalents, and subscribes to 2697 serial publications. Such on-line databases and networks as LEXIS, DIALOG, WESTLAW, NEXIS, Legal Track, and CIS Index are available to law students for research. Special library collections include the Anglophonic Collection, African Collection, Rawle History Collection, Ellsberg Watergate Collection, and Temple Trial Collection. Recently, the library added WESTLAW and LEXIS training centers, a web-based on-line catalog system with access to more than 200 CD-ROM titles, wired library carrels, an affordable PC laptop loaner program, and a wireless network in the main lobby. The ratio of library volumes to faculty is 8978 to 1 and to students, 462 to 1. The ratio of seats in the library to students is 1 to 2.

Faculty

The law school has 57 full-time and 191 part-time faculty members, of whom 74 are women. According to AAUP standards for Category I institutions, faculty salaries are well above average. About 28% of full-time faculty have a graduate law degree in addition to the J.D. The ratio of full-time students to full-time

Placement

J.D.s awarded:	320

Services available through: separate law school placement center

Special features: programs on federal and state judicial clerkships; specific outreach to small and medium-size firms; access to Emplawyernet and other on-line career planning resources; and cosponsorship of regional job fairs. Temple is a founder of the Philadelphia Area Minority Job Fair. Counseling on public interest and public service careers is handled by a newly created Public Interest Law Programs Office.

Full-time job interviews:	78 employers
Summer job interviews:	78 employers
Placement by graduation:	58% of class
Placement within 9 months:	92% of class
Average starting salary:	$30,000 to $76,000

Areas of placement:
Private practice 2-10 attorneys	15%
Private practice 11-25 attorneys	8%
Private practice 26-50 attorneys	4%
Private practice 51-100 attorneys	22%
Business/industry	20%
Judicial Clerkships	11%
Government	11%
Public interest	6%
Academic	2%
Military	1%

faculty in an average class is 18 to 1. The law school has a regular program of bringing visiting professors and other distinguished lecturers and visitors to campus.

Students

About 47% of the student body are women; 24%, minorities; 11%, African American; 7%, Asian American; and 3%, Hispanic. The majority of students come from Pennsylvania (72%). The average age of entering students is 26; age range is 20 to 54. About 31% of students enter directly from undergraduate school, 15% have a graduate degree, and 64% have worked full-time prior to entering law school. About 4% drop out after the first year for academic or personal reasons; 96% remain to receive a law degree.

Thurgood Marshall School of Law

3100 Cleburne Avenue
Houston, TX 77004

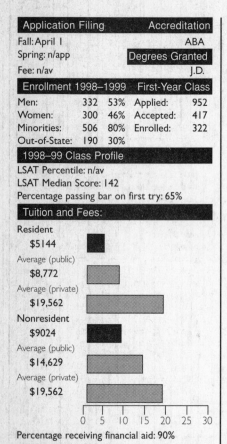

Application Filing			Accreditation
Fall: April 1			ABA
Spring: n/app			**Degrees Granted**
Fee: n/av			J.D.
Enrollment 1998–1999			**First-Year Class**
Men:	332	53%	Applied: 952
Women:	300	46%	Accepted: 417
Minorities:	506	80%	Enrolled: 322
Out-of-State:	190	30%	

1998–99 Class Profile

LSAT Percentile: n/av
LSAT Median Score: 142
Percentage passing bar on first try: 65%

Tuition and Fees:

Resident
$5144

Average (public)
$8,772

Average (private)
$19,562

Nonresident
$9024

Average (public)
$14,629

Average (private)
$19,562

0   5   10   15   20   25   30

Percentage receiving financial aid: 90%

ADMISSIONS

In the fall 1999 first-year class, 952 applied, 417 were accepted, and 322 enrolled. The median GPA of the most recent first-year class was 2.76 on a 4.0 scale.

Requirements

Applicants must have a bachelor's degree from an accredited institution and take the LSAT. The most important admission factors include LSAT results, GPA, and motivations. No specific undergraduate courses are required. Candidates are interviewed.

Procedure

The application deadline for fall entry is April 1. Applicants should submit an application form, LSAT results, a nonrefundable application fee, and 2 letters of recommendation. Check with the school for current fee. Notification of the admission decision is between February and May (majority). The latest acceptable LSAT test date for fall entry is February, but June of the same year is also considered. The law school uses the LSDAS.

Special

The law school recruits minority and disadvantaged students through the Office of Admissions' Candidate Referral Service program and college campus visits. The majority of students are members of minority groups. Requirements are different for out-of-state students in that they must, generally, have stronger credentials. Transfer students must have attended an ABA-approved law school and have been academically successful at the first school of attendance. Preadmissions courses consist of the Legal Education Advancement Program, available during the summers by invitation.

Costs

Tuition and fees for the 1999-2000 academic year are $5144 for full-time in-state students and $9024 for out-of-state students. Books and supplies run $1022.

Financial Aid

In a recent year, about 90% of current law students received some form of aid. The average annual amount of aid from all sources combined, including scholarships, loans, and work contracts, was $18,500; maximum, $18,500. Awards are based on need and merit. The required financial statement is FAFSA. Check with the school for current application deadline. Special funds for minority or disadvantaged students consist of a number of scholarships. First-year students are notified about their financial aid application at the time of acceptance.

About the Law School

Texas Southern University Thurgood Marshall School of Law was established in 1947 and is a public institution. The 6-acre campus is in an urban area 7 miles south of downtown Houston. The primary mission of the law school is in keeping with its designation by the Texas Legislature as a special purpose institution for urban programming to meet not only the needs of students in general but of minority and disadvantaged students as well. Students have access to federal, state, county, city, and local agencies, courts, correctional facilities, law firms, and legal aid organizations in the Houston area. There are also adjunct faculty in certain areas of specialty and 2 writing-skills specialists. There is a strong clinical program and a very competitive moot court program. Facilities of special interest to law students include several computer rooms offering terminals for on-line legal research as well as for off-line student use. Housing for law students consists of a privately managed campus apartment community, for which law students receive priority consideration. All law school facilities are accessible to the physically disabled.

Calendar

The law school operates on a traditional semester basis. Courses for full-time students are offered days only and must be completed within 4 years. There is no part-time program. New full-time students are admitted in the fall. There is a 9-week summer session. Transferable summer courses are offered.

Programs

Students may take relevant courses in other programs and apply credit toward the J.D.; a maximum of 6 credits may be applied.

Phone: 713-313-7114
Fax: 713-313-1049
E-mail: cgardner@tsulaw.edu
Web: www.tsulaw.edu

Contact

Carolyn Gardner, Admissions Officer, 713-313-7114 for general inquiries; Pamela Jones, Student Record Coordinator, 713-313-7243 for financial aid information.

Required

To earn the J.D., candidates must complete 90 total credits, of which 70 are for required courses. They must maintain a minimum GPA of 2.0 in the required courses. The following first-year courses are required of all students: Case Analysis and Legal Writing, Civil Procedure, Property, Contracts, Torts, Constitutional Law, and Criminal Law. Required upper-level courses consist of Appellate Litigation, Evidence, Criminal Procedure, Trial Simulation, Business Associations, Commercial Law, Consumer Rights, Basic Federal Income Taxation, Professional Responsibility, Wills and Trusts, Federal Jurisdiction and Procedure, a writing seminar, and Texas Practice. The required orientation program for first-year students consists of a 1-week introduction and lectures on skills.

Electives

The Thurgood Marshall School of Law offers concentrations in litigation and tax law. In addition, clinics include criminal law, homeless advocacy law, elderly law, family law, immigration law, housing law, tax law, environmental justice, AIDS law, Mediation, and general civil law. Seminars include criminal trial practice; writing; First Amendment; jurisprudence; estate-planning; commercial torts; environmental law; sports law; immigration law; patent, trademarks, and copyright law; medical malpractice, and health law. Internships are available through the clinics offered, including a judicial internship with federal and state judges. Research programs allow for independent research and thesis research. A special lecture series, the Quodlibet, is a faculty- and student-sponsored program on current legal issues that are debated by faculty. Students may participaate in study-abroad programs sponsored by other ABA-approved law schools. Each first-year section is assigned a student tutor who reviews substantive materials, discusses hypotheticals, and provides study help for each professor's class. The Legal Education Advancement Program (LEAP) is a 6-week summer program to develop oral and written legal analysis skills. Minority students are offered the third-year Mentor Program in which students are assigned alumni mentors in the third year through the bar examination. Academic counseling on course selection and personal goals is available. The most widely taken electives are estate planning, legal clinics, and oil and gas law.

Graduation Requirements

In order to graduate, candidates must have a GPA of 2.0 and have completed the upper-division writing requirement.

Organizations

The primary law review is the *Thurgood Marshall Law Review*. The student magazine is *The Solicitor*. The James M. Douglas Board of Advocates sponsors numerous moot court and mock trial programs. Law student organizations include the Student Bar Association, Black Law Students Association, and Chicano Law Students Association. There are local chapters of Asian Pacific American Law Students Association, Phi Alpha Delta, and Phi Delta Phi.

Library

The law library contains 229,464 hardcopy volumes and 100,536 microform volume equivalents, and subscribes to 385 serial publications. Such on-line databases and networks as LEXIS, DIALOG, WESTLAW, and Legal-Trac are available to law students for research. Special library collections include the Dominion Reports and federal government depositories. Recently, the library completed a modern, state-of-the-art research and study facility, and added an interoffice library network. The ratio of library volumes to faculty is 7402 to 1 and to students, 353 to 1. The ratio of seats in the library to students is 1 to 2.

Faculty

The law school has 34 full-time and 19 part-time faculty members, of whom 14 are women. About 39% of full-time faculty have a graduate law degree in addition to the J.D. The ratio of full-time students to full-time faculty in an average class is 60 to 1; in a clinic, 10 to 1.

Placement

J.D.s awarded:	140
Services available through: A separate law school placement center.	
Services: participate in numerous job fairs in and out of state.	
Special features: Attorneys address students about legal career opportunities and participate in interview role-playing. Resumes are also individually critiqued. In addition, mock interview seminars are conducted, as well as workshops in preparation for summer legal internships.	
Full-time job interviews:	n/av
Summer job interviews:	28 employers
Placement by graduation:	72% of class
Placement within 9 months:	72% of class
Average starting salary:	$47,000
Areas of placement:	
Private practice 2-100 attorneys	88%
Government	7%
Business/industry	4%
Public interest	2%

Students

About 46% of the student body are women; 80%, minorities; 46%, African American; 3%, Asian American; 29%, Hispanic; and 2%, Native American. The majority of students come from Texas (70%). The average age of entering students is 27; age range is 25 to 35. About 60% of students enter directly from undergraduate school, 10% have a graduate degree, and 40% have worked full-time prior to entering law school. About 35% drop out after the first year for academic or personal reasons; 65% remain to receive a law degree.

TEXAS TECH UNIVERSITY

School of Law

1802 Hartford
Lubbock, TX 79409

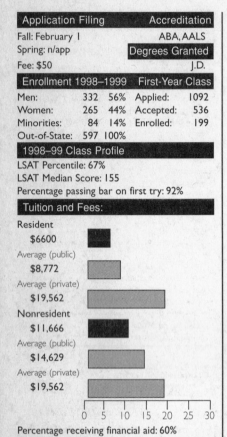

Application Filing	Accreditation
Fall: February 1	ABA, AALS
Spring: n/app	**Degrees Granted**
Fee: $50	J.D.

Enrollment 1998–1999		First-Year Class	
Men:	332 56%	Applied:	1092
Women:	265 44%	Accepted:	536
Minorities:	84 14%	Enrolled:	199
Out-of-State:	597 100%		

1998–99 Class Profile

LSAT Percentile: 67%
LSAT Median Score: 155
Percentage passing bar on first try: 92%

Tuition and Fees:

Resident
$6600

Average (public)
$8,772

Average (private)
$19,562

Nonresident
$11,666

Average (public)
$14,629

Average (private)
$19,562

0 5 10 15 20 25 30

Percentage receiving financial aid: 60%

ADMISSIONS

In the fall 1999 first-year class, 1092 applied, 536 were accepted, and 199 enrolled. Sixteen transfers enrolled. The median LSAT percentile of the most recent first-year class was 67; the median GPA was 3.4 on a scale of 4.0. The lowest LSAT percentile accepted was 17; the highest was 97.

Requirements

Applicants must have a bachelor's degree from an accredited institution and take the LSAT. Minimum acceptable LSAT score is 50 and minimum acceptable GPA is 2.5 on a scale of 4.0. The most important admission factors include LSAT results, GPA, and academic achievement. No specific undergraduate courses are required. Candidates are not interviewed.

Procedure

The application deadline for fall entry is February 1. Applicants should submit an application form, LSAT results, a nonrefundable application fee of $50, and a personal statement and resume. Notification of the admission decision begins in November. The latest acceptable LSAT test date for fall entry is February. The law school uses the LSDAS.

Special

The law school recruits minority and disadvantaged students by encouraging campus visitation by minority faculty and students and recruiting at many Texas universities. Transfer students must have one year of credit, have attended an ABA-approved law school, have ranked in the upper 25% of the first-year class, and be in good standing.

Costs

Tuition and fees for the 1999-2000 academic year are $6600 for full-time in-state students and $11,666 for out-of-state students. On-campus room and board costs about $5434 annually; books and supplies run $832.

Financial Aid

About 60% of current law students receive some form of aid. The average annual amount of aid from all sources combined, including scholarships, loans, and work contracts, is $13,344; maximum, $16,674. Awards are based on need and merit. The required financial statement is the FAFSA. The aid application deadline for fall entry is March. First-year students are notified about their financial aid application usually by late summer.

About the Law School

Texas Tech University School of Law was established in 1967 and is a public institution. The 1839-acre campus is in an urban area in Lubbock. The primary mission of the law school is to train men and women for the practice of law in the United States, whether as an advocate, counselor, judge, or law teacher, in accordance with the highest traditions of professional responsibility. At the same time, the use of law as a stepping-stone to a career in government, politics, or business is recognized. Students have access to federal, state, county, city, and local agencies, courts, correctional facilities, law firms, and legal aid organizations in the Lubbock area. Housing for law students is available on-campus, as well as in plentiful rental property close to the law school and throughout the city. All law school facilities are accessible to the physically disabled.

Calendar

The law school operates on a traditional semester basis. Courses for full-time students are offered days only and must be completed within 3 years. There is no part-time program. New full-time students are admitted in the fall. There are 2 6- week summer sessions. Transferable summer courses are offered.

Programs

Students may take relevant courses in other programs and apply credit toward the J.D.; a maximum of 12 hours may be applied, but ponly if the student is in a joint-degree program. The following joint degrees may be earned: J.D./M.B.A. (Juris Doctor/Master of Business Administration), J.D./M.P.A. (Juris Doctor/Master of Public Administration), J.D./M.S. (Juris Doctor/Master of Science in agriculture economics), and J.D./M.S.A.C. (Juris Doctor/Master of Accounting).

Phone: 806-742-3985
Fax: 806-742-1629
E-mail: xydaw@ttacs.ttu.edu
Web: http://www.law.ttu.edu

Contact

Donna Williams, Admissions Assistant, 806-742-3985 for general inquiries; and financial aid information.

TEXAS

Required

To earn the J.D., candidates must complete 90 total credits, of which 55 are for required courses. They must maintain a minimum GPA of 2.0 in the required courses. The following first-year courses are required of all students: Property, Legal Practice I, Legal Practice II, Criminal Law, Constitutional Law, Civil Procedure, Torts, and Contracts. Required upper-level courses consist of Business Entities, Commercial Law, Criminal Procedure, Income Taxation, Professional Responsibility, Wills and Trusts, and Evidence. The required orientation program for first-year students lasts 1 week.

Electives

There are no established areas of concentration. Students select an area and take electives offered in those areas. In addition, second- and third-year students who have completed prerequisites may take seminar courses. A number of internships are available to second- and third-year students for credit. Independent research programs are available for advanced students for a maximum of 4 credit hours. There is a study-abroad program in Guanajuato, Mexico. A tutor is provided for each section of all first-year classes except legal practice. In addition, every first-year student will be provided with a mentor from the second- or third-year class if desired. The most widely taken electives are Family Law, Oil and Gas, and Trial Advocacy.

Graduation Requirements

In order to graduate, candidates must have a GPA of 2.0 and have completed the upper-division writing requirement.

Organizations

Students edit the *Texas Tech Law Review, the Administrative Law Journal, The Texas Bank Lawyer,Texas Bank Lawyer*, and *Texas Judges Bench Book*. Moot court competitions include the American Bar Association, Texas State Bar Association, and New York Bar Association. Other competitions include the ATLA Mock Trial, Tournament of Champions, American Bar Association Mock Trial, National Negotiations, and Client Counseling. Law student organizations include the Texas Tech Student Bar Association, Student Academic Support Services, and Criminal Trial Lawyers Association. Local chapters of national associations include Delta Theta Phi, Phi Alpha Delta, and Phi Delta Phi. Other organizations include Women In Law, Minority Law Students Association, and Board of Barristers.

Library

The law library contains 280,153 hardcopy volumes and 492,945 microform volume equivalents, and subscribes to 534 serial publications. Such on-line databases and networks as LEXIS, DIALOG, WESTLAW, and Datatimes are available to law students for research. Special library collections include a federal government documents depository. Recently, the library added a 12,000-square foot addition with a computer in each of 250 student carrels. The computers are on-line to LEXIS, WESTLAW, and the Internet and are connected to printers. The ratio of library volumes to faculty is 7000 to 1 and to students, 466 to 1. The ratio of seats in the library to students is 1 to 1.

Faculty

The law school has 28 full-time and 10 part-time faculty members, of whom 12 are women. According to AAUP standards for Category I institutions, faculty salaries are below average. About 68% of full-time faculty have a graduate law degree in addition to the J.D.; about 54% of part-time faculty have one. The ratio of full-time students to full-time faculty in an average class is 21 to 1. The law school has a regular program of bringing visiting professors and other distinguished lecturers and visitors to campus. There is a chapter of the Order of the Coif; 26 faculty are members.

Placement

J.D.s awarded:	212
Services available through: a separate law school placement center.	
Services:	
Special features: participation in 4 off-campus recruitment programs in conjunction with various law schools.	
Full-time job interviews:	10 employers
Summer job interviews:	55 employers
Placement by graduation:	42% of class
Placement within 9 months:	93% of class
Average starting salary:	$24,000 to $87,000
Areas of placement:	
Private practice 2-10 attorneys	13%
Private practice 11-25 attorneys	29%
Private practice 26-50 attorneys	19%
Private practice 51-100 attorneys	24%
Government	10%
Judicial clerkships	5%

Students

About 44% of the student body are women; 14%, minorities; 2%, African American; 1%, Asian American; 10%, Hispanic; and 1%, Native American. The average age of entering students is 25; age range is 19 to 52. About 15% drop out after the first year for academic or personal reasons; 80% remain to receive a law degree.

School of Law

1515 Commerce Street
Fort Worth, TX 76102

Application Filing		Accreditation
Fall: open		ABA
Spring: n/app		**Degrees Granted**
Fee: n/av		J.D.

Enrollment 1998–1999			First-Year Class
Men:	244	54%	Applied: 942
Women:	208	41%	Accepted: 238
Minorities:	86	19%	Enrolled: 223
Out-of-State:	68	15%	

1998–99 Class Profile

LSAT Percentile: 50%
LSAT Median Score: 150
Percentage passing bar on first try: 70%

Tuition and Fees:

Resident
$8000
Average (public)
$8,772
Average (private)
$19,562
Nonresident
$8000
Average (public)
$14,629
Average (private)
$19,562

0   5   10   15   20   25   30

Percentage receiving financial aid: 80%

ADMISSIONS

In the fall 1999 first-year class, 942 applied, 238 were accepted, and 223 enrolled. Eleven transfers enrolled. The median LSAT percentile of the most recent first-year class was 50; the median GPA was 3.1 on a scale of 4.0.

Requirements

Applicants must have a bachelor's degree from an accredited institution and take the LSAT. The most important admission factors include GPA and LSAT results. No specific undergraduate courses are required. Candidates are not interviewed.

Procedure

The application deadline for fall entry is open. Applicants should submit an application form, LSAT results, transcripts, a nonrefundable application fee, 2 letters of recommendation, personal statement of no less than 500 words, and a letter of good standing from an undergraduate university. Check with the school for current fee. Notification of the admission decision is ongoing. The latest acceptable LSAT test date for fall entry is June. The law school uses the LSDAS.

Special

Transfer students must have one year of credit, have a minimum GPA of 3.0, have attended an ABA-approved law school, and have a letter of good standing from the home law school, the application fee, a professor's recommendation, and a letter of request to transfer. A maximum of 30 credits is transferable; no pass/fail credits transfer.

Costs

Tuition and fees for the 1999-2000 academic year are $8000 for all full-time students. Tuition for all part-time students is $5920 annually, or $520 per credit. Books and supplies run $700.

Financial Aid

In a recent year, about 80% of current law students received some form of aid. The average annual amount of aid from all sources combined, including scholarships, loans, and work contracts, was $20,000; maximum, $21,180. Awards are based on need and merit. The required financial statement is FAFSA. Check with the school for current aid application deadline. First-year students are notified about their financial aid application at the time of acceptance or time of file completion, whichever is later.

About the Law School

Texas Wesleyan University School of Law was established in 1989 and is a private institution. The campus is in an urban area in downtown Fort Worth. The primary mission of the law school is to provide legal education to a diverse student body, recognizing the need for both knowledge and skills, as well as professionalism. Students have access to federal, state, county, city, and local agencies, courts, correctional facilities, law firms, and legal aid organizations in the Fort Worth area. Housing for law students is at the main campus (10 minute drive).

Calendar

The law school operates on a traditional semester basis. Courses for full-time students are offered both day and evening and must be completed within 5 years. For part-time students, courses are offered both day and evening and must be completed within 6 years. New full-and d part-time students are admitted in the fall. There are 2 5-week and 1 7-week summer sessions. Transferable summer courses are offered.

Phone: 817-212-4040
800-733-9529
Fax: 817-212-4002
E-mail: law-admissions@law.txwes.edu
Web: law.txwes.edu

Contact

Assistant Director of Admissions, 817-212-4040 for general inquiries; Doug Akins, Financial Aid Officer, 817-212-4090 for financial aid information.

TEXAS

Programs

Required

To earn the J.D., candidates must complete 88 total credits, of which 50 are for required courses. They must maintain a minimum grade average of 70 in the required courses. The following first-year courses are required of all students: Contracts, Torts, Property, Civil Procedure, Criminal Law, Constitutional Law, Legal Analysis, Research, and Writing, and Introduction to Law. Required upper-level courses consist of Professional Responsiblity, Business Associations, Criminal Procedure, Estates and Trusts, and Evidence. The required orientation program for first-year students is a 1-week orientation that includes Introduction to Law class in Case Analysis, Legal History, Jurisprudence, Professionalism, Procedure, and Statutory Interpretation.

Electives

There is a Law Clinic, Family Mediation Clinic, and Mediation Clinic. Seminars, open to upper-level students include Law and Elderly, Computers and Law, and Race and Racism. After completing 45 hours and maintaining a minimum grade average of 72, a student can earn up to 6 hours working with a private attorney under the supervision of a faculty member. Directed Research programs and Directed Readings are available. An Academic Support Program provides assistance to students, including facilitated study groups and exam-taking workshops. The most widely taken electives are Tax, Family Law, and Texas Procedure.

Graduation Requirements

In order to graduate, candidates must have a grade average of 70 and have completed the upper-division writing requirement.

Organizations

Students edit the *Texas Wesleyan Law Review*. There are fall and spring intraschool moot court competitions, as well as the ABA/LSD National Moot Court, Texas Young Lawyers Moot Court, and Jessup International Moot Court competitions. Other competitions include the ABA/LSD National Negotiations competition. Law student organizations include Texas Aggie Wesleyan Legal society, Criminal Justice Society, and Intellectual Property Association. There are local chapters of Delta Theta Phi and Phi Delta Phi.

Library

The law library contains 152,556 hardcopy volumes and 441,501 microform volume equivalents, and subscribes to 617 serial publications. Such on-line databases and networks as LEXIS, WESTLAW, and CD-ROM towers that support '98 CD-ROM drives, which are networked to the faculty and student computer laboratories,w are available to law students for research. Special library collections include Microfiche - CIS Congressional Library. Recently, the library moved to a new facility, added carrel seating, and increased its overall seating capacity. The ratio of library volumes to faculty is 5867 to 1 and to students, 290 to 1. The ratio of seats in the library to students is 1 to 2.

Faculty

The law school has 26 full-time and 24 part-time faculty members, of whom 12 are women. According to AAUP standards for Category IIA institutions, faculty salaries are above average. About 40% of full-time faculty have a graduate law degree in addition to the J.D. The ratio of full-time students to full-time faculty in an average class is 25 to 1; in a clinic, 8 to 1. There is a chapter of the Order of the Coif; 6 faculty are members.

Students

About 41% of the student body are women; 19%, minorities; 5%, African American; 2%, Asian American; 9%, Hispanic; 2%, Native American; and 6%, unknown. The majority of students come from Texas (85%). The average age of entering students is 32; age range is 21 to 68. About 15% drop out after the first year for academic or personal reasons; 85% remain to receive a law degree.

Placement

J.D.s awarded:	166
Services available through: A separate law school placement center.	
Services:	
Special features: job fairs, career services library, job search workshop, career services handbook and packet given to students at orientation, and alumni outreach	
Full-time job interviews:	18 employers
Summer job interviews:	40 employers
Placement by graduation:	49% of class
Placement within 9 months:	83% of class
Average starting salary:	$33,000 to $80,000
Areas of placement:	
Private practice 2-10 attorneys	56%
Private practice 11-25 attorneys	9%
Private practice 26-50 attorneys	4%
Government	14%
Business/industry	12%
Judicial clerkships	3%
Academic	1%
Public interest	1%

THOMAS JEFFERSON SCHOOL OF LAW

2121 San Diego Avenue
San Diego, CA 92110

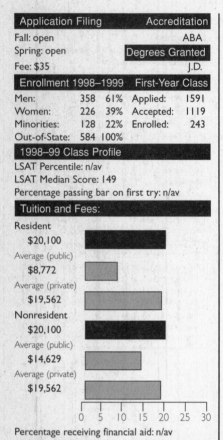

Application Filing	Accreditation
Fall: open	ABA
Spring: open	**Degrees Granted**
Fee: $35	J.D.

Enrollment 1998–1999		First-Year Class	
Men:	358 61%	Applied:	1591
Women:	226 39%	Accepted:	1119
Minorities:	128 22%	Enrolled:	243
Out-of-State:	584 100%		

1998–99 Class Profile
LSAT Percentile: n/av
LSAT Median Score: 149
Percentage passing bar on first try: n/av

Tuition and Fees:

Resident
$20,100

Average (public)
$8,772

Average (private)
$19,562

Nonresident
$20,100

Average (public)
$14,629

Average (private)
$19,562

0 5 10 15 20 25 30

Percentage receiving financial aid: n/av

ADMISSIONS

In the fall 1999 first-year class, 1591 applied, 1119 were accepted, and 243 enrolled. The median GPA of the most recent first-year class was 2.8 on a 4.0 scale. The lowest LSAT percentile accepted was 9; the highest was 95.

Requirements

Generally, applicants must have a bachelor's degree from an accerited school and must take the LSAT. Minimum acceptable GPA is 2.0 on a scale of 4.0. The most important admission factors include LSAT results, academic achievement, and life experience. No specific undergraduate courses are required. Candidates are interviewed.

Procedure

The application deadline's for fall and spring entry are open. Applicants should submit an application form, LSAT results, transcripts, a nonrefundable application fee of $35, 2 letters of recommendation, and a personal statement. The latest acceptable LSAT test date for fall entry is June. The law school uses the LSDAS.

Costs

Tuition and fees for the 1999-2000 academic year are $20,100 for all full-time students. Tuition for all part-time students is $12,550 annually, and $663 per credit. Books and supplies run $864.

Financial Aid

The average annual amount of aid from all sources combined, including scholarships, loans, and work contracts, is $21,900; maximum, $33,736. Awards are based on need and merit. The required financial statement is FAFSA. The aid application deadline for fall and spring entry is February 14. First-year students are notified about their financial aid application at the time of acceptance.

About the Law School

Thomas Jefferson School of Law was established in 1969 and is a private institution. The campus is in an urban area in the Old Town area of San Diego. The primary mission of the law school is to provide legal education for a nationally-based student body in a collegiate and supportive environment with attention to newly emerging areas of law, particularly those related to technological development, globalization, and the quest for social justice. Students have access to federal, state, county, city, and local agencies, courts, correctional facilities, law firms, legal aid organizations, and county law libraries in the San Diego area. The school has no on-site housing. The Student Services Department can assist with various housing alternatives. All law school facilities are accessible to the physically disabled.

Calendar

The law school operates on a traditional semester basis. Courses for full-time students are offered both day and evening and must be completed within 5 years. For part-time students, courses are offered both day and evening and must be completed within 6 years. New full- and part-time students are admitted in the fall and spring. There is an 8-week summer session. Transferable summer courses are offered.

Programs

Students may take relevant courses in other programs and apply credit toward the J.D.; a maximum of 8 credits may be applied.

Required

To earn the J.D., candidates must complete 88 total credits, of which 55 are for required courses. The following first-year courses are required of all students: Contracts I and II, Legal Writing I, Civil Procedure I and II, Torts I and II, Criminal Law, Criminal Procedure, and Property I. Required upper-level courses consist of Legal Writing II, Constitutional Law I and II, Evidence, Corporations, Property II, Remedies, and Professional Responsibility.

Phone: 619-297-9700
800-936-7529
Fax: 619-294-4713
E-mail: adm@tjsl.edu
Web: www.tjsl.edu

Contact

Carl Tusinski, Senior Admissions Counselor, 619-297-9700, ext. 1694 for general inquiries; Miriam Safer, Director of Financial Assistance, 619-297-9700, ext. 1353 for financial aid information.

CALIFORNIA

Electives

The Thomas Jefferson School of Law offers concentrations in corporate law, criminal law, entertainment, environmental law, family law, international law, litigation, media law, sports law. Litigation includes Dispute Resolution; Constitutional and Civil Rights; government and administrative law; intellectual property; and health law. In addition, students can earn a maximum of 5 units by working in various government agencies, state and federal courts, or legal aid clinics. Small seminars are offered in specialty areas and are open to all students. Topics vary. A judicial internship program places qualified students in state and federal courts. Research assistantships are available through individual instructors. An Alumni Perspectives series annually features successful alumni who share their practice experience and expertise with students. Native American Law Students Association, Iranian Jurisprudence Society, Christian Legal Society, Jewish Student Union, Women's Law Association, La Raza, Pan Asian Lawyers Student Association, and Black Law Students Association offer mentoring and networking programs for minority students.

Graduation Requirements

In order to graduate, candidates must have a GPA of 2.0 and have completed the upper-division writing requirement.

Organizations

Students edit the *Thomas Jefferson Law Review*. Other publications include *The Thomas Jefferson School of Law News* and *The SBA Informer*. Moot court competitions include the National Appellate Advocacy Competition and Roger J. Traynor Moot Court Competition. Other competitions include A.T.L.A. Mock Trial, Young Texas Lawyers Association Mock Trial, San Diego Defense Lawyers, Intra-School National Mock Trial, and John Marshall Moot Court Competition. Among the student organizations are the Black Law Students Association, Pan Asian Law Students Association, and La Raza Law Students Association. Local chapters of national associations are the National Lawyers Guild, Civil Liberties Society, and ABA/Law Student Division. Campus clubs include the International Law Society, Public Interest Law Foundation, and Sports and Entertainment Law Society.

Library

The law library contains 221,247 hard-copy volumes and 121,154 microform volume equivalents, and subscribes to 934 serial publications. Such on-line databases and networks as LEXIS, WESTLAW, and the Internet; Congressional Universe, Matthew Bender-Authority on Demand; Loislaw.com; Legaltrac; and Legal Scholarship Network are available to law students for research. Special library collections include Thomas Jefferson's writings and any books, videos, and other material about Thomas Jefferson. Recently, the library expanded its space, installed new shelving, and acquired major microform collections for congressional documents, historical treatises, and U.S. Supreme Court documents. The ratio of library volumes to faculty is 7629 to 1 and to students, 417 to 1. The ratio of seats in the library to students is 1 to 7.

Faculty

The law school has 29 full-time and 20 part-time faculty members, of whom 18 are women. About 17% of full-time faculty have a graduate law degree in addition to the J.D. The law school has a regular program of bringing visiting professors and other distinguished lecturers and visitors to campus.

Students

About 39% of the student body are women; 22%, minorities; 4%, African American; 8%, Asian American; and 8%, Hispanic.

Placement

J.D.s awarded:	128
Services available through: A separate law school placement center.	
Services: several lecture series and individual lectures throughout the school year.	
Full-time job interviews:	n/av
Summer job interviews:	n/av
Placement by graduation:	n/av
Placement within 9 months:	90% of class
Average starting salary:	$30,000 to $75,000
Areas of placement:	
Private practice 2-10 attorneys	33%
Private practice 11-25 attorneys	2%
Private practice 26-50 attorneys	2%
Solo practice or firm size unknown	14%
Business/industry	28%
Government	12%
Academic	7%
Judicial clerkships	1%
Public interest	1%
Military	1%

THOMAS M. COOLEY LAW SCHOOL

300 South Capitol Avenue
Lansing, MI 48901

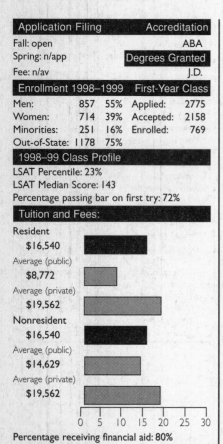

Application Filing	Accreditation
Fall: open	ABA
Spring: n/app	Degrees Granted
Fee: n/av	J.D.

Enrollment 1998–1999		First-Year Class	
Men:	857 55%	Applied:	2775
Women:	714 39%	Accepted:	2158
Minorities:	251 16%	Enrolled:	769
Out-of-State:	1178 75%		

1998–99 Class Profile

LSAT Percentile: 23%
LSAT Median Score: 143
Percentage passing bar on first try: 72%

Tuition and Fees:

Resident
$16,540

Average (public)
$8,772

Average (private)
$19,562

Nonresident
$16,540

Average (public)
$14,629

Average (private)
$19,562

Percentage receiving financial aid: 80%

ADMISSIONS

In the fall 1999 first-year class, 2775 applied, 2158 were accepted, and 769 enrolled. Three transfers enrolled. The median LSAT percentile of the most recent first-year class was 23; the median GPA was 2.9 on a scale of 4.0. The lowest LSAT percentile accepted was 6; the highest was 97.

Requirements
Applicants must have a bachelor's degree from an accredited institution and take the LSAT. Minimum acceptable GPA is 2.0 on a scale of 4.0. The most important admission factors include GPA and LSAT results. No specific undergraduate courses are required. Candidates are not interviewed.

Procedure
The application deadline for fall entry is open. Applicants should submit an application form, LSAT results, transcripts, and a nonrefundable application fee. New students pay a $25 nonrefundable enrollment fee. Notification of the admission decision is on a rolling basis. The latest acceptable LSAT test date for fall entry is June. The law school uses the LSDAS.

Special
The Assistant to the Director of Admissions recruits minorities by attending law forums and job fairs. Transfer students must have one year of credit, have a minimum GPA of 2.0, and have attended an ABA-approved law school. Students can transfer up to 30 credits for classes in which they have received a grade of C or better. They must be in good standing at their last school.

Costs

Tuition and fees for the 1999-2000 academic year are $16,540 for all full-time students. Tuition for all part-time students is $13,240 annually; $605 per credit. Books and supplies run $775 for full-time students and $516 for part-time students.

Financial Aid

About 80% of current law students receive some form of aid. The average annual amount of aid from all sources combined, including scholarships, loans, and work contracts, is $18,500; maximum, $26,743. Awards are based on need and merit. The required financial statement is FAFSA. Check with the school for current application deadline. First-year students are notified about their financial aid application at the time of acceptance.

About the Law School

Thomas M. Cooley Law School was established in 1972. The campus is in an urban area in Lansing, the state capital. The primary mission of the law school is to integrate the study of law with practical experience in government, business, and the courts. Students have access to federal, state, county, city, and local agencies, courts, correctional facilities, law firms, and legal aid organizations in the Lansing area. The law school is located within walking distance of the State Law Library, state and local courts, City Hall, and state agencies. Facilities of special interest to law students include a new legal research library, opened in 1991. Housing for law students is available on a limited basis through Michigan State University. Most students choose from the wide variety of apartments in the Lansing area. All law school facilities are accessible to the physically disabled.

Calendar

The law school operates on a trimester basis. Courses for full-time students are offered both day and evening and on weekends and must be completed within 5 years. For part-time students, courses are offered both day and evening and on weekends and must be completed within 6 years. New full-and part-time students are admitted in the fall, winter, and spring. There is a 15-week summer session. Transferable summer courses are offered.

Phone: 517-371-5140
800-874-3511
Fax: 517-334-5718
E-mail: admissions@cooley.edu
Web: www.cooley.edu

Contact

Stephanie Gregg, Assistant Director for Admissions, 517-371-5140 ext. 2250 for general inquiries; Richard Boruszewski, Financial Aid Director, 517-371-5140 ext. 2216 for financial aid information.

Programs

Required

To earn the J.D., candidates must complete 90 total credits, of which 63 are for required courses. They must maintain a minimum GPA of 2.0 in the required courses. The following first-year courses are required of all students: Introduction to Law I and II, Professional Responsibility, Contracts I and II, Property I and II, Torts I and II, Criminal Law, Research and Writing, Civil Procedure I and II, and Criminal Procedure. Required upper-level courses consist of Constitutional Law I and II, Evidence, Remedies, Secured Transactions, Administrative Law or Law Practice or Sales (choose 1 of 3), Business Organizations, Taxation, and Wills, Estates, and Trusts. The required orientation program for first-year students a 1-week course.

Electives

Clinics include the Cooley Law Clinic, which offers services to nonprofit organizations and criminal law and civil law clinics, which offer live client contact. Credits vary. Practice seminars are conducted in civil procedure, district court practice, criminal practice, and client counseling. A variety of internship and externship opportunities is made available through the Academic Program and the Career and Student Services Office. Research and Writing and Advocacy courses provide training in brief writing and oral argument conducted before sitting Circuit Court Judges. Cooley has an extensive third-year externship program, which places senior students in work settings for 1 or 2 terms. Special lecture series include the Krinock lecture. Through the Student Tutorial Services, upper-class students help new students form study groups. Faculty members may offer special seminars on study techniques. The most widely taken electives are Civil Practice, Family Law, and Law Office Management.

Graduation Requirements

In order to graduate, candidates must have a GPA of 2.0 and have completed the upper-division writing requirement.

Organizations

Students edit the *Cooley Law Review*, the *Thomas M. Cooley Journal of Practical and Clinical Law*, the newspaper *The Pillar*, *Benchmark*, a magazine published each trimester, and *Catalog*, an annual publication. The school sponsors moot court, mock trial, and client counseling competitions, and sends teams to national and regional contests. Law student organizations include the Student Bar Association, the ABA-Law Student Division, and the National Lawyers Guild. The Law School has more than 30 student organizations including the Black Law Students Association, the Computer Law Society, and the Criminal Law Society.

Library

The law library contains 361,885 hardcopy volumes and 182,620 microform volume equivalents, and subscribes to 5259 serial publications. Such on-line databases and networks as LEXIS and WESTLAW are available to law students for research. Special library collections include a depository for U.S. government documents, a full set of Michigan Supreme Court records and briefs, and a Congressional Information Service Microfiche library. Recently, the library made available a large computer laboratory, 2 electronic classrooms for computer-assisted research instruction, and INNOPAC, a state-of-the-art integrated automated library system.

Faculty

The law school has 60 full-time and 129 part-time faculty members, of whom 55 are women. According to AAUP standards for Category IIA institutions, faculty salaries are well above average. About 21% of full-time faculty have a graduate law degree in addition to the J.D. The ratio of full-time students to full-time faculty in an average class is 25 to 1; in a clinic, 9 to 1.

Placement

J.D.s awarded:	421
Services available through:	A separate law school placement center.
Services:	24-hour toll-free job hotline recording

Special features: a complete career library including audio and visual resources, weekly workshops and programs, job bulletins from more than 123 law schools nationwide, a newsletter, mock interview program, and roommate directory

Full-time job interviews:	5 employers
Summer job interviews:	4 employers
Placement by graduation:	23% of class
Placement within 9 months:	88% of class
Average starting salary:	$16,500 to $104,000

Areas of placement:

Private practice 2-10 attorneys	50%
Private practice 11-25 attorneys	9%
Private practice 26-50 attorneys	2%
Private practice 51-100 attorneys	2%
Government	22%
Business/industry	9%
Public interest	4%
Academic	1%
Judicial clerkships	1%

Students

About 39% of the student body are women; 16%, minorities; 5%, African American; 4%, Asian American; 4%, Hispanic; and 1%, Native American. The majority of students come from Michigan (25%). The average age of entering students is 26; age range is 20 to 68. About 12% of students have a graduate degree. About 30% drop out after the first year for academic or personal reasons; 70% remain to receive a law degree.

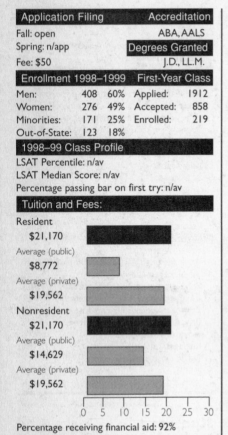

Enrollment 1998–1999		First-Year Class	
Men:	408 60%	Applied:	1912
Women:	276 49%	Accepted:	858
Minorities:	171 25%	Enrolled:	219
Out-of-State:	123 18%		

1998–99 Class Profile

LSAT Percentile: n/av
LSAT Median Score: n/av
Percentage passing bar on first try: n/av

Tuition and Fees:

Resident
$21,170

Average (public)
$8,772

Average (private)
$19,562

Nonresident
$21,170

Average (public)
$14,629

Average (private)
$19,562

0   5   10   15   20   25   30

Percentage receiving financial aid: 92%

ADMISSIONS

In the fall 1999 first-year class, 1912 applied, 858 were accepted, and 219 enrolled. Twenty transfers enrolled. The lowest LSAT percentile accepted was 18; the highest was 92.

Requirements

Applicants must have a bachelor's degree from an accredited institution and take the LSAT. In certain circumstances, students may commence law school upon completion of three fourths of the credits required for a bachelor's degree. The most important admission factors include academic achievement, LSAT results, and general background. No specific undergraduate courses are required. Candidates are interviewed.

Procedure

The application deadline for fall entry is open. Applicants should submit an application form, LSAT results, transcripts, the TOEFL for international students, a non-refundable application fee of $50, optional letters of recommendation, and a personal statement. Notification of the admission decision is on a rolling basis. The latest acceptable LSAT test date for fall entry is June. The law school uses the LSDAS.

Special

The law school recruits minority and disadvantaged students by means of visits to historically black colleges, as well as colleges and universities with significant minority populations; the use of Law Services' Candidate Referral Service; Council on Legal Education Opportunity (CLEO); the Legal Education Access Program; and other projects. Transfer students must have one year of credit and be in good academic standing, and submit a copy of the LSDAS Report, an official transcript, and a letter of good standing from the law school currently attended.

Costs

Tuition and fees for the 1999-2000 academic year are $21,170 for all full-time students. Tuition for part-time students is $16,520 per year. Books and supplies run $500.

Financial Aid

About 92% of current law students receive some form of aid. The average annual amount of aid from all sources combined, including scholarships, loans, and work contracts, is $18,500; maximum, $40,330. Awards are based on need and merit. The required financial statement is the FAFSA. The aid application deadline for fall entry is June 1. Special funds for minority or disadvantaged students consist of the Touro Grant, awarded based on financial need; Perkins Loan and College Work Study, awarded based on need; and incentive awards, based on need and merit. First-year students are notified about their financial aid application at time of acceptance.

About the Law School

Touro College Jacob D. Fuchsberg Law Center was established in 1980 and is a private institution. The 11-acre campus is in a suburban area 25 miles east of New York City. The primary mission of the law school is to produce graduates ready for real-world practice. The student experience is characterized by extensive faculty-student interaction, innovative student support systems, and a commitment to a lawyer's moral and ethical obligations. Students have access to federal, state, county, city, and local agencies, courts, correctional facilities, law firms, and legal aid organizations in the Huntington area. The school is planning to relocate to become part of the Central Islip court complex, with a state-of-the-art interactive facility. Facilities of special interest to law students include law firms, local and New York City attorneys' offices, and public interest agencies and firms. Housing for law students is available on-campus and off-campus. The school's Housing Information Network and mailings identify available accommodations and students who wish to share housing. About 98% of the law school facilities are accessible to the physically disabled.

Calendar

The law school operates on a traditional semester basis. Courses for full-time students are offered days only and must be completed within 6 years. For part-time students, courses are offered both day and evening and must be completed within 6 years. New full- and part-time students are admitted in the fall. There is a 4- and a 7- week summer session. Transferable summer courses are offered.

Programs

In addition to the J.D., the law school offers the LL.M. in U.S. legal studies for foreign law graduates and in general studies. The following joint degrees may be earned: J.D./M.S.W. (Juris Doctor/Master of Social Work, with State University of New York at Stony Brook University, C.W. Post Campus, and Dowling College, J.D./M.B.A. (Juris Doctor/Master of Business Administration, with Long Island), and J.D./M.P.A. (Juris Doctor/Master of Public Administration in Health Care).

Required

To earn the J.D., candidates must complete 87 total credits, of which 55 to 56 are for required courses. They must maintain a minimum GPA of 2.0 in the required courses. The following first-year courses are required of all students: Torts I and II, Civil Procedure I and II, Contracts I and II, Legal Methods I and II, Criminal Law I, and Property I. Required upper-level courses consist of Property II, Constitutional Law I and II, Professional Responsibility, perspective requirement, advanced writing requirement, public interest requirement, Business Organizations I,

Phone: 631-421-2244 ext. 312
Fax: 631-421-9708
E-mail: admissions@tourolaw.edu
Web: http://www.tourolaw.edu

Contact

William A. Imbriale, Director of Admissions, 631-421-2244, ext. 312 for general inquiries; Gail Drapala, Director of Financial Aid, 631-421-2244, ext. 322 for financial aid information.

NEW YORK

Evidence, Sales, Trusts and Estates, and Second-Year Writing Tutorial. All students may satisfy the public interest requirement by taking a clinical course, and are strongly encouraged to do so. The required 5- to 6-day orientation program deals mostly with legal methods and provides an introduction to law; case assignments are given in advance for students to read, brief, and discuss.

Electives

The Jacob D. Fuchsberg Law Center offers concentrations in corporate law, criminal law, family law, international law, litigation, public interest and civil rights, intellectual property, real estate, and health law. In addition, clinical offerings include Family Law (6 credits), Elder Law, Criminal Law, Civil Practice, and Judicial Clerskship (5 credits each); Civil Rights Litigation (3 or 6 credits); International Human Rights/ Immigration Litigation (4 credits); and Not-for-Profit Corporation Law (2 credits). Seminars are open to all students who have satisfied the prerequisites: Law and Medicine: Selected Topics in Law, Medicine, and Ethics; Patent Practice Seminar; and Supreme Court. Internships are arranged through the Career Planning Office for positions during the semester, and in the summer. Externships are also available in-house, at the Law Center's Domestic Violence Project and at the Housing Rights Project. Second- and third-year students may apply to be paid research assistants for a faculty member. Also, students may take Independent Research for 1 to 3 credits. Field work may be done through Career Planning externships, through the pro bono requirement, and through clinical offerings. Annually, the Law Center hosts the 3 lecture series: Distinguished Jurist in Residence, Distinguished Public Interest Lawyer in Residence, and Distinguished Israeli Jurist in Residence. Any student in good academic standing may take up to 6 credits at an ABA-approved summer program. Such programs are evaluated on a case-by-case basis. The Office of Student Affairs arranges summer placements abroad in London, Paris, Lisbon, Brussels, Cork, Tel Aviv, Jerusalem, and Moscow. The Writing Clinic provides writing specialists to assist students. The Professional Development Program, designed to help first-year students adapt to the rigors of law school, provides teaching assistants in most required courses, as well as TA mentors and TA tutors for writing skills. Minority stu-

dents may take advantage of the Legal Education Access Program (LEAP), which offers an orientation program, a lecture series, discussion groups, a mentor program, and individual counseling. Special interest groups include the Institute for Jewish Law and the Institute of Local and Suburban Law. The most widely taken electives are New York Practice, Family Law, and Criminal Procedure.

Graduation Requirements

In order to graduate, candidates must have a GPA of 2.0, have completed the upper-division writing requirement, and have successfully completed 87 credits, including all the required courses and additional requirements.

Organizations

Students edit the *Touro Law Review, Touro International Law Review,* and the *Journal of the Suffolk Academy of Law* (produced in conjunction with the Suffolk County Bar Association). The student newspaper is *The Restatement,* and the yearbook is *Res Ipsa.* Students compete in the ABA-National Moot Court Competition, Benjamin N. Cardozo National Moot Court in Entertainment Law, and Brooklyn Law School's Jerome Prince Invitational Evidence Competition. Other competitions include the New York State Bar Association Legal Ethics Writing and Nathan Burkan Copyright Law competitions. Law student organizations include the Student Bar Association, Delta Theta Phi International Law Fraternity, and Women's Bar Association. There are local chapters of ABA-Law Student Division, National Jewish Students Network, and American Civil Liberties Union. Other organizations include Minority Students Bar Association, Federalist Society, and International Law Society.

Library

The law library contains 380,000 hard-copy volumes, and subscribes to 1300 serial publications. Such on-line databases and networks as LEXIS, DIALOG, WESTLAW, the internet access, Dow Jones News Retrieval, OCLC, and Auto-Cite are available to law students for research. Special library collections include an official depository for selected U.S. government publications, a New York State depository, an extensive Judaica collection, and rare English, American, and foreign legal works. Recently, the library added titles, volumes, and physical space.

Placement

J.D.s awarded:	170
Services available through: a separate law school placement center	
Services: employer panels, resource library, judicial clerkship screening committee, job prospectus, and alumni newsletter on-line daily	
Special features: computers, laser printers, on-line services, Directories on Disk, and Pro Bono Students America	
Full-time job interviews:	n/av
Summer job interviews:	n/av
Placement by graduation:	n/av
Placement within 9 months:	78% of class
Average starting salary:	n/av
Areas of placement:	
Private practice 2-10 attorneys	33%
Private practice 11-25 attorneys	12%
Private practice 26-50 attorneys	2%
Private practice 51-100 attorneys	12%
Private practice 100+ attorneys	2%
Government	17%
Business/industry	16%
Judicial clerkships	5%
Public interest	4%
Military	1%
Academic	1%

The ratio of library volumes to faculty is 5672 to 1 and to students, 512 to 1. The ratio of seats in the library to students is 1 to 2.

Faculty

The law school has 37 full-time and 30 part-time faculty members, of whom 19 are women. About 33% of full-time faculty have a graduate law degree in addition to the J.D. The ratio of full-time students to full-time faculty in an average class is 35 to 1; in a clinic, 8 to 1. The law school has a regular program of bringing visiting professors and other distinguished lecturers and visitors to campus. There is a chapter of the Order of the Coif; 2 faculty are members.

Students

About 49% of the student body are women; 25%, minorities; 14%, African American; 6%, Asian American; and 6%, Hispanic. The majority of students come from New York (82%). The average age of entering students is 29; age range is 19 to 74. About 5% drop out after the first year for academic or personal reasons; 90% remain to receive a law degree.

TULANE UNIVERSITY

Law School

Weinmann Hall, 6329 Freret Street
New Orleans, LA 70118

Application Filing		Accreditation
Fall: May 1		ABA, AALS
Spring: n/app		**Degrees Granted**
Fee: $50		J.D., LL.M., S.J.D.

Enrollment 1998–1999		First-Year Class	
Men:	510 52%	Applied:	2805
Women:	470 47%	Accepted:	1295
Minorities:	245 25%	Enrolled:	323
Out-of-State:	813 83%		

1998–99 Class Profile
LSAT Percentile: 83%
LSAT Median Score: 159
Percentage passing bar on first try: n/av

Tuition and Fees:

Resident
$24,288

Average (public)
$8,772

Average (private)
$19,562

Nonresident
$24,288

Average (public)
$14,629

Average (private)
$19,562

0 5 10 15 20 25 30

Percentage receiving financial aid: 80%

ADMISSIONS

In the fall 1999 first-year class, 2805 applied, 1295 were accepted, and 323 enrolled. Twenty transfers enrolled. The median LSAT percentile of the most recent first-year class was 83; the median GPA was 3.3 on a scale of 4.0. The lowest LSAT percentile accepted was 25; the highest was 99.

Requirements
Applicants must take the LSAT. Minimum acceptable LSAT score is 25 and minimum acceptable GPA is 2.0 on a scale of 4.0. The most important admission factors include academic achievement, LSAT results, and GPA. No specific undergraduate courses are required. Candidates are interviewed.

Procedure
The application deadline for fall entry is May 1. Applicants should submit an application form, LSAT results, transcripts, LSDAS report, and a nonrefundable application fee of $50. Notification of the admissions decision is from January 15 through the summer. The latest acceptable LSAT test date for fall entry is February. The law school uses the LSDAS.

Special
The law school recruits minority and disadvantaged students by actively visiting undergraduate schools, using the CRS, and following up. Transfer students must have one year of credit and have a good law school record.

Costs

Tuition and fees for the 1999-2000 academic year are $24,288 for all students. On-campus room and board costs about $7180 annually; and books and supplies run $780.

Financial Aid

About 80% of current law students receive some form of aid. Loans are based on need, while scholarships are based on merit and on need and merit combined. The required financial statement is the FAFSA. The aid application deadline for fall entry is February 15. Special funds for minority or disadvantaged students are available. First-year students are notified about their financial aid application at time of acceptance.

About the Law School

Tulane University Law School was established in 1847 and is a private institution. The 110-acre campus is in an urban area in uptown New Orleans, Louisiana. The primary mission of the law school is to provide the best possible professional training so that graduates will become effective and ethical lawyers with skills that qualify them to practice law anywhere in the United States or the world. Figures given in the above capsule are approximate. Students have access to federal, state, county, city, and local agencies, courts, correctional facilities, law firms, and legal aid organizations in the New Orleans area. There are five levels of courts in New Orleans: state trial, appellate, and supreme, and federal trial and appellate. In addition, there are many law firms, public interest organizations, and governmental entities. Facilities of special interest to law students are the Reily Recreation Center, the Freeman School of Business, and numerous recreational and entertainment opportunities throughout the city. Housing for law students is available on and off campus. About 95% of the law school facilities are accessible to the physically disabled.

Calendar

The law school operates on a traditional semester basis. Courses are offered days only with some elective courses offered during the evening, and must be completed within 6 semesters, although limited leaves are permitted. There is no part-time progarm. New students are admitted in the fall. There is a 6-week summer session in New Orleans and 2- and 4-week study-abroad sessions. Transferable summer courses are offered.

Phone: 504-865-5930
Fax: 504-865-6710
E-mail: admissions@law.tulane.edu
Web: www.law.tulane.edu

Contact

Admissions, 504-865-5930 for general inquiries; Georgia Whiddon, 504-865-5931 for financial aid information.

LOUISIANA

Programs

In addition to the J.D., the law school offers the LL.M., S.J.D., and LL.M. in admiralty; energy and environment, and international and comparative law. The following joint degrees may be earned: J.D./M.B.A. (Juris Doctor/ Master of Business Administration), J.D./M.H.A. (Juris Doctor/ Master of Health Administration), J.D./M.P.H. (Juris Doctor/ Master of Public Health in environmental health), J.D./M.A. (Juris Doctor/Master of Arts in Latin American studies and in political science), J.D./M.Acc. (Juris Doctor/Master of Accounting), and J.D./ M.S.W. (Juris Doctor/Master of Social Work).

Required

To earn the J.D., candidates must complete 88 total credits, of which 31 are for required courses. They must maintain a minimum GPA of 2.0 in the required courses. The following first-year courses are required of all students: Criminal Law, Constitutional Law, Civil Procedure, Property (Civil or Common), Contracts I, Legal Profession (can be taken in first year or later), Torts, Contracts II or Obligations I, Legal Research and Writing, and a first-year elective. Required upper-level courses consist of 20 hours of community service. The required orientation program for first-year students is 1 day of logistical information plus sessions on case briefing.

Electives

Students must take 15 to 16 in their area of concentration. The Law School offers concentrations in environmental law, maritime law, sports law, and European legal studies. In addition, 8 different clinics including representation for actual clients are available for third-year students for 8 credits. Second- and third-year students may earn 2 to 3 credits for seminars that are offered in various advanced legal areas. Judicial and other 1-year (2-semester) externship programs worth 4 credits are offered to third-year students. Upper-level students may undertake directed research with individual faculty members for a maximum of 3 credits. Field work in some courses, particularly advanced environmental law courses, are offered. Many special lecture series are also offered each year. Students may earn 3 to 6 credits for the summer study-abroad program, offered in 8 countries and held for 2 to 4 weeks. In addition, some semester-long exchange programs are available with universities abroad. Selected first-year students may take the tutorial course Legal Analysis for 1 credit. Support and placement programs for minority students are sponsored by the school. Special interest group programs are provided by 20 student organizations. The most widely taken electives are Business Enterprises, Evidence, and Trusts and Estates.

Graduation Requirements

In order to graduate, candidates must have a GPA of 2.0, and have performed 20 hours of mandatory pro bono work.

Organizations

Students edit the *Tulane Law Review*, the *Tulane Maritime Law Journal*, the *Tulane Environmental Law Journal*, the *Journal of Law and Sexuality*, the *Tulane Journal of International and Comparative Law*, *Civil Law Forum*, the *Sports Law Journal*, and the student newspaper *Dicta*. There are separate intraschool trial and appellate competitions for second- and third-year students, including the Jessup International, Negotiations, and Trial competitions. Law student organizations include the Historic Preservation Law Society, Environmental Law Society, and National Public Interest Law Foundation. There are local chapters of the National Lawyers Guild, Phi Alpha Delta, and the American Civil Liberties Union.

Library

The law library contains 500,000 hardcopy volumes, and subscribes to 3000 serial publications. Such on-line databases and networks as LEXIS, DIALOG, and WESTLAW are available to law students for research. Special library collections include canon law, European law, civil law, and maritime law. Recently, the library opened a law school building and law library with excellent computer facilities for student use. The ratio of library volumes to faculty is 8000 to 1 and to students, 400 to 1. The ratio of seats in the library to students is 1 to 2.

Placement	
J.D.s awarded:	321
Services available through: separate law school placement center	
Services: videotaped mock interviews, law firm tours and orientations, job fairs and placement consortia, and introduction to new cities	
Special features: a minority clerkship program and individual sessions with career services staff	
Full-time job interviews:	n/av
Summer job interviews:	n/av
Placement by graduation:	60% of class
Placement within 9 months:	85% of class
Average starting salary:	$33,189 to $75,000
Areas of placement:	
Private practice 2-100 attorneys	48%
Judicial clerkships	16%
Government	12%
Business/industry	10%
Unknown	10%
Public interest	2%
Academic	2%

Faculty

The law school has 50 full-time and 49 part-time faculty members, of whom 21 are women. According to AAUP standards for Category I institutions, faculty salaries are above average. About 26% of full-time faculty have a graduate law degree in addition to the J.D.; about 18% of part-time faculty have one. The ratio of full-time students to full-time faculty in an average class is 34 to 1; in a clinic, 8 to 1. The law school has a regular program of bringing visiting professors and other distinguished lecturers and visitors to campus. There is a chapter of the Order of the Coif; all faculty and the top 10% of graduates are members.

Students

About 47% of the student body are women; 25%, minorities; 11%, African American; 4%, Asian American; and 6%, Hispanic. The majority of students come from the South (42%). The average age of entering students is 24; age range is 21 to 55. About 33% of students enter directly from undergraduate school, 5% have a graduate degree, and 65% have worked full time prior to entering law school. About 5% drop out after the first year for academic or personal reasons; 92% remain to receive a law degree.

Albany Law School

80 New Scotland Avenue
Albany, NY 12208

Application Filing	Accreditation
Fall: March 15	ABA, AALS
Spring: n/app	**Degrees Granted**
Fee: $50	J.D.

Enrollment 1998–1999			First-Year Class	
Men:	325	47%	Applied:	1455
Women:	363	53%	Accepted:	851
Minorities:	131	19%	Enrolled:	254
Out-of-State:	76	11%		

1998–99 Class Profile

LSAT Percentile: 47%
LSAT Median Score: 150
Percentage passing bar on first try: 78%

Tuition and Fees:

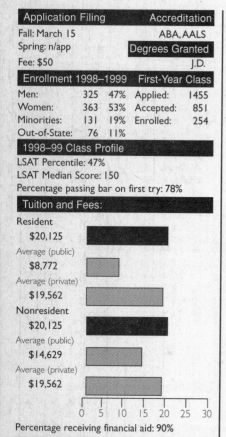

Resident
$20,125
Average (public)
$8,772
Average (private)
$19,562
Nonresident
$20,125
Average (public)
$14,629
Average (private)
$19,562

0 5 10 15 20 25 30

Percentage receiving financial aid: 90%

ADMISSIONS

In the fall 1999 first-year class, 1455 applied, 851 were accepted, and 254 enrolled. Six transfers enrolled. The median LSAT percentile of the most recent first-year class was 47; the median GPA was 3.1 on a scale of 4.0. The lowest LSAT percentile accepted was 11; the highest was 94.

Requirements

Applicants must have a bachelor's degree from an accredited institution and take the LSAT. Students without a baccalaurette degree are admitted only with exceptional undergraduate records. The most important admission factors include academic achievement, LSAT results, and general background. No specific undergraduate courses are required. Candidates are not interviewed.

Procedure

The application deadline for fall entry is March 15. Applicants should submit an application form, LSAT results, transcripts, a nonrefundable application fee of $50, and 2 letters of recommendation. Notification of the admission decision is on a rolling basis. The latest acceptable LSAT test date for fall entry is February. The law school uses the LSDAS.

Special

The law school recruits minority and disadvantaged students through current minority students who assist the Admissions Office by recruiting at colleges and universities with large minority populations and by offering tuition scholarships that are awarded to more than half of the accepted minority applicants. Transfer students must have one year of credit and have attended an ABA-approved law school.

Costs

Tuition and fees for the 1999-2000 academic year are $20,125 for all full-time students. Tuition for part-time students is $15,126 per year. On-campus room and board costs about $2730 annually; books and supplies run $595.

Financial Aid

About 90% of current law students receive some form of aid. The average annual amount of aid from all sources combined, including scholarships, loans, and work contracts, is $22,300; maximum, $31,100. Awards are based on need and merit, along with diversity. The required financial statement is the FAFSA. Special funds for minority or disadvantaged students include diversity scholarships and full- or partial-tuition waivers. First-year students are notified about their financial aid application at time of acceptance.

About the Law School

Union University Albany Law School was established in 1851. The 6-acre campus is in an urban area 150 miles north of New York City. The primary mission of the law school is to provide students with a quality education in accordance with ethical principles and professional standards. The curriculum is traditional, yet innovative, and stresses legal knowl-
edge, professional skills, thought habits, and contemporary techniques and technologies. Students have access to federal, state, county, city, and local agencies, courts, correctional facilities, law firms, and legal aid organizations in the Albany area. The school is located in Albany, the state capital. Facilities of special interest to law students are the Government Law Center, Science and Technology Law Center, Moot Court Program, and the Schaeffer Law Library. Housing for law students is limited on campus, but readily available and inexpensive off campus. About 90% of the law school facilities are accessible to the physically disabled.

Calendar

The law school operates on a traditional semester basis. Courses for full-time students are offered days only and must be completed within 3 years. For part-time students, courses are offered days only and must be completed within 4 years. New full- and part-time students are admitted in the fall. There is a 7-week summer session. Transferable summer courses are offered.

Programs

Students may take relevant courses in other programs and apply credit toward the J.D.; a maximum of 4 credits may be applied. The following joint degrees may be earned: J.D./M.B.A. (Juris Doctor/Master of Business Administration) and J.D./M.P.A. (Juris Doctor/Master of Public Administration).

Required

To earn the J.D., candidates must complete 87 total credits, of which 31 are for required courses. They must maintain a minimum GPA of 1.7 in the required courses. The following first-year courses are required of all students: Contracts, Constitutional Law, Criminal Law, Introduction to Civil Procedure, Introduction to Lawyering, Property I and II, Torts, and Legal Methods. Required upper-level courses consist of an upperclass writing requirement and The Legal Professional/Professional Responsibility seminar. The required orientation program for first-year students is a week long program that includes a 1 credit "Legal Methods" class, social activities, and administrative activities.

Phone: 518-445-2326
Fax: 518-445-2369
E-mail: admissions@mail.als.edu
Web: www.als.edu

Contact

Dawn M. Chamberlaine, Assistant Dean, 518-445-2326 for general inquiries; and at 518-445-2357 for financial aid information.

NEW YORK

Electives

Students must take 24 in their area of concentration. The Albany Law School offers concentrations in corporate law, criminal law, environmental law, family law, international law, labor law, litigation, securities law, tax law, commercial law, constitutional law, civil procedure, health law, estate law, government administration and regulation, intellectual property, and prospectives on law and legal systems. In addition, a clinical program enables upper-level students to obtain practical experience in a public law office. A classroom component is available; students may earn 8 credits, 2 or 3 each semester. Clinics include Civil Rights and Disabilities Law Clinic, AIDS Law Clinic, Civil Litigation Clinic, and Domestic Violence Clinic. Seminars, worth 2 or 3 credits each semester, and research assistantships are open to upper-level students. Internships in government agencies are offered through the Government Law Center, and externships in public law offices are arranged through the Placement Clinic. Annual special lectures include the Justice Jackson and the Edward L. Swobota Memorial Lecture Series. Study abroad may be arranged for upper-level students. The Lewis A. Swyer Academic Success Program provides small groups and individual instruction in legal reasoning, case analysis and synthesis, writing, and study skills. Entering students who have been out of the academic environment for several years, those whose academic backgrounds differ substantially, and those with language, physical, or emotional handicaps are eligible to participate in the program. Minority programs are offered through student organizations, faculty, the administration, and alumni. Several societies offer lectures, symposia, and other events, including the International Law Society and Environmental Law Society. The most widely taken electives are Business Organizations, Evidence, and New York Practice.

Graduation Requirements

In order to graduate, candidates must have a GPA of 2.0 and have completed the upper-division writing requirement.

Organizations

Students edit the *Albany Law Review, Albany Law Journal of Science and Technology*, the student newspaper *The Issue*, the yearbook *The Verdict*, the *Literary Review*, and *Environmental Outlook*. Intraschool moot court competitions include the Gabrielli Appellate Advocacy Competition, the Senior Prize Trial Competition, and the Morse Client Counseling Competition. Interschool competitions include the Association of Trial Lawyers of America *(ATLA) Trial Advocacy Competition and National Trial Competition*. Other interschool competitions include ABA Client Counseling, ABA Negotiations, National Appellate Advocacy, Medical/Legal Ethics, First Amendment, Products Liability, Civil Rights, and Constitutional law. Law student organizations include the People's Law Project, International Law Society, and Intellectual Property Law Society. There are local chapters of Phi Alpha Delta, the National Lawyers Guild, and the Lambda Law Students Association. Other organizations are the Nontraditional Students Association, Black Law Students Association, and Latino Law Students Association.

Library

The law library contains 247,669 hard-copy volumes and 1,421,190 microform volume equivalents, and subscribes to 1464 serial publications. Such on-line databases and networks as LEXIS, DIALOG, WESTLAW, New York Legislature Retrieval System, Court of Appeals on-line information service, the Internet, and NELLCO Intranet are available to law students for research. Special library collections include a U.S. government documents depository, New York State documents research depository, and a New York Court of Appeals oral argument videotape repository. The ratio of library volumes to faculty is 6041 to 1 and to students, 360 to 1. The ratio of seats in the library to students is 1 to 1.

Faculty

The law school has 41 full-time and 41 part-time faculty members, of whom 27 are women. According to AAUP standards for Category IIA institutions, faculty salaries are well above average. About 20% of full-time faculty have a graduate law degree in addition to the J.D.; about 8% of part-time faculty have one. The ratio of full-time students to full-time faculty in an average class is 17 to 1; in a clinic, 9 to 1. The law school has a regular program of bringing visiting professors and other distinguished lecturers and visitors to campus.

Placement

J.D.s awarded:	229

Services available through: a separate law school placement center.

Services: off-campus interview programs in selected cities; job fairs; recruitment programs for full-time, summer, and part-time employment opportunities; judicial clerkship, fellowship, and internship assistance; resume and cover letter writing assistance; job search workshops; employment reports listing summer and full-time employers; job listing newsletters for alumni and recent graduates; Public Service Law Net Worldwide (PS LawNet); and computer services for job searches (LEXIS and Westlaw)

Special features: career planning staff of six committed to personalized service; quarterly career bulletin; career education seminars featuring alumni and faculty members; *Alumni Career Advisory Network*; and videotape mock interviews with alumni practitioners.

Full-time job interviews:	95 employers
Summer job interviews:	95 employers
Placement by graduation:	n/av
Placement within 9 months:	95% of class
Average starting salary:	$26,500 to $101,000

Areas of placement:

Private practice 2-10 attorneys	26%
Private practice 11-25 attorneys	9%
Private practice 26-50 attorneys	6%
Private practice 51-100 attorneys	9%
Government	21%
Business/industry	16%
Judicial clerkships	7%
Academic	2%
Public interest	2%

Students

About 53% of the student body are women; 19%, minorities; 8%, African American; 6%, Asian American; 4%, Hispanic; and 1%, Native American. The majority of students come from New York (89%). The average age of entering students is 26; age range is 21 to 65. About 41% of students enter directly from undergraduate school and 3% have a graduate degree. About 10% drop out after the first year for academic or personal reasons; 90% remain to receive a law degree.

UNIVERSITY OF AKRON

School of Law

Corner Wolf Ledges and
University Avenue
Akron, OH 44325-2901

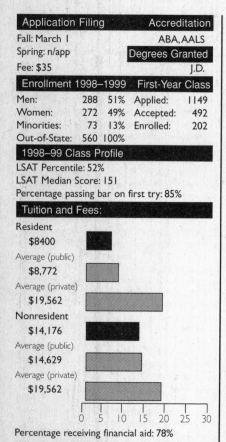

Application Filing	Accreditation
Fall: March 1	ABA, AALS
Spring: n/app	**Degrees Granted**
Fee: $35	J.D.

Enrollment 1998–1999		First-Year Class	
Men:	288 51%	Applied:	1149
Women:	272 49%	Accepted:	492
Minorities:	73 13%	Enrolled:	202
Out-of-State:	560 100%		

1998–99 Class Profile
LSAT Percentile: 52%
LSAT Median Score: 151
Percentage passing bar on first try: 85%

Tuition and Fees:

Resident
$8400

Average (public)
$8,772

Average (private)
$19,562

Nonresident
$14,176

Average (public)
$14,629

Average (private)
$19,562

0 5 10 15 20 25 30

Percentage receiving financial aid: 78%

ADMISSIONS

In the fall 1999 first-year class, 1149 applied, 492 were accepted, and 202 enrolled. The median LSAT percentile of the most recent first-year class was 52; the median GPA was 3.15 on a scale of 4.0. The lowest LSAT percentile accepted was 13; the highest was 98.

Requirements
Applicants must have a bachelor's degree from an accredited institution and take the LSAT. Minimum acceptable GPA is 2.0 on a scale of 4.0. The most important admission factors include academic achievement, LSAT results, and general background. No specific undergraduate courses are required. Candidates are not interviewed.

Procedure
The application deadline for fall entry is March 1. Applicants should submit an application form, LSAT results, transcripts, and a nonrefundable application fee of $35. 2 to 3 letters of recommendation are strongly recommended. Notification of the admission decision is 4 to 6 weeks after the application is complete. The latest acceptable LSAT test date for fall entry is June. The law school uses the LSDAS.

Special
The law school recruits minority and disadvantaged students by means of visiting colleges with a large percentage of minority students, sending mailings, holding recruitment days, participating in minority law fairs, publishing a minority brochure, granting scholarships, and advertising in various publications. In addition, minority law students call minority admittees to welcome them. Transfer students must have one year of credit, have attended an ABA-approved law school, and show strong academic performance. Preadmissions courses consist of optional legal skills workshops, traditionally offered in the summer.

Costs

Tuition and fees for the 1999-2000 academic year are $8400 for full-time in-state students and $14,176 for out-of-state students. Tuition for part-time students is $6572 annually, or $232 per credit in-state and $11,084 annually, or $413 per credit out-of-state. Books and supplies run $600.

Financial Aid

About 78% of current law students receive some form of aid. The average annual amount of aid from all sources combined, including scholarships, loans, and work contracts, is $13,875; maximum, $24,344. Awards are based on need and merit. The required financial statements are FAFSA and the institutional aid application. The aid application deadline for fall entry is May 1. First-year students are notified about their financial aid application at the time of acceptance.

About the Law School

University of Akron School of Law was established in 1921 and is a public institution. The 170-acre campus is in an urban area 40 miles south of Cleveland. The primary mission of the law school is to prepare students to become outstanding members of the bench and bar. Students have access to federal, state, county, city, and local agencies, courts, correctional facilities, law firms, and legal aid organizations in the Akron area. The Akron Municipal Court and the Summit County Court of Common Pleas (including Domestic Relations and Probate) are within a 5-minute walk; the Ohio Court of Appeals, Ninth District, within a 7-minute walk; and the U.S. District Court is within a 10-minute walk. Facilities of special interest to law students are the Legal Clinic offices located at the law school. Housing for law students is available on campus in graduate housing; many off-campus affordable housing options are available within walking distance or a short drive away. All law school facilities are accessible to the physically disabled.

Calendar

The law school operates on a traditional semester basis. Courses for full-time students are offered both day and evening and must be completed within 5 years. For part-time students, courses are offered both day and evening and must be completed within 6 years. New full- and part-time students are admitted in the fall. There are 5- and 10-week summer sessions. Transferable summer courses are offered.

Programs

Students may take relevant courses in other programs and apply credit toward the J.D.; a maximum of 6 graduate work credits may be applied. The following joint degrees may be earned: J.D./M.B.A. (Juris Doctor/Master of Business Administration), J.D./M.Tax. (Juris Doctor/Master of Taxation), and J.D./M.P.A. (Juris Doctor/Master of Public Administration).

Required
To earn the J.D., candidates must complete 88 total credits, of which 44 are for required courses. They must maintain a minimum GPA of 2.0 in the required courses. The following first-year courses are required of all students: Civil Procedure I and II, Contracts I and II, Criminal Law, Property I and II, Torts I and II, Basic Legal Communications, Intermediate

Phone: 330-972-7331
800-4-AKRON-U
Fax: 330-258-2343
E-mail: lawadmissions@uakron.edu
Web: www.uakron.edu/law

Contact

Lauri S. File, Assistant to the Dean, Director of Admissions and Financial Assistance, 330-972-7331 for general inquiries; University Financial Aid Office, 330-972-7032 for financial aid information.

OHIO

Legal Communications, Legal Research, and Introduction: Law and Legal Systems. Required upper-level courses consist of Advanced Legal Communications, Constitutional Law I and II, Evidence, Legal Profession, and a general writing requirement. Elective clinical courses, which are offered for 2 or 3 credits and may be repeated up to 6 credits, include Trial Litigation Clinic, Appellate Review, Inmate Assistance Program, and external placements in government and nonprofit organizations. The required orientation program for first-year students, Introduction to Law and Legal Systems, is a 1-week course held during the first week of classes. This course offers an overview of the U.S. legal system, a discussion of how to brief and outline, and study tips for final exams. Students are provided with a framework for understanding the basic premises of our system of law, both substantive and procedural, and the ways in which law is made.

Electives

The School of Law offers concentrations in corporate law, criminal law, international law, labor law, litigation, tax law, and intellectual property and technology; public interest. In addition, the Trial Litigation Clinic allows third-year students to be certified legal interns, whereas in the Clinical Seminar, students with strong academic records may clerk for judges. There is also a clinic in Appellate Review. Clinic students may be placed in-house or externally for credit after their first year. Students with an intern certficate may represent clients in civil and misdemeanor cases in court. Seminars include Advanced Corporate Taxation, Alternative Dispute Resolution, and Business Planning. Internships and research programs are offered through the School of Law Legal Clinic and the Career Planning and Placement Office. Upper-division students may apply to become a research assistant for a law faculty member. Special lecture series are held during the fall and spring semesters. Study abroad is available through any ABA-accredited law school's study-abroad program. With permission of the associate dean, students may assume visiting status at another ABA-accredited law school and transfer credits back to Akron. Tutoring is available through the Stoller Tutorial Program. The Black Law Student Association (BLSA) sponsors outlining and exam-taking seminars, adopt-a-school, scholarships, an annual dinner/dance, regionl job fairs,

Frederick Douglass Moot Court Competition, and travel to regional and national BLSA events. The most widely taken electives are Family Law, Wills, Trusts and Estates, and Corporations.

Graduation Requirements

In order to graduate, candidates must have a GPA of 2.0, have completed the upper-division writing requirement, and fulfill residency weeks requirements as established by the ABA.

Organizations

Students edit the *Akron Law Review*. The moot court team attends the ABA/LSD-National Appellate Advocacy competition, National Moot Court competition (N.Y. Bar Association), and Jessup International Law Competition. A trial team attends competitions sponsored by the American College of Trial Lawyers, the American Trial Lawyers Association, National Institute for Trial Advocacy, the Academy of Trial Lawyers of Allegheny County, PA, and other associations. There is also a negotiation team. Law student organizations include the International Law Society, Student Bar Association, and Law Association for Women's Rights. Campus clubs and other organizations incude the Intellectual Property and Technology Law Association, National Association of Criminal Defense Lawyers, and Sports and Entertainment Law Society.

Library

The law library contains 261,818 hardcopy volumes and 371,921 microform volume equivalents, and subscribes to 3477 serial publications. Such on-line databases and networks as LEXIS, WESTLAW, and Ohio Link (containing 60 commercial databases) are available to law students for research. Special library collections include a government documents depository (intellectual property). Recently, the library created a networked student microcomputer system, with access to LEXIS, WESTLAW, and the Web, recarpeted the entire library and renovated the computer laboratory. The ratio of library volumes to faculty is 9696 to 1 and to students, 559 to 1. The ratio of seats in the library to students is 1 to 2.

Placement

J.D.s awarded:	188

Services available through: A separate law school placement center and the university placement center.

Services: Alumni and Student Affairs Committee, Judicial Clerkship Committee, Reference Letter Program, Mentor Program, and preparatory career planning workshops and seminars

Special features: individualized one-to-one counseling and assisting students with all phases of the job search; computerized job postings, participation in off-campus hiring programs for intellectual property and public interest law, participation in several off-campus hiring programs for minority students and coordination of events through the Ohio Law Placement Consortium (OLPC) for all students.

Full-time job interviews:	23 employers
Summer job interviews:	8 employers
Placement by graduation:	39% of class
Placement within 9 months:	97% of class
Average starting salary:	$39,328
Areas of placement:	
Private practice 2-10 attorneys	24%
Private practice 11-25 attorneys	5%
Private practice 26-50 attorneys	1%
Private practice 51-100 attorneys	3%
Private practice 100+ attorneys	5%
Government	26%
Business/industry	22%
Judicial clerkships	6%
Military	2%
Academic	1%

Faculty

The law school has 27 full-time and 37 part-time faculty members, of whom 28 are women. According to AAUP standards for Category I institutions, faculty salaries are below average. About 11% of full-time faculty have a graduate law degree in addition to the J.D. The ratio of full-time students to full-time faculty in an average class is 27 to 1.

Students

About 49% of the student body are women; 13%, minorities; 8%, African American; 2%, Asian American; 2%, Hispanic; and 1%, Native American. The average age of entering students is 29; age range is 21 to 59. About 23% drop out after the first year for academic or personal reasons; 70% remain to receive a law degree.

UNIVERSITY OF ALABAMA

School of Law

Box 870382
Tuscaloosa, AL 35487-0382

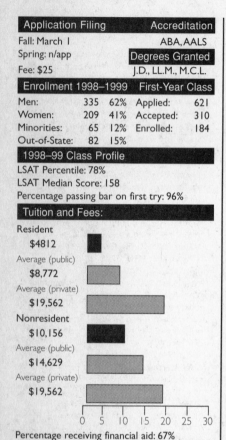

Application Filing			Accreditation
Fall: March 1			ABA, AALS
Spring: n/app			**Degrees Granted**
Fee: $25			J.D., LL.M., M.C.L.

Enrollment 1998–1999			First-Year Class	
Men:	335	62%	Applied:	621
Women:	209	41%	Accepted:	310
Minorities:	65	12%	Enrolled:	184
Out-of-State:	82	15%		

1998–99 Class Profile
LSAT Percentile: 78%
LSAT Median Score: 158
Percentage passing bar on first try: 96%

Tuition and Fees:

Resident
$4812

Average (public)
$8,772

Average (private)
$19,562

Nonresident
$10,156

Average (public)
$14,629

Average (private)
$19,562

0   5   10   15   20   25   30

Percentage receiving financial aid: 67%

ADMISSIONS

In the fall 1999 first-year class, 621 applied, 310 were accepted, and 184 enrolled. Two transfers enrolled. The median LSAT percentile of the most recent first-year class was 78; the median GPA was 3.3 on a scale of 4.0.

Requirements
Applicants must have a bachelor's degree from an accredited institution and take the LSAT. The most important admission factors include LSAT results, GPA, and academic achievement. No specific undergraduate courses are required. Candidates are not interviewed.

Procedure
The application deadline for fall entry is March 1. Applicants should submit an application form, LSAT results, transcripts, the TOEFL for M.C.L. candidates, a nonrefundable application fee of $25, and 2 personal statements, correspondence cards, and a personal information card. Notifica-

tion of the admission decision is on a rolling basis, beginning in November. The latest acceptable LSAT test date for fall entry is February. The law school uses the LSDAS.

Special
The law school recruits minority and disadvantaged students by means of recruiters visiting undergraduate institutions and participating annually in the Law Forums. Requirements are different for out-of-state students. Because it is a state school, more residents than nonresidents are admitted to The University of Alabama School of Law. Transfer students must have one year of credit, have generally high grades, have attended an ABA-approved law school, and have a collegiate academic record and an LSAT score that would have qualified the student for entry-level admission to the school. They must be in good standing at the current law school, as evidenced by a letter from the dean of that school, must not be on any kind of probationary status, and must rank academically high at that school.

Costs

Tuition and fees for the 1999-2000 academic year are $4812 for full-time in-state students and $10,156 for out-of-state students. On-campus room and board costs about $3570 annually, and books and supplies run $930.

Financial Aid

About 67% of current law students receive some form of aid. The maximum annual amount of aid from all sources combined, including scholarships, loans, and work contracts, is $25,742 for out-of-state students, and $18,500 for in-state students. Awards are based on need and merit. The School of Law provides significant scholarship support. Outstanding nonresident students may receive a nonresident fee waiver. The required financial statement is FAFSA. The aid application deadline for fall entry is March 1. First-year students are notified about their financial aid application at time of acceptance.

About the Law School

University of Alabama School of Law was established in 1872 and is a public institution. The campus is in a small town 60 miles south of Birmingham. The primary mission of the law school is to prepare future lawyers for their critical role in society, as well as to become a dynamic part of the community. Students have access to federal, state, county, city, and local agencies, courts, correctional facilities, law firms, and legal aid organizations in the Tuscaloosa area. Facilities of special interest to law students include the moot court and trial advocacy rooms, student lounge, and student areas. Housing for law students is available in residence halls and university-owned and operated apartments and efficiency units. The majority of the law students live off campus. All law school facilities are accessible to the physically disabled.

Calendar

The law school operates on a traditional semester basis. Courses for full-time students are offered days only and must be completed within 3 years. There is no part-time program. New full-time students are admitted in the fall. There is a 7-week summer session. Transferable summer courses are not offered.

Programs

In addition to the J.D., the law school offers the LL.M., M.C.L., and LL.M. in taxation. Students may take relevant courses in other programs and apply credit toward the J.D.; a maximum of 6 credits may be applied. The following joint degree may be earned: J.D./M.B.A. (Juris Doctor/Master of Business Administration).

Phone: 205-348-5440
Fax: 205-348-3917
E-mail: admissions@law.ua.edu
Web: http://www.law.ua.edu

Contact

Betty McGinley, Admissions Coordinator, 205-348-5440 for general inquiries; Noah Funderburg, Assistant Dean, 205-348-4508 for financial aid information.

ALABAMA

Required

To earn the J.D., candidates must complete 90 total credits, of which 36 are for required courses. They must maintain a minimum GPA of 2.0 in the required courses. The following first-year courses are required of all students: Contracts, Property, Torts, Criminal Law, Civil Procedure, Constitutional Law, Federal Income Tax, Legal Writing, Moot Court, and Legal Research. Required upper-level courses consist of Evidence, The Legal Profession, and seminar. The required 4-day orientation program for first-year students is geared toward making the transition into law school as smooth as possible.

Electives

The School of Law offers concentrations in corporate law, criminal law, litigation, and tax law. In addition, clinics are offered for 3 credit hours. Students may take 2-credit hour internships under the Alabama Student Practice Rule, in which a student clerks for a judge. Seminars are usually small groups of third-year students. Instruction is on a more informal and advanced basis than in basic courses. A written paper is required. First-year students are required to carry out a closely supervised program in legal research and writing. They must also participate in a moot court program in appellate advocacy involving substantial library research. A course in advanced legal research is offered as a 2-hour elective for upper-level students. Several minority programs support a diversified student body. Special lecture series, study abroad, and externships are available. The most widely taken electives are Family Law, Criminal Procedure, and Trial Advocacy.

Graduation Requirements

In order to graduate, candidates must have a GPA of 2.0 and have completed the upper-division writing requirement.

Organizations

Students edit the *Alabama Law Review*, *Law and Psychology Review*, *Journal of the Legal Profession*, and *American Journal of Tax Policy*. The student newspaper is *Alabama Column*. The school participates annually in the John A. Campbell Moot Court, National Moot Court, Phillip C. Jessup International Law Moot Court, and Frederick Douglass Moot Court competitions. The law school also participates in 3 to 4 trial advocacy competitions each year. Student organizations include the Bench and Bar Society, Environmental Law Society, and Law Spouses Club. There is a local chapter of the American Civil Liberties Union. Legal fraternities include Phi Alpha Delta, Phi Delta Phi, and Delta Theta Phi.

Library

The law library contains 379,165 hard-copy volumes and 97,668 microform volume equivalents, and subscribes to 3219 serial publications. Such on-line databases and networks as LEXIS, DIALOG, WESTLAW, and NEXIS, and OCLC are available to law students for research. Special library collections include all decisions of appellate-level state and federal courts, all state and federal codes, Alabama and federal rules and regulations, and the decisions of selected agencies and of principal courts of the Commonwealth nations. There are also extensive treatise holdings. Recently, the library reassigned or upgraded many library staff to enhance technical services, and added a new Special Collections area. The ratio of library volumes to faculty is 11,000 to 1 and to students, 700 to 1. The ratio of seats in the library to students is 1 to 1.

Faculty

The law school has 35 full-time and 41 part-time faculty members, of whom 11 are women. According to AAUP standards for Category I institutions, faculty salaries are below average. About 37% of full-time faculty have a graduate law degree in addition to the J.D.; about 10% of part-time faculty have one. The ratio of full-time students to full-time faculty in an average class is 18 to 1; in a clinic, 6 to 1. The law school has a regular program of bringing visiting professors and other distinguished lecturers and visitors to campus. There is a chapter of the Order of the Coif; 23 faculty and 18 graduates are members.

Placement

J.D.s awarded:	165

Services available through: a separate law school placement center.

Special features: fall and spring on-campus interviewing and resume forwarding programs and participation in job fairs, seminars, various publications, telephone and message/mail delivery service, LEXIS and WESTLAW computers, and programs in nontraditional law.

Full-time job interviews:	26 employers
Summer job interviews:	65 employers
Placement by graduation:	70% of class
Placement within 9 months:	99% of class
Average starting salary:	$35,000 to $56,000

Areas of placement:

Private practice 2-10 attorneys	36%
Private practice 11-25 attorneys	9%
Private practice 26-50 attorneys	10%
Private practice 51-100 attorneys	15%
Judicial clerkships	10%
Government	9%
Business/industry	6%
Public interest	3%
Academic	1%

Students

About 41% of the student body are women; 12%, minorities; 9%, African American; 1%, Asian American; 1%, Hispanic; and 1%, Native American. The majority of students come from Alabama (85%). The average age of entering students is 24. About 49% of students enter directly from undergraduate school, 9% have a graduate degree, and 49% have worked full-time prior to entering law school. About 2% drop out after the first year for academic or personal reasons; 98% remain to receive a law degree.

UNIVERSITY OF ARIZONA

James E. Rogers College of Law

Mountain and Speedway
P.O. Box 210176
Tucson, AZ 85721-0176

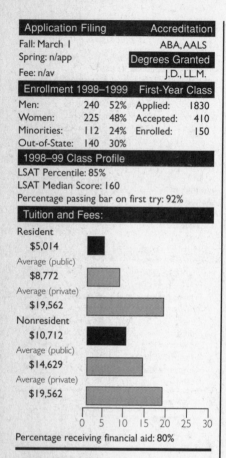

Application Filing			Accreditation
Fall: March 1			ABA, AALS
Spring: n/app			**Degrees Granted**
Fee: n/av			J.D., LL.M.

Enrollment 1998–1999		First-Year Class	
Men:	240 52%	Applied:	1830
Women:	225 48%	Accepted:	410
Minorities:	112 24%	Enrolled:	150
Out-of-State:	140 30%		

1998–99 Class Profile
LSAT Percentile: 85%
LSAT Median Score: 160
Percentage passing bar on first try: 92%

Tuition and Fees:

Resident
$5,014

Average (public)
$8,772

Average (private)
$19,562

Nonresident
$10,712

Average (public)
$14,629

Average (private)
$19,562

Percentage receiving financial aid: 80%

ADMISSIONS

In the fall 1999 first-year class, 1830 applied, 410 were accepted, and 150 enrolled. Eight transfers enrolled. The median LSAT percentile of the most recent first-year class was 85; the median GPA was 3.4 on a scale of 4.0. The lowest LSAT percentile accepted was 36; the highest was 99.

Requirements
Applicants must have a bachelor's degree from an accredited institution and take the LSAT. Minimum acceptable GPA is 2.2 on a scale of 4.0. The most important admission factors include academic achievement and LSAT results. No specific undergraduate courses are required. Candidates are not interviewed.

Procedure
The application deadline for fall entry is March 1. Applicants should submit an application form, LSAT results, TOEFL for foreign applicants, a nonrefundable application fee, 2 letters of recommendation, use of the LSDAS, a personal statement, and a resume. Check with the school for current application fee. Notification of the admission decision is January through May. The latest acceptable LSAT test date for fall entry is February. The law school uses the LSDAS.

Special
The law school recruits minority and disadvantaged students through a strong minority recruitment and retention program. Ethnicity is one of many qualitative factors considered by the Admissions Committee. Requirements are different for out-of-state students in that there are a limited number of openings for nonresident students. Generally 70% of enrollees are residents and 30% are nonresidents; however, approximately 50% of admission offers go to nonresidents. Transfer students must have one year of credit, have attended an ABA-approved law school, and should be ranked in the top tenth to top quarter of their class. Space in the class and nature of law school attended are always factors, as are undergraduate record, LSAT score, admissibility as a first-year applicant, personal statement, and letters of recommendation from law faculty with whom the applicant has studied.

Costs

Tuition and fees for the 1999-2000 academic year are $5014 for full-time in-state students and $12,348 for out-of-state students. On-campus room and board costs about $7334 annually; and books and supplies run $700.

Financial Aid

In a recent year, about 80% of current law students received some form of aid. The average annual amount of aid from all sources combined, including scholarships, loans, and work contracts, was $10,000 maximum, $18,500. Awards are based on need and merit. The required financial statement is FAFSA. Check with the school for current deadline. Special funds for minority or disadvantaged students and special scholarships for Native Americans are available. First-year students are notified about their financial aid application between acceptance and enrollment; generally between May and June.

About the Law School

University of Arizona James E. Rogers College of Law was established in 1925 and is a public institution. The 325-acre campus is in an urban area near downtown Tucson. The primary mission of the law school is to integrate the study of modern issues with the traditional legal course of study in a small law school of approximately 450 students, with a rigorous yet collegial atmosphere. Students have access to federal, state, county, city, and local agencies, courts, correctional facilities, law firms, and legal aid organizations in the Tucson area. In addition, Arizona is home to many Native American tribes, all with their own tribal governments and tribal court systems. Facilities of special interest to law students include videotape-equipped classrooms, a moot court room, seminar rooms, a student lounge, a library, a computer laboratory for students, and a fully equipped computerized courtroom. Housing for law students includes university-affiliated apartments for families and plenty of affordable off-campus rental housing. About 99% of the law school facilities are accessible to the physically disabled.

Calendar

The law school operates on a traditional semester basis. Most courses for full-time students are offered days only, there are some late afternoon and early evening elective courses. Course work must be completed within 3 years. There is no part-time program. New full-time students are admitted in the fall. There is a 5-week summer session. Transferable summer courses are offered.

Programs

In addition to the J.D., the law school offers the LL.M and LL.M. in international trade law. Students may take relevant courses in other programs and apply credit toward the J.D.; a maximum of 6 credits may be applied. The following joint degrees may be earned: J.D./M.B.A. (Juris Doctor/Master of Business Administration), J.D./M.A. (Juris Doctor/Master of Arts in economics and American Indians), J.D./Ph.D. (Juris Doctor/Doctor of Philosophy in psychology, philosophy, economics, and J.D./M.P.A. (Juris Doctor/Master of Public Administration).

Phone: 520-621-3477
Fax: 520-621-9140
E-mail: admissions@nt.law.arizona.edu
Web: http://www.law.arizona.edu

Contact

Assistant Dean, 520-621-3477 for general inquiries; Henrietta Stover, Assistant Dean, Financial Services, 520-621-8101 for financial aid information.

Required

To earn the J.D., candidates must complete 85 total credits, of which 39 are for required courses. They must maintain a minimum GPA of 2.0 in the required courses. The following first-year courses are required of all students: Contracts, Torts, Civil Procedure, Criminal Procedure, Legal Research and Writing, Property, Constitutional Law, and Appellate Practice and Moot Court. Required upper-level courses consist of Evidence, Professional Responsibility, and an advanced writing seminar. The required orientation program for first-year students is 1 day and encompasses academic and cultural aspects of the law school experience; 3 follow-up sessions during the first 2 weeks of school are held on ethics, stress, and various other matters.

Electives

The James E. Rogers College of Law offers concentrations in corporate law, criminal law, environmental law, family law, international law, litigation, securities law, tax law, and torts and insurance. In addition, students work for legal aid, the county and city prosecutor's office, public defender's office, and the state attorney general's office. Additionally, the College has an active legal clinic program with several Native American tribes located in Arizona. The College has a diverse set of offerings for its advanced research and writing seminars, ranging from the Warren Court to a death penalty seminar. Internships may be taken with the state legislature and with the offices of U.S. senators and representatives, and on the Navajo, Tohono O'odham, and White Mountain Apache reservations. Students may take up to 5 units of independent study with faculty supervision. Students may hear special lectures through the Isaac Marks Memorial Lectures, Rosenstiel Scholar-in-Residence Program, McCormick Society lectures, and the Jeanne Kiewit Taylor Visiting Faculty Program. Study abroad is possible in London and Puerto Rico. All first-year students may take tutorial programs. Special scholarship efforts, orientation programs, mentoring, tutorial assistance, and a weeklong bridge program are offered to minority students. The most widely taken electives are Federal Income Tax, Corporations, and Employment Law.

Graduation Requirements

In order to graduate, candidates must have a GPA of 2.0 and have completed the upper-division writing requirement. All students must write a paper of "publishable quality" to fulfill the upper-division writing requirement.

Organizations

The primary law review is the *Arizona Law Review*. Students also edit *The Arizona Journal for International Law*, and *The Journal of Psychology, Public Policy and Law. The Arizona Advocate* is the student newspaper. Students may participate in a wide range of regional, national, and international moot court competitions. Law student organizations include the Student Bar Association, Phi Alpha Delta, and Phi Delta Phi. There are local chapters of the American Civil Liberties Union and ABA-Law Student Division.

Library

The law library contains 380,000 hard-copy volumes and 426,000 microform volume equivalents, and subscribes to 3650 serial publications. Such on-line databases and networks as LEXIS, DIALOG, and WESTLAW are available to law students for research. Special library collections include an extensive collection of materials on Latin American law. Recently, the library refurbished and recarpeted the computer lab and library. There are also extensive electronic databases. The ratio of library volumes to faculty is 12,500 to 1 and to students, 777 to 1. The ratio of seats in the library to students is 1 to 1.

Faculty

The law school has 33 full-time and 33 part-time faculty members, of whom 16 are women. According to AAUP standards for Category I institutions, faculty salaries are above average. About 47% of full-time faculty have a graduate law degree in addition to the J.D.; about 2% of part-time faculty have one. The ratio of full-time students to full-time faculty in an average class is 15 to 1; in a clinic, 7 to 1. There is a chapter of the Order of the Coif; 14 faculty and 325 graduates are members.

Placement

J.D.s awarded:	146
Services available through: a separate law school placement center.	
Services: extensive career counseling and direction, creative programming, and participation of faculty and alumni	
Special features: the college has a very active Career Services Office with a full-time director. The office takes a proactive approach to career services, educating, and assisting students.	
Full-time job interviews:	50 employers
Summer job interviews:	110 employers
Placement by graduation:	65% of class
Placement within 9 months:	93% of class
Average starting salary:	$28,000 to $94,000
Areas of placement:	
Private practice 2-10 attorneys	12%
Private practice 11-25 attorneys	8%
Private practice 26-50 attorneys	10%
Private practice 51-100 attorneys	15%
Government	17%
Judicial clerkships	15%
Business/industry	13%
Academic	5%
Public interest	3%
Military	2%

Students

About 48% of the student body are women; 24%, minorities; 4%, African American; 5%, Asian American; 15%, Hispanic; and 3%, Native American. The majority of students come from Arizona (70%). The average age of entering students is 25; age range is 20 to 59. About 40% of students enter directly from undergraduate school, 15% have a graduate degree, and 60% have worked full-time prior to entering law school. About 1% drop out after the first year for academic or personal reasons; 98% remain to receive a law degree.

School of Law

Robert A. Leflar Law Center,
Waterman Hall
Fayetteville, AR 72701

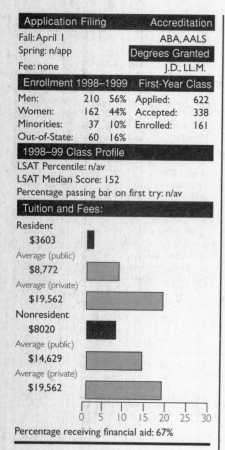

Application Filing		Accreditation
Fall: April 1		ABA, AALS
Spring: n/app		**Degrees Granted**
Fee: none		J.D., LL.M.

Enrollment 1998–1999			First-Year Class	
Men:	210	56%	Applied:	622
Women:	162	44%	Accepted:	338
Minorities:	37	10%	Enrolled:	161
Out-of-State:	60	16%		

1998–99 Class Profile

LSAT Percentile: n/av
LSAT Median Score: 152
Percentage passing bar on first try: n/av

Tuition and Fees:

Resident
$3603
Average (public)
$8,772
Average (private)
$19,562
Nonresident
$8020
Average (public)
$14,629
Average (private)
$19,562

0 5 10 15 20 25 30

Percentage receiving financial aid: 67%

ADMISSIONS

In the fall 1999 first-year class, 622 applied, 338 were accepted, and 161 enrolled. Four transfers enrolled. The median GPA of the most recent first-year class was 3.34 on scale of 4.0.

Requirements

Applicants must have a bachelor's degree from an accredited institution and take the LSAT. The most important admission factors include GPA and LSAT results. No specific undergraduate courses are required. Candidates are not interviewed.

Procedure

The application deadline for fall entry is April 1. Applicants should submit an application form, LSAT results, and transcripts. Accepted students must submit a nonrefundable $75 preregistration fee, which is applied to the regular registration fee for the semester. Notification of the admission decision is on a rolling basis. The latest acceptable LSAT test date for fall entry is February. The law school uses the LSDAS.

Special

Requirements are different for out-of-state students in that index admission is granted to those nonresident applicants who have prediction indexes of 200 or above on the 120 to 180 scale. If space permits, index admission is offered to other applicants. A small number of non-residents who do not qualify for index admission may be admitted by the Admissions Committee. Transfer students must have one year of credit, have attended an ABA-approved law school, and apply to the Dean of the School of Law, indicating previous attendance at another school. Transfer students must complete the last 4 semesters at the University of Arkansas School of Law.

Costs

Tuition and fees for the 1999-2000 academic year are $3603 for full-time in-state students and $8020 for out-of-state students. On-campus room and board costs about $3868 annually; books and supplies run $1000.

Financial Aid

About 67% of current law students receive some form of aid. Awards are based on need and merit, along with the probability of success in law school. The aid application deadline for fall entry is April 1. Special funds for minority or disadvantaged students consist of selected scholarships.

About the Law School

University of Arkansas School of Law was established in 1924 and is a public institution. The campus is in a small town. The primary mission of the law school is to prepare students as lawyers who will provide professional service to their clients, who are interested in and capable of advancing legal process and reform, and who are prepared to fill the vital role of the lawyer as a community leader. Students have access to federal, state, county, city, and local agencies, courts, correctional facilities, law firms, and legal aid organizations in the Fayetteville area. Housing for law students consists of on-campus residence halls, sorority and fraternity houses, and 2-bedroom units. Housing for married students is limited. A housing service helps students find off-campus housing.

Calendar

The law school operates on a traditional semester basis. Courses for full-time students are offered days only and must be completed within 3 years. There is no part-time program. New full-time students are admitted in the fall. There is a summer session. Transferable summer courses are offered.

Programs

In addition to the J.D., the law school offers the LL.M. in agricultural law. The following joint degrees may be earned: J.D./M.B.A. (Juris Doctor/Master of Business Administration) and J.D./M.P.A. (Juris Doctor/Master of Public Administration).

Contact

James Miller, Associate Dean for Students, 501-575-3102 for general inquiries; Terry Finney, Director of Financial Aid, 501-575-3806 for financial aid information.

ARKANSAS

Required

To earn the J.D., candidates must complete 90 total credits, of which 43 are for required courses. They must maintain a minimum GPA of 2.0 in the required courses. The following first-year courses are required of all students: Legal Research and Writing I, Legal Research and Writing II, Contracts A and B, Criminal Law, Torts, Property A and B, and Civil Procedure A and B. Required upper-level courses consist of Constitutional Law, Legal Research and Writing III, and Professional Responsibility. The required orientation program for first-year students is a 6-day introduction to the study of law that includes an introduction to the library, law school and campus tours, and university resources and student life planning suggestions.

Electives

The School of Law offers concentrations in agricultural law. In addition, students with 48 or more hours who have completed Civil Procedure A and B, Criminal Procedure, Basic Evidence and Professional Responsibility may take civil or criminal clinic. Upper-level students who have taken Professional Responsibility may take Federal Practice clinic. Seminars for 2 or 3 hours of credit are available to upper-level students. Seminars offered include Bankruptcy, Bioethics, Comparative Law, Criminal Law, Elder Law, Indian Law, Judicial Administration Jurisprudence, Juvenile Justice, Privacy Law, Supreme Court, and UCC. Faculty may hire research assistants. Several scholarships are available for minority students.

Graduation Requirements

In order to graduate, candidates must have earned a GPA of 2.0, completed the upper-division writing requirement, and completed an upper-level research and writing project. Seminar papers may be used to satisfy this requirement. Grades are usually based on a single final exam.

Organizations

Students edit the *University of Arkansas Law Review*. The school participates in a variety of national and regional moot court competitions. Student organizations include the Student Bar Association, the Women's Law Student Association, Arkansas Coalition for Public Interest Law, and Christian Legal Society. Local chapters of national associations include Phi Alpha Delta, Phi Delta Phi, Black Law Students Association, Delta Theta Phi, and the Student Honor Council.

Library

The law library contains 243,962 hardcopy volumes and 43,584 microform volume equivalents, and subscribes to 2240 serial publications. Such on-line databases and networks as LEXIS and WESTLAW are available to law students for research. Special library collections include a growing collection of agricultural law materials developed through the National Center for Agricultural Law Research and Information. The Young Law Library is a depository for federal documents. Recently, the library expanded the Leflar Law Center, which created additional library space. The ratio of library volumes to faculty is 5433 to 1 and to students, 511 to 1. The ratio of seats in the library to students is 1 to 105.

Faculty

The law school has 35 full-time and 5 part-time faculty members, of whom 9 are women. About 26% of full-time faculty have a graduate law degree in addition to the J.D.

Students

About 44% of the student body are women; 10%, minorities. The majority of students come from Arkansas (84%). The average age of entering students is 26.

Placement	
J.D.s awarded:	136
Services available through: a separate law school placement center and the university placement center.	
Special features: monthly placement newsletters, including internships and fellowships, and alumni and monthly job list postings by mail or E-mail, including those exchanged at other schools.	
Full-time job interviews:	18 employers
Summer job interviews:	37 employers
Placement by graduation:	48% of class
Placement within 9 months:	95% of class
Average starting salary:	$18,000 to $82,000
Areas of placement:	
Private practice 2-10 attorneys	32%
Private practice 11-25 attorneys	9%
Private practice 51-100 attorneys	3%
Private practice 101-250 attorneys	3%
Private practice 251+ attorneys	4%
Solo practice	3%
Business/industry	21%
Government	14%
Judicial clerkships	9%
Academic	2%
Public interest	2%

School of Law

1201 McAlmont Street
Little Rock, AR 72202-5142

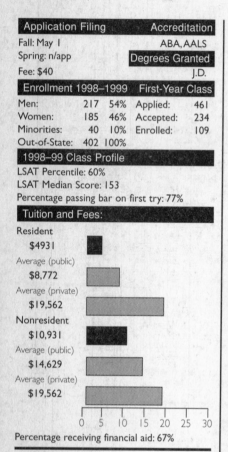

Application Filing	Accreditation
Fall: May 1	ABA, AALS
Spring: n/app	**Degrees Granted**
Fee: $40	J.D.

Enrollment 1998–1999		First-Year Class	
Men:	217 54%	Applied:	461
Women:	185 46%	Accepted:	234
Minorities:	40 10%	Enrolled:	109
Out-of-State:	402 100%		

1998–99 Class Profile
LSAT Percentile: 60%
LSAT Median Score: 153
Percentage passing bar on first try: 77%

Tuition and Fees:

Resident
$4931

Average (public)
$8,772

Average (private)
$19,562

Nonresident
$10,931

Average (public)
$14,629

Average (private)
$19,562

0 5 10 15 20 25 30

Percentage receiving financial aid: 67%

ADMISSIONS

In the fall 1999 first-year class, 461 applied, 234 were accepted, and 109 enrolled. Fourteen transfers enrolled. The median LSAT percentile of the most recent first-year class was 60; the median GPA was 3.3 on a scale of 4.0. The lowest LSAT percentile accepted was 23; the highest was 96.

Requirements
Applicants must have a bachelor's degree from an accredited institution and take the LSAT. The most important admission factors include LSAT results, academic achievement, and life experience. No specific undergraduate courses are required. Candidates are not interviewed.

Procedure
The application deadline for fall entry is May 1. Applicants should submit an application form, LSAT results, transcripts, a nonrefundable application fee of $40, 2 letters of recommendation, and a prescribed-format personal statement. Notification of the admission decision is on a rolling basis. The latest acceptable LSAT test date for fall entry is February. The law school uses the LSDAS.

Special
The law school recruits minority and disadvantaged students by means of scholarships that take race, ethnicity, and life experience into account. Transfer students must have attended an ABA-approved law school and have an official law school transcript showing completion of 20 semester hours, a letter of good standing stating class rank, LSAT score, official undergraduate transcript, a letter explaining the need to transfer, an application, and the $40 application fee. Preadmissions courses consist of a 1-week experience for nonindex admittees that is designed to introduce students to legal education processes. Staffed by a professor of law and upper-level students who serve as mentors, the experience centers around a simulated Criminal Law course.

Costs

Tuition and fees for the 1999-2000 academic year are $4931 for full-time in-state students and $10,931 for out-of-state students. Tuition and fees for part-time students are $2993 annually in-state and $6593 out-of-state, or $160 per credit hour in-state and $360 out-of-state. Books and supplies run $750.

Financial Aid

About 67% of current law students receive some form of aid. The average annual amount of aid from all sources combined, including scholarships, loans, and work contracts, is $12,000; maximum, $14,500 for residents; $19,100 for non-residents. Awards are based on need and merit. The required financial statement is FAFSA. The aid application deadline for fall entry is March 1. Special funds for minority or disadvantaged students include Bowen Scholarships. First-year students are notified about their financial aid application 8 to 10 weeks after application.

About the Law School

University of Arkansas at Little Rock School of Law was established in 1975 and is a public institution. The 5-acre campus is in an urban area downtown, 6 miles from the main campus. The primary mission of the law school is to provide a high-quality legal education that equips students with the knowledge, skills, and ethical concepts to function as competent attorneys, public officials, business persons, and other professionals, and to think critically about the efficacy of the law and legal institutions and to work for their improvement. Students have access to federal, state, county, city, and local agencies, courts, correctional facilities, law firms, and legal aid organizations in the Little Rock area. Little Rock is Arkansas's capital city; thus, students have a wide range of employment opportunities, from all branches of state government to legal services to law firms. Housing for law students consists of many rental properties varying in cost. All law school facilities are accessible to the physically disabled.

Calendar

The law school operates on a traditional semester basis. Courses for full-time students are offered principally day, with some upper-level electives at night, and must be completed within 6 years. For part-time students, courses are offered principally evenings, with some upper-level electives in the daytime, and must be completed within 6 years. New full-time and part-time students are admitted in the fall. There is an 8- week summer session. Transferable summer courses are offered.

Contact

501-324-9439 for general inquiries; Cari Wickliffe, Director of Student Services, (501) 569-3130 for financial aid information.

ARKANSAS

Programs

Students may take relevant courses in other programs and apply credit toward the J.D.; a maximum of 6 credits may be applied for the joint degree. The following joint degrees may be earned: J.D./M.B.A. (Juris Doctor/Master of Business Administration) and J.D./M.P.A. (Juris Doctor/Master of Public Administration).

Required

To earn the J.D., candidates must complete 87 total credits, of which 48 are for required courses. They must maintain a minimum GPA of 2.0 in the required courses. The following first-year courses are required of all students: Contracts I and II, Torts I and II, Civil Procedure I and II, Criminal Law, Property I and II, Legal Research I and II, and Reasoning, Writing, and Advocacy I and II. Required upper-level courses consist of Constitutional Law I and II, Legal Profession, Evidence, and Trial Advocacy. The required orientation program for first-year students is 4 days long and covers the academic and personal skills needed to succeed in law school.

Electives

Of special curricular note are the two clinics, litigation and mediation. The latter is offered at night as well as in the day. Students can choose from a number of highly interesting seminar topics, as well as writing their own independent paper under the supervision of a faculty member. Outside speakers participate in an annual symposium, and nationally notable speakers offer several lectures a year as well. Brand new this year is an ABA-approved summer program at the University of Haifa offering courses in comparative law. A number of scholarships are available to students. Many factors are considered in the awarding of scholarships, including race, ethnicity and background. An academic mentoring tutorial program is available to all first-year students. The most widely taken electives are Family Law, Debtor-Creditor, and Corporations.

Graduation Requirements

In order to graduate, candidates must have a GPA of 2.0, completed the upper-division writing requirement, and upper-level jurisprudential requirement, which can be fulfilled by a number of courses, e.g., jurisprudence and legal history.

Organizations

During the current year there are 12 registered student organizations that sponsor various activities during the school year, ranging from community service to bringing in outside speakers. In addition to the student organizations, students edit the *UALR Law Review*, a quarterly publication containing scholarly articles. Students staff the Moot Court Board, which sends several teams each year to participate in national competitions. Since its inception, UALR has also sent teams to the National Trial Competition. Each year UALR and UAF student trial teams compete in the Henry Woods competition.

Library

The law library contains 164,039 hardcopy volumes and 528,208 microform volume equivalents, and subscribes to 3168 serial publications. Such on-line databases and networks as LEXIS, DIALOG, WESTLAW, and LOIS are available to law students for research. Special library collections include a federal documents depository, a state documents depository going back to 1993, and Arkansas Supreme Court records and briefs for 1836-1926. Recently, the library initiated a web catalog; on-line interlibrary loan; and expanded access to electronic resources. The ratio of library volumes to faculty is 4100 to 1 and to students, 408 to 1. The ratio of seats in the library to students is 1 to 1.

Faculty

The law school has 29 full-time and 29 part-time faculty members, of whom 23 are women. According to AAUP standards for Category IIA institutions, faculty salaries are above average. About 32% of full-time faculty have a graduate law degree in addition to the J.D.; about 13% of part-time faculty have one. The ratio of full-time students to full-time faculty in an average class is 30 to 1; in a clinic, 8 to 1. The law school has a regular program of bringing visiting professors and other distinguished lecturers and visitors to campus. The school has the Altheimer Lectures and Jurists-in-Residence program.

Placement

J.D.s awarded:	109
Services available through: a separate law school placement center.	
Services: computer access to WESTLAW and NALPLine, and brown-bag lunches on various aspects of career planning and the job search.	
Special features: an annual graduate brochure that is mailed to all judges and attorneys in Arkansas. The brochure features each student's picture along with information on GPA, honors, past work experience, type of legal practice desired, and geographic preference.	
Full-time job interviews:	4 employers
Summer job interviews:	8 employers
Placement by graduation:	n/av
Placement within 9 months:	95% of class
Average starting salary:	$16,000 to $90,000
Areas of placement:	
Private practice 2-10 attorneys	33%
Private practice 11-25 attorneys	4%
Private practice 26-50 attorneys	1%
Private practice 51-100 attorneys	1%
Private practice- solo	4%
Private practice- size unknown	2%
Business/industry	21%
Government	20%
Judicial clerkships	11%
Public interest	2%
Academic	1%

Students

About 46% of the student body are women; 10%, minorities; 7%, African American; 1%, Asian American; and 1%, Hispanic. The average age of entering students is 28; age range is 21 to 69. About 1% drop out after the first year for academic or personal reasons; 99% remain to receive a law degree.

UNIVERSITY OF BALTIMORE

School of Law

1420 North Charles Street
Baltimore, MD 21201-5779

Application Filing			Accreditation
Fall: April 1			ABA, AALS
Spring: n/app			**Degrees Granted**
Fee: n/av			J.D., LL.M.
Enrollment 1998–1999			**First-Year Class**
Men:	438	48%	Applied: 1473
Women:	466	49%	Accepted: 892
Minorities:	172	19%	Enrolled: 305
Out-of-State:	145	16%	

1998–99 Class Profile

LSAT Percentile: n/av
LSAT Median Score: 149
Percentage passing bar on first try: 65%

Tuition and Fees:

Resident
$9617

Average (public)
$8,772

Average (private)
$19,562

Nonresident
$16,700

Average (public)
$14,629

Average (private)
$19,562

0   5   10   15   20   25   30

Percentage receiving financial aid: 65%

ADMISSIONS

In the fall 1999 first-year class, 1473 applied, 892 were accepted, and 305 enrolled. Sixteen transfers enrolled. The median GPA of the most recent first-year class was 2.9 on a 4.0 scale. The lowest LSAT percentile accepted was 15; the highest was 97.

Requirements
Applicants must have a bachelor's degree from an accredited institution and take the LSAT. The most important admission factors include GPA, LSAT results, and work experience. No specific undergraduate courses are required. Candidates are not interviewed.

Procedure
The application deadline for fall entry is April 1. Applicants should submit an application form, LSAT results, transcripts, a nonrefundable application fee, and 2 letters of recommendation. LSAT scores and transcripts must come through LSDAS. Check with the school for current fee. Notification of the admission decision is on a rolling basis. The latest acceptable LSAT test date for fall entry is February. The law school uses the LSDAS.

Special
The law school recruits minority and disadvantaged students by means of an on-campus minority law forum, recruiting at historically black colleges, and recruiting minorities during visits to undergraduate institutions. Transfer students must have one year of credit, have attended an ABA-approved law school, and have files individually reviewed by committee, which does so subject to availability of space. The Summer Institute, a conditional admission program, offers the opportunity to demonstrate ability for law school through successful completion of an intensive case analysis and legal writing program to individuals whose grades or test scores may be somewhat lower than those ordinarily required for admission.

Costs

Tuition and fees for the 1999-2000 academic year are $9617 for full-time in-state students and $16,700 for out-of-state students. Tuition for part-time students is $373 per credit in-state and $630 per credit out-of-state. Fees are $520. Books and supplies run $850.

Financial Aid

About 65% of current law students receive some form of aid. The average annual amount of aid from all sources combined, including scholarships, loans, and work contracts, is $7500; maximum, $20,000. Awards are based on need and merit combined need only for federal programs; scholarships on need and/or merit. The required financial statement is FAFSA. Check with the school for current application deadlines. The law school offers Diversity Grants to entering and continuing students. First-year students are notified about their financial aid application in mid-June.

About the Law School

University of Baltimore School of Law was established in 1925 and is a public institution. The campus is in an urban area in Baltimore. The primary mission of the law school is to draw together students and faculty from a variety of backgrounds in a common search for knowledge and understanding. Students have access to federal, state, county, city, and local agencies, courts, correctional facilities, law firms, and legal aid organizations in the Baltimore area. Area corporations and nonprofit organizations are also accessible. Facilities of special interest to law students consist of 2 small personal computer laboratories for student use and on-line databases and networks. Housing for law students is available off campus; there is a roommate referral service offered. Nearby, many apartments range from inexpensive studios to luxury apartment buildings. About 95% of the law school facilities are accessible to the physically disabled.

Calendar

The law school operates on a traditional semester basis. Courses for full-time students are offered both day and evening and must be completed within 5 years. For part-time students, courses are offered both day and evening and must be completed within 6 years. New full- and part-time students are admitted in the fall. There are 6- and 8-week summer sessions. Transferable summer courses are offered.

Programs

In addition to the J.D., the law school offers the LL.M. Students may take relevant courses in other programs and apply credit toward the J.D.; a maximum of 6 credits may be applied. The following joint degrees may be earned: J.D./M.P.A. (Juris Doctor/ Master of Public Administration), J.D./M.S. (Juris Doctor/ Master of Science in criminal justice), J.D./M.B.A. (Juris Doctor/ Master of Business Administration), and J.D./Ph.D. (Juris Doctor/ Doctor of Philosophy in policy sciences).

Required
To earn the J.D., candidates must complete 90 total credits, of which 39 are for required courses. They must maintain a minimum GPA of 2.0 in the required

Phone: 410-837-4459
Fax: 410-837-4450
E-mail: lwadmiss@ubmail.ubalt.edu
Web: lawschool@ubalt.edu

Contact

Office of Law Admissions, 410-837-4459 for general inquiries; 410-837-4763, for financial aid information.

courses. The following first-year courses are required of all students: Civil Procedure I and II, Contracts I and II, Criminal Law, Legal Analysis, Research, and Writing, Moot Court, Property, Torts, and Constitutional Law. Required upper-level courses consist of Evidence, Professional Responsibility, an advocacy requirement, and 2 upper-level research and writing projects. All students take clinics as part of upper-level elective courses. The required orientation program for first-year students is 4 days; students meet with faculty and peer advisers, attend case analysis and other seminars, and attend an Information Fair on school services and student activities.

Electives

Students must take 36 in their area of concentration. The School of Law offers concentrations in corporate law, criminal law, environmental law, family law, international law, litigation, securities law, tax law, torts and insurance, civil rights, estate planning, public and government law, property, general practice, intellectual property, business law, criminal practice, environmental law, estate planning, family law, general practice, intellectual property, international and comparative law, litigation and advocacy, public interest law, real estate practice, and theories of the law. In addition, clinics offer the opportunity to work under the direct supervision of attorneys. Upper-level students undertake the representation of real clients in actual cases and perform all tasks necessary for proper representation. Students earn 6 credits in the Criminal Practice Clinic, Family Law Clinic, and Appellate Advocacy Clinic. Students earn 8 credits in the Civil Litigation Clinic. Seminars are 3-credit advanced discussion classes that require independent research, writing, and discussion leadership by students. The Internship Program allows upper-level students to learn about the lawyering and judicial process by working closely with supervising attorneys and judges. Internships are open to any upper-level student in good standing and are worth 3 to 4 credits. Special lecture series include the Liss Memorial Lectures, A.M. Law Series, Hoffberger Center for Professional Ethics, and the Center for International and Comparative Law. Study abroad is open to any student after the first year of study. The school offers a program in international comparative law in conjunction with the University of Aberdeen,

Scotland. First-year students may receive tutorial assistance through the Law Achievement Workshop, which consists of weekly tutorial sessions for almost every first-year class. Other tutorial programs are handled on an individual basis. Programs for minority students include the Law Achievement Workshop, Attorney Mentors, Exam Writing Workshop, Afro-American Lectures in Law, Black Law Student Orientation, and the Black Law Student Adviser Program. The most widely taken electives are Federal Income Tax, Maryland Civil Procedure, and Trusts and Estates.

Graduation Requirements

In order to graduate, candidates must have a GPA of 2.0, completed the upper-division writing requirement, and fulfill the upper-level advocacy requirement.

Organizations

Students edit *The University of Baltimore Law Review*, the *University of Baltimore Law Forum*, the *University of Baltimore Journal of Environmental Law*, the *University of Baltimore Intellectual Property Journal*, and the newspaper *The Advance Sheet*. Annually, teams compete at the American Trial Lawyers Association Trial Advocacy and Client Counseling competitions, Client Negotiation Moot Court, Pace National Environmental Law Moot Court, Tax Moot Court, and Trial Advocacy competitions. Law student organizations include the Intellectual Property Legal Society, Christian Legal Society, and Criminal Law Association. There are local chapters of Phi Alpha Delta, Phi Delta Kappa, and Phi Delta Phi. Campus clubs and other organizations include the Graduate Tax Students Association and the university's basketball league.

Library

The law library contains 287,125 hard-copy volumes and 561,053 microform volume equivalents, and subscribes to 3215 serial publications. Such on-line databases and networks as LEXIS, DIALOG, and WESTLAW are available to law students for research. Special library collections include a U.S. government selective depository. Recently, a Bibliographical Instruction Center with 10 terminals, primarily LEXIS and WESTLAW was added to the library. The ratio of library volumes to faculty is 2600 to 1 and to students, 213 to 1. The ratio of seats in the library to students is 1 to 3.

Placement

J.D.s awarded:	320

Services available through: a separate law school placement center.

Services: some 20 different panels and workshops on job search techniques, specialty areas, and career opportunities

Special features: Public Interest Career Fair and the Small Employer Career Fair, a joint program with the University of Maryland, and EXPLOR, a summer legal experience program for first year students

Full-time job interviews:	n/av
Summer job interviews:	30 employers
Placement by graduation:	77% of class
Placement within 9 months:	92% of class
Average starting salary:	$39,391
Areas of placement:	
Private practice 2-10 attorneys	47%
Private practice 11-25 attorneys	47%
Private practice 26-50 attorneys	47%
Private practice 51-100 attorneys	47%
Judicial clerkships	31%
Government	14%
Business/industry	6%
Public interest	3%

Faculty

The law school has 45 full-time and 79 part-time faculty members, of whom 37 are women. According to AAUP standards for Category IIA institutions, faculty salaries are well above average. About 30% of full-time faculty have a graduate law degree in addition to the J.D. The ratio of full-time students to full-time faculty in an average class is 19 to 1; in a clinic, 6 to 1.

Students

About 49% of the student body are women; 19%, minorities; 13%, African American; and 4%, Asian American. The majority of students come from Maryland (84%). The average age of entering students is 28; age range is 21 to 56. About 6% of students enter directly from undergraduate school, 13% have a graduate degree, and 82% have worked full-time prior to entering law school. About 2% drop out after the first year for academic or personal reasons; 93% remain to receive a law degree.

Hastings College of the Law

200 McAllister Street
San Francisco, CA 94102

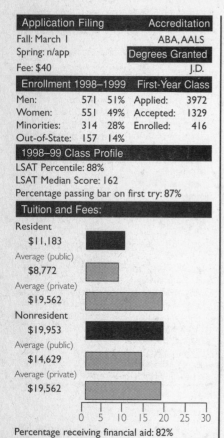

Application Filing	Accreditation
Fall: March 1	ABA, AALS
Spring: n/app	Degrees Granted
Fee: $40	J.D.

Enrollment 1998–1999		First-Year Class	
Men:	571 51%	Applied:	3972
Women:	551 49%	Accepted:	1329
Minorities:	314 28%	Enrolled:	416
Out-of-State:	157 14%		

1998–99 Class Profile

LSAT Percentile: 88%
LSAT Median Score: 162
Percentage passing bar on first try: 87%

Tuition and Fees:

Resident
$11,183

Average (public)
$8,772

Average (private)
$19,562

Nonresident
$19,953

Average (public)
$14,629

Average (private)
$19,562

Percentage receiving financial aid: 82%

ADMISSIONS

In the fall 1999 first-year class, 3972 applied, 1329 were accepted, and 416 enrolled. The median LSAT percentile of the most recent first-year class was 88; the median GPA was 3.4 on a scale of 4.0. The lowest LSAT percentile accepted was 23; the highest was 100.

Requirements

Applicants must have a bachelor's degree from an accredited institution and take the LSAT. The most important admission factors include LSAT results, academic achievement, and GPA. No specific undergraduate courses are required. Candidates are not interviewed.

Procedure

The application deadline for fall entry is March 1. Applicants should submit an application form, LSAT results, a nonrefundable application fee of $40, and optional letters of recommendation. Notification of the admission decision is January and May. The latest acceptable LSAT test date for fall entry is December. The law school uses the LSDAS.

Special

The law school recruits minority and disadvantaged students by enrolling 20% of the class through the LEOP program, an alternative means of evaluating disadvantaged students. Transfer students must have one year of credit, have a minimum GPA of 3.0, have attended an ABA-approved law school, and the school must be AALS-approved.

Costs

Tuition and fees for the 1999-2000 academic year are $11,183 for full-time in-state students and $19,953 for out-of-state students. On-campus room and board costs about $10,800 annually, and books and supplies run $840.

Financial Aid

About 82% of current law students receive some form of aid. The average annual amount of aid from all sources combined, including scholarships, loans, and work contracts, in $18,500; maximum, $31,800. Awards are based on need and merit. The required financial statement is FAFSA. The aid application deadline for fall entry is March 1. First-year students are notified about their financial aid application at as soon after acceptance as possible.

About the Law School

University of California Hastings College of the Law was established in 1878 and is a public institution. The campus is in an urban area in San Francisco. The primary mission of the law school is to prepare new members of the legal profession who are capable of and willing to serve all segments of the public as lawyers, judges, legislators, legal scholars, and in other roles in society. Students have access to federal, state, county, city, and local agencies, courts, correctional facilities, law firms, and legal aid organizations in the San Francisco area. Facilities of special interest to law students include the Public Interest Clearinghouse, the Public Law Research Institute, and the Land Conservation Institute. Housing for law students is offered at McAllister Tower, which accomodates approximately 450 students. There are studios, 1-bedroom, and 2-bedroom units available. About 90% of the law school facilities are accessible to the physically disabled.

Calendar

The law school operates on a traditional semester basis. Courses for full-time students are offered days only and must be completed within 3 years. There is no part-time program. New full-time students are admitted in the fall. There is no summer session. Transferable summer courses are not offered.

Programs

In addition to the J.D., the following joint degree may be earned: JD/MBA (Juris Doctor/Master of Business Administration).

Required

To earn the J.D., candidates must complete 86 total credits, of which 34 are for required courses. They must maintain a minimum GPA of 2.0 in the required courses. The following first-year courses are required of all students: Criminal Law, Torts, Contracts, Property, Civil Procedure, Legal Writing and Research, Moot Court, and a statutory course, either Employment Discrimination or Environmental Law. Required upper-

Phone: 415-565-4623
Fax: 415-565-4863
E-mail: admiss@uchastings.edu
Web: u.c.hastings.edu

Contact

Director of Admissions, 415-565-4885 for general inquiries; Linda Bisesi, Director of Financial Aid, 415-565-4624 for financial aid information.

level courses consist of Professional Responsibility and seminar or independent study with a substantial writing compon. The required orientation program for first-year students is a 2 1/2-day program that includes mock classes taught by first-year faculty, assignments, and discussions of study habits, test-taking, and diversity issues.

Electives

The Hastings College of the Law offers concentrations in corporate law, criminal law, entertainment, environmental law, international law, litigation, media law, securities law, tax law, and public interest law. In addition, upper-level students may act as a judicial extern for one of the state or federal courts. Students also may participate in a clinical seminar and gain practice experience under the supervision of an attorney. Clinics include Civil Justice, Criminal Practice, and Environmental Law. Enrollment in seminars is limited to 24 second- and third-year students. Upper-level students whose academic work is of superior quality may conduct research under the supervision of a full-time faculty member. There are exchange programs with Leiden University in the Netherlands and the University of British Columbia. An outstanding second- or third-year student may be chosen by the dean to serve as a discussion group leader for each of the first-year classes and for certain elective courses. The Legal Education Opportunity Program (LEOP) offers academic support to selected students with backgrounds that include some serious disadvantage that has been encountered and overcome. Incoming students have a special 1-week orientation introducing them to case briefing, legal writing, and analysis. Other programming for LEOP students includes the First-Year Study Program for the California bar examination, which is taught by and for LEOP students. An exchange program is offered with Vermont Law School. The most widely taken electives are Constitutional Law, Evidence, and Criminal Procedure.

Graduation Requirements

In order to graduate, candidates must have a GPA of 2.0 and have completed the upper-division writing requirement.

Organizations

Students edit the *Hastings Law Journal*, the *Constitutional Law Quarterly*, *International and Comparative Law Review*, *Communications and Entertainment Law Journal*, *Women's Law Journal*, and *North/Northwest Journal of Environmental Law and Policy*. The student newspaper is the *Hastings Law News*. Moot court competitions include the Giles Sutherland Rich Moot Court, National Appellate Advocacy, and the Frederick Douglass Moot Court. Two credit hours are awarded for participation. Among the 40 student organizations are the Associated Students of Hastings, La Raza Law Students Association, and the Black Law Students Association. There are local chapters of the National Lawyers Guild, Phi Delta Phi, and Amnesty International.

Library

The law library contains 627,035 hard-copy volumes and 1,229,584 microform volume equivalents, and subscribes to 8332 serial publications. Such on-line databases and networks as LEXIS, DIALOG, WESTLAW, and NEXIS, InfoTrac, EPIC, and First Search are available to law students for research. Special library collections include a state and federal depository, a state and federal records and briefs collection, and documents of the U.S. Supreme Court and U.S. Court of Appeals for the 9th Circuit and California appellate courts. Recently, the library expanded student computer facilities for legal research and word processing at the Learning Resources Center. Students access to e-mail is now available in the library. The ratio of library volumes to faculty is 11,400 to 1 and to students, 567 to 1. The ratio of seats in the library to students is 1 to 1.

Placement

J.D.s awarded:	445

Services available through: a separate law school placement center.

Special features: The center is a co-sponsor of an annual public interest and public service conference; it also conducts on-campus interviewing twice a year.

Full-time job interviews:	200 employers
Summer job interviews:	225 employers
Placement by graduation:	57% of class
Placement within 9 months:	95% of class
Average starting salary:	$26,000 to $90,000

Areas of placement:

Private practice 2-10 attorneys	15%
Private practice 11-25 attorneys	4%
Private practice 26-50 attorneys	5%
Private practice 51-100 attorneys	8%
Private practice 101-500 attorneys	24%
Private practice - unknown size	10%
Business/industry	13%
Government	10%
Judicial clerkships	7%
Public interest	3%
Academic	1%

Faculty

The law school has 47 full-time and 73 part-time faculty members, of whom 43 are women. According to AAUP standards for Category I institutions, faculty salaries are above average. About 28% of full-time faculty have a graduate law degree in addition to the J.D. The ratio of full-time students to full-time faculty in an average class is 20 to 1; in a clinic, 18 to 1. The law school has a regular program of bringing visiting professors and other distinguished lecturers and visitors to campus. There is a chapter of the Order of the Coif; 38 faculty and 1400 graduates are members.

Students

About 49% of the student body are women; 28%, minorities; 4%, African American; 19%, Asian American; 8%, Hispanic; and 1%, Native American. The majority of students come from California (86%). The average age of entering students is 25; age range is 21 to 53. About 11% of students have a graduate degree. About 5% drop out after the first year for academic or personal reasons; 93% remain to receive a law degree.

Boalt Hall

5 Boalt Hall
Berkeley, CA 94720

Application Filing	Accreditation
Fall: February I	ABA, AALS
Spring: n/app	**Degrees Granted**
Fee: $40	J.D., LL.M., S.J.D.

Enrollment 1998–1999		First-Year Class	
Men:	n/av	Applied:	4717
Women:	n/av	Accepted:	867
Minorities:	n/av	Enrolled:	269
Out-of-State:	n/av		

1998–99 Class Profile

LSAT Percentile: 93%
LSAT Median Score: 165
Percentage passing bar on first try: n/av

Tuition and Fees:

Resident
$10,865

Average (public)
$8,772

Average (private)
$19,562

Nonresident
$20,669

Average (public)
$14,629

Average (private)
$19,562

0 5 10 15 20 25 30

Percentage receiving financial aid: 80%

ADMISSIONS

In the fall 1999 first-year class, 4717 applied, 867 were accepted, and 269 enrolled. Fifty-nine transfers enrolled. The median LSAT percentile of the most recent first-year class was 93; the median GPA was 3.8 on a scale of 4.0. The lowest LSAT percentile accepted was 37; the highest was 99.

Requirements
Applicants must have a bachelor's degree from an accredited institution and take the LSAT. The most important admission factors include academic achievement, LSAT results, and life experience. No specific undergraduate courses are required. Candidates are not interviewed.

Procedure
The application deadline for fall entry is February 1. Applicants should submit an application form, LSAT results, transcripts, a nonrefundable application fee of $40, and a personal statement. Although letters of recommendation are not mandatory, they are highly recommended. Notification of the admission decision is from January to May. The latest acceptable LSAT test date for fall entry is December. The law school uses the LSDAS.

Special
The law school recruits minority and disadvantaged students by means of special programs for statewide visits and outreach, and national recruitment via mail campaigns and selected visits. Transfer students must have one year of credit, have attended an ABA-approved law school, and be in the top 5% at their home law school.

Costs

Tuition and fees for the 1999-2000 academic year are $10,865 for full-time in-state students and $20,669 for out-of-state students. On-campus room and board costs about $9558 annually; and books and supplies run $936.

Financial Aid

About 80% of current law students receive some form of aid. The average annual amount of aid from all sources combined, including scholarships, loans, and work contracts, is $20,826; maximum, $34,724. Awards are based on need and merit. The required financial statements are FAFSA and supplemental aid application (if applicable). The aid application deadline for fall entry is March 2. First-year students are notified about their financial aid application at in late spring.

About the Law School

University of California at Berkeley Boalt Hall was established in 1903 and is a public institution. The campus is in an urban area 12 miles east of San Francisco. The primary mission of the law school is to educate men and women not only for the practice of law, but for all the varied roles lawyers perform in a modern society. Students have access to federal, state, county, city, and local agencies, courts, correctional facilities, law firms, and legal aid organizations in the Berkeley area. All other facilities of the Berkeley campus are available to law students. Housing for law students is available at the law studio apartment complex, International House, and off campus. All law school facilities are accessible to the physically disabled.

Calendar

The law school operates on a traditional semester basis. Courses for full-time students are offered days only and must be completed within 3 years. There is no part-time program. New full-time students are admitted in the fall. There is no summer session. Transferable summer courses are not offered.

Programs

In addition to the J.D., the law school offers the LL.M and S.J.D. Students may take relevant courses in other programs and apply credit toward the J.D.; the maximum number of credits that may be applied varies. The following joint degrees may be earned: J.D./M.A. (Juris Doctor/Master of Arts in Asian Studies: jurisprudence and social policy; economics; international and area studies; information management and systems), J.D./M.A.L.D. (Juris Doctor/Master of Arts in law and diplomacy), J.D./M.B.A. (Juris Doctor/Master of Business Administration), J.D./M.C.P. (Juris Doctor/Master of City Planning), J.D./M.J. (Juris Doctor/Master of Journalism), J.D./M.P.P. (Juris Doctor/Master of Public Policy), J.D./Ph.D. (Juris Doctor/Doctor of Philosophy in legal history, jurisprudence).

Phone: 510-642-2274
Fax: 510-643-6222
E-mail: admissions@law.berkeley.edu
Web: www.law.berkeley.edu

Contact

510-642-2274 for general inquiries; 510-642-1563 for financial aid information.

Required

To earn the J.D., candidates must complete 85 total credits, of which 30 are for required courses. The following first-year courses are required of all students: Civil Procedure, Constitutional Law, Contracts, Criminal Law, Legal Writing, Research, and Advocacy, Property, and Torts. Required upper-level courses consist of Professional Responsibility. The required orientation program for first-year students, consists of 2 days of basic material for new students including the curriculum and services.

Electives

Boalt Hall offers concentrations in environmental law, international law, and law and technology. In addition, many clinics, with varying credit, mostly open to second-and third-year students, are available. Research programs can be undertaken at the Earl Warren Legal Institute, and field work may be done at the Berkeley Community Law Center or Boalt Hall's International Human Rights Clinic. Special lecture series are offered through the Sho Sato Japanese Legal Studies program and the Berkeley-Cologne Program. Additionally, tutorials are offered by the Academic Support Program.

Graduation Requirements

In order to graduate, candidates must have completed the upper-division writing requirement.

Organizations

Students edit *The California Law Review, Ecology Law Quarterly, Berkeley Technology Journal, Berkeley Journal of Employment and Labor Law, Berkeley Journal of International Law, Berkeley Women's Law Journal, African American Law and Policy Report, La Raza Journal,* and *Asian Law Journal.* The *Cross-Examiner* is the student newspaper. Annual moot court competitions are held at the school and include the McBaine and Jessup competitions. Among the student organizations are the Asian Pacific American Law Students, Law Students of African Descent, and La Raza. There are local chapters of the Federalist Society, Phi Alpha Delta, and the ABA/Law Student Division.

Library

The law library contains 680,000 hardcopy volumes and 660,000 microform volume equivalents, and subscribes to 7000 serial publications. Such on-line databases and networks as LEXIS, DIALOG, WESTLAW, and Legal-trac are available to law students for research. Special library collections include the Robbins Collection of ecclesiastical, foreign, comparative and international law, and the Goodrich and Matthew collections of commerical, conservation, and ecology law. Recently, the library increased word processing facilities for students. The ratio of library volumes to faculty is 5600 to 1 and to students, 850 to 1. The ratio of seats in the library to students is 1 to 3.

Faculty

The law school has 61 full-time and 102 part-time faculty members, of whom 51 are women. According to AAUP standards for Category I institutions, faculty salaries are well above average. About 10% of full-time faculty have a graduate law degree in addition to the J.D.; about 2% of part-time faculty have one. The ratio of full-time students to full-time faculty in an average class is 25 to 1; in a clinic, 6 to 1. The law school has a regular program of bringing visiting professors and other distinguished lecturers and visitors to campus. There is a chapter of the Order of the Coif; 22 faculty are members.

Placement

J.D.s awarded:	277

Services available through: a separate law school placement center and the university placement center.

Services: Job listings are available on the school's Web site.

Special features: numerous career programs including a Career Symposium for first-year students offered the first Saturday in November as well as a Mock Job Interviews Program in the spring and fall. There is also a "World of Law" career series in the spring. A full-time counselor is available for public interest/public sector jobs.

Full-time job interviews:	213 employers
Summer job interviews:	344 employers
Placement by graduation:	91% of class
Placement within 9 months:	97% of class
Average starting salary:	$27,000 to $145,000

Areas of placement:

Private practice 2-10 attorneys	2%
Private practice 11-25 attorneys	5%
Private practice 26-50 attorneys	3%
Private practice 51-100 attorneys	4%
Private practice 101+ attorneys	50%
Private practice - unknown type	4%
Judicial clerkships	12%
Government	8%
Public interest	6%
Business/industry	5%
Academic	1%

Students

About 50% of the student body are women; 31%, minorities; 5%, African American; 14%, Asian American; 11%, Hispanic; and 1%, Native American. The majority of students come from California (75%). The average age of entering students is 24; age range is 18 to 48. About 19% of students have a graduate degree.

School of Law

P.O. Box 951445
Los Angeles, CA 90095-1445

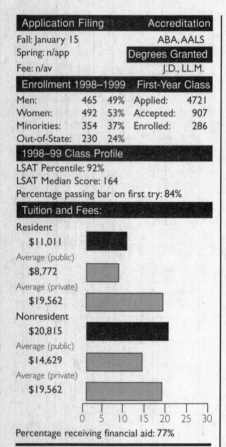

Application Filing	Accreditation
Fall: January 15	ABA, AALS
Spring: n/app	**Degrees Granted**
Fee: n/av	J.D., LL.M.

Enrollment 1998–1999		First-Year Class	
Men:	465 49%	Applied:	4721
Women:	492 53%	Accepted:	907
Minorities:	354 37%	Enrolled:	286
Out-of-State:	230 24%		

1998–99 Class Profile

LSAT Percentile: 92%
LSAT Median Score: 164
Percentage passing bar on first try: 84%

Tuition and Fees:

Resident
$11,011

Average (public)
$8,772

Average (private)
$19,562

Nonresident
$20,815

Average (public)
$14,629

Average (private)
$19,562

0   5   10   15   20   25   30

Percentage receiving financial aid: 77%

ADMISSIONS

In the fall 1999 first-year class, 4721 applied, 907 were accepted, and 286 enrolled. Fifty transfers enrolled. The median LSAT percentile of the most recent first-year class was 92; the median GPA was 3.65 on a scale of 4.0. The lowest LSAT percentile accepted was 36; the highest was 99.

Requirements

Applicants must have a bachelor's degree from an accredited institution and take the LSAT. The most important admission factors include GPA, LSAT results, and academic achievement. No specific undergraduate courses are required. Candidates are not interviewed.

Procedure

The application deadline for fall entry is January 15. Applicants should submit an application form, LSAT results, and transcripts. Check with the school for the current fee. Notification of the admission decision is from February through late May. The latest acceptable LSAT test date for fall entry is December. The law school uses the LSDAS.

Special

The law school recruits minority and disadvantaged students by means of visits to undergraduate schools, participation in LSAC forums, and programs arranged by law school student organizations. Transfer students must have one year of credit, have attended an ABA-approved law school, and must have an outstanding academic performance in the first year of law school. The law school offers a limited enrollment, 8-day summer program designed for students who are the first in their family to attend college or law school, those who have been out of school for a number of years, or those who are unfamiliar with the American legal system.

Costs

Tuition and fees for the 1999-2000 academic year are $11,011 for in-state students and $20,815 for out-of-state students. On-campus room and board costs about $9009 annually; and books and supplies run $1221.

Financial Aid

In a recent year, about 77% of current law students received some form of aid. The average annual amount of aid from all sources combined, including scholarships, loans, and work contracts, was $17,154. Awards are based on need along with departmental scholarships are awarded on the basis of need, and merit. The required financial statement is the FAFSA. Check with the school for cu;rrent application deadlines. Graduate Opportunity Fellowship Program funds are available to disadvantaged students. First-year students are notified about their financial aid application at some time prior to the beginning of the semester.

About the Law School

University of California at Los Angeles School of Law was established in 1948 and is a public institution. The 419-acre campus is in an urban area in Los Angeles. The primary mission of the law school is to admit outstanding students who will bring a wide range of backgrounds to the classroom and the legal profession. UCLA's central purpose is to train attorneys of professional excellence and integrity who will exercise civic responsibility. Students have access to federal, state, county, city, and local agencies, courts, correctional facilities, law firms, and legal aid organizations in the Los Angeles area. The law school offers a mediation clinic where students work on cases in the municipal courts. The school also has a partnership with Public Counsel, the pro bono arm of the Los Angeles County and Beverly Hills bar associations. Housing for law students is widely available. They may choose from privately owned rental housing, university-owned apartments, and graduate student apartments and dormitories. About 99% of the law school facilities are accessible to the physically disabled.

Calendar

The law school operates on a traditional semester basis. Courses are offered days only and must be completed within 5 years. There is no part-time program. New students are admitted in the fall. There is no summer session. Transferable summer courses are not offered.

Programs

In addition to the J.D., the law school offers the LL.M. Students may take relevant courses in other programs and apply credit toward the J.D.; a maximum of 6 credits may be applied. The following joint degrees may be earned: J.D./M.B.A. (Juris Doctor/Master of Business Administration), J.D./M.A. (Juris Doctor/Master of Arts in urban planning), and J.D./M.A. (Juris Doctor/Master of Arts in American Indian studies).

Required

To earn the J.D., candidates must complete 87 total credits, of which 35 are for required courses. They must maintain a minimum GPA of 1.7 in first-year

Phone: 310-825-2080
Fax: 310-825-9450
E-mail: admissions@law.ucla.edu
Web: www.law.ucla.edu

Contact

Andrea Sossin-Bergman, Assistant Dean for Admissions, 310-825-2080 for general inquiries; Veronica Wilson, 310-825-2459 for financial aid information.

required courses, 1.9 thereafter. The following first-year courses are required of all students: Constitutional Law I, Contracts, Lawyering Skills, Torts, Criminal Law, Property, and Civil Procedure. Required upper-level courses consist of Legal Profession. All students must take clinical courses. There is an optional 2-day orientation program designed to acquaint first-year students with classmates, professors and deans, and with the study of law and to handle a variety of administrative tasks. It incorporates a law skills workshop, panel and group discussions, and a substantive course lecture.

Electives

The School of Law offers concentrations in corporate law, and international law, and UCLA offers specializations in these areas with specific course requirements and special notations on diploma upon completion. In addition, clinics are offered to advanced students in environmental law, trial advocacy, public policy advocacy, fact investigation, alternative dispute resolution, pre trial procedures, and other subjects. Credit ranges from 4 to 13 units, depending on the course. Seminars are offered to advanced students and credit ranges from 2 to 4 units, depending on the course. Externships are offered to students in their fourth and fifth semesters and are worth 13 units: 11 units for the placement and 2 units for a paper. The externships range from the State Department's Office of General Counsel, the White House Counsel, government law offices, and public interest law firms, to non-profit agencies and the chambers of many federal judges. Directed research, for which students must produce original scholarship of publishable quality, offers 1 to 5 units. Academic support programs that include tutorials are available for some first-year courses, exam workshops, and Bar preparatory sessions for advanced students. Remedial programs for students in academic difficulty include an intensive section of Legal Lawyering Skills and Wills and Trusts. Summer programs for students admitted on a diversity basis are available. The most widely taken electives are those subjects tested on the California bar exam, such as Constitutional Law II, Constitutional Criminal Procedure, and Wills and Trusts.

Graduation Requirements

In order to graduate, candidates must have a GPA of 1.9, and have 6 semesters of residence credit in regular session.

Organizations

Students edit the *UCLA Law Review* and the newspaper The *Docket*. Other student-edited publications include the *Asian Pacific American Law Journal, Journal of Environmental Law and Policy, National Black Law Journal, Pacific Basin Law Journal, Women's Law Journal, Chicano/Latino Law Review, UCLA Journal of International Law and Foreign Affairs,* the online *Bulletin of Law and Technology,* and *Entertainment Law Review.* There is a Moot Court Honors Program, a Roscoe Pound Competition, and the National Hispanic Moot Court Competition. Law student organizations include the American Indian Law Students Association, Immigration Law Society, and Health Care Law Society. Local chapters of national associations include Phi Alpha Delta and Phi Delta Phi.

Library

The law library contains 470,789 hardcopy volumes and 319,675 microform volume equivalents, and subscribes to 6967 serial publications. Such on-line databases and networks as LEXIS, DIALOG, WESTLAW, and Legal-Trac are available to law students for research. Special library collections include a U.S. government depository, a California depository, an East Asian law collection, and a Mexican law collection. The newly expanded and renovated Hugh and Hazel Darling Law Library nearly doubles the size of the former library and adds state-of-the-art technological enhancements. The ratio of library volumes to faculty is 4483 to 1 and to students, 470 to 1. The ratio of seats in the library to students is 1 to 1.

Faculty

The law school has 79 full-time and 26 part-time faculty members, of whom 33 are women. According to AAUP standards for Category I institutions, faculty salaries are well above average. About 15% of full-time faculty have a graduate law degree in addition to the J.D.; about

Placement

J.D.s awarded:	324

Services available through: separate law school placement center

Services: a twice-yearly on-campus interview program. The office hosts public interest, government, and small firm events as well.

Special features: individual counseling and workshops on career planning and interviewing skills. Job listings can be accessed by students and alumni by the Internet.

Full-time job interviews:	250 employers
Summer job interviews:	350 employers
Placement by graduation:	80% of class
Placement within 9 months:	98% of class
Average starting salary:	$87,000

Areas of placement:

Private practice 2-10 attorneys	8%
Private practice 11-25 attorneys	7%
Private practice 26-50 attorneys	10%
Private practice 51-100 attorneys	9%
unknown	41%
Judicial clerkships	8%
Government	5%
Public interest	3%
Academic	1%

12% of part-time faculty have one. The ratio of full-time students to full-time faculty in an average class is 13 to 1; in a clinic, 6 to 1. There is a chapter of the Order of the Coif; 32 faculty and 1050 graduates are members.

Students

About 53% of the student body are women; 37%, minorities; 5%, African American; 20%, Asian American; 11%, Hispanic; and 1%, Native American. The majority of students come from California (76%). The average age of entering students is 24; age range is 20 to 42. About 35% of students enter directly from undergraduate school. About 5% drop out after the first year for academic or personal reasons; 95% remain to receive a law degree.

UNIVERSITY OF CALIFORNIA, DAVIS

School of Law

King Hall - 400 Mrak Hall Drive
Davis, CA 95616-5201

Application Filing	Accreditation
Fall: February 1	ABA, AALS
Spring: n/app	**Degrees Granted**
Fee: $40	J.D., LL.M.

Enrollment 1998–1999		First-Year Class	
Men:	243 48%	Applied:	2290
Women:	268 52%	Accepted:	796
Minorities:	123 24%	Enrolled:	161
Out-of-State:	72 14%		

1998–99 Class Profile
LSAT Percentile: 81%
LSAT Median Score: 160
Percentage passing bar on first try: 83%

Tuition and Fees:

Resident
$10,882

Average (public)
$8,772

Average (private)
$19,562

Nonresident
$20,266

Average (public)
$14,629

Average (private)
$19,562

0 5 10 15 20 25 30

Percentage receiving financial aid: 92%

ADMISSIONS
In the fall 1999 first-year class, 2290 applied, 796 were accepted, and 161 enrolled. One transfer enrolled. The median LSAT percentile of the most recent first-year class was 81; the median GPA was 3.42 on a scale of 4.0. The lowest LSAT percentile accepted was 30; the highest was 99.

Requirements
Applicants must have a bachelor's degree from an accredited institution and take the LSAT. The most important admission factors include LSAT results, personal statement, and GPA. No specific undergraduate courses are required. Candidates are not interviewed.

Procedure
The application deadline for fall entry is February 1. Applicants should submit an application form, LSAT results, a nonrefundable application fee of $40, 2 letters of recommendation, and a personal statement; applicants should directly submit supplementary transcripts covering the fall semester, and successful applicants must submit a final transcript. Notification of the admission decision is from January to May. The latest acceptable LSAT test date for fall entry is December. The law school uses the LSDAS.

Special
The law school recruits minority and disadvantaged students by means of visits to undergraduate campuses, the Candidate Referral Service, graduate/professional information days, and the Western Name Exchange. Requirements are different for out-of-state students in that they pay tuition not required of California residents. Transfer students must have one year of credit, have attended an ABA-approved law school, with admitted students usually in the top 5% to 10% of their first-year class.

Costs
Tuition and fees for the 1999-2000 academic year are $10,882 for full-time in-state students and $20,266 for out-of-state students. Books and supplies run $889.

Financial Aid
About 92% of current law students receive some form of aid. The average annual amount of aid from all sources combined, including scholarships, loans, and work contracts, is $16,600; maximum, $30,700. Awards are based on need. The required financial statement is FAFSA. The aid application deadline for fall entry is March 2. First-year students are notified about their financial aid application at the time of acceptance.

About the Law School
University of California, Davis School of Law was established in 1965 and is a public institution. The 5200-acre campus is in a small town 15 miles west of Sacramento. The primary mission of the law school is to combine the best of traditional legal education with modern techniques of providing practical experience. Students have access to federal, state, county, city, and local agencies, courts, correctional facilities, law firms, and legal aid organizations in the Davis area. The law school is located about 15 miles from downtown Sacramento, the state capital. Facilities of special interest to law students include the instructional computer laboratory, the library, which allows 24-hour access, and a day care co-op where care is provided by parents for children 12 months and younger. Housing for law students is available through university housing facilities for single graduate students and student families; off campus housing is available through the ASUCD Community Housing Listing Service and a variety of community resource listings (e.g., newspapers). All law school facilities are accessible to the physically disabled.

Calendar
The law school operates on a traditional semester basis. Courses for full-time students are offered days only and must be completed within 3 years, unless special circumstances arise. There is no part-time program. New full-time students are admitted in the fall. There is no summer session. Transferable summer courses are not offered.

Programs
In addition to the J.D., the law school offers the LL.M. Students may take relevant courses in other programs and apply credit toward the J.D.; a maximum of 10 semester units as part of a combined degree program begun at the law school may be applied. The following joint degrees may be earned: J.D./M.A. (Juris Doctor/Master of Arts in most programs offered by UC Davis Graduate Studies Division) and J.D./M.B.A. (Juris Doctor/Masters in Business Administration).

Phone: 530-752-6477
E-mail: lawadmissions@ucdavis.edu
Web: kinghall.ucdavis.edu

Contact

530-752-6477 for general inquiries; Delecia Nunnally, Financial Aid Director, 530-752-6573 for financial aid information.

Required

To earn the J.D., candidates must complete 88 total credits, of which 33 are for required courses. They must maintain a minimum GPA of 2.0 in the required courses. The following first-year courses are required of all students: Introduction to Law, Property, Contracts, Civil Procedure, Torts, Constitutional Law, Criminal Law, and Legal Research and Legal Writing. Required upper-level courses consist of Professional Responsibility and an advanced legal writing project. The required orientation program for first-year students is an introductory week that includes meeting the Academic Assistance Program tutors, a tour of the law library, a photo session, class registration, a financial aid information session, dean's orientation, and social activities. The primary focus is a 1-unit course, Introduction to Law.

Electives

Students must take 15 credits in their area of concentration. The School of Law offers a certificate program in public interest law. In addition, clinics are open to upper-level students. Placements are available with selected public agencies, judges, and some private attorneys through such formal clinical programs as Administration of Criminal Justice (2 to 6 or 12 units), Civil Rights (2 to 6 units), and Employment Relations (2 to 6 units). Seminars for 2 or 3 credits, open to upper-level students, include areas of constitutional law, criminal law, and estate planning. There is an Academic Assistance Program whereby a second- or third-year student is assigned to each first-year class. The tutors are available for assistance with substantive course work as well as note taking, briefing, and outlining skills. Special interest group programs include the King Hall Pro Bono Program and the Public Interest Law Program. The most widely taken electives are Negotiations and Trial Practice.

Graduation Requirements

In order to graduate, candidates must have a GPA of 2.0, completed the upper-division writing requirement, and the required courses.

Organizations

Students edit the *UC Davis Law Review*; the newspaper, *Advocate*; the *Environs*, a publication of the Environmental Law Society; the *Journal of International Law and Policy*, a publication of the International Law Society; and the *Journal of Juvenile Law and Policy*. Moot court competitions held annually include the Moot Court Trial Competition, Client Counseling, and National Moot Court. Student organizations include the Law Student Association, ABA-Law Student Division, and American Civil Liberties Union. There are local chapters of Phi Alpha Delta and Phi Delta Phi. Other campus organizations include the Alumni Association.

Library

The law library contains 276,361 hardcopy volumes and 617,054 microform volume equivalents, and subscribes to 5043 serial publications. Such on-line databases and networks as LEXIS, DIALOG, WESTLAW, and MELVYL-UC system, First Search, WORLDCAT, CQ, and MEDLINE are available to law students for research. Special library collections include federal and California documents depositories. Special emphasis is in intellectual property and environmental law. Recently, the library added wireless access to the Internet and on-line resources through the library. The ratio of library volumes to faculty is 5221 to 1 and to students, 585 to 1.

Faculty

The law school has 31 full-time and 34 part-time faculty members, of whom 28 are women. According to AAUP standards for Category I institutions, faculty salaries are well above average. About 3% of full-time faculty have a graduate law degree in addition to the J.D. The ratio of full-time students to full-time faculty in an average class is 40 to 1; in a clinic, 10 to 1. The law school has a regular program of bringing visiting professors and other distinguished lecturers and visitors to campus. There is a chapter of the Order of the Coif; 26 faculty and 448 graduates are members.

Placement

J.D.s awarded:	146

Services available through: A separate law school placement center.

Special features: NEXIS and LEXIS systems are available for student use; there is a career services library as well as career-related panels and presentations. UC Davis is a member of the Public Interest Clearinghouse's Public Interest Law Certificate Program, which includes specialized job listings and career advising.

Full-time job interviews:	n/av
Summer job interviews:	107 employers
Placement by graduation:	51% of class
Placement within 9 months:	92% of class
Average starting salary:	$26,400 to $95,000
Areas of placement:	
Private practice 2-10 attorneys	15%
Private practice 11-25 attorneys	16%
Private practice 26-50 attorneys	8%
Private practice 51-100 attorneys	8%
Private practice 101+ attorneys	16%
Solo practice	1%
Government	14%
Judicial clerkships	12%
Public interest	7%
Academic	1%
Business/industry	1%

Students

About 52% of the student body are women; 24%, minorities; 3%, African American; 13%, Asian American; 6%, Hispanic; and 1%, Native American. The majority of students come from California (86%). The average age of entering students is 25; age range is 20 to 52. About 38% of students enter directly from undergraduate school and 13% have a graduate degree. About 6% drop out after the first year for academic or personal reasons; 90% remain to receive a law degree.

Law School

1111 East 60th Street
Chicago, IL 60637

Application Filing		Accreditation
Fall: see profile		ABA, AALS
Spring: n/app		**Degrees Granted**
Fee: $60	J.D., LL.M., M.C.L., J.S.D., D.C.L.	

Enrollment 1998–1999		First-Year Class	
Men:	333 59%	Applied:	2972
Women:	231 41%	Accepted:	883
Minorities:	96 17%	Enrolled:	182
Out-of-State:	457 81%		

1998–99 Class Profile

LSAT Percentile: 97%
LSAT Median Score: 169
Percentage passing bar on first try: n/av

Tuition and Fees:

Resident
$26,796

Average (public)
$8,772

Average (private)
$19,562

Nonresident
$26,796

Average (public)
$14,629

Average (private)
$19,562

0   5   10   15   20   25   30

Percentage receiving financial aid: 75%

ADMISSIONS

In the fall 1999 first-year class, 2972 applied, 883 were accepted, and 182 enrolled. Twenty-two transfers enrolled. The median LSAT percentile of the most recent first-year class was 97; the median GPA was 3.7 on a scale of 4.0.

Requirements

Applicants must have a bachelor's degree from an accredited institution and take the LSAT. No specific undergraduate courses are required. Candidates are interviewed.

Procedure

The application deadlines for fall entry are December 1, earlly, February 1, regular, and April 1, late. Applicants should submit an application form, LSAT results, transcripts, a nonrefundable application fee of $60, 2 letters of recommendation, a personal statement and resume. Notification of the admissions decision is sent by January 1, March 1, or May 30. The latest acceptable LSAT test date for fall entry is December for most cases. The law school uses the LSDAS.

Special

The law school recruits minority and disadvantaged students by using the Law School Data Assembly Service's Candidate Referral Service and outreach at law school forums, colleges, and minority fairs. Transfer students must have one year of credit and must be planning to spend at least 2 years at the school.

Costs

Tuition and fees for the 1999-2000 academic year are $26,796 for all students. On-campus room and board costs about $10,500 annually; and books and supplies run $1500.

Financial Aid

About 75% of current law students receive some form of aid. Awards are based on need and merit. The required financial statement is the FAFSA. The aid application deadline for fall entry is March 1.

About the Law School

University of Chicago Law School was established in 1902 and is a private institution. The 203-acre campus is in an urban area 7 miles from downtown Chicago. The primary mission of the law school is not to certify lawyers but to train well-rounded, critical, and socially conscious thinkers and doers. Three cornerstones provide the foundation for Chicago's educational mission: the life of the mind, participatory learning, and interdisciplinary inquiry. Students have access to federal, state, county, city, and local agencies, courts, correctional facilities, law firms, and legal aid organizations in the Chicago area. Housed in the Arthur Cane Center, Chicago's clinics involve more than 100 students each year and permit them to represent clients with real-world legal problems under the guidance of clinical faculty. Facilities of special interest to law students include the law quadrangle, made up of buildings surrounding a reflecting pool and housing the law library, classrooms, offices, the legal aid clinics, an auditorium, and a moot court room. About a third of first-year students live in the school's dormitory, located 2 blocks from the school. Two-thirds of the first-year students and half of the upper-class students live in Hyde Park's 3-story walk-ups, highrises, single-family homes, and townhouses. The remainder commute from other neighborhoods in Chicago.

Calendar

The law school operates on a quarter basis. Courses are offered days only and must be completed within a 3-year course of study. There is no part-time program. New students are admitted in the fall. There is no summer session.

Programs

In addition to the J.D., the law school offers the LL.M, M.C.L., J.S.D., and D.C.L. Students may take relevant courses in other programs and apply credit toward the J.D.; a maximum of 12 credits may be applied. Students may earn joint degrees with any other division of the university, but must be accepted in both divisions.

Phone: 773-702-9484
Fax: 773-834-0942
E-mail: admissions@law.uchicago.edu
Web: law.uchicago.edu

Contact
Anna Praschma or Genita Robinson, Associate Directors of Admission, 773-702-9484 for general inquiries and for financial aid information.

ILLINOIS

Required
To earn the J.D., candidates must complete 105 total credits, of which 40 are for required courses. They must maintain a minimum grade average of 68 in the required courses. The following first-year courses are required of all students: Elements of the Law, Contracts, Criminal Law, Civil Procedures, Property, Torts, Legal Research and Writing, and 1 elective. All upper-level courses are elective with the exception of a professional responsibility course. Two substantial writings, beyond those required in the first-year Legal Research and Writing course, must also be completed. The optional orientation program for first-year students consists of 4 days of presentations, tours, and social events, including a dinner, a Lake Michigan boat cruise, a picnic, and a visit to the Second City Comedy Review.

Electives
The school's clinical program includes the Mandel Legal Aid Clinic, the Institute for Justice Clinic on Entrepreneurship, and the MacArthur Justice Center. These clinics are open to second- and third-year students. Credit is given for both the classroom and the practical component. 68 of the school's 155 courses are seminars. They are open to second- and third-year students. Examples include Cyberlaw, Race and Criminal Justice, Entrepreneurship, and Issues in International Refugee Law. The Career Services Center helps students locate summer internships. Approximately 92% of first-year students and 99% of second-year students are employed during the summer. The Chicago Law Foundation, a student-run charitable organization, awards grants to students working in public-interest jobs during the summer. The school encourages student and faculty research in the law as well as the social sciences. Faculty-supervised research may be done in the Individual Research program for credit. Lectures, open to the law school community, occur several times a year in workshops such as constitutional Law, International Law, Law and Economics, Law and Philosophy, and regular lunchtime lectures with a variety of speakers. The most widely taken electives are Evidence, Constitutional Law, and Taxation of Individual Income.

Graduation Requirements
In order to graduate, candidates must have a grade average of 68, have completed the upper-division writing requirement, and have completed a Professional Responsibility course.

Organizations
Students edit the *University of Chicago Law Review*, the *University of Chicago Legal Forum*, the University of Chicago Roundtable, and the Journal of International Legal Studies. About a third of students participate. There are 4 faculty-edited journals: the *Supreme Court Review, the Journal of Law and Economics, the Journal of Legal Studies*, and *Law and Economics: Working Papers*. The student newspaper is *The Phoenix*. While first-year students have moot court practice in their Legal Research and Writing class, upper-level students participate in the Hinton Moot Court Program. The school has about 40 student organizations that include the Intellectual Property and Entertainment Law Society, International Law Society, and the Law and Internet Forum. Local chapters of national associations include the Black Law Students Association, the Federalist Society, and ACLU. Other organizations include Habitat for Humanity, Outdoor Adventure Club, and Simply Theater.

Library
The law library contains 640,000 hard-copy volumes and 61,756 microform volume equivalents, and subscribes to 7816 serial publications. Such on-line databases and networks as LEXIS and WESTLAW are available to law students for research. Special library collections include a federal document depository, Supreme Court briefs and records, and Kare Llewellyn Papers. Recently, the library added power and data ports to desks. The ratio of library volumes to faculty is 5614 to 1 and to students, 1135 to 1. The ratio of seats in the library to students is 1 to 1.

Faculty
The law school has 54 full-time and 60 part-time faculty members. According to AAUP standards for Category I institutions, faculty salaries are well above average. The law school has a regular program of bringing visiting professors and other distinguished lecturers and visitors to campus. There is a chapter of the Order of the Coif.

Placement

Placement	
J.D.s awarded:	191
Services available through: a separate law school placement center.	
Services: seminars and publications	
Full-time job interviews:	221 employers
Summer job interviews:	333 employers
Placement by graduation:	97% of class
Placement within 9 months:	98% of class
Average starting salary:	$37,000 to $125,000
Areas of placement:	
Private practice	67%
Judicial clerkships	25%
Business/industry	7%
Government	1%
Public interest	1%

Students
About 41% of the student body are women; 17%, minorities; 4%, African American; 9%, Asian American; and 5%, Hispanic. The majority of students come from the Midwest (39%). The average age of entering students is 24; age range is 20 to 42. About 40% of students enter directly from undergraduate school, 14% have a graduate degree, and 58% have worked full time prior to entering law school. About 1% drop out after the first year for academic or personal reasons; 99% remain to receive a law degree.

UNIVERSITY OF CINCINNATI

College of Law

P.O. Box 210040
Cincinnati, OH 45221-0040

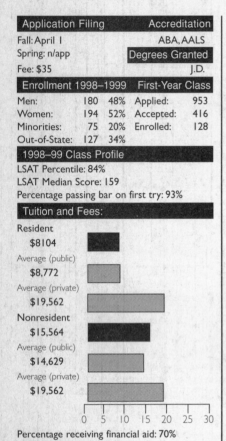

Application Filing			Accreditation
Fall: April 1			ABA, AALS
Spring: n/app			**Degrees Granted**
Fee: $35			J.D.
Enrollment 1998–1999			**First-Year Class**
Men:	180	48%	Applied: 953
Women:	194	52%	Accepted: 416
Minorities:	75	20%	Enrolled: 128
Out-of-State:	127	34%	

1998–99 Class Profile
LSAT Percentile: 84%
LSAT Median Score: 159
Percentage passing bar on first try: 93%

Tuition and Fees:

Resident
$8104

Average (public)
$8,772

Average (private)
$19,562

Nonresident
$15,564

Average (public)
$14,629

Average (private)
$19,562

0 5 10 15 20 25 30

Percentage receiving financial aid: 70%

ADMISSIONS

In the fall 1999 first-year class, 953 applied, 416 were accepted, and 128 enrolled. Fifteen transfers enrolled. The median LSAT percentile of the most recent first-year class was 84; the median GPA was 3.5 on a scale of 4.0. The lowest LSAT percentile accepted was 20; the highest was 99.

Requirements
Applicants must have a bachelor's degree from an accredited institution and take the LSAT. The most important admission factors include GPA, LSAT results, and academic achievement. No specific undergraduate courses are required. Candidates are not interviewed.

Procedure
The application deadline for fall entry is April 1. Applicants should submit an application form, LSAT results, transcripts, TOEFL for international applicants, a nonrefundable application fee of $35, and 2 letters of recommendation. Notification of the admission decision is on a rolling basis. The latest acceptable LSAT test date for fall entry is February. The law school uses the LSDAS.

Special
The law school recruits minority and disadvantaged students by giving special consideration to competitive applications for admission by candidates from minority groups under-represented in the legal profession. Particular effort is made to provide adequate financial assistance to minority students. Transfer students must have one year of credit, have attended an ABA-approved law school, supply their class rank, give the reason(s) for the transfer, and generally be in the top 20% of the class. The applicant must also have attended a member law school of AALS.

Costs

Tuition and fees for the 1999-2000 academic year are $8104 for full-time in-state students and $15,564 for out-of-state students. On-campus room and board costs about $9899 annually; books and supplies run $723.

Financial Aid

About 70% of current law students receive some form of aid. Awards are based on need and merit. The required financial statement is FAFSA. The aid application deadline for fall entry is March 1. First-year students are notified about their financial aid application at time of acceptance.

About the Law School

University of Cincinnati College of Law was established in 1833 and is a public institution. The campus is in an urban area in the Clifton area of Cincinnati. The primary mission of the law school is to provide students with an opportunity to equip themselves for effective and creative participation in the roles lawyers play in our society. Students have access to federal, state, county, city, and local agencies, courts, correctional facilities, law firms, and legal aid organizations in the Cincinnati area. Students also have access to a variety of legal externships in Cincinnati coordinated through the Office of Public Service and Professional Development. Facilities of special interest to law students are the U.S. Court of Appeals for the Sixth Circuit and the District Court for the Southern District of Ohio; the 3000-plus members of the Cincinnati Bar Association; the more than 300 law firms; and the Legal Aid Society of Cincinnati. Housing for law students is plentiful, and most law students live off campus in housing within walking distance of campus. The average rent is $375 to $425 a month. All law school facilities are accessible to the physically disabled.

Calendar

The law school operates on a traditional semester basis. Courses for full-time students are offered days only and must be completed within 3 years unless special circumstances exist. There is no part-time program. New full-time students are admitted in the fall. There is no summer session. Transferable summer courses are offered.

Programs

Students may take relevant courses in other programs and apply credit toward the J.D.; a maximum of 8 credits may be applied. The following joint degrees may be earned: J.D./M.B.A. (Juris Doctor/Master of Business Administration), J.D./M.C.P. (Juris Doctor/Master of Community Planning), and J.D./M.A. (Juris Doctor/Master of Arts in women's studies).

Contact

513-556-6805 for general inquiries; Al Watson, Assistant Dean and Director of Admissions, 513-556-6805 for financial aid information.

OHIO

Required

To earn the J.D., candidates must complete 90 total credits, of which 35 are for required courses. They must maintain a minimum GPA of 2.0 in the required courses. The following first-year courses are required of all students: Introduction to Law, Civil Procedure I and II, Constitutional Law I and II, Contracts, Legal Research and Writing, Torts, Advocacy, Criminal Law, and Property. Required upper-level courses consist of Professional Responsibility and 2 writing requirements. Externships are strongly encouraged but not required. The required orientation program for first-year students is 1 week long and includes the Introduction to Law course, registration, a photo identification session, a tour of the facilities, assignment of faculty and student advisers, a meeting with student advisers, a social event with upper-level students, information about the law library, and bar association membership opportunities.

Electives

The College of Law offers concentrations in corporate law, environmental law, international law, litigation, tax law, and intellectual property. In addition, seminar topics include corporate law, constitutional law, and banking. An externship program is offered to 50 or 60 students and is worth 3 credit hours. Speakers can be heard at the Human Rights Institute, which invites international visitors, the Center for Corporate Law, the Center for Mental Health Law, and the Health Care Law symposium. Study abroad may be done at any ABA/AALS-approved program with special permission. A maximum of 8 credit hours from outside the law school can be applied toward the J.D. An academic support program is also available. Minority programs include the Minority Access Program and a summer clerkship program with federal judges, local corporations, and law firms. The most widely taken electives are Corporations and Evidence.

Graduation Requirements

In order to graduate, candidates must have a GPA of 2.0, complete the upper-division writing requirement, and have completed the Professional Responsibility course.

Organizations

Students edit the *University of Cincinnati Law Review*, the *Immigration and Nationality Law Review*, and the *Human Rights Quarterly*. Students compete at the Jessup International Law Moot Court, the J. Braxton Craven, Jr. Memorial Moot Court, and the Giles Sutherland Rich Moot Court in patent law. Also, the College of Law hosts the National Product Liability Competition and participates in all other national competitions. Law student organizations include the ABA-Law Student Division, International Law Society, and Intellectual Property Society. There are local chapters of Order of the Barristers and Order of the Coif.

Library

The law library contains 385,617 hard-copy volumes and 673,095 microform volume equivalents, and subscribes to 2599 serial publications. Such on-line databases and networks as LEXIS, WESTLAW, and UCLID, Ohio Link databases, and the U.N. Optical Disk System are available to law students for research. Special library collections include the Urban Morgan Human Rights Collection; the Segoe Collection on Land Use and Urban Planning; the Goldstein Collection on the Law of Church and State; Manuscript collections: papers of William J. Butler, trustee and benefactor of the Urban Morgan Institute for Human Rights; records of the 1987 Merit Plan constitutional amendment campaign regarding judicial selection in Ohio; U.S. government depository (1978 - present). Recently, the library participated in Ohio Link, which facilitates resource sharing with more than 70 other Ohio academic libraries; created a public Web site http://www.law.uc.edu; and expanded access to the College of Law LAN in the Law Library. The ratio of library volumes to faculty is 16,765 to 1 and to students, 1031 to 1. The ratio of seats in the library to students is 1 to 1.

Faculty

The law school has 26 full-time and 58 part-time faculty members, of whom 12 are women. According to AAUP standards for Category I institutions, faculty salaries are above average. About 19% of full-time faculty have a graduate law degree in addition to the J.D. The ratio of full-time students to full-time faculty in an average class is 14 to 1. The law school has a regular program of bringing visiting professors and other distinguished lecturers and visitors to campus. There is a chapter of the Order of the Coif.

Placement

J.D.s awarded:	124

Services available through: a separate law school placement center.

Special features: focused career planning and career counseling sessions, an extensive library on career issues including nonlegal and specialty practice, federal job options program, and a local government/public interest career fair

Full-time job interviews:	30 employers
Summer job interviews:	45 employers
Placement by graduation:	60% of class
Placement within 9 months:	93% of class
Average starting salary:	$23,900 to $103,000

Areas of placement:

Private practice 2-10 attorneys	10%
Private practice 11-25 attorneys	8%
Private practice 26-50 attorneys	5%
Private practice 51-100 attorneys	4%
Business/industry	19%
Judicial clerkships	9%
Public interest	4%
Government	4%
Military	3%

Students

About 52% of the student body are women; 20%, minorities; and 12%, African American. The majority of students come from Ohio (66%). The average age of entering students is 25; age range is 20 to 60. About 45% of students enter directly from undergraduate school, 10% have a graduate degree, and 55% have worked full-time prior to entering law school. About 1% drop out after the first year for academic or personal reasons; 96% remain to receive a law degree.

School of Law

Campus Box 403
Boulder, CO 80309-0403

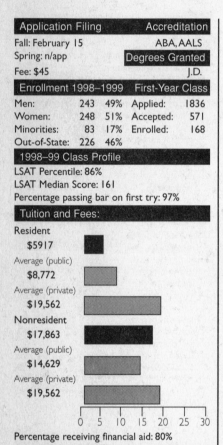

Application Filing		Accreditation
Fall: February 15		ABA, AALS
Spring: n/app		Degrees Granted
Fee: $45		J.D.

Enrollment 1998–1999		First-Year Class	
Men:	243 49%	Applied:	1836
Women:	248 51%	Accepted:	571
Minorities:	83 17%	Enrolled:	168
Out-of-State:	226 46%		

1998–99 Class Profile

LSAT Percentile: 86%
LSAT Median Score: 161
Percentage passing bar on first try: 97%

Tuition and Fees:

Resident
$5917

Average (public)
$8,772

Average (private)
$19,562

Nonresident
$17,863

Average (public)
$14,629

Average (private)
$19,562

0 5 10 15 20 25 30

Percentage receiving financial aid: 80%

ADMISSIONS

In the fall 1999 first-year class, 1836 applied, 571 were accepted, and 168 enrolled. Three transfers enrolled. The median LSAT percentile of the most recent first-year class was 86; the median GPA was 3.5 on a scale of 4.0. The lowest LSAT percentile accepted was 23; the highest was 99.

Requirements

Applicants must have a bachelor's degree from an accredited institution and take the LSAT. Minimum acceptable LSAT percentile is 1 and minimum acceptable GPA is 1.0 on a scale of 4.0. The most important admission factors include writing ability, LSAT results, GPA, and academic achievement. No specific undergraduate courses are required. Candidates are not interviewed.

Procedure

The application deadline for fall entry is February 15. Applicants should submit an application form, LSAT results, transcripts, a nonrefundable application fee of $45, 1 letter of recommendation, and a personal statement. Notification of the admission decision is mid-January through May. The latest acceptable LSAT test date for fall entry is December. The law school uses the LSDAS.

Special

The law school recruits minority and disadvantaged students by means of law school forums, candidate referral services through LSAS, and special outreach by the Associate Dean for Student Affairs/Professional Programs. Transfer students must have one year of credit, and have attended an ABA-approved law school; it is recommended that students be in the top 10% to 20% of their current law school class.

Costs

Tuition and fees for the 1999-2000 academic year are $5917 for full-time in-state students and $17,863 for out-of-state students. On-campus room and board costs about $8146 annually; books and supplies run $695.

Financial Aid

About 80% of current law students receive some form of aid. The average annual amount of aid from all sources combined, including scholarships, loans, and work contracts, is $18,943 (resident) or $30,899 (nonresident). Awards are based on need and merit, loans are based on need. Scholarships are usually based on a combination of need and merit. The required financial statement is FAFSA. The aid application deadline for fall entry is March 1. Special funds for minority or disadvantaged students cosist of a mix of need-based, merit, and diversity scholarships. First-year students are notified about their financial aid application at the time of the initial inquiry; information on financial aid is included in the catalog. Admitted students are encouraged to apply for financial aid as early as possible.

About the Law School

University of Colorado School of Law was established in 1892 and is a public institution. The 873-acre campus is in a small town 30 miles northwest of Denver. The primary mission of the law school is to develop the skills, ethics, and habits of mind to be an excellent lawyer with a strong sense of the legal profession's greatest traditions and to develop an equal dedication to public service. Students have access to federal, state, county, city, and local agencies, courts, correctional facilities, law firms, and legal aid organizations in the Boulder area. Facilities of special interest to law students include the law school facility, which contains all aspects of academic, administrative, clinical, research, career services, social, and audiovisual offerings under one roof. Housing for law students is primarily in apartments within 10 minutes of the law school. Less expensive accommodations are available in nearby towns. About 95% of the law school facilities are accessible to the physically disabled.

Calendar

The law school operates on a traditional semester basis. Courses for full-time students are offered days only and must be completed within 3 years. There is no part-time program. New full-time students are admitted in the fall. There is an 8-week summer session. Transferable summer courses are not offered.

Programs

Students may take relevant courses in other programs and apply credit toward the J.D.; the maximum number of credits that may be applied varies. The following joint degrees may be earned: J.D./M.B.A. (Juris Doctor/Master of Business Administration), J.D./M.P.A. (Juris Doctor/Master of Public Administration), and J.D./M.I.A. (Juris Doctor/Master of International Affairs).

Required

To earn the J.D., candidates must complete 89 total credits, of which 43 are for required courses. They must maintain a minimum grade average of 72 in the required courses. The following first-year courses are required of all students:

Contact

Carol Nelson-Douglas, Assistant Dean for Admissions and Financial Aid, 303-492-7203 for general inquiries; 303-492-7203 for financial aid information.

COLORADO

Contracts I and II, Torts, Civil Procedure I and II, Property I and II, Criminal Law, Legal Writing, and Appellate Court Advocacy. Required upper-level courses consist of Constitutional Law, Evidence, Professional Responsibility, and a seminar and practice requirement. All students must take clinical courses. The required orientation program for first-year students is 4 days and includes class registration, legal writing exercises, social activities, and an introduction to faculty, law school, and university facilities.

Electives

The School of Law offers concentrations in corporate law, criminal law, environmental law, family law, international law, juvenile law, labor law, litigation, media law, securities law, tax law, torts and insurance, and natural resources. In addition, clinics are available for either a year or 1 semester, with a maximum of 11 credits awarded. Clinics include Indian Law, Appellate Advocacy, Natural Resources Litigation, and Legal Aid (civil and criminal practice). A minimum of 1 seminar must be chosen from a variety of subjects. Externships allow students to earn up to 4 hours of academic credit for work in a governmental agency, private nonprofit institution, or a private law office. Independent study is occasionally permitted for 1 credit. Field work is offered through some seminars. Special no-credit lectures are offered to all students on a variety of topics. There is one tutor per each first-year class section. Students on academic probation are furnished with tutors. The most widely taken electives are Natural Resources and Environmental Law and Corporate Law.

Graduation Requirements

In order to graduate, candidates must have a grade average of 72, complete the upper-division writing requirement, and submit a paper of publishable quality for the required seminar.

Organizations

Students edit the *University of Colorado Law Review, Colorado Journal of International Environmental Law and Policy*, and the newspaper, *Class Action*. The school competes in the Rothgerber Moot Court, held annually at the law school, the Jessup International Moot Court, held each year regionally, nationally, and internationally, and the Carrigan Cup Competition, an internal competition in which participants are selected for regional competitions. From time to time the law school participates in the national mock trial competition sponsored by the ABA. Law student organizations include Telecom/High Tech Association, Women's Law Caucus, and Student Trial Lawyers Association. There is a local chapter of Phi Alpha Delta Julius Gunther Chapter.

Library

The law library contains 383,000 hardcopy volumes and 725,704 microform volume equivalents, and subscribes to 970 serial publications. Such on-line databases and networks as LEXIS, DIALOG, WESTLAW, Congressional Universe, Academic Universe, Statistical Universe, UNCOVER, OCLC, RLIN, First Search, Encyclopedia Britannica, Innovative Interfaces' Library System, Legaltrac, and Index to Legal Periodicals are available to law students for research. Special library collections include a federal publications depository and strengths in environmental and Native American Law and Constitutional Law. Recently, the library installed a wireless LAN that allows students to check out laptops that access the Internet via a radio frequency. The ratio of library volumes to faculty is 7660 to 1 and to students, 730 to 1. The ratio of seats in the library to students is 1 to 1.

Faculty

The law school has 40 full-time and 30 part-time faculty members, of whom 23 are women. According to AAUP standards for Category I institutions, faculty salaries are above average. About 2% of full-time faculty have a graduate law degree in addition to the J.D.; about 4% of part-time faculty have one. The ratio of full-time students to full-time faculty in an average class is 14 to 1; in a clinic, 12 to 1. There is a chapter of the Order of the Coif; 39 faculty and 573 graduates are members.

Placement

J.D.s awarded:	156

Services available through: separate law school placement center.

Services: group information in addition to individual advising; access to computer career search resources; written documents providing job search information.

Special features: an on-campus interview program, lunch-time informational sessions on job-seeking skills and various types of employment (traditional and nontraditional), Internet access to job postings, career workshops for law school graduates, a mock interview program, annual legal career options day program, government/public interest career fair.

Full-time job interviews:	31 employers
Summer job interviews:	49 employers
Placement by graduation:	51% of class
Placement within 9 months:	89% of class
Average starting salary:	$25,000 to $94,000

Areas of placement:

Private practice 2-10 attorneys	17%
Private practice 11-25 attorneys	3%
Private practice 26-50 attorneys	2%
Private practice 51-100 attorneys	4%
Private practice 100+ & firms size	
Unknown	13%
Judicial clerkships	14%
Government	13%
Business/industry	10%
Military	5%
Public interest	3%

Students

About 51% of the student body are women; 17%, minorities; 4%, African American; 4%, Asian American; 6%, Hispanic; and 3%, Native American. The majority of students come from Colorado (54%). The average age of entering students is 26; age range is 20 to 45. About 29% of students enter directly from undergraduate school, 11% have a graduate degree, and 73% have worked full-time prior to entering law school. About 5% drop out after the first year for academic or personal reasons; 90% remain to receive a law degree.

UNIVERSITY OF CONNECTICUT

School of Law

55 Elizabeth Street
Hartford, CT 06105

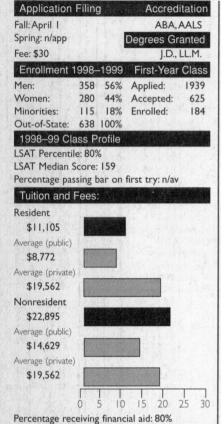

Application Filing	Accreditation
Fall: April 1	ABA, AALS
Spring: n/app	Degrees Granted
Fee: $30	J.D., LL.M.

Enrollment 1998–1999		First-Year Class	
Men:	358 56%	Applied:	1939
Women:	280 44%	Accepted:	625
Minorities:	115 18%	Enrolled:	184
Out-of-State:	638 100%		

1998–99 Class Profile
LSAT Percentile: 80%
LSAT Median Score: 159
Percentage passing bar on first try: n/av

Tuition and Fees:

Resident
$11,105

Average (public)
$8,772

Average (private)
$19,562

Nonresident
$22,895

Average (public)
$14,629

Average (private)
$19,562

0 5 10 15 20 25 30

Percentage receiving financial aid: 80%

ADMISSIONS

In the fall 1999 first-year class, 1939 applied, 625 were accepted, and 184 enrolled. The median LSAT percentile of the most recent first-year class was 80; the median GPA was 3.3 on a scale of 4.0.

Requirements
Applicants must have a bachelor's degree from an accredited institution and take the LSAT. No specific undergraduate courses are required. Candidates are not interviewed.

Procedure
The application deadline for fall entry is April 1. Applicants should submit an application form, LSAT results, transcripts, a nonrefundable application fee of $30, 2 letters of recommendation, and a personal statement. Notification of the admission decision is January through May. The latest acceptable LSAT test date for fall entry is February. The law school uses the LSDAS.

Special
The law school recruits minority and disadvantaged students by means of an annual Minority Law Day conference at the school, BLSA, ALSA, and LLSA students, and contacts with various minority undergraduate student organizations, centers, and advisers. Transfer students must have one year of credit, have attended an ABA-approved law school, should be within the top 10% of their class, and must show compelling reason(s) for transfer.

Costs

Tuition and fees for the 1999-2000 academic year are $11,105 for full-time in-state students and $22,895 for out-of-state students. Tuition for part-time students is $7049 per year in-state and $14,447 out-of-state. Books and supplies run $900.

Financial Aid

About 80% of current law students receive some form of aid. The average annual amount of aid from all sources combined, including scholarships, loans, and work contracts, is $12,100; maximum, $36,000. Awards are based on need, but some loans are non-need-based. The required financial statements are FAFSA and institutional financial aid application. The aid application deadline for fall entry is April 1. Special funds for minority or disadvantaged students consist of several grants that are awarded each year to entering students from economically and educationally disadvantaged backgrounds who demonstrate promise. First-year students are notified about their financial aid application at the time of acceptance.

About the Law School

University of Connecticut School of Law was established in 1921 and is a public institution. The 21-acre campus is in an urban area 100 miles southwest of Boston. The primary mission of the law school is to provide a legal education of high quality, serve the state and the bar, and prepare students to practice law in any jurisdiction. Students have access to federal, state, county, city, and local agencies, courts, correctional facilities, law firms, and legal aid organizations in the Hartford area. Housing for law students is ample and affordable in the surrounding areas; there are no on-campus housing facilities.

Calendar

The law school operates on a traditional semester basis. Courses for full-time students are offered days only, and days and evenings after the first year and must be completed within 5 years. For part-time students, courses are offered both day and evening and must be completed within 6 years. New full- and part-time students are admitted in the fall. There is a 4-week summer session. Transferable summer courses are offered.

Programs

In addition to the J.D., the law school offers the LL.M. Students may take relevant courses in other programs and apply credit toward the J.D.; a maximum of 6 credits may be applied. The following joint degrees may be earned: J.D./M.S.W. (Juris Doctor/Master of Social Work), J.D./M.L.S. (Juris Doctor/Master of Library Science), J.D./M.P.A. (Juris Doctor/Master of Public Affairs Administration), J.D./M.A. (Juris Doctor/Master of Public Policy), J.D./M.B.A. (Juris Doctor/Master of Business Administration), and J.D./M.P.H. (Juris Doctor/Master of Public Health).

Phone: 937-229-3555
Fax: 937-229-4194
E-mail: lawinfo@udayton.edu
Web: www.law.udayton.edu

Contact

Admissions Office, 937-229-3555 for general inquiries; Janet L. Hein, Director of Admission and financial Aid, 937-229-3555 for financial aid information.

OHIO

Programs

Students may take relevant courses in other programs and apply credit toward the J.D.; a maximum of 6 credits may be applied. The following joint degrees may be earned: J.D./M.B.A. (Juris Doctor/Master of Business Administration).

Required

To earn the J.D., candidates must complete 87 total credits, of which 36 are for required courses. They must maintain a minimum GPA of 2.0 in the required courses. The following first-year courses are required of all students: Constitutional Law I, Contracts I and II, Legal Profession I and II, Legislation, Property, and Torts I and II. Required upper-level courses consist of Constitutional Law II, Legal Profession III, and Professional Responsibility. The required orientation program for first-year students is a 3-1/2 day program primarily aimed at introducing students to the structure of their course of studies, to administrative matters such as registration and notebook computer set-up, and to provide them with an opportunity to gather in social settings and establish relationships with fellow students, faculty, and staff.

Electives

The School of Law offers concentrations in corporate law, criminal law, family law, international law, labor law, litigation, securities law, tax law, and intellectual property, patent law, and computer/cyberspace law. In addition, clinics worth 5 credits are available to any third-year student who possesses an intern's license. Seminars are open to any student with upper-level standing. Topics include poverty law, product liability, health care law, complex litigation, cyberspace law, and e-commerce law. An internship in the area of patent law is open to upper-level students who have taken a patent law course. Research programs may be undertaken with individual law faculty members. Second- and third-year law students are able to act as

law clerks to area judges for 3 credits. Special lecture series include the Scholar-in-Residence, Law and Technology Symposium, and the Law and Technology Scholar-in-Residence. The voluntary Academic Excellence Program is designed to assist first-year students from educationally or economically disadvantaged backgrounds and is conducted by law faculty and upper-level teaching assistants for one credit. The most widely taken electives are Evidence, Tax, Corporations, and Criminal Law.

Graduation Requirements

In order to graduate, candidates must have a GPA of 2.0 and have completed the upper-division writing requirement.

Organizations

Students edit the *University of Dayton Law Review*, the Journal of Law and Technology, and the student newspaper, *Equitable Relief*. Students typically participate in moot court competitions including tax, patent law, and international law. The School of Law also hosts the Carl A. Stickel National Cybercrimes Moot Court competition. There is also a mock trial competition. Law student organizations include the Student Bar Association, Cyberspace Law Association, and the Women's Caucus. There are local chapters of Phi Alpha Delta, Delta Theta Phi, and Phi Delta Phi.

Library

The law library contains 270,003 hardcopy volumes and 640,225 microform volume equivalents, and subscribes to 4044 serial publications. Such on-line databases and networks as LEXIS and WESTLAW are available to law students for research. Recently, the Zimmerman Law Library opened offering data and power outlets at each seat. Students are able to access the Law School Network and on-line research services from 500 different locations within the library. The ratio of library volumes to faculty is 9643 to 1 and to students, 599 to 1. The ratio of seats in the library to students is 1 to 1.

Placement	
J.D.s awarded:	162
Services available through: a separate law school placement center.	
Full-time job interviews:	19 employers
Summer job interviews:	19 employers
Placement by graduation:	38% of class
Placement within 9 months:	88% of class
Average starting salary:	$23,000 to $80,000
Areas of placement:	
Private practice 2-10 attorneys	27%
Private practice 11-25 attorneys	7%
Private practice 26-50 attorneys	5%
Private practice 51-100 attorneys	9%
Business/industry	24%
Government	20%
Judicial clerkships	7%
Unknown	6%
Public interest	4%
Continued education	4%
Military	2%

Faculty

The law school has 28 full-time and 34 part-time faculty members, of whom 19 are women. According to AAUP standards for Category IIA institutions, faculty salaries are well above average. About 21% of full-time faculty have a graduate law degree in addition to the J.D.; about 5% of part-time faculty have one. The ratio of full-time students to full-time faculty in an average class is 18 to 1; in a clinic, 8 to 1. The law school has a regular program of bringing visiting professors and other distinguished lecturers and visitors to campus.

Students

About 42% of the student body are women; 17%, minorities; 8%, African American; 4%, Asian American; 5%, Hispanic; and 1%, Native American. The majority of students come from the Midwest (72%). The average age of entering students is 26; age range is 19 to 59. About 35% of students enter directly from undergraduate school, 7% have a graduate degree, and 64% have worked full-time prior to entering law school. About 6% drop out after the first year for academic or personal reasons; 94% remain to receive a law degree.

College of Law

7039 E. 18th Avenue
Denver, CO 80220

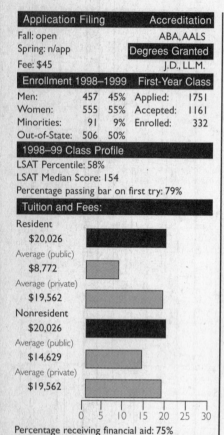

Application Filing	Accreditation
Fall: open	ABA, AALS
Spring: n/app	**Degrees Granted**
Fee: $45	J.D., LL.M.

Enrollment 1998–1999		First-Year Class	
Men:	457 45%	Applied:	1751
Women:	555 55%	Accepted:	1161
Minorities:	91 9%	Enrolled:	332
Out-of-State:	506 50%		

1998–99 Class Profile

LSAT Percentile: 58%
LSAT Median Score: 154
Percentage passing bar on first try: 79%

Tuition and Fees:

Resident
$20,026

Average (public)
$8,772

Average (private)
$19,562

Nonresident
$20,026

Average (public)
$14,629

Average (private)
$19,562

0 5 10 15 20 25 30

Percentage receiving financial aid: 75%

ADMISSIONS

In the fall 1999 first-year class, 1751 applied, 1161 were accepted, and 332 enrolled. Thirty transfers enrolled. The median LSAT percentile of the most recent first-year class was 58; the median GPA was 3.2 on a scale of 4.0. The lowest LSAT percentile accepted was 33; the highest was 98.

Requirements

Applicants must have a bachelor's degree from an accredited institution and take the LSAT. The most important admission factors include GPA and academic achievement. No specific undergraduate courses are required. Candidates are not interviewed.

Procedure

There is no application deadline. Applicants should submit an application form, a nonrefundable application fee of $45, 2 letters of recommendation, a personal statement, and a resume. Notification of the admission decision is on a rolling basis. The latest acceptable LSAT test date for fall entry is February. The law school uses the LSDAS.

Special

The law school recruits minority and disadvantaged students by means of special scholarships and the intervention and support of the Assistant Dean of Student Affairs' office. Transfer students must have one year of credit and have attended an ABA-approved law school.

Costs

Tuition and fees for the 1999-2000 academic year are $20,026 for all full-time students. Tuition for all part-time students is $12,920 annually. Books and supplies run $706.

Financial Aid

About 75% of current law students receive some form of aid. The average annual amount of aid from all sources combined, including scholarships, loans, and work contracts, is $20,000; maximum, $32,800. Awards are based on need and merit. Award letters offer aid (scholarships, loans, work-study) up to cost of attendance (approximately $32,800 including room and board for 2000-2001). The required financial statement is FAFSA. The aid application deadline for fall entry is February 15. First-year students are notified about their financial aid application shortly after receipt of admissions application.

About the Law School

University of Denver College of Law was established in 1892 and is a private institution. The 33-acre campus is in an urban area 10 minutes from downtown Denver. The primary mission of the law school is to support and foster significant legal research while being actively involved in the profession and in the society it serves. Students have access to federal, state, county, city, and local agencies, courts, correctional facilities, law firms, and legal aid organizations in the Denver area. Facilities of special interest to law students include the Lowell Thomas Law Building, which houses the law library, classrooms and auditorium, faculty offices, and courtrooms. Adjoining buildings provide space for administration, student examination, dining facilities, an on-campus child care center, student residences, and apartments. Housing for law students is on campus and consists of apartments and dormitories. About 85% of the law school facilities are accessible to the physically disabled.

Calendar

The law school operates on a traditional semester basis. Courses for full-time students are offered days only and must be completed within 4 years. For part-time students, courses are offered evenings only and must be completed within 5 years. New full-and part-time students are admitted in the fall. There is an 11-week summer session. Transferable summer courses are offered.

Programs

In addition to the J.D., the law school offers the LL.M. Students may take relevant courses in other programs and apply credit toward the J.D.; a maximum of 10 credits may be applied. The following joint degrees may be earned: J.D./M.B.A. (Juris Doctor/Master of Business Administration), J.D./M.I.M. (Juris Doctor/Master of International Management), J.D./M.A. (Juris Doctor/Master of Arts in geography, and judicial administration), J.D./G.S.I.S. (Juris Doctor/Graduate School International Studies), J.D./MSLA (Juris Doctor/ Master of Legal Administration), and J.D./M.T. (Juris Doctor/Master in Taxation).

Contact
Karen Higganbotham; Assistant Director of Admissions, 303-871-6135 for general inquiries; Donna Ellis, 303-871-6136 for financial aid information.

COLORADO

Required

To earn the J.D., candidates must complete 90 total credits, of which 44 are for required courses. They must maintain a minimum GPA of 2.0 in the required courses. The following first-year courses are required of all students: Contracts, Torts, Civil Procedure, Criminal Law, Property, Lawyering Process, and a perspective elective. Required upper-level courses consist of Constitutional Law, Evidence, Administrative Law, and Legal Profession and Legal Writing. The required orientation program for first-year students orients students to law school programs, facilities, organizations, and procedures and is 3 days long.

Electives

The College of Law offers concentrations in corporate law, criminal law, environmental law, international law, litigation, tax law, business and commercial law, natural resources, advocacy skills, transportation law, and public interest law. In addition, upper-level students receive 5 credit hours for a clinic. Clinic topics include public interest, civil, criminal, human rights, and mediation/arbitration. Seminars offered to upper-level students are worth 2 to 3 credit hours. Seminar topics include Criminal Justice, Advertising Regulations, Appellate Advocacy, Business and Commercial Law, Computers and the Law, Constitutional Law, Government Contracts, International Law, Law and Society, Legislation, Natural Resources, Professional Ethics, and Torts. Internships are available in the offices of prosecutors; public defenders; the attorney general; and judicial, legislative, corporate, immigration, and natural resources agencies. Internships are only open to upper-level students for 3 credits. Directed research may be undertaken under a professor's supervision. Research positions are open only to upper-level students for 2 to 3 credits. Externships are equal to 10 credits and are available to upper-level students. A study-abroad option is available. The no-credit Academic Achievement Program is a tutorial program offered to first-year students. The most widely taken electives are Basic Tax, Corporations, and Trusts and Estates.

Graduation Requirements

In order to graduate, candidates must have a GPA of 2.0.

Organizations

Students edit the *University of Denver Law Journal, Water Court Reporter, Transportation Law Journal, Denver Journal of International Law and Policy,* and the newspaper, *Student Writ.* Moot court competitions running through the school year include the Negotiations Competition, Jessup International Law Competition, and Hoffman Cup Trial Competition. Among the student organizations are Christian Legal Society, Colorado Council of Mediators Organization, and Entertainment Law Society. Chapters of national associations include Delta Theta Phi, Phi Alpha Delta, and Phi Delta Phi.

Library

The law library contains 274,284 hardcopy volumes and 48,685 microform volume equivalents, and subscribes to 3100 serial publications. Such on-line databases and networks as LEXIS, DIALOG, WESTLAW, InfoTrac, and NEXIS are available to law students for research. Special library collections include a government document selective depository and the Hughes Rare Book Room. Recently, the library upgraded computer equipment and rearranged seating to maximize outside lighting. The ratio of library volumes to faculty is 6102 to 1 and to students, 261 to 1. The ratio of seats in the library to students is 1 to 1.

Faculty

The law school has 38 full-time and 35 part-time faculty members, of whom 20 are women. According to AAUP standards for Category I institutions, faculty salaries are below average. About 25% of full-time faculty have a graduate law degree in addition to the J.D.; about 5% of part-time faculty have one. The ratio of full-time students to full-time faculty in an average class is 18 to 1; in a clinic, 8 to 1. The law school has a regular program of bringing visiting professors and other distinguished lecturers and visitors to campus.

Placement

J.D.s awarded:	296

Services available through: separate law school placement center and the university placement center.

Services: self-assessment

Special features: out-of-town alumni networks, DU alumni links, mentors, and individualized networking strategies

Full-time job interviews:	45 employers
Summer job interviews:	n/av
Placement by graduation:	69% of class
Placement within 9 months:	86% of class
Average starting salary:	$28,000 to $72,000

Areas of placement:

Private practice 2-10 attorneys	45%
Private practice 11-25 attorneys	10%
Private practice 26-50 attorneys	4%
Private practice 51-100 attorneys	3%
Government	17%
Business/industry	14%
judicial clerkships	4%
Military	2%
Public interest	2%
Academic	1%

Students

About 55% of the student body are women; 9%, minorities; 1%, African American; 3%, Asian American; 4%, Hispanic; and 1%, Native American. The majority of students come from Colorado (50%). The average age of entering students is 27; age range is 20 to 55. About 25% of students enter directly from undergraduate school, 15% have a graduate degree, and 40% have worked full-time prior to entering law school. About 4% drop out after the first year for academic or personal reasons; 95% remain to receive a law degree.

UNIVERSITY OF DETROIT MERCY

School of Law

651 East Jefferson Avenue
Detroit, MI 48226

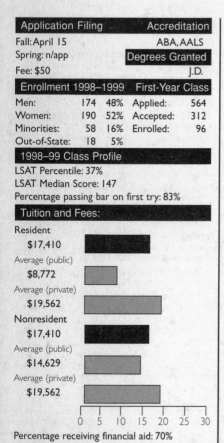

Application Filing		Accreditation
Fall: April 15		ABA, AALS
Spring: n/app		**Degrees Granted**
Fee: $50		J.D.

Enrollment 1998–1999			First-Year Class	
Men:	174	48%	Applied:	564
Women:	190	52%	Accepted:	312
Minorities:	58	16%	Enrolled:	96
Out-of-State:	18	5%		

1998–99 Class Profile
LSAT Percentile: 37%
LSAT Median Score: 147
Percentage passing bar on first try: 83%

Tuition and Fees:

Resident
$17,410

Average (public)
$8,772

Average (private)
$19,562

Nonresident
$17,410

Average (public)
$14,629

Average (private)
$19,562

0   5   10   15   20   25   30

Percentage receiving financial aid: 70%

ADMISSIONS

In the fall 1999 first-year class, 564 applied, 312 were accepted, and 96 enrolled. Two transfers enrolled. The median LSAT percentile of the most recent first-year class was 37; the median GPA was 3.0 on a scale of 4.0. The lowest LSAT percentile accepted was 15; the highest was 81.

Requirements
Applicants must have a bachelor's degree from an accredited institution and take the LSAT. The most important admission factors include academic achievement, LSAT results, and GPA. No specific undergraduate courses are required. Candidates are not interviewed.

Procedure
The application deadline for fall entry is April 15. Applicants should submit an application form, LSAT results, transcripts, TOEFL results, if appropriate, a nonrefundable application fee of $50, and 2 letters of recommendation. Notification of the admission decision is on a rolling basis. The latest acceptable LSAT test date for fall entry is June. The law school uses the LSDAS.

Special
The law school recruits minority and disadvantaged students by attending law fairs at colleges and universities targeted to reach students of color by using the LSAC Candidate Referral Service. Transfer students must have one year of credit, have attended an ABA-approved law school, and be in good standing their current law school. Preadmissions courses consist of an 8-week conditional admission program offered during the summer for minority and disadvantaged students who do not meet current admission standards but who demonstrate potential for success in law school. Satisfactory demonstration of ability in the program permits admission as a regular student in the fall semester.

Costs

Tuition and fees for the 1999-2000 academic year are $17,410 for all full-time students. Tuition for part-time students is $12,450 per year. Books and supplies run $850.

Financial Aid

About 70% of current law students receive some form of aid. The average annual amount of aid from all sources combined, including scholarships, loans, and work contracts, is $18,500; maximum, $32,500. Scholarships are based on merit; all other aid, except unsubsidized loans, is based on need. The required financial statement is the FAFSA. The aid application deadline for fall entry is April 1. First-year students are notified about their financial aid application at time of acceptance.

About the Law School

University of Detroit Mercy School of Law was established in 1912 and is a private institution. The 4-acre campus is in an urban area in downtown Detroit. The primary mission of the law school is to provide a rigorous, value-oriented education in the Jesuit tradition. Students have access to federal, state, county, city, and local agencies, courts, correctional facilities, law firms, and legal aid organizations in the Detroit area. The Career Services Office provides a wide array of resources to enable students to obtain short- and long-term positions in these areas. Facilities of special interest to law

students include a full range of extracurricular activities, and organizations like the St. Thomas More Society, the Student Bar Association, the Black Law Student's Association, and Phi Alpha Delta offer the chance to exercise leadership skills and perform community service. There is a large quantity of housing within walking distance of the Law School. For students who do not mind a short commute, there are many residential suburbs from which to choose. The School of Law will assist students with housing needs. All law school facilities are accessible to the physically disabled.

Calendar

The law school operates on a traditional semester basis. Courses for full-time students are offered both day and evening and must be completed within 3 years. For part-time students, courses are offered both day and evening and must be completed within 5 years. New full- and part-time students are admitted in the fall. There is a 7-week summer session. Transferable summer courses are offered.

Programs

The following joint degree may be earned: J.D./M.B.A. (Juris Doctor/Master of Business Administration).

Required
To earn the J.D., candidates must complete 90 total credits, of which 49 are for required courses. They must maintain a minimum GPA of 2.0 in the required courses. The following first-year courses are required of all students: Contracts, Civil Procedure, Property, Torts, and Applied Legal Theory and Analysis. Required upper-level courses consist of Tax A, Criminal Law I and II, Constitutional Law I, Evidence, Professional Responsibility, and a seminar course. The required orientation program for first-year students is a 3-day session that includes presentations by faculty and administrators, alumni panel discussions, and an overview of the first-year curriculum.

Phone: 313-596-0264
Fax: 313-596-0280
E-mail: udmlawao@udmercy.edu
Web: www.law.udmercy.edu

Contact

Kathleen H. Caprio, Assistant Dean, Admissions and Student Affairs, 313-596-0264 for general inquiries; Denise Daniel, Financial Aid Coordinator, 313-596-0214 for financial aid information.

Electives

The School of Law offers concentrations in corporate law, criminal law, entertainment, environmental law, family law, international law, labor law, litigation, tax law, torts and insurance, health law, constitutional law, and intellectual property law. In addition, the Urban Law Clinic (clinical intern program) is available to upper-level students who have successfully completed at least 30 credits; Criminal Procedure and Evidence coures are prerequisites for eligibility for 1 of the 12 slots each semester for the 4-credit Urban Law Clinic course. Upper-level students who have successfully completed all of their first-year courses and who meet the upper-level course prerequisites for any given seminar may apply for 1 of the 16 slots in any of the 2-credit seminars offered each semester. A variety of 2-credit clinical externships is also available to upper-class students. Students with a GPA of 2.5 may work under the supervision of faculty attorneys in preparing cases for local civil and criminal courts, federal district courts, and state and federal administrative courts. The clinic places students with such agencies as the Wayne County Prosecutor's Office, the U.S. Attorney's Office, the Attorney Grievance Commission, the American Civil Liberties Union, the City of Detroit Law Department, and local health care systems. Students may undertake independent research projects through the Urban Law Clinic. A special program gives students credit for teaching law to high school students. One feature of the Applied Legal Theory and Analysis course is the Analytical Tools Section Lectures, including Structure of Legal Argument, History of Legal Education, The Common Law, Equity, and American Reception of the Common Law. The School of Law also hosts the annual McElroy Lecture on Law and Religion. The University of Detroit Mercy School of Law London Law Programme offers second- and third-year students from UDM and other ABA-accredited law schools an opportunity to study international and comparative law abroad for a fall or spring semester. The Associate Director of Recruitment and Academic Support is available to provide individual tutorial sessions to students in an effort to assist students in improving study skills. Minority and disadvantaged students who do not meet the standard of those currently being admitted, but who have strong qualifications that indicate possible success in law school, may be admitted to the Special Summer Program (SSP). Students who successfully complete the SSP may matriculate with the fall class. Through a consortium with 2 other law schools, students interested in intellectual property law may choose from a wide array of intellectual property law electives. The most widely taken electives are Trial Practice, Estates and Trusts, and Criminal Procedure.

Graduation Requirements

In order to graduate, candidates must have a GPA of 2.0 and have completed the upper-division writing requirement.

Organizations

The primary law review is the *University of Detroit Mercy Law Review*. Another law review is the *Michigan Business Law Journal*. The student newspaper is *In Brief*. Moot court competitions include the Gallagher Competition, the G. Mennen Williams Annual Moot Court Competition, and the Professional Responsibility Competition. Law student organizations include the Student Bar Association, the St. Thomas More Society, and the Black Law Students Association. Local chapters of national associations include Phi Alpha Delta and Delta Theta Phi. Other organizations include the Justice Frank Murphy Honor Society (named for a former faculty member who became a U.S. Attorney General and Associate Justice of the U.S. Supreme Court), intramural team sports, and the Film Society.

Library

The law library contains 307,767 hardcopy volumes and 94,430 microform volume equivalents, and subscribes to 3537 serial publications. Such on-line databases and networks as LEXIS, DIALOG, WESTLAW, and LANs are available to law students for research. Special library collections include English and Canadian law, government documents, records, legal periodical indexes on CD-ROM, and several hundred databases in related fields. Recently, the library installed 38 state-of-the-art computers for students' use. The ratio of library volumes to faculty is 16,200 to 1 and to students, 845 to 1. The ratio of seats in the library to students is 1 to 1.

Faculty

The law school has 19 full-time and 20 part-time faculty members, of whom 11 are women. About 18% of full-time faculty have a graduate law degree in addition to the J.D. The ratio of full-time students to full-time faculty in an average class is 23 to 1; in a clinic, 12 to 1. The law school has a regular program of bringing visiting professors and other distinguished lecturers and visitors to campus.

Students

About 52% of the student body are women; 16%, minorities; 10%, African American; 3%, Asian American; and 2%, Hispanic. The majority of students come from Michigan (95%). The average age of entering students is 27; age range is 21 to 48. About 60% of students enter directly from undergraduate school, 10% have a graduate degree, and 30% have worked full-time prior to entering law school. About 10% drop out after the first year for academic or personal reasons; 90% remain to receive a law degree.

Placement

J.D.s awarded:	127
Services available through: a separate law school placement center	
Special features: The Career Services Office operates on-campus interview programs in the fall and spring, provides seminars and individual advice on such topics as interviewing and resume preparation, and sponsors the weekly "Lunch with a Lawyer" Series and the Alumni Mentor Program. The Career Services Office also provides employment letters for alumni and students and an alumni job telephone hot line.	
Full-time job interviews:	17 employers
Summer job interviews:	32 employers
Placement by graduation:	n/av
Placement within 9 months:	85% of class
Average starting salary:	$41,000
Areas of placement:	
Private practice 2-10 attorneys	18%
Private practice 11-25 attorneys	5%
Private practice 26-50 attorneys	2%
Private practice 51-100 attorneys	3%
Private practice 100+ attorneys	5%
Solo practice	5%
Business/industry	20%
Government	20%
Judicial clerkships	9%
Public interest	3%
Academic	3%

College of Law

325 Holland Hall P.O. Box 117622
Gainesville, FL 32611-7622

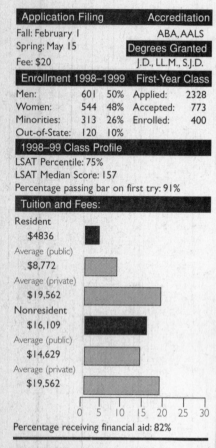

Application Filing		Accreditation
Fall: February 1		ABA, AALS
Spring: May 15		**Degrees Granted**
Fee: $20		J.D., LL.M., S.J.D.

Enrollment 1998–1999		First-Year Class	
Men:	601 50%	Applied:	2328
Women:	544 48%	Accepted:	773
Minorities:	313 26%	Enrolled:	400
Out-of-State:	120 10%		

1998–99 Class Profile

LSAT Percentile: 75%
LSAT Median Score: 157
Percentage passing bar on first try: 91%

Tuition and Fees:

Resident
$4836

Average (public)
$8,772

Average (private)
$19,562

Nonresident
$16,109

Average (public)
$14,629

Average (private)
$19,562

0 5 10 15 20 25 30

Percentage receiving financial aid: 82%

ADMISSIONS

In the fall 1999 first-year class, 2328 applied, 773 were accepted, and 400 enrolled. Twenty-three transfers enrolled. The median LSAT percentile of the most recent first-year class was 75; the median GPA was 3.5 on a scale of 4.0.

Requirements
Applicants must have a bachelor's degree from an accredited institution and take the LSAT. No specific undergraduate courses are required. Candidates are not interviewed.

Procedure
The application deadline for fall entry is February 1. Applicants should submit an application form, LSAT results, transcripts, a nonrefundable application fee of $20, and a personal statement to the Admissions Committee. Three letters of recommendation are recommended but not required. Candidates are strongly encouraged to use the LSDAS letter option. Notification of the admission decision is in April for fall; July for spring. The latest acceptable LSAT test date for fall entry is December for fall; February for spring. The law school uses the LSDAS.

Special
The College of Law is represented at a large number of Law Day programs in Florida and other southern states. This activity is supplemented by individual campus visits and other visits to historically black colleges in Florida and the south. The law school actively seeks a diverse student body. Requirements are different for out-of-state students in that their credentials must be significantly better. State law limits non-Floridian enrollment to 10%. Transfer students must have one year of credit, have attended an ABA-approved law school, and must rank in at least the top one-third of their class to be considered.

Costs

Tuition and fees for the 1999-2000 academic year are $4836 for full-time in-state students and $16,109 for out-of-state students. On-campus room and board costs about $9120 annually; books and supplies run $700.

Financial Aid

About 82% of current law students receive some form of aid. The average annual amount of aid from all sources combined, including scholarships, loans, and work contracts, is $13,000; maximum, $26,740. Awards are based on need and merit. The required financial statement is FAFSA. The aid application deadline for fall entry is April 1. Special funds for minority or disadvantaged students include the Minority Participation in Legal Education (MPLE) Scholarship of $15,000, the Virgil Hawkins Scholarship of $15,000, and the Florida Bar Foundation Council on Legal Education Opportunity. First-year students are notified about their financial aid application at time of acceptance.

About the Law School

University of Florida College of Law was established in 1909 and is a public institution. The 2000-acre campus is in a small town 70 miles southwest of Jacksonville, Florida. The primary mission of the law school is to prepare students for a life of creative problem solving, dispute resolution, planning, and counseling. Students have access to federal, state, county, city, and local agencies, courts, correctional facilities, law firms, and legal aid organizations in the Gainesville area. Housing for law students is available in university dormitories, family housing, and apartments. About 90% of the law school facilities are accessible to the physically disabled.

Calendar

The law school operates on a traditional semester basis. Courses for full-time students are offered days only and must be completed within 5 years. There is no part-time program. New full-time students are admitted in the fall and spring. There is an 8-week summer session. Transferable summer courses are offered.

Phone: 352-392-2087
Fax: 352-392-2087
E-mail: patrick@law.ufl.edu
Web: http://www.law.ufl.edu

Contact

J. Michael Patrick, Assistant Dean for Admissions, 352-392-2087 for general inquiries; Trish Varnes, Director of Financial Aid, 352-392-0421 for financial aid information.

Programs

In addition to the J.D., the law school offers the LL.M and S.J.D. Students may take relevant courses in other programs and apply credit toward the J.D.; a maximum of 6 credits may be applied. The following joint degrees may be earned: J.D./M.B.A. (Juris Doctor/ Master of Business Administration), J.D./M.A. (Juris Doctor/ Master of Arts in accounting and mass communication), J.D./Ph.D (Juris Doctor/Doctor of Philosophy in history and educational leadership), J.D./M.Acc. (Master of accounting), J.D./M.S. (Master of sciences in anthropology, environmental, engineering, exercise and sports science, forest resources and conservation, medical sciences, real estate and scoiology), J.D./M.A. (Master of Arts in history, Latin American studies, and political science), J.D./M.D. (Doctor of Medicine), J.D./M.H.A. (Master of Health Administration), J.D./M.U.R.P. (Master of Urban and Regional Planning), J.D. Ph.D. (psychology and educational leadership), and J.D./Certificate Program in Gender Studies.

Required

To earn the J.D., candidates must complete 88 total credits, of which 34 are for required courses. They must maintain a minimum GPA of 2.0 in the required courses. The following first-year courses are required of all students: Contracts, Torts, Civil Procedure, Property, Constitutional Law, Legal Research and Writing, Appellate Advocacy, and Introduction to Law. Required upper-level courses consist of Legal Drafting and Professional Responsibility. The required orientation program for first-year students is incorporated into the 4-day (1-credit) Introduction to Law class.

Electives

The College of Law offers concentrations in corporate law, criminal law, entertainment law, environmental law, family law, international law, juvenile law, labor law, litigation, maritime law, media law, securities law, sports law, tax law, and torts and insurance. Clinics include the Virgil Hawkins Civil Clinic for 9 credits, Prosecutor-Criminal Clinic for 6 credits, and Public Defender-Criminal Clinic for 6 credits. The clinics are open to students who have completed at least 48 hours and Professional Responsibility. Criminal Clinics also require Trial Practice. Seminars are available in a variety of legal topics for 2 credits and are open to students who have completed the first-year curriculum. The Council of Ten is a non-credit tutorial program for any first-year student. Academic Support workshops for students at risk of being placed on academic probation are available. The no-credit program is open to any student who has completed at least 1 semester of law school. The Virgil Hawkins Summer Program is available to any African American admitted for the following fall class, with no credit. The most widely taken electives are legal skills courses.

Graduation Requirements

In order to graduate, candidates must have a GPA of 2.0, and have scompleted the upper-division writing requirement and a senior writing project seminar.

Organizations

Students edit the *Florida Law Review*, the *Florida International Law Journal*, *Journal of Law and Public Policy*, the *Florida Tax Review*, *FLA-LAW*, and the student newspaper, *The Docket*. Law student organizations include the Justice Campbell Thornal Moot Court Team, Trial Competition Team, and Achieving a Barrier-Free Legal Education. Local chapters of national associations include The National Lawyers Guild, Phi Alpha Delta, and Phi Delta Phi.

Library

The law library contains 592,000 hardcopy volumes and 200,000 microform volume equivalents, and subscribes to 8100 serial publications. Such on-line databases and networks as LEXIS, DIALOG, WESTLAW, and Internet access are available to law students for research. Special library collections include tax, Latin American, U.S. government documents, and video and multimedia collections. Recently, the library installed an extensive computer system for on-line searching, with student E-mail access throughout the law complex. The ratio of library volumes to faculty is 7283 to 1 and to students, 432 to 1. The ratio of seats in the library to students is 1 to 1.

Placement

J.D.s awarded:	388
Services available through: a separate law school placement center	
Services: mock interviews, off-campus job fairs on-line a interview sign-up job listings	
Special features: large numbers of on-campus interviewers and on-line job listings; three full-time professionals to advise students, mock interviews, and off-campus job fairs	
Full-time job interviews:	153 employers
Summer job interviews:	165 employers
Placement by graduation:	65% of class
Placement within 9 months:	85% of class
Average starting salary:	$28,000 to $75,000
Areas of placement:	
Private practice 2-10 attorneys	9%
Private practice 11-25 attorneys	7%
Private practice 26-50 attorneys	5%
Private practice 51-100 attorneys	5%
Private practice 101-250 attorneys	4%
Private practice 251+ attorneys	7%
Private practice (unknown size)	17%
Government	19%
Judicial clerkships	6%
Business/industry	6%
Public interest	1%

Faculty

The law school has 69 full-time and 18 part-time faculty members, of whom 28 are women. According to AAUP standards for Category I institutions, faculty salaries are above average. About 32% of full-time faculty have a graduate law degree in addition to the J.D. The ratio of full-time students to full-time faculty in an average class is 18 to 1; in a clinic, 10 to 1. There is a chapter of the Order of the Coif.

Students

About 48% of the student body are women; 26%, minorities; 9%, African American; 4%, Asian American; 12%, Hispanic; and 1%, Native American. The majority of students come from Florida (90%). The average age of entering students is 25. About 4% drop out after the first year for academic or personal reasons.

School of Law

Hirsch Hall, 225 Herty Drive
Athens, GA 30602-6012

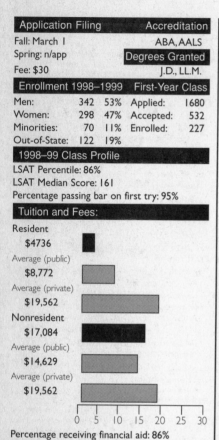

Application Filing	Accreditation
Fall: March 1	ABA, AALS
Spring: n/app	**Degrees Granted**
Fee: $30	J.D., LL.M.

Enrollment 1998–1999		First-Year Class	
Men:	342 53%	Applied:	1680
Women:	298 47%	Accepted:	532
Minorities:	70 11%	Enrolled:	227
Out-of-State:	122 19%		

1998–99 Class Profile

LSAT Percentile: 86%
LSAT Median Score: 161
Percentage passing bar on first try: 95%

Tuition and Fees:

Resident
$4736

Average (public)
$8,772

Average (private)
$19,562

Nonresident
$17,084

Average (public)
$14,629

Average (private)
$19,562

0 5 10 15 20 25 30

Percentage receiving financial aid: 86%

ADMISSIONS

In the fall 1999 first-year class, 1680 applied, 532 were accepted, and 227 enrolled. Eleven transfers enrolled. The median LSAT percentile of the most recent first-year class was 86; the median GPA was 3.6 on a scale of 4.3. The lowest LSAT percentile accepted was 20; the highest was 99.

Requirements

Applicants must take the LSAT. Minimum acceptable GPA is 2.0 on a scale of 4.0. No specific undergraduate courses are required. Candidates are not interviewed.

Procedure

The application deadline for fall entry is March 1. Applicants should submit an application form, LSAT results, transcripts, a nonrefundable application fee of $30, 2 letters of recommendation, and a 200-word statement indicating the applicant's reasons for obtaining a legal education. Notification of the admission decision is from October through August. The latest acceptable LSAT test date for fall entry is February. The law school uses the LSDAS.

Special

The law school recruits minority and disadvantaged students by means of the Candidate Referral Service of Law Services, LSAC Law Forums, and campus visitations. Transfer students must have one year of credit, have attended an ABA-approved law school, and transfer from an AALS member school. A copy of the LSDAS Law School Report, law school transcript, dean's certification letter, and 2 letters of recommendation, must be submitted.

Costs

Tuition and fees for the 1999-2000 academic year are $4736 for full-time in-state students and $17,084 for out-of-state students. On-campus room and board costs about $4902 annually; books and supplies run $1000.

Financial Aid

About 86% of current law students receive some form of aid. Awards are based on need and merit. The required financial statement is FAFSA. First-year students are notified about their financial aid application on or about March 1 for academic scholarships; on or about June 1 for need-based aid.

About the Law School

University of Georgia School of Law was established in 1859 and is a public institution. The 1,289-acre campus is in a small town 65 miles northeast of Atlanta. Students have access to federal, state, county, city, and local agencies, courts, correctional facilities, law firms, and legal aid organizations in the Athens area. Facilities of special interest to law students are the Dean Rusk Center for International and Comparative Law, the Institute for Continuing Legal Education, and the Institution for Continuing Judicial Education. Housing for law students is available on campus for single students in residence halls; students with a spouse and/or children may live in University Village, an on-campus apartment complex. About 99% of the law school facilities are accessible to the physically disabled.

Calendar

The law school operates on a traditional semester basis. Courses for full-time students are offered days only and must be completed within 5 years. There is no part-time program. new full-time students are admitted in the fall. There is a 7-week summer session. Transferable summer courses are offered.

Programs

In addition to the J.D., the law school offers the LL.M. Students may take relevant courses in other programs and apply credit toward the J.D.; a maximum of 4 credits may be applied. The following joint degrees may be earned: J.D./M.B.A. (Juris Doctor/Master of Business Administration), J.D./M.H.P. (Juris Doctor/Master of Historic Preservation), and J.D./M.P.A. (Juris Doctor/Master of Public Administration).

GEORGIA

Contact

Giles W. Kennedy, Director of Law Admissions, 706-542-7060 for general inquiries; D. Ray Tripp, Director, Office of Student Financial Aid, 706-542-6147 for financial aid information.

Required

To earn the J.D., candidates must complete 88 total credits, of which 33 are for required courses. They must maintain a minimum GPA of 1.7 in the required courses. The following first-year courses are required of all students: Civil Procedure, Contracts and Sales, Criminal Law, Legal Research and Writing, Property, and Torts. Required upper-level courses consist of Legal Profession. The required orientation program for first-year students is a 2-day program that provides an introduction to the school's activities, programs, and requirements, to the case method and legal study, and to new and returning students.

Electives

The School of Law offers concentrations in corporate law, criminal law, entertainment law, environmental law, family law, international law, juvenile law, labor law, litigation, sports law, tax law, torts and insurance, and intellectual property law. Upper-level students may take Legal Aid and Defender Clinic, Civil Clinic, and Prosecutorial Clinic; credit varies. Seminars, worth 2 credits, and supervised research and independent projects worth a maximum of 4 credits, are also open to upper-level students. Internships include the Civil Externship, variable credit; Public Interest Practicum, variable credit; and Protective Order Project, variable credit. Dean Rusk Center for International and Comparative Law, variable credit, provides research programs. Field work includes a summer clerkship program for University of Georgia students in England. All students may attend the following special, non-credit lecture series offered on a number of topics: Horace Sibley Lecture Series and Edith House Lecture Series. Study-abroad programs may be undertaken with permission; the law school is a member of the London Law Consortium, and sponsor of Brussels Seminar on Law and Institutions of the European Union and Community. Several tutorial and mentoring programs are offered for no credit. The most widely taken electives are Constitutional Law I and II, Evidence, and Federal Income Tax.

Graduation Requirements

In order to graduate, candidates must have a GPA of 1.7 and have completed the upper-division writing requirement.

Organizations

Students edit the *Georgia Law Review, Georgia Journal of International and Comparative Law, Journal of Intellectual Property Law*, and the newspaper *Georgia Scales*. Annually, moot court teams participate in 8 moot court competitions, including the National the Phillip C. Jessup and the ABA National. Other competitions are the National Mock Trial and the American Trial Lawyers Association competitions. Law student organizations include the Student Bar Association, Women Law Students Association, and Equal Justice Foundation. There are local chapters of the Black Law Students Association, Christian Legal Society, and Jewish Law Students Association. Law students may participate in the various clubs and associations on the college campus as well.

Library

The law library contains 480,005 hardcopy volumes and 490,965 microform volume equivalents, and subscribes to 7152 serial publications. Such on-line databases and networks as LEXIS, DIALOG, WESTLAW, and more than 100 databases are available to law students for research. Special library collections include complete English and Canadian law collections and a European Community depository library. Recently, the library upgraded wiring for computers. The ratio of library volumes to faculty is 10,000 to 1 and to students, 750 to 1. The ratio of seats in the library to students is 1 to .7.

Placement

J.D.s awarded:	224

Services available through: separate law school placement center

Services: 12 off-campus job fairs, a computer and laser printer laboratory, Internet, LEXIS, WESTLAW access, E-mail, and Web distribution of job announcements

Special features: a career lecture series and videotaping of mock interviews, shadow programs, mentor programs, and 12 or more interviewing consortiams

Full-time job interviews:	58 employers
Summer job interviews:	103 employers
Placement by graduation:	74% of class
Placement within 9 months:	96% of class
Average starting salary:	$20,000 to $82,000

Areas of placement:

Private practice 2-10 attorneys	22%
Private practice 11-25 attorneys	11%
Private practice 26-50 attorneys	6%
Private practice 51-100 attorneys	4%
Private practice 100 + attorneys	4%
Private practice (firm size unknown)	4%
Judicial clerkships	16%
Business/industry	14%
Government	6%
Public interest	4%
Self-employed	1%

Faculty

The law school has 48 full-time and 36 part-time faculty members, of whom 23 are women. According to AAUP standards for Category I institutions, faculty salaries are above average. About 39% of full-time faculty have a graduate law degree in addition to the J.D.; about 10% of part-time faculty have one. The ratio of full-time students to full-time faculty in an average class is 18 to 1; in a clinic, 6 to 1. There is a chapter of the Order of the Coif.

Students

About 47% of the student body are women; 11%, minorities; 8%, African American; 3%, Asian American; 1%, Hispanic; and 8%, unknown. The majority of students come from the South (90%). The average age of entering students is 24; age range is 21 to 47. About 5% drop out after the first year for academic or personal reasons; 95% remain to receive a law degree.

UNIVERSITY OF HAWAII-MANOA

William S. Richardson School of Law

2515 Dole Street
Honolulu, HI 96822

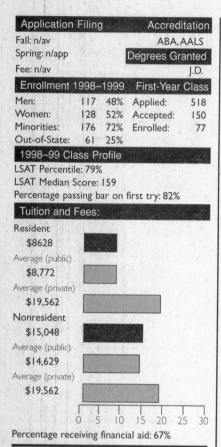

Application Filing			Accreditation
Fall: n/av			ABA, AALS
Spring: n/app			Degrees Granted
Fee: n/av			J.D.

Enrollment 1998–1999			First-Year Class	
Men:	117	48%	Applied:	518
Women:	128	52%	Accepted:	150
Minorities:	176	72%	Enrolled:	77
Out-of-State:	61	25%		

1998–99 Class Profile
LSAT Percentile: 79%
LSAT Median Score: 159
Percentage passing bar on first try: 82%

Tuition and Fees:

Resident
$8628

Average (public)
$8,772

Average (private)
$19,562

Nonresident
$15,048

Average (public)
$14,629

Average (private)
$19,562

0 5 10 15 20 25 30

Percentage receiving financial aid: 67%

ADMISSIONS
In the fall 1999 first-year class, 518 applied, 150 were accepted, and 77 enrolled. Four transfers enrolled. The median LSAT percentile of the most recent first-year class was 79; the median GPA was 3.39 on a scale of 4.0. The lowest LSAT percentile accepted was 21; the highest was 99.

Requirements
Applicants must have a bachelor's degree from an accredited institution and take the LSAT. The most important admission factors include academic achievement, GPA, and LSAT results. No specific undergraduate courses are required. Candidates are not interviewed.

Procedure
Checkl with the school for current application deadlines. Applicants should submit an application form, LSAT results, transcripts, TOEFL, if applicable, 2 letters of recommendation, and residency declaration. Check with the school for the current

fee. Notification of the admissions decision is in early April. The latest acceptable LSAT test date for fall entry is February. The law school uses the LSDAS.

Special
The law school recruits minority and disadvantaged students by means of the Pre-Admission Program and by targeting certain affinity and ethnic groups. Requirements are different for out-of-state students in that there is a higher admission threshold on LSAT scores and the GPA for nonresidents. Transfer students must have one year of credit, have attended an ABA-approved law school, and have a law school rank at least in the top half of their class, and must submit 2 letters of recommendation, including one from a law professor, and a complete application. Preadmissions courses consist of a 1-year course for 12 students selected from groups underrepresented in the Hawaii Bar. Students enroll in Contracts I and II, Civil Procedure I and II, tutorials for each of those 4 courses, Legal Bibliography, and a Pre-Admission Seminar, held each semester, which is designed for the group.

Costs
Tuition and fees for the 1999-2000 academic year are $8628 for in-state students and $15,048 for out-of-state students. On-campus room and board costs about $7550 annually; and books and supplies run $800.

Financial Aid
In a recent year, about 67% of current law students received some form of aid. The average annual amount of aid from all sources combined, including scholarships, loans, and work contracts, was $12,680; maximum, $23,614. Awards are based on need and merit. Some merit grants are available. The required financial statement is the FAFSA. Check with the school for current application deadlines. Special funds for minority or disadvantaged students consist of grants from the Bishop Estate for Native Hawaiians and, through the university, special tuition waivers for state residents; Native Hawaiians qualify for resident tuition rates regardless of residency. First-year students are notified about their financial aid application at some time after acceptance, which occurs in March or April, but before enrollment in August. Most students are notified about financial aid in June.

About the Law School
University of Hawaii-Manoa William S. Richardson School of Law was established in 1973 and is a public institution. The 300-acre campus is in a suburban area 2 miles east of Honolulu. The primary mission of the law school is to provide a legal education for the state and its people, as well as those committed to the state, while developing special programs in Pacific and Asian law and ocean and environmental law. Students have access to federal, state, county, city, and local agencies, courts, correctional facilities, law firms, and legal aid organizations in the Honolulu area. Students have full access to virtually every aspect of the legal community as the law school is Hawaii's only law school; the legal community is active at the school via adjunct teaching, live client clinics, mentoring, and speaking. Facilities of special interest to law students consist of expertise, degree programs, and/or research units in ocean studies, resource management, land use, water resources, natural energy, and marine biology; additionally, there are Centers for Chinese, Hawaiian, Japanese, Korean, Pacific Island, Philippine, South Asian, and South East Asian studies. Housing for law students is very limited on campus; nearly all law students live off campus in nearby apartments. All law school facilities are accessible to the physically disabled.

Calendar
The law school operates on a traditional semester basis. Courses are offered primarily during the day, with a few evening courses and must be completed within 5 years. There is no part-time program. New students are admitted in the fall. There is no summer session. Transferable summer courses are not offered.

Programs
Students may take relevant courses in other programs and apply credit toward the J.D.; the maximum number of credits that may be applied varies. The following joint degrees may be earned: J.D./M.B.A. (Juris Doctor/Master of Business Adminstration), J.D./M.A. (Juris Doctor/Master of Arts in Asian studies), J.D./M.U.R.P. (Juris Doctor/Master of Urban and Regional Planning), J.D./M.P.H. (Juris Doctor/Master of Public Health), J.D./M.S.W. (Juris Doctor/Master of Social Work), and J.D./Ph.D. (Juris Doctor/Doctor of Philosophy in psychology).

Phone: 808-956-7966
Fax: 808-956-3813
E-mail: lawadm@hawaii.edu

Contact

Assistant Dean, 808-956-7966 for general inquiries; Gail Koki, Director of Financial Aid, (808) 956-7251 for financial aid information.

HAWAII

Required

To earn the J.D., candidates must complete 89 total credits, of which 42 are for required courses. They must maintain a minimum GPA of 2.0 in the required courses. The following first-year courses are required of all students: Torts Process I and II, Contracts I and II, Civil Procedure I and II, Criminal Justice, Real Property Law I, Legal Method Seminar, Appellate Advocacy, and Legal Bibliography. Required upper-level courses consist of Constitutional Law I, Second Year Seminar, Professional Responsibility, one clinical course, and pro bono legal service (60 hours). All students must take clinical courses. The required orientation program for first-year students is 1 week consisting of introductions to faculty, students, career issues, registration, and academic regulations; discussion of stress and personal issues; and a group introduction to the Legal Method Seminar.

Electives

The William S. Richardson School of Law offers concentrations in corporate law, criminal law, environmental law, family law, international law, labor law, litigation, maritime law, tax law, torts and insurance, and Pacific Asian legal studies. In addition, clinics for 3 or 4 credits each are assigned by lottery to upper-level students who meet the prerequisites. Clinics include Prosecution, Elder Law, Native Hawaiian Rights, and others. Upper-level students are offered a variety of seminars in advanced legal studies and Pacific-Asian legal studies for 1 to 3 credits per seminar. The required Second Year Seminar is offered for 4 credits. One externship per semester may be taken by upper-level students; a maximum of 2 externships may be taken for 2 credits each. Alternatively, a 14-credit externship in an approved Pacific Island jurisdiction may be taken. Under the directed studies program, any upper-level student may elect to conduct special research for 1 to 3 credits. Research can be repeated. Field work is linked to those clinics that include live client representation as well as actual court appearances under a special state Supreme Court rule. Special lecture series are offered for no credit; any student may attend. Annually, there is a Distinguished Fujiyama Visiting Professor, a George Johnson Visiting Scholar, and

Jurist-in-Residence Program. There is also a Pacific-Asian Legal Studies lecture series for visiting Asian legal scholars. Study abroad can be accomplished by special arrangement for varying credits or by a full-semester externship in certain Pacific Island jurisdictions for 14 credits. Tutorial programs are available and administered through the Student Bar Association for no credit. Special interest group programs, offered for no credit, include the Filipino Law Students Association, 'Ahahui 'O Hawai'i (a Native Hawaiian organization), Advocates for Public Interest Law, and the Pacific-Asian Legal Studies Organization. The most widely taken electives are Evidence, Wills and Trusts, and Corporations.

Graduation Requirements

In order to graduate, candidates must have a GPA of 2.0 and have completed the upper-division writing requirement.

Organizations

Students edit the *University of Hawaii Law Review* and the *Pacific Asian Legal Journal*. Students participate in the annual Susan McKay Moot Court Competition, held internationally and in Honolulu; the Environmental Law Moot Court, held in New York; and the Jessup International Moot Court competition. Other competitions include client counseling and Mock Trial. Law student organizations include the Student Bar Association, Environmental Law Society, and Hawaii Association of Women Law Students. Local chapters of national associations include the American Inns of Court, ABA-Student Division, and Phi Delta Phi, Rutherford chapter.

Library

The law library contains 248,838 hardcopy volumes and 875,305 microform volume equivalents, and subscribes to 2736 serial publications. Such on-line databases and networks as LEXIS, DIALOG, WESTLAW, NEXIS, Legal Track, ERIC, and ABI/INFORM are available to law students for research. Special library collections include a partial federal government depository. Recently, the library upgraded its computer lab. The ratio of library volumes to faculty is 13,097 to 1 and to students, 1046 to 1. The ratio of seats in the library to students is 1 to 1.

Placement

J.D.s awarded:	n/av
Services available through:	separate law school placement center
Services:	career information series
Special features: Nearly all placement activity is focused on the Hawaii market, as are on-campus interviews, since 95% of graduates remain in the state	
Full-time job interviews:	n/av
Summer job interviews:	n/av
Placement by graduation:	n/av
Placement within 9 months:	93% of class
Average starting salary:	$24,000 to $70,000
Areas of placement:	
Private practice 2-10 attorneys	13%
Private practice 11-25 attorneys	8%
Private practice 26-50 attorneys	7%
Private practice 51-100 attorneys	8%
Judicial clerkships	36%
Government	15%
Business/industry	12%
Public interest	3%

Faculty

The law school has 19 full-time and 29 part-time faculty members, of whom 16 are women. About 37% of full-time faculty have a graduate law degree in addition to the J.D.; about 25% of part-time faculty have one. The ratio of full-time students to full-time faculty in an average class is 13 to 1; in a clinic, 12 to 1.

Students

About 52% of the student body are women; 72%, minorities; 1%, African American; 47%, Asian American; 1%, Hispanic; 1%, Native American; and 22%, Hawaiian and Pacific Islander. The majority of students come from Hawaii (75%). The average age of entering students is 27; age range is 22 to 56. About 37% of students enter directly from undergraduate school, 15% have a graduate degree, and 63% have worked full time prior to entering law school. About 5% drop out after the first year for academic or personal reasons; 92% remain to receive a law degree.

UNIVERSITY OF HOUSTON

Law Center

Office of Admissions
Houston, TX 77204-6391

Application Filing		Accreditation
Fall: February 15		ABA, AALS
Spring: n/app		**Degrees Granted**
Fee: $50		J.D., LL.M.

Enrollment 1998–1999		First-Year Class	
Men:	532 54%	Applied:	2441
Women:	457 46%	Accepted:	881
Minorities:	198 20%	Enrolled:	289
Out-of-State:	168 17%		

1998–99 Class Profile

LSAT Percentile: 73%

LSAT Median Score: 158

Percentage passing bar on first try: 90%

Tuition and Fees:

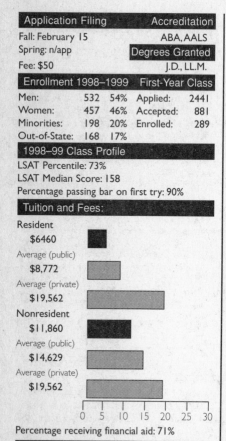

Resident
$6460

Average (public)
$8,772

Average (private)
$19,562

Nonresident
$11,860

Average (public)
$14,629

Average (private)
$19,562

0   5   10   15   20   25   30

Percentage receiving financial aid: 71%

ADMISSIONS

In the fall 1999 first-year class, 2441 applied, 881 were accepted, and 289 enrolled. Fifty-nine transfers enrolled. The median LSAT percentile of the most recent first-year class was 73; the median GPA was 3.3 on a scale of 4.0. The lowest LSAT percentile accepted was 18; the highest was 99.9.

Requirements

Applicants must have a bachelor's degree from an accredited institution and take the LSAT. The most important admission factors include LSAT results, GPA, and general background. No specific undergraduate courses are required. Candidates are not interviewed.

Procedure

The application deadline for fall entry is February 15. Applicants should submit an application form, a nonrefundable application fee of $50, a personal statement, a work resume, and the LSDAS. Letters of recommendation are optional. Notification of the admission decision is January 15 through May 1. The latest acceptable LSAT test date for fall entry is February. The law school uses the LSDAS.

Special

The law school recruits minority and disadvantaged students through scholarship programs, a strong support system on campus, and well-funded BLSA, HLSA, and ALSA organizations. Requirements are different for out-of-state students in that there is a 20% cap for nonresident students. Transfer students must have one year of credit, have attended an ABA-approved law school, and rank typically within the top 10%.

Costs

Tuition and fees for the 1999-2000 academic year are $6460 for full-time in-state students and $11,860 for out-of-state students. Tuition for part-time students is $160 per credit in-state and $340 out-of-state. On-campus room and board costs about $4624 annually; books and supplies run $824.

Financial Aid

About 71% of current law students receive some form of aid. The average annual amount of aid from all sources combined, including scholarships, loans, and work contracts, is $14,559; maximum, $16,948. Awards are based on need and merit; need-based financial aid is handled by the University's Director of Financial Aid. Scholarships are handled by the Assistant Dean for Student Affairs at the Law Center. The Financial Aid Counselor at the Law Center assists students with their paperwork. The required financial statement is the FAFSA. The aid application deadline for fall entry is April 1. Typically, 50% of law scholarship funding is allocated to minority students. No separate application is required. First-year students are notified about their financial aid application at time of acceptance.

About the Law School

University of Houston Law Center was established in 1947 and is a public institution. The 540-acre campus is in an urban area 3 miles south of downtown Houston. The primary mission of the law school is to attract a student body characterized by social and ethnic diversity that will be exposed to a diverse educational and social experience and that will enter the legal profession in positions of responsibility. Students have access to federal, state, county, city, and local agencies, courts, correctional facilities, law firms, and legal aid organizations in the Houston area. Special attention given to accommodating students with disabilities. Housing for law students is available, including housing for married students. About 98% of students live 15 to 20 minutes from campus. About 95% of the law school facilities are accessible to the physically disabled.

Calendar

The law school operates on a traditional semester basis. Courses for full-time students are offered both day and evening and must be completed within 4 years. For first-year studetns, courses are offered day only. For part-time students, courses are offered both day and evening and must be completed within 6 years. For first-year students, courses are offered evenings only. New full-time students are admitted in the fall; part-time, summer. There are 2 6-week summer sessions and 1- 12 week session. Transferable summer courses are offered.

Programs

In addition to the J.D., the law school offers the LL.M. Students may take relevant courses in other programs and apply credit toward the J.D.; a maximum of 12 semester hours may be applied. The following joint degrees may be earned: J.D./M.B.A. (Juris Doctor/Master of Business Administration), J.D./M.P.H. (Juris Doctor/Master of Public Health), J.D./M.A. (Juris Doctor/Master of Arts in history), and J.D./Ph.D. (Juris Doctor/Doctor of Philosophy in medical humanities).

Phone: 713-743-1070
Fax: 713-743-2194
E-mail: admission@www.law.uh.edu
Web: www.law.uh.edu

Contact

Sondra C. Richardson, Assistant Dean for Admissions, 713-743-1070 for general inquiries; Laura Neal, Financial Aid Counselor, 713-743-2269 for financial aid information.

TEXAS

Required

To earn the J.D., candidates must complete 90 total credits, of which 35 are for required courses. They must maintain a minimum GPA of 2.0 in the required courses. The following first-year courses are required of all students: Torts I and II, Criminal Law, Contracts I and II, Legal Research, Procedure, Property I and II, Legal Writing, and Constitutional Law. Required upper-level courses consist of Professional Responsibility and the senior writing requirement. The optional orientation program for first-year students is 2 days of general information and mock classroom instruction taught by faculty, plus ongoing activities throughout the semester.

Electives

The Law Center offers concentrations in corporate law, criminal law, environmental law, international law, litigation, tax law, and health law, and intellectual property. In addition, students can choose among 20 to 25 clinics, both civil and criminal, including the Health Law Clinic and Environmental Law Clinic. Seminar courses are available in all areas. There are judicial internships at federal, state, district, and county municipal levels. Research programs include the Environmental Liability Law Program, Health Law and Policy Institute, National Institute of Trial Advocacy (NITA), Institute of Higher Education Law and Governance, Intellectual Property Institute, and International Law Institute. There is a Young Scholars lecture series. Study abroad may be done through the Mexican Legal Studies Program. The Academic Enrichment Program provides tutorial assistance. The most widely taken electives are Commercial Transactions, Business Organizations, and Evidence.

Graduation Requirements

In order to graduate, candidates must have a GPA of 2.0 and have completed the upper-division writing requirement.

Organizations

Students edit the *Houston Law Review, Houston Journal of International Law, Environmental Resource Newsletter, Environmental Law Society, Health Law News, Environmental Liability Law Report,* International Law in Houston, and the newspaper *Legalese.* Intra-scholastic moot court competitions include the Blakely, Hippard, and New-house Mediation competitions. Law student organizations include Advocates, Corporate Law Society, and Environmental Law Society. There are local chapters of ABA-Law Student Division, Phi Alpha Phi, and Order of the Coif. Law students have access to more than 250 campus clubs and other organizations on the university campus.

Library

The law library contains 460,569 hard-copy volumes and 911,626 microform volume equivalents, and subscribes to 2750 serial publications. Such on-line databases and networks as LEXIS, DIALOG, WESTLAW, and NEXIS are available to law students for research. Special library collections include a U.S. government depository, Mexican Law Collection, Admiralty and Maritime Law Collection, and John R. Brown Archives. Recently, the library added additional computer laboratories and expanded the law school network. Major renovation of the law library building was completed in 1996. The ratio of seats in the library to students is 1 to 1.

Placement

J.D.s awarded:	300

Services available through: separate law school placement center.

Services: Public Interest/Public Sector Fellowship Program

Special features: A comprehensive career education series is held every spring, and includes networking events, speaker panels and mock inerview for first year students. UHLC participates in 6 off-campus recruitment programs during the year.

Full-time job interviews:	56 employers
Summer job interviews:	121 employers
Placement by graduation:	70% of class
Placement within 9 months:	93% of class
Average starting salary:	$45,000 to $78,000

Areas of placement:

Private practice 2-100 attorneys	65%
Judicial clerkships	27%
Business/industry	21%
Academic	17%
Government	10%
Public interest	1%

Faculty

The law school has 46 full-time and 67 part-time faculty members, of whom 29 are women. According to AAUP standards for Category I institutions, faculty salaries are above average. About 28% of full-time faculty have a graduate law degree in addition to the J.D.; about 13% of part-time faculty have one. The ratio of full-time students to full-time faculty in an average class is 19 to 1; in a clinic, 5 to 1. The law school has a regular program of bringing visiting professors and other distinguished lecturers and visitors to campus. There is a chapter of the Order of the Coif; 26 faculty and 337 graduates are members.

Students

About 46% of the student body are women; 20%, minorities; 3%, African American; 7%, Asian American; 9%, Hispanic; and 1%, Native American. The majority of students come from Texas (83%). The average age of entering students is 25; age range is 20 to 60. About 60% of students enter directly from undergraduate school and 13% have a graduate degree. About 3% drop out after the first year for academic or personal reasons; 85% remain to receive a law degree.

College of Law

P.O. Box 442321
Moscow, ID 83844-2321

Application Filing		Accreditation
Fall: February 1		ABA, AALS
Spring: n/app		Degrees Granted
Fee: $40		J.D.

Enrollment 1998–1999		First-Year Class	
Men:	217 74%	Applied:	479
Women:	78 26%	Accepted:	307
Minorities:	12 4%	Enrolled:	100
Out-of-State:	n/av		

1998–99 Class Profile

LSAT Percentile: 60%
LSAT Median Score: 153
Percentage passing bar on first try: 83%

Tuition and Fees:

Resident
$4076

Average (public)
$8,772

Average (private)
$19,562

Nonresident
$10,076

Average (public)
$14,629

Average (private)
$19,562

0 5 10 15 20 25 30

Percentage receiving financial aid: 28%

ADMISSIONS

In the fall 1999 first-year class, 479 applied, 307 were accepted, and 100 enrolled. Two transfers enrolled. The median LSAT percentile of the most recent first-year class was 60; the median GPA was 3.3 on a scale of 4.0. The lowest LSAT percentile accepted was 23; the highest was 99.

Requirements
Applicants must have a bachelor's degree from an accredited institution and take the LSAT. The most important admission factors include state or country of residence, LSAT results, and GPA. No specific undergraduate courses are required. Candidates are interviewed.

Procedure
The application deadline for fall entry is February 1. Applicants should submit an application form, and a nonrefundable application fee of $40. LSDAS registration is required. Personal statements are encouraged, as well as current resumes. Notification of the admission decision is by April 1. The latest acceptable LSAT test date for fall entry is December. The law school uses the LSDAS.

Special
The law school recruits minority and disadvantaged students by means of the Candidate Referral Service. Transfer students must have one year of credit, have attended an ABA-approved law school, submit a letter of good standing, rank in the top half of class, and have competitive LSAT results and UGPA.

Costs

Tuition and fees for the 1999-2000 academic year are $4076 for full-time in-state students and $10,076 for out-of-state students. On-campus room and board costs about $4000 annually; books and supplies run $750.

Financial Aid

About 28% of current law students receive some form of aid. The average annual amount of aid from all sources combined, including scholarships, loans, and work contracts, is $3171; maximum, $11,290. Awards are based on need and merit. The required financial statements are FAFSA and University of Idaho special forms. The aid application deadline for fall entry is February 15. Special funds for minority or disadvantaged students consist of scholarships.

About the Law School

University of Idaho College of Law was established in 1909 and is a public institution. The 160-acre campus is in a small town 85 miles southeast of Spokane, Washington. The primary mission of the law school is to prepare students for the practice of law and leadership in the community. Students have access to federal, state, county, city, and local agencies, courts, correctional facilities, law firms, and legal aid organizations in the Moscow area. Facilities of special interest to law students include the law building, which is especially designed for the study of law. Law students also have access to the extensive university athletic facilities. Housing for law students is available and includes university graduate student dorms, married student housing, and apartments in the local community. All law school facilities are accessible to the physically disabled.

Calendar

The law school operates on a traditional semester basis. Courses for full-time students are offered days only and must be completed within 6 years. There is no part-time program. New full-time students are admitted in the fall. There is an 8- week summer session. Transferable summer courses are not offered.

Phone: 208-885-6423
Fax: 208-885-5709
E-mail: adewitt@uidaho.edu
Web: http:\\www.uidaho.edu\

Contact
Amy E. DeWitt, Admissions Coordinator, 208-885-6423 for general inquiries; Rod Dunn, Associate Director, 208-885-6312 for financial aid information.

IDAHO

Programs
The following joint degrees may be earned: J.D./M.S. (Master of Environmental Science).

Required

To earn the J.D., candidates must complete 88 total credits, of which 31 are for required courses. They must maintain a minimum GPA of 2.0 in the required courses. The following first-year courses are required of all students: Introduction to Law, Property I and II, Torts I and II, Legal Research and Writing, Procedure, Contracts I and II, and Criminal Law. Required upper-level courses consist of Professional Responsibility and an upper-division writing requirement. The required orientation program for first-year students is a 3-day introduction to the study of law which includes professional responsibility, the court system, and trial process.

Electives

The College of Law offers concentrations in corporate law, environmental law, and lawyering skills. In addition, third-year students only may take general practice clinic, tax clinic, Ninth Circuit Court of Appeals, and Nez Perce, and Coeur D'Alene Indian Reservation defense clinics for a maximum of 8 credits. Second- and third-year students may take seminars for 1 to 3 credits. The school offers non-class and resident credit for semesters with the U.S. Attorney, the Attorney General, state and federal districts, appellate courts, and other similar experiences. Second- and third-year students may participate in research programs for 1 to 2 credits. Tutorial programs are provided to first-year students as requested. Minority programs are sponsored by the Minority Law Student Association. The most widely taken electives are Natural Resources, Lawyering Skills, and bar courses.

Graduation Requirements

In order to graduate, candidates must have a GPA of 2.0 and have completed the upper-division writing requirement.

Organizations
The *Idaho Law Review* is the student-edited law publication. Teams compete in the National Moot Court, Jessup International Moot Court, and Environmental Law Moot Court competitions. Other competitions include the McNichols Moot Court competition. Law student organizations include the ABA-Law Student Division, Board of Student Advocates, and Environmental Law Society. There are local chapters of Delta Theta Phi, Phi Delta Phi, and Phi Alpha Delta.

Library
The law library contains 180,892 hard-copy volumes, and subscribes to 2820 serial publications. Such on-line databases and networks as LEXIS, DIALOG, WESTLAW, Legal Resource Index, and Carl are available to law students for research. Special library collections include archives of Idaho materials. Recently, the library added carrels, new compact shelving, and a computer lab. The ratio of library volumes to faculty is 6712 to 1 and to students, 541 to 1. The ratio of seats in the library to students is 1 to 1.

Faculty
The law school has 1 part-time and 16 full-time faculty members, of whom 4 are women. According to AAUP standards for Category I institutions, faculty salaries are below average. About 1% of full-time faculty have a graduate law degree in addition to the J.D. The ratio of full-time students to full-time faculty in an average class is 50 to 1; in a clinic, 10 to 1. The law school has a regular program of bringing visiting professors and other distinguished lecturers and visitors to campus.

Students
About 26% of the student body are women; 4%, minorities; 1%, African American; 1%, Asian American; 1%, Hispanic; and 1%, Native American. The majority of students come from foreign countries (1%). The average age of entering students is 28; age range is 21 to 59. About 9% drop out after the first year for academic or personal reasons; 90% remain to receive a law degree.

Placement	
J.D.s awarded:	80
Services available through: separate law school placement center	
Full-time job interviews:	n/av
Summer job interviews:	n/av
Placement by graduation:	64% of class
Placement within 9 months:	93% of class
Average starting salary:	$36,500
Areas of placement:	
Private practice 2-10 attorneys	42%
Judicial clerkships	29%
Government	16%
Business/industry	8%
Academic	3%

College of Law

504 East Pennsylvania Avenue
Champaign, IL 61820

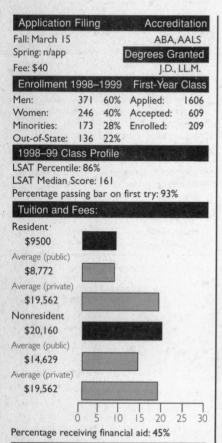

Application Filing			Accreditation
Fall: March 15			ABA, AALS
Spring: n/app			Degrees Granted
Fee: $40			J.D., LL.M.

Enrollment 1998–1999		First-Year Class	
Men:	371 60%	Applied:	1606
Women:	246 40%	Accepted:	609
Minorities:	173 28%	Enrolled:	209
Out-of-State:	136 22%		

1998–99 Class Profile

LSAT Percentile: 86%
LSAT Median Score: 161
Percentage passing bar on first try: 93%

Tuition and Fees:

Resident
$9500

Average (public)
$8,772

Average (private)
$19,562

Nonresident
$20,160

Average (public)
$14,629

Average (private)
$19,562

Percentage receiving financial aid: 45%

ADMISSIONS

In the fall 1999 first-year class, 1606 applied, 609 were accepted, and 209 enrolled. Eighteen transfers enrolled. The median LSAT percentile of the most recent first-year class was 86; the median GPA was 3.4 on a scale of 4.0. The lowest LSAT percentile accepted was 33; the highest was 99.

Requirements

Applicants must have a bachelor's degree from an accredited institution and take the LSAT. The most important admission factors include LSAT results, GPA, and undergraduate curriculum. No specific undergraduate courses are required. Candidates are not interviewed.

Procedure

The application deadline for fall entry is March 15. Applicants should submit an application form, LSAT results, transcripts, a nonrefundable application fee of $40, 2 letters of recommendation, a personal statement, and a resume. Notification of the admissions decision is on a rolling basis from December to May. The latest acceptable LSAT test date for fall entry is February. The law school uses the LSDAS.

Special

The law school recruits minority and disadvantaged students by participating in recruiting fairs and by visiting schools where there are a large number of minority students. Transfer students must have one year of credit, have a minimum GPA of 3.0, and have attended an ABA-approved law school. Preadmissions courses consist of the Law Minority Access Program to expose college juniors to law school. Students take classes in legal analysis and legal research and writing for 4 weeks and then spend 4 weeks as interns with Chicago law firms. Another program, Minority Access to Law School, has a similar intent but is designed for college sophomores.

Costs

Tuition and fees for the 1999-2000 academic year are $9500 for in-state students and $20,160 for out-of-state students. On-campus room and board costs about $6950 annually; and books and supplies run $930.

Financial Aid

About 45% of current law students receive some form of aid. The maximum annual amount of aid from all sources combined, including scholarships, loans, and work contracts, is $18,500. Loans are need based and scholarships are merit based. The required financial statement is the FAFSA. The aid application deadline for fall entry is March 15. Special funds for minority or disadvantaged students are available. First-year students are notified about their financial aid application at the time application is made, and again in a letter of acceptance.

About the Law School

University of Illinois College of Law was established in 1897 and is a public institution. The 710-acre campus is in an urban area 130 miles south of Chicago. The primary mission of the law school is to foster excellence in legal education through a close community of professors and students, where teaching goes hand in hand with scholarship and public service. Students have access to federal, state, county, city, and local agencies, courts, correctional facilities, law firms, and legal aid organizations in the Champaign area. Housing for law students is available in inexpensive apartments in Champaign-Urbana. Two graduate student dormitories are available for law students. All law school facilities are accessible to the physically disabled.

Calendar

The law school operates on a traditional semester basis. Courses are offered days only and must be completed within 3 years. There is no part-time program. New students are admitted in the fall. There are two 5-week summer sessions. Transferable summer courses are not offered.

Programs

In addition to the J.D., the law school offers the LL.M. Students may take relevant courses in other programs and apply credit toward the J.D.; a maximum of 12 credits may be applied. The following joint degrees may be earned: J.D./M.B.A. (Juris Doctor/ Master of Business Administration), J.D./M.D. (Juris Doctor/ Doctor of Medicine), J.D./M.A.L.I.R. (Juris Doctor/ Master of Arts in Labor and Industrial Relations), J.D./M.Ed. (Juris Doctor/ Master of Education), J.D./D.V.M. (Juris Doctor/ Doctor of Veterinary Medicine), J.D./Ph.D. (Juris Doctor/ Doctor of Philosophy in Education), J.D./M.S. (Juris Doctor/Master of Science in journalism, chemistry, or natural resources), and J.D./M.U.P. (Juris Doctor/Master of Urban Planning).

Phone: 217-244-6415
Fax: 217-244-1478
Web: http://www.law.uiuc.edu or
admissions@law.uiuc.edu

Contact

Pamela Coleman, Director of Admissions, 217-244-6415 for general inquiries; Ann K. Perry, Assistant Dean for Student Affairs, 217-333-6438 for financial aid information.

Required

To earn the J.D., candidates must complete 90 total credits, of which 34 are for required courses. They must maintain a minimum GPA of 2.0 in the required courses. The following first-year courses are required of all students: Contracts, Property, Criminal Law and Procedure, Civil Procedure, Torts, Legal Research and Writing, Introduction to Advocacy, Constitutional Law I, and Statutory Interpretation Electives. Required upper-level courses consist of Professional Responsibility and Upper-Level Writing. The required orientation program for first-year students lasts 2 days and is designed to familiarize students with the college. Mock class and group discussions introduce students to law study.

Electives

The College of Law offers concentrations in corporate law, criminal law, environmental law, family law, international law, labor law, litigation, securities law, sports law, tax law, torts and insurance, intellectual property, and public interest law. In addition, clinics are open to second- and third year students for 4 credit hours. Seminar enrollment is generally limited to 12 students. Numerous seminars are offered each semester and are open to second- and third-year students for 2 to 3 credit hours. Student interns may receive up to 4 credit hours for working in such agencies as a local legal services agency, the state's attorney's office, and the public defender's office. Students may also work as research assistants for faculty members and may receive up to 4 credit hours for independent research projects working with individual faculty members. Field work may be carried out through the Prisoners' Rights Research Project, where students provide legal research for federal and state inmates in Illinois institutions; no academic credit is offered. The David C. Baum Memorial Lectures are presented twice each year by distinguished scholars in the areas of civil liberties and civil rights. Students may receive credit for ABA-approved study-abroad programs. First-year students with the lowest predictive indices may attend tutorial sessions with 2 of their professors. The most widely taken electives are Trial Advocacy, Business Organizations, and Evidence.

Graduation Requirements

In order to graduate, candidates must have a GPA of 3.0, have completed the upper-division writing requirement, and have 90 weeks residency, 90 semester hours of passing grades, and 56 hours earned from the University of Illinois.

Organizations

Students edit the *University of Illinois Law Review*, the *Elder Law Journal*, and the newspaper *Pro Se*; law students write the "Recent Decisions" section of the *Illinois Bar Journal*. Teams are sent to the National Moot Court, Philip C. Jessup International Moot Court, and Environmental Moot Court competitions. Other competitions are the ABA Negotiations and ABA Client Counseling competitions. Law student organizations are the Public Interest Law Foundation, Sports Law Society, and Student Bar Association. Local chapters of national associations include the Black Law Students Association, ABA-Law Student Division, and Christian Legal Society. Other campus clubs include intramural basketball and darts, Law Revue, and Volunteer Outreach Program.

Library

The law library contains 565,660 hardcopy volumes and 775,212 microform volume equivalents, and subscribes to 8190 serial publications. Such on-line databases and networks as LEXIS and WESTLAW are available to law students for research. Special library collections include a federal government depository and a European Union depository. Recently, the library added 2 public terminals and a government document workstation and wired south balcony carrels for network access.

Faculty

The law school has 45 full-time and 33 part-time faculty members. About 10% of full-time faculty have a graduate law degree in addition to the J.D. The ratio of full-time students to full-time faculty in an average class is 17 to 1; in a clinic, 7 to 1. The law school has a regular program of bringing visiting professors and other distinguished lecturers and visitors to campus. There is a chapter of the Order of the Coif; 40 faculty and 20 graduates are members.

Placement

J.D.s awarded:	185
Services available through: a separate law school placement center and the university placement center	
Special features: the Alumni-Student Job Search Conference, where 50 alumni provide counseling and programs for students about the job search process	
Full-time job interviews:	62 employers
Summer job interviews:	108 employers
Placement by graduation:	70% of class
Placement within 9 months:	96% of class
Average starting salary:	$22,200 to $91,500
Areas of placement:	
Private practice 2-10 attorneys	11%
Private practive 11-25 attorneys	13%
Private practice 26-50 attorneys	6%
Private practice 51-100 attorneys	12%
Private practice 101-250 attorneys	19%
Private practice 251-500 attorneys	24%
Private practice 500+ attorneys	11%
Business/industry	21%
Judicial clerkships	20%
Government	16%

Students

About 40% of the student body are women; 28%, minorities; 11%, African American; 8%, Asian American; and 9%, Hispanic. The majority of students come from Illinois (78%). The average age of entering students is 24; age range is 21 to 43. About 1% drop out after the first year for academic or personal reasons; 99% remain to receive a law degree.

College of Law

276 Boyd Law Building,
Melrose at Byington Street
Iowa City, IA 52242

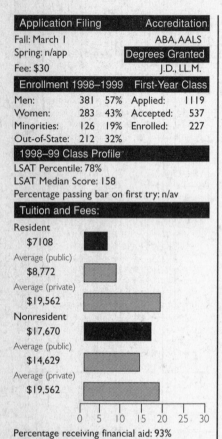

Application Filing		Accreditation
Fall: March 1		ABA, AALS
Spring: n/app		**Degrees Granted**
Fee: $30		J.D., LL.M.

Enrollment 1998–1999			First-Year Class
Men:	381	57%	Applied: 1119
Women:	283	43%	Accepted: 537
Minorities:	126	19%	Enrolled: 227
Out-of-State:	212	32%	

1998–99 Class Profile

LSAT Percentile: 78%
LSAT Median Score: 158
Percentage passing bar on first try: n/av

Tuition and Fees:

Resident
$7108

Average (public)
$8,772

Average (private)
$19,562

Nonresident
$17,670

Average (public)
$14,629

Average (private)
$19,562

Percentage receiving financial aid: 93%

ADMISSIONS

In the fall 1999 first-year class, 1119 applied, 537 were accepted, and 227 enrolled. Four transfers enrolled. The median LSAT percentile of the most recent first-year class was 78; the median GPA was 3.49 on a scale of 4.0.

Requirements
Applicants must have a bachelor's degree from an accredited institution and take the LSAT. The most important admission factors include academic achievement, LSAT results, and motivation. No specific undergraduate courses are required. Candidates are not interviewed.

Procedure
The application deadline for fall entry is March 1. Applicants should submit an application form, LSAT results, and transcripts. Prior standardized test scores may be submitted as well as TOEFL, for foreign applicants who have not received a degree from a U.S. institution and a nonrefundable application fee of $30,

($50 for foreign applicants) letters of recommendation are recommended. Notification of the admission decision begins in October. The latest acceptable LSAT test date for fall entry is February, although a February tester will be at a disadvantage. The law school uses the LSDAS.

Special
In addition to extensive travel, the law school has sponsored, for more than 20 years, "Bridging the Gap," a minority recruitment conference held at the law school. The law school participates in and supports CLEO and PLSI. Requirements are different for out-of-state students in that preference is given to applicants who are residents of Iowa. Approximately 70% of the entering class is comprised of Iowa residents. Transfer students must have one year of credit, have attended an ABA-approved law school, have credentials that would have made the students admissible as first-year students, and have attended an AALS- and ABA-approved law school.

Costs

Tuition and fees for the 1999-2000 academic year are $7108 for full-time in-state students and $17,670 for out-of-state students. On-campus room and board costs about $4370 annually; books and supplies run $1350.

Financial Aid

About 93% of current law students receive some form of aid. The average annual amount of aid from all sources combined, including scholarships, loans, and work contracts, is $17,183; maximum, $27,756. Awards are based on need and merit. The required financial statements are the FAFSA, students federal tax returns, and the institutional form. The aid application deadline for fall entry is on a rolling basis after January 1. The Law Opportunity Fellowship program funds a limited number of 3-year tuition and research assistant positions to persons from groups and backgrounds historically underrepresented in the legal profession. First-year students are notified about their financial aid application after admission, and once all required financial aid documents are submitted to the university.

About the Law School

University of Iowa College of Law was established in 1865 and is a public institution. The 1900-acre campus is in a small town 125 miles east of Des Moines. The primary mission of the law school is to challenge students to set high standards for themselves and to strive for the best professional education they can obtain from the curriculum, the faculty, and the academic environment. Students have access to federal, state, county, city, and local agencies, courts, correctional facilities, law firms, and legal aid organizations in the Iowa City area. Facilities of special interest to law students include the $25 million law building that features state-of-the-art computer equipment, audiovisual technology, and 3 full-scale courtrooms. Housing for law students is available as family housing for married or single parent students, as dormitory housing offered through Residence Services, and as apartments, rooms, and duplexes off campus. All law school facilities are accessible to the physically disabled.

Calendar

The law school operates on a traditional semester basis. Courses for full-time students are offered days only and must be completed within 3 years. There is no part-time program. New students are admitted in the fall and summer. There is an 11-week summer session broken down into 2 5-1/2 week sessions. Transferable summer courses are offered.

Programs

In addition to the J.D., the law school offers the LL.M. Students may take relevant courses in other programs and apply credit toward the J.D.; a maximum of 6 credits may be applied. The following joint degrees may be earned: J.D./M.B.A. (Juris Doctor/Master of Business Administration) and J.D./M.A. (Juris Doctor/Master of Arts in urban and regional planning and in hospital and health administratrion).

Phone: 319-335-9095 or 319-335-9142
553-IOWA, ext. 9142
Fax: 319-335-9019
E-mail: law-admissions@uiowa.edu
Web: www.uiowa.edu/~lawcoll

Contact

College of Law Admissions Staff, 319-335-9095 or 319-335-9142 for general inquiries; Susan Palmer, Associate Director of Admissions, 319-335-9142 for financial aid information.

IOWA

Required

To earn the J.D., candidates must complete 90 total credits, of which 35 are for required courses. The following first-year courses are required of all students: Contracts I and II, Property I and II, Criminal Law, Torts, Civil Procedure, Constitutional Law I, and Introduction to Legal Reasoning. Required upper-level courses consist of Appellate Advocacy I, Professional Responsibility, and Constitutional Law II. The required orientation program for first-year students is 1 week; the course component covers an overview of the American legal system, legal education, the legal profession and perspectives on law. The program component covers academic and other support services, bar requirements, dealing with stress, professional conduct standards, and social events.

Electives

There are a variety of civil and criminal law programs including specialized clinics representing financially distressed farmers and persons with HIV-related problems. Clinics are open to students in the second half of their law study for up to 15 credit hours. Seminars are offered in a variety of subject areas. They normally run for 2 semesters; 5-credits and an upper-level writing credit are awarded.If there is overenrollment in the seminars, priority is given to third-year students and those seeking maximum credit. Occasionally, externship placements are approved with nonprofit entities that offer a strong educational experience. They may be arranged in the summer or during the academic year. Credit is normally 6 hours, though a maximum of 15 credits may be awarded in extraordinary circumstances. Students may arrange an independent research project with faculty members in areas of mutual interest. The Academic Achievement Program sponsors an academic skills lecture series throughout the year, which is open to all students, though the emphasis is on the needs of first-year students. The college participates in the London Law Consortium and sponsors a summer semester in Archachon, France. In addition, many students transfer credits from programs sponsored by other institutions. Faculty members provide mentoring for students needing special assistance. In addition, the Writing Center works with students individually. Students of color are involved in the full array of opportunities offered by the law school, as well as in the minority student organizations. Minority

and special interest programming is also sponsored by student organizations. The most widely taken electives are Clinics, Trial Advocacy, and Evidence.

Graduation Requirements

In order to graduate, candidates must have completed the upper-division writing requirement.

Organizations

Students edit the *Iowa Law Review*, the *Journal of Corporation Law*, and the *Iowa Journal of Transnational Law and Contemporary Problems*. Newsletters are produced by the Student Bar Association and the Organization of Women Law Students. Annually, students compete in internal competitions such as the Appellate Advocacy I and II and external competitions such as National Moot Court. Additionally, the Stepenson Competition is a competitive version of the full trials completing the trial advocacy course. Student organizations include the Iowa Student Bar Association, Environmental Law Society, and Trial Advocacy Board. There are local chapters of Phi Delta Phi and Phi Alpha Delta.

Library

The law library contains 642,872 hardcopy volumes and 290,909 microform volume equivalents, and subscribes to 8301 individual titles. Such on-line databases and networks as LEXIS, DIALOG, WESTLAW, NEXIS, RLIN, Wilson Indexes, PAIS, and OCLC are available to law students for research. Special library collections include a U.S. Government Printing Office and Iowa depositories as well as (United Nations collection. Recently, the library wired all 381 student carrels with access to LAN (Internet, Westlaw, Lexis, OPAC and so on). The ratio of library volumes to faculty is 18,677 to 1 and to students, 1394 to 1. The ratio of seats in the library to students is 1 to 1.

Placement

J.D.s awarded:	235

Services available through: separate law school placement center.

Services: 2 full-time professionals provide individual advising and mock interview training.

Special features: weekly programs on career areas in the law.

Full-time job interviews:	n/av
Summer job interviews:	n/av
Placement by graduation:	75% of class
Placement within 9 months:	99% of class
Average starting salary:	$30,000 to $110,000

Areas of placement:

Private practice 2-10 attorneys	16%
Private practice 11-25 attorneys	6%
Private practice 26-50 attorneys	5%
Private practice 51-100 attorneys	4%
Private practice 100 + attorneys	25%
Judicial clerkships	14%
Business/industry	10%
Government	8%
Public interest	7%
Military	2%
Academic	2%

Faculty

The law school has 52 full-time and 29 part-time faculty members, of whom 26 are women. According to AAUP standards for Category I institutions, faculty salaries are well above average. About 20% of full-time faculty have a graduate law degree in addition to the J.D.; about 10% of part-time faculty have one. The ratio of full-time students to full-time faculty in an average class is 13 to 1; in a clinic, 7 to 1. The law school has a regular program of bringing visiting professors and other distinguished lecturers and visitors to campus. There is a chapter of the Order of the Coif; 50 faculty and 800 graduates are members.

Students

About 43% of the student body are women; 19%, minorities; 6%, African American; 7%, Asian American; 4%, Hispanic; and 2%, Native American. The majority of students come from the Midwest (83%). The average age of entering students is 25; age range is 21 to 53. About 11% of students have a graduate degree. About 6% drop out after the first year for academic or personal reasons; 94% remain to receive a law degree.

School of Law

205 Green Hall
Lawrence, KS 66045

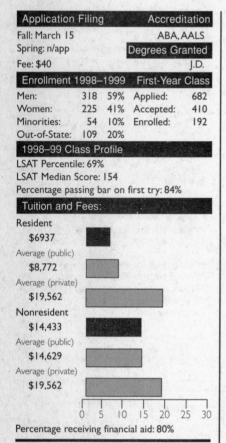

Application Filing		Accreditation
Fall: March 15		ABA, AALS
Spring: n/app		**Degrees Granted**
Fee: $40		J.D.

Enrollment 1998–1999			First-Year Class	
Men:	318	59%	Applied:	682
Women:	225	41%	Accepted:	410
Minorities:	54	10%	Enrolled:	192
Out-of-State:	109	20%		

1998–99 Class Profile
LSAT Percentile: 69%
LSAT Median Score: 154
Percentage passing bar on first try: 84%

Tuition and Fees:

Resident
$6937

Average (public)
$8,772

Average (private)
$19,562

Nonresident
$14,433

Average (public)
$14,629

Average (private)
$19,562

0 5 10 15 20 25 30

Percentage receiving financial aid: 80%

ADMISSIONS

In the fall 1999 first-year class, 682 applied, 410 were accepted, and 192 enrolled. Five transfers enrolled. The median LSAT percentile of the most recent first-year class was 69; the median GPA was 3.3 on a scale of 4.0. The lowest LSAT percentile accepted was 20; the highest was 99.

Requirements
Applicants must have a bachelor's degree from an accredited institution and take the LSAT. The most important admission factors are state or country of residence, GPA, and LSAT results. No specific undergraduate courses are required. Candidates are not interviewed.

Procedure
The application deadline for fall entry is March 15. Applicants should submit an application form, LSAT results, a nonrefundable application fee of $40, 1 letter of recommendation, and a personal statement. Notification of the admission decision is on a rolling basis. The latest acceptable LSAT test date for fall entry is February; however, December is preferred. The law school uses the LSDAS.

Special
The law school recruits minority and disadvantaged students by means of minority scholarship opportunities. The law school also sponsors a Minority-in-Law Day program. Letters are sent to students from the Western Name Exchange program. The Law Service Candidate Referral Service is also used. In addition, the law school recruits in areas with a large minority population. Requirements are different for out-of-state students in that preference is given to Kansas residents. Transfer students must have one year of credit, have a minimum GPA of 3.0, and have attended an ABA-approved law school. No more than 31 hours from the student's previous law school can be transferred.

Costs

Tuition and fees for the 1999-2000 academic year are $6937 for full-time in-state students and $14,433 for out-of-state students. On-campus room and board costs about $6465 annually; books and supplies run $700.

Financial Aid

About 80% of current law students receive some form of aid. The average annual amount of aid from all sources combined, including scholarships, loans, and work contracts, is $8500; maximum, $18,500. Awards are based on need and merit. The required financial statement is the FAFSA. The aid application deadline for fall entry is March 1. Special funds for minority or disadvantaged students consist of an amount close to tuition, which is generally available. First-year students are notified about their financial aid application at any point in time of acceptance through the time of enrollment.

About the Law School

University of Kansas School of Law was established in 1878 and is a public institution. The 1000-acre campus is in a suburban area 40 miles west of Kansas City. The primary mission of the law school is to prepare students for practice in the legal profession by focusing on a general education in the law as well as on the details of legal rules and practice. Students have access to federal, state, county, city, and local agencies, courts, correctional facilities, law firms, and legal aid organizations in the Lawrence area. Of special interest to law students is the Paul E. Wilson Defender Project, which allows students to counsel and perform legal service for indigent inmates of the U.S. Penitentiary at Leavenworth, the Kansas State Penitentiary, and Kansas Correctional Institution; the project was the first of its kind in the country. Housing for law students is available in a university residence hall or apartment complex and also in apartments or houses off campus. Married student housing is also available. All law school facilities are accessible to the physically disabled.

Calendar

The law school operates on a traditional semester basis. Courses for full-time students are offered days only and must be completed within 5 years. There is no part-time program. New full-time students are admitted in the fall and summer. There are 2 5-week summer sessions. Transferable summer courses are offered.

Programs

Students may take relevant courses in other programs and apply credit toward the J.D.; a maximum of 6 hours credits may be applied. The following joint degrees may be earned: J.D./M.B.A. (Juris Doctor/Master of Business Administration), J.D./M.A. (Juris Doctor/Master of Arts in economics and in philosophy), J.D./M.S. (Juris Doctor/Master of Science in health services administration), J.D./M.P.A. (Juris Doctor/Master of Public Administration), J.D./M.S.W. (Juris Doctor/Master of Social Work), and J.D./M.U.P. (Juris Doctor/Master of Urban Planning).

Phone: 785-864-4378
Fax: 785-864-5054
E-mail: lindeman@law.wpo.ukans.edu
Web: www.law.ukans.edu

Contact

Diane Lindeman, Director of Admissions, 913-864-4378 for general inquiries; Diane Del Buono, Director of Financial Aid, 913-864-4700 for financial aid information.

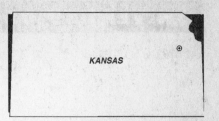

KANSAS

Required

To earn the J.D., candidates must complete 90 total credits, of which 43 to 45 are for required courses. They must maintain a minimum GPA of 2.0 in the required courses. The following first-year courses are required of all students: Civil Procedure I and II, Contracts I and II, Criminal Law, Criminal Procedure, Property I and II, Torts I, and Lawyering I and II. Required upper-level courses consist of Commercial Law I, Constitutional Law *or* Constitutional Law A and B, Evidence, Professional Responsibility, and a writing requirement. The required orientation program for first-year students is a 1 1/2-day program that includes sessions on preparing for class, briefing and studying techniques, a mock class, small group sessions, and tours of the library and building.

Electives

The School of Law offers concentrations in corporate law, criminal law, environmental law, family law, international law, juvenile law, labor law, litigation, media law, securities law, tax law, torts and insurance, and agricultural law, civil rights law, constitutional law, energy law, industrial relations law, tribal law, and patent law. In addition, clinics are offered to second- and third-year students for 1 to 3 hours of credit. Clinics include Criminal Justice, the Paul E. Wilson Defender Project, and the Legal Aid Clinic. Periodically, research workshops are offered for all students. Second-and third-year students may take advantage of available internship opportunities available; usually no academic credit is awarded. Guest lecture programs are offered for no credit. Students may study at University College in London through the London Law Consortium, of which the University of Kansas is a member. Students may also participate in other ABA-approved study-abroad programs. Tutorial programs are voluntary. Academic support programs are available for students who may be in need assistance. The most widely taken electives are Business Associations I and II, Income Tax, and Family Law.

Graduation Requirements

In order to graduate, candidates must have a GPA of 2.0 and fulfill the upper-division writing requirement by successfully completing 2 hours of independent research, and a 2- to 3-hour seminar, workshop, clinic, or other course that a faculty member has certified involves close faculty supervision of writing, or publishing a student note or comment in the law review or journal.

Organizations

Students edit the *Kansas Law Review* and the *Kansas Journal of Law and Public Policy*. Other publications include *KU Laws*, the alumni newsletter. There is an in-house moot court competition for second-year students who compete for the Robert C. Foulston and George Siefkin Prizes for Excellence in Appellate Advocacy. The National Moot Court Competition is held annually in the fall, whereas the Jessup International Moot Court Competition is held annually in the spring. Student organizations include the American Trial Lawyers Association, Black Law Students Association, and Environmental Law Society. Local chapters of national associations include Phi Alpha Delta, Phi Delta Phi, and National Lawyers Guild.

Library

The law library contains 325,000 hardcopy volumes and 333,169 microform volume equivalents, and subscribes to 4165 serial publications. Such on-line databases and networks as LEXIS, DIALOG, WESTLAW, and LRIN are available to law students for research. Special library collections include selective government depositories for both state and federal documents. Recently, the library wired study carrels for Internet access. The ratio of library volumes to faculty is 7692 to 1 and to students, 535 to 1. The ratio of seats in the library to students is 1 to 1.

Placement

J.D.s awarded:	166
Services available through: a separate law school placement center.	
Special features: a mentoring program that matches current law students with practicing alumni.	
Full-time job interviews:	150 employers
Summer job interviews:	n/av
Placement by graduation:	n/av
Placement within 9 months:	94% of class
Average starting salary:	$23,000 to $52,000
Areas of placement:	
Private practice 2-10 attorneys	26%
Private practice 11-25 attorneys	14%
Private practice 26-50 attorneys	6%
Private practice 51-100 attorneys	11%
Judicial clerkships	7%
Business/industry	26%
Judicial clerkships	7%
Public interest	4%
Academic	2%
Government	2%
Military	2%

Faculty

The law school has 34 full-time and 7 part-time faculty members, of whom 11 are women. According to AAUP standards for Category I institutions, faculty salaries are average. About 28% of full-time faculty have a graduate law degree in addition to the J.D.; about 50% of part-time faculty have one. The ratio of full-time students to full-time faculty in an average class is 16 to 1; in a clinic, 10 to 1. The law school has a regular program of bringing visiting professors and other distinguished lecturers and visitors to campus. There is a chapter of the Order of the Coif; 17 faculty and 450 graduates are members.

Students

About 41% of the student body are women; 10%, minorities; 3%, African American; 2%, Asian American; 4%, Hispanic; and 1%, Native American. The majority of students come from Kansas (80%). The average age of entering students is 23; age range is 20 to 52. About 51% of students enter directly from undergraduate school, 8% have a graduate degree, and 40% have worked full-time prior to entering law school. About 3% drop out after the first year for academic or personal reasons; 94% remain to receive a law degree.

UNIVERSITY OF KENTUCKY

College of Law

209 Law Building
Lexington, KY 40506-0048

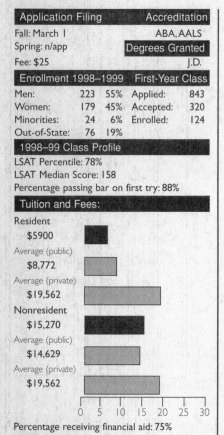

Application Filing			Accreditation
Fall: March 1			ABA, AALS
Spring: n/app			**Degrees Granted**
Fee: $25			J.D.

Enrollment 1998–1999			First-Year Class	
Men:	223	55%	Applied:	843
Women:	179	45%	Accepted:	320
Minorities:	24	6%	Enrolled:	124
Out-of-State:	76	19%		

1998–99 Class Profile
LSAT Percentile: 78%
LSAT Median Score: 158
Percentage passing bar on first try: 88%

Tuition and Fees:

Resident
$5900

Average (public)
$8,772

Average (private)
$19,562

Nonresident
$15,270

Average (public)
$14,629

Average (private)
$19,562

0 5 10 15 20 25 30

Percentage receiving financial aid: 75%

ADMISSIONS

In the fall 1999 first-year class, 843 applied, 320 were accepted, and 124 enrolled. Thirteen transfers enrolled. The median LSAT percentile of the most recent first-year class was 78; the median GPA was 3.5 on a scale of 4.0. The lowest LSAT percentile accepted was 33; the highest was 98.

Requirements
Applicants must have a bachelor's degree from an accredited institution and take the LSAT. Minimum acceptable LSAT score is 25 and minimum acceptable GPA is 2.2 on a scale of 4.0. The most important admission factors include writing ability, LSAT results, and GPA. No specific undergraduate courses are required. Candidates are not interviewed.

Procedure
The application deadline for fall entry is March 1. Applicants should submit an application form, LSAT results, transcripts, TOEFL if a foreign student, and a nonrefundable application fee of $25; and 2 letters of recommendation are recommended but not required. Notification of the admissions decision is weekly on a rolling basis. The latest acceptable LSAT test date for fall entry is February. The law school uses the LSDAS.

Special
The law school recruits minority and disadvantaged students by means of the Fall Minority Visitation Conference, scholarships and stipends, visits to campuses, participation in CLEO, the provision of tutors during the first year, and general academic support offerings. Transfer students must have one year of credit, have a minimum GPA of 2.7, have attended an ABA-approved law school, and must provide reasons for wanting to transfer. As transfers are not encouraged, applications are reviewed on a case-by-case basis. Preadmissions courses consist of a 1-week summer workshop prior to the first day of classes.

Costs

Tuition and fees for the 1999-2000 academic year are $5900 for in-state students and $15,270 for out-of-state students. On-campus room and board costs about $6990 annually; and books and supplies run $500.

Financial Aid

About 75% of current law students receive some form of aid. The average annual amount of aid from all sources combined, including scholarships, loans, and work contracts, is $14,000; maximum, $25,500. Awards are based on need and merit. Special funds are available that have specific criteria that must be met by the applicants. The required financial statement is the FAFSA. The aid application deadline for fall entry is April 1. Special funds for minority or disadvantaged students consist of tuition and monthly stipends available through the combined efforts of the college's and university's administration. First-year students are notified about their financial aid application 1 month after acceptance for scholarships, and in June for loans.

About the Law School

University of Kentucky College of Law was established in 1908 and is a public institution. The 673-acre campus is in an urban area 80 miles east of Louisville, Kentucky, and 75 miles south of Cincinnati, Ohio. The primary mission of the law school is to provide a legal education to individuals so that they might render a high quality of professional service to Kentucky and the nation. Students have access to federal, state, county, city, and local agencies, courts, correctional facilities, law firms, and legal aid organizations in the Lexington area and elsewhere in Kentucky. Facilities of special interest to law students include a civil law clinic; students have their own clients and caseloads under the supervision of a former trial attorney. Housing for law students is plentiful both on and off campus. Most law students choose off-campus housing, some of which is located across the street from the law school. All law school facilities are accessible to the physically disabled.

Calendar

The law school operates on a traditional semester basis. Courses are offered days only and are usually completed within 3 to 4 years. There is no part-time program. New students are admitted in the fall. There is an 8-week summer session. Transferable summer courses are offered.

Programs

Students may take relevant courses in other programs and apply credit toward the J.D.; a maximum of 6 credits may be applied. The following joint degrees may be earned: J.D./M.B.A. (Juris Doctor/Master of Business Administration) and J.D./M.P.A. (Juris Doctor/Master of Public Administration).

Phone: 606-257-7938
E-mail: dbakert@pop.uky.edu

Contact

Drusilla V. Bakert, Associate Dean, 606-257-1678 for general inquiries; University of Kentucky Student Financial Aid Office, 606-257-3172 for financial aid information.

Required

To earn the J.D., candidates must complete 90 total credits, of which 34 are for required courses. They must maintain a minimum GPA of 2.0 in the required courses. The following first-year courses are required of all students: Contracts and Sales I and II, Torts, Property, Criminal Law, Constitutional Law I, Civil Procedure I and II, and Legal Research and Writing. Required upper-level courses consist of Professional Responsibility and a seminar with a writing requirement. The required orientation program for first-year students is 2 days long and includes an introduction to the community, to the case method, to the faculty, and to the current students.

Electives

The College of Law offers concentrations in corporate law, criminal law, environmental law, family law, international law, labor law, litigation, securities law, tax law, torts and insurance, and alternate dispute resolution. In addition, clinics include Prison Counsel for upper-level students for 3 credit hours and Civil-Law Clinic for upper-level students for 3 credit hours. Numerous seminars are offered, including Gender Discrimination, Housing Law, and Intellectual Property. Internships with prosecutors for third-year students for 3 credit hours are available. Independent research may be done on topics of special interest for 1 to 3 credit hours. Third-year students receive 1 to 3 credit hours for clerking with judges in state district, circuit, and appellate division courts, or in either of 2 federal district courts. The Roy Ray and Virginia Ray and Judge Mac Swinford lecture series bring national figures to speak at the college. Other lecture series are given by scholars such as Dean Guido Calabresi to the Honorable Justice William H. Rehnquist. Study abroad is available via transient work at a number of ABA-approved law schools. Academic support is offered for all first-year students in the first semester and in later semesters for those in academic difficulty. Tutorials are offered to minority students. The most widely taken electives are Evidence, Business Associations, and Tax.

Graduation Requirements

In order to graduate, candidates must have a GPA of 2.0 and have completed the upper-division writing requirement.

Organizations

Students edit the *Kentucky Law Journal*, the *Journal of Natural Resources and Environmental Law*, and the newspapers *Class Action* and *Week in Brief*. Students compete in the National Moot Court Competition, Jessup Competition, and Frederick Douglass Black Law Student Association Competition. Other competitions include the Trial Advocacy Competition, the Wilhelm Vis International Commercial Law Moot, and competitions in sports law, space law, and telecommunications law. Student organizations include the Student Bar Association, Environmental Law Society, and Womens' Law Caucus. Henry Clay Inns of Court and several legal fraternities have local chapters.

Library

The law library contains 408,276 hardcopy volumes and 976,440 microform volume equivalents, and subscribes to 3418 serial publications. Such on-line databases and networks as LEXIS, DIALOG, and WESTLAW are available to law students for research. Special library collections include human rights and mineral law and policy, as well as a selective government document depository. Recently, the library added a 50-station computer lab for student use, a 42-carrel study room wired for laptop use of the Internet, LEXIS, WESTLAW, and other library resources. The ratio of library volumes to faculty is 12,891 to 1 and to students, 750 to 1. The ratio of seats in the library to students is 1 to 1.

Faculty

The law school has 28 full-time and 20 part-time faculty members, of whom 14 are women. According to AAUP standards for Category I institutions, faculty salaries are average. About 25% of full-time faculty have a graduate law degree in addition to the J.D.; about 10% of part-time faculty have one. The ratio of full-time students to full-time faculty in an average class is 19 to 1; in a clinic, 8 to 1. The law school has a regular program of bringing visiting professors and other distinguished lecturers and visitors to campus. There is a chapter of the Order of the Coif; 23 faculty and 395 graduates are members.

KENTUCKY

Placement

J.D.s awarded:	135
Services available through: aA separate law school placement center	
Services: computer database on Kentucky law firms and 5 recruitment conferences	
Special features: individual attention from an associate dean with 8 years of practice experience in a law firm setting	
Full-time job interviews:	90 employers
Summer job interviews:	120 employers
Placement by graduation:	51% of class
Placement within 9 months:	98% of class
Average starting salary:	$22,000 to $78,000
Areas of placement:	
Private practice 2-10 attorneys	30%
Private practice 11-25 attorneys	7%
Private practice 26-50 attorneys	6%
Private practice 51-100 attorneys	7%
Private practice 100+ attorneys	9%
Solo practice	1%
Business/industry	14%
Judicial clerkships	14%
Government	7%
Public interest	4%
Military	1%

Students

About 45% of the student body are women; 6%, minorities; 5%, African American; 1%, Asian American; and 1%, Hispanic. The majority of students come from Kentucky (81%). The average age of entering students is 23; age range is 21 to 50. About 4% drop out after the first year for academic or personal reasons; 90% remain to receive a law degree.

Louis D. Brandeis School of Law

University of Louisville
Belknap Campus-Wilson W. Wyatt Hall
Louisville, KY 40292

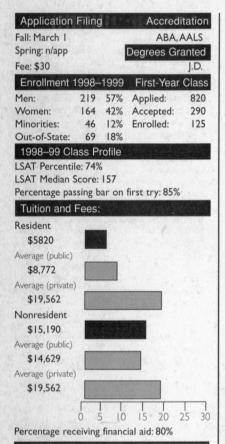

Application Filing		Accreditation
Fall: March 1		ABA, AALS
Spring: n/app		**Degrees Granted**
Fee: $30		J.D.

Enrollment 1998–1999		First-Year Class	
Men:	219 57%	Applied:	820
Women:	164 42%	Accepted:	290
Minorities:	46 12%	Enrolled:	125
Out-of-State:	69 18%		

1998–99 Class Profile
LSAT Percentile: 74%
LSAT Median Score: 157
Percentage passing bar on first try: 85%

Tuition and Fees:

Resident
$5820

Average (public)
$8,772

Average (private)
$19,562

Nonresident
$15,190

Average (public)
$14,629

Average (private)
$19,562

0 5 10 15 20 25 30

Percentage receiving financial aid: 80%

ADMISSIONS
In the fall 1999 first-year class, 820 applied, 290 were accepted, and 125 enrolled. Twelve transfers enrolled. The median LSAT percentile of the most recent first-year class was 74; the median GPA was 3.4 on a scale of 4.0. The lowest LSAT percentile accepted was 27; the highest was 99.

Requirements
Applicants must have a bachelor's degree from an accredited institution and take the LSAT. Minimum acceptable GPA is 2.0 on a scale of 4.0. The most important admission factors include academic achievement, LSAT results, and GPA. No specific undergraduate courses are required. Candidates are not interviewed.

Procedure
The priority application deadline for fall entry is March 1. Applicants should submit an application form, a nonrefundable application fee of $30, and a personal statement. Recommendations are suggested, but not required. Notification of the admission decision is on a rolling basis. The latest acceptable LSAT test date for fall entry is February. The law school uses the LSDAS.

Special
The law school recruits minority and disadvantaged students by sponsoring a minority prelaw day and attending minority fairs and programs at other schools. Minority scholarships are also available. Transfer students must have one year of credit, have attended an ABA-approved law school, be in good standing, have met entrance requirements for the school had they applied for initial admission, and be in the upper quarter of their law school class. Preadmissions courses vary from year to year.

Costs
Tuition and fees for the 1999-2000 academic year are $5820 for full-time in-state students and $15,190 for out-of-state students. Tuition and fees for part-time students is $5160 per year in-state and $13,760 out-of-state. On-campus room and board costs about $4200 annually; books and supplies run $824.

Financial Aid
About 80% of current law students receive some form of aid. The average annual amount of aid from all sources combined, including scholarships, loans, and work contracts, is $8000; maximu;m, $16,500 (resident) and $26,000 (nonresident). Awards are based on need and merit. The required financial statement is the FAFSA. The aid application deadline for fall entry is June 1. Special funds for minority or disadvantaged students consist of a number of recruiting scholarships. First-year students are notified about their financial aid application at the time of acceptance.

About the Law School
University of Louisville Louis D. Brandeis School of Law was established in 1846 and is a public institution. The campus is in an urban area 4 miles south of downtown Louisville. The primary mission of the law school is to provide students with a quality legal education and prepare them for professional life through a curriculum that emphasizes fundamental lawyering skills and the development of professional values, while also affording students the opportunity to take advanced courses in a wide variety of specialty areas. Students have access to federal, state, county, city, and local agencies, courts, correctional facilities, law firms, and legal aid organizations in the Louisville area. Facilities of special interest to law students include the school's physical facility that provides students with a large, comfortable environment in which to attend class and study. Many student gathering places and study group rooms are available. Housing for law students is available in a university dormitory and in affordable rental housing close to campus. All law school facilities are accessible to the physically disabled.

Calendar
The law school operates on a traditional semester basis. Courses for full-time students are offered days only, but full-time students may enroll in evening classes after the first year; courses must be completed within 5 years. For part-time students, courses are offered evenings only, but part-time students may enroll in day classes and must be completed within 6 years. New full-and part-time students are admitted in the fall. There is an 8-week summer session. Transferable summer courses are offered.

Programs
The following joint degrees may be earned: M.B.A./J.D. (Juris Doctor/Master of Business Administration) and J.D./M.Div. (Juris Doctor/Master of Divinity).

Phone: 502-852-6364
334-8634
Fax: 502-852-0862
E-mail: charlene.olivia@louisville.edu
Web: www.louisville.edu/brandeislaw/

Contact

Charlene Taylor, Admissions Office, 502-852-6364 for general inquiries; Jerie Torbeck, Assistant Dean for Law Admissions, 502-852-6096 for financial aid information.

KENTUCKY

Required

To earn the J.D., candidates must complete 90 total credits, of which 44 are for required courses. They must maintain a minimum GPA of 2.0 in the required courses. The following first-year courses are required of all students: Basic Legal Skills, Civil Procedure, Contracts, Torts, Property, Legal Research, and Criminal Law. Required upper-level courses consist of Professional Responsibility, Constitutional Law I and II, a perspective course, a writing requirement, and 24 hours of core courses. The required orientation program for first-year students is 2½ days devoted to skills development and orientation to legal education and the profession. There is also time for social events.

Electives

The Louis D. Brandeis School of Law offers concentrations in corporate law, criminal law, family law, international law, labor law, securities law, and tax law. In addition, there is a required pro bono program (minimum 30 hours of work). Externships in the courts and the P.D. and D.A. offices are available to those who have completed 60 credit hours. Tahe school offers a wide variety of seminars to second-third-and fourth-year students in specialized fields of law; 2 to 3 credit hours are awarded. Several internships, worth 2 to 4 hours, are available, including a judicial internship and a civil and criminal internship. All students are required to complete Legal Research, a 3-hour Basic Legal Skills course, and a seminar that requires a substantial research paper. Special lecture series include the Brandeis and Harlan Lecture Series. Students may earn credit for participation in foreign study in an ABA-accredited program. Students with adequate language abilities may be foreign exchange students with several law schools throughout the world. An academic support program is offered to provide tutorial assistance to students with academic problems. Tutors run study sessions in first-year courses. The school has several minority recruiting activities each year and a number of scholarships for minority students. A diversity committee presents programs to the student body on topics such as gay/lesbian issues and women in politics. The most widely taken electives are Tax, Evidence, and Business Organizations.

Graduation Requirements

In order to graduate, candidates must have a GPA of 2.0, have completed the upper-division writing requirement, and have performed 30 hours of law-related public service at a placement approved by the school.

Organizations

Students edit the *Brandeis Law Journal*, the *Brandeis Brief Magazine*, and, in conjunction with the University of South Carolina, the *Journal of Law and Education*. Annually, students participate in the National Moot Court, the Jessup International Law, and the American Association of Trial Lawyers Mock Trial. Other competitions include a Trial Advocacy Moot Court exercise in a student's first year and the Pirtle-Washer Moot Court in a student's second year. Law student organizations include the Student Bar Association, Environmental Law Society, and the International Law Society. There are local chapters of Delta Theta Phi, Phi Alpha Delta, and the Federalist Society.

Library

The law library contains 325,639 hardcopy volumes and 403 microform volume equivalents, and subscribes to 5242 serial publications. Such on-line databases and networks as LEXIS and WESTLAW are available to law students for research. Special library collections include the Justice Brandeis papers, Justice Harlan papers, Supreme Court briefs, and a U.S. government documents depository. Recently, the library upgraded the computer laboratory to 486 processors and Ethernet connections as well as carrels with connections for laptop computers. The ratio of library volumes to faculty is 6705 to 1 and to students, 619 to 1. The ratio of seats in the library to students is 1 to 2.

Faculty

The law school has 32 full-time and 19 part-time faculty members, of whom 19 are women. According to AAUP standards for Category I institutions, faculty salaries are below average. About 54% of full-time faculty have a graduate law degree in addition to the J.D. The ratio of full-time students to full-time faculty in an average class is 42 to 1. The law school has a regular program of bringing visiting professors and other distinguished lecturers and visitors to campus.

Placement

J.D.s awarded:	157

Services available through: separate law school placement center.

Special features: participation in recruiting consortia in the southeast and Kentucky.

Full-time job interviews:	16 employers
Summer job interviews:	20 employers
Placement by graduation:	50% of class
Placement within 9 months:	94% of class
Average starting salary:	$19,300 to $65,000

Areas of placement:

Private practice 2-10 attorneys	28%
Government	18%
Business/industry	16%
Private practice 51-100 attorneys	12%
Private practice 11-25 attorneys	11%
Private practice 26-50 attorneys	9%
Judicial clerkships	3%
Academic	2%
Public interest	2%
Military	1%

Students

About 42% of the student body are women; 12%, minorities; 6%, African American; 3%, Asian American; 2%, Hispanic; and 1%, Native American. The majority of students come from Kentucky (82%). The average age of entering students is 24; age range is 20 to 52. About 35% of students enter directly from undergraduate school, 20% have a graduate degree, and 65% have worked full-time prior to entering law school. About 5% drop out after the first year for academic or personal reasons; 94% remain to receive a law degree.

School of Law

246 Deering Avenue
Portland, ME 04102

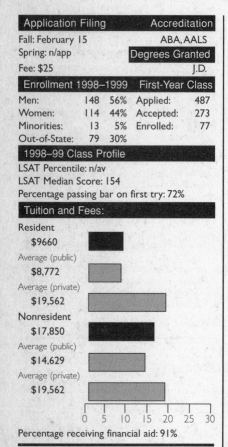

Application Filing		Accreditation
Fall: February 15		ABA, AALS
Spring: n/app		Degrees Granted
Fee: $25		J.D.

Enrollment 1998–1999		First-Year Class	
Men:	148 56%	Applied:	487
Women:	114 44%	Accepted:	273
Minorities:	13 5%	Enrolled:	77
Out-of-State:	79 30%		

1998–99 Class Profile
LSAT Percentile: n/av
LSAT Median Score: 154
Percentage passing bar on first try: 72%

Tuition and Fees:

Resident
$9660

Average (public)
$8,772

Average (private)
$19,562

Nonresident
$17,850

Average (public)
$14,629

Average (private)
$19,562

0   5   10   15   20   25   30

Percentage receiving financial aid: 91%

ADMISSIONS

In the fall 1999 first-year class, 487 applied, 273 were accepted, and 77 enrolled. Three transfers enrolled. The median GPA of the most recent first-year class was 3.1. The lowest LSAT percentile accepted was 15; the highest was 99.

Requirements

Applicants must have a bachelor's degree from an accredited institution and take the LSAT. The most important admission factor is academic achievement. No specific undergraduate courses are required. Candidates are not interviewed.

Procedure

The application deadline for fall entry is February 15. Applicants should submit an application form, LSAT results, transcripts (through LSDAS), a nonrefundable application fee of $25, and 1 letter of recommendation. Notification of the admission decision in mid-April. The latest acceptable LSAT test date for fall entry is February, but December is recommended. The law school uses the LSDAS.

Special

The law school recruits minority and disadvantaged students through law school admissions forums, scholarship assistance, and contacts with law school minority organizations. Transfer students must have one year of credit and have superior academic credentials.

Costs

Tuition and fees for the 1999-2000 academic year are $9660 for full-time in-state students and and $17,850 for out-of-state students. Tuition for part-time students is $325 per credit in-state and $578, out of state. On-campus room and board costs about $7726 annually; and books and supplies run $1050.

Financial Aid

About 91% of current law students receive some form of aid. The average annual amount of aid from all sources combined, including scholarships, loans, and work contracts, is $15,625; maximum, $27,204. Awards are based on need. The required financial statement is the FAFSA. The aid application deadline for fall entry is February 1. Special funds for minority or disadvantaged students consist of 3 full-tuition scholarships available for each class. First-year students are notified about their financial aid application when a nonrefundable tuition deposit is due.

About the Law School

University of Maine School of Law was established in 1962 and is a public institution. The campus is in an urban area in Portland. The primary mission of the law school is to educate students to serve the public and private sectors with distinction; to contribute to the advancement of the law through scholarly and professional research and writing; and to engage in public services aimed at improving the legal system. Students have access to federal, state, county, city, and local agencies, courts, correctional facilities, law firms, and legal aid organizations in the Portland area. Portland is the major urban and legal center in the state. Facilities of special interest to law students are the Cumberland County Superior Court, the Maine Supreme Judicial Court, and the Federal District Court. Housing for law students is available in university dorms, but most students prefer to find housing in and around Portland. All law school facilities are accessible to the physically disabled.

Calendar

The law school operates on a traditional semester basis. Courses for full-time students are offered days only and must be completed within 3 years. For part-time students, courses are offered days only and must be completed within 5 years. New full-and part-time students are admitted in the fall. There is a 7-week summer session. Transferable summer courses are offered.

Programs

Students may take relevant courses in other programs and apply credit toward the J.D.; the maximum of credits that may be applied varies, and must be approved by the curriculum committee. The following joint degree may be earned: J.D./M.A. (Juris Doctor/Master of Arts in public policy and management, health policy management, and community planning and development).

Contact
Barbara Gauditz, Assistant Dean, 207-780-4341 for general inquiries; Norma Catalano, Assistant Director, 207-780-5250 for financial aid information.

MAINE

Required
To earn the J.D., candidates must complete 89 total credits, of which 40 are for required courses. They must maintain a minimum GPA of 2.0 in the required courses. The following first-year courses are required of all students: Constitutional Law I, Contracts I and II, Civil Procedure I and II, Property, Torts, Criminal Law, and Legal Research and Writing I and II. Required upper-level courses consist of Professional Responsibility, a perspectives course, an independent writing requirement, and Constitutional Law II. The required orientation program for first-year students is 2 days. The first day includes mini classes, then discussion with alumni on the same case, and small group discussions with faculty; the second day is information on university services, student organizations, and a session on professional responsibility.

Electives
There are no formal concentration areas. A number of clinics are offered: General Practice Clinic is open to third-year students for 6 credits; Criminal Law and Family Law practicums are open to third-year students for 6 credits; and the Environmental Law Clinic is open to second- and third-year students for 3 credits. Seminars in commercial law, consumer law, constitutional law international law are open to second- and third-year students. The Frank M. Coffin Lecture on Law and Public Service is held annually. The Student Bar Association and other student organizations also offer guest lectures. There is a 1-semester option at Dalhousie Law School in Halifax, Nova Scotia; the University of New Brunswick, Canada; University College, Galway, Ireland; University of Buckingham, England; or Universite de Maine, Le Mans, France. Tutorial assistance is available for students identified as requiring additional work in writing skills and legal analysis. The most widely taken electives are Trial Practice, Business Associations, and Evidence.

Graduation Requirements
In order to graduate, candidates must have a GPA of 1.6; have completed the upper-division writing requirement, which may be fulfilled with *Law Review, Ocean and Coastal Law Journal* Moot Court, or an independent writing project; and have taken Constitutional Law II, one course that places the law in a broader philosophic, historic, or comparative context, and a course in professional responsibility.

Organizations
Students edit the *Maine Law Review, Ocean and Coastal Law Journal*, and *The Advocate*, the weekly career services newsletter. The second-year Moot Court Board is chosen by internal competition. Board members compete in a number of regional, national, and international competitions, such as the National Moot Court Competition, Jessup International, and National Mock Trial Competition. Student organizations include the Environmental Law Society; Lesbian, Gay and Bisexual Law Caucus; and Maine Association for Public Interest Law. Local chapters of national associations include the National Lawyers Guild, International Law Society, and Federalist Society.

Library
The law library contains 300,000 hard-copy volumes. Such on-line databases and networks as LEXIS and WESTLAW are available to law students for research. Special library collections include a U.S. government publications depository and Canadian and British Commonwealth law reports and statutes. Recently, the library completed an addition that provides more shelf space and student study space. The ratio of library volumes to faculty is 17,500 to 1 and to students, 1037 to 1.

Faculty
The law school has 17 full-time and 4 part-time faculty members, of whom 6 are women. About 30% of full-time faculty have a graduate law degree in addition to the J.D. The ratio of full-time students to full-time faculty in an average class is 40 to 1; in a clinic, 6 to 1. The law school has a regular program of bringing visiting professors and other distinguished lecturers and visitors to campus.

Placement

J.D.s awarded:	98
Services available through: separate law school placement center	
Full-time job interviews:	40 employers
Summer job interviews:	53 employers
Placement by graduation:	n/av
Placement within 9 months:	84% of class
Average starting salary:	$20,000 to $50,000
Areas of placement:	
Private practice 2-10 attorneys	30%
Private practice 11-25 attorneys	12%
Private practice 26-50 attorneys	4%
Private practice 51-100 attorneys	5%
Judicial clerkships	22%
Business/industry	13%
Government	10%
Public interest	7%

Students
About 44% of the student body are women; 5%, minorities; 2%, African American; 1%, Asian American; 2%, Hispanic; and 2%, Native American. The majority of students come from Maine (70%). The average age of entering students is 30; age range is 21 to 55. About 16% of students enter directly from undergraduate school, 22% have a graduate degree, and 85% have worked full time prior to entering law school. About 3% drop out after the first year for academic or personal reasons; 97% remain to receive a law degree.

UNIVERSITY OF MARYLAND

School of Law

515 West Lombard Street
Baltimore, MD 21201

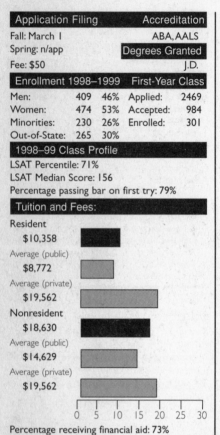

Application Filing		Accreditation
Fall: March 1		ABA, AALS
Spring: n/app		**Degrees Granted**
Fee: $50		J.D.

Enrollment 1998–1999		First-Year Class	
Men:	409 46%	Applied:	2469
Women:	474 53%	Accepted:	984
Minorities:	230 26%	Enrolled:	301
Out-of-State:	265 30%		

1998–99 Class Profile

LSAT Percentile: 71%
LSAT Median Score: 156
Percentage passing bar on first try: 79%

Tuition and Fees:

Resident
$10,358
Average (public)
$8,772
Average (private)
$19,562
Nonresident
$18,630
Average (public)
$14,629
Average (private)
$19,562

0 5 10 15 20 25 30

Percentage receiving financial aid: 73%

ADMISSIONS

In the fall 1999 first-year class, 2469 applied, 984 were accepted, and 301 enrolled. The median LSAT percentile of the most recent first-year class was 71; the median GPA was 3.4 on a scale of 4.0. The lowest LSAT percentile accepted was 10; the highest was 99.

Requirements

Applicants must have a bachelor's degree from an accredited institution and take the LSAT. Outstanding applicants, at minimum age 23 with 3 years of college, are also considered. The most important admission factors include GPA, general background, and faculty recommendation. No specific undergraduate courses are required. Candidates are not interviewed.

Procedure

The application deadline for fall entry is March 1. Applicants should submit an application form, LSAT results, transcripts, a non-refundable application fee of $50, 2 letters of recommendation, and a personal statement. Notification of the admission decision is Jan-

uary through April. The latest acceptable LSAT test date for fall entry is February. The law school uses the LSDAS.

Special

The law school recruits minority and disadvantaged students by encouraging applications from African American students and other students of color, and from disadvantaged persons who will enrich the law school and the profession. Transfer students must have one year of credit, have attended an ABA-approved law school, and have competitive academic credentials.

Costs

Tuition and fees for the 1999-2000 academic year are $10,358 for full-time in-state students and $18,630 for out-of-state students. Tuition for part-time students is $7793 annually in-state and $13,995 out-of-state. Books and supplies run $1100.

Financial Aid

About 73% of current law students receive some form of aid. Awards are based on need and merit. The average annual amount of aid from all sources combined, including scholarships, loans, and work contracts, is $17,042, based on need. There is a limit of no more than 10 merit awards annually. The required financial statement is FAFSA. The priority aid application deadline for fall entry is March 15. Special funds for minority or disadvantaged students consist of grants that are available for students whose enrollment would add significantly to student diversity. First-year students are notified about their financial aid application in April provided their financial aid applications are completed by the March deadline.

About the Law School

University of Maryland School of Law was established in 1816 and is a public institution. The campus is in an urban area in downtown Baltimore. The primary mission of the law school is to prepare students for professional leadership as lawyers, business executives, legislators, and public policymakers, community advocates, and agents of social, political, and economic progress. Students have access to federal, state, county, city, and local agencies, courts, correctional facilities, law firms, and legal aid organizations in the Baltimore area. The law school is within walking dis-

tance of local and federal courthouses. It is less than an hour from both Annapolis, the state capital, and Washington, D.C. Facilities of special interest to law students include clinical programs that involve student practice, under close faculty supervision, in courts and government agencies; Certificate programs in environmental law and health care law are also offered. Housing for law students is available in campus apartments and at the Baltimore Student Union; board is not offered. The university's Residence Life Office assists in finding off-campus housing. All law school facilities are accessible to the physically disabled.

Calendar

The law school operates on a traditional semester basis. Courses for full-time students are offered day only for required courses; day and evening for electives. They must be completed within 3 years. For part-time students, courses are offered evening only for required courses; for electives, day and evening. Courses must be completed within 4 years. New full- and part-time students are admitted in the fall. There is a 7-week summer session. Transferable summer courses are offered.

Programs

Students may take relevant courses in other programs and apply credit toward the J.D.; a maximum of 9 credits may be applied. The following joint degrees may be earned: J.D./Ph.D. (Juris Doctor/Doctor of Philosophy in policy science), J.D./M.A. (Juris Doctor/Master of Arts in criminal justice, liberal education, applied and professional ethics, community planning, and public management), J.D./M.B.A. (Juris Doctor/Master of Business Administration), J.D./M.S.W. (Juris Doctor/Master of Social Work), and J.D./Pharm.D. (Juris Doctor/Doctor of Pharmacy).

Required

To earn the J.D., candidates must complete 85 total credits, of which 35 to 38 are for required courses. They must maintain a minimum GPA of C- in the required courses. The following first-year courses are required of all students: Cardin Program (day students only), Civil Procedure I and II, Constitutional Law I and II, Contracts I and II, Criminal Law, Criminal Procedure, Introduction to Appellate Advocacy, Legal Method Process, Legal Profession, Property I and II, and Torts I and II. All students must take clinical courses. The optional

Phone: 410-706-3492
Fax: 410-706-4045
E-mail: admissions@law.umaryland.edu
Web: http://www.law.umaryland.edu

Contact

James F. Forsyth, Associate Dean, 410-706-3492 for general inquiries; Mary S. Vansickle, 410-706-7347 for financial aid information.

orientation program for first-year students is a brief introduction to case analysis and synthesis, including a sample class, a lunch with faculty, and a small group meeting with upper-class peer advisers. The program lasts for 2 1/2 days.

Electives

Students must take approximately 40 credits in their area of concentration, although few students concentrate in one area. The School of Law offers concentrations in corporate law, criminal law, environmental law, family law, international law, juvenile law, labor law, litigation, securities law, tax law, and torts and insurance. Through a broad range of electives, students may (but need not) focus on a particular topic. In addition, clinical practice specialties include AIDS, appellate advocacy, and bail and access to Justice. Appoximately 60 seminars are offered. Externships are available in public agencies and nonprofit organizations for 1 to 13 credits. Externships are coordinated with classroom discussion and a writing requirement. Research may be undertaken through 4 legal journals, through independent research/writing under faculty supervision, by acting as research assistants for faculty, and in courses and seminars. Several annual lectures are sponsored by alumni gifts, student organizations, law school faculty/administration, and campus administration. A summer-abroad program is held at Aberdeen, Scotland and a semester-long program in South Africa. Also, credits are accepted for work done in other ABA-approved summer programs. Tutorials may be done as independent study on a topic of choice for 1 to 7 credits. The Director of Academic Support provides group and individual assistance. The Student Peer Advisers provide individual and program support. Maryland's enrollment is 26% minority, including 15% African American. Administration/faculty and student initiatives provide a supportive learning environment. There is a pre-enrollment program before orientation begins that is targeted at minority students, returning students, and students with disabilities. There is a varied and diverse group of student organizations that sponser events such as the latino Gala, BLSA Banquet and the MPILP auction. The most widely taken electives are Clinical Law Program, Business Associations, and Sales and Secured Transactions.

Graduation Requirements

In order to graduate, candidates must complete the upper-division writing requirement and meet the residency requirements of 6 semesters of attendance for full-time students, and 8 semesters for part-time students.

Organizations

The primary law review is the *Maryland Law Review*. Other law reviews include the *Journal of Health Care Law & Policy*, *The Business Lawyer*, a joint publication of the law school and the ABA Section of Business Law, and *Margins*. The student newspaper is *The Raven*, published monthly. Moot court competitions include Morris B. Myerowits Competition, the Albert R. Mogel National Tax Moot Court Competition, and the Pace University National Environmental Law Moot Court Competition. Other competitions include the Health Law Moot Court, Robert R. Merhige, Jr. National Environmental Negotiation Competition, Jessup International Moot Court, American College of Trial Lawyers, and Association of Trial Lawyers of America. Law student organizations include Maryland Environmental Law Society, Student Health Law Organization, and Maryland Intellectual Property Association. Local chapters of national associations are the Asian/Pacific-American Law Student Association, Black Law Students Association, and Latino Law Students Association.

Library

The law library contains 273,129 hardcopy volumes and 442,334 microform volume equivalents, and subscribes to 4074 serial publications. Such on-line databases and networks as LEXIS, DIALOG, WESTLAW, and and many others are available to law students for research. Special library collections include a partial federal government depository. Recently, the library remodeled its library and research services office. It will move into a new building with expanded library facilities in summer 2002. The ratio of library volumes to faculty is 5153 to 1 and to students, 309 to 1.

Placement

J.D.s awarded:	262
Services available through: a separate law school placement center.	
Services: job fairs	
Special features: Career Development staff assists in developing job search strategies, facilitates on-campus interviewing, and provides workshops and seminars.	
Full-time job interviews:	n/av
Summer job interviews:	96 employers
Placement by graduation:	84% of class
Placement within 9 months:	96% of class
Average starting salary:	n/av
Areas of placement:	
Private practice 2-10 attorneys	7%
Private practice 11-25 attorneys	24%
Private practice 26-50 attorneys	4%
Private practice 51-100 attorneys	4%
Private practice, 100+ attorneys	16%
Business/industry	14%
Academic	2%
Public interest	2%
Military	2%

Faculty

The law school has 53 full-time and 68 part-time faculty members, of whom 36 are women. According to AAUP standards for Category I institutions, faculty salaries are average. About 21% of full-time faculty have a graduate law degree in addition to the J.D.; about 8% of part-time faculty have one. The ratio of full-time students to full-time faculty in an average class is 16 to 1; in a clinic, 8 to 1. The law school has a regular program of bringing visiting professors and other distinguished lecturers and visitors to campus. There is a chapter of the Order of the Coif.

Students

About 53% of the student body are women; 26%, minorities; 14%, African American; 8%, Asian American; and 3%, Hispanic. The majority of students come from Maryland (70%). The average age of entering students is 26; age range is 20 to 60. About 32% of students enter directly from undergraduate school, 17% have a graduate degree, and 68% have worked full-time prior to entering law school. About 4% drop out after the first year for academic or personal reasons; 91% remain to receive a law degree.

UNIVERSITY OF MEMPHIS

Cecil C. Humphreys School of Law

Campus Box 526513
Memphis, TN 38152-6513

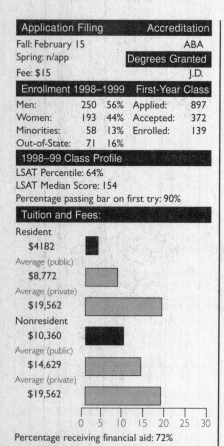

Application Filing	Accreditation
Fall: February 15	ABA
Spring: n/app	**Degrees Granted**
Fee: $15	J.D.

Enrollment 1998–1999		First-Year Class	
Men:	250 56%	Applied:	897
Women:	193 44%	Accepted:	372
Minorities:	58 13%	Enrolled:	139
Out-of-State:	71 16%		

1998–99 Class Profile
LSAT Percentile: 64%
LSAT Median Score: 154
Percentage passing bar on first try: 90%

Tuition and Fees:

Resident
$4182

Average (public)
$8,772

Average (private)
$19,562

Nonresident
$10,360

Average (public)
$14,629

Average (private)
$19,562

0 5 10 15 20 25 30

Percentage receiving financial aid: 72%

ADMISSIONS

In the fall 1999 first-year class, 897 applied, 372 were accepted, and 139 enrolled. Nine transfers enrolled. The median LSAT percentile of the most recent first-year class was 64; the median GPA was 3.2 on a scale of 4.0. The lowest LSAT percentile accepted was 15; the highest was 98.

Requirements

Applicants must have a bachelor's degree from an accredited institution and take the LSAT. Minimum acceptable GPA is 2.0 on a scale of 4.0. The most important admission factors include LSAT results, GPA, and academic achievement. No specific undergraduate courses are required. Candidates are not interviewed.

Procedure

The application deadline for fall entry is February 15. Applicants should submit an application form, LSAT results, transcripts, a nonrefundable application fee of $15, 1 letter of recommendation, a dean's certification form, a personal statement, and a domicile certificate. Notification of the admission decision is from January to May. The latest acceptable LSAT test date for fall entry is February. The law school uses the LSDAS.

Special

The law school recruits minority and disadvantaged students by means of the Tennessee Pre-Law Fellowship Program, graduate and professional fairs, law school forums, workshops, and a candidate referral service with Law Services. Out-of-state applicants may be required to have higher GPA and LSAT results. Transfer students must have attended an ABA-approved law school and meet the admission index set by the school or be in the upper third of their class.

Costs

Tuition and fees for the 1999-2000 academic year are $4182 for full-time in-state students and $10,360 for out-of-state students. Tuition and fees for part-time students are $3320 per year in-state and $8144 out-of-state. On-campus room and board costs about $6000 annually; books and supplies run $1100.

Financial Aid

About 72% of current law students receive some form of aid. The maximum annual amount of aid from all sources combined, including scholarships, loans, and work contracts, is $21,774. Awards are based on need and merit. The required financial statement is the FAFSA. The aid application deadline for fall entry is April 1. Special funds for minority or disadvantaged students include law stipends for African American Tennessee residents. First-year students are notified about their financial aid application after seat deposit and orientation fees are paid, usually May 1.

About the Law School

University of Memphis Cecil C. Humphreys School of Law was established in 1962 and is a public institution. The campus is in a suburban area located within Memphis. The primary mission of the law school is to provide a sound, traditional, and quality study of law and to promote legal scholarship and research. Students have access to federal, state, county, city, and local agencies, courts, correctional facilities, law firms, and legal aid organizations in the Memphis area, and the University of Memphis library and departmental libraries. Facilities of special interest to law students are the law school and library, which are housed in a single building on the north side of campus. Housing for law students consists of traditional residence halls as well as on-campus apartments and townhouses. Local privately owned apartments are available off campus. About 98% of the law school facilities are accessible to the physically disabled.

Calendar

The law school operates on a traditional semester basis. Courses for full- and part-time students are offered days only, though limited elective courses are offered in the evenings, and must be completed within 6 years. New full- and part-time students are admitted in the fall. part-time, fall. There is an 8-week summer session. Transferable summer courses are offered.

Programs

The following joint degree may be earned: J.D./M.B.A. (Juris Doctor/Master of Business Administration).

Contact

Dr. Sidney Evans, Director of Law, 901-678-2073 for general inquiries; Karen Smith, Assistant Director, Office of Student Aid, 901-678-4825, direct line 901-678-3687 for financial aid information.

TENNESSEE

Required

To earn the J.D., candidates must complete 90 total credits, of which 56 are for required courses. They must maintain a minimum GPA of 2.0 in the required courses. The following first-year courses are required of all students: Contracts I and II, Torts I and II, Property I and II, Civil Procedure I and II, Legal Method I and II, and Criminal Law. Required upper-level courses consist of Income Tax, Secured Transactions, Criminal Procedure I, Evidence, Constitutional Law, Business Organizations I, Decedents' Estates, Professional Responsibility, and Advanced Research. The required orientation program for first-year students consists of a 2-day mandatory program that takes place immediately before the beginning of fall classes.

Electives

The Cecil C. Humphreys School of Law offers concentrations in corporate law, criminal law, entertainment, environmental law, family law, international law, juvenile law, labor law, litigation, securities law, tax law, torts and insurance, and commercial law, and real estate law. In addition, clinics on subject areas that include civil litigation, elder law, and juvenile law (worth 3 credit hours each) are available to upper-class students as an elective. Seminars include: Procedure (2 hours), Evidence (2 hours), and Law and Society (2 hours). Internships are available with NLRB (2 hours), EEOC (2 hours), U.S. Attorney (2 hours), and Bankruptcy Court (2 hours). Three research programs are available: Research I, Research II, and Law Review. Field work consists of the Bankruptcy, National Labor Relations Board, U.S. Attorney, Death Penalty, Criminal Justice, and Judicial externships. There is an annual alumni distinguished lecture series and an academic support program offered on a voluntary basis to first-year students. The Tennessee Pre-Law Fellowship Program is available to African-Americans who are Tennessee residents, beginning in their sophomore year of undergraduate school. The most widely taken electives are Sales, Commercial Paper, and Trial Advocacy.

Graduation Requirements

In order to graduate, candidates must have a GPA of 2.0 and have completed the upper-division writing requirement.

Organizations

The primary law review is *The University of Memphis Law Review*. The Tennessee Journal of Practice and Procedure is also published. The *Docket* is published by the Dean's office to provide information to students. Moot court competitions include Intraschool Trial, Intraschool Advanced, and First-Year Intraschool. Other competitions include National Environmental Moot Court, Frederick Douglass Moot Court, ATLA National Mock Trial, and National Mock Trial. Law student organizations include the Student Bar Association, International Law Society, and Environmental Law Society. There are local chapters of Phi Delta Phi, Phi Alpha Delta, and Black Law Students Association. Campus clubs and other organizations include the American Trial Lawyers Association and Entertainment Law Society.

Library

The law library contains 267,566 hardcopy volumes and 502,848 microform volume equivalents, and subscribes to 3015 serial publications. Such on-line databases and networks as LEXIS, DIALOG, WESTLAW, and NEXIS are available to law students for research. Special library collections include a selective federal depository. Recently, the library installed a 30-station computer laboratory with a Novell Network and laser printers. The ratio of library volumes to faculty is 12,741 to 1 and to students, 525 to 1. The ratio of seats in the library to students is 1 to 1.

Faculty

The law school has 21 full-time and 35 part-time faculty members, of whom 18 are women. About 57% of full-time faculty have a graduate law degree in addition to the J.D.; about 32% of part-time faculty have one. The ratio of full-time students to full-time faculty in an average class is 21 to 1; in a clinic, 6 to 1.

Placement

J.D.s awarded:	136
Services available through: a separate law school placement center	
Services: workshops, seminars, and nontraditional legal career advice	
Special features: membership in regional, national, and minority law placement consortiums	
Full-time job interviews:	24 employers
Summer job interviews:	24 employers
Placement by graduation:	n/av
Placement within 9 months:	96% of class
Average starting salary:	$35,068 to $60,760
Areas of placement:	
Private practice 2-10 attorneys	31%
Private practice 11-25 attorneys	13%
Private practice 26-50 attorneys	6%
Private practice 51-100 attorneys	2%
Business/industry	11%
Government	11%
Judicial clerkships	10%
Public interest	3%
Academic	1%
Military	1%

Students

About 44% of the student body are women; 13%, minorities; 10%, African American; 1%, Asian American; and 1%, Hispanic. The majority of students come from Tennessee (84%). The average age of entering students is 26; age range is 20 to 50. About 43% of students enter directly from undergraduate school and 12% have a graduate degree. About 10% drop out after the first year for academic or personal reasons; 85% remain to receive a law degree.

UNIVERSITY OF MIAMI

School of Law

P.O. Box 248087, 1311 Miller Drive
Coral Gables, FL 33124-8087

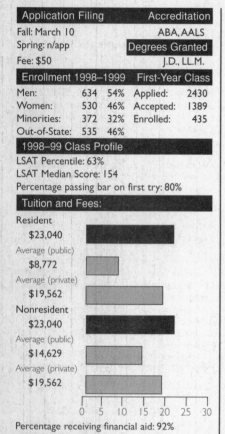

Application Filing		Accreditation
Fall: March 10		ABA, AALS
Spring: n/app		**Degrees Granted**
Fee: $50		J.D., LL.M.

Enrollment 1998–1999		First-Year Class	
Men:	634 54%	Applied:	2430
Women:	530 46%	Accepted:	1389
Minorities:	372 32%	Enrolled:	435
Out-of-State:	535 46%		

1998–99 Class Profile
LSAT Percentile: 63%
LSAT Median Score: 154
Percentage passing bar on first try: 80%

Tuition and Fees:

Resident
$23,040

Average (public)
$8,772

Average (private)
$19,562

Nonresident
$23,040

Average (public)
$14,629

Average (private)
$19,562

0 5 10 15 20 25 30

Percentage receiving financial aid: 92%

ADMISSIONS

In the fall 1999 first-year class, 2430 applied, 1389 were accepted, and 435 enrolled. Fourteen transfers enrolled. The average LSAT percentile of the most recent first-year class was 63; the average GPA was 3.2 on a scale of 4.0. The lowest LSAT percentile accepted was 13; the highest was 98.

Requirements

Applicants must have a bachelor's degree from an accredited institution and take the LSAT. No specific undergraduate courses are required. Candidates are not interviewed.

Procedure

The application deadline for fall entry is March 10. Applicants should submit an application form, LSAT results, TOEFL for foreign students, a nonrefundable application fee of $50, and 2 letters of recommendation. Graduates from foreign institutions should submit transcript evaluations. All students must possess a bachelor's degree or its equivalent from a regionally accredit-

ed institution prior to the first day of classes. Notification of the admission decision is on a rolling basis. The latest acceptable LSAT test date for fall entry is June. The law school uses the LSDAS.

Special

The law school recruits minority and disadvantaged students by means of a committee reviewing all files, sending information to prelaw advisers at historically minority institutions, hosting diversity admissions fairs, and participating in recruiting events at historically black schools and locations at schools where minority population is strong; also, current minority students call newly admitted minority students. Transfer students must have one year of credit, have a minimum GPA of 3.0, have attended an ABA-approved law school, and have their LSAT and undergraduate performance reviewed.

Costs

Tuition and fees for the 1999-2000 academic year are $23,040 for all full-time students. Tuition and fees for all part-time students is $17,030 annually, or $988 per credit. On-campus room and board costs about $8325 annually; and books and supplies run $700.

Financial Aid

About 92% of current law students receive some form of aid. The average annual amount of aid from all sources combined, including scholarships, loans, and work contracts, is $32,487; maximum, $37,500. Awards are based on need and merit, but the majority of scholarships are merit-based. The required financial statement is FAFSA. The aid application deadline for fall entry is March 1. Special funds for minority or disadvantaged students include need-based scholarships and merit scholarships, both institutional and donor, including the Colson Scholarship Fund, Florida Bar Minority Scholarships, and the Spellman and Baker McKenzie scholarships. First-year students are notified about their financial aid application on a rolling basis as the files are complete.

About the Law School

University of Miami School of Law was established in 1926 and is a private institution. The 260-acre campus is in an urban area 7 miles south of Miami. The primary mission of the law school is to teach students the craft as well as the theory of law,

develop the research and writing skills necessary to the legal profession, and expose students to other skills necessary for effective professional service, such as client counseling, fact investigation, and trial skills. Students have access to federal, state, county, city, and local agencies, courts, correctional facilities, law firms, and legal aid organizations in the Coral Gables area. The legal institutions and firms of Miami, Ft. Lauderdale, and the Palm Beach areas are also available to students. Facilities of special interest to law students include the Litigation Skills and Clinical programs, the Moot Court Board, which runs one of the nation's largest mock trial competitions, 7 LL.M. programs, the London Summer Program, the Summer Program in Spain, and the Summer Public Interest Program. Housing for law students is available on campus. Ample apartments are also available in the area, and roommate referral and apartment listings are supplied to admitted students. About 98% of the law school facilities are accessible to the physically disabled.

Calendar

The law school operates on a traditional semester basis. Courses for full-time students are offered both day and evening. After the first year, there is some flexibility courses must be completed within 5 years. For part-time students, courses are offered both day and evening and must be completed within 5 years. New full-and part-time students are admitted in the fall. There is an 8-week summer session. Transferable summer courses are not offered.

Programs

In addition to the J.D., the law school offers the LL.M and LL.M. in comparative law, tax, real estate, estate planning, international law, and ocean and coastal law. Students may take relevant courses in other programs and apply credit toward the J.D.; a maximum of 6 credits may be applied. The following joint degrees may be earned: J.D./M.B.A. (Juris Doctor/Master of Business Administration), J.D./M.P.H. (Juris Doctor/Master of Public Health), and J.D/M.M.S. (Juris Doctor/Master of Marine Science).

Required

To earn the J.D., candidates must complete 88 total credits, of which 73 are for required courses. They must maintain a minimum

Phone: 305-284-2523
E-mail: admissions@law.miami.edu
Web: law.miami.edu

Contact

Therese Lambert, Director of Student Recruiting, 305-284-6746 for general inquiries; Felicita Colon, Director of Financial Aid, 305-284-3115; finaid@law.miami.edu for financial aid information.

GPA of 2.0 in the required courses. The following first-year courses are required of all students: Contracts, Torts, Elements, Civil Procedure I, Legal Writing and Research I and II, Property, Criminal Procedure, Constitutional Law I, and a first-year elective. Required upper-level courses consist of Legal Professions, Personal and Business Transactions, public law and process courses, and perspective courses. The required orientation program for first-year students is a 2-day formal program combined with a writing seminar and various activities organized by students.

Electives

The School of Law offers concentrations in corporate law, criminal law, entertainment, environmental law, family law, international law, labor law, litigation, maritime law, securities law, sports law, tax law, and torts and insurance. In addition, clinical placement is worth 6 credits and Litigations Skills I is a prerequisite. Students are placed in more than a dozen participating agencies and handle actual cases under the supervision of agency attorneys. Seminars providing intensive study, research, and writing opportunities in specialized areas are worth 2 credits and are open to second- and third-year students. The Public Interest Seminar Program focuses on a public interest topic; students are selected to pursue an application and interview process. Second- and third-year students are also able to take part in individual research projects, worth 1 to 3 credits. The Cole Lecture Series brings distinguished jurists such as U.S. Supreme Court Justices to campus. Other special lectures bring distinguished judges, scholars, and practicing attorneys from around the world to the campus. Study abroad is possible through the London Summer Program, an intensive 5-week, 6-credit program conducted at the University of London. Tutorial programs are a component of the first-year curriculum. A research and writing program is taught by instructors in a small group setting. It is worth 2 credits. Selected minority students may be chosen to participate in the James Weldon Johnson Institute. This is a 5-week summer fellowship program designed to develop the legal, analytical, and writing skills. The Institute is held prior to the beginning of fall classes and all financial aspects are covered by grants. A special orientation for first-year African American students is conducted by the Black Law Students Association. The most widely taken electives are Litigation Skills and Clinical Program, Civil Procedure II, and Evidence.

Graduation Requirements

In order to graduate, candidates must have a GPA of 2.0 and have completed the upper-division writing requirement. Many offerings in the upper division require substantial papers.

Organizations

Student-edited publications include the *University of Miami Law Review; Inter-American Law Review; Entertainment and Sports Law Review; Business Law Journal; Yearbook of International Law; Psychology, Public Policy, and Law; Res Ipsa Loquitur* (newspaper), *Amicus Curiae* (yearbook), and *The Hearsay* (weekly newsletter). The Moot Court Board runs one of the nation's largest mock trial competitions, involving more than 200 experienced lawyers. This organization also sponsors several local, state, and regional moot court competitions, as well as negotiation and client counseling competitions. Other competitions include International Moot Court. Law student organizations include Black Law Students Association, Association of Caribbean Law Students, and Asian/Pacific Law Students Association. Local chapters of national associations include the ABA-Law Student Division, Association of Trial Lawyers of America, and Hispanic Law Students Association.

Library

The law library contains 348,552 hard-copy volumes and 775,463 microform volume equivalents, and subscribes to 1785 serial publications. Such on-line databases and networks as LEXIS, DIALOG, WESTLAW, and Internet are available to law students for research. Special library collections include taxation, estate planning, labor theory, ocean law, international law, the law of Latin American and Caribbean countries, Soia Mentschikoff papers, and Everglades litigation files. It is a selective depository for U.S. government documents. The expanded and renovated law library features a 600-node local area network for accessing on-line legal research, communications, and internal library systems. The ratio of library volumes to faculty is 7921 to 1 and to students, 264 to 1. The ratio of seats in the library to students is 1 to 2.

Placement

J.D.s awarded:	415
Services available through: a separate law school placement center and the university placement center.	
Services: off-campus interview programs/job fairs	
Special features: a professional staff consisting of 4 attorneys and a certified adult counselor; a minority mentor program; a public interest program; a judicial internship program; an on- and off-campus interview program, including lottery selections for students, and various job fairs nationwide.	
Full-time job interviews:	49 employers
Summer job interviews:	61 employers
Placement by graduation:	52% of class
Placement within 9 months:	91% of class
Average starting salary:	n/av
Areas of placement:	
Private practice 2-100 attorneys	59%
Government	14%
Business/industry	12%
Unknown	7%
Public interest	4%
Judicial clerkships	3%
Military	1%

Faculty

The law school has 58 full-time and 103 part-time faculty members, of whom 40 are women. According to AAUP standards for Category I institutions, faculty salaries are above average. About 10% of full-time faculty have a graduate law degree in addition to the J.D. The ratio of full-time students to full-time faculty in an average class is 20 to 1; in a clinic, 15 to 1. The law school has a regular program of bringing visiting professors and other distinguished lecturers and visitors to campus. There is a chapter of the Order of the Coif; 39 graduates are members.

Students

About 46% of the student body are women; 32%, minorities; 8%, African American; 3%, Asian American; 20%, Hispanic; and 1%, Native American. The majority of students come from the South (64%). The average age of entering students is 26; age range is 19 to 60. About 40% of students enter directly from undergraduate school. About 5% drop out after the first year for academic or personal reasons; 90% remain to receive a law degree.

Law School

625 South State Street
Ann Arbor, MI 48109-1215

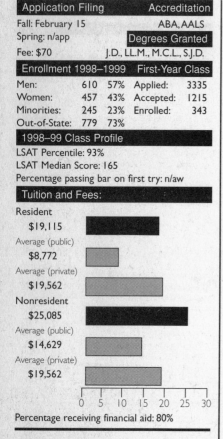

Application Filing	Accreditation
Fall: February 15	ABA, AALS
Spring: n/app	**Degrees Granted**
Fee: $70	J.D., LL.M., M.C.L., S.J.D.

Enrollment 1998–1999		First-Year Class	
Men:	610 57%	Applied:	3335
Women:	457 43%	Accepted:	1215
Minorities:	245 23%	Enrolled:	343
Out-of-State:	779 73%		

1998–99 Class Profile

LSAT Percentile: 93%

LSAT Median Score: 165

Percentage passing bar on first try: n/aw

Tuition and Fees:

Resident
$19,115

Average (public)
$8,772

Average (private)
$19,562

Nonresident
$25,085

Average (public)
$14,629

Average (private)
$19,562

(bar chart axis: 0 5 10 15 20 25 30)

Percentage receiving financial aid: 80%

ADMISSIONS

In the fall 1999 first-year class, 3335 applied, 1215 were accepted, and 343 enrolled. Twenty-two transfers enrolled. The median LSAT percentile of the most recent first-year class was 93; the median GPA was 3.6 on a scale of 4.0. The lowest LSAT percentile accepted was 40; the highest was 99.

Requirements

Applicants must have a bachelor's degree from an accredited institution and take the LSAT. No specific undergraduate courses are required. Candidates are not interviewed.

Procedure

The application deadline for fall entry is February 15. Applicants should submit an application form, LSAT results, transcripts, a nonrefundable application fee of $70, 1 letter of recommendation (although 3 are encouraged), and a personal statement. Transcripts and LSAT results must be sent via LSDAS. Notification of the admission decision is on a rolling basis from December 1. The latest acceptable LSAT test date for fall entry is December; September is encouraged. The law school uses the LSDAS.

Special

The law school recruits minority and disadvantaged students by reaching out to student populations that are likely to have these students in significant concentrations. Specific means of recruiting minority students include attending minority Law Days, writing to all admissible minority students who participate in the candidate referral service, and holding alumni receptions in various nationwide settings. The Law School attempts to attract economically disadvantaged students by providing need-based financial aid packages, as well as some merit-based financial aid awards. Requirements are different for out-of-state students in that Michigan residency is a slight advantage in the admissions process. Typically one-third of the entering class will be Michigan residents. Credentials of matriculating residents and nonresidents are comparable. Transfer students must have one year of credit, have attended an ABA-approved law school, and typically must be in the top 5% to 10% of their first-year class.

Costs

Tuition and fees for the 1999-2000 academic year are $19,115 for full-time instate students and $25,085 for out-of-state students. On-campus room and board costs about $8150 annually; and books and supplies run $800.

Financial Aid

About 80% of current law students receive some form of aid. The average annual amount of aid from all sources combined, including scholarships, loans, and work contracts, is $21,300; maximum, $50,400. Awards are based on need and merit. Most aid is need-based. A small number of merit-based grants are awarded each year. The required financial statement is FAFSA. First-year students are notified about their financial aid application 3 to 5 working days from the admission date or March 15, whichever is later.

About the Law School

University of Michigan Law School was established in 1859 and is a public institution. The 2665-acre campus is in a small town 45 miles west of Detroit. The primary mission of the law school is to bring the whole of human insight to bear on the study of law and its institutions, drawing on the resources of the University and an interdisciplinary faculty. It seeks to share with its students a knowledge of the past and present forms and functions of law,

together with a sense of engaged understanding of the law's evolution and future development. Students have access to federal, state, county, city, and local agencies, courts, correctional facilities, law firms, and legal aid organizations in the Ann Arbor area. Other resources come from the school's integration in an international university. Facilities of special interest to law students are the law libraries, containing study space for each student and extensive mainframe and microcomputer facilities. Housing for law students is available at the Lawyers Club, a residence hall that is part of the Law Quadrangle; in university family housing; in graduate dormitories; and in other dormitories for those students who serve as resident advisers. Off-campus housing is available in the Ann Arbor area. All law school facilities are accessible to the physically disabled.

Calendar

The law school operates on a traditional semester basis. Courses for full-time students are offered days only and must be completed within 5 years. There is no part-time program. New full-time students are admitted in the fall and summer. There is a 11-week summer session.

Programs

In addition to the J.D., the law school offers the LL.M, M.C.L., and S.J.D. Students may take relevant courses in other programs and apply credit toward the J.D.; a maximum of 9 credits may be applied. The following joint degrees may be earned: J.D./M.B.A. (Juris Doctor/Master of Business Administration), J.D./M.P.P. (Juris Doctor/Master of Public Policy Studies), J.D./M.S. (Juris Doctor/Master of Science in natural resources), J.D./M.A. (Juris Doctor/Master of Arts in world politics), J.D./A.M. (Juris Doctor/Master of Arts in Russian and East European studies), J.D./Ph.D. (Juris Doctor/Doctor of Philosophy in economics), J.D./A.M. (Juris Doctor/Master of Arts in modern Middle Eastern and North African studies), J.D./M.H.S.A. (Juris Doctor/Master of Health Services Administration), J.D./M.S.W. (Juris Doctor/Masters in Social Work), J.D./M.S.I. (Juris Doctor/Master of Science in Information), J.D./M.A. (Juris Doctor/Master of Arts in Japanese Studies), and J.D./M.P.H. (Juris Doctor/Master of Public Health).

Required

To earn the J.D., candidates must complete at least 83 total credits, of which 37 are for required courses. They must maintain a

Contact

734-764-0537 for general inquiries; Katherine Gottschalk, Director of Financial Aid, 734-764-5289 for financial aid information.

minimum GPA of 2.0 in the required courses. The following first-year courses are required of all students: Civil Procedure, Contracts I and II, Criminal Law, Introduction to Constitutional Law, Legal Practice I and II, Property I and II, Torts, and an elective. Required upper-level courses consist of 1 seminar and a course meeting the professional responsibility requirement. The required orientation program for first-year students consists of 2 days of presentations by deans, faculty, and upper-class students; tours; information about the school and Ann Arbor; and an introduction to the study of law. The school day of orientation has traditionally become "Service Day." New students, along with participating orientation leaders, administrators and faculty, are brought to various sites in the Ann Arbor and Detroit areas to engage in a community service project.

Electives

The Law School offers concentrations in corporate law, criminal law, environmental law, family law, international law, juvenile law, labor law, litigation, media law, securities law, sports law, tax law, torts and insurance, and civil rights, feminist legal theory, law and literature, psychology, sociology, economics, philosophy, and refugee and asylum. In addition, upper-class students may take clinical and externship courses for up to 12 hours of credit. These clinics include Child Advocacy, Clinical Law I, Advanced Clinical Law, Asylum and Refugee Law, criminal Appellate Practice, Environmental Law, and Legal Assistance for Urban communities. Students must take at least one seminar in their second or third year; most recently, 71 seminars were offered. Externships may be arranged for up to 12 hours of credit, 3 of which are devoted to a significant research paper under the direction of a faculty member. Under the supervision of a school faculty member, students may pursue up to six hours of independent research. Many noncredit opportunities exist for field work, including the Family Law Project and Pro Bono Students America (PBSA) placements. Special lecture series include the William W. Cook Lecture Series, Thomas M. Cooley Lectureship, Helen L. DeRoy Fellowship, and Sunderland Faculty Fellowship. Study abroad is available at Leiden University in the Netherlands, University College in London, the University of Freiburg in Germany, Katholiecke University in Leuven, Belgium, and the University of Paris II in France; special fellowships

support student-initiated study for third-year students and recent graduates. Individual tutors are available to students who request them. The Minority Affairs program (MAP) represents a commitment by the Law School to its students of color through the program, which is voluntary, students receive both academic and social support from upper-class students who serve MAP instructors. An average, about half of the eligible students choose to attend. The most widely taken electives are Evidence, Tax I, and Jurisdiction and Choice of Law.

Graduation Requirements

In order to graduate, candidates must have a GPA of 2.0 and have completed the upper-division writing requirement.

Organizations

Students edit the *Michigan Law Review, Michigan Journal of International Law, University of Michigan Journal of Law Reform, Michigan Journal of Gender and Law, Michigan Journal of Race and Law, Michigan Telecommunications and Technology Law Review,* the newspaper *Res Gestae,* and the yearbook *The Quadrangle.* Annual moot court competitions include the Henry M. Campbell Memorial and the Philip C. Jessup International Moot Court. Other competitions include the Negotiation Client Counseling, ABA Criminal Trial, NACDL Bennett, and Georgetown White Collor Crime Competitions. Law student organizations include the Environmental Law Society, Law School Student Senate and Women's Law Student Association. There are local chapters of Phi Alpha Delta, Phi Delta Phi, and the ABA-Law Student Division.

Library

The law library contains 845,328 hard-copy volumes and 1,142,830 microform volume equivalents, and subscribes to 9794 serial publications. Such on-line databases and networks as LEXIS, DIALOG, WESTLAW, and MIRLYN (University of Michigan on-line catalog), the Internet, RLG/RLIN, and MENTOR (University of Michigan Business School on-line catalog) are available to law students for research. Special library collections include a depository for U.S. and E.C. documents, U.N. documents, and foreign and international law as well as U.S. state and federal material. There are also extensive special collections in the fields of Roman law, international law, comparative law, trials, biography, and legal bibliography. Recently, the library added an on-line

Placement

J.D.s awarded:	337

Services available through: a separate law school placement center.

Services: databases to assist in job searches and mailings.

Special features: a separate office dedicated to public interest placement, and access to an innovative nationwide database program that helps students obtain volunteer legal experience under the supervision of lawyers in a variety of nonprofit offices, government agencies, and law firms.

Full-time job interviews:	n/av
Summer job interviews:	n/av
Placement by graduation:	93% of class
Placement within 9 months:	99% of class
Average starting salary:	$39,270 to $87,000

Areas of placement:

Private practice 2-100 attorneys	75%
Judicial clerkships	15%
Unknown	5%
Business/industry	3%
Public interest	1%

public access catalog, Lexcalibur. Also added were a separate secure area for EC documents, reserved books, a rare book room, and study carrels. The ratio of seats in the library to students is 1 to 1.

Faculty

The law school has 74 full-time and 49 part-time faculty members, of whom 37 are women. According to AAUP standards for Category IIA institutions, faculty salaries are well above average. About 23% of full-time faculty have a graduate law degree in addition to the J.D.; about 12% of part-time faculty have one. The ratio of full-time students to full-time faculty in an average class is 14 to 1; in a clinic, 8 to 1. The law school has a regular program of bringing visiting professors and other distinguished lecturers and visitors to campus. There is a chapter of the Order of the Coif.

Students

About 43% of the student body are women; 23%, minorities; 7%, African American; 9% Asian American; 5%, Hispanic; and 2%, Native American. The majority of students come from the Midwest (56%). The average age of entering students is 23; age range is 21 to 56. About 43% of students enter directly from undergraduate school. About 1% drop out after the first year for academic or personal reasons; 99% remain to receive a law degree.

UNIVERSITY OF MINNESOTA
Law School

229 19th Avenue S.,
Minneapolis, MN 55455

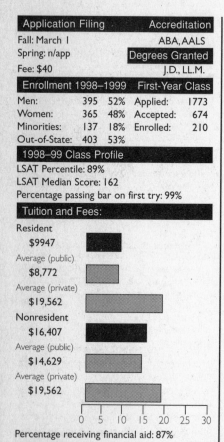

Application Filing | **Accreditation**

Fall: March 1 — ABA, AALS
Spring: n/app

Degrees Granted

Fee: $40 — J.D., LL.M.

Enrollment 1998–1999 | First-Year Class

Men: 395 52% | Applied: 1773
Women: 365 48% | Accepted: 674
Minorities: 137 18% | Enrolled: 210
Out-of-State: 403 53%

1998–99 Class Profile

LSAT Percentile: 89%
LSAT Median Score: 162
Percentage passing bar on first try: 99%

Tuition and Fees:

Resident
$9947

Average (public)
$8,772

Average (private)
$19,562

Nonresident
$16,407

Average (public)
$14,629

Average (private)
$19,562

0 5 10 15 20 25 30

Percentage receiving financial aid: 87%

ADMISSIONS

In the fall 1999 first-year class, 1773 applied, 674 were accepted, and 210 enrolled. Twenty transfers enrolled. The median LSAT percentile of the most recent first-year class was 89; the median GPA was 3.6 on a scale of 4.0. The lowest LSAT percentile accepted was 40; the highest was 99.

Requirements

Applicants must have a bachelor's degree from an accredited institution and take the LSAT. The most important admission factors include academic achievement, motivation, and character/personality. No specific undergraduate courses are required. Candidates are interviewed.

Procedure

The application deadline for fall entry is March 1. Applicants should submit an application form, LSAT results, transcripts, a nonrefundable application fee of $40, 2 letters of recommendation, and a personal statement. Notification of the admission decision is on a rolling basis. The latest acceptable LSAT test date for fall entry is February. The law school uses the LSDAS.

Special

The law school recruits minority and disadvantaged students by means of national recruitment, CLEO, Candidate Referral Service, and the National Name Exchange. Requirements are different for out-of-state students in that admission standards are slightly higher. Transfer students must have one year of credit, have attended an ABA-approved law school, have credentials to be admitted as a first-year law student, and exhibit good standing with quality work at a comparable law school; space availability is also a factor.

Costs

Tuition and fees for the 1999-2000 academic year are $9947 for full-time in-state students and $16,407 for out-of-state students. On-campus room and board costs about $7732 annually; and books and supplies run $1666.

Financial Aid

About 87% of current law students receive some form of aid. The average annual amount of aid from all sources combined, including scholarships, loans, and work contracts, is $12,000; maximum, $29,000. Awards are based on need and merit. The required financial statement is FAFSA. The aid application deadline for fall entry is February 1. Special funds for minority or disadvantaged students are available. First-year students are notified about their financial aid application some time between March and June.

About the Law School

University of Minnesota Law School was established in 1888 and is a public institution. The campus is in an urban area in Minneapolis. The primary mission of the law school is to provide students with the theoretical, analytical, and practical skills necessary to contribute professionally and creatively to U.S. and international society. Students have access to federal, state, county, city, and local agencies, courts, correctional facilities, law firms, and legal aid organizations in the Minneapolis area. Facilities of special interest to law students consist of the clinic law office, 2 courtrooms, a computer laboratory, the placement office, a bookstore, group study rooms, student publication and organization offices, and 2 lounge areas with an adjoining outdoor plaza. Housing for law students is plentiful. Apartments, efficiencies, houses near campus, and on-campus housing, are available. All law school facilities are accessible to the physically disabled.

Calendar

The law school operates on a traditional semester basis. Courses for full-time students are offered days only and must be completed within 5 years. New students are admitted in the fall. There is no part-time program. There is a 5- week summer session.

Programs

In addition to the J.D., the law school offers the LL.M for students with foreign law degrees, and a Master of Arts in American Legal institutions. Students may take relevant courses in other programs and apply credit toward the J.D.; a maximum of 6 to 12 credits may be applied. The following joint degrees may be earned: J.D./M.A. (Juris Doctor/Master of Arts), J.D./M.P. (Juris Doctor/Master of Planning), J.D./M.B.A. (Juris Doctor/Master of Businss Administration), and J.D./M.P.P. (Juris Doctor/Master of Public Policy).

Contact

Collins Byrd, Admissions Director, 612-625-3487 for general inquiries; Office of Admissions, 612-625-3487 for financial aid information.

MINNESOTA

Required

To earn the J.D., candidates must complete 88 total credits, of which 32 are for required courses. They must maintain a minimum GPA of 8.0 (on a scale of 4 to 16) in the required courses. The following first-year courses are required of all students: Constitutional Law, Contracts, Criminal Law, Legislation, Civil Procedure, Property, Torts, and Legal Research and Writing. Required upper-level courses consist of Professional Responsibility. Clincal courses are not required, but they are quite popular, with a 65% participation rate. The required orientation program for first-year students consists of $3\frac{1}{2}$ days in which the entering class is introduced to each other and the law school faculty and staff.

Electives

The Law School offers concentrations in corporate law, criminal law, environmental law, family law, international law, juvenile law, labor law, litigation, securities law, tax law, torts and insurance, and commercial transactions, real estate, estate planning, and theories of law. In addition, clinics, generally worth 2 credits, are offered in bankruptcy, family, and international human rights. Upper-level students may enroll in numerous seminars and earn from 1 to 3 credit hours. There is the Jurist-in-Residence program and the William B. Lockhart Distinguished Lecture Series. Study abroad is available in France, Sweden, Germany, Mexico, Poland, the People's Republic of China, Ireland, and the Netherlands. Tutorial programs are available. Academic support programs are available to minority students. The most widely taken electives are Business/Corporations, Tax, and Evidence.

Graduation Requirements

In order to graduate, candidates must have a GPA of 8.0 on a scale of 4 to 16 and have completed the upper-division writing requirement.

Organizations

Students edit the *Minnesota Law Review, Law and Inequality: A Journal of Theory and Practice*, the *Minnesota Journal of Global Trade*, and the *Journal of Technology, Law and Business*. The student newspaper is *The Source*. Moot court competitions include the Jessup International Law, Wagner Labor Law, and Civil Rights. An independent writing competition also is held at the school. Student organizations include the Law School Council, Environmental Law Society, and International and Comparative Law Society. The ABA, Delta Theta Phi, and Federalist Society have local chapters.

Library

The law library contains 875,000 hardcopy volumes and 300,000 microform volume equivalents, and subscribes to 8809 serial publications. Such on-line databases and networks as LEXIS, DIALOG, WESTLAW, and LUMINA, an on-line library catalog of University of Minnesota libraries, and LEGI-SLATE are available to law students for research. Special library collections include a U.S. documents depository as well as collections on the United Nations, European Community, and human rights. Recently, the library renovated the reference office and library classroom, and the lounge is now a 24-hour study area. The ratio of library volumes to faculty is 20,833 to 1 and to students, 1151 to 1. The ratio of seats in the library to students is 1 to 1.

Faculty

The law school has 42 full-time faculty members, of whom 13 are women. According to AAUP standards for Category I institutions, faculty salaries are well above average. About 35% of full-time faculty have a graduate law degree in addition to the J.D. The ratio of full-time students to full-time faculty in an average class is 17 to 1; in a clinic, 9 to 1. The law school has a regular program of bringing visiting professors and other distinguished lecturers and visitors to campus. There is a chapter of the Order of the Coif.

Placement

J.D.s awarded:	243
Services available through: A separate law school placement center.	
Special features: extensive career programming, an alumni networking program for students, and listings of employers by type, size, and city.	
Full-time job interviews:	125 employers
Summer job interviews:	125 employers
Placement by graduation:	92% of class
Placement within 9 months:	99% of class
Average starting salary:	$25,000 to $99,000
Areas of placement:	
Private practice 2-10 attorneys	4%
Private practice 11-25 attorneys	5%
Private practice 26-50 attorneys	9%
Private practice 51-100 attorneys	29%
Judicial clerkships	24%
Business/industry	15%
Government	7%
Public interest	3%
Academic	2%

Students

About 48% of the student body are women; 18%, minorities; 5%, African American; 9%, Asian American; 4%, Hispanic; and 2%, Native American. The majority of students come from Minnesota (47%). The average age of entering students is 25; age range is 20 to 58. About 35% of students enter directly from undergraduate school, 11% have a graduate degree, and 40% have worked full-time prior to entering law school. About 4% drop out after the first year for academic or personal reasons; 98% remain to receive a law degree.

School of Law

Lamar Hall
Oxford, MS 38677

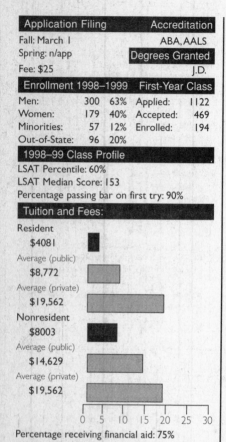

Application Filing		Accreditation
Fall: March 1		ABA, AALS
Spring: n/app		**Degrees Granted**
Fee: $25		J.D.

Enrollment 1998–1999		First-Year Class	
Men:	300 63%	Applied:	1122
Women:	179 40%	Accepted:	469
Minorities:	57 12%	Enrolled:	194
Out-of-State:	96 20%		

1998–99 Class Profile

LSAT Percentile: 60%
LSAT Median Score: 153
Percentage passing bar on first try: 90%

Tuition and Fees:

Resident
$4081

Average (public)
$8,772

Average (private)
$19,562

Nonresident
$8003

Average (public)
$14,629

Average (private)
$19,562

0 5 10 15 20 25 30

Percentage receiving financial aid: 75%

ADMISSIONS

In the fall 1999 first-year class, 1122 applied, 469 were accepted, and 194 enrolled. Three transfers enrolled. The median LSAT percentile of the most recent first-year class was 60; the median GPA was 3.0 on a scale of 4.0. The lowest LSAT percentile accepted was 7; the highest was 97.

Requirements

Applicants must have a bachelor's degree from an accredited institution and take the LSAT. The most important admission factors include state or country of residence, LSAT results, and GPA. No specific undergraduate courses are required. Candidates are not interviewed.

Procedure

The application deadline for fall entry is March 1. Applicants should submit an application form, LSAT results, transcripts, TOEFL for non-U.S. citizens whose native language is not English, and a nonrefundable application fee of $25. Not required but strongly recommended are letters of recommendation. Notification of the admission decision is no later than April 15. The latest acceptable LSAT test date for fall entry is December. The law school uses the LSDAS.

Special

The law school recruits minority and disadvantaged students by means of an extensive recruiting program aimed at historically black colleges and universities in Mississippi and in other states as well as participation in Law School Forums. Requirements are different for out-of-state students in that slightly higher credentials are required and the percentage of nonresidents admitted is limited. Transfer students must have one year of credit and the law school from which the transfer is made must be both ABA and AALS accredited.

Costs

Tuition and fees for the 1999-2000 academic year are $4081 for full-time in-state students and $8003 for out-of-state students. On-campus room and board costs about $7000 annually, and books and supplies run $800.

Financial Aid

About 75% of current law students receive some form of aid. The average annual amount of aid from all sources combined, including scholarships, loans, and work contracts, is $10,000; maximum, $18,500. Awards are based on need and merit. The required financial statement is CSS Profile or FAFSA. The aid application deadline for fall entry is March 1. Special funds for minority or disadvantaged students are available as tuition grants; some grants, based on both merit and need, exceed tuition. First-year students are notified about their financial aid application at time of acceptance.

About the Law School

University of Mississippi School of Law was established in 1854 and is a public institution. The 1900-acre campus is in a small town 80 miles southeast of Memphis, Tennessee. The primary mission of the law school is to provide a quality legal education that prepares graduates for the practice of law in the United States and for entry into government and public service or any profession in which a legal education is a helpful or necessary background. Students have access to federal, state, county, city, and local agencies, courts, correctional facilities, law firms, and legal aid organizations in the Oxford area. Oxford, where the University is located, has federal, circuit, chancery, and justice courts, the North Mississippi Rural Legal Services, and approximately 31 law firms. Housing for law students is primarily off campus and is described as adequate and reasonably priced. About 75% of the law school facilities are accessible to the physically disabled.

Calendar

The law school operates on a traditional semester basis. Courses for full-time students are offered days only. There is no part-time program. New full-time students are admitted in the fall and summer. There is an 8-week summer session. Transferable summer courses are offered.

Programs

Students may take relevant courses in other programs and apply credit toward the J.D.; a maximum of 6 credits may be applied. The following joint degrees may be earned: J.D./M.B.A. (Juris Doctor/Master of Business Administration).

Phone: 601-915-6910
Fax: 601-915-1289
E-mail: bvinson@olemiss.edu

Contact
Office of Law Admissions, 601-915-6910 for general inquiries; Larry Ridgeway, Director of Financial Aid, 601-915-7175 for financial aid information.

Required
To earn the J.D., candidates must complete 90 total credits, of which 54 to 57 are for required courses. They must maintain a minimum GPA of 2.0 in the required courses. The following first-year courses are required of all students: Contracts, Torts, Civil Procedure I, Property, Constitutional Law, Legal Research and Writing I and II, and Criminal Law. Required upper-level courses consist of Civil Procedure II, Evidence, Legal Profession, Moot Court, 2 business/ commercial courses, 1 procedure course, 1 perspective course, and 1 senior skills/ writing course. All students must take clinical courses. The required orientation program for first-year students is a 2-day program incorporating an introduction to the study of law, including analytical, case briefing, and exam-taking skills.

Electives
The School of Law offers concentrations in corporate law, labor law, litigation, and tax law. In addition, School Law, Family Law, and Constitutional Law seminars are offered. Public Service Internships, awarded 12 hours of pass/fail credit, are offered to senior students with more than 60 hours, a GPA of 2.2, and the permission of the Director. Law students work with judges, prosecuting attorneys, and public defenders under the Student Limited Practice Act. The Mississippi Law Research Institute, operated as an auxiliary program, offers students the opportunity to perform legal research. Students receive wages for their work but no law school credit. Field work opportunities are available. Special lectures include the Dunbar Lectures in Philosophy and the Law, the Currie Lectures, which relate law, religion, and the behavioral sciences, and the McClure Memorial Lectures in Law. Upper-class students may take 6 hours in the study-abroad program in Cambridge, England, where various courses are offered. Students may also earn up to 6 hours in the summer study program in Hawaii. All first-year students may take advantage of a tutorial program in which upper-class students serve as teaching assistants. The program is under the direction of the Assistant to the Dean. Minority programs consist of the Minority Tuition Scholarship Program and programs offered through the BLSA. There are various active special-interest organizations. The most widely taken electives are Insurance, Family Law, and Environmental Law.

Graduation Requirements
In order to graduate, candidates must have a GPA of 2.0 and have completed the upper-division writing requirement.

Organizations
Student-edited publications include the *Mississippi Law Journal, National Security Law Journal*, the student newspaper *The Solicitor*, and *The Advocate*, the School of Law yearbook. Moot court competitions include the Steen-Reynolds Competition in the fall semester and trial competitions and appellate competitions each semester. Other competitions include the National Moot Court, Douglass Moot Court, Student Trial, Craven Moot Court, Heidelberg, Woodliff Oral Advocacy, and Jessup International Law. Law student organizations include the Lamar Society of International Law, Moot Court Board, and Law School Student Body Association as well as student divisions of ABA, Delta Theta Phi, and Phi Delta Phi.

Library
The law library contains 296,871 hardcopy volumes and 846,235 microform volume equivalents, and subscribes to 2704 serial publications. Such on-line databases and networks as LEXIS, DIALOG, WESTLAW, Benner Full Authority, CIS Universe, and mslawyer.com are available to law students for research. Special library collections include a depository of federal documents and a space law collection. There are 363 seats in the library.

Faculty
The law school has 26 full-time and 11 part-time faculty members, of whom 10 are women. According to AAUP standards for Category I institutions, faculty salaries are below average. About 28% of full-time faculty have a graduate law degree in addition to the J.D.; about 18% of part-time faculty have one. The ratio of full-time students to full-time faculty in an average class is 19 to 1; in a clinic, 8 to 1.

Placement

J.D.s awarded:	175
Services available through: a separate law school placement center.	
Services: a course in general practice offers insight into establishing a solo practice.	
Special features: personalized service based on the small student body.	
Full-time job interviews:	15 employers
Summer job interviews:	35 employers
Placement by graduation:	60% of class
Placement within 9 months:	96% of class
Average starting salary:	$21,000 to $90,000
Areas of placement:	
Private practice 2-10 attorneys	26%
Private practice 11-25 attorneys	10%
Private practice 26-50 attorneys	7%
Private practice 51-100 attorneys	4%
Private practice 101-500 attorneys	15%
Solo Practice	7%
Judicial clerkships	16%
Government	9%
Business/industry	9%
Academic	4%
Public interest	1%
Military	1%

Students
About 40% of the student body are women; 12%, minorities; 11%, African American; 1%, Asian American; 1%, Hispanic; and 1%, Native American. The majority of students come from Mississippi (80%). The average age of entering students is 24; age range is 21 to 49. About 75% of students enter directly from undergraduate school, 5% have a graduate degree, and 25% have worked full-time prior to entering law school. About 9% drop out after the first year for academic or personal reasons; 90% remain to receive a law degree.

UNIVERSITY OF MISSOURI-COLUMBIA

School of Law

103 Hulston Hall
Columbia, MO 65211

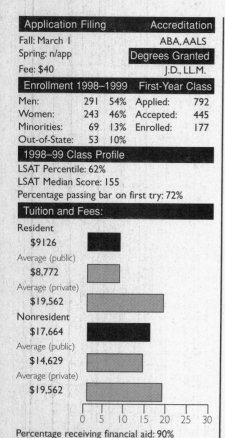

Application Filing	Accreditation
Fall: March 1	ABA, AALS
Spring: n/app	**Degrees Granted**
Fee: $40	J.D., LL.M.

Enrollment 1998–1999		First-Year Class	
Men:	291 54%	Applied:	792
Women:	243 46%	Accepted:	445
Minorities:	69 13%	Enrolled:	177
Out-of-State:	53 10%		

1998–99 Class Profile
LSAT Percentile: 62%
LSAT Median Score: 155
Percentage passing bar on first try: 72%

Tuition and Fees:

Resident
$9126

Average (public)
$8,772

Average (private)
$19,562

Nonresident
$17,664

Average (public)
$14,629

Average (private)
$19,562

0 5 10 15 20 25 30

Percentage receiving financial aid: 90%

ADMISSIONS

In the fall 1999 first-year class, 792 applied, 445 were accepted, and 177 enrolled. Nine transfers enrolled. The median LSAT percentile of the most recent first-year class was 62; the median GPA was 3.3 on a scale of 4.0. The lowest LSAT percentile accepted was 28; the highest was 99.

Requirements

Applicants must have a bachelor's degree from an accredited institution and take the LSAT. Minimum acceptable LSAT score is 30. The most important admission factors include LSAT results, GPA, and academic achievement. No specific undergraduate courses are required. Required undergraduate courses are those that stress writing, accounting basics, and analytical reasoning. Candidates are not interviewed.

Procedure

The application deadline for fall entry is March 1. Applicants should submit an application form, LSAT results, transcripts, and a nonrefundable application fee of $40. There is also a $200 nonrefundable deposit after admission that is credited toward tuition. Notification of the admission decision is usually by May 1. The latest acceptable LSAT test date for fall entry is February. The law school uses the LSDAS.

Special

The law school recruits minority and disadvantaged students actively and has a special admissions policy. Transfer students must have one year of credit, have attended an ABA-approved law school, and must be in good standing.

Costs

Tuition and fees for the 1999-2000 academic year are $9126 for in-state students and $17,664 for out-of-state students. On-campus room and board costs about $6615 annually; and books and supplies run $1169.

Financial Aid

About 90% of current law students receive some form of aid. The average annual amount of aid from all sources combined, including scholarships, loans, and work contracts, is $15,200; maximum, $21,500. Awards are based on need and merit. The required financial statement is the FAFSA. The aid application deadline for fall entry is March 1. Special funds for minority or disadvantaged students consist of need- and merit-based law school scholarships, ranging from $500 to full tuition. First-year students are notified about their financial aid application at time of acceptance.

About the Law School

University of Missouri-Columbia School of Law was established in 1872 and is a public institution. The 1348-acre campus is in a suburban area 125 miles west of St. Louis. The primary mission of the law school is to educate students about the fundamentals of legal thinking, including the analysis and synthesis of court opinions, preparation and argument of cases, and the resolution of client problems and ethical issues that attorneys must face. Students have access to federal, state, county, city, and local agencies, courts, correctional facilities, law firms, and legal aid organizations in the Columbia area. Housing for law students is available in on- and off-campus apartments and dormitories. All law school facilities are accessible to the physically disabled.

Calendar

The law school operates on a traditional semester basis. Courses are offered days only. There is no part-time program. New students are admitted in the fall. There is a 7-week summer session. Transferable summer courses are offered.

Programs

In addition to the J.D., the law school offers the LL.M. Students may take relevant courses in other programs and apply credit toward the J.D.; a maximum of 3 to 6 credits may be applied. The following joint degrees may be earned: J.D./M.B.A. (Juris Doctor/Master of Business Administration), J.D./M.P.A. (Juris Doctor/Master of Public Administration), J.D./M.A. (Juris Doctor/Master of Arts in economics), and J.D./M.A. (Juris Doctor/Master of Human Development and Family Studies).

Required

To earn the J.D., candidates must complete 89 total credits, of which 57 are for required courses. They must maintain a minimum grade average of 70 in the required courses. The following first-year courses are required of all students: Contracts I and II, Torts I and II, Civil Procedure I and II, Criminal Law, Property I and II, Legal Research and Writing, and Advocacy and Research. Required upper-level courses consist of

Phone: 573-882-6042
888-685-2948
Fax: 573-882-9625
E-mail: umclawadmissions@missouri.edu
Web: www.law.missouri.edu

Contact

Sheryl Gregory, Admissions Adviser, 573-882-6042 or 888-MULAW4U (685-2948) for general inquiries; Financial Aid Adviser, 573-882-1383 for financial aid information.

Evidence, Constitutional Law, Legislation, Public Law Module (Administrative Law or Criminal Procedure), Transactions Module (Business Organizations, Real Estate Finance, or Secured Transactions), Professional Responsibility, Law of Personal Relationships (Estates and Trusts or Family Law), Skills Module (Trial Practice, Pretrial Litigation, Arbitration, Negotiation, Mediation, client Interviewing and Counseling, or Business Planning), and completion of a writing requirement. The required 3-day orientation program for first-year students consists of meeting with administration, faculty, and student organizations, learning rules and regulations, learning to brief a case, and registering for classes.

Electives

The School of Law offers concentrations in corporate law, criminal law, environmental law, family law, labor law, litigation, securities law, tax law, torts and insurance, and trial law. In addition, the school offers a criminal clinic and a domestic violence clinic. Internship programs are available to upper-level students who wish to experience the practice of civil and criminal law in various state and federal agencies; 3 credit hours are offered. Seminars are open to upper-level students on Communication Law, Criminal Law, Environmental Law, Law and Medicine, and other selected topics for 2 credit hours. Upper-level students may perform independent research for a faculty member and earn up to 3 credit hours. The main lecture series at the Law School is the Nelson Lecture, in which noted national legal scholars deliver a major address. The School of Law participates in the London Law Consortium, in cooperation with the universities of Kansas, Utah, Iowa, Arizona, Indiana, IIT Chicago-Kent, and Georgia. A semester in the Bloomsbury district of London, each January through May, is available to second- and third-year law students in good standing; the courses are taught by regular faculty from the participating American universities. Students also may enroll in classes taught by British professors. The school has a full-time academic counselor available to assist students with academic concerns. Minority scholarship funds are available. The most widely taken electives are Trial Practice, Family Law, and Secured Transactions.

Graduation Requirements

In order to graduate, candidates must have an average of 70 and must have completed the upper-division writing requirement.

Organizations

Students edit the *Missouri Law Review,* the *Environmental Law and Policy Review,* and the *Journal of Dispute Resolution.* The student newspaper is the *Student Bar Association Newsletter* and *The Gavel.* Moot court competitions include the Midwest Moot Court Competition, National Moot Court, and the ABA Moot Court. Other competitions are the Negotiation, Trial, Client Counseling, and First Year Moot Court. Student organizations include the Board of Advocates, the Student Bar Association, and the Women's Law Association. Phi Alpha Delta, the ABA-Law School Division, and the Association of Trial Lawyers of America have local chapters.

Library

The law library contains 320,000 hardcopy volumes and 444,865 microform volume equivalents, and subscribes to 3637 serial publications. Such on-line databases and networks as LEXIS, DIALOG, WESTLAW, and OCLC, Merlin, Legal-Trac, LOIS, the Internet, and the World Wide Web are available to law students for research. Special library collections include U.S. and Missouri state documents and a nineteenth-century criminal trial collection. Recently, the library Upgraded its computer lab to Windows NT and Netware 5, and added new carrel seating. The ratio of library volumes to faculty is 9142 to 1 and to students, 592 to 1. The ratio of seats in the library to students is 4 to 5.

Faculty

The law school has 36 full-time and 15 part-time faculty members, of whom 16 are women. According to AAUP standards for Category I institutions, faculty salaries are average. About 14% of full-time faculty have a graduate law degree in addition to the J.D.; about 2% of part-time faculty have one. The ratio of full-time students to full-time faculty in an average class is 15 to 1; in a clinic, 8 to 1. The law school has a regular program of bringing visiting professors and other distinguished lecturers and visitors to campus. There is a chapter of the Order of the Coif; 45 faculty and 533 graduates are members.

Placement

J.D.s awarded:	187
Services available through: a separate law school placement center and the university placement center	
Services: access to electronic and hard copy resume databases	
Special features: an active and successful judicial clerkship committee and CLAWSNET, an organized alumni network which serves as an informational interview resource	
Full-time job interviews:	37 employers
Summer job interviews:	66 employers
Placement by graduation:	78% of class
Placement within 9 months:	90% of class
Average starting salary:	$19,000 to $70,000
Areas of placement:	
Private practice 2-10 attorneys	38%
Private practice 11-25 attorneys	22%
Private practice 26-50 attorneys	10%
Private practice 51-100 attorneys	7%
Government	22%
Judicial clerkships	13%
Business/industry	13%
LL.M. program	2%
Public interest	1%

Students

About 46% of the student body are women; 13%, minorities; 8%, African American; 2%, Asian American; 1%, Hispanic; and 1%, Native American. The majority of students come from Missouri (90%). The average age of entering students is 23; age range is 20 to 44. About 85% of students enter directly from undergraduate school, 10% have a graduate degree, and 5% have worked full time prior to entering law school. About 5% drop out after the first year for academic or personal reasons; 95% remain to receive a law degree.

School of Law

500 East 52nd Street
Kansas City, MO 64110-2499

Application Filing		Accreditation
Fall: open		ABA, AALS
Spring: n/app		Degrees Granted
Fee: n/av		J.D., LL.M.

Enrollment 1998–1999			First-Year Class	
Men:	238	49%	Applied:	667
Women:	249	46%	Accepted:	386
Minorities:	34	7%	Enrolled:	165
Out-of-State:	136	28%		

1998–99 Class Profile
LSAT Percentile: 52%
LSAT Median Score: 151
Percentage passing bar on first try: n/av

Tuition and Fees:

Resident
$9108

Average (public)
$8,772

Average (private)
$19,562

Nonresident
$17,645

Average (public)
$14,629

Average (private)
$19,562

0 5 10 15 20 25 30

Percentage receiving financial aid: 82%

ADMISSIONS

In the fall 1999 first-year class, 667 applied, 386 were accepted, and 165 enrolled. Eight transfers enrolled. The median LSAT percentile of the most recent first-year class was 52; the median GPA was 3.2 on a scale of 4.0. The lowest LSAT percentile accepted was 23; the highest was 99.

Requirements
Applicants must take the LSAT. Minimum acceptable LSAT score is 45 and minimum acceptable GPA is 2.0 on a scale of 4.0. The most important admission factors include LSAT results, GPA, and academic achievement. No specific undergraduate courses are required. Required undergraduate courses are those that provide opportunities for development of critical thinking and oral and written skills. Candidates are not interviewed.

Procedure
The application deadline for fall entry is open. Applicants should submit an application form, LSAT results, transcripts, a nonrefundable application fee, 2 letters of recommendation, and a personal statement. Check with the school for current fee. Notification of the admission decision is on a rolling basis. The latest acceptable LSAT test date for fall entry is June. The law school uses the LSDAS.

Special
The law school recruits minority and disadvantaged students by means of minority recruitment, forums, personal letters, and telephone calls to potential applicants. Transfer students must have one year of credit, have a minimum GPA of 2.7, have attended an ABA-approved law school. Had the student not been admissible when applying for initial admission to the school, then a minimum GPA of 3.0 is required.

Costs

Tuition and fees for the 1999-2000 academic year are $9108 for full-time in-state students and $17,645 for out-of-state students. The cost per credit hour for full-time and part-time is $355 in-state and $660 for out-of-state students. Books and supplies run $500 for full-time students and $400 for part-time students.

Financial Aid

About 82% of current law students receive some form of aid. The average annual amount of aid from all sources combined, including scholarships, loans, and work contracts, is $6775. Awards are based on need and merit. The required financial statement is FAFSA. Check with the school for current application deadline. Special funds for minority or disadvantaged students include special admissions scholarships and out-of-state tuition waivers for minority students. First-year students are notified about their financial aid application at the time of acceptance.

About the Law School

University of Missouri-Kansas City School of Law was established in 1895 and is a public institution. The 93-acre campus is in an urban area in Kansas City. The primary mission of the law school is to prepare men and women for the general practice of law and for policy-forming functions in government, business, and organization community life, while providing a sound curriculum that offers a rigorous learning experience for students to obtain knowledge and skills in breadth and depth. Students have access to federal, state, county, city, and local agencies, courts, correctional facilities, law firms, and legal aid organizations in the Kansas City area. Clerkship opportunities are available in the numerous nearby law firms. Facilities of special interest to law students include the placement of study stations in office suites shared by law faculty. These student stations include study carrels and double occupancy student offices that are available to second- and third-year students, and provide student-faculty interaction. Housing for law students is described as limited on campus, while a large selection of housing is available off campus from private owners. About 95% of the law school facilities are accessible to the physically disabled.

Calendar

The law school operates on a traditional semester basis. Courses for full-time students are offered both day and evening, with most courses being offered during the day, and must be completed within 3 years. For part-time students, courses are offered days only and must be completed within 5 years. New full-and part-time students are admitted in the fall. There is an 8-week summer session.

Phone: 816-235-1644
Fax: 816-235-5276
E-mail: klosterman@umkc.edu
Web: law.umkc.edu

Contact

Jean Klosterman, Admissions Director, 816-235-1672 for general inquiries; Pat McTee, Director of Financial Aid, 816-235-1154 for financial aid information.

MISSOURI

Programs

In addition to the J.D., the law school offers the LL.M in 2 emphasis areas: tax and general. Students may take relevant courses in other programs and apply credit toward the J.D.; a maximum of 10 credits may be applied. The following joint degrees may be earned: J.D./M.B.A. (Juris Doctor/Master of Business Administration) and J.D./LL.M. (Juris Doctor/Master of Laws in taxation).

Required

To earn the J.D., candidates must complete 91 total credits, of which 52 are for required courses. They must maintain a minimum GPA of 2.0 in the required courses. The following first-year courses are required of all students: Contracts I and II, Torts I and II, Property I and II, Introduction to Law I and II, Criminal Law, Constitutional Law, and Civil Procedure I. Required upper-level courses consist of Business Organizations, Civil Procedure II, Evidence, Commercial Transaction or Secured Transaction, Criminal Procedure, Professional Responsibility, a federal agency familiarity requirement, a jurisprudential requirement, and Federal Taxation. The required orientation program for first-year students is a 2-day program that introduces students to all aspects of law school, legal study, registration and rules, and includes discussion groups and lunch with members of the local judiciary and bar.

Electives

The School of Law offers concentrations in corporate law, criminal law, environmental law, family law, international law, labor law, litigation, securities law, tax law, torts and insurance, and urban affairs, estates and trust/planning. Clinics from 2 to 6 credit hours include legal aid, public defender trial, and death penalty. Seminars for 2 or 3 credit hours include Civil Rights Litigation, Constitutional Problems, and Famous Trials. Research is conducted as part of the research and writing requirement for all students. Introduction to Law and Legal Processes, for 5 credit hours, requires all students to engage in research case analysis and synthesis, and Advanced Legal Writing, a 3-credit-hour course for upper-level students, focuses on drafting seminars in corporate law and litigation. Structured study groups are offered in one substantive course in each first-year section. Trained upper-level study leaders

model effective learning strategies and assist with writing/synthesis skills. An academic enrichment program, focusing on analytical, organization, and exam-writing skills, also is offered. A special summer preparatory workshop is available to minority candidates, who are encouraged to apply via the Special Admissions Program. The most widely taken electives are Family Law, Debtor-Creditor, Trial Advocacy, and Estates and Trusts.

Graduation Requirements

In order to graduate, candidates must have a GPA of 2.0, have completed the upper-division writing requirement, the jurisprudential requirement, and the federal agency familiarity requirement.

Organizations

Students edit the *UMKC Law Review*, the *Urban Lawyer*, and the *Journal of the American Academy of Matrimonial Lawyers*. Annual moot court competitions include the National Moot Court, Jessup International Law, and Giles Sutherland Rich. Other competitions include the National Trial, ATLA Trial, Client Counseling, and the yearly ABA Negotiation. Student organizations include the Student Bar Association and the Law Council. The ABA/Law School Division, Black Law Students Association, and National Lawyers Guild have local chapters.

Library

The law library contains 178,058 hardcopy volumes and 77,000 microform volume equivalents, and subscribes to 3802 serial publications. Such on-line databases and networks as LEXIS, DIALOG, WESTLAW, and OCLC Merlin, the library catalog of the 4 University of Missouri campuses and INNOPAC for serials control and budgeting are available to law students for research. Special library collections include a depository for federal, Missouri, and Kansas documents, an urban law collection, and a tax law concentration. Recently, the library provided a LAN for students, access to the Internet, and a computer word-processing lab. The ratio of library volumes to faculty is 8697 to 1 and to students, 526 to 1. The ratio of seats in the library to students is 1 to 1.

Placement	
J.D.s awarded:	151
Services available through: A separate law school placement center.	
Services: career services news bulletin and the career services library	
Full-time job interviews:	34 employers
Summer job interviews:	n/av
Placement by graduation:	50% of class
Placement within 9 months:	94% of class
Average starting salary:	$20,000 to $70,000
Areas of placement:	
Private practice 2-10 attorneys	23%
Private practice 11-25 attorneys	2%
Private practice 26-50 attorneys	1%
Private practice 51-100 attorneys	1%
Private practice 100+ attorneys	14%
Solo pracice	3%
Government	21%
Business/industry	14%
Judicial clerkships	11%
Military	1%

Faculty

The law school has 29 full-time and 35 part-time faculty members, of whom 17 are women. According to AAUP standards for Category I institutions, faculty salaries are average. About 43% of full-time faculty have a graduate law degree in addition to the J.D. The ratio of full-time students to full-time faculty in an average class is 30 to 1; in a clinic, 6 to 1.

Students

About 46% of the student body are women; 7%, minorities; 4%, African American; 3%, Asian American; and 3%, Hispanic. The majority of students come from the Midwest (92%). The average age of entering students is 27. About 12% of students have a graduate degree. About 5% drop out after the first year for academic or personal reasons; 89% remain to receive a law degree.

UNIVERSITY OF MONTANA

School of Law

Missoula, MT 59812

Application Filing		Accreditation
Fall: March 1		ABA, AALS
Spring: n/app		Degrees Granted
Fee: $60		J.D.

Enrollment 1998–1999			First-Year Class	
Men:	137	59%	Applied:	352
Women:	97	41%	Accepted:	235
Minorities:	16	7%	Enrolled:	73
Out-of-State:	80	34%		

1998–99 Class Profile

LSAT Percentile: 60%

LSAT Median Score: 153

Percentage passing bar on first try: 96%

Tuition and Fees:

Resident
$6695

Average (public)
$8,772

Average (private)
$19,562

Nonresident
$12,298

Average (public)
$14,629

Average (private)
$19,562

0   5   10   15   20   25   30

Percentage receiving financial aid: 86%

ADMISSIONS

In the fall 1999 first-year class, 352 applied, 235 were accepted, and 73 enrolled. One transfer enrolled. The median LSAT percentile of the most recent first-year class was 60; the median GPA was 3.2 on a scale of 4.0. The lowest LSAT percentile accepted was 3; the highest was 97.

Requirements

Applicants must have a bachelor's degree from an accredited institution and take the LSAT. The most important admission factors include GPA, LSAT results, and writing ability. No specific undergraduate courses are required. Candidates are not interviewed.

Procedure

The application deadline for fall entry is March 1. Applicants should submit an application form, LSAT results, transcripts, TOEFL for foreign applicants, a nonrefundable application fee of $60, 3 letters of recommendation, and personal statements. Notification of the admission decision is from March to June. The latest acceptable LSAT test date for fall entry is February. The law school uses the LSDAS.

Special

The law school recruits minority and disadvantaged students by means of special recruiting efforts aimed at Native American and other minority students. Transfer students must have one year of credit, have attended an ABA-approved law school, and be in the top third of their class; the average in all law studies must be equivalent to that required for graduation from the institution attended.

Costs

Tuition and fees for the 1999-2000 academic year are $6695 for full-time in-state students and $12,298 for out-of-state students. On-campus room and board costs about $7510 annually; books and supplies run $910.

Financial Aid

About 86% of current law students receive some form of aid. The average annual amount of aid from all sources combined, including scholarships, loans, and work contracts, is $14,254; maximum, $18,500. Awards are based on need and merit. The required financial statement is FAFSA. The aid application deadline for fall entry is March 1. Special funds for minority or disadvantaged students consists of Native American fee waivers and scholarships. First-year students are notified about their financial aid application at a time determined by the University Financial Aid Office.

About the Law School

University of Montana School of Law was established in 1911 and is a public institution. The campus is in the small town of Missoula, Montana. The primary mission of the law school is to teach a competency-based curriculum. Legal writing, trial practice, and clinical programs require students to demonstrate their abilities to apply highly technical legal knowledge to practical situations. Students have access to federal, state, county, city, and local agencies, courts, correctional facilities, law firms, and legal aid organizations in the Missoula area. Students in clinics benefit from natural resource groups and Native American tribal courts and governments. Facilities of special interest to law students include 9 computerized courtroom facility and first-year moot "law firms". Housing for law students is available for married students in university housing and dormitories; apartments and houses are available for rent in the community. All law school facilities are accessible to the physically disabled.

Calendar

The law school operates on a traditional semester basis. Courses for full-time students are offered days only and must be completed within 3 years. There is no part-time program. New students are admitted in the fall. There is no summer session.

Programs

The following joint degrees may be earned: J.D./M.P.A. (Juris Doctor/Master of Public Administration) and J.D./M.S. (Juris Doctor/Master of Science in environmental studies).

Phone: 406-243-2698
E-mail: lawadmis@selway.umt.edu
Web: http://www.umt.edu/law

Contact
Heidi Fanslow, Director of Admissions, 406-243-2698 for general inquiries; Elizabeth Oleson, Administrative Officer, 406-243-4311 for financial aid information.

MONTANA

Required
To earn the J.D., candidates must complete 90 total credits, of which 59 are for required courses. They must maintain a minimum GPA of 2.0 in the required courses. The following first-year courses are required of all students: Civil Procedure I and II, Contracts I and II, Pre-trial Advocacy I and II, Legal Writing I, Criminal Law and Procedure I and II, Torts I and II, and Legal Research and Analysis. Required upper-level courses consist of Business Organizations, Federal Tax, Constitutional Law I and II, Evidence, Commercial requirement, Property I and II, advanced writing component, Estate Planning, Professional Responsibility, Trial Practice, clinical training, and Business Transactions. All students must take clinical courses. The required orientation program for first-year students is 2 1/2 weeks long and includes concepts of jurisprudence, the role of lawyers in society, legal history, and other topics.

Electives
The School of Law offers concentrations in corporate law, criminal law, environmental law, family law, labor law, litigation, tax law, torts and insurance, and Indian law. In addition, clinics, field work, and internships include the Criminal Defense Clinic, Montana Legal Services, and Natural Resource Clinic for 1 to 4 credit hours for third-year students. Seminars include Contemporary Problems in Constitutional Law, Problems in Estate Planning, and Problems in Indian Law Regulation for 2 credit hours each, open to second- and third-year students. Independent study programs designed by law students and professors for 1 to 2 credit hours for third-year students and periodic law reform projects for second- and third-year students, for no credit, are available. Special lectures include the Blankenbaker Lecture in Ethics and the Judge William B. Jones and Judge Edward A. Tamm Judicial Lecture Series. Tutorial programs include the Academic Assistance Program. Minority programs are sponsored by the Native American Law Students Association. Periodic programs are offered by the Federalist Society, Women's Law Caucus, Phi Delta Phi, Student Bar Association, and 8 other student groups. The most widely taken electives are Family Law, Environmental Law, and Real Estate Transactions.

Graduation Requirements
In order to graduate, candidates must have a GPA of 2.0 and have completed the upper-division writing requirement.

Organizations
Students edit the *Montana Law Review* and the *Public Land and Resource Law Review*. Moot court competitions include National Moot Court Team, NALSA Moot Court Team, and Pace Environmental Law Moot Court Team. Other competitions include ATLA Trial Team, ABA Negotiations Team, and ABA Client Counseling Team. Student organizations include the Student Bar Association, Phi Delta Phi, and Women's Law Caucus. Local chapters of national organizations include American Trial Lawyers and ACLU.

Library
The law library contains 108,599 hardcopy volumes and 57,584 microform volume equivalents, and subscribes to 1717 serial publications. Such on-line databases and networks as LEXIS, WESTLAW, and MONTLAW are available to law students for research. Recently, the library increased staffing, added computers, and completed renovation of a basement which added seminar rooms and a presentation center. The ratio of library volumes to faculty is 3109 to 1 and to students, 464 to 1. The ratio of seats in the library to students is 1 to 1.

Faculty
The law school has 19 full-time and 16 part-time faculty members, of whom 10 are women. According to AAUP standards for Category I institutions, faculty salaries are well below average. About 43% of full-time faculty have a graduate law degree in addition to the J.D.; about 27% of part-time faculty have one. The ratio of full-time students to full-time faculty in an average class is 12 to 1; in a clinic, 10 to 1. The law school has a regular program of bringing visiting professors and other distinguished lecturers and visitors to campus.

Placement

J.D.s awarded:	69
Services available through: A separate law school placement center.	
Special features: semiannual on-campus recruitment conferences	
Full-time job interviews:	40 employers
Summer job interviews:	n/av
Placement by graduation:	n/av
Placement within 9 months:	93% of class
Average starting salary:	$33,750
Areas of placement:	
Private practice	43%
Judicial clerkships	20%
Government	12%
Business/industry	9%
Pursuing advanced degree	4%
Public interest	3%
Academic	1%

Students
About 41% of the student body are women; 7%, minorities; 1%, African American; 1%, Asian American; 2%, Hispanic; and 4%, Native American. The majority of students come from Montana (66%). The average age of entering students is 27; age range is 21 to 60. About 22% of students enter directly from undergraduate school, 14% have a graduate degree, and 60% have worked full-time prior to entering law school. About 1% drop out after the first year for academic or personal reasons; 99% remain to receive a law degree.

College of Law

P.O. Box 830902
Lincoln, NE 68583-0902

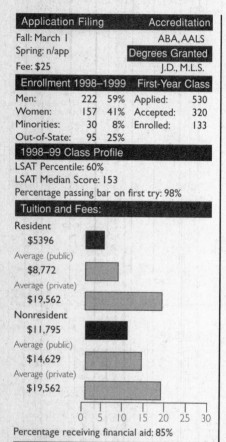

Application Filing		Accreditation
Fall: March 1		ABA, AALS
Spring: n/app		Degrees Granted
Fee: $25		J.D., M.L.S.

Enrollment 1998–1999		First-Year Class	
Men:	222 59%	Applied:	530
Women:	157 41%	Accepted:	320
Minorities:	30 8%	Enrolled:	133
Out-of-State:	95 25%		

1998–99 Class Profile
LSAT Percentile: 60%
LSAT Median Score: 153
Percentage passing bar on first try: 98%

Tuition and Fees:

Resident
$5396

Average (public)
$8,772

Average (private)
$19,562

Nonresident
$11,795

Average (public)
$14,629

Average (private)
$19,562

0 5 10 15 20 25 30

Percentage receiving financial aid: 85%

ADMISSIONS

In the fall 1999 first-year class, 530 applied, 320 were accepted, and 133 enrolled. Three transfers enrolled. The median LSAT percentile of the most recent first-year class was 60; the median GPA was 3.54 on a scale of 4.0. The lowest LSAT percentile accepted was 12; the highest was 97.

Requirements
Applicants must have a bachelor's degree from an accredited institution and take the LSAT. The most important admission factors include LSAT results, GPA, and academic achievement. No specific undergraduate courses are required. Required undergraduate courses are those that develop analytical and logical reasoning and communication skills. Candidates are not interviewed.

Procedure
The application deadline for fall entry is March 1. Applicants should submit an application form, LSAT results, transcripts, and a nonrefundable application fee of $25. Two letters of recommendation are recommended. Notification of the admission decision is on a rolling basis. The latest acceptable LSAT test date for fall entry is February. The law school uses the LSDAS.

Special
The law school recruits minority and disadvantaged students through sponsoring an annual Diversity Law Day and participating in career fairs and the CLEO program. The college takes special care when evaluating applications from members of minority groups that historically have not been well represented in the legal profession. Transfer students must have one year of credit and must be in good standing at the end of a full year of study and eligible to continue at their current law school. Other requirements may apply.

Costs

Tuition and fees for the 1999-2000 academic year are $5396 for full-time in-state students and $11,795 for out-of-state students. On-campus room and board costs about $4870 annually, and books and supplies run $990.

Financial Aid

About 85% of current law students receive some form of aid. The maximum annual amount of aid from all sources combined, including scholarships, loans, and work contracts, is $21,742. Awards are based on need and merit. The required financial statement is FAFSA. The aid application deadline for fall entry is March 1. Special funds for minority or disadvantaged students consist of college funds for need-based grants and opportunity grants. First-year students are notified about their financial aid application from January to April for scholarships and grants, and June through August for loans.

About the Law School

University of Nebraska College of Law was established in 1891 and is a public institution. The campus is in a suburban area on the east campus of the University of Nebraska-Lincoln. The primary mission of the law school is to provide an excellent, affordable legal education with a balance between legal theory and professional skills in the atmosphere of a small law school. Students have access to federal, state, county, city, and local agencies, courts, correctional facilities, law firms, and legal aid organizations in the Lincoln area. As Lincoln is the state capital, the legislature, the State Supreme Court, and the Intermediate Court of Appeals are nearby. The Nebraska State Penitentiary is also located in Lincoln. There are 2 clinical programs. 1 clinic is located at the college, providing civil legal services to the poor, and the other clinic is located within the Lancaster County Attorney's Office, permitting third-year students to prosecute misdemeanor cases. The federal and state appellate courts frequently hear cases at the college. The Shermon S. Welpton, Jr. courtroom is used for actual trials as well as practical skills training. Housing for law students is available both as on-campus graduate housing and off-campus apartments and homes. All law school facilities are accessible to the physically disabled.

Calendar

The law school operates on a traditional semester basis. Courses for full-time students are offered days only and must be completed within 5 years; 3 years is normal. There is no part-time program. New full-time students are admitted in the fall. There are 2 5-week summer sessions as well as a 3-week pre-session. Transferable summer courses are offered.

Phone: 402-472-2161
Fax: 402-472-5185
E-mail: lawadm@unlinfo.unl.edu
Web: http://www.unl.edu/lawcoll

Contact

Glenda J. Pierce, Assistant Dean, 402-472-2161 for general inquiries and financial aid information.

NEBRASKA

Programs

In addition to the J.D., the law school offers the M.L.S.(Master of Legal Studies). Students may take relevant courses in other programs and apply credit toward the J.D.; a maximum of 6 nonlaw graduate hours credits may be applied. The following joint degrees may be earned: J.D./M.B.A. (Juris Doctor/Master of Business Administration), J.D./M.P.A. (Juris Doctor/Master of Professional Accountancy), J.D./M.A. (Juris Doctor/Master of Arts in psychology, economics, political science, and international affairs), J.D./M.C.R.P. (Juris Doctor/Master of Community and Regional Planning), and J.D./Ph.D (Juris Doctor/Doctor of Philosophy in psychology and education).

Required

To earn the J.D., candidates must complete 96 total credits, of which 45 are for required courses. They must maintain a minimum GPA of 4.0 (C) in the required courses. The following first-year courses are required of all students: Torts, Civil Procedure, Contracts, Legal Process, Criminal Law, Legal Research and Writing, and Property. Required upper-level courses consist of Constitutional Law I, Legal Professional Responsibility, and a seminar with substantial writing requirements. The required orientation program for first-year students is 2 days prior to the beginning of the fall semester. Students listen to speakers, tour the college, meet faculty and upper-level students, and attend a legal writing class.

Electives

The College of Law offers concentrations in corporate law, criminal law, environmental law, litigation, and tax law. In addition, students who have obtained senior standing are eligible to take either a 6-credit hour civil or criminal clinic. Second- or third-year students must take a 3-credit-hour seminar with a substantial writing requirement. A 3-credit-hour research program in a selected field under the supervision of a faculty member is available to any upper-level student. Any student may apply to have transfer credit for courses taken in a summer abroad program where the student received a grade of C or better. The Academic Resource Program offers a noncredit skills seminar for first-year students to assist in developing such skills as note taking, case briefing, and exam

taking. Participation in the program is by invitation. Minority programs include a voluntary 2-day "adjustment to law college" for which no credit is given. The most widely taken electives are Corporations, Evidence, and Wills and Trusts.

Graduation Requirements

In order to graduate, candidates must complete the upper-division writing requirement, have taken a Legal Professional Responsibility Course and Constitutional Law I, and have completed 96 credit hours.

Organizations

Students edit the *Nebraska Law Review*. Moot court competitions include the Allen Moot Court Competition for first-year students each spring, Allen Moot Court Competition for second-year students each fall and spring, and the National Moot Court competition each fall. Other competitions include Client Counseling and National Trial. Student organizations include the Black Law Students Association, Nebraska Civil Liberties Union Chapter, and Community Legal Education Project. Delta Theta Phi, ABA-Law Student Division, and Phi Alpha Delta have local chapters. Other organizations include the Multi-Cultural Legal Society.

Library

The law library contains 358,016 hard-copy volumes and 860,864 microform volume equivalents, and subscribes to 1906 serial publications. Such on-line databases and networks as LEXIS, DIALOG, WESTLAW, and and Expanded Academic Index Full Text are available to law students for research. Special library collections include a selected federal government depository and the Great Plains Tax Library. Recently, the library added a CD-ROM network. The ratio of library volumes to faculty is 12,786 to 1 and to students, 944 to 1. The ratio of seats in the library to students is 1 to 2.

Faculty

The law school has 28 full-time and 24 part-time faculty members, of whom 12 are women. According to AAUP standards for Category I institutions, faculty salaries are average. About 21% of full-time faculty have a graduate law degree in addition to the J.D.; about 4% of part-time faculty have one. The ratio of full-time students to full-time faculty in an average class is 20 to 1; in a clinic, 8 to 1. There is a chapter of the Order of the Coif; 18 faculty and 637 graduates are members.

Placement

J.D.s awarded:	126
Services available through: a separate law school placement center and the university placement center.	
Full-time job interviews:	18 employers
Summer job interviews:	32 employers
Placement by graduation:	45% of class
Placement within 9 months:	96% of class
Average starting salary:	$24,000 to $70,000
Areas of placement:	
Private practice 2-10 attorneys	21%
Private practice 11-25 attorneys	9%
Private practice 26-50 attorneys	1%
Private practice 51-100 attorneys	3%
Government	23%
Business/industry	17%
Public interest	4%
Academic	4%

Students

About 41% of the student body are women; 8%, minorities; 3%, African American; 3%, Asian American; and 2%, Hispanic. The majority of students come from the Midwest (83%). The average age of entering students is 26; age range is 21 to 52. About 43% of students enter directly from undergraduate school and 3% have a graduate degree. About 10% drop out after the first year for academic or personal reasons; 90% remain to receive a law degree.

School of Law

1117 Stanford Drive N.E.
Albuquerque, NM 87131-1431

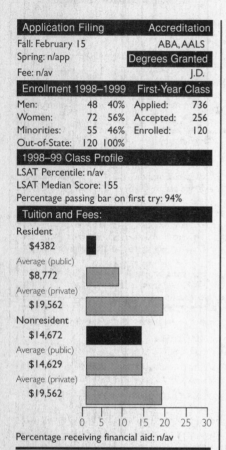

Application Filing		Accreditation
Fall: February 15		ABA, AALS
Spring: n/app		**Degrees Granted**
Fee: n/av		J.D.

Enrollment 1998–1999			First-Year Class	
Men:	48	40%	Applied:	736
Women:	72	56%	Accepted:	256
Minorities:	55	46%	Enrolled:	120
Out-of-State:	120	100%		

1998–99 Class Profile

LSAT Percentile: n/av
LSAT Median Score: 155
Percentage passing bar on first try: 94%

Tuition and Fees:

Resident
$4382

Average (public)
$8,772

Average (private)
$19,562

Nonresident
$14,672

Average (public)
$14,629

Average (private)
$19,562

0 5 10 15 20 25 30

Percentage receiving financial aid: n/av

ADMISSIONS

In the fall 1999 first-year class, 736 applied, 256 were accepted, and 120 enrolled. Five transfers enrolled. The median GPA of the most recent first-year class was 3.2.

Requirements
Applicants must have a bachelor's degree from an accredited institution and take the LSAT. No specific undergraduate courses are required. Candidates are not interviewed.

Procedure
The application deadline for fall entry is February 15. Applicants should submit an application form, a nonrefundable application fee, 1 required letter of recommendation, a personal statement, and the LSDAS report. Check with the school for current fee. Notification of the admission decision is on a rolling basis. The latest acceptable LSAT test date for fall entry is December. The law school uses the LSDAS.

Special
The law school recruits minority and disadvantaged students by means of special prelaw programs such as CLEO, which are taken into consideration by the Admission Committee. Requirements are different for out-of-state students in that very substantial preference is given to applicants who are New Mexico residents. Transfer students must have one year of credit, have attended an ABA-approved law school, and a letter from the dean of the previously attended school. The applicant must be in good academic standing.

Costs

Tuition and fees for the 1999-2000 academic year are $4382 for full-time in-state students and $14,672 for out-of-state students. There is no part-time program. Books and supplies run $824.

Financial Aid

Awards are based on need. The required financial statement is GAPSFAS or FAF-SA. Check with the school for current application deadline.

About the Law School

University of New Mexico School of Law was established in 1947 and is a public institution. The 600-acre campus is in an urban area in the city of Albuquerque. The primary mission of the law school is to offer a legal education that combines training in legal doctrine, theory, and policy with the development of practical lawyering skills. Emphasis is placed on student-faculty interaction. Students have access to federal, state, county, city, and local agencies, courts, correctional facilities, law firms, and legal aid organizations in the Albuquerque area. Facilities of special interest to law students is Bratton Hall, which, in addition to housing the classrooms, seminar rooms, and faculty, staff, and student organization offices, is home to the Natural Resources Center, the American Indian Law Center, and the Law Practice Clinic. Housing for law students consists of off-campus rental homes and apartments, where most students live, and 200 student family apartments. The university helps with finding housing.

Calendar

The law school operates on a traditional semester basis. Courses for full-time students are offered days only and must be completed within 3 years. New full-time students are admitted in the fall.

Programs

Students may take relevant courses in other programs and apply credit toward the J.D.; a maximum of 6 to 9 credits may be applied. The following joint degrees may be earned: J.D./M.B.A. (Juris Doctor/Master of Business Administration), J.D./M.P.A. (Juris Doctor/Master of Public Administration), J.D./M.A.L.A.S. (Juris Doctor/Master of Arts in Latin American Studies), and J.D./M.A., M.S., or Ph.D. (All degrees are available in various academic fields.)

Phone: 505-277-5072
Fax: 505-277-9958

Contact

Susan Mitchell, Director of Admissions and Financial Aid, 505-277-0959 for general inquiries; Susan Mitchell, Dir. of Admissions and Fin. Aid, 505-277-0959 for financial aid information.

Required

To earn the J.D., candidates must complete 86 total credits, of which 33 are for required courses. They must maintain a minimum GPA of 2.0 in the required courses. The following first-year courses are required of all students: Contracts I, Legal Reasoning, Research and Writing, Historical Introduction to Law, Property I, Legislative and Administrative Process, Criminal Law, Torts, Civil Procedure I, and Advocacy. Required upper-level courses consist of Constitutional Law, a course in Professional Responsibility, and 6 hours of clinical courses. All students must take clinical courses. The required orientation program for first-year students lasts 3 days.

Electives

The School of Law offers concentrations in Indian law, natural resources, and environmental law. In addition, the Law Practice Clinic operates as a law firm, with each student assigned to a group that is managed by a professor. Students can handle cases in areas such as family law, criminal law, and tax and business. The District Attorney Program is directed by a professor who is appointed as an assistant district attorney. Eight students prosecute criminal misdemeanor cases, with considerable opportunity for court experience. Judicial and law office externships are available. Individual research, worth 1, 2, or 3 credits, is available under the direction of faculty. There is also an Advanced Legal Research elective. Work-study programs are available. Summer abroad programs are available through the Guanajuato Summer Law Institute. The Natural Resource Center develops programs that enable students to understand resource problems more effectively than if they were handled strictly as legal problems. Summer-abroad options are available through the Guanajuato Summer Law Institute. Tutorials in each substantive course are available in the spring semester to first-year students. Special prelaw programs for minority and disadvantaged applicants provide information about their ability to succeed in law school. The school has a summer prelaw program and is also a member of the Southwest CLEO consortium. The school offers an extensive Indian law curriculum. The school also has a number of special centers, or institutes: the American Indian Law Center, the International Transboundary Resource Center, the Institute of Public Law, the Center for Health Law and Ethics, the center for Wildlife Law, and the Center for the Study and Resolution of Disputes.

Graduation Requirements

In order to graduate, candidates must have a GPA of 2.0, completed the upper-division writing requirement, and at least 3 full academic years in residence. Either the Ethics or the Role of the Lawyer in Society course must be passed.

Organizations

The primary law review is the *New Mexico Law Review*, which is published 3 times a year. Students also edit the *Natural Resources Journal*. The student newspaper is the *Bratton Hall Bulletin*. Moot court teams attend the Mock Trial Competition, Helene Simson Memorial Client Counseling Competition, and Frederick Douglas's Moot Court Competition. Law student organizations include the Student Bar Association, Environmental Law Society, and International Law Students Association. There are campus chapters of Phi Alpha Delta, Phi Delta Phi, and Association of Trial Lawyers of America/New Mexico.

Library

The law library contains 300,000 hardcopy volumes. Such on-line databases and networks as LEXIS, WESTLAW, and CD-ROM are available to law students for research. Special library collections include an extensive collection of New Mexico appellate briefs and records. The library is also developing collections in American Indian law, Mexican and Latin American law, and community landgrant law. The ratio of seats in the library to students is 1 to 1.

Placement

J.D.s awarded:	96
Services available through: A separate law school placement center.	
Services: autumn job fair	
Full-time job interviews:	11 employers
Summer job interviews:	15 employers
Placement by graduation:	n/av
Placement within 9 months:	93% of class
Average starting salary:	$25,000 to $150,000
Areas of placement:	
Private practice 2-10 attorneys	28%
Private practice 11-25 attorneys	8%
Private practice 26-50 attorneys	3%
Private practice 51-100 attorneys	3%
Government	26%
Judicial clerkships	16%
Unknown	9%
Business/industry	6%
Public interest	1%

Faculty

The law school has 32 full-time and 27 part-time faculty members. According to AAUP standards for Category I institutions, faculty salaries are below average. About 22% of full-time faculty have a graduate law degree in addition to the J.D. The ratio of full-time students to full-time faculty in an average class is 11 to 1. There is a chapter of the Order of the Coif.

Students

About 56% of the student body are women; 46%, minorities; 4%, African American; 4%, Asian American; 30%, Hispanic; and 8%, Native American. The average age of entering students is 25. About 31% of students enter directly from undergraduate school.

School of Law

Campus Box 3380,
101 Van Hecke-Wettach Hall
Chapel Hill, NC 27599-3380

Application Filing		Accreditation
Fall: February 1		ABA, AALS
Spring: n/app		**Degrees Granted**
Fee: n/av		J.D.

Enrollment 1998–1999			First-Year Class	
Men:	352	52%	Applied:	2481
Women:	331	49%	Accepted:	621
Minorities:	143	21%	Enrolled:	237
Out-of-State:	171	25%		

1998–99 Class Profile

LSAT Percentile: n/av
LSAT Median Score: 160
Percentage passing bar on first try: 89%

Tuition and Fees:

Resident
$3602

Average (public)
$8,772

Average (private)
$19,562

Nonresident
$15,702

Average (public)
$14,629

Average (private)
$19,562

0 5 10 15 20 25 30

Percentage receiving financial aid: 80%

ADMISSIONS

In the fall 1999 first-year class, 2481 applied, 621 were accepted, and 237 enrolled. One transfer enrolled. The median GPA of the most recent first-year class was 3.6. The lowest LSAT percentile accepted was 24; the highest was 99.

Requirements

Applicants must have a bachelor's degree from an accredited institution and take the LSAT. The most important admission factors include LSAT results, GPA, and academic achievement. No specific undergraduate courses are required. Required undergraduate courses are economics, philosophy, accounting, and logic. Candidates are not interviewed.

Procedure

The application deadline for fall entry is February 1. Applicants should submit an application form, LSAT results, transcripts, a nonrefundable application fee, and 2 letters of recommendation. Check with the school for current fee. Notification of the admission decision is on a rolling basis from January. The latest acceptable LSAT test date for fall entry is February. The law school uses the LSDAS.

Special

The law school recruits minority and disadvantaged students by means of the Candidate Referral Service and a special open house for minority students. Transfer students must have one year of credit, have attended an ABA-approved law school, and have a superior academic performance, be in good academic standing, have been originally admissible.

Costs

Tuition and fees for the 1999-2000 academic year are $3602 for full-time in-state students and $15,702 for out-of-state students. There is no part-time program. On-campus room and board, books and supplies costs about $11,284 annually.

Financial Aid

In a recent year, about 80% of current law students received some form of aid. Awards are based on need. The required financial statement is FAFSA. Check with the school for current application deadline. Special funds for minority or disadvantaged students consist of the Minority Presence Grant Program. First-year students are notified about their financial aid application in June.

About the Law School

University of North Carolina at Chapel Hill School of Law was established in 1845 and is a public institution. The 700-acre campus is in a small town 23 miles northwest of Raleigh. The primary mission of the law school is to educate future practitioners and leaders of the bench and bar. Students have access to federal, state, county, city, and local agencies, courts, correctional facilities, law firms, and legal aid organizations in the Chapel Hill area. Housing for law students is available in the residence hall for graduate and professional students located near the law school; there are also many apartments in the area.

Calendar

The law school operates on a traditional semester basis. Courses for full-time students are offered days only and must be completed within 3 years. There is no part-time program. New full-time students are admitted in the fall. There is a 6-week summer session.

Programs

Students may take relevant courses in other programs and apply credit toward the J.D.; a maximum of 3 credits may be applied. The following joint degrees may be earned: J.D./M.B.A. (Juris Doctor/Master of Business Administration), J.D./M.P.H. (Juris Doctor/Master of Public Health), J.D./M.R.P. (Juris Doctor/Master of Regional Planning), J.D./M.P.A. (Juris Doctor/Master of Public Administrator), J.D./M.P.P.S. (Juris Doctor/Master of Public Policy Sciences), and J.D./M.S.W. (Juris Doctor/Master of Social Work).

Phone: 919-962-5109
Fax: 919-843-7939
E-mail: law_admission@unc.edu
Web: http://www.law.unc.edu

Contact

Winston Crisp, Associate Dean, 919-962-5109 for general inquiries; Sue Burdick, Financial Aid Officer, 919-962-8396 for financial aid information.

NORTH CAROLINA

Required

To earn the J.D., candidates must complete 86 total credits, of which 33 are for required courses. They must maintain a minimum GPA of 1.7 in the required courses. The following first-year courses are required of all students: Civil Procedure, Contracts, Property, Torts, Criminal Law, and Research and Writing. Required upper-level courses consist of Professional Responsibility. The required orientation program for first-year students is 2 1/2 days and includes an introduction to case study method and briefing, and social activities.

Electives

The School of Law offers concentrations in corporate law, criminal law, environmental law, family law, international law, juvenile law, labor law, litigation, securities law, and tax law. In addition, third-year students may participate in Trial Advocacy to gain experience in pretrial and trial settings. Some 24 students participate in the Criminal Law Clinic, representing defendants and convicted prisoners under faculty supervision. The Civil Law Clinic is also open to some 24 students. There are approximately 40 seminars offered to upper-level students for 3 credit hours; preference is given to third-year students, then second-year students. Research may be undertaken for no more than 3 credit hours and only with faculty permission. Students may study in Lyon, France; Nijmegen, The Netherlands; Glasgow, Scotland; Mexico City, Mexico; or Manchester, England during the spring semester of the second or third year for 12 credit hours. Courses focus on international law. The LEAP program is a first-year academic support program for a select group of entering students.

Graduation Requirements

In order to graduate, candidates must have a GPA of 1.7, completed the upper-division writing requirement, have completed the second-year writing class and the seminar requirement in the third year.

Organizations

Students edit the *North Carolina Law Review*, *North Carolina Journal of International Law and Commercial Regulation*, the student newspaper *Mere Dictum*, and *The Banking Institute*. The Holderness Moot Court Bench consists of the negotiations team, client counseling team, invitational team, national team, constitutional team, and international team, and sponsors the annual Craven Moot Court competition. Other competitions include American Jurisprudence Award, Block Improvement, Burkan Memorial, Millard S. Breckenridge, Judge Heriot Clarkson, Chief Justice Walter Clark, Albert Coates, Investors Title Insurance, William T. Jayner, James William Morrow III, and U.S. Law Week. Law student organizations include Order of the Barristers, Environmental Law Project, and the Federalist Society.

Library

The law library contains 447,320 hardcopy volumes and 11,302 microform volume equivalents, and subscribes to 5926 serial publications. Such on-line databases and networks as LEXIS and WESTLAW are available to law students for research. Special library collections include Anglo-American legal materials.

Faculty

The law school has 44 full-time and 35 part-time faculty members, of whom 29 are women. According to AAUP standards for Category I institutions, faculty salaries are well above average. The ratio of full-time students to full-time faculty in an average class is 20 to 1. There is a chapter of the Order of the Coif.

Students

About 49% of the student body are women; 21%, minorities; 13%, African American; 4%, Asian American; 2%, Hispanic; and 1%, Native American. The majority of students come from North Carolina (75%). The average age of entering students is 23; age range is 21 to 53. About 12% of students have a graduate degree. About 1% drop out after the first year for academic or personal reasons; 95% remain to receive a law degree.

Placement

J.D.s awarded:	233
Services available through: A separate law school placement center and the university placement center.	
Services:	
Special features: associate director for public service employment opportunities	
Full-time job interviews:	117 employers
Summer job interviews:	n/av
Placement by graduation:	73% of class
Placement within 9 months:	98% of class
Average starting salary:	$23,000 to $100,000
Areas of placement:	
Private practice 2-10 attorneys	15%
Private practice 11-25 attorneys	4%
Private practice 26-50 attorneys	4%
Private practice 51-100 attorneys	4%
Private practice 100+ attorneys	22%
Unknown	12%
Government	11%
Business/industry	10%
Judicial clerkships	10%
Public interest	6%
Military	1%

UNIVERSITY OF NORTH DAKOTA

School of Law

Box 9003
Grand Forks, ND 58202

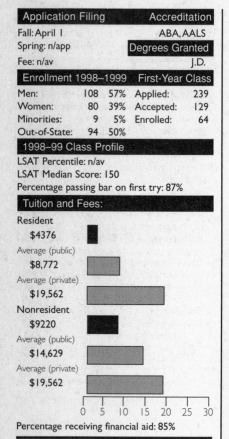

Application Filing		Accreditation
Fall: April 1		ABA, AALS
Spring: n/app		**Degrees Granted**
Fee: n/av		J.D.

Enrollment 1998–1999			First-Year Class	
Men:	108	57%	Applied:	239
Women:	80	39%	Accepted:	129
Minorities:	9	5%	Enrolled:	64
Out-of-State:	94	50%		

1998–99 Class Profile
LSAT Percentile: n/av
LSAT Median Score: 150
Percentage passing bar on first try: 87%

Tuition and Fees:

Resident
$4376

Average (public)
$8,772

Average (private)
$19,562

Nonresident
$9220

Average (public)
$14,629

Average (private)
$19,562

0   5   10   15   20   25   30

Percentage receiving financial aid: 85%

ADMISSIONS

In the fall 1999 first-year class, 239 applied, 129 were accepted, and 64 enrolled. Two transfers enrolled. The median GPA of the most recent first-year class was 3.3. The lowest LSAT percentile accepted was 11; the highest was 95.

Requirements

Applicants must have a bachelor's degree from an accredited institution and take the LSAT. The most important admission factors include academic achievement, GPA, and LSAT results. No specific undergraduate courses are required. Candidates are not interviewed.

Procedure

The application deadline for fall entry is April 1. Applicants should submit an application form and a non-refundable fee. Check with the school for current fee. Notification of the admission decision is on a rolling basis. The latest acceptable LSAT test date for fall entry is that which ensures the score is received by the application deadline. The law school uses the LSDAS.

Special

The law school recruits minority and disadvantaged students as part of the school's philosophy of promoting diversity in the student body. Requirements are different for out-of-state students in that preference is given to qualified state residents, depending on the number of applications received. Transfer students must have a minimum GPA of 2.0 and have attended an ABA-approved law school. Generally, no more than 2 semesters of course work are eligible for transfer.

Costs

Tuition and fees for the 1999-2000 academic year are $4376 for full-time in-state students and $9220 for out-of-state students. On-campus room and board costs about $7200 annually; and books and supplies run $800.

Financial Aid

In a recent year, about 85% of current law students received some form of aid. The average annual amount of aid from all sources combined, including scholarships, loans, and work contracts, was $9266; maximum, $14,475. Awards are based on need and merit. The required financial statement is FAFSA. Check with the school for current deadline. Special funds for minority or disadvantaged students include Cultural Diversity Tuition Waivers. First-year students are notified about their financial aid application at the time of acceptance.

About the Law School

University of North Dakota School of Law was established in 1899 and is a public institution. The campus is in a small town 320 miles northwest of Minneapolis-St. Paul, Minnesota. The primary mission of the law school is to provide education and training in legal analysis and the application of legal principles leading to professional competence. Students have access to federal, state, county, city, and local agencies, courts, correctional facilities, law firms, and legal aid organizations in the Grand Forks area. Housing for law students is in residence halls, single-student apartments, family housing apartments, and a trailer court, all adjacent to the campus. About 95% of the law school facilities are accessible to the physically disabled.

Calendar

The law school operates on a traditional semester basis. Courses for full-time students are offered days only and must be completed within 5 years. There is no part-time program. New full-time students are admitted in the fall. There is a 6- week summer session. Transferable summer courses are offered.

Programs

Students may take relevant courses in other programs and apply credit toward the J.D.; a maximum of 6 credits may be applied. The following joint degrees may be earned: J.D/M.P.A. (Juris Doctor/Master of Public Administration).

Phone: 701-777-2104
Fax: 701-777-2217
E-mail: linda.kohoutek@thor.law.und.nodak.edu
Web: http://www.law.und.nodak.edu

Contact

Admissions and Records Associate, 701-777-2260 for general inquiries; Mark Bricksom, Student Financial Aid Office, 701-777-2269 for financial aid information.

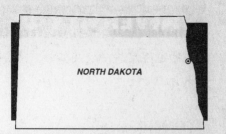

NORTH DAKOTA

Required

To earn the J.D., candidates must complete 90 total credits, of which 34 are for required courses. They must maintain a minimum GPA of 2.0 in the required courses. The following first-year courses are required of all students: Brief Writing and Appellate Advocacy, Civil Procedure, Contracts I and II, Criminal Law, Legal Process, Property I and II, Torts I and II, and Constitutional Law I and II. Required upper-level courses consist of Professional Responsibility. The required orientation program for first-year students lasts 1 week.

Electives

Clinics are conducted under the supervision of the Director of Legal Aid, and other clinical instructors, including a family law clinic and a Native American law project. Clinical Education I, II, III, and IV are also available. Internships are available with the North Dakota District Court, North Dakota Legislative Assembly, Grand Forks County States Attorney, and the Office of the Staff Judge Advocate at the Grand Forks Air Force Base. Various supervised research projects are available through the Special Projects Committee. Also, Central Legal Research employs second- and third-year students to work on current legal research questions. The Rocky Mountain Mineral Law Foundation, through grants, scholarships, seminars, and publications, promotes research in natural resources law. The Fode Lecture is a special lecture series. Students may receive credit for summer law study at the University of Oslo, Norway. The Canadian-American Law Institute encourages interchange among law students and faculty from North Dakota and several Canadian provinces. The most widely taken electives are bar courses, skills courses, and trial advocacy.

Graduation Requirements

In order to graduate, candidates must have a GPA of 2.0, completed the upper-division writing requirement, have completed Legal Process, Brief Writing, and Professional Responsibility, 2 significant writing projects, and have fulfilled the residency requirements of the last 4 semesters of study at the school.

Organizations

Students edit the *North Dakota Law Review* and the student newspaper, *Rhadamanthus*. The North Dakota Agricultural Law Institute serves the state's agricultural industry by publishing bulletins related to agriculture. Members of the Moot Court Association participate in an appellate moot court intraschool competition. During the past few years, members have also participated in the National Moot Court Competition, the Tulane Sports Law Competition, and various regional competitions. Student organizations include the Student Bar Association, Native American Law Students Association, Christian Law Students Society, the Federalist Society, Student Trial Lawyers Association, and the Law Women's Caucus. There are campus chapters of Phi Alpha Delta, Phi Delta Phi, and Order of the Coif.

Library

The law library contains 251,320 hardcopy volumes and 129,554 microform volume equivalents, and subscribes to 2710 serial publications. Such on-line databases and networks as LEXIS, DIALOG, WESTLAW, and OCLC, ODIN, Internet, CALI, Legal-Trac are available to law students for research. Special library collections include a good Canadian collection, partial U.S. government documents depository, and a Norwegian law collection. Recently, the library added a computer laboratory and walk-up computer information kiosks. The ratio of library volumes to faculty is 10,927 to 1 and to students, 1315 to 1. The ratio of seats in the library to students is 1 to 1.

Faculty

The law school has 14 full-time and 9 part-time faculty members, of whom 8 are women. About 29% of full-time faculty have a graduate law degree in addition to the J.D. There is a chapter of the Order of the Coif.

Students

About 39% of the student body are women; 5%, minorities; 1%, African American; 1%, Asian American; 1%, Hispanic; and 3%, Native American. The majority of students come from North Dakota (50%). The average age of entering students is 26; age range is 21 to 48. About 6% drop out after the first year for academic or personal reasons.

Placement

J.D.s awarded:	66
Services available through:	A separate law school placement center.
Services: job board, on which full- and part-time positions are listed	
Special features: a job-seeking resource and reference library, files on individual firms or organizations, and files on job bulletins from more than 80 other law schools around the nation. Internet, legal, and job-seeking sites are bookmarked from the school's web page.	
Full-time job interviews:	6 employers
Summer job interviews:	10 employers
Placement by graduation:	60% of class
Placement within 9 months:	100% of class
Average starting salary:	$19,000 to $70,000
Areas of placement:	
Private practice 2-10 attorneys	32%
Private practice 11-25 attorneys	3%
Private practice 26-50 attorneys	2%
Judicial clerkships	35%
Business/industry	14%
Government	10%
Military	4%

UNIVERSITY OF NOTRE DAME

Notre Dame Law School

P.O. Box 959
Notre Dame, IN 46556-0959

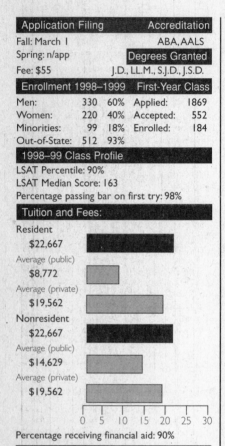

Application Filing		Accreditation
Fall: March 1		ABA, AALS
Spring: n/app		**Degrees Granted**
Fee: $55		J.D., LL.M., S.J.D., J.S.D.

Enrollment 1998–1999			First-Year Class	
Men:	330	60%	Applied:	1869
Women:	220	40%	Accepted:	552
Minorities:	99	18%	Enrolled:	184
Out-of-State:	512	93%		

1998–99 Class Profile

LSAT Percentile: 90%
LSAT Median Score: 163
Percentage passing bar on first try: 98%

Tuition and Fees:

Resident
$22,667

Average (public)
$8,772

Average (private)
$19,562

Nonresident
$22,667

Average (public)
$14,629

Average (private)
$19,562

0   5   10   15   20   25   30

Percentage receiving financial aid: 90%

ADMISSIONS

In the fall 1999 first-year class, 1869 applied, 552 were accepted, and 184 enrolled. Seven transfers enrolled. The median LSAT percentile of the most recent first-year class was 90; the median GPA was 3.4 on a scale of 4.0. The lowest LSAT percentile accepted was 42; the highest was 98.

Requirements
Applicants must have a bachelor's degree from an accredited institution and take the LSAT. The most important admission factors include academic achievement, college extracurricular activities, and LSAT results. No specific undergraduate courses are required. Candidates are not interviewed.

Procedure
The application deadline for fall entry is March 1. Applicants should submit an application form, LSAT results, transcripts, a nonrefundable application fee of $55, 2 letters of recommendation, and a personal statement. Notification of the admissions decision is on a rolling basis. The law school uses the LSDAS.

Special
The law school recruits minority and disadvantaged students by considering as positive factors an applicant's ethnic or minority background and economic disadvantage. Transfer students must have one year of credit and have attended an ABA-approved law school.

Costs

Tuition and fees for the 1999-2000 academic year are $22,667 for all students. On-campus room and board costs about $4800 annually; and books and supplies run $925.

Financial Aid

About 90% of current law students receive some form of aid. Awards are based on need and merit, with 30% of first year students receiving scholarships ranging from $5000 to $22,630; and 90% receiving loans with an average financial package ranging up to $18,500. Although there is no work- study for first-year students, a limited number of research assistantships are available to qualified upper-level students. The required financial statement is the FAF-SA. The aid application deadline for fall entry is March 1. Special funds for minority or disadvantaged students consist of grants. First-year students are notified about their financial aid application as soon as possible after acceptance and after financial documents are received.

About the Law School

University of Notre Dame, Notre Dame Law School was established in 1869 and is a private institution. The 1250-acre campus is in a small town just north of South Bend. The primary mission of the law school is to provide capable and compassionate lawyers for practice in the profession, and to play a leadership role in legal education and in the development of the law. Students have access to federal, state, county, city, and local agencies, courts, correctional facilities, law firms, and legal aid organizations in the Notre Dame area, as well as the courts and legal aid clinics of South Bend, Chicago, and Michigan. Housing for law students is available as on-campus apartments for single students. There are also apartments for married students and townhouses for graduate and law students. The university assists students in finding off-campus housing. About 70% of the law school facilities are accessible to the physically disabled.

Calendar

The law school operates on a traditional semester basis. Courses for full-time students are offered days only and must be completed within 3 years. There is no part-time program. New students are admitted in the fall. There is a 6- week summer session. Transferable summer courses are offered.

Programs

In addition to the J.D., the law school offers the LL.M., and S.J.D. The J.S.D. is offered to those studying international human rights. Students may take relevant courses in other programs and apply credit toward the J.D.; a maximum of 9 credits may be applied. The following joint degrees may be earned: J.B./M.B.A. (Juris Doctor/Master of Business Administration), J.D./M.A. (Juris Doctor/Master of Arts in English and law, and peace studies), and J.D./M.S. (Juris Doctor/Master of Science in engineering).

Phone: 219-631-6626
Fax: 219-631-3980
E-mail: law.bulletin.1@nd.edu
Web: http://www.law.nd.edu

Contact

Rev. James E. McDonald, 219-631-6626 for general inquiries; Financial Aid Office, 219-631-6626 for financial aid information.

INDIANA

Required

To earn the J.D., candidates must complete 90 total credits, of which 52 are for required courses. They must maintain a minimum GPA of 2.0 in the required courses. The following first-year courses are required of all students: Torts I and II, Contracts I and II, Procedure I and II, Criminal Law or Criminal Procedure, Property I, Legal Research I and II-Moot Court, Legal Writing, and Introduction to Law and Ethics. Required upper-level courses consist of Constitutional Law, Business Associates, Federal Taxation, Jurisprudence, and Ethics II. The required orientation program for first-year students is 2 days.

Electives

The Notre Dame Law School offers concentrations in corporate law, criminal law, international law, and litigation. In addition, clinical training is avaiable in Indiana and Michigan through Legal Aid, Appellate Advocacy, Criminal Practice, Public Interest Practice, and Trial Advocacy programs. Special seminars are offered in criminal law, trial advocacy, business law, and general law. Internships are available through the Thomas C. White Center on Law and Government and the Public Defender and Prosecutor's office. Students may carry out research projects through the Center for Civil and Human Rights and the White Center on Law and Government. A study-abroad program allows students to take their second year or a summer session at the law school's London campus. Tutorial programs are tailored to meet the needs of individual students. Diversity groups are actively involved in the law school. The most widely taken electives are Conflicts of Laws, Trial Advocacy, and Securities Regulation.

Graduation Requirements

In order to graduate, candidates must have a GPA of 2.0.

Organizations

Students edit the *Notre Dame Law Review*, published 5 times a year. Other publications are the *American Journal of Jurisprudence, the Journal of Legislation, the Journal of College and University Law,* and the *Journal of Law, Ethics, and Public Policy.* Moot court competitions include the National Moot Court and the Jessup International Moot Court competitions. Other competitions include the National Trial Competition and Client Counseling. Law student organizations include Phi Alpha Delta. There are local chapters of the Black Law Students Association, Hispanic Law Students Association, Asian Law Students Association, and Native American Law Students Association. Other organizations include Federalist Society, Irish Law Society, and Women's Law Forum.

Library

The law library contains 501,071 hardcopy volumes and 1,340,615 microform volume equivalents, and subscribes to 5055 serial publications. Such on-line databases and networks as LEXIS, DIALOG, and WESTLAW are available to law students for research. Special library collections include the U.S. Civil Rights Commission archived records. There is also an auxiliary library in London. Recently, the library added networking. The ratio of library volumes to faculty is 18,558 to 1 and to students, 861 to 1. The ratio of seats in the library to students is 1 to 1.

Faculty

The law school has 27 full-time and 33 part-time faculty members, of whom 13 are women. According to AAUP standards for Category I institutions, faculty salaries are well above average. About 4% of full-time faculty have a graduate law degree in addition to the J.D. The ratio of full-time students to full-time faculty in an average class is 20 to 1; in a clinic, 4 to 1. The law school has a regular program of bringing visiting professors and other distinguished lecturers and visitors to campus.

Placement

J.D.s awarded:	168
Services available through: separate law school placement center	
Services: conducting seminars and surveys, maintaining a library, and networking through a national alumni network	
Full-time job interviews:	180 employers
Summer job interviews:	180 employers
Placement by graduation:	76% of class
Placement within 9 months:	96% of class
Average starting salary:	$60,000
Areas of placement:	
Private practice 2-10 attorneys	6%
Private practice 11-25 attorneys	6%
Private practice 26-50 attorneys	3%
Private practice 51-100 attorneys	6%
Private practice 101-250 attorneys	16%
Judicial clerkships	11%
Business/industry	9%
Government	6%
Academic	3%
Military	3%
Public interest	3%

Students

About 40% of the student body are women; 18%, minorities; 3%, African American; 7%, Asian American; 5%, Hispanic; and 2%, Native American. The majority of students come from the Midwest (43%). The average age of entering students is 23; age range is 22 to 45. About 67% of students enter directly from undergraduate school, 15% have a graduate degree, and 35% have worked full-time prior to entering law school. About 1% drop out after the first year for academic or personal reasons; 99% remain to receive a law degree.

College of Law

300 Timberdell Road
Norman, OK 73019

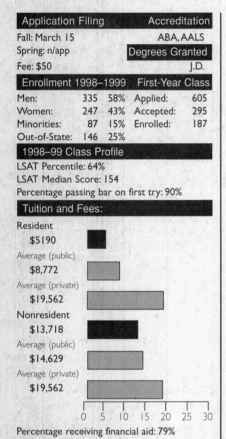

Application Filing		Accreditation
Fall: March 15		ABA, AALS
Spring: n/app		**Degrees Granted**
Fee: $50		J.D.

Enrollment 1998–1999		First-Year Class	
Men:	335 58%	Applied:	605
Women:	247 43%	Accepted:	295
Minorities:	87 15%	Enrolled:	187
Out-of-State:	146 25%		

1998–99 Class Profile
LSAT Percentile: 64%
LSAT Median Score: 154
Percentage passing bar on first try: 90%

Tuition and Fees:

Resident
$5190

Average (public)
$8,772

Average (private)
$19,562

Nonresident
$13,718

Average (public)
$14,629

Average (private)
$19,562

0   5   10   15   20   25   30

Percentage receiving financial aid: 79%

ADMISSIONS

In the fall 1999 first-year class, 605 applied, 295 were accepted, and 187 enrolled. Thirteen transfers enrolled. The median LSAT percentile of the most recent first-year class was 64; the median GPA was 3.4 on a scale of 4.0. The lowest LSAT percentile accepted was 64; the highest was 75.

Requirements
Applicants must have a bachelor's degree from an accredited institution and take the LSAT. The most important admission factors include academic achievement, college attended, and GPA. No specific undergraduate courses are required. Candidates are not interviewed.

Procedure
The application deadline for fall entry is March 15. Applicants should submit an application form, LSAT results, transcripts, and a nonrefundable application fee of $50. Notification of the admission decision is by May 15. The latest acceptable LSAT test date for fall entry is February. The law school uses the LSDAS.

Special
The law school recruits minority and disadvantaged students through prelaw fairs and counseling days at undergraduate institutions and through personal correspondence and contacts. Requirements are different for out-of-state students in that a state Regents' mandate limits nonresident admissions to 15%. Further, the college is prohibited from admitting a nonresident whose scores are lower than those of a resident to whom we have denied admission. Transfer students must have one year of credit and have attended an ABA-approved law school.

Costs

Tuition and fees for the 1999-2000 academic year are $5190 for in-state students and $13,718 for out-of-state students. On-campus room and board costs about $5911 annually; and books and supplies run $846.

Financial Aid

About 79% of current law students receive some form of aid. The average annual amount of aid from all sources combined, including scholarships, loans, and work contracts, is $15,641; maximum, $18,500. Awards are based on need. The required financial statement is the FAFSA. The aid application deadline for fall entry is March 1. Special funds for minority or disadvantaged students include State Regents grants of about $4000 per year for those with outstanding undergraduate academic records. First-year students are notified about their financial aid application when the file is completed, which is generally during the summer.

About the Law School

University of Oklahoma College of Law was established in 1909 and is a public institution. The campus is in a small town 20 miles south of Oklahoma City. The primary mission of the law school is to prepare qualified students to practice law or to use the law in their disciplines, to enable law graduates to remain qualified; and to promote further understanding of law and legal institutions. Students have access to federal, state, county, city, and local agencies, courts, correctional facilities, law firms, and legal aid organizations in the Norman area. Housing for law students is in dormitories and nearby off-campus apartments. About 90% of the law school facilities are accessible to the physically disabled.

Calendar

The law school operates on a traditional semester basis. Courses for full-time students are offered days only and must be completed within 5 years. There is no part-time program. New students are admitted in the fall. There is an 8-week summer session.

Programs

Students may take relevant courses in other programs and apply credit toward the J.D.; a maximum of 6 credits may be applied. The following joint degrees may be earned: J.D./M.B.A. (Juris Doctor/ Master of Business Administration), J.D./M.P.H. (Juris Doctor/Master of Public Health), and J.D./M.S. (Juris Doctor/Master of Science in health administration, environmental science, and occupational health).

Phone: 405-325-4726
888-298-0891
Fax: 405-325-0502
E-mail: kmadden@ou.edu
Web: www.law.ou.edu

Contact
Ms. Kathie Madden, Admissions Counselor, 405-325-4728 for general inquiries; 405-325-4521, for financial aid information.

OKLAHOMA

Required

To earn the J.D., candidates must complete 90 total credits, of which 42 are for required courses. They must maintain a minimum GPA of 4 on a scale of 12 in the required courses. The following first-year courses are required of all students: Contracts I; Contracts II, Property, Civil Procedure I, Civil Procedure II, Torts I, Torts II, Legal Research & Writing I, Legal Research and Writing II, Constitutional Law, and Criminal Law. Required upper-level courses consist of Professional Responsibility, Evidence, graduation writing requirement, and Criminal Procedure I. No clinical courses are required, but many students participate in a strong clinical program. The required orientation program for first-year students is a 1-day orientation that provides a basic introduction to legal study and the OU Law Center.

Electives

The College of Law offers concentrations in corporate law, criminal law, environmental law, family law, international law, labor law, litigation, media law, securities law, sports law, tax law, and torts and insurance. In addition, clinical programs include the Legal Aid Clinic (civil) and the Criminal Defense Clinic (criminal) for 3 hours per semester with no limit. The Judicial Clinic (employment with a judge) is limited to 3 hours. All students who have completed their first year of law studies may take seminars. Each semester several are offered for 2 credit hours each. There is no limit, though students generally take no more than 2 or 3. Environmental internships are available for 10 credit hours. Legal externships are available for 2 credit hours. Second- and third-year students may be research assistants for law professors for no credit while receiving an hourly wage. All students may attend enrichment programs for no credit. A summer program is available at Brasenose College, Oxford University, Oxford, England. In addition, students have the opportunity to study abroad for a semester or full academic year after they have completed at least the first year of law studies and are in good academic standing. Students can create individual study programs at foreign law schools, and if approved by the College of Law and the American Bar Association, they can receive up to 30 hours of credit. Such study programs are particularly relevant to students who have an interest in international law or

international business. Tutorial programs are available for students in the summer. Admission by Performance Groups (APG) is a special admission program for disadvantaged students. Student tutors receive 1 hour credit. Also, teaching assistantships are available for second- and third-year students in the first-year legal writing program. Assistants receive 1 credit hour per semester up to 4 semesters and also receive a stipend. A voluntary remedial writing class for entering first-year students is available for those whose LSAT writing samples are substandard. Minority law student organizations host programs for undergraduates throughout the academic year. The most widely taken electives are Administrative Law, Commercial Law, and Tax Law.

Graduation Requirements

In order to graduate, candidates must have a GPA of 4.0 on a scale of 12, and have completed the upper-division writing requirement.

Organizations
Students edit the *Oklahoma Law Review* and the *American Indian Law Review*. Moot court competitions include the National Moot Court, ABA Client Counseling, and ATLA Student Trial. Other competitions include first-year competitions within the law school. Law student organizations include the Student Bar Association, Board of Advocates, and Association of Public Interest Lawyers. Local chapters of national associations include Phi Alpha Delta, Phi Delta Phi, and ABA/Law Student Division.

Library
The law library contains 302,738 hardcopy volumes and 80,603 microform volume equivalents, and subscribes to 3977 serial publications. Such on-line databases and networks as LEXIS, DIALOG, WESTLAW, OCLC, First Search, and Legal-Trac are available to law students for research. Special library collections include the Native Peoples Collection and GPO depository. Recently, the library replaced all student computers, added 2 laser printers and a variety of software, and provided access to the Internet. The ratio of library volumes to faculty is 7123 to 1 and to students, 362 to 1. The ratio of seats in the library to students is 1 to 2.

Placement

J.D.s awarded:	161
Services available through: a separate law school placement center	
Special features: personal student counseling and on-campus seminars	
Full-time job interviews:	12 employers
Summer job interviews:	38 employers
Placement by graduation:	63% of class
Placement within 9 months:	87% of class
Average starting salary:	$20,000 to $80,000
Areas of placement:	
Private practice 2-10 attorneys	25%
Private practice 11-25 attorneys	24%
Private practice 26-50 attorneys	6%
Private practice 51-100 attorneys	6%
Government	19%
Business/industry	9%
Judicial clerkships	4%
Military	3%
Academic	3%
Public interest	1%

Faculty
The law school has 33 full-time and 20 part-time faculty members, of whom 8 are women. According to AAUP standards for Category I institutions, faculty salaries are below average. About 50% of full-time faculty have a graduate law degree in addition to the J.D. The ratio of full-time students to full-time faculty in an average class is 40 to 1; in a clinic, 15 to 1. The law school has a regular program of bringing visiting professors and other distinguished lecturers and visitors to campus. There is a chapter of the Order of the Coif; 37 faculty and 856 graduates are members.

Students
About 43% of the student body are women; 15%, minorities; 3%, African American; 3%, Asian American; 3%, Hispanic; and 7%, Native American. The majority of students come from Oklahoma (75%). The average age of entering students is 24; age range is 20 to 54. About 80% of students enter directly from undergraduate school. About 4% drop out after the first year for academic or personal reasons; 95% remain to receive a law degree.

School of Law, William W. Knight Law Center

1515 Agate Street
Eugene, OR 97403-1221

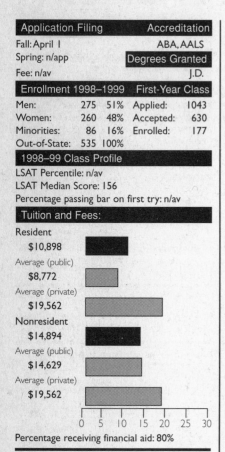

Application Filing	Accreditation
Fall: April 1	ABA, AALS
Spring: n/app	**Degrees Granted**
Fee: n/av	J.D.

Enrollment 1998–1999		First-Year Class	
Men:	275 51%	Applied:	1043
Women:	260 48%	Accepted:	630
Minorities:	86 16%	Enrolled:	177
Out-of-State:	535 100%		

1998–99 Class Profile

LSAT Percentile: n/av
LSAT Median Score: 156
Percentage passing bar on first try: n/av

Tuition and Fees:

Resident
$10,898
Average (public)
$8,772
Average (private)
$19,562
Nonresident
$14,894
Average (public)
$14,629
Average (private)
$19,562

0 5 10 15 20 25 30

Percentage receiving financial aid: 80%

ADMISSIONS

Information in the above capsule is approximate. In the fall 1999 first-year class, 1043 applied, 630 were accepted, and 177 enrolled. The median GPA of the most recent first-year class was 3.5. The lowest LSAT percentile accepted was 17; the highest was 96.

Requirements
Applicants must have a bachelor's degree from an accredited institution and take the LSAT. The most important admission factors include GPA, LSAT results, and academic achievement. No specific undergraduate courses are required. Candidates are not interviewed.

Procedure
The application deadline for fall entry is April 1. Applicants should submit an application form and a personal statement and resume. Check with the school for the current fee. Notification of the admissions decision is January through May. The latest acceptable LSAT test date for fall entry is February. The law school uses the LSDAS.

Special
The law school recruits minority and disadvantaged students by attending law school fairs throughout the country and contacting prospective minori[ty applicants who attend; having students and alumni contact admitted minorities; inviting qualified minorities and disadvantaged students to apply to the law school through the LSAS's Candidate Referral Service (CRS); and by eliciting recruitment support from current students of color. Transfer students must have one year of credit and have attended an ABA-approved law school, and The Admissions Committee considers each application on an individual basis.

Costs

Tuition and fees for the 1999-2000 academic year are $10,898 for in-state students and $14,894 for out-of-state students. On-campus room and board costs about $4000 annually; and books and supplies run $450.

Financial Aid

in a recent year about 80% of current law students received some form of aid. Awards are based on need and merit. The required financial statement is the FAFSA. Check with the school for current application deadlines. Special funds for minority or disadvantaged students are available through Oregon State Bar scholarships and loans and Derrick Bell, Jr., scholarships. Other general university scholarships and loans are possible. First-year students are notified about their financial aid application as early as possible after acceptance.

About the Law School

University of Oregon School of Law, William W. Knight Law Center was established in 1884 and is a public institution. The 250-acre campus is in a small town, Eugene. The primary mission of the law school is to serve the state, the nation, and the world through a constantly renewed commitment to excellence. Students are challenged to excel in the service of both clients and community. The school is committed to providing a technological as well as a legal education. Students have access to federal, state, county, city, and local agencies, courts, correctional facilities, law firms, and legal aid organizations in the Eugene area. The law school is aggressive in its commitment to nationwide networks that provide both summer and permanent employment. Housing for law students is readily available. All law school facilities are accessible to the physically disabled.

Calendar

The law school operates on a traditional semester basis. Courses are offered days only and must be completed within 3 years. There is no part-time program. New students are admitted in the fall. There is an 8-week summer session. Transferable summer courses are offered.

Programs

Students may take relevant courses in other programs and apply credit toward the J.D.; a maximum of 5 credits may be applied. The following joint degrees may be earned: J.D./M.B.A. (Juris Doctor/ Master of Business Administration) and J.D./M.S. (Juris Doctor/Master of Science).

Required
To earn the J.D., candidates must complete 85 total credits, of which 37 are for required courses. They must maintain a minimum GPA of 2.0 in the required courses. The following first-year courses are required of all students: Civil Proce-

Phone: 541-346-1553
800-825-6687
Fax: 541-346-3984
E-mail: bmcolure@law.uoregon.edu
Web: www.uoregon.edu

Contact
Bonnie, 541-346-1553 for general inquiries; Edward Vignoul, Financial Aid Director, 541-346-3221 or 800-760-6953 for financial aid information.

OREGON

dure, Contracts, Criminal Law, Legal Research and Writing, Legislative and Administrative Processes, Property, and Torts. Required upper-level courses consist of Legal Profession, a comprehensive writing requirement, a basic writing requirement, and Constitutional Law. The required orientation program for first-year students consists of a 2-day orientation and registration before the first day of classes. Orientation includes a convocation, small group sessions, peer advising sessions, a library tour, and an all-school picnic. Peer and faculty advising continues throughout the J.D. program.

Electives
The School of Law, William W. Knight Law Center offers concentrations in corporate law, criminal law, environmental law, family law, international law, juvenile law, labor law, litigation, maritime law, securities law, tax law, torts and insurance, legal theory and ethics, litigation and procedure, property and estate, public law and policy, business law, clinical programs, and transnational legal problems. In addition, a variety of clinics is offered. The Civil Clinic is with the Legal Aid Office; the Prosecution Clinic involves working with local prosecutors; and the Criminal Defense Clinic involves working through the public defender services. More than 20 seminars are offered. Students have excellent opportunities for internships as a result of an established network and alumni relationships. Faculty-supervised research may be done for a total of 6 credits, but no more than 3 per semester. A reciprocal study-abroad exchange has been established with the University of Adelaide in Australia. The Academic Support Program, offered on a voluntary basis, addresses the needs of nontraditional law students. It involves a 2-week summer orientation prior to registration and tutorial assistance during the academic year. Minority programs include a Minority Law Students Association (MLSA) and an Oregon State Bar Affirmative Action Program, which offers financial assistance through scholarships and loans. Additionally, the law school offers placement assistance, scholarships, and partial fee waivers to minority students.

Graduation Requirements
In order to graduate, candidates must have a GPA of 2.0 and have completed the upper-division writing requirement.

Organizations
Students edit the *Oregon Law Review*, the *Journal of Environmental Law and Litigation*, and the newspaper *The Weekly Dissent*. There is an alumni magazine, the *Oregon Lawyer* and a monthly administrative publication for students, *In The Loop*. Students compete at the Client Counseling Competition, Mock Trial Competition, and Environmental Moot Court Competition. Other competitions are held for appointments to the *Oregon Law Review* and the *Journal of Environmental Law and Litigation*. Student organizations are the Black American Law Students Association, Christian Legal Society, and Federalist Society. There are local chapters of Phi Alpha Delta, Phi Delta Phi, and Partners and Spouses.

Library
The law library contains 177,409 hardcopy volumes and 169,187 microform volume equivalents, and subscribes to 3092 serial publications. Such on-line databases and networks as LEXIS, DIALOG, WESTLAW, EPIC, OLIS, BRS, FirstSearch, and the Internet are available to law students for research. Special library collections include a selected U.S. government depository, an Ocean and Coastal Law Library, and a rare book collection. Recently, the library installed 78 drop sites for laptop computer access to a local area network. The ratio of library volumes to faculty is 4126 to 1 and to students, 338 to 1. The ratio of seats in the library to students is 1 to 3.

Placement
J.D.s awarded:	n/av
Services available through: separate law school placement center	
Services: a Career Services Library with more than 500 references, and information on fellowships, graduate and summer writing programs, and writing competitions	
Special features: weekly bulletin of job notices to students; semi-monthly bulletin for interested alumni.	
Full-time job interviews:	n/av
Summer job interviews:	n/av
Placement by graduation:	n/av
Placement within 9 months:	n/av
Average starting salary:	n/av
Areas of placement:	n/av

Faculty
The law school has 32 full-time and 11 part-time faculty members, of whom 10 are women. According to AAUP standards for Category I institutions, faculty salaries are below average. About 19% of full-time faculty have a graduate law degree in addition to the J.D. The ratio of full-time students to full-time faculty in an average class is 5 to 1; in a clinic, 10 to 1. There is a chapter of the Order of the Coif.

Students
About 48% of the student body are women; 16%, minorities; 2%, African American; 14%, Asian American; 4%, Hispanic; 1%, Native American; and 2%, foreign nationals. The average age of entering students is 25; age range is 20 to 49. About 2% drop out after the first year for academic or personal reasons; 98% remain to receive a law degree.

Law School

3400 Chestnut Street
. Philadelphia, PA 19104-6204

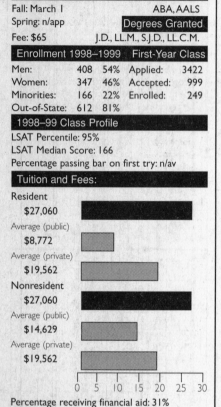

Application Filing		Accreditation
Fall: March 1		ABA, AALS
Spring: n/app		Degrees Granted
Fee: $65		J.D., LL.M., S.J.D., LL.C.M.

Enrollment 1998–1999		First-Year Class	
Men:	408 54%	Applied:	3422
Women:	347 46%	Accepted:	999
Minorities:	166 22%	Enrolled:	249
Out-of-State:	612 81%		

1998–99 Class Profile

LSAT Percentile: 95%
LSAT Median Score: 166
Percentage passing bar on first try: n/av

Tuition and Fees:

Resident
$27,060

Average (public)
$8,772

Average (private)
$19,562

Nonresident
$27,060

Average (public)
$14,629

Average (private)
$19,562

0 5 10 15 20 25 30

Percentage receiving financial aid: 31%

ADMISSIONS

In the fall 1999 first-year class, 3422 applied, 999 were accepted, and 249 enrolled. Six transfers enrolled. The median LSAT percentile of the most recent first-year class was 95; the median GPA was 3.6 on a scale of 4.0. The lowest LSAT percentile accepted was 21; the highest was 99.

Requirements

Applicants must have a bachelor's degree from an accredited institution and take the LSAT. The most important admission factors include academic achievement, LSAT results, and undergraduate curriculum. No specific undergraduate courses are required. Candidates are not interviewed.

Procedure

The application deadline for fall entry is March 1. Applicants should submit an application form, LSAT results, transcripts, a nonrefundable application fee of $65, a dean's letter, and 2 letters of recommendation. Accepted students must pay two $250 deposits to hold a place in the class. Notification of the admission decision is on a rolling basis. The latest acceptable LSAT test date for fall entry is December. The law school uses the LSDAS.

Special

The law school recruits minority and disadvantaged students as part of the school's policy to achieve diversity in the student body. Transfer students must have one year of credit, and have attended an ABA-and AALS-approved law school.

Costs

Tuition and fees for the 1999-2000 academic year are $27,060 for all full-time students. On-campus room and board costs about $8800 annually; books and supplies run $850.

Financial Aid

About 31% of current law students receive some form of aid. The average annual amount of aid from all sources combined, including scholarships, loans, and work contracts, in $9810. Awards are based on need and merit. The required financial statements are the FAFSA and the institution's financial aid form. The aid application deadline for fall entry is March 1. First-year students are notified about their financial aid application shortly after acceptance.

About the Law School

University of Pennsylvania Law School was established in 1852 and is a private institution. The 260-acre campus is in an urban area 2 miles from central Philadelphia. The primary mission of the law school is to prepare students for effective, enlightened, and socially responsible careers in law. The school is sensitive to the problems confronting

society. Students have access to federal, state, county, city, and local agencies, courts, correctional facilities, law firms, and legal aid organizations in the Philadelphia area. The Pennsylvania Supreme Court is in Philadelphia. The federal courthouse headquarters the U.S. District Court for the Eastern District of Pennsylvania and the Court of Appeals for the Third Circuit. Housing for law students is in on-campus facilities for single and married students in the university's 2 high-rise apartment residences. An International House is available for international students. A university office helps students secure off-campus housing.

Calendar

The law school operates on a traditional semester basis. Courses are offered days only and must be completed within 3 years. There is no part-time program. New students are admitted in the fall. There is no summer session.

Programs

In addition to the J.D., the law school offers the LL.M, S.J.D., and LL.C.M. Students may take relevant courses in other programs and apply credit toward the J.D.; a maximum of 12 credits may be applied. The following joint degrees may be earned: J.D./M.B.A. (Juris Doctor/Master of Business Administration), J.D./M.A. (Juris Doctor/Master of Arts in public policy and management), J.D./M.C.P. (Juris Doctor/Master of City Planning), J.D./M.A. (Juris Doctor/Master of Arts in Asian and Middle East studies), J.D./Ph.D. (Juris Doctor/Doctor of Philosophy in economics and public policy), J.D./M.S.W. (Juris Doctor/Master of Social Work), and J.D./M.D. (Juris Doctor/Doctor of Medicine).

Phone: 215-898-7400
E-mail: admissions@oyez.law.upenn.edu
Web: http://www.law.upenn.edu

Contact

Janice Austin, Assistant Dean, Admissions and Financial Aid, 215-898-7400 for general inquiries; Denise McGarry, Associate Director, 215-898-7743 for financial aid information.

PENNSYLVANIA

Required

To earn the J.D., candidates must complete 89 total credits, of which 28 are for required courses. The following first-year courses are required of all students: Civil Procedure, Contracts, Criminal Law, Torts, Constitutional Law, Property, and Legal Writing. Required upper-level courses consist of Professional Responsibility. The required orientation program for first-year students lasts 2 days.

Electives

The Law School offers concentrations in corporate law, criminal law, family law, international law, labor law, securities law, tax law, regulation of business, property and land development, perspectives on the law, law and the health services, constitutional law, courts and administration of justice, commercial law, urban and public interest law, and clinical, professional responsibility, and cocurricular courses. In addition, clinics and extern programs are available for credit in law-related agencies outside of the school. The clinical program includes courses in litigation, small-business planning, and mediation and criminal defense. Seminars are available in Administrative Due Process, Advanced Issues in Secured Transactions, American Legal History, Bankruptcy: Practice and Theory, Bankruptcy Reorganization, Comparative Labor Law, and numerous other areas. Each year a substantial number of students are employed as research assistants for faculty members. The Center for Advanced Studies in Legal History encourages teaching, research, and scholarship in legal history. The school requires that all students complete 70 hours of service in public interest.

Graduation Requirements

In order to graduate, candidates must have completed the upper-division writing requirement.

Organizations

Students edit the *University of Pennsylvania Law Review*, *Journal of Employment and Labor Law*, the *Journal of International Economic Law*, the *Constitutional Law Journal*, the *Hybrid: A Journal of Law and Social Change*, and the newspaper *The Forum*. The student Moot Court Board, made up of third-year students, administers the Moot Court Program, which holds a voluntary intramural competition for the Edwin R. Keedy Trophy. The school also participates in several competitions sponsored by bar associations or other law schools, including the Jessup International Moot Court Competition. There are 38 student groups, including organizations for black, Asian-American, and Hispanic students. The Law Alumni Society sponsors gatherings of alumni and involves alumni in programs at the school.

Library

The law library contains 685,675 hardcopy volumes and 868,948 microform volume equivalents, and subscribes to 2914 serial publications. Such on-line databases and networks as LEXIS, DIALOG, WESTLAW, NEXIS, BRS, VUTEXT, and Dow Jones are available to law students for research. Special library collections include foreign, international, and rare-book collections, archives of the American Law Institute and the National Conference of Commissioners on Uniform State Laws, and the papers of Judge Bazelon and Bernard G. Segal. The Biddle Library incorporates a variety of study environments totaling 525 seats and more than 650 computer ports. The ratio of library volumes to faculty is 16,326 to 1 and to students, 908 to 1. The ratio of seats in the library to students is 1 to 1.

Faculty

The law school has 42 full-time and 54 part-time faculty members, of whom 35 are women. According to AAUP standards for Category I institutions, faculty salaries are well above average. About 3% of full-time faculty have a graduate law degree in addition to the J.D. The ratio of full-time students to full-time faculty in an average class is 15 to 1. The law school has a regular program of bringing visiting professors and other distinguished lecturers and visitors to campus. There is a chapter of the Order of the Coif; 10 graduates are members.

Placement

J.D.s awarded: 269

Services available through: separate law school placement center

Services: The placement library contains material on a wide variety of subjects and includes all major legal press.

Special features: Students work individually with counselors on their career searches. The office holds panel discussions and small-group meetings during the year to explore the practice of law and career opportunities. Additionally, first-year students work in small groups on issues such as resume writing and career opportunities.

Full-time job interviews:	340 employers
Summer job interviews:	340 employers
Placement by graduation:	94% of class
Placement within 9 months:	99% of class
Average starting salary:	$30,000 to $100,000

Areas of placement:

Private practice 51-100 attorneys	70%
Judicial clerkships	19%
Business/industry	5%
Public interest	3%
Unknown	1%
Private practice 26-50 attorneys	1%
Government	1%

Students

About 46% of the student body are women; 22%, minorities; 8%, African American; 7%, Asian American; and 7%, Hispanic. The average age of entering students is 24. About 39% of students enter directly from undergraduate school and 12% have a graduate degree. About 1% drop out after the first year for academic or personal reasons; 99% remain to receive a law degree.

UNIVERSITY OF PITTSBURGH

School of Law

3900 Forbes Avenue
Pittsburgh, PA 15260

Application Filing		Accreditation
Fall: March 1		ABA, AALS
Spring: n/app		**Degrees Granted**
Fee: $50		J.D., LL.M.

Enrollment 1998–1999		First-Year Class	
Men:	382 56%	Applied:	1220
Women:	303 44%	Accepted:	765
Minorities:	69 10%	Enrolled:	263
Out-of-State:	206 30%		

1998–99 Class Profile
LSAT Percentile: 64%
LSAT Median Score: 154
Percentage passing bar on first try: 73%

Tuition and Fees:

Resident
$12,868

Average (public)
$8,772

Average (private)
$19,562

Nonresident
$19,842

Average (public)
$14,629

Average (private)
$19,562

0 5 10 15 20 25 30

Percentage receiving financial aid: see

ADMISSIONS
In the fall 1999 first-year class, 1220 applied, 765 were accepted, and 263 enrolled. Five transfers enrolled. The median LSAT percentile of the most recent first-year class was 64; the median GPA was 3.2 on a scale of 4.0. The highest LSAT percentile was 99.

Requirements
Applicants must have a bachelor's degree from an accredited institution and take the LSAT. The most important admission factors include LSAT results, GPA, and academic achievement. No specific undergraduate courses are required. Candidates are not interviewed.

Procedure
The application deadline for fall entry is March 1. Applicants should submit an application form, LSAT results, transcripts, a nonrefundable application fee of $50, and 2 suggested letters of recommendation. Notification of the admissions decision is on a rolling basis. The latest acceptable LSAT test date for fall entry is February. The law school uses the LSDAS.

Special
The law school recruits minority and disadvantaged students by means of inhouse programs, visits to minority institutions, direct mail, and phone solicitation. Transfer students must have one year of credit and have attended an ABA-approved law school.

Costs
Tuition and fees for the 1999-2000 academic year are $12,868 for full-time in-state students and $19,842 for out-of-state students. Books and supplies run $500.

Financial Aid
About 35% of current law students receive scholarships, 85% loans. The average annual amount of aid from all sources combined, including scholarships, loans, and work contracts, in $18,500. Awards are based on need and merit. The required financial statement is the FAFSA. The aid application deadline for fall entry is March 1. Special funds for minority or disadvantaged students are available through scholarships provided by the school and the university. First-year students are notified about their financial aid application at time of acceptance.

About the Law School
University of Pittsburgh School of Law was established in 1895 and is a public institution. The campus is in an urban area 3 miles from downtown Pittsburgh. The primary mission of the law school is to provide education, research, and public service. Students have access to federal, state, county, city, and local agencies, courts, correctional facilities, law firms, and legal aid organizations in the Pittsburgh area. Facilities of special interest to law students are the law library, classrooms, seminar rooms, courtroom complex, student lounge, student activities offices, meeting rooms, and administrative offices. Housing for law students is in rental apartments that cost $350 to $450 and are available within 1 to 3 miles of the law school. On-campus housing is not available. All law school facilities are accessible to the physically disabled.

Calendar
The law school operates on a traditional semester basis. Courses for full-time students are offered days only and must be completed within 3 years. For flex-time students, courses are offered day and must be completed within 5 years. New full-time students are admitted in the fall; flex-time, fall. There is no summer session. Transferable summer courses are not offered.

Programs
In addition to the J.D., the law school offers the LL.M. Students may take relevant courses in other programs and apply credit toward the J.D.; a maximum of 6 credits may be applied. The following joint degrees may be earned: J.D./M.B.A. (Juris Doctor/ Master of Business Administration), J.D./M.P.A. (Juris Doctor/ Master of Public Administration), J.D./M.P.I.A. (Juris Doctor/ Master of Public and International Affairs), J.D./M.P.H. (Juris Doctor/ Master of Public Health), J.D./M.S.I.A. (Juris Doctor/ Master of Science in industrial management), J.D./M.S. (Juris Doctor/ Master of Science in law and public management), and J.D./M.A. (Juris Doctor/Master of Arts in bioethics).

Phone: 412-648-1412
Fax: 412-648-2647
E-mail: admissions@law.pitt.edu
Web: www.pitt.law.edu

Contact

Fredi Miller, Assistant Dean for Admissions and Financial Aid, 412-648-1412 for general inquiries, and 412-648-1415 for financial aid information.

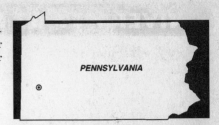

PENNSYLVANIA

Required

To earn the J.D., candidates must complete 88 total credits, of which 34 are for required courses. They must maintain a minimum GPA of 2.0 in the required courses. The following first-year courses are required of all students: Contracts, Torts, Property, Legal Process and Civil Procedure, Legal Analysis and Writing, Criminal Law, Criminal Procedure, and Constitutional Law. Required upper-level courses consist of Legal Profession and an upper-level writing requirement. The required orientation program for first-year students is conducted over a 2-day period including a formal program, diversity training, discussion groups, family and friends orientation, and cookout.

Electives

The School of Law offers concentrations in corporate law, criminal law, environmental law, family law, international law, labor law, litigation, tax law, torts and insurance, and health law. In addition, the clinical program includes the Family Support Clinic, which can be taken for 5 or 7 credits, and is open to students who have completed 3 semesters. Also offered are the Child Welfare Clinic, for 2 credits, and Corporate Counsel Clinic for 2 credits each. These 2 clinics are limited to third-year students. Second- and third-year students may receive 2 credits for a variety of seminars, which can satisfy the upper-level writing requirement. Internships and externships opportunities are available with 47 local federal and state judges, 32 other judges throughout Pennsylvania, and 13 judges in other states. Students are also placed in 49 Pennsylvania and federal agencies and 18 out-of-state agencies; including Legal Aid societies, the Urban Redevelopment Authority, U.S. attorneys, neighborhood legal services, public defenders, the National Labor Relations Board, hospitals, and housing authorities. The Colloquium Committee sponsors the Caplan Lecture, the Mellon Lecture, a Faculty Colloquium series, and the Martin Luther King Lecture annually. The Law School also sponsors a lecture in honor of Black History Month. The Law School invites minority and other students to participate in the Mellon Legal Writing Program, which is designed to provide additional academic and social support for students confronting special challenges. The Law School is cosponsor of the CLEO (The Council for Legal Educational Opportunity) Institute every year. The Law School

hosted the Institute in 1993, and 1995, 1998. The Black Law Students Association sponsors a Big Brother and Sister Program that assigns each first-year student to an upper-level student. Student organizations sponsor programs reflecting the interest of the group, such as Sports and Entertainment Law, International Law, and Environmental Law. The most widely taken electives are Federal Income Tax, Corporations, and Evidence.

Graduation Requirements

In order to graduate, candidates must have a GPA of 2.0 and have completed the upper-division writing requirement and the Legal Profession Ethics course.

Organizations

Students edit the *University of Pittsburgh Law Review, University of Pittsburgh Journal of Law and Commerce*, and the newspaper *Pitt Law Chronicle*. Moot court competitions include the Annual Cardozo Entertainment Law, Frederick Douglass Competition, and Wagner Labor Law. Law student organizations are the Student Bar Association, International Law Society, and Environmental Law Society. There are local chapters of Phi Alpha Delta, SBA, and BLSA.

Library

The law library contains 375,000 hard-copy volumes and 105,202 microform volume equivalents, and subscribes to 4964 serial publications. Such on-line databases and networks as LEXIS, DIALOG, WESTLAW, and more than 75 separate databases available through the University of Pittsburgh Digital Library are available to law students for research. Special library collections include international law, tax and labor law, health law, and a selective federal depository. Recently, the library installed a law school local area network with a CD-ROM server, added the CIS legislative history archives collection on microfiche, and tripled the capacity of the library. The ratio of library volumes to faculty is 8963 to 1 and to students, 529 to 1. The ratio of seats in the library to students is 1 to 1.

Faculty

The law school has 42 full-time and 38 part-time faculty members, of whom 23 are women. According to AAUP standards for Category I institutions, faculty salaries are

Placement

J.D.s awarded:	259

Services available through: separate law school placement center

Services: computerized job search, weekly workshops, publication of a weekly student newletter as well as a monthly alumni bulletin, formal assessment availability, mentoring program, and participation in minority and other specialized job fairs

Special features: an emphasis on exploring career options and long-range career planning and developing and refining job procurement and retention skills. The professional staff consists of an assistant dean and the director of placement and public interest opportunities, both of whom remain active in state and local bar associations and bring an array of legal practice experience to their work.

Full-time job interviews:	62 employers
Summer job interviews:	37 employers
Placement by graduation:	59% of class
Placement within 9 months:	94% of class
Average starting salary:	$16,000 to $94,000

Areas of placement:

Private practice 2-10 attorneys	19%
Private practice 11-25 attorneys	5%
Private practice 26-50 attorneys	7%
Private practice 51-100 attorneys	5%
Private practice 101 + attorneys	20%
Business/industry	16%
Judicial Clerkships	13%
Government	10%
Military	7%
Public interest	3%
Academic	1%

above average. About 24% of full-time faculty have a graduate law degree in addition to the J.D.; about 14% of part-time faculty have one. The ratio of full-time students to full-time faculty in an average class is 23 to 1; in a clinic, 8 to 1. There is a chapter of the Order of the Coif.

Students

About 44% of the student body are women; 10%, minorities; 7%, African American; 2%, Asian American; and 1%, Hispanic. The majority of students come from Pennsylvania (70%). The average age of entering students is 24; age range is 20 to 42. About 40% of students enter directly from undergraduate school and 10% have a graduate degree. About 3% drop out after the first year for academic or personal reasons; 95% remain to receive a law degree.

School of Law

P.O. Box 23349, UPR Station
Rio Piedras, PR 00931

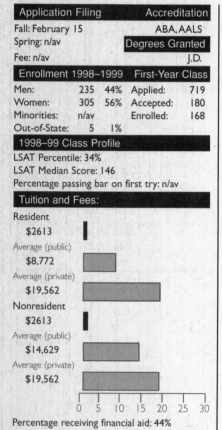

Application Filing		Accreditation
Fall: February 15		ABA, AALS
Spring: n/av		Degrees Granted
Fee: n/av		J.D.

Enrollment 1998–1999			First-Year Class	
Men:	235	44%	Applied:	719
Women:	305	56%	Accepted:	180
Minorities:	n/av		Enrolled:	168
Out-of-State:	5	1%		

1998–99 Class Profile
LSAT Percentile: 34%
LSAT Median Score: 146
Percentage passing bar on first try: n/av

Tuition and Fees:

Resident
$2613

Average (public)
$8,772

Average (private)
$19,562

Nonresident
$2613

Average (public)
$14,629

Average (private)
$19,562

0 5 10 15 20 25 30

Percentage receiving financial aid: 44%

ADMISSIONS

In the fall 1999 first-year class, 719 applied, 180 were accepted, and 168 enrolled. Eleven transfers enrolled. The median LSAT percentile of the most recent first-year class was 34; the median GPA was 3.6 on a scale of 4.0. The lowest LSAT percentile accepted was 4; the highest was 99.

Requirements

Applicants must have a bachelor's degree from an accredited institution and take the LSAT. Minimum acceptable GPA is 2.0 on a scale of 4.0. No specific undergraduate courses are required. Candidates are not interviewed.

Procedure

The application deadline for fall entry is February 15. Applicants should submit an application form, LSAT results, transcripts, and PAEG. Accepted students must pay a $45 seat deposit. Notification of the admission decision is May. The latest acceptable LSAT test date for fall entry is February. The law school uses the LSDAS.

Special

Transfer students must have a minimum GPA of 3.3, have attended an ABA-approved law school, and and have completed at least 60 credit hours in residence.

Costs

Tuition and fees for the 1999-2000 academic year are $2613 for all full-time students. Tuition and fees for all part-time students is $1712 per credit in-state. On-campus room and board costs about $2880 annually; and books and supplies run $1800.

Financial Aid

About 44% of current law students receive some form of aid. The average annual amount of aid from all sources combined, including scholarships, loans, and work contracts, is $2000; maximum, $8000. Awards are based on need and merit. The required financial statement is the CSS Profile. The aid application deadline for fall entry is April 1. First-year students are notified about their financial aid application at time of acceptance.

About the Law School

University of Puerto Rico School of Law was established in 1913 and is a public institution. The 5-acre campus is in an urban area in metropolitan San Juan. The primary mission of the law school is to train competent lawyers and jurists with a strong sense of professional, ethical, and social responsibility. Students have access to federal, state, county, city, and local agencies, courts, correctional facilities, law firms, and legal aid organizations in the Rio Piedras area. Housing for law students is available in dormitories on campus. About 95% of the law school facilities are accessible to the physically disabled.

Calendar

The law school operates on a traditional semester basis. Courses for full-time students are offered both day and evening and must be completed within 6 semesters. For part-time students, courses are offered both day and evening and must be completed within 8 semesters. New full-and part-time students are admitted in the fall. There is a 6- week summer session.

Programs

Students may take relevant courses in other programs and apply credit toward the J.D.; a maximum of 6 credits may be applied. The following joint degrees may be earned: J.D./M.B.A. (Juris Doctor/Master of Business Administration), J.D./Lic.en Derecho (a Dual degree program with the University of Barcelona), and J.D./M.P.P. (Juris Doctor/Master of Public Policy).

Contact

Director of Admissions, (787)-764-0000, ext. 2413 or (787)-764-1655 for general inquiries; Michael Ayala, (787)-764-0000, ext 3148-2413; (787) 764-1655 for financial aid information.

PUERTO RICO

Required

To earn the J.D., candidates must complete 92 total credits, of which 46 are for required courses. They must maintain a minimum GPA of 2.0 in the required courses. The following first-year courses are required of all students: Introduction to Law, Torts, Property, Family Law, Legal Research, Criminal Law, Obligations and Contracts Law, Civil Procedure, Constitutional Law, and Problems in International Law. Required upper-level courses consist of Evidence, Theory of Law, Business Associations and Corporations, and Legal Aid Clinic I and II. All students must take clinical courses. The required orientation program for first-year students lasts 1 week.

Electives

All students are required to take clinics, worth 6 credits, and 2 2-credit seminars. During the summer an elective legal practice workshop is offered; it is worth 2 credits. Legal research in urban planning, housing, poverty, and related subjects is encouraged in a number of courses. There is a summer course in Barcelona, worth up to 5 credits, that is open to all students in good standing. There is also a dual-degree program with the University of Barcelona. The most widely taken electives are Bankruptcy, Taxation, and Criminology.

Graduation Requirements

In order to graduate, candidates must have a GPA of 2.0 and have completed the upper-division writing requirement.

Organizations

Students edit the *Revista Juridica de la Universidad de Puerto Rico* and the newspaper *El Nuevo Jurista*. Law student organizations include El Consejo de Estudiantes de Derecho, which is an elected student government; the National Association of Law Students; and ABA-Law Student Division. Student representatives chosen by the student coucil serve on all law school committees, except the personnel committee.

Library

The law library contains 346,360 hardcopy volumes and 641,402 microform volume equivalents, and subscribes to 4487 serial publications. Such on-line databases and networks as LEXIS, DIALOG, WESTLAW, NEXIS, MicroJuris, PRONLINE, other CD-ROM bases services, Compuclerk, Compuley, and LexCo are available to law students for research. Special library collections include extensive collections in Latin American and comparative law, a U.S. government depository, Specialized European Communities Documentation Centre, and a depository for the Central American Parliament. Recently, the library was developing a comprehensive collection of legal materials from Mexico, Central America, Colombia, Venezuela, and the jurisdictions of the Caribbean. The ratio of library volumes to faculty is 8060 to 1 and to students, 511 to 1. The ratio of seats in the library to students is 1 to 1.

Faculty

The law school has 35 full-time and 29 part-time faculty members, of whom 15 are women. According to AAUP standards for Category IIB institutions, faculty salaries are average. About 70% of full-time faculty have a graduate law degree in addition to the J.D.; about 50% of part-time faculty have one. The ratio of full-time students to full-time faculty in an average class is 15 to 1; in a clinic, 13 to 1. The law school has a regular program of bringing visiting professors and other distinguished lecturers and visitors to campus.

Students

About 56% of the student body are women. The majority of students come from Puerto Rico (99%). The average age of entering students is 23; age range is 20 to 60. About 91% of students enter directly from undergraduate school, 9% have a graduate degree, and 14% have worked full-time prior to entering law school. About 5% drop out after the first year for academic or personal reasons; 95% remain to receive a law degree.

Placement

J.D.s awarded:	114
Services available through: separate law school placement center.	
Full-time job interviews:	n/av
Summer job interviews:	n/av
Placement by graduation:	n/av
Placement within 9 months:	n/av
Average starting salary:	$28,000 to $35,000
Areas of placement:	
Private practice 2-10 attorneys	9%
Private practice 11-25 attorneys	13%
Private practice 26-50 attorneys	15%
Private practice 51-100 attorneys	16%
Judicial clerkships	10%
unknown	5%
Business/industry	1%
Public interest	1%

The T.C. Williams School of Law

University of Richmond, VA 23173

Application Filing		Accreditation
Fall: January 15		ABA, AALS
Spring: n/app		**Degrees Granted**
Fee: $35		J.D.

Enrollment 1998–1999		First-Year Class	
Men:	251 53%	Applied:	1246
Women:	225 46%	Accepted:	543
Minorities:	90 19%	Enrolled:	156
Out-of-State:	286 60%		

1998–99 Class Profile

LSAT Percentile: 74%

LSAT Median Score: 157

Percentage passing bar on first try: 79%

Tuition and Fees:

Resident
$19,940

Average (public)
$8,772

Average (private)
$19,562

Nonresident
$19,940

Average (public)
$14,629

Average (private)
$19,562

Percentage receiving financial aid: 94%

ADMISSIONS

In the fall 1999 first-year class, 1246 applied, 543 were accepted, and 156 enrolled. Three transfers enrolled. The median LSAT percentile of the most recent first-year class was 74; the median GPA was 3.18 on a scale of 4.0. The highest LSAT percentile was 99.

Requirements

Applicants must have a bachelor's degree from an accredited institution and take the LSAT. No specific undergraduate courses are required. Candidates are not interviewed.

Procedure

The application deadline for fall entry is January 15. Applicants should submit an application form, LSAT results, transcripts, a nonrefundable application fee of $35, 2 are optional letters of recommendation, and a narrative statement. Notification of the admissions decision is by May 1. The latest acceptable LSAT test date for fall entry is February. The law school uses the LSDAS.

Special

The law school recruits minority and disadvantaged students by attending minority law forums, being a Council for Legal Education Opportunity (CLEO) sponsor, and being a CLEO Regional Summer Institute site (3 of last 7 years). Transfer students must have one year of credit, have attended an ABA-approved law school, and must be in good standing at an ABA-approved law school.

Costs

Tuition and fees for the 1999-2000 academic year are $19,940 for all full-time students. Tuition for part-time students is $995 per credit hour. On-campus room and board costs about $4325 annually; and books and supplies run $900.

Financial Aid

About 94% of current law students receive some form of aid. The average annual amount of aid from all sources combined, including scholarships, loans, and work contracts, is $23,340. All admitted students who file the FAFSA and supplemental application by February 25 of each year are considered for grants based on both merit and need at the time they enter the law school. Students maintain the level of grant awarded for the first year unless they experience a change in financial circumstances. The required financial statement is the FAFSA. The aid application deadline for fall entry is February 25. Special funds for minority or disadvantaged students consist of scholarships. First-year students are notified about their financial aid application at the time of acceptance.

About the Law School

University of Richmond's T.C. Williams School of Law was established in 1870 and is a private institution. The 350-acre campus is in a suburban area 2 miles west of Richmond. The primary mission of the law school is to train its graduates to practice law. Its relatively small size helps fashion a close and open relationship between students and faculty. Students have access to federal, state, county, city, and local agencies, courts, correctional facilities, law firms, and legal aid organizations in the University of Richmond area. Facilities of special interest to law students include the law library with a legal research and writing computer laboratory, and individualized study carrels that are electronically networked via students' personal computers to the Legal Information Center, a schoolwide computer system that gives instant access to the electronic age in law. Housing for law students is available in 1 law dormitory with 8 single rooms. Attractively priced apartments are available very close to the campus. All law school facilities are accessible to the physically disabled.

Calendar

The law school operates on a traditional semester basis. Courses for full-and part time students are offered days only and must be completed within 5 years. New full and part-time students are admitted in the fall and summer. There are 3- and 8- week summer sessions. Transferable summer courses are offered.

Programs

Students may take relevant courses in other programs and apply credit toward the J.D.; a maximum of up to 9 approved non law school credit hours, credits may be applied. The following joint degrees may be earned: J.D./M.B.A. (Juris Doctor/Master of Business Administration), J.D./M.S.W. (Juris Doctor/Master of Social Work with Virginia Commonwealth), J.D./M.U.R.P. (Juris Doctor/ Master of Urban and Regional Planning with Virginia Commonwealth), J.D./ M.H.A. (Juris Doctor/Master of Health Administration with Medical College of Virginia), and J.D./M.P.A. (Juris Doctor/Master of Public Administration with Virginia Commonwealth).

Phone: 804-289-8189
E-mail: admissions@uofrlaw.richmond.edu
Web: law.richmond.edu

Contact

Michelle L. Rahman, Admissions Director, 804-289-8189 for general inquiries; C. Bolger, Director of Financial Aid, 804-289-8438 for financial aid information.

VIRGINIA

Required

To earn the J.D., candidates must complete 86 total credits, of which 38 are for required courses. The following first-year courses are required of all students: Contracts, Constitutional Law, Property, Civil Procedure, Lawyering Skills I and II, Criminal Law, Torts, and Environmental Law. Required upper-level courses consist of Professional Responsibility, upper-level writing requirements, and upper-level Lawyering Skills III and IV. The required orientation program for first-year students lasts 3 days and includes network and computer training and an introduction to lawyering skills as well as the law school administration, faculty, staff, student organizations, and law student advisers.

Electives

The T.C. Williams School of Law offers concentrations in corporate law, criminal law, entertainment, environmental law, family law, international law, juvenile law, labor law, litigation, maritime law, securities law, sports law, tax law, and torts and insurance. In addition, third-year students may participate in either the outplacement clinic or the school's in-house Youth Advocacy, Worker's Protection and Advocacy, and Mental Disabilities clinics. The outplacement clinic allows students to work in various legal offices in the community, and is complemented by a classroom component. The Youth Advocacy and Mental Disabilities clinics, supervised by a staff attorney, allow students to represent clients in business, civil, criminal, and judicial matters. Students may also participate in the D.C. Summer Environmental Internship Program in Washington, D.C. Credit varies for these programs. Special lecture series include the Allen Chair Lecture, Emroch Lecture, Austin Owen Lecture, and Legal Forum. There is a study-abroad option. Students may study international law for 5 weeks at Emmanuel College in Cambridge, England, or for a semester at any one of 9 foreign universities with which the law school has an exchange program. There is an academic support program.

Graduation Requirements

In order to graduate, candidates must have a GPA of 2.0 and have completed the upper-division writing requirement.

Organizations

Students edit the *University of Richmond Law Review, Journal of Law Technology* (which is completely on-line), *Perspectives on Law and the Public Interest*, and the newspaper, *Juris Publici*. Moot court teams attend the Appellate Advocacy Moot Court Competition in the fall, and the Motions and Interscholastic Motions Competition in the spring as well as the Judge John R. Brown Admiralty Moot Court Competition. There are intramural competitions in both client counseling and negotiations. The winning teams enter respective ABA competitions. Annually, the National Environmental Negotiation Competition is entered. The school has hosted the ABA regional competition. Law student organizations include the Student Bar Association, Client Counseling and Negotiation Board, and Federalist Society for Law and Public Policy Studies. There are local chapters of ABA-Student Division and the Black Law Students Association. Additionally, there are intramural sports including soccer and softball.

Library

The law library contains 279,403 hardcopy volumes and 115,790 microform volume equivalents, and subscribes to 4170 serial publications. Such on-line databases and networks as LEXIS, DIALOG, WESTLAW, Virginia Legislative Search Service, NEXIS, On-line University Catalog, and Internet access are available to law students for research. Special library collections include a U.S. government documents depository. Recently, the library doubled space to 52,000 square feet and added completely wired study carrels. A Novell computer network, which provides for E-mail, file transfers, WESTLAW and LEXIS searching, information sharing, notice boards, course discussions, and so on, has been installed, linking all computers in the law school, including student computers in the carrels. The ratio of library volumes to faculty is 9548 to 1 and to students, 590 to 1. The ratio of seats in the library to students is 1 to 1.

Placement

J.D.s awarded:	144

Services available through: separate law school placement center and the university placement center

Services: programs on law practice, marketing projects for targeted employers, minority job fairs, and job search support groups

Special features: Computerized mail merge files for employers are available to students, as is resume and cover letter preparation software.

Full-time job interviews:	60 employers
Summer job interviews:	n/av
Placement by graduation:	57% of class
Placement within 9 months:	99% of class
Average starting salary:	n/av

Areas of placement:

Private practice 2-10 attorneys	22%
Private practice 11-25 attorneys	5%
Private practice 26-50 attorneys	4%
Private practice 51-100 attorneys	5%
Private practice 100+ attorneys	10%
Business/industry	15%
Judicial clerkships	14%
Government	12%
Public interest	4%
Military	2%

Faculty

The law school has 26 full-time and 40 part-time faculty members, of whom 27 are women. According to AAUP standards for Category IIA institutions, faculty salaries are well above average. About 70% of full-time faculty have a graduate law degree in addition to the J.D. The ratio of full-time students to full-time faculty in an average class is 13 to 1; in a clinic, 5 to 1. The law school has a regular program of bringing visiting professors and other distinguished lecturers and visitors to campus.

Students

About 46% of the student body are women; 19%, minorities; 10%, African American; 7%, Asian American; 2%, Hispanic; and 1%, Native American. The majority of students come from Virginia (40%). The average age of entering students is 25; age range is 21 to 46. About 46% of students enter directly from undergraduate school, 10% have a graduate degree, and 54% have worked full time prior to entering law school. About 1% drop out after the first year for academic or personal reasons; 99% remain to receive a law degree.

University of Richmond   **483**

UNIVERSITY OF SAN DIEGO

School of Law

5998 Alcala Park
San Diego, CA 92110

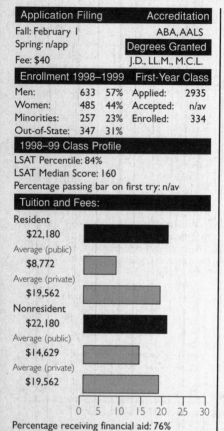

Application Filing		Accreditation
Fall: February 1		ABA, AALS
Spring: n/app		Degrees Granted
Fee: $40		J.D., LL.M., M.C.L.

Enrollment 1998–1999		First-Year Class	
Men:	633 57%	Applied:	2935
Women:	485 44%	Accepted:	n/av
Minorities:	257 23%	Enrolled:	334
Out-of-State:	347 31%		

1998–99 Class Profile
LSAT Percentile: 84%
LSAT Median Score: 160
Percentage passing bar on first try: n/av

Tuition and Fees:

Resident
$22,180

Average (public)
$8,772

Average (private)
$19,562

Nonresident
$22,180

Average (public)
$14,629

Average (private)
$19,562

0 5 10 15 20 25 30

Percentage receiving financial aid: 76%

ADMISSIONS

In the fall 1999 first-year class, 2935 applied and 334 enrolled. Fifty-six transfers enrolled. The median LSAT percentile of the most recent first-year class was 84; the median GPA was 3.2 on a scale of 4.0.

Requirements
Applicants must have a bachelor's degree from an accredited institution and take the LSAT. No specific undergraduate courses are required. Candidates are not interviewed.

Procedure
The application deadline for fall entry is February 1. Applicants should submit an application form, LSAT results, a nonrefundable application fee of $40, a personal statement, and any other information that the applicants wants to provide. Notification of the admission decision is from January through midsummer. The latest acceptable LSAT test date for fall entry is February (day program) and June (evening program). The law school uses the LSDAS.

Special
The law school recruits minority and disadvantaged students by welcoming and respecting those whose lives are formed by different traditions, recognizing that diversity of viewpoint, background, and experience (including race, ethnicity, cultural diversity, gender, religion, age, socioeconomic status, and disability) among its student body is essential to the full and informed exchange of ideas and to the quality of legal education it seeks to provide. Transfer students must have one year of credit, have attended an ABA-approved law school, and should have a rank in the top quintile of the first-year class.

Costs

Tuition and fees for the 1999-2000 academic year are $22,180 for all full-time students. Tuition for part-time students is $15,750 annually. On-campus room and board costs about $12,542 annually; books and supplies run $750.

Financial Aid

About 76% of current law students receive some form of aid. The average annual amount of aid from all sources combined, including scholarships, loans, and work contracts, is $12,878; maximum, $35,472. Awards are based on need and merit. The required financial statement is FAFSA. The aid application deadline for fall entry is March 2. Need-based, full- and partial-tuition scholarships are available to entering students. These scholarships are based on the applicant's academic promise, financial need, potential for service to the community, and contribution of diversity to the student body. First-year students are notified about their financial aid application at time of acceptance.

About the Law School

University of San Diego School of Law was established in 1954 and is a private institution. The 180-acre campus is in a suburban area 5 miles north of downtown San Diego. The primary mission of the law school is to foster an environment of stimulating and rigorous intellectual exchange between teacher and student in which teaching and learning engage the full attention of faculty and students while maintaining concern for the broader personal and moral development of the law student. Students have access to federal, state, county, city, and local agencies, courts, correctional facilities, law firms, and legal aid organizations in the San Diego area. Safe and affordable housing is available near campus. The Admissions Office maintains a listing of students seeking roommates among other resources. About 90% of the law school facilities are accessible to the physically disabled.

Calendar

The law school operates on a traditional semester basis. Courses for full-time students are offered days only and must be completed within 5 years. For part-time students, courses are offered evenings only and must be completed within 5 years. New full-and part-time students are admitted in the fall. There is an 8-week summer session. Transferable summer courses are offered.

Programs

In addition to the J.D., the law school offers the LL.M, M.C.L.; LL.M in Taxation; LL.M. in International Law; LL.M. in Comparative Law; and LL.M in Business and Comparative Law. Students may take relevant courses in other programs and apply credit toward the J.D.; a maximum of 6 credits may be applied. The following joint degrees may be earned: J.D./M.B.A. (Juris Doctor/Master of Business Administration), J.D./I.M.B.A. (Juris Doctor/International. Master of Business Administration), and J.D./M.A (Juris Doctor/Master of Arts in international relations).

Phone: 619-260-4528

248-4873

Fax: 619-260-2218

E-mail: jdinfo@acusd.edu

Web: acusd.edu/usdlaw

Contact

Carl J. Eging, Director of Admissions and Financial Aid, 619-260-4528 for general inquiries; 619-260-4570 for financial aid information.

Required

To earn the J.D., candidates must complete 85 total credits, of which 48 are for required courses. They must maintain a minimum grade average of 75 in the required courses. The following first-year courses are required of all students: Civil Procedure, Contracts, Criminal Law, Lawyering Skills I, Property, and Torts. Required upper-level courses consist of Constitutional Law, Criminal Procedure I, Evidence, Professional Responsibility, and Tax I. The optional orientation program for first-year students is offered to incoming students, who attend a 1-day orientation hosted by the Student Bar Association. Many topics are presented for discussion, including the Socratic method, time management, and how to study for law school exams.

Electives

The School of Law offers concentrations in corporate law, criminal law, environmental law, family law, international law, juvenile law, labor law, litigation, tax law, torts and insurance, and public interest/children's advocacy. In addition, students may enroll for up to 10 credits of clinical field work. They represent actual clients in consumer housing, family, administrative, mental health, environmental, immigration, criminal, and juvenile law matters. Internships are available in-house through the Clinical Education Program, as well as with local agencies, government offices, and law firms in a variety of areas. Research programs are available at the Center for Public Interest Law, Patient Advocacy Program, and the Children's Advocacy Institute. Field work may be done for credit through the Clinical Education Program as well as Summer Community Service grants. Students may also receive credit for judicial field placements with state and federal courts. Special lecture series include the Nathanson Series, featuring such speakers as U.S. Supreme Court Justices Sandra Day O'Connor, and Antonin Scalia, and the Seigan Series, featuring such speakers as Nobel Laureate Milton Friedman and Judge Robert Bork. The Institute on International and Comparative Law sponsors the Summer Law Study Programs, held in England, France, Ireland, Italy, and Spain. Internships for credit are available in England and France. The Academic Support Program makes special services available to eligible students. A faculty member provides academic counseling and sets up study groups for each class. The most widely taken electives are courses relevant to international law, environmental law, and corporate law.

Graduation Requirements

In order to graduate, candidates must have a grade average of 75 and have completed the upper-division writing requirement.

Organizations

Students edit the *San Diego Law Review*, the newspaper *Motions*, the *Journal of Contemporary Legal Issues* published by the law school; and *Legal Theory*, a quarterly journal published by Cambridge University Press in conjuction with Yale, Harvard, and USD law schools. Moot court competitions include the Alumni Tort, Annual USD National Criminal Procedure Competition, and Jessup International Law. All are held annually on the university campus, except for the National, which is held at the San Diego Court House. Other competitions include Advanced Trial Advocacy and Mock Trial, Lou Kerig Criminal Law Competition, Thomas More Constituitional Law Competition, National Criminal Procedure Competition, and John Winters Competition. Student organizations include Student Bar Association, Environmental Law Society, and International Law Society. Phi Delta Phi and Phi Alpha Delta have local chapters.

Library

The law library contains 453,301 hardcopy volumes and 1,415,092 microform volume equivalents, and subscribes to 5305 serial publications. Such on-line databases and networks as LEXIS, DIALOG, WESTLAW, NEXIS, OCLC, RLIN, Legal-Trac, Netscape, and Undocs are available to law students for research. Special library collections include state and federal depositories, tax collection, and California collection. A new computer instructional lab provides state-of-the-art access to legal research tools, the Internet, and law office technology.

Placement

J.D.s awarded:	284

Services available through: separate law school placement center.

Special features: panel discussions sponsored by the Alumni Association that focus on law practice, alternative careers, and law clerk training.

Full-time job interviews:	n/av
Summer job interviews:	n/av
Placement by graduation:	n/av
Placement within 9 months:	89% of class
Average starting salary:	$30,000 to $85,000

Areas of placement:

Private practice 2-10 attorneys	29%
Private practice 11-25 attorneys	14%
Private practice 26-50 attorneys	9%
Private practice 51-100 attorneys	11%
Government	17%
Business Industry	15%
Judicial clerkships	2%
Academic	1%
Public interest	1%
Military	1%

Faculty

The law school has 61 full-time and 56 part-time faculty members, of whom 36 are women. According to AAUP standards for Category I institutions, faculty salaries are above average. The ratio of full-time students to full-time faculty in an average class is 20 to 1. The law school has a regular program of bringing visiting professors and other distinguished lecturers and visitors to campus. There is a chapter of the Order of the Coif; 62 faculty and 187 graduates are members.

Students

About 44% of the student body are women; 23%, minorities; 2%, African American; 12%, Asian American; 8%, Hispanic; and 1%, Native American. The majority of students come from California (69%). The average age of entering students is 24; age range is 20 to 63. About 7% drop out after the first year for academic or personal reasons; 90% remain to receive a law degree.

University of San Diego **485**

School of Law

2130 Fulton Street
San Francisco, CA 94117-1080

Application Filing	Accreditation
Fall: April 1	ABA, AALS
Spring: n/app	Degrees Granted
Fee: $40	J.D., LL.M.

Enrollment 1998–1999		First-Year Class	
Men:	268 44%	Applied:	2445
Women:	346 56%	Accepted:	1148
Minorities:	172 28%	Enrolled:	228
Out-of-State:	68 11%		

1998–99 Class Profile

LSAT Percentile: 68%
LSAT Median Score: 155
Percentage passing bar on first try: n/av

Tuition and Fees:

Resident
$22,234

Average (public)
$8,772

Average (private)
$19,562

Nonresident
$22,354

Average (public)
$14,629

Average (private)
$19,562

0   5   10   15   20   25   30

Percentage receiving financial aid: 89%

ADMISSIONS
In the fall 1999 first-year class, 2445 applied, 1148 were accepted, and 228 enrolled. The median LSAT percentile of the most recent first-year class was 68; the median GPA was 3.2 on a scale of 4.0.

Requirements
Applicants must have a bachelor's degree from an accredited institution and take the LSAT. The most important admission factors include LSAT results, GPA, and academic achievement. No specific undergraduate courses are required. Candidates are not interviewed.

Procedure
The application deadline for fall entry is April 1. Applicants should submit an application form, LSAT results, transcripts, a nonrefundable application fee of $40, 2 letters of recommendation, and a personal essay. Notification of the admission decision is on a rolling basis. The latest acceptable LSAT test date for fall entry is February. The law school uses the LSDAS.

Special
The law school recruits minority and disadvantaged students by actively recruiting under the special admissions program. Transfer students must have one year of credit, and have attended an ABA-approved law school; deadline for transfer is July 1.

Costs
Tuition and fees for the 1999-2000 academic year are $22,234 for all full-time students. On-campus room and board costs about $7900 annually; and books supplies run $750.

Financial Aid
About 89% of current law students receive some form of aid. The average annual amount of aid from all sources combined, including scholarships, loans, and work contracts, in $30,000; maximum, $37,144. Awards are based on merit. The required financial statement is FAFSA. The aid application deadline for fall entry is on a rolling basis. The Special Admissions Program provides a grant that varies in amount not exceeding $5000. First-year students are notified about their financial aid application at the time of acceptance.

About the Law School
University of San Francisco School of Law was established in 1912 and is a private institution. The 55-acre campus is in an urban area in the center of San Francisco, adjacent to Golden Gate Park. The primary mission of the law school is to educate students to be skilled lawyers with a social conscience and a global perspective, emphasizing analytical ability and other fundamental skills, along with full awareness of special obligations to society. Students have access to federal, state, county, city, and local agencies, courts, correctional facilities, law firms, and legal aid organizations in the San Francisco area. The law

school is minutes away from federal, state, and municipal courts as well as cultural, social, and recreational resources in San Francisco and throughout the greater Bay Area. Facilities of special interest to law students are the law building, Kendrick Hall, which contains classrooms, the library, and faculty and administrative offices. A newer addition houses a moot court room, seminar rooms, offices, and library space. The Koret Center, a large health and recreational center on campus, is available to all law students. Housing for law students is limited on campus; listings of off-campus accommodations are also available.

Calendar
The law school operates on a traditional semester basis. Courses for full-time students are offered both day and evening and must be completed within 5 years; required courses are offered during the day and elective courses both day; and evening. For part-time students, courses are offered both day and evening (mostly evenings) and must be completed within 5 years. New full-and part-time students are admitted in the fall; part-time, fall. There is an 8-week summer session. Transferable summer courses are offered.

Programs
In addition to the J.D., the law school offers the LL.M. The following joint degrees may be earned: J.D./M.B.A. (Juris Doctor/Master of Business Administration).

Required
To earn the J.D., candidates must complete 86 total credits, of which 48 are for required courses. They must maintain a minimum GPA of 2.0 in the required courses. The following first-year courses are required of all students: Civil Procedure I and II, Contracts I and II, Criminal Law (second-year, part-time), Torts I and II, Legal Research, Writing, and Analysis I and II, Criminal Procedure (second-year, part-time), and Moot Court (second-year, part-time). Required upper-level courses consist of Property I and II, Constitutional Law I and II, Evidence, Professional Responsibility, and a research and writing requirement. The required orientation program for first-year students is a 1-week program.

Phone: 415-422-6586
Fax: 415-422-6433

Contact

Director of Admissions, 415-422-6586 for general inquiries; Office of Financial Aid, 415-422-6210 for financial aid information.

CALIFORNIA

Electives

The School of Law offers concentrations in corporate law, criminal law, environmental law, family law, international law, juvenile law, labor law, litigation, maritime law, securities law, tax law, torts and insurance, and intellectual property (including entertainment, sports, and media law). Clinics include the USF Law Clinic, a teaching law firm staffed by faculty and students with a caseload half-criminal, half-civil; the narcotics prosecution clinic, with the city's District Attorney's office; the Mediation Clinic, with Family Court Services; and the Judicial Clerkship and Externship. The Cambodian Law and Democracy Project allows law students to assist efforts to reestablish legal institutions and legal education in Cambodia through research into American and foreign legal systems. Summer research and tutoring positions are available in Phnom Penh for interested USF law students. Summer study-abroad programs are offered at Trinity College, Dublin; Charles University, Prague; and Udayana University, Bali. There is a special Admission Program to promote enhanced opportunity for students who have been deprived of equal educational opportunity or who are members of groups underrepresented in higher education. Tutorial programs are available for Special Admission Program's students through the Academic Support Program. Special interest group programs include the Street Law Project, a program to promote legal literacy among 30 Bay Area high schools, and Asian Pacific Legal Studies Program, a special international law focus on Pacific Rim nations. The most widely taken electives are Corporations, Wills and Trusts, and Remedies.

Graduation Requirements

In order to graduate, candidates must have a GPA of 2.0 and have completed the upper-division writing requirement.

Organizations

Students edit the *University of San Francisco Law Review*, and the *University of San Francisco Maritime Law Journal*, one of only 2 maritime law reviews published in the United States. The student newspaper is *The Forum*. Students participate in the National Moot Court, Jessup International Law Moot Court, and Roger Memorial Moot Court competitions. Other competitions include the Advocate of the Year and the Nathan Burkan Memorial competitions. Law student organizations include the McAuliffe Honor Society, Student Bar Association, and Admiralty and Maritime Law Society. There are local chapters of Environmental Law Society, American Trial Lawyers Association, and Intellectual Property Association. Campus clubs and other organizations include the Public Interest Law Foundation, St. Thomas More Society, and Entertainment Law Society.

Library

The law library contains 295,317 hardcopy volumes and 161,252 microform volume equivalents, and subscribes to 2693 serial publications. Such on-line databases and networks as LEXIS, DIALOG, WESTLAW, Innovative OPAC; and Internet legal resources are available to law students for research. Special library collections include California and federal government documents depository collections. Recently, the library installed a CD-ROM network, a computer lab network, and a Web-based integrated automated library system (Millennium II). The ratio of library volumes to faculty is 10,938 to 1 and to students, 491 to 1. The ratio of seats in the library to students is 1 to 2.

Faculty

The law school has 24 full-time and 59 part-time faculty members, of whom 26 are women. About 15% of full-time faculty have a graduate law degree in addition to the J.D.; about 5% of part-time faculty have one. The ratio of full-time students to full-time faculty in an average class is 20 to 1; in a clinic, 8 to 1. The law school has a regular program of bringing visiting professors and other distinguished lecturers and visitors to campus.

Placement

J.D.s awarded:	200

Services available through: separate law school placement center.

Services: career seminars, on-campus interviewing

Special features: Mentor Program, Public Interest Law Program

Full-time job interviews:	25 employers
Summer job interviews:	45 employers
Placement by graduation:	n/av
Placement within 9 months:	81% of class
Average starting salary:	$52,000 to $57,073

Areas of placement:

Private practice 2-100 attorneys	60%
Private practice 101-501+ attorneys	7%
Business/industry	15%
Government	7%
Judicial clerkships	5%
Public interest	5%
Academic	1%

Students

About 56% of the student body are women; 28%, minorities; 4%, African American; 14%, Asian American; 7%, Hispanic; and 3%, multi-ethnic. The majority of students come from California (89%). The average age of entering students is 25; age range is 20 to 42. About 19% of students enter directly from undergraduate school and 5% have a graduate degree. About 9% drop out after the first year for academic or personal reasons; 90% remain to receive a law degree.

UNIVERSITY OF SOUTH CAROLINA

School of Law

Main and Greene Streets
Columbia, SC 29208

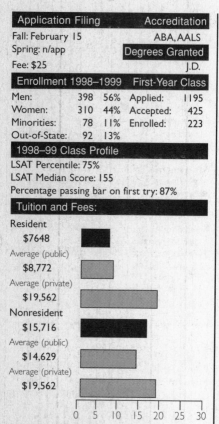

Application Filing		Accreditation
Fall: February 15		ABA, AALS
Spring: n/app		Degrees Granted
Fee: $25		J.D.

Enrollment 1998–1999		First-Year Class	
Men:	398 56%	Applied:	1195
Women:	310 44%	Accepted:	425
Minorities:	78 11%	Enrolled:	223
Out-of-State:	92 13%		

1998–99 Class Profile
LSAT Percentile: 75%
LSAT Median Score: 155
Percentage passing bar on first try: 87%

Tuition and Fees:

Resident
$7648

Average (public)
$8,772

Average (private)
$19,562

Nonresident
$15,716

Average (public)
$14,629

Average (private)
$19,562

0 5 10 15 20 25 30

Percentage receiving financial aid: 85%

ADMISSIONS
In the fall 1999 first-year class, 1195 applied, 425 were accepted, and 223 enrolled. Twenty transfers enrolled. The median LSAT percentile of the most recent first-year class was 75; the median GPA was 3.23 on a scale of 4.0. The highest LSAT percentile was 99.

Requirements
Applicants must have a bachelor's degree from an accredited institution and take the LSAT. Minimum acceptable GPA is 2.0 on a scale of 4.0. The most important admission factors include GPA, LSAT results, and class rank. No specific undergraduate courses are required. Candidates are interviewed.

Procedure
The application deadline for fall entry is February 15. Applicants should submit an application form, LSAT results, transcripts, a nonrefundable application fee of $25, 2 letters of recommendation, use of the LSDAS, a personal statement, and dean's certification. Notification of the admission decision is from mid-February to May. The latest acceptable LSAT test date for fall entry is February. The law school uses the LSDAS.

Special
The law school recruits minority and disadvantaged students through campus visits and a minority recruitment day that is held on campus in the fall; students are invited to attend. Requirements are different for out-of-state students in that their LSAT and GPA scores must be better than residents' scores. Transfer students must have one year of credit, have a minimum GPA of 3.0, have attended an ABA-approved law school, be in good standing, and be eligible to return to their current law school.

Costs
Tuition and fees for the 1999-2000 academic year are $7648 for full-time in-state students and $15,716 for out-of-state students. Books and supplies run $500.

Financial Aid
About 85% of current law students receive some form of aid. The average annual amount of aid from all sources combined, including scholarships, loans, and work contracts, is $12,000; maximum, $18,983. Awards are based on need and merit. The required financial statements are the FAFSA and the School of Law scholarship application. The aid application deadline for fall entry is April 15. Special funds for minority or disadvantaged students are provided through the Minority Scholarship program and other law school sources. First-year students are notified about their financial aid application at time of acceptance.

About the Law School
University of South Carolina School of Law was established in 1866 and is a public institution. The campus is in an urban area in downtown Columbia, . The primary mission of the law school is to develop professional competence and responsibility. The school seeks to qualify its graduates for the highest opportunities in professional legal services and to instill a sense of perspective about what the law is capable of doing for the good of society. Students have access to federal, state, county, city, and local agencies, courts, correctional facilities, law firms, and legal aid organizations in the Columbia area. The U.S. Department of Justice's Legal Education Program has moved from Washington, D.C. to Columbia and is affiliated with the law school. Facilities of special interest to law students are the 2 courtrooms in the school. One is designed as a moot courtroom, and the other is an actual courtroom periodically used by the state court system. There is also a computer laboratory for student use. Housing for law students is available in numerous apartments within commuting distance of the school. The university has apartments for married students near the campus. All law school facilities are accessible to the physically disabled.

Calendar
The law school operates on a traditional semester basis. Courses for full-time students are offered days only and must be completed within 3 years. There is no part-time program. New students are admitted in the fall. There is an 8- week summer session. Transferable summer courses are offered.

Programs
Students may take relevant courses in other programs and apply credit toward the J.D.; a maximum of 9 hours if in joint-degree program and 6 hours, if not, may be applied. The following joint degrees may be earned: J.D./M.B.A (Juris Doctor/Master of Business Administration), J.D./M.I.B.S. (Juris Doctor/Masters of International Business), J.D./M.P.A. (Juris Doctor/Master of Public Administration), J.D./M.C.J. (Juris Doctor/Master of Criminal Justice), J.D./M.S.W. (Juris Doctor/Master of Social Work), J.D./M.E.S. (Juris Doctor/Master of Environmental Science), J.D./H.R.M. (Juris Doctor/Master of Human Resource Management), and J.D./M.T. (Juris Doctor/Master of Taxation).

Phone: 803-777-6605
Fax: 803-777-7751
E-mail: usclaw@law.law.sc.edu
Web: www.law.sc.edu/

Contact

Assistant Dean for Admissions, 803-777-6605 for general inquiries; Director of Financial Aid, 803-777-6605 for financial aid information.

SOUTH CAROLINA ◉

Required

To earn the J.D., candidates must complete 90 total credits, of which 46 are for required courses. They must maintain a minimum GPA of 2.0 in the required courses. The following first-year courses are required of all students: Civil Procedure, Constitutional Law, Contracts I and II, Property I and II, Torts I and II, Introduction to Legal System and Legal Writing, and Introduction to Legal Research and Lawyering. Required upper-level courses consist of Criminal Process, Professional Responsibility, a perspective course, and a writing requirement. The required orientation program for first-year students is 1 day before the start of classes. Accepted students are also invited to a reception in the spring prior to the start of the first fall semester.

Electives

The School of Law offers concentrations in corporate law, labor law, litigation, tax law, business law, commercial law and bankruptcy, probate and estate planning, and real estate. In addition, there are several types of clinics, usually for 3 credit hours, including Consumer Bankruptcy and Criminal Practice. Students gain closely supervised training experience in the representation of clients. A number of seminars are offered each semester, such as Death Penalty and Environmental Law. All have limited enrollment, require a paper to be written, and are for 3 credit hours. In the area of research programs, students may take the course Supervised Legal Research for 2 credit hours. It is an independent study performed under the supervision of a faculty member and requires a research paper. Many upper-level students clerk for law firms during the school year. A special lecture series is open to all students. First-year students offered a tutorial program. All first-year courses have an assigned tutor. A minority peer assistance tutorial program is also available. Special interest group programs include the Pro Bono Program, which provides opportunities for volunteer law students to obtain practical legal training. The most widely taken electives are litigation, business, and commercial law.

Graduation Requirements

In order to graduate, candidates must have a GPA of 2.0 and have completed the upper-division writing requirement.

Organizations

The primary law review is the *South Carolina Law Review*; the other law reviews are *ABA Real Property, Probate, and Trust Journal* and *The South Carolina Environmental Law Journal*. The student newspaper is the *Gavel Raps*. The school sponsors teams in the National, International, American Bar Association, and Labor Law Moot Court competitions as well as the National Trial competitions. Other competitions include J. Woodrow Lewis Intramural Moot Court Competition in appellate advocacy. Law student organizations are the Student Bar Association, Black Law Studetns Assoction, and Women in Law. Local chapters of national associations are Phi Alpha Delta and Phi Delta Phi. Campus clubs and other organizations include the Society of International Law, Wig and Robe, and the Federalist Society.

Library

The law library contains 330,000 hardcopy volumes and 2718 microform volume equivalents, and subscribes to 972 serial publications. Such on-line databases and networks as LEXIS, DIALOG, WESTLAW, and NEXIS are available to law students for research. Special library collections include a South Carolina legal history collection and a selective GPO depository. Recently, the library installed 2 new electronic classrooms. The ratio of library volumes to faculty is 8250 to 1 and to students, 418 to 1.

Faculty

The law school has 43 full-time and 26 part-time faculty members, of whom 9 are women. According to AAUP standards for Category I institutions, faculty salaries are average. About 55% of full-time faculty have a graduate law degree in addition to the J.D. The ratio of full-time students to full-time faculty in an average class is 45 to 1; in a clinic, 12 to 1. The law school has a regular program of bringing visiting professors and other distinguished lecturers and visitors to campus. There is a chapter of the Order of the Coif; 19 faculty and 281 graduates are members.

Placement

J.D.s awarded:	242
Services available through: separate law school placement center.	
Services:	
Special features: monthly job opportunity newsletter for a nominal fee, free job opportunities postings on the Internet, Directory of the South Carolina Legal Profession, which lists virtually all law firms in the state, including very small firms, their number of lawyers and practice areas, and also lists judiciary, state agencies, solicitors, and public defenders.	
Full-time job interviews:	31 employers
Summer job interviews:	46 employers
Placement by graduation:	59% of class
Placement within 9 months:	92% of class
Average starting salary:	$26,000 to $91,000
Areas of placement:	
Private practice 2-10 attorneys	32%
Private practice 11-25 attorneys	11%
Private pratice 26-50 attorneys	3%
Private practice 51-100 attorneys	4%
Judicial clerkships	24%
Government	11%
Business/industry	6%
Public interest	2%
Military	1%

Students

About 44% of the student body are women; 11%, minorities; 9%, African American; and 1%, Asian American. The majority of students come from South Carolina (87%). The average age of entering students is 23; age range is 21 to 51. About 55% of students enter directly from undergraduate school, 6% have a graduate degree, and 45% have worked full-time prior to entering law school. About 3% drop out after the first year for academic or personal reasons; 97% remain to receive a law degree.

UNIVERSITY OF SOUTH DAKOTA

School of Law

414 East Clark Street
Vermillion, SD 57069-2390

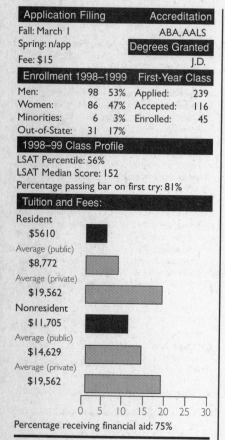

Application Filing		Accreditation
Fall: March 1		ABA, AALS
Spring: n/app		Degrees Granted
Fee: $15		J.D.

Enrollment 1998–1999			First-Year Class	
Men:	98	53%	Applied:	239
Women:	86	47%	Accepted:	116
Minorities:	6	3%	Enrolled:	45
Out-of-State:	31	17%		

1998–99 Class Profile
LSAT Percentile: 56%
LSAT Median Score: 152
Percentage passing bar on first try: 81%

Tuition and Fees:

Resident
$5610

Average (public)
$8,772

Average (private)
$19,562

Nonresident
$11,705

Average (public)
$14,629

Average (private)
$19,562

0 5 10 15 20 25 30

Percentage receiving financial aid: 75%

ADMISSIONS

In the fall 1999 first-year class, 239 applied, 116 were accepted, and 45 enrolled. Three transfers enrolled. The median LSAT percentile of the most recent first-year class was 56; the median GPA was 3.28 on a scale of 4.0. The lowest LSAT percentile accepted was 5; the highest was 93.

Requirements

Applicants must have a bachelor's degree from an accredited institution and take the LSAT. The most important admission factors include LSAT results, GPA, and character, personality. No specific undergraduate courses are required, but those that require writing reports and papers and logical, analytic reasoning are recommended. In addition, an understanding of the basic principles of accounting may be helpful for the practice of business-related law. Candidates are not interviewed.

Procedure

The application deadline for fall entry is March 1. Applicants should submit an application form, LSAT results, a nonrefundable application fee of $15, 2 letters of recommendation, a personal statement, and the LSDAS report. Notification of the admission decision is on a rolling basis. The latest acceptable LSAT test date for fall entry is February. The law school uses the LSDAS.

Special

The law school recruits minority and disadvantaged students by mail solicitation and meeting in person with prospects. Transfer students must have one year of credit, have attended an ABA-approved law school, and be in good standing at their present law school.

Costs

Tuition and fees for the 1999-2000 academic year are $5610 for full-time in-state students and $11,705 for out-of-state students. On-campus room and board costs about $3550 annually; and books and supplies run $1000.

Financial Aid

About 75% of current law students receive some form of aid. Awards are based on need and merit. The required financial statement is FAFSA. Check with the school for current aid application deadline. First-year students are notified about their financial aid application at the time of acceptance.

About the Law School

University of South Dakota School of Law was established in 1901 and is a public institution. The 216-acre campus is in a small town 50 miles south of Sioux Falls. The primary mission of the law school is to prepare students for the practice of law and to train professionally competent graduates capable of achieving their career goals and serving their profession. Students have access to federal, state, county, city, and local agencies, courts, correctional facilities, law firms, and legal aid organizations in the Vermillion area. Housing for law students is described as adequate. All law school facilities are accessible to the physically disabled.

Calendar

The law school operates on a traditional semester basis. Courses for full-time students are offered days only and must be completed within 6 semesters. There is no part-time program. New full-time students are admitted in the fall. There is a 6-week summer session. Transferable summer courses are offered.

Programs

Students may take relevant courses in other programs and apply credit toward the J.D.; a maximum of 9 credits may be applied. The following joint degrees may be earned: J.D./M.B.A. (Juris Doctor/Master of Business Administration), J.D./M.P.A. (Juris Doctor/Master of Public Administration), J.D./M.A. (Juris Doctor/Master of Arts in English, history, psychology, and political science, J.D./M.P.Acc. (Juris Doctor/Master of Professional Accountancy), , J.D./M.A. (Juris Doctor/Master of Education Administration), and J.D./M.S.A.S. (Juris Doctor/Master of Science in Administrative Studies).

Phone: 605-677-5443
Fax: 605-677-5417
E-mail: lawreq@usd.edu
Web: http://www.usd.edu/law

Contact

Jean Henriques, Admission Officer/Registrar, 605-677-5443 for general inquiries; University Financial Aid Office, 605-677-5446 for financial aid information.

SOUTH DAKOTA

Required

To earn the J.D., candidates must complete 90 total credits, of which 43 are for required courses. They must maintain a minimum grade average of 60 in the required courses. The following first-year courses are required of all students: Torts, Contracts, Property, Criminal Law and Procedure, Civil Procedure, Legal Writing, Legal Research, and Appellate Advocacy. Required upper-level courses consist of Constitutional Law, Evidence, Legal Profession, and code course (Commercial Law, Secured Transactions, or Federal Income Tax. The required orientation program for first-year students lasts for 2 1/2 days.

Electives

The School of Law offers concentrations in corporate law, criminal law, environmental law, international law, tax law, and Indian law. In addition, externships are available for third-year students, amounting to 15 hours a semester (or 6 hours during the summer). Research programs, amounting to 1 or 2 hours of credit, are available for second- and third-year students. Study abroad opportunities are available if approved and the student has an average of at least 75. The most widely taken electives are Trusts and Wills, Family Law, and Commercial Law.

Graduation Requirements

In order to graduate, candidates must have a grade average of 70 and have upper-division writing requirement.

Organizations

The primary law review is the *South Dakota Law Review*. Other publications include the *Great Plains Natural Resources Journal*. Moot court competitions are held at intramural, regional, and national levels. Other competitions include Client Counseling and Negotiations, which are available on the local and regional level. Law student organizations include Women in law, Native American Law Students Association, Christian Legal Society, and Law Caucus. Local chapters of national associations are Delta Theta Phi and Phi Alpha Delta.

Library

The law library contains 188,061 hardcopy volumes and 11,824 microform volume equivalents, and subscribes to 750 serial publications. Such on-line databases and networks as LEXIS, DIALOG, and WESTLAW are available to law students for research. Special library collections include a government documents depository collection, which is an extension of the main university library's collection. Other collections include reference, reserve, and Indian law. Recently, the library provided students and faculty with 24/7 access to the library. The ratio of seats in the library to students is 1 to 1.

Faculty

The law school has 15 full-time and 2 part-time faculty members, of whom 3 are women. About 27% of full-time faculty have a graduate law degree in addition to the J.D. The ratio of full-time students to full-time faculty in an average class is 15 to 1. The law school has a regular program of bringing visiting professors and other distinguished lecturers and visitors to campus.

Students

About 47% of the student body are women; 3%, minorities; 1%, African American; 1%, Asian American; 2%, Native American; and 1%, African. The majority of students come from South Dakota (83%). The average age of entering students is 27; age range is 21 to 45. About 47% of students enter directly from undergraduate school and 2% have a graduate degree. About 7% drop out after the first year for academic or personal reasons; 93% remain to receive a law degree.

Placement

J.D.s awarded:	69
Services available through: A separate law school placement center.	
Special features: alumni network	
Full-time job interviews:	12 employers
Summer job interviews:	26 employers
Placement by graduation:	56% of class
Placement within 9 months:	94% of class
Average starting salary:	$25,000 to $30,000
Areas of placement:	
Private practice 2-10 attorneys	31%
Private practice 11-25 attorneys	2%
Private practice 51-100 attorneys	2%
Judicial clerkships	33%
Government	18%
Business/industry	12%
Academic	2%

Law School

Application Filing

Fall: February 1
Spring: n/app
Fee: $60

Accreditation

ABA, AALS

Degrees Granted

J.D.

Enrollment 1998–1999   First-Year Class

Men:	315	52%	Applied:	3878
Women:	293	48%	Accepted:	869
Minorities:	249	41%	Enrolled:	199
Out-of-State:	243	40%		

1998–99 Class Profile

LSAT Percentile: 92%
LSAT Median Score: 164
Percentage passing bar on first try: 90%

Tuition and Fees:

Resident
$26,522

Average (public)
$8,772

Average (private)
$19,562

Nonresident
$26,522

Average (public)
$14,629

Average (private)
$19,562

0 5 10 15 20 25 30

Percentage receiving financial aid: 80%

ADMISSIONS

In the fall 1999 first-year class, 3878 applied, 869 were accepted, and 199 enrolled. Four transfers enrolled. The median LSAT percentile of the most recent first-year class was 92; the median GPA was 3.5 on a scale of 4.0.

Requirements

Applicants must have a bachelor's degree from an accredited institution and take the LSAT. No specific undergraduate courses are required. Candidates are not interviewed.

Procedure

The application deadline for fall entry is February 1. Applicants should submit an application form, LSAT results, transcripts, a nonrefundable application fee of $60, 1 letter of recommendation, and a personal statement. Notification of the admission decision is in the spring. The latest acceptable LSAT test date for fall entry is December. The law school uses the LSDAS.

Special

The law school recruits minority and disadvantaged students by means of mail outreach campaigns, school visits, and minority receptions; the minority student organizations also help recruit and retain qualified candidates. Transfer students must have one year of credit, have attended an ABA-approved law school, and be in the top 20% of their first-year class.

Costs

Tuition and fees for the 1999-2000 academic year are $26,522 for all full-time students. On-campus room and board costs about $7282 annually; books and supplies run $800.

Financial Aid

About 80% of current law students receive some form of aid. The average annual amount of aid from all sources combined, including scholarships, loans, and work contracts, is $15,000; maximum, $38,000. Awards are based on need and merit. The required financial statements are FAFSA and Law School financial aid application. The aid application deadline for fall entry is February 15. Special funds for minority or disadvantaged students consist of scholarships that are used in part to assist disadvantaged and minority students. First-year students are notified about their financial aid application at time of acceptance.

About the Law School

University of Southern California Law School was established in 1900 and is a private institution. The 150-acre campus is in an urban area 3½ miles south of downtown Los Angeles. The primary mission of the law school is to offer an innovative program focusing on the law as an expression of social values and as an instrument for implementing social goals. Students have access to federal, state, county, city, and local agencies, courts, correctional facilities, law firms, and legal aid organizations in the Los Angeles area. Facilities of special interest to law students include a computer lab, multimedia classrooms, large and high-tech library facilities, a spacious student lounge, and clinical law offices. The USC campus features a 24-hour library, fitness center, specialty libraries, theaters, and restaurants. Housing for law students consists of an on-campus apartment house designated for law students.

Calendar

The law school operates on a traditional semester basis. Courses for full-time students are offered days only and must be completed within 4 years. There is no part-time program. New full-time students are admitted in the fall. There is no summer session. Transferable summer courses are not offered.

Programs

Students may take relevant courses in other programs and apply credit toward the J.D.; a maximum of 12 credits may be applied. The following joint degrees may be earned: J.D./M.B.A. (Juris Doctor/Master of Business Administration), J.D./M.B.T. (Juris Doctor/Master of Business Taxation), J.D./M.A. (Juris Doctor/Master of Arts in economics), J.D./M.R.E.D. (Juris Doctor/Master of Real Estate Development), J.D./M.S.W. (Juris Doctor/Master of Social Work), J.D./M.P.A. (Juris Doctor/Master of Public Administration), J.D./Ph.D. (Juris Doctor/Doctor of Philosophy in Economics), J.D./M.A.P. (Juris Doctor/Master of Philosophy), J.D./M.A. (Juris Doctor/Master of Arts in international relations), J.D./M.A. (Juris Doctor/Master of Arts in communications management), J.D./M.A. (Juris Doctor/Master of Arts in religion), J.D./M.S. (Juris Doctor/Master of Science in gerontology), J.D./M.P.P. (Juris Doctor/Master of Public Policy), J.D./M.A. (Juris Doctor/Master of Arts in political science), and J.D./Ph.D. (Juris Doctor/Doctor of Philosophy in political science).

Contact

William J. Hoye, Assistant Dean, 213-740-7331 for general inquiries; Mary Bingham, Director of Financial Aid, 213-740-7331 for financial aid information.

CALIFORNIA

Required

To earn the J.D., candidates must complete 88 total credits, of which 31 are for required courses. They must maintain a minimum grade average of 70 in the required courses. The following first-year courses are required of all students: Law Language and Ethics, Torts I, Civil Procedure, Contracts, Criminal Law, Constitutional Law, Property, Legal Research and Introduction to Lawyering Skills, and Legal Profession. Required upper-level courses consist of a writing requirement. The required orientation program for first-year students is a 1-day program that includes a welcoming address, luncheon, financial aid counseling, meetings with second-year advisers assigned to incoming students, and a barbecue. A student-run mentor program for first-year students has year-round activities.

Electives

The Law School offers concentrations in corporate law, criminal law, entertainment, environmental law, family law, international law, juvenile law, labor law, litigation, media law, securities law, tax law, torts and insurance, and public interest, constitutional law, and civil rights. In addition, actual and simulated clinics are available for upper-level students. Actual clinics include the Post-Conviction Justice project or the Children's Legal Issues Clinic. Internships, worth 4 credits, are available for upper-level students with government or public interest nonprofit organizations. Judicial externships allow students to clerk for a state or federal judge. There is a Pacific Center research program as well as individual research projects with faculty. Special lecture series include the Roth lecture, Olin faculty workshops, and faculty workshops. There is no study-abroad program, but credit may be given for work done in other accredited law schools' study-abroad programs. Tutorials are arranged on a case-by-case basis. The school also offers a 5-part workshop on studying. An exam-taking skills course is offered to first-year students in the spring and upper-division students in the fall. Student-run organizations geared at specific areas of the legal profession include the Entertainment Law Society, International Law Society, Corporate Law Society, and Public Interest Law Foundation. The most widely taken electives are Entertainment Law, What Lawyers Should Know About Business, and Gender Discrimination.

Graduation Requirements

In order to graduate, candidates must have completed the upper-division writing requirement.

Organizations

Students edit the *Southern California Law Review, Southern California Interdisciplinary Law Journal, Southern California Review of Law and Womens Studies*, the newspaper, *The Law Street Journal. Advance Sheet*, a weekly newsletter, and *USC Law*, a semiannual alumni/ae magazine. All first-year students participate in moot court competitions; the 40 best advocates are selected to compete, in their second year, in the Hale Moot Court Honors Program. In addition, the best advocates from the Hale Moot Court Competition participate in numerous national competitions. Student organizations include the Environmental Law Society, the Health Law Society, and the Sports, Music and Entertainment Society. Local chapters of national associations are Phi Alpha Delta and Phi Delta Phi.

Library

The law library contains 366,333 hardcopy volumes and 493,817 microform volume equivalents, and subscribes to 2127 serial publications. Such on-line databases and networks as LEXIS, DIALOG, WESTLAW, NEXIS, Dataquick, and ADVOCAT are available to law students for research. Special library collections include a selected depository. Among the important holdings are health law/bioethics, law and economics, law and philosophy, law and social sciences, taxation, preventive law and historic documents concerning President Lincoln. Recently, the library expanded facilities with an addition and renovation, including new computer laboratories and classrooms, and increased seating and study areas; library carrels are wired for laptop Internet access. The ratio of seats in the library to students is 1 to 2.

Faculty

The law school has 46 full-time and 40 part-time faculty members, of whom 18 are women. According to AAUP standards for Category I institutions, faculty salaries are well above average. About 35% of full-time faculty have a graduate law degree in addition to the J.D. The ratio of full-time students to full-time faculty in an average class is 15 to 1; in a

Placement

J.D.s awarded:	205

Services available through: separate law school placement center.

Services: lists of public interest contacts, counseling regarding wide array of alternatives, a major on-campus placement program, videotaped practice interviews, 1-to-1 mentor program with graduates for first-year students in the second semester

Special features: videotaped interviews for practice and a 1-to-1 mentor program with graduates for first-year students in the second semester; the Career Services Office's a *Guide to Public Interest Law* for its students/graduates; Alumni-Student Mock Interview Program

Full-time job interviews:	175 employers
Summer job interviews:	225 employers
Placement by graduation:	92% of class
Placement within 9 months:	95% of class
Average starting salary:	$87,000 to $91,000

Areas of placement:

Private practice 2-10 attorneys	5%
Private practice 11-25 attorneys	10%
Private practice 26-50 attorneys	20%
Private practice 51-100 attorneys	30%
Business/industry	14%
Judicial Clerkships	10%
Public interest	6%
Government	5%

clinic, 5 to 1. The law school has a regular program of bringing visiting professors and other distinguished lecturers and visitors to campus. There is a chapter of the Order of the Coif; 15 faculty and the top 10% of every graduating class are members.

Students

About 48% of the student body are women; 41%, minorities; 12%, African American; 15%, Asian American; 14%, Hispanic; and 1%, Native American. The majority of students come from California (60%). The average age of entering students is 24; age range is 20 to 50. About 40% of students enter directly from undergraduate school, 25% have a graduate degree, and 35% have worked full-time prior to entering law school. About 1% drop out after the first year for academic or personal reasons; 99% remain to receive a law degree.

College of Law

1505 W. Cumblerland Avenue
Knoxville, TN 37996-1810

Application Filing		Accreditation	
Fall: February 1		ABA, AALS	
Spring: n/app		**Degrees Granted**	
Fee: $15			J.D.

Enrollment 1998–1999		First-Year Class	
Men:	266 55%	Applied:	1049
Women:	218 45%	Accepted:	387
Minorities:	63 13%	Enrolled:	168
Out-of-State:	73 15%		

1998–99 Class Profile
LSAT Percentile: 70%
LSAT Median Score: 156
Percentage passing bar on first try: 88%

Tuition and Fees:

Resident
$5126

Average (public)
$8,772

Average (private)
$19,562

Nonresident
$13,432

Average (public)
$14,629

Average (private)
$19,562

0 5 10 15 20 25 30

Percentage receiving financial aid: 77%

ADMISSIONS

In the fall 1999 first-year class, 1049 applied, 387 were accepted, and 168 enrolled. Three transfers enrolled. The median LSAT percentile of the most recent first-year class was 70; the median GPA was 3.48 on a scale of 4.0. The lowest LSAT percentile accepted was 20; the highest was 99.

Requirements

Applicants must have a bachelor's degree from an accredited institution and take the LSAT. Admission factors are not ranked; all are considered during a subjective review of each complete file. No specific undergraduate courses are required. Candidates are not interviewed.

Procedure

The application deadline for fall entry is February 1. Applicants should submit an application form, a nonrefundable application fee of $15, 2 letters of recommendation, a personal statement, an essay, and a dean's certification form. Notification of the admission decision varies. The latest acceptable LSAT test date for fall entry is December. The law school uses the LSDAS.

Special

The law school recruits minority and disadvantaged students through a number of initiatives, including on-campus visits, LSAC forums, on-campus workshops, Tennessee Pre-Law Day (each spring), and LSAC CRS Service. Transfer students must have one year of credit, have a minimum GPA of 2.0, and have attended an ABA-approved law school. Transfer admission is limited and very competitive.

Costs

Tuition and fees for the 1999-2000 academic year are $5126 for full-time in-state students and $13,432 for out-of-state students. On-campus room and board costs about $5666 annually; and books and supplies run $1172.

Financial Aid

About 77% of current law students receive some form of aid. The average annual amount of aid from all sources combined, including scholarships, loans, and work contracts, is $14,082; maximum, $24,580. Awards are based on need and merit. The required financial statement is FAFSA. The aid application deadline for fall entry is February 14. Special funds for minority or disadvantaged students consist of scholarships that are awarded on the basis of demonstrated financial need and merit. First-year students are notified about their financial aid application before acceptance; usually in January.

About the Law School

University of Tennessee College of Law was established in 1890 and is a public institution. The 417-acre campus is in an urban area in Knoxville, Tennessee, in the heart of the university. The primary mission of the law school is to provide a first-rate legal education to a diverse group of students. Students have access to federal, state, county, city, and local agencies, courts, correctional facilities, law firms, and legal aid organizations in the Knoxville area. The College of Law is located approximately 1 mile from the courts and legal employers in downtown Knoxville. Facilities of special interest to law students include a fairly new law center, which houses civil and criminal clinics, a mediation program, the center for entrepreneurial law, classrooms, law library, and faculty offices. Several off-campus university apartment complexes are available to single and married students. Seven apartment complexes are located within a 5-mile radius of the campus. All law school facilities are accessible to the physically disabled.

Calendar

The law school operates on a traditional semester basis. Courses for full-time students are offered days only and must be completed within 5 years. There is no part-time program. New full-time students are admitted in the fall. There is an 8-week summer session. Transferable summer courses are offered.

Programs

Students may take relevant courses in other programs and apply credit toward the J.D.; a maximum of 6 credits may be applied. The following joint degrees may be earned: J.D./M.B.A. (Juris Doctor/Master of Business Administration).

Phone: 865-974-4131
Fax: 865-974-1572
E-mail: lawadmit@libra.law.utk.edu
Web: http://www.law.utk.edu

Contact
Carolyn Dossett, Admissions Assistant, 865-974-4131 for general inquiries; Janet Hatcher, Admissions and Financial Aid Adviser, 865-974-4131 for financial aid information.

Required
To earn the J.D., candidates must complete 89 total credits, of which 46 are for required courses. They must maintain a minimum GPA of 2.0 in the required courses. The following first-year courses are required of all students: Introduction to the Study of Law, Civil Procedure I and II, Contracts I and II, Criminal Law, Legal Process I and II, Torts I and II, and Property. Required upper-level courses consist of Constitutional Law, Legal Profession, a perspective course, an expository writing course, and a planning and drafting course. The Introductory Period begins with orientation, offers 3 1/2 days of mini courses in Civil Litigation Process and Case Analysis and Briefing, and concludes with one regular class meeting in Criminal Law, Contracts, and Torts.

Electives
The College of Law offers concentrations in business transactions, advocacy and dispute resolution. In addition, an advocacy clinic is open to third-year students who have completed trial practice. Students receive 6 hours credit. A mediation clinic is open to all upper-division students for 3 credits. A variety of seminars is available for 2 hours credit. An experimental prosecutorial internship is open to third-year students, who preferably have completed both Criminal Procedure I and II. Students receive 4 credit hours. An advanced legal research course is offered. Special lecture series include the Alumni Distinguished Lecture in Jurisprudence, the Charles Henderson Miller Lecture in Professional Responsibility, and the Speaker Series, which hosts nationally known speakers to address issues of importance to a wide spectrum of Tennesseans. Any student may study abroad through ABA-approved summer abroad programs. A maximum of 8 credits may be transferred. Students with a first-semester average below 2.0 are invited to participate, in the second semester, in tutorials in Contracts, Civil Procedure, and Torts. First-year students may attend a series of Law School Success Seminars on topics such as Managing Time and Energy in Law School; Outlining; sample exams in Civil Procedure, Torts, and Contracts; and Final Exams. The most widely taken electives are Commercial Law, Trial Practice, and Criminal Procedure.

Graduation Requirements
In order to graduate, candidates must have a GPA of 2.0, have completed the upper-division writing requirement, and the perspective requirement, the planning and drafting requirement.

Organizations
Students edit the *Tennessee Law Review* and the student newspapers *The Informant* and *UTK Daily Beacon*. Moot court competitions include the National Moot Court, National Trial, and Jerome Prince Evidence. Other competitions include the Jenkins Trial and Advocates Prize Moot Court. Law student organizations include the American Bar Association—Law Student Division, Association of Trial Lawyers of America—Student Chapter, and Hamilton Barrett Chapter of the American Inns of Court. There are local chapters of the Black Law Students Association, Phi Delta Phi, and Tennessee Association for Public Interest Law.

Library
The law library contains 469,108 hardcopy volumes and 1,145,172 microform volume equivalents, and subscribes to 6465 serial publications. Such on-line databases and networks as LEXIS, WESTLAW, and World Wide Web and Internet access, NEXIS, INFOTRAC are available to law students for research. Special library collections include a selective federal document depository and a Tennessee depository. The ratio of library volumes to faculty is 15,637 to 1 and to students, 969 to 1. The ratio of seats in the library to students is 1 to 1.

Faculty
The law school has 30 full-time and 27 part-time faculty members, of whom 18 are women. About 22% of full-time faculty have a graduate law degree in addition to the J.D.; about 5% of part-time faculty have one. The ratio of full-time students to full-time faculty in an average class is 16 to 1; in a clinic, 8 to 1. There is a chapter of the Order of the Coif.

Placement

J.D.s awarded:	155

Services available through: A separate law school placement center.

Services: off-campus recruiting events, the Southeastern Minority Job Fair, the Southeastern Law Placement Consortium, National Association for Public Interest Law Career Information Fair, Mid-South Law Placement Consortium, Patent Law Interview Program, and the Nashville Bar Association Minority Clerkship Program

Special features: small-group orientations, the Career Services Handbook; a resource library with more than 1000 employer files, books, and videotapes; an annual picturebook of students; a booklet series of alumni career narratives; and a Web-based information system.

Full-time job interviews:	28 employers
Summer job interviews:	56 employers
Placement by graduation:	58% of class
Placement within 9 months:	93% of class
Average starting salary:	$28,000 to $70,000

Areas of placement:

Private practice 2-10 attorneys	27%
Private practice 11-25 attorneys	11%
Private practic 26-50 attorneys	5%
Private practice 51-100 attorneys	2%
Private practice 100+ attorneys	11%
Solo practice	3%
Judicial clerkships	14%
Government	11%
Business/industry	7%
Public interest	6%
Military	3%

Students
About 45% of the student body are women; 13%, minorities; 10%, African American; 1%, Asian American; 1%, Hispanic; and 1%, Native American. The majority of students come from Tennessee (85%). The average age of entering students is 25; age range is 21 to 50. About 68% of students enter directly from undergraduate school, 5% have a graduate degree, and 42% have worked full-time prior to entering law school. About 4% drop out after the first year for academic or personal reasons; 96% remain to receive a law degree.

School of Law

727 East Dean Keeton Street
Austin, TX 78705

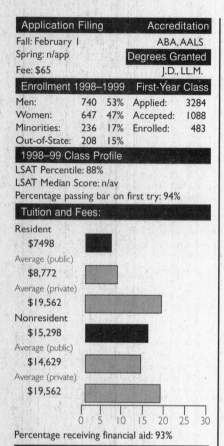

Application Filing		Accreditation
Fall: February 1		ABA, AALS
Spring: n/app		**Degrees Granted**
Fee: $65		J.D., LL.M.

Enrollment 1998–1999			First-Year Class	
Men:	740	53%	Applied:	3284
Women:	647	47%	Accepted:	1088
Minorities:	236	17%	Enrolled:	483
Out-of-State:	208	15%		

1998–99 Class Profile
LSAT Percentile: 88%
LSAT Median Score: n/av
Percentage passing bar on first try: 94%

Tuition and Fees:

Resident
  $7498
Average (public)
  $8,772
Average (private)
  $19,562
Nonresident
  $15,298
Average (public)
  $14,629
Average (private)
  $19,562

0   5   10   15   20   25   30

Percentage receiving financial aid: 93%

ADMISSIONS

In the fall 1999 first-year class, 3284 applied, 1088 were accepted, and 483 enrolled. Twenty transfers enrolled. The median LSAT percentile of the most recent first-year class was 88. The lowest LSAT percentile accepted was 30; the highest was 100.

Requirements
Applicants must have a bachelor's degree from an accredited institution and take the LSAT. Minimum acceptable GPA is 2.2 on a scale of 4.0. No specific undergraduate courses are required. Candidates are interviewed.

Procedure
The application deadline for fall entry is February 1. Applicants should submit an application form, a nonrefundable application fee of $65, and registration with LSDAS by January 10 or by October 10 for early decision. Payment of $200 as an enrollment fee for admitted students is required as well as a personal statement and a resume. Notification of the admission decision is made January through May. The latest acceptable LSAT test date for fall entry is December. The law school uses the LSDAS.

Special
The law school recruits minority and disadvantaged students through campus visits and law forums. Requirements are different for out-of-state students in that Texas' state legislature limits nonresident enrollment to 20% of the entering class. Therefore, nonresidents face tougher competition. Transfer students must have one year of credit, have a minimum GPA of 2.2, have attended an ABA-approved law school, and demonstrate good cause for the transfer, and have a strong academic record prior to and during law school.

Costs

Tuition and fees for the 1999-2000 academic year are $7498 for full-time in-state students and $15,298 for out-of-state students. On-campus room and board costs about $6732 annually; books and supplies run $866.

Financial Aid

About 93% of current law students receive some form of aid. The average annual amount of aid from all sources combined, including scholarships, loans, and work contracts, is $18,598; maximum, $26,578. Awards are based on need and merit. The required financial statement is the FAFSA. The aid application deadline for fall entry is March 31. First-year students are notified about their financial aid application at the time of acceptance.

About the Law School

University of Texas at Austin School of Law was established in 1883 and is a public institution. The 40-acre campus is in an urban area within Austin. The primary mission of the law school is to educate students for the practice of law by advancing knowledge of the law as an institution to effect social change. Students have access to federal, state, county, city, and local agencies, courts, correctional facilities, law firms, and legal aid organizations in the Austin area. Facilities of special interest to law students Townes Hall and Tarlton Law Library, which is housed in the Joseph D. Jamail Center for Legal Research, 2 connected buildings that house the law library, classrooms, seminar rooms, student organization areas, and other support facilities. Housing for law students is available off campus. Few students select on-campus housing. All law school facilities are accessible to the physically disabled.

Calendar

The law school operates on a traditional semester basis. Courses for full-time students are offered days only and must be completed within within five years. There is no part-time program. New full-time students are admitted in the fall. There is a 6-week summer session. Transferable summer courses are offered.

Programs

In addition to the J.D., the law school offers the LL.M. Students may take relevant courses in other programs and apply credit toward the J.D.; a maximum of 6 credits may be applied. The following joint degrees may be earned: J.D./M.B.A. (Juris Doctor/Master of Business Administration), J.D./M.P.A. (Juris Doctor/Master of Public Affairs), J.D./M.S. (Juris Doctor/Master of Science in community and regional planning), J.D./M.A. (Juris Doctor/Master of Arts in Russian, Latin American, Middle Eastern, East European, and Eurasian studies).

Required
To earn the J.D., candidates must complete 86 total credits, of which 39 are for required courses. They must maintain a minimum GPA of 1.9 in the required courses. The following first-year courses are required of all students: Contracts, Criminal Law, Torts, Property, Legal Research and Legal Writ-

Contact

Assistant Dean for Admissions, 512-232-1200 for general inquiries; Linda Alba, Financial Aid Counselor, 512-232-1130 for financial aid information.

ing, Civil Procedure, and Constitutional Law I. Required upper-level courses consist of Professional Responsibility, a writing seminar, and Constitutional Law II. The required orientation program for first-year students is a 3-day program that familiarizes them with the physical facilities, rules, and procedures of the law school and the university. Students receive initial class assignments and attend a general welcome and social event.

Electives

The School of Law offers concentrations in corporate law, criminal law, entertainment, environmental law, family law, international law, juvenile law, labor law, litigation, maritime law, media law, securities law, tax law, torts and insurance, and natural resources law, civil liberties, commercial law, and intellectual property law. In addition, clinics are offered in Capital Punishment, Children's Rights, and Criminal Defense. An individual research clinic is available for advanced clinical students. Seminars include those classified as either "nonwriting seminars" or "writing seminars." A writing seminar is a requirement for graduation. Judicial internships are available with the Texas Supreme Court, the Texas Court of Criminal Appeals, and the Texas Third Court of Appeals, through which a small number of students earn law school credit for work done under the supervision of an individual justice. Empirical legal research projects sponsored and directly supervised by a faculty member are available. An advanced student may also conduct individual research projects. The school has a semester-long exchange program with Queen Mary College and Westfield College, which are both colleges of the University of London. Up to 30 upper-class students enroll for 4 approved courses in international or comparative law. Students can create their own study-abroad program as well. Students on scholastic probation, or in danger of being placed on scholastic probation, are assigned tutors. There are student organizations focusing on almost any area of the law. The most widely taken electives are Wills and Estates, Business Associations, and Federal Income Tax.

Graduation Requirements

In order to graduate, candidates must have a GPA of 1.9 and have completed the upper-division writing requirement.

Organizations

Students edit the *Texas Law Review, Texas International Law Journal, American Journal of Criminal Law, The Review of Litigation*, the *Texas Forum on Civil Liberties and Civil Rights, Hispanic Law Journal, Texas Environmental Law Journal, Texas Intellectual Property Law Journal, Texas Journal of Women and the Law, Texas Journal of Hispanic Law and Policy, Texas Review of Law and Politics*, the SBA newsletter *The Writ*, and the *Texas Business Law Journal*. The Board of Advocates directs a range of moot court, mock trial, and client counseling contests both in the school and with other law schools. Law student organizations include the Student Bar Association, the Legal Research Board, and the International Law Society. There are local chapters of the Thurgood Marshall Society and Phi Alpha Delta. The Chancellors is the school's most prestigious honor society. The Order of Barristers recognizes outstanding participation in the moot court competition.

Library

The law library contains 936,000 hard-copy volumes and 879,118 microform volume equivalents, and subscribes to 9500 serial publications. Such on-line databases and networks as LEXIS, DIALOG, and WESTLAW are available to law students for research. Special library collections include an extensive collection of foreign law (Western Europe, Latin America), papers of Tom C. Clark, Associate Justice of the U.S. Supreme Court; ABA Gavel Committee Award Entries; EC depository; law in popular culture; and U.S. Supreme Court briefs. Recently, the library added Web access to its collection through TALLONS (Tartlton Law Library Online System), and to the resources of the other UT libraries and the Harry Ransom Humanities Research Center through UTCAT. The Law Library's Computer Learning Center (CLC) provides a networked environment for research, E-mail, and word processing applications with laser-printed output. The CLC has doubled in size, with more than 100 networked PCs now available for student use. The ratio of library volumes to faculty is 4167 to 1 and to students, 497 to 1. The ratio of seats in the library to students is 1 to 1.

Placement

J.D.s awarded:	450

Services available through: separate law school placement center.

Special features: member of Pro Bono Students of America; Public Interest Law Center

Full-time job interviews:	n/av
Summer job interviews:	300 employers
Placement by graduation:	73% of class
Placement within 9 months:	98% of class
Average starting salary:	$61,626
Areas of placement:	
Private Practice 2-10 attorneys	30%
Private practice 11-25 attorneys	9%
Private practice 26-50 attorneys	5%
Private practice 51-100 attorneys	5%
Judicial clerkships	10%
Government	9%
Business/industry	9%
Unknown	9%
Public interest	2%
Military	1%

Faculty

The law school has 75 full-time and 73 part-time faculty members, of whom 38 are women. According to AAUP standards for Category I institutions, faculty salaries are above average. About 2% of full-time faculty have a graduate law degree in addition to the J.D.; about 4% of part-time faculty have one. The ratio of full-time students to full-time faculty in an average class is 21 to 1; in a clinic, 15 to 1. There is a chapter of the Order of the Coif; 57 graduates are members.

Students

About 47% of the student body are women; 17%, minorities; 2%, African American; 7%, Asian American; and 8%, Hispanic. The majority of students come from Texas (85%). The average age of entering students is 25; age range is 20 to 57. About 50% of students enter directly from undergraduate school and 11% have a graduate degree.

David A. Clarke School of Law

4200 Connecticut Avenue, N.W.
Washington, DC 20008

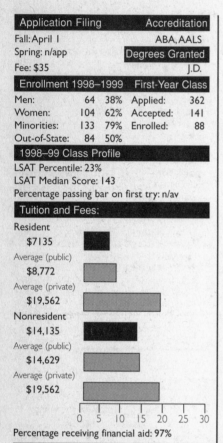

Application Filing			Accreditation
Fall: April 1			ABA, AALS
Spring: n/app			**Degrees Granted**
Fee: $35			J.D.

Enrollment 1998–1999			First-Year Class
Men:	64	38%	Applied: 362
Women:	104	62%	Accepted: 141
Minorities:	133	79%	Enrolled: 88
Out-of-State:	84	50%	

1998–99 Class Profile
LSAT Percentile: 23%
LSAT Median Score: 143
Percentage passing bar on first try: n/av

Tuition and Fees:

Resident
$7135

Average (public)
$8,772

Average (private)
$19,562

Nonresident
$14,135

Average (public)
$14,629

Average (private)
$19,562

Percentage receiving financial aid: 97%

ADMISSIONS

In the fall 1999 first-year class, 362 applied, 141 were accepted, and 88 enrolled. One transfer enrolled. The median LSAT percentile of the most recent first-year class was 23; the median GPA was 2.7 on a scale of 4.0. The lowest LSAT percentile accepted was 2; the highest was 75.

Requirements
Applicants must have a bachelor's degree from an accredited institution and take the LSAT. Minimum acceptable LSAT score is 140 and minimum acceptable GPA is 2.5 on a scale of 4.0. The most important admission factors include general background, GPA, and LSAT results. No specific undergraduate courses are required. Candidates are interviewed.

Procedure
The application deadline for fall entry is April 1. Applicants should submit an application form, LSAT results, transcripts, a nonrefundable application fee of $35, 2 letters of recommendation, and 3 essays. Notification of the admission decision is on a rolling basis. The latest acceptable LSAT test date for fall entry is February. The law school uses the LSDAS.

Special
The law school recruits minority and disadvantaged students by direct mail recruitment campaigns such as LSAC Candidate Referral Service and GRE Minority Locator Service; through visits to historically black and minority institutions; by maintaining contact with local community groups and organizations; holding Open House programs; and through ads in school papers and local government periodicals. Transfer students must have one year of credit, have a minimum GPA of 2.0, and have attended an ABA-approved law school. The school offers a pre-admission summer program.

Costs

Tuition and fees for the 1999-2000 academic year are $7135 for full-time in-state students and $14,135 for out-of-state students. Books and supplies run $4500.

Financial Aid

About 97% of current law students receive some form of aid. The average annual amount of aid from all sources combined, including scholarships, loans, and work contracts, is $22,600; maximum, $41,421. Awards are based on need and merit. Students may apply for non-need-based alternative loans with eligibility based on creditworthiness. The required financial statements for institutional scholarships are FAFSA and NEED ACCESS. The aid application deadline for fall entry is May 1. Special funds for minority or disadvantaged students are available through need-based named scholarships donated to the law school's scholarship fund for minority student awards. First-year students are notified about their financial aid application at time of acceptance.

About the Law School

University of the District of Columbia David A. Clarke School of Law was established in 1987 and is a public institution. The campus is in an urban area of upper Northwest Washington, D.C. The primary mission of the law school is to represent the legal needs of low-income persons, particularly those who reside in the District of Columbia, while recruiting, enrolling, and training persons from racial, ethnic, or other population groups who have been traditionally underrepresented at the Bar. Students have access to federal, state, county, city, and local agencies, courts, correctional facilities, law firms, and legal aid organizations in the Washington area. Other resources include the Supreme Court, Capitol Hill, Library of Congress, and public interest groups and organizations. Facilities of special interest to law students are local and federal government offices, including courts, and administrative agencies, public interest organizations, and Capitol Hill. There is no on-campus housing. The School of Law assists incoming students with locating housing in the Washington metropolitan area. All law school facilities are accessible to the physically disabled.

Calendar

The law school operates on a traditional semester basis. Courses for full-time students are offered both day and evening and must be completed within 3 years. There is no part-time program. New full-time students are admitted in the fall. There is an 8- to 10-week summer session. Transferable summer courses are offered.

Programs

Students may take relevant courses in other programs and apply credit toward the J.D.; a maximum of 30 credits may be applied if they are taken at an ABA-approved school.

Required
To earn the J.D., candidates must complete 90 total credits, of which 66 are for required courses. They must maintain a minimum GPA of 2.0 in the required courses. The following first-year courses are required of all students: Civil Procedure I and II, Contracts I and II, Criminal Law, Lawyering Process I and II,

Fax: 202-274-5583
E-mail: vcanty@law.udc.edu
Web: www.law.udc.edu

Contact

Vivian W. Canty, 202-274-7341 for general inquiries; Anne El-Shazli, Financial Aid Officer, 202-274-7337 for financial aid information.

DISTRICT OF COLUMBIA

Torts, Criminal Procedure, and Law and Justice. Required upper-level courses consist of Evidence, Clinic I and II, Property, Constitutional Law I and II, Professional Responsibility, and Moot Court. All students must take clinical courses. Students are required to take a 14-credit serving low-income D.C. residents clinic in order to graduate. The required orientation program for first-year students is approximately 1 week in length. Usually given in mid-August, it includes the course Lawyering Process I and such activities as tours of the Supreme Court, student and faculty presentations, and a dean's reception.

Electives

The David A. Clarke School of Law offers concentrations in criminal law, juvenile law, litigation, and public interest law. In addition, clinics are offered in Public Entitlements Law, Housing/Consumer Law, and HIV/AIDS Law. Seven credits are awarded per clinic. Seminars are offered each semester. A 2-credit internship seminar is required of all students who do an internship. Internships are offered for advanced students who have completed 14 credits of clinic and are in good standing. The internship must be with a public or nonprofit private agency. The internship is for 8 credits. Students may be selected to be research assistants on faculty research projects. The clinics involve students in various forms of field work. In addition, the internship program provides full-time field work. The Academic Support Program (ASP) provides small group and individual tutorials for first-year students. The ASP does diagnostic testing, counseling, and tutoring for students whose GPA falls below 2.0, but is still above the threshold for termination. The ASP also makes use of CALI exercises and diagnostic exercises on the computer, which were designed at the school. The most widely taken electives are Conflicts of Laws, Business Organizations I, and Uniform Commercial Code.

Graduation Requirements

In order to graduate, candidates must have a GPA of 2.0 and have completed the upper-division writing requirement.

Organizations

Students edit *The District of Columbia Law Review, The Advocate,* and the newspaper, *The Sidebar.* Moot court competitions in which students compete include the District of Columbia Moot Court Association, Burton D. Wechsler First Amendment Moot Court, and the William B. Spong, Jr. Invitational Moot Court competitions. Law student organizations include the DCSL Student Bar Association, Women's Society, and Joseph Raub Equal Justice Fund. There are local chapters of the American Trial Lawyers Association, Delta Theta Phi, and Federalist Society.

Library

The law library contains 181,000 hardcopy volumes and 90 microform volume equivalents, and subscribes to 550 serial publications. Such on-line databases and networks as LEXIS, DIALOG, WESTLAW, and CALI, INFOTRAC, Matthew Bender, BNA, and the Internet are available to law students for research. Special library collections include District of Columbia law. Recently, the library has expanded its computer laboratory and audiovisual department, and has automated its public catalog and other library operations. The ratio of library volumes to faculty is 7826 to 1 and to students, 1233 to 1. The ratio of seats in the library to students is 1 to 1.

Faculty

The law school has 16 full-time and 18 part-time faculty members, of whom 19 are women. About 10% of full-time faculty have a graduate law degree in addition to the J.D.; about 22% of part-time faculty have one. The ratio of full-time students to full-time faculty in an average class is 17 to 1; in a clinic, 10 to 1. The law school has a regular program of bringing visiting professors and other distinguished lecturers and visitors to campus.

Placement

J.D.s awarded:	48
Services available through: a separate law school placement center.	
Services: lists of judicial clerkships, fellowships, and writing competitions. Bar exam applications and information are also available.	
Full-time job interviews:	13 employers
Summer job interviews:	2 employers
Placement by graduation:	56% of class
Placement within 9 months:	83% of class
Average starting salary:	n/av
Areas of placement:	
Private practice 2-10 attorneys	50%
Solo Practice	6%
Government	20%
Business/Industry	17%
Public interest	4%
Judicial clerkships	2%
Academic	1%

Students

About 62% of the student body are women; 79%, minorities; 62%, African American; 9%, Asian American; 9%, Hispanic; and 10%, Middle Eastern, etc. The majority of students come from the District of Columbia (50%). The average age of entering students is 29; age range is 21 to 55. About 50% of students enter directly from undergraduate school, 11% have a graduate degree, and 70% have worked full-time prior to entering law school. About 15% drop out after the first year for academic or personal reasons; 85% remain to receive a law degree.

McGeorge School of Law

3200 Fifth Avenue
Sacramento, CA 95817

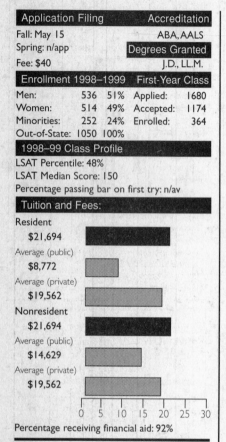

Application Filing	Accreditation
Fall: May 15	ABA, AALS
Spring: n/app	**Degrees Granted**
Fee: $40	J.D., LL.M.

Enrollment 1998–1999		First-Year Class	
Men:	536 51%	Applied:	1680
Women:	514 49%	Accepted:	1174
Minorities:	252 24%	Enrolled:	364
Out-of-State:	1050 100%		

1998–99 Class Profile

LSAT Percentile: 48%
LSAT Median Score: 150
Percentage passing bar on first try: n/av

Tuition and Fees:

Resident
$21,694

Average (public)
$8,772

Average (private)
$19,562

Nonresident
$21,694

Average (public)
$14,629

Average (private)
$19,562

Percentage receiving financial aid: 92%

ADMISSIONS

In the fall 1999 first-year class, 1680 applied, 1174 were accepted, and 364 enrolled. The median LSAT percentile of the most recent first-year class was 48; the median GPA was 3.0 on a scale of 4.3. The lowest LSAT percentile accepted was 30; the highest was 99.

Requirements
Applicants must take the LSAT. The most important admission factors include academic achievement, LSAT results, and general background. No specific undergraduate courses are required. Candidates are not interviewed.

Procedure
The application deadline for fall entry is May 15. Applicants should submit an application form, LSAT results, transcripts, a nonrefundable application fee of $40, optional letters of recommendation, and personal statement. Notification of the admission decision begins in February. The law school uses the LSDAS.

Special
The law school recruits minority and disadvantaged students through recruiting events, publications, letters, contacts with McGeorge students, and scholarship and grant programs. Transfer students must have one year of credit. Acceptance of transfer students is dependent upon space availability; preference is given to students with compelling reasons to request transfer.

Costs

Tuition and fees for the 1999-2000 academic year are $21,694 for all full-time students. Tuition for all part-time students is $14,434 annually. Books and supplies run $610.

Financial Aid

About 92% of current law students receive some form of aid. The average annual amount of aid from all sources combined, including scholarships, loans, and work contracts, is $26,500; maximum, $35,600. Awards are based on need and merit. The required financial statement is FAFSA. The aid application deadline for fall entry is open. Diversity factors are considered in the award of scholarships and grants. First-year students are notified about their financial aid application at the time of acceptance.

About the Law School

University of the Pacific McGeorge School of Law was established in 1924 and is a private institution. The 22-acre law school campus is in an urban area in Sacramento, California. The primary mission of the law school is to educate practice-ready graduates, able to repre-

sent clients skillfully and ethically, through a rigorous curriculum that unifies classroom study with development of professional skills. Students have access to federal, state, county, city, and local agencies, courts, correctional facilities, law firms, and legal aid organizations in the Sacramento area. Sacramento, the state capital, has numerous federal and state agencies that provide internship opportunities and resources for the school's Governmental Affairs Program. Special facilities include the trial courtroom, the LawLab equipped with computer technology, the "live-client" clinical facilities, student Center with food service, library with ample study and computer areas, and recreational facilities. Housing for law students consists of 158 on-campus apartments; housing off campus is readily available in the Sacramento area at a reasonable cost. About 95% of the law school facilities are accessible to the physically disabled.

Calendar

The law school operates on a traditional semester basis. Courses for full-time students are offered both day and evening and must be completed within 4 years. For part-time students, courses are offered both day and evening and must be completed within 5 years. New full- and part-time students are admitted in the fall. There are 7 1/2- week and intensive 1 to 3-week summer session. Transferable summer courses are offered.

Programs

In addition to the J.D., the law school offers the LL.M. Students may take relevant courses in other programs and apply credit toward the J.D.; a maximum of 6 credits, from another law school, 3.0 for transfer student, and 6 to 12 for joint degree candidates, may be applied. The following joint degrees may be earned: J.D./M.B.A. (Juris Doctor/Master of Business Administration), J.D./M.P.P.A. (Juris Doctor/Master of Public Policy and Administration), and J.D./M.A. or M.S. (Juris Doctor/Master of Arts or Master of Science).

Phone: 916-739-7105
Fax: 916-739-7134
E-mail: admissionsmcgeorge@uop.edu
Web: www.mcgeorge.edu

Contact

916-739-7105 for general inquiries; Financial Aid Office, 916-739-7158 for financial aid information.

CALIFORNIA

Required

To earn the J.D., candidates must complete 88 total credits, of which 58 are for required courses. The following first-year courses are required of all students: Civil Procedure, Contracts, Criminal Law, Legal Process, Property, and Torts. Required upper-level courses consist of Business Associations, Constitutional Law, Criminal Procedure, Evidence, Professional Responsibility, Remedies, and Appellate Advocacy. The required orientation program for first-year students is a 3-day program at the beginning of the year that includes orientation classes, small group sessions, and social activities. First-year faculty provide special feedback programs, including practice examinations, throughout the first year.

Electives

The McGeorge School of Law offers concentrations in corporate law, criminal law, environmental law, family law, international law, juvenile law, litigation, securities law, tax law, torts and insurance, and intellectual roperty, and a Governmental Affairs program for both private practice and government positions in legislative administrative, and regulatory areas. On-campus, Clinics include Community Legal Services, which provides legal services for those not otherwise able to afford them; it is available to advanced students, carries a 2-semester commitment and is worth 6 credits. Other campus-based clinics available to advanced students are Administrative Adjudication Clinic (2 credits); Legislation and the Law of Politics Clinic (2); and Parole Representation Clinic (3). A number of elective courses are in a seminar format with limited enrollment. More than 40 off-campus internships are available in non-profit and local, state, and federal governmental offices and agencies. Internships are available to advanced students and are usually worth 3 credits per semester. Directed research, available as an elective for advanced students, is offered for 1 or 2 credits. Individual professors also have student research assistants. Additionally, the Research Pool undertakes research projects for practictioners. Lecture series such as the Distinguished Speaker's Series, Hefner Memorial Lecture Series, and Lou Ashe Symposium bring outstanding guest speakers to campus. A summer institute in International Legal

Studies is offered in Salzburg, Austria, in cooperation with the University of Salzburg. The Minority Student Program provides a peer support and networking system as well as special orientation sessions, student-led discussion groups, and course review sessions. A Governmental Affairs curriculum for both private practice and government positions in legislative, administrative, and regulatory areas leads to a certificate awarded concurrently with the J.D. degree. The most widely taken electives are Trial Advocacy, clinical offerings, and business courses.

Graduation Requirements

In order to graduate, candidates must have a GPA of 2.3 and have completed the upper-division writing requirement.

Organizations

Students edit the *McGeorge Law Review* and the *Transnational Lawyer*. *Appellate Advocacy or International Advocacy are required second-year courses.* McGeorge teams compete in the National and ABA Moot Court competitions, and the Jessup International Moot Court Competition. Other competitions are the Client Counseling Competition, the American Trial Lawyers competition, the Texas Young Lawyers Competition, the San Diego Consumer Attorneys Association competition, and the San Diego Defense Attorneys Competition. More than 30 law student organizations represent a wide range of social, political, and law-related interests. Local chapters of national organizations include the ABA-Law Student Division, Student Trial Lawyers Association (ATLA), and Phi Alpha Delta legal fraternity.

Library

The law library contains 436,384 hardcopy volumes and 1,189,824 microform volume equivalents, and subscribes to 4509 serial publications. Such on-line databases and networks as LEXIS, DIALOG, and WESTLAW are available to law students for research. Special library collections include California legal materials, California and U.S. documents depository, and tax and international law special collections. Recently, the library expanded and remodeled 6000 square feet that provided room for automated systems, LEXIS/WESTLAW Permanent

Placement

J.D.s awarded:	300
Services available through: separate law school placement center.	
Special features: Practice interview program; alumni network program; first-year Career Development orientation program	
Full-time job interviews:	n/av
Summer job interviews:	n/av
Placement by graduation:	n/av
Placement within 9 months:	85% of class
Average starting salary:	$39,000 to $55,000
Areas of placement:	
Private practice 2-100 attorneys	56%
Government	26%
Business/industry	11%
Judicial clerkships	4%
Public interest	2%
Academic	1%

Learning Centers, additional study rooms, microform/media/CD-ROM Center, expanded circulation, and upgraded photocopy facilities. The ratio of library volumes to faculty is 9918 to 1 and to students, 416 to 1. The ratio of seats in the library to students is 1 to 2.

Faculty

The law school has 44 full-time and 59 part-time faculty members, of whom 27 are women. According to AAUP standards for Category IIA institutions, faculty salaries are below average. About 23% of full-time faculty have a graduate law degree in addition to the J.D.; about 17% of part-time faculty have one. The ratio of full-time students to full-time faculty in an average class is 24 to 1; in a clinic, 10 to 1. The law school has a regular program of bringing visiting professors and other distinguished lecturers and visitors to campus. There is a chapter of the Order of the Coif; 34 faculty and 650 graduates are members.

Students

About 49% of the student body are women; 24%, minorities; 3%, African American; 12%, Asian American; 8%, Hispanic; and 1%, Native American. The average age of entering students is 24; age range is 20 to 54. About 44% of students enter directly from undergraduate school. About 11% drop out after the first year for academic or personal reasons.

UNIVERSITY OF TOLEDO

College of Law

2801 West Bancroft Street
Toledo, OH 43606-3390

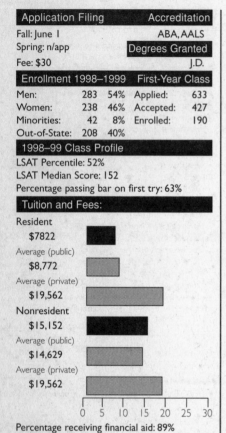

Application Filing		Accreditation
Fall: June 1		ABA, AALS
Spring: n/app		**Degrees Granted**
Fee: $30		J.D.

Enrollment 1998–1999		First-Year Class	
Men:	283 54%	Applied:	633
Women:	238 46%	Accepted:	427
Minorities:	42 8%	Enrolled:	190
Out-of-State:	208 40%		

1998–99 Class Profile
LSAT Percentile: 52%
LSAT Median Score: 152
Percentage passing bar on first try: 63%

Tuition and Fees:
Resident
$7822

Average (public)
$8,772

Average (private)
$19,562

Nonresident
$15,152

Average (public)
$14,629

Average (private)
$19,562

0 5 10 15 20 25 30

Percentage receiving financial aid: 89%

ADMISSIONS
In the fall 1999 first-year class, 633 applied, 427 were accepted, and 190 enrolled. Five transfers enrolled. The median LSAT percentile of the most recent first-year class was 52; the median GPA was 3.24 on a scale of 4.0. The lowest LSAT percentile accepted was 15; the highest was 97.

Requirements
Applicants must have a bachelor's degree from an accredited institution and take the LSAT. Minimum acceptable GPA is 2.0 on a scale of 4.0. No specific undergraduate courses are required. Candidates are not interviewed.

Procedure
The application deadline for fall entry is June 1. Applicants should submit an application form, LSAT results, transcripts, a nonrefundable application fee of $30, and 2 letters of recommendation, and they should indicate preference for full- or part-time study. Accepted applicants must submit a $75 nonrefundable deposit, which is credited toward tuition. Notification of the admission decision is on a rolling basis. The latest acceptable LSAT test date for fall entry is February. The law school uses the LSDAS.

Special
Transfer students must have attended an ABA-approved law school and be in good standing at the previous school.

Costs
Tuition and fees for the 1999-2000 academic year are $7822 for full-time in-state students and $15,152 for out-of-state students. Tuition for part-time students is $6688 per year in-state and $12,797 out-of-state. Books and supplies run $1025.

Financial Aid
About 89% of current law students receive some form of aid. The average annual amount of aid from all sources combined, including scholarships, loans, and work contracts, is $16,896; maximum, $31,041. Awards are based on need and merit. The required financial statement is the FAFSA. The aid application deadline for fall entry is April 1. First-year students are notified about their financial aid application at time of acceptance.

About the Law School
University of Toledo College of Law was established in 1906 and is a public institution. The 210-acre campus is in a suburban area west of downtown Toledo. The primary mission of the law school is to familiarize prospective lawyers with the major areas of the law while at the same time introducing them to the basic skills for competent lawyering. The college integrates theory and practice. Students have access to federal, state, county, city, and local agencies, courts, correctional facilities, law firms, and legal aid organizations in the Toledo area. Facilities of special interest to law students include a state-of-the-art mock courtroom, which is available for trial practice and appellate advocacy programs. Housing for law students consists of living accommodations located near the campus. The university assists students in finding housing. All law school facilities are accessible to the physically disabled.

Calendar
The law school operates on a traditional semester basis. Courses for full-time students are offered both day and evening and must be completed within 5 years. For part-time students, courses are offered evenings only and must be completed within 6 years. New full- and part-time students are admitted in the fall. There is a 10-week summer session. Transferable summer courses are offered.

Programs
Students may take relevant courses in other programs and apply credit toward the J.D.; a maximum of 7 credits may be applied. The following joint degrees may be earned: J.D./M.B.A. (Juris Doctor/Master of Business Administration) and J.D./M.E. (Juris Doctor/Master of Engineering).

Phone: 419-530-4131
Fax: 419-530-4345
E-mail: law.utoledo.edu
Web: utoledo.edu/law

Contact

Carol E. Frendt, Assistant Dean of Law Admissions, 419-530-4131 for general inquiries; Beth Solo, Assistant Director, Law Financial Aid, 419-530-7929 for financial aid information.

OHIO

Required

To earn the J.D., candidates must complete 89 total credits, of which 42 are for required courses. They must maintain a minimum GPA of 2.0 in the required courses. The following first-year courses are required of all students: Civil Procedure I and II, Contracts I and II, Torts, Legal Research, Writing, Appellate Advocacy I and II, Property, Criminal Law, and Constitutional Law. Required upper-level courses consist of Legal Ethics and Professional Responsibility, Evidence, and a seminar that involves researching and writing a scholarly paper. The required orientation program for first-year students lasts 2 days.

Electives

The College of Law offers concentrations in corporate law, criminal law, environmental law, family law, international law, juvenile law, labor law, sports law, tax law, torts and insurance, business and commercial law, civil practice and procedure, estate and trust law, governmental regulation, health care law, intellectual property, jurisprudence, legal history and philosophy, personal and family law, property/real estate law, public interest law, public law, and skills and values. In addition, clinical programs include the College of Law Legal Clinic, the Criminal Law Practice Program, and the Dispute Resolution Clinic. These are offered to all upper-level students (4 to 6 hours of credit). Seminars, of which 1 is required for graduation, are scheduled to provide maximum flexibility in meeting the needs and interests of the students. Internships are available through the Criminal Law Practice Program. A Judicial Internship Program offers field experience in the chambers of a federal judge or magistrate or state appellate judge. The college offers a number of research assistantships to students who have completed 1 academic year. Individual research programs allow students to develop their own research projects, which are pursued in consultation with a faculty committee. The Cannon Lecture Series and the Stranghan National Issues Forum have hosted individuals of national prominence who provide the college and general public with timely discussions of legal and policy issues. The College of Law, in cooperation with the Inns of Court Law School in London, arranges summer internships with British barristers and solicitors. A special first-year course for academically disadvantaged students is available. The most widely taken electives are Administrative Law, Corporations, and Evidence.

Graduation Requirements

In order to graduate, candidates must have a GPA of 2.0 and have completed the upper-division writing requirement.

Organizations

Students edit the *University of Toledo Law Review, Toledo Transcript, Toledo Journal of Great Lakes' Law, Sciences and Policy,* and the student newspaper *No Holds Bar Review.* The Moot Court program helps build skills in the arts of brief writing and oral advocacy through participation in national and intraschool competitions, such as the Charles W. Fornoff Intra-School Competition. Competitions are managed by a student Moot Court Board. Law student organizations include the Student Bar Association, Business Law Society, and Federalist Society. There are local chapters of the Order of the Coif, Delta Theta Phi, and Phi Alpha Delta. The Law Alumni Association has more than 5000 members across the country.

Library

The law library contains 320,727 hard-copy volumes and 117,964 microform volume equivalents, and subscribes to 3251 serial publications. Such on-line databases and networks as LEXIS, WESTLAW, the Internet, a significant CD-ROM collection, and an Innovative Interfaces automated system are available to law students for research. Special library collections include significant holdings of primary materials for the United Kingdom, Canada, Australia, and New Zealand, and primary and secondary materials for studying international law; the library is a federal depository. Recently, the library installed nearly 45 networked computers to support various kinds of on-line legal research. The ratio of library volumes to faculty is 10,346 to 1 and to students, 616 to 1. The ratio of seats in the library to students is 1 to 1.

Faculty

The law school has 31 full-time and 25 part-time faculty members, of whom 16 are women. According to AAUP standards for Category I institutions, faculty salaries are below average. About 20% of full-time faculty have a graduate law degree in addition to the J.D.; about 1% of part-time faculty have one. The ratio of full-time students to full-time faculty in an average class is 17 to 1; in a clinic, 10 to 1. The law school has a regular program of bringing visiting professors and other distinguished lecturers and visitors to campus. There is a chapter of the Order of the Coif; 37 faculty and 292 graduates are members.

Students

About 46% of the student body are women; 8%, minorities; 4%, African American; 1%, Asian American; 2%, Hispanic; and 1%, Native American. The majority of students come from Ohio (60%). The average age of entering students is 26; age range is 22 to 65. About 85% of students enter directly from undergraduate school and 15% have a graduate degree. About 8% drop out after the first year for academic or personal reasons; 89% remain to receive a law degree.

Placement

J.D.s awarded:	166

Services available through: a separate law school placement center.

Services: arrange interviews using video conferencing equipment, organize mentor program, and arrange for reciprocity with other law schools

Special features: the Law Career Services Employment Resource Library and the Law Career Services Student Handbook

Full-time job interviews:	10 employers
Summer job interviews:	25 employers
Placement by graduation:	80% of class
Placement within 9 months:	97% of class
Average starting salary:	$19,200 to $75,000

Areas of placement:

Private practice 2-10 attorneys	31%
Private practice 11-25 attonreys	10%
Private practice 26-50 attorneys	5%
Private practice 51-100 attorneys	5%
Business/industry	22%
Government	18%
Judicial clerkships	5%
Military	2%
Academic	1%
Public interest	1%

College of Law

3120 East Fourth Place
Tulsa, OK 74104-2499

Application Filing		Accreditation
Fall: open		ABA, AALS
Spring: open		**Degrees Granted**
Fee: $30		J.D., LL.M.

Enrollment 1998–1999		First-Year Class	
Men:	314 56%	Applied:	844
Women:	247 35%	Accepted:	518
Minorities:	73 13%	Enrolled:	181
Out-of-State:	320 57%		

1998–99 Class Profile
LSAT Percentile: 50%
LSAT Median Score: 149
Percentage passing bar on first try: 78%

Tuition and Fees:

Resident
$17,060

Average (public)
$8,772

Average (private)
$19,562

Nonresident
$17,060

Average (public)
$14,629

Average (private)
$19,562

0 5 10 15 20 25 30

Percentage receiving financial aid: 75%

ADMISSIONS

In the fall 1999 first-year class, 844 applied, 518 were accepted, and 181 enrolled. Twenty transfers enrolled. The median LSAT percentile of the most recent first-year class was 50; the median GPA was 3.1 on a scale of 4.0. The lowest LSAT percentile accepted was 25; the highest was 93.

Requirements
Applicants must have a bachelor's degree from an accredited institution and take the LSAT. Minimum acceptable GPA is 2.0 on a scale of 4.0. The most important admission factors include GPA, class rank, and academic achievement. No specific undergraduate courses are required. Candidates are not interviewed.

Procedure
The application deadline for fall entry is open. Applicants should submit an application form, LSAT results, transcripts, a nonrefundable application fee of $30, 2 letters of recommendation, and a personal statement. Notification of the admission decision is on an ongoing basis. The latest acceptable LSAT test date for fall entry is June. The law school uses the LSDAS.

Special
The law school recruits minority and disadvantaged students through CLEO and an academic support program in summer. Transfer students must have one year of credit and have attended an ABA-approved law school.

Costs

Tuition and fees for the 1999-2000 academic year are $17,060 for all full-time students. Tuition for part-time students is $11,460 per year. On-campus room and board costs about $5850 annually; books and supplies run $1500.

Financial Aid

About 75% of current law students receive some form of aid. The average annual amount of aid from all sources combined, including scholarships, loans, and work contracts, is $22,162; maximum, $30,000. Awards are based on need and merit. The required financial statement is the FAFSA. The aid application deadline for fall entry is open. Special funds for minority or disadvantaged students consist of need-based scholarship awards. First-year students are notified about their financial aid application at time of acceptance.

About the Law School

University of Tulsa College of Law was established in 1923 and is a private institution. The 160-acre campus is in a suburban area 3 miles east of Tulsa. The primary mission of the law school is to provide an education responsive to the legal affairs of the country, particularly in the areas of energy development, natural resources, environmental ethics, international and comparative law, dispute resolution, American Indian law

and history, health law, and public policy and regulation. Students have access to federal, state, county, city, and local agencies, courts, correctional facilities, law firms, and legal aid organizations in the Tulsa area. Housing for law students is available in dormitories and university apartments. Accommodations are available in nonuniversity facilities at reasonable cost.

Calendar

The law school operates on a traditional semester basis. Courses for full-time students are offered both day and evening and must be completed within 3 years. For part-time students, courses are offered both day and evening and must be completed within 5 years. New full-time students are admitted in the fall and spring; part-time, fall. There are 4- and 8-week summer sessions. Transferable summer courses are offered.

Programs

In addition to the J.D., the law school offers the LL.M. Students may take relevant courses in other programs and apply credit toward the J.D.; a maximum of 6 credits may be applied. The following joint degrees may be earned: J.D./M.B.A. (Juris Doctor/Master of Business Administration), J.D./M.A. (Juris Doctor/Master of Arts), and J.D./M.S. (Juris Doctor/Master of Science).

Required
To earn the J.D., candidates must complete 88 total credits, of which 42 are for required courses. They must maintain a minimum GPA of 2.0 in the required courses. The following first-year courses are required of all students: Civil Procedure I and II, Contracts I and II, Criminal Law and Administration, Legal Authorities, Introduction to Legal Reasoning and Writing, Torts, Property I and II, and Legal Reasoning and Writing. Required upper-level courses consist of Constitutional Law I and II, Introduction to Appellate Advocacy, and electives. The required orientation program for first-year students is the week-long Legal Authorities course. It starts 1 week before the beginning of other courses.

Phone: 918-631-2709
Fax: 918-631-3630

Contact

Velda Stoves, Admissions Director, 918-631-2709 for general inquiries; David Gruen, Director of Financial Aid, 918-631-2526 for financial aid information.

OKLAHOMA

Electives

The College of Law offers concentrations in corporate law, criminal law, environmental law, family law, international law, juvenile law, labor law, litigation, securities law, sports law, tax law, torts and insurance, Indian law, and health law. In addition, at the University of Tulsa Legal Clinic, students represent needy clients in a variety of civil cases. All students are supervised by a faculty member, and credit is offered. The Neighbor-to-Neighbor clinic offers the opportunity to provide volunteer assistance to low-income clients on issues such as landlord-tenant, consumer fraud, benefit problems, and domestic disputes. Seminars offered have a limited enrollment. Topics include banking, corrections, and criminal justice. Through the college's Legal Internship Program, students may obtain academic credit for practical experience gained under the supervision of practicing attorneys and the college. The Judicial Internships program offers students supervised educational experience in the Oklahoma District Court, Oklahoma Court of Appeals, U.S. District Court, U.S. Magistrate's Office, and U.S. Bankruptcy Court. There are also advanced appellate advocacy, law journal, and legal internships. Qualified students may pursue independent study in specific areas of the law under the supervision of 2 law professors. In addition, all entering students are invited to participate in the Enrichment Program, an orientation developed by the college and the BLSA. During this 2-week program, students receive a special tort lecture, review reading and comprehension skills, and have personal conferences. Minority programs include the Indian Law Certificate, in which students learn to do legal work on issues of importance to Native Americans. The Comparative and International Law Center coordinates and develops activities related to study and research in international law and teaching and research. The Center on Dispute Resolution offers a resource for students, attorneys, judges, and the general public in the field of dispute resolution.

Graduation Requirements

In order to graduate, candidates must have a GPA of 2.0 and have completed the upper-division writing requirement.

Organizations

Students edit the *Tulsa Law Journal*, *Energy Law Journal*, *International Law Journal*, and the newspaper *Baculus*. The First Board of Advocates sponsors 7 moot court competitions including the first-year Client Counseling, Client Counseling (regional and national), and ABA Negotiation (regional and national). Student organizations include ABA-Law Student Division, Federalist Society, and Student Bar Association. There are local chapters of Delta Theta Phi, Phi Alpha Delta, and Phi Delta Phi.

Library

The law library contains 280,000 hardcopy volumes and 688,772 microform volume equivalents, and subscribes to 3891 serial publications. Such on-line databases and networks as LEXIS, DIALOG, WESTLAW, CCH Access, LOIS, First Search, and 125 other subscription databases are available to law students for research. Special library collections include literature and information on environmental law and Indian law. In January 2000, the College of Law completed construction of a major addition to the law library, the Mabee Legal Information Center. Existing library space was completely renovated, and two additional floors were constructed. The addition permits the College of Law to nearly double its library collection space, increase seating capacity to accommodate the entire student body, introduce expanded technologies, provide additional facilities for law school programs, and offer more services to members of Tulsa's professional legal community who use the library extensively. The ratio of library volumes to faculty is 8667 to 1 and to students, 388 to 1. The ratio of seats in the library to students is 1 to 1.

Faculty

The law school has 37 full-time and 34 part-time faculty members, of whom 32 are women. About 50% of full-time faculty have a graduate law degree in addition to the J.D.; about 13% of part-time faculty have one. The ratio of full-time students to full-time faculty in an average class is 20 to 1; in a clinic, 6 to 1. The law school has a regular program of bringing visiting professors and other distinguished lecturers and visitors to campus.

Placement

J.D.s awarded:	185

Services available through: a separate law school placement center and the university placement center

Services: seminars and panel presentations on various aspects of law practice and career options

Special features: video library and taping equipment; the *Career Counseling Handbook*, and career services library resources, including directories, reference books, computer terminals equipped with WESTLAW, LEXIS, the Internet, and word-processing software, job advertisements, periodicals, and job sharing with 99 other law schools

Full-time job interviews:	9 employers
Summer job interviews:	20 employers
Placement by graduation:	48% of class
Placement within 9 months:	91% of class
Average starting salary:	$38,000
Areas of placement:	
Private practice 2-10 attorneys	37%
Private practice 11-25 attorneys	4%
Private practice 26-50 attorneys	2%
Private practice 51-100 attorneys	1%
Solo practice	3%
Unknown	9%
Business/industry	25%
Government	11%
Public interest	4%
Military	2%
Judicial clerkships	2%

Students

About 35% of the student body are women; 13%, minorities; 5%, African American; 3%, Asian American; 3%, Hispanic; and 8%, Native American. The average age of entering students is 27; age range is 20 to 58. About 40% of students enter directly from undergraduate school, 11% have a graduate degree, and 50% have worked full-time prior to entering law school. About 8% drop out after the first year for academic or personal reasons; 92% remain to receive a law degree.

UNIVERSITY OF UTAH

College of Law

332 South 1400 East Front
Salt Lake City, UT 84112

Application Filing	Accreditation
Fall: February 1	ABA, AALS
Spring: n/app	**Degrees Granted**
Fee: $40	J.D., LL.M.

Enrollment 1998–1999		First-Year Class	
Men:	212 57%	Applied:	805
Women:	157 43%	Accepted:	304
Minorities:	52 14%	Enrolled:	125
Out-of-State:	89 24%		

1998–99 Class Profile

LSAT Percentile: 84%
LSAT Median Score: 159
Percentage passing bar on first try: 89%

Tuition and Fees:

Resident
$5127

Average (public)
$8,772

Average (private)
$19,562

Nonresident
$11,439

Average (public)
$14,629

Average (private)
$19,562

0 5 10 15 20 25 30

Percentage receiving financial aid: 75%

ADMISSIONS

In the fall 1999 first-year class, 805 applied, 304 were accepted, and 125 enrolled. Nine transfers enrolled. The median LSAT percentile of the most recent first-year class was 84; the median GPA was 3.5 on a scale of 4.0. The lowest LSAT percentile accepted was 32; the highest was 99.

Requirements

Applicants must have a bachelor's degree from an accredited institution and take the LSAT. The most important admission factors include academic achievement, writing ability, and GPA. No specific undergraduate courses are required. Candidates are not interviewed.

Procedure

The application deadline for fall entry is February 1. Applicants should submit an application form, LSAT results, transcripts, a nonrefundable application fee of $40, 1 letter of recommendation, a personal statement, and a resume. Notification of the admission decision is from January on. The latest acceptable LSAT test date for fall entry is December. The law school uses the LSDAS.

Special

The law school recruits minority and disadvantaged students through extensive mailing to prospective applicants located through the Candidate Referral Service of LSAC and through special targeted recruitment programs. Council on Legal Opportunity fellows are recruited. Transfer students must have one year of credit, have attended an ABA-approved law school, and be in the top 15% to 20% of the first-year class.

Costs

Tuition and fees for the 1999-2000 academic year are $5127 for full-time in-state students and $11,439 for out-of-state students. On-campus room and board costs about $5940 annually; books and supplies run $1672.

Financial Aid

About 75% of current law students receive some form of aid. The average annual amount of aid from all sources combined, including scholarships, loans, and work contracts, is $10,500; maximum, $15,500. Awards are based on need and merit. The required financial statement is the FAFSA. The aid application deadline for fall entry is February 15. Special funds for minority or disadvantaged students include need and merit scholarships, stipend for a summer intern program, and tuition waivers that accompany CLEO fellowships. First-year students are notified about their financial aid application between April and June.

About the Law School

University of Utah College of Law was established in 1914 and is a public institution. The 1535-acre campus is in an urban area 1 1/2 miles east of Salt Lake City. The primary mission of the law school is to edu-cate students to deal effectively with the complex legal, social, and ethical problems of modern society. Students have access to federal, state, county, city, and local agencies, courts, correctional facilities, law firms, and legal aid organizations in the Salt Lake City area. Facilities of special interest to law students include the library, which features individual study carrels with connections to laptop computers and extensive computing and on-line facilities. Housing for law students is abundant and affordable on and off campus in safe neighborhoods within walking distance of campus. All law school facilities are accessible to the physically disabled.

Calendar

The law school operates on a traditional semester basis. Courses for full-time students are offered days only and must be completed within 6 semesters. There is no part-time program. New students are admitted in the fall. There is a 5-week summer session. Transferable summer courses are offered.

Programs

In addition to the J.D., the law school offers the LL.M. Students may take relevant courses in other programs and apply credit toward the J.D.; a maximum of 15 semester hours credits may be applied. The following joint degrees may be earned: J.D./M.B.A. (Juris Doctor/Master of Business Administration), J.D./M.P.A. (Juris Doctor/Master of Public Administration), and others by special arrangement.

Required

To earn the J.D., candidates must complete 88 total credits, of which 40 are for required courses. They must maintain a minimum GPA of 2.0 in the required courses. The following first-year courses are required of all students: Contracts, Torts, Property, Criminal Law, Constitutional Law, Civil Procedure, and Legal Writing and Research. Required upper-level courses consist of Professional Ethics, Advanced Constitutional Law, a seminar, and a perspective course. Clinical courses are not required but all students are strongly encouraged to participate. The required orientation program for first-year students is a 4-day course before classes begin to help students understand the role of law, the tasks of a lawyer, and the method of legal education and study.

Phone: 801-581-7479
800-444-8638
Fax: 801-581-6897
E-mail: gormleyl@law.utah.edu
Web: www.law.utah.edu

Contact

Laura Gormley, Asistant Director of Admissions a, 801-581-7479 for general inquiries; Marie Eastman, Law School Financial Aid Counselo, 801-585-5828 for financial aid information.

UTAH

Electives

The College of Law offers concentrations in corporate law, criminal law, environmental law, family law, labor law, litigation, natural resources, public lands and energy, and constitutional law. In addition, live and simulation component clinics are offered for 2 to 4 credit hours. Clinics may be criminal, in which students work at the offices of the county attorney or Salt Lake Legal Defenders; civil, in which students represent actual clients from a public-interest law firm; or judicial, in which students act as law clerks to state and federal judges. In seminars, students perform closely supervised research, analysis, and writing. Topics have included American Legal History, Appellate Advocacy, and Civil Rights. Students may spend a semester as full-time law clerks in the Judical Extern Program as part of the Judicial Clinic. Numerous opportunites exist for students to be paid as research assistants for faculty, or to undertake directed research for credit or advanced legal research courses. Field placements with a public interest law office, Utah Legal Services, Legal Aid Society of Salt Lake, Legal Center for People with Disabilities, Catholic Community Services, and the ACLU are part of the clinical program. Annual lecture series include the Leary Lecture, Fordham Debate, Distinguished Jurist in Residence, Law Review Symposium, and the Natural Resources Law Forum. Study abroad is possible for upper-level students in the London Law Consortium, a one-semester, ABA-approved program. Academic support for eligible minority, disadvantaged, and nontraditional students is offered and includes a legal process course, a tutorial program, and academic counseling. The college sponsors a summer intern program, funded with private donations, for minority students. Selected students intern with major Salt Lake City law firms for 6 weeks following the completion of their first year and receive a $3000 stipend. The college has hosted and regularly recruits participants for the Council on Legal Education Opportunity summer institute. Special interest groups include the Natural Resources Law Forum and the Family Law Symposium. The most widely taken electives are Evidence, Criminal Procedure, and Business Organization.

Graduation Requirements

In order to graduate, candidates must have a GPA of 2.0 and have completed the upper-division writing requirement.

Organizations

Students edit the *Utah Law Review, Journal of Law and Family Studies, Journal of Land Resources and Enviornmental Law, and Western Energy Bulletin,, and the newspaper* Utah Law Forum. Moot court competitions include the annual Traynor Moot Court and National Moot Court. In addition, several writing and research competitions are offered in connection with scholarships and awards. Law student organizations include the Natural Resources Law Forum, Women's Law Caucus, and Minority Law Caucus. There are local chapters of Phi Alpha Delta, Phi Delta Phi, and the Federalist Society.

Library

The law library contains 300,000 hard-copy volumes and 98,000 microform volume equivalents, and subscribes to 1280 serial publications. Such on-line databases and networks as LEXIS, DIALOG, WESTLAW, NEXIS, Capitol Hill Services, Utah Courts Information Xchange, and Internet services are available to law students for research. Special library collections include environmental and natural resources law, Utah/Western United States law, tax and commercial law, U.S. government document depository, energy and public utilities regulation, and labor and employment law. Recently, the library expanded the reference room to provide additional workstations for access to legal research databases, added shelving, and attached network nodes to study carrels. The ratio of library volumes to faculty is 13,071 to 1 and to students, 1000 to 1. The ratio of seats in the library to students is 1 to 1.

Faculty

The law school has 28 full-time and 32 part-time faculty members, of whom 16 are women. According to AAUP standards for Category I institutions, faculty salaries are average. About 35% of full-time faculty have a graduate law degree in addition to the J.D. The ratio of full-time students to full-time faculty in an average class is 30 to 1; in a clinic, 12 to 1. The law school has a regular program

Placement

J.D.s awarded:	96

Services available through: A separate law school placement center.

Special features: Computer-maintained records of current and former students may be transmitted to prospective employers to facilitate both on- and off-campus recruiting. The Legal Career Services Office offers personal counseling, maintains a resource library, and sponsors seminars to aid students in their self-directed job search.

Full-time job interviews:	n/av
Summer job interviews:	50 employers
Placement by graduation:	68% of class
Placement within 9 months:	93% of class
Average starting salary:	$18,000 to $78,000

Areas of placement:

Private practice 2-10 attorneys	20%
Private practice 11-25 attorneys	11%
Private practice 26-50 attorneys	7%
Private practice 51-100 attorneys	3%
Private practice 101+ attorneys	10%
Government	33%
Judicial clerkships	19%
Business/industry	9%
Public interest	2%
Academic	1%
Military	1%

of bringing visiting professors and other distinguished lecturers and visitors to campus. There is a chapter of the Order of the Coif; 15 faculty and 10 graduates are members.

Students

About 43% of the student body are women; 14%, minorities; 2%, African American; 4%, Asian American; 7%, Hispanic; and 1%, Native American. The majority of students come from the West (79%). The average age of entering students is 26; age range is 19 to 60. About 60% of students enter directly from undergraduate school, 10% have a graduate degree, and 36% have worked full-time prior to entering law school. About 3% drop out after the first year for academic or personal reasons; 97% remain to receive a law degree.

UNIVERSITY OF VIRGINIA

School of Law

580 Massie Road
Charlottesville, VA 22903-1789

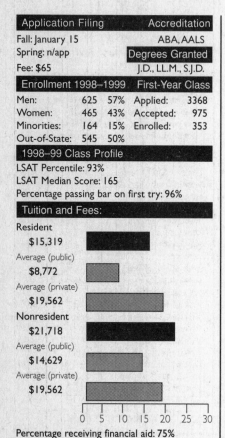

Application Filing	Accreditation
Fall: January 15	ABA, AALS
Spring: n/app	**Degrees Granted**
Fee: $65	J.D., LL.M., S.J.D.

Enrollment 1998–1999		First-Year Class	
Men:	625 57%	Applied:	3368
Women:	465 43%	Accepted:	975
Minorities:	164 15%	Enrolled:	353
Out-of-State:	545 50%		

1998–99 Class Profile
LSAT Percentile: 93%
LSAT Median Score: 165
Percentage passing bar on first try: 96%

Tuition and Fees:

Resident
$15,319

Average (public)
$8,772

Average (private)
$19,562

Nonresident
$21,718

Average (public)
$14,629

Average (private)
$19,562

0   5   10   15   20   25   30

Percentage receiving financial aid: 75%

ADMISSIONS

In the fall 1999 first-year class, 3368 applied, 975 were accepted, and 353 enrolled. Eighteen to 22 transfers enroll per year. The median LSAT percentile of the most recent first-year class was 93; the median GPA was 3.7 on a scale of 4.0.

Requirements
Applicants must have a bachelor's degree from an accredited institution and take the LSAT. No specific undergraduate courses are required. Candidates are interviewed.

Procedure
The application deadline for fall entry is January 15. Applicants should submit an application form, LSAT results, transcripts, a nonrefundable application fee of $65, 2 letters of recommendation, a personal statement, and a dean's certification form. Notification of the admission decision is by April 15. The latest acceptable LSAT test date for fall entry is December. The law school uses the LSDAS.

Special
The law school recruits minority and disadvantaged students through the Candidate Referral Service and by providing scholarship aid. Transfer students must have one year of credit and be in the top 5% of their class.

Costs

Tuition and fees for the 1999-2000 academic year are $15,319 for full-time in-state students and $21,718 for out-of-state students. On-campus room and board costs about $10,465 annually; books and supplies run $800.

Financial Aid

About 75% of current law students receive some form of aid. The average annual amount of aid from all sources combined, including scholarships, loans, and work contracts, is $23,263. Awards are based on need and merit. The required financial statements are the FAFSA and institutional forms. The aid application deadline for fall entry is February 15. Special funds for minority or disadvantaged students are available need is an important factor in scholarship allocations. First-year students are notified about their financial aid application when they are offered admission, if the appropriate needs analysis form is submitted.

About the Law School

University of Virginia School of Law was established in 1826 and is a public institution. The 1050-acre campus is in a suburban area 120 miles southwest of Washington D.C. and 70 miles west of Richmond. The primary mission of the law school is to help build a new dedication in society to the classical roles and skills of lawyering, and to foster an intellectual environment rich in the transmission of traditional values and character as well as immersed in new and creative legal thinking, analysis, and research. Students have access to federal, state, county, city, and local agencies, courts, correctional facilities, law firms, and legal aid organizations in the Charlottesville area. The Public Service Center and numerous student organizations offer pro bono opportunities and other practice situations. Facilities of special interest to law students include an extensive library, modern classrooms, and moot court rooms, student organization offices, lounges, computer laboratories, and outdoor gardens and recreational areas. Housing for law students is available in university housing for both single and married students; the Off-Grounds Housing Office also helps students find off-campus accommodations. All law school facilities are accessible to the physically disabled.

Calendar

The law school operates on a traditional semester basis. Courses for full-time students are offered days only and must be completed within a time set on a case-by-case basis. There is no part-time program. New students are admitted in the fall. There is no summer session. Transferable summer courses are not offered.

Programs

In addition to the J.D., the law school offers the LL.M, S.J.D., and LL.M. in the Judicial Process. Students may take relevant courses in other programs and apply credit toward the J.D.; a maximum of 12 credits may be applied. The following joint degrees may be earned: J.D./M.B.A. (Juris Doctor/Master of Business Administration), J.D./M.P. (Juris Doctor/Master of Planning with the Architecture School), J.D./M.A. (Juris Doctor/Master of Arts in several areas), and J.D./M.S. (Juris Doctor/Master of Science in accounting).

Phone: 804-924-7351
Fax: 804-982-2128
E-mail: lawadmit@virginia.edu
Web: http://www.law.virginia.edu

Contact
Elaine M. Hadden, Associate Dean, Management and, 804-924-7343 for general inquiries; Jerome Stokes, Assistant Dean, 804-924-7805 for financial aid information.

VIRGINIA

Required
To earn the J.D., candidates must complete 86 total credits, of which 27 are for required courses. They must maintain a minimum GPA of 2.3 in the required courses. The following first-year courses are required of all students: Criminal Law, Civil Procedure, Constitutional Law, Contracts, Property, Torts, and Legal Writing. Required upper-level courses consist of Professional Responsibility and a writing requirement. The required orientation program for first-year students is 1 day, scheduled the week classes begin.

Electives
The School of Law offers concentrations in corporate law, criminal law, family law, international law, labor law, litigation, media law, tax law, administrative law and regulations, business organizations and finance; commercial; constitutional; health; human rights and civil liberties, intellectual property, legal history; jurisprudence and comparative law. In addition, clinical offerings include the family law clinic, criminal practice clinic, and housing law. Students may gain practical experience through the school's clinical seminars; other seminars are offered by resident and adjunct faculty. Students may work with local judges in the surrounding jurisdictions, in commonwealth attorneys' offices, and with public defenders. Students may also work with individual faculty on independent research projects and may also assist faculty in research and publication projects. There are numerous special lecture series held throughout the year, including the Contemporary Legal Thought series. Students may also gain experience through the University of Virginia's Legal Assistance Society, the Post-Conviction Assistance Project, the John M. Olin Program in Law and Economics, the Center for Oceans Law and Policy, and the Institute of Law, Psychiatry, and Public Policy. The most widely taken electives are Corporations, Evidence, and Federal Income Tax I.

Graduation Requirements
In order to graduate, candidates must have a GPA of 2.3 and have completed the upper-division writing requirement.

Organizations
Students edit the *Virginia Law Review; Virginia Tax Review; Virginia Environmental Law Journal; Virginia Journal of International Law*, the oldest continuously published student-edited international law review in the country; *Journal of Law and Politics; Virginia Journal of Social Policy and the Law; Journal of Law and Technology*; and the newspaper *Virginia Law Weekly*. Students participate in in-house, intramural, and national competitions with more than 100 teams entered in the William Minor Lile moot court competition. Law student organizations include the John B. Moore Society of International Law, Environmental Law Forum, and Moot Court Board. National societies with chapters on campus are Delta Theta Phi, Phi Alpha Delta, and Phi Delta Phi.

Library
The law library contains 794,529 hardcopy volumes and 1,150,000 microform volume equivalents, and subscribes to 11,740 serial publications. Such on-line databases and networks as LEXIS, DIALOG, and WESTLAW are available to law students for research. Special library collections include oceans law and historic preservation law materials as well as U.S. Government documents. Recently, the library added a 3-story main reading room, expanded space with all new furnishings and more seating, and installed additional computer terminals. The ratio of seats in the library to students is .7 to 1.

Faculty
The law school has 64 full-time and 63 part-time faculty members, of whom 22 are women. According to AAUP standards for Category I institutions, faculty salaries are well above average. About 25% of full-time faculty have a graduate law degree in addition to the J.D. The ratio of full-time students to full-time faculty in an average class is 17 to 1; in a clinic, 10 to 1. The law school has a regular program of bringing visiting professors and other distinguished lecturers and visitors to campus. There is a chapter of the Order of the Coif; 1200 graduates are members.

Placement
J.D.s awarded:	373

Services available through: separate law school placement center.

Special features: computer network-based information on law firms and other employment opportunities, on-line interview sign-ups, and an extensive public service opportunities database. There is also an active and extensive national alumni network.

Full-time job interviews:	500 employers
Summer job interviews:	850 employers
Placement by graduation:	92% of class
Placement within 9 months:	97% of class
Average starting salary:	$30,000 to $110,000

Areas of placement:
Private practice 2-100 attorneys	68%
Judicial clerkships	17%
Government	6%
Business/industry	5%
Academic	1%
Public interest	1%
Military	1%
Unknown	1%

Students
About 43% of the student body are women; 15%, minorities; 8%, African American; 5%, Asian American; 2%, Hispanic; and 1%, Native American. The majority of students come from Virginia (50%). Current students come from 47 states, the District of Columbia and Puerto Rico. The average age of entering students is 24; age range is 21 to 46. About 40% of students enter directly from undergraduate school and 15% have a graduate degree. Less than 270 drop out after the first year for academic or personal reasons; more than 98% remain to receive a law degree.

UNIVERSITY OF WASHINGTON

School of Law

1100 Northeast Campus Parkway
Seattle, WA 98105-6617

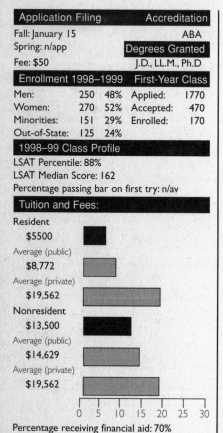

Application Filing	Accreditation
Fall: January 15	ABA
Spring: n/app	Degrees Granted
Fee: $50	J.D., LL.M., Ph.D

Enrollment 1998–1999		First-Year Class	
Men:	250 48%	Applied:	1770
Women:	270 52%	Accepted:	470
Minorities:	151 29%	Enrolled:	170
Out-of-State:	125 24%		

1998–99 Class Profile

LSAT Percentile: 88%
LSAT Median Score: 162
Percentage passing bar on first try: n/av

Tuition and Fees:

Resident
$5500

Average (public)
$8,772

Average (private)
$19,562

Nonresident
$13,500

Average (public)
$14,629

Average (private)
$19,562

0 5 10 15 20 25 30

Percentage receiving financial aid: 70%

ADMISSIONS

Information in the above capsule is approximate. In the fall 1999 first-year class, 1770 applied, 470 were accepted, and 170 enrolled. Nine transfers enrolled. The median LSAT percentile of the most recent first-year class was 88; the median GPA was 3.5 on a scale of 4.0. The lowest LSAT percentile accepted was 28; the highest was 99.

Requirements

Applicants must have a bachelor's degree from an accredited institution and take the LSAT. The most important admission factors include LSAT results, GPA, and academic achievement. No specific undergraduate courses are required. Candidates are not interviewed.

Procedure

The application deadline for fall entry is January 15. Applicants should submit an application form, LSAT results, transcripts, a nonrefundable application fee, 2 optional letters of recommendation, a dean's certificate, and a personal statement. Check with the school for current fee. Notification of the admission decision is April 1. The latest acceptable LSAT test date for fall entry is December. The law school uses the LSDAS.

Special

The law school recruits minority and disadvantaged students through West Coast law fairs, Washington undergraduate schools, law forums, and personal referrals. Transfer students must have one year of credit and have attended an ABA-approved law school.

Costs

Tuition and fees for the 1999-2000 academic year are approximately $5500 for full-time in-state students and $13,500 for out-of-state students. On-campus room and board costs about $7700 annually; and books and supplies run $1000.

Financial Aid

In a recent year, about 70% of current law students received some form of aid. The average annual amount of aid from all sources combined, including scholarships, loans, and work contracts, was $12,000; maximum, $17,000. Awards are based on need. The required financial statement is FAFSA. Check with the school for current deadline. Special funds for minority or disadvantaged students include scholarships that are available from the school's privately donated scholarship funds. Scholarships are awarded based on demonstrated financial need. First-year students are notified about their financial aid application in late spring for on-time applicants who have been admitted.

About the Law School

University of Washington School of Law was established in 1899 and is a public institution. The 20-acre campus is in an urban area 3 miles from downtown Seattle. The primary mission of the law school is a commitment to excellence in teaching, scholarship, and public service. Students have access to federal, state, county, city, and local agencies, courts, correctional facilities, law firms, and legal aid organizations in the Seattle area. Facilities of special interest to law students include a well-stocked law library. Housing for law students is available for single and married students to a limited degree in university housing; the Student Housing Affairs Office maintains listings of off-campus accommodations. All law school facilities are accessible to the physically disabled.

Calendar

The law school operates on a quarter basis. Courses for full-time students are offered days only. There is no part-time program. New full-time students are admitted in the fall. There are 2 4-week summer session's. Transferable summer courses are offered.

Contact

206-543-4078 for general inquiries; Brenda Ringer-Cote, Financial Aid Coordinator, 206-543-4552 for financial aid information.

WASHINGTON

Programs

In addition to the J.D., the law school offers the LL.M and Ph.D in Asian law. Students may take relevant courses in other programs and apply credit toward the J.D.; a maximum of 15 quarter credits may be applied. Joint degree programs can be set up with 90 other graduate programs at the school.

Required

To earn the J.D., candidates must complete 135 total credits. The following first-year courses are required of all students: Contracts, Civil Procedure, Property, Torts, Criminal Law, Basic Legal Skills, and Constitutional Law. Required upper-level courses consist of Advanced Writing, Professional Responsibility, and 60 hours of pro bono legal work. The required orientation program for first-year students is 2 days.

Electives

The School of Law offers concentrations in corporate law, criminal law, environmental law, family law, international law, labor law, litigation, maritime law, securities law, tax law, and torts and insurance. In addition, clinics open to second- and third-year students for 7 or 8 credits are avilable in mediation, child advocacy, unemployment, criminal law, affordable housing, immigration, and refugee and immigrant advocacy law. Seminars earning 3 to 6 credits and internships worth 1 to 15 credits are also open to second- and third-year students. Also available are independent research programs earning 1 to 6 credits. The most widely taken electives are Trial Advocacy, Payment Systems, and Evidence.

Graduation Requirements

In order to graduate, candidates must have a GPA of 2.7, have completed the upper-division writing requirement, and have 9 quarters in residence.

Organizations

Students edit the *Washington Law Review*, the *Pacific Rim and Policy Journal*, and the newspaper *Condor Crier*. Moot court competitions include the Jessup and International Jessup. Law student organizations include the Student Bar Association, Women's Law Caucus, and Minority Law Students Association. Other organizations include Law and Alternative Dispute Resolution, Phi Delta Phi, and Public Interest Law Association.

Library

The law library contains 506,334 hardcopy volumes and 152,681 microform volume equivalents, and subscribes to 1000 serial publications. Such on-line databases and networks as LEXIS, WESTLAW, UW Information Navigator, and CD Law as well as full Internet access, are available to law students for research. Special library collections include Japanese and other East Asian law materials. The library has been designated as a depository for U.S. government documents. The ratio of library volumes to faculty is 11,252 to 1 and to students, 803 to 1. The ratio of seats in the library to students is 1 to 2.

Faculty

The law school has 43 full-time faculty members, of whom 14 are women. According to AAUP standards for Category I institutions, faculty salaries are average. About 25% of full-time faculty have a graduate law degree in addition to the J.D. The ratio of full-time students to full-time faculty in an average class is 18 to 1. There is a chapter of the Order of the Coif.

Students

About 52% of the student body are women; 29%, minorities; 3%, African American; 15%, Asian American; 8%, Hispanic; and 3%, Native American. The majority of students come from Washington (76%). The average age of entering students is 25; age range is 20 to 50. About 33% of students enter directly from undergraduate school, 14% have a graduate degree, and 50% have worked full-time prior to entering law school. About 2% drop out after the first year for academic or personal reasons; 98% remain to receive a law degree.

Placement

J.D.s awarded:	151
Services available through: a separate law school placement center.	
Services:	
Special features: first-year student job workshops, first-year student mock interview program, and other career programs throughout the school year	
Full-time job interviews:	35 employers
Summer job interviews:	69 employers
Placement by graduation:	82% of class
Placement within 9 months:	86% of class
Average starting salary:	n/av
Areas of placement:	
Private practice 2-10 attorneys	19%
Private practice 11-25 attorneys	9%
Private practice 26-50 attorneys	10%
Private practice 51-100 attorneys	13%
Solo practice	4%
Business/industry	12%
Government	12%
Judicial clerkships	9%
Public interest	7%
Academic	3%
Military	2%

UNIVERSITY OF WISCONSIN-MADISON

Law School

975 Bascom Mall
Madison, WI 53706

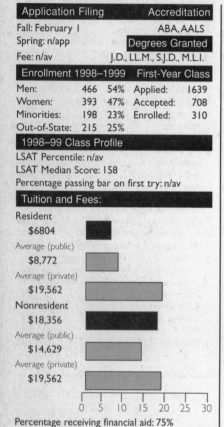

Application Filing		Accreditation
Fall: February 1		ABA, AALS
Spring: n/app		**Degrees Granted**
Fee: n/av		J.D., LL.M., S.J.D., M.L.I.

Enrollment 1998–1999			First-Year Class	
Men:	466	54%	Applied:	1639
Women:	393	47%	Accepted:	708
Minorities:	198	23%	Enrolled:	310
Out-of-State:	215	25%		

1998–99 Class Profile

LSAT Percentile: n/av
LSAT Median Score: 158
Percentage passing bar on first try: n/av

Tuition and Fees:

Resident
$6804

Average (public)
$8,772

Average (private)
$19,562

Nonresident
$18,356

Average (public)
$14,629

Average (private)
$19,562

0 5 10 15 20 25 30

Percentage receiving financial aid: 75%

ADMISSIONS

In the fall 1999 first-year class, 1639 applied, 708 were accepted, and 310 enrolled. Six transfers enrolled. The median GPA of the most recent first-year class was 3.8 on a scale of 4.0.

Requirements

Applicants must have a bachelor's degree from an accredited institution and take the LSAT. The most important admission factors include academic achievement, GPA, and LSAT results. No specific undergraduate courses are required. Candidates are not interviewed.

Procedure

The application deadline for fall entry is February 1. Applicants should submit an application form, LSAT results, transcripts, and a nonrefundable application fee. Although not required, letters of recommendation from teachers or employers are strongly encouraged. Check with the school for current fee. Notification of the admission decision is on a rolling basis. The latest acceptable LSAT test date for fall entry is February. The law school uses the LSDAS.

Special

The law school recruits minority and disadvantaged students through mailings, law school and graduate school days, and minority career fairs. Transfer students must have one year of credit and have attended an ABA-approved law school. Due to enrollment pressures, transfer applications are accepted primarily on the basis of class rank in the transferring law school, or, if class rank is unavailable, on the basis of other evidence of academic performance.

Costs

Tuition and fees for the 1999-2000 academic year are $6804 for full-time in-state students and $18,356 for out-of-state students. Tuition for part-time students is $285 per credit in-state, and $767 per credit out-of-state. On-campus room and board costs about $5790 annually; and books and supplies run $1740.

Financial Aid

In a recent year, about 75% of current law students received some form of aid. The average annual amount of aid from all sources combined, including scholarships, loans, and work contracts, was $12,000; maximum, $19,900. Awards are based on need. The required financial statement is FAFSA. Check with the school for current deadline. Special funds for minority or disadvantaged students are available. First-year students are notified about their financial aid application at the time they apply to law school.

About the Law School

University of Wisconsin-Madison Law School was established in 1868 and is a public institution. The 928-acre campus is in an urban area 120 miles north of Chicago. The primary mission of the law school is to emphasize the dynamics of the law: how the law relates to society as a whole and to social changes. Students have access to federal, state, county, city, and local agencies, courts, correctional facilities, law firms, and legal aid organizations in the Madison area. Facilities of special interest to law students include the State Capitol, State Supreme Court, Federal District Court, and County Court located in Madison. Housing for law students is limited at the university, but there is an abundance of private rental property. All law school facilities are accessible to the physically disabled.

Calendar

The law school operates on a traditional semester basis. Courses for full-and part-time students are offered both day and evening and must be completed within 6 years. New full-and part-time students are admitted in the fall. There is a 13-week summer session. Transferable summer courses are offered.

Programs

In addition to the J.D., the law school offers the LL.M, S.J.D., and M.L.I. (Master of Arts or Master of Science in Legal Institutions. Students may take relevant courses in other programs and apply credit toward the J.D.; a maximum of 6 credits may be applied unless the student is in one of the school's joint degree programs. The following joint programs may be pursued: Law and Public Affairs; Law and Library and Information Services; Law and Philosophy (Ph.D. level only); Law and Latin American and Iberian Studies; Law and Business; Law and Environmental Studies; Law and Industrial Relations; and Law and Sociology (Ph.D.) and Rural Sociology.

Phone: 608-262-5914
Fax: 608-262-5485
E-mail: Admissions@law.wisc.educ
Web: www.law.wisc.educ

Contact

Marilyn Johnson, Secretary, 608-262-5914 for general inquiries; Dorothy Davis, 608-262-1815 for financial aid information.

WISCONSIN

Required

To earn the J.D., candidates must complete 90 total credits, of which 30 to 31 are for required courses. They must maintain a minimum grade average of 77 in the required courses. The following first-year courses are required of all students: Contracts, Introduction to Substantive Criminal Law, Civil Procedure, Criminal Procedure, Torts, Legal Research and Writing, and Property. Required upper-level courses consist of Legal Process and Professional Responsibilities. The required orientation program for first-year students is a 3-day program that includes a check-in with the Admissions Office staff, diagnostic writing exercise, case briefing workshop, first-year convocation, informal gatherings, and student photos.

Electives

The Law School offers concentrations in corporate law, criminal law, environmental law, international law, labor law, litigation, and public interest law. In addition, clinics include Legal Assistance to Institutionalized Persons, Legal Defense Project, and Labor Law. Numerous seminars are available, as well as internships, research programs, field work, tutorial programs, and special interest group programs. Study abroad is possible through the Germany, Holland, Italy, Chile, and Asian Programs. The Legal Education Opportunities Program is available for minorities. The most widely taken electives are Trusts and Estates, Evidence, and Business Organizations.

Graduation Requirements

In order to graduate, candidates must have a grade average of 77 and have completed the upper-division writing requirement.

Organizations

Students edit the *Wisconsin Law Review, Environmental Law Journal, Wisconsin International Law Journal, Women's Law Journal,* and the student newspaper *The Advocate.* Moot court competitions include the Jessup International Law and National Constitutional Law teams, which are offered every year. Civil Rights Law and other teams are offered according to student interest. Law student organizations include the ABA-Law Student Division, Association of Trial Lawyers of America, and Asian Law Students Association. Local chapters of national associations include Phi Alpha Delta, Edward G. Ryan Chapter of Phi Delta Phi, and National Lawyers Guild.

Library

The law library contains 475,000 hard-copy volumes and 695,000 microform volume equivalents, and subscribes to 5000 serial publications. Such on-line databases and networks as LEXIS, DIALOG, WESTLAW, and lwocal and Internet access to a wide range of resources are available to law students for research. Special library collections include criminal justice and foreign and international law materials. The library is a federal depository. Recently, the library underwent an extensive expansion and renovation project, which resulted in a significant enhancement. The ratio of library volumes to faculty is 7500 to 1 and to students, 420 to 1.

Faculty

The law school has 47 full-time faculty members, of whom 11 are women. According to AAUP standards for Category I institutions, faculty salaries are well above average. About 4% of full-time faculty have a graduate law degree in addition to the J.D. The ratio of full-time students to full-time faculty in an average class is 18 to 1; in a clinic, 5 to 1. There is a chapter of the Order of the Coif.

Placement

J.D.s awarded:	263
Services available through: a separate law school placement center.	
Special features: The school operates a mentoring and tag-along program in cooperation with the State Bar of Wisconsin.	
Full-time job interviews:	50 employers
Summer job interviews:	95 employers
Placement by graduation:	70% of class
Placement within 9 months:	98% of class
Average starting salary:	$37,085 to $67,000
Areas of placement:	
Private practice 2-10 attorneys	16%
Private practice 11-25 attorneys	8%
Private practice 26-50 attorneys	6%
Private practice 51-100 attorneys	5%
Private practice 100+ attorneys	21%
Government	15%
Business/industry	10%
Judicial clerkships	9%
Academic	2%
Public interest	2%
Military	2%

Students

About 47% of the student body are women; 23%, minorities; 10%, African American; 3%, Asian American; 7%, Hispanic; and 3%, Native American. The majority of students come from Wisconsin (75%). The average age of entering students is 25; age range is 21 to 55. About 38% of students enter directly from undergraduate school, 8% have a graduate degree, and 60% have worked full-time prior to entering law school. About 1% drop out after the first year for academic or personal reasons; 99% remain to receive a law degree.

UNIVERSITY OF WYOMING

College of Law

P.O. Box 3035
Laramie, WY 82071

ADMISSIONS

In the fall 1999 first-year class, 379 applied, 249 were accepted, and 83 enrolled. The median LSAT percentile of the most recent first-year class was 55; the median GPA was 3.3 on a scale of 4.0. The lowest LSAT percentile accepted was 29; the highest was 93.

Requirements

Applicants must have a bachelor's degree from an accredited institution and take the LSAT. The most important admission factors include GPA, LSAT results, and writing ability. No specific undergraduate courses are required. Candidates are not interviewed.

Procedure

The application deadline for fall entry is March 15. Applicants should submit an application form, LSAT results, transcripts, and a nonrefundable application fee of $35. Notification of the admission decision is no later than May 15. The latest acceptable LSAT test date for fall entry is February. The law school uses the LSDAS.

Special

The law school recruits minority and disadvantaged students by means of participation in the CLEO Summer Institutes and by hosting a law day session for minority undergraduate students at the university. Transfer students must have one year of credit, have attended an ABA-approved law school, and rank in the top quarter of their first-year class.

Costs

Tuition and fees for the 1999-2000 academic year are $4424 for full-time in-state students and $9692 for out-of-state students. On-campus room and board costs about $7236 annually; and books and supplies run $800.

Financial Aid

About 80% of current law students receive some form of aid. The average annual amount of aid from all sources combined, including scholarships, loans, and work contracts, is $8500; maximum, $11,000. Awards are based on need and merit. The required financial statement is FAFSA. The aid application deadline for fall entry is February 1. Special funds for minority or disadvantaged students consist of minority graduate assistantships offered on a competitive basis. First-year students are notified about their financial aid application at the time of acceptance.

About the Law School

University of Wyoming College of Law was established in 1920 and is a public institution. The 735-acre campus is in a small town 125 miles north of Denver, Colorado. The primary mission of the law school is to provide students with the knowledge and training necessary to meet the responsibilities of the profession; students must secure a broad and basic knowlege of legal principles, understand the social and economic factors underlying these principles, and learn to judge the effectiveness of these principles in solving client and societal problems. Students have access to federal, state, county, city, and local agencies, courts, correctional facilities, law firms, and legal aid organizations in the Laramie area. All state and federal judicial and government agencies are located in the state capital, Cheyenne. Housing for law students is available in a university residence hall for single students. The university also maintains 2-bedroom furnished apartments for married students. About 90% of the law school facilities are accessible to the physically disabled.

Calendar

The law school operates on a traditional semester basis. Courses for full-time students are offered days only and must be completed within 3 years. New full-time students are admitted in the fall. There is no summer session. Transferable summer courses are not offered.

Programs

The following joint degree may be earned: J.D./M.P.A. (Juris Doctor/Master of Public Administration).

Required

To earn the J.D., candidates must complete 88 total credits, of which 52 are for required courses. They must maintain a minimum GPA of 2.0 in the required courses. The following first-year courses are required of all students: Contracts I and II, Property I and II, Torts I and II, Criminal Law, Judicial Remedies, Legal Writing and Research, Appellate Advocacy, Civil Procedure I, and Constitutional Law I. Required upper-level courses consist of Civil Procedure II, Constitutional Law II, Evidence, Professional Responsibility, and an

Phone: 307-766-6416
E-mail: lawadmis@uwyo.edu
Web: uwyo.edu/law

Contact

Robin Kniffen, Admissions Secretary, 307-766-6416 for general inquiries; Office of Student Financial Aid, 307-766-2116 for financial aid information.

advanced writing requirement. Students must complete 2 of the following 3 courses: Administrative Law, Business Organizations, or Trusts and Estates. Students must complete 1 of the following 3 courses: Creditors' Rights, Income Taxation, or Secured Transactions. The first-year orientation program is 2 days of lectures on legal analysis, legal reasoning, the study of law, case briefing sessions, and a speech by a member of the Wyoming judiciary.

Electives

The College of Law offers concentrations in corporate law and environmental law. In addition, Defender Aid, Legal Services, and Prosecution Assistance programs are available to third-year students; 1 clinic per semester may be taken for 3 credit hours. In order to graduate, the advanced writing requirement must be fulfilled; a variety of seminars that meet this requirement is offered for 1 to 2 credits. Second- and third-year students may participate in the externship program for 1 or 2 credit hours per semester. Externs are placed with the Wyoming Attorney General's Office, Wyoming Supreme Court, State Department of Revenue and Taxation, and the U.S. District Court and Court of Appeals judges for Wyoming. A retention program is offered each spring to first-year students who have GPAs near or below 2.0 after the first semester. The most widely taken electives are Secured Transactions, Family Law, and Water Law.

Graduation Requirements

In order to graduate, candidates must have a GPA of 2.0 and have completed the upper-division writing requirement.

Organizations

Students edit the *Land and Water Law Review*. Moot court competitions include the National Moot Court, National Environmental Law Moot Court at Pace University, and Natural Resources Law Moot Court at the University of Denver. Other competitions include the National Client Counseling and the National Student Trial Advocacy. Law student organizations include the Potter Law Club, Natural Resources Law Forum, and Women's Law Forum. There are local chapters of Phi Alpha Delta, Phi Delta Phi, and Delta Theta Phi.

Library

The law library contains 134,028 hard-copy volumes and 453,081 microform volume equivalents, and subscribes to 2312 serial publications. Such on-line databases and networks as LEXIS, DIALOG, and WESTLAW are available to law students for research. Special library collections include a selective government depository and a Roman law collection. Recently, the library increased the number of WESTLAW and LEXIS terminals. The ratio of library volumes to faculty is 11,154 to 1 and to students, 613 to 1. The ratio of seats in the library to students is 1 to 1.

Faculty

The law school has 14 full-time faculty members, of whom 6 are women. According to AAUP standards for Category I institutions, faculty salaries are well below average. About 6% of full-time faculty have a graduate law degree in addition to the J.D. The ratio of full-time students to full-time faculty in an average class is 30 to 1; in a clinic, 8 to 1. The law school has a regular program of bringing visiting professors and other distinguished lecturers and visitors to campus. There is a chapter of the Order of the Coif; 14 faculty and 79 graduates are members.

Students

About 43% of the student body are women; 4%, minorities; 1%, African American; 1%, Asian American; 2%, Hispanic; and 1%, Native American. The majority of students come from Wyoming (68%). The average age of entering students is 27; age range is 21 to 48. About 37% of students enter directly from undergraduate school, 13% have a graduate degree, and 57% have worked full-time prior to entering law school. About 8% drop out after the first year for academic or personal reasons; 85% remain to receive a law degree.

Placement

J.D.s awarded:	65
Services available through: A separate law school placement center and the university placement center.	
Services:	
Special features:	
Full-time job interviews:	10 employers
Summer job interviews:	11 employers
Placement by graduation:	n/av
Placement within 9 months:	86% of class
Average starting salary:	$18,000 to $86,000
Areas of placement:	
Private practice 2-10 attorneys	53%
Government	18%
Judicial clerkships	16%
Unknown	9%
Public interest	2%
Military	2%

School of Law

Wesemann Hall
Valparaiso, IN 46383-6493

Application Filing	Accreditation
Fall: April 15	ABA, AALS
Spring: n/app	**Degrees Granted**
Fee: $30	J.D., LL.M.

Enrollment 1998–1999		First-Year Class	
Men:	231 53%	Applied:	734
Women:	206 47%	Accepted:	532
Minorities:	61 14%	Enrolled:	166
Out-of-State:	197 45%		

1998–99 Class Profile
LSAT Percentile: 52%
LSAT Median Score: 151
Percentage passing bar on first try: 86%

Tuition and Fees:

Resident
$18,438

Average (public)
$8,772

Average (private)
$19,562

Nonresident
$18,438

Average (public)
$14,629

Average (private)
$19,562

0　5　10　15　20　25　30

Percentage receiving financial aid: 90%

ADMISSIONS

In the fall 1999 first-year class, 734 applied, 532 were accepted, and 166 enrolled. Five transfers enrolled. The median LSAT percentile of the most recent first-year class was 52; the median GPA was 3.1 on a scale of 4.0. The lowest LSAT percentile accepted was 17; the highest was 95.

Requirements
Applicants must have a bachelor's degree from an accredited institution and take the LSAT. The most important admission factors include academic achievement, general background, and LSAT results. No specific undergraduate courses are required. Candidates are not interviewed.

Procedure
The application deadline for fall entry is April 15. Applicants should submit an application form, LSAT results, transcripts, and a nonrefundable application fee of $30. TOEFL is required of international applicants. Notification of the admission decision is on a rolling basis. The latest acceptable LSAT test date for fall entry is February. The law school uses the LSDAS.

Special
The law school recruits minority and disadvantaged students with the assistance of the minority alumni and members of the black and Hispanic student groups, who assist the admissions office by making recruitment trips, writing letters, and making phone calls. Also, scholarships are available for qualified minority students. Transfer students must have one year of credit, have a minimum GPA of 2.0, have attended an ABA-approved law school, and have their application reviewed by the admissions committee.

Costs

Tuition and fees for the 1999-2000 academic year are $18,438 for all full-time students. Tuition for all part-time students is $945 per credit. Off-campus room and board costs about $6600 annually; books and supplies run $750.

Financial Aid

About 90% of current law students receive some form of aid. The maximum annual amount of aid from all sources combined, including scholarships, loans, and work contracts, is $28,798. Awards are based on need and merit. The required financial statement is FAFSA. The aid application deadline for fall entry is March. Special funds for minority or disadvantaged students are available based on academic merit and need. First-year students are notified about their financial aid application at the time the financial aid file is complete.

About the Law School

Valparaiso University School of Law was established in 1879 and is a private institution. The 310-acre campus is in a suburban area 55 miles southeast of Chicago in Northwest Indiana. The primary mission of the law school is to foster a learning environment; to maintain a community of teacher-scholars committed to excellence in legal research and publication that will shape the development of the law; and to embody an inter-action between demands of the law and the Lutheran heritage of Valparaiso University. Students have access to federal, state, county, city, and local agencies, courts, correctional facilities, law firms, and legal aid organizations in the Valparaiso area. Valparaiso is the county seat of Porter County. Students also have access to charitable and community organizations for volunteer/pro bono work in Porter and Lake counties, Indiana, and Cook County, Illinois (Chicago). Facilities of special interest to law students are the Wesemann Hall, which houses classrooms, a courtroom, and an administrative complex; and Heritage Hall, which is listed on the National Register of Historic places, housing the law clinic. Housing for law students includes limited on-campus apartments; local apartments and large apartment complexes; and modest lakeside summer homes and cottages available for rent. The Admissions Office provides assistance in locating housing. About 75% of the law school facilities are accessible to the physically disabled.

Calendar

The law school operates on a traditional semester basis. Courses for full- and part-time students are offered both day and evening and must be completed within 5 years. New full- and part-time students are admitted in the fall. There is an 8-week summer session. Transferable summer courses are offered.

Programs

In addition to the J.D., the law school offers the LL.M. The following joint degree may be earned: J.D./M.A. (Juris Doctor/Master of Arts in psychological foundations).

Required
To earn the J.D., candidates must complete 90 total credits, of which 46 are for required courses. They must maintain a minimum GPA of 2.0 in the required courses. The following first-year courses are required of all students: Contracts, Criminal Law, Property, Civil Procedure, Torts, Constitutional Law I, and Legal Writing, Reasoning, and Research. Required upper-level courses consist of Constitutional Law II, Jurisprudence, Legal Profession, a seminar, and 1 of 7

INDIANA

Phone: 219-465-7829
888-VALPOLAW (825-7652)
Fax: 219-465-7808
E-mail: heike.spahn@valpo.edu
Web: www.valpo.edu/law/

Contact

Heike Spahn, Assistant Dean, 219-465-7829 for general inquiries; Kimberly Jenkins, Financial Aid Counselor, 219-465-7818 for financial aid information.

perspective courses, Evidence, and 1 of 5 advanced writing courses. All third-year (and some second-year) law students in Indiana are permitted to represent clients in court, under supervision. The law clinic is available to third-year students and handles civil, criminal, environmental, domestic violence, and juvenile mediation law matters. The required orientation program for first-year students is 2 days, usually the Thursday and Friday before classes begin. Formal registration and meetings with current students, deans, and faculty advisers are included.

Electives
Students must take 19 credits in their area of concentration. The School of Law offers concentrations in criminal law, entertainment, environmental law, international law, labor law, litigation, alternative dispute resolution, and state and local Government/civil rights. In addition, clinics are available to second- and third-year students for 2 or 3 credits a semester for a maximum of 12 credit hours. A seminar is required of all third-year students not on the *Law Review*, and a substantial paper is required. Second- and third-year students may also participate in up to 15 credit hours of an extern program. The law school supports 55 externship programs. Students may assist faculty with current representation or in research assistantships in which they work one-on-one with a professor in his or her area of current interest and research. No credit is given for the 20 hours of pro bono public service. Special lecture series include the Monsanto Annual Lecture on Tort Law Reform, the annual Seegers Lecture Series, the Distinguished Visitors Program, and the annual Tabor Institute on Legal Ethics. There is a summer study-abroad program in Cambridge, England. There is also a voluntary Academic Support Program; no credit is given and participation is by invitation only. Other tutorials are led by first-year faculty with student tutors available for individual consultation. The Hispanic Law Students Association and Black Law Students Association sponsor minority programming. Special interest group progrmas include the Intellectual Property Association, Health Law Association, Sports and Entertainment Law Association, Coalition for Choice, Jus Vitae, Equal Justice Alliance, Third World Legal Studies, International

Law, Pastoral Ministry, ATLA, and ABA. The most widely taken electives are Trusts and Estates, Trial Advocacy, and business and commercial law courses.

Graduation Requirements
In order to graduate, candidates must have a GPA of 2.0, have completed the upper-division writing requirement, and have completed the pro bono service requirement of 20 hours, for which there is no grade or credit.

Organizations

Students edit the *Valparaiso University Law Review*. The *Third World Legal Studies* is published by the International Third World Legal Studies Association and the School of Law. The student newspaper is *The Forum.* Annually, moot court teams are sent to the Environmental Moot Court held at Pace University, the Giles Sutherland Rich Moot Court (1995 National Champions), and the Jessup International Moot Court. Other annual competitions are the Negotiations, the National Mock Trial, Association of Trial Lawyers of America, and Client Counseling. Law student organizations include the Sports and Entertainment Law Association, Midwest Environmental Law Caucus, and Christian Legal Society. Local chapters of national associations include Delta Theta Phi, Phi Alpha Delta, and Phi Delta Phi. Other groups include the Fine Arts Committee, Law Spouses Association, and university intramural sports.

Library

The law library contains 283,803 hard-copy volumes and 774,186 microform volume equivalents, and subscribes to 2806 serial publications. Such on-line databases and networks as LEXIS, DIALOG, and WESTLAW, are available to law students for research. All students are offered E-mail/Internet accounts and have access to the World Wide Web and CALI materials. Special library collections include a selected United States Government Printing Office Depository, a Readex United Nations basic law library collection, and briefs from the Indiana Supreme Court and Indiana Court of Appeals. Recently, the library expanded computer facilities; installed an integrated, automated library system; added shelving and a new staff position. The ratio of library volumes to faculty is 14,190 to 1 and to students, 652 to 1. The ratio of seats in the library to students is 1 to 8.

Placement

J.D.s awarded:	141

Services available through: a separate law school placement center
Services: annually participate in 12 job fairs, produce newletters for students, and hold numerous seminars and workshops, including Bridge the Gap and Client Relations and Retention.
Special features: participates in NAPIL, Pro Bono Students of America, and Alliance for Justice and assists in locating intern/externships and pro bono opportunities. The Assistant Dean of Career Services was the 1993-94 president of the National Association for Law Placement.

Full-time job interviews:	27 employers
Summer job interviews:	39 employers
Placement by graduation:	72% of class
Placement within 9 months:	95% of class
Average starting salary:	$26,000 to $96,000

Areas of placement:

Private practice 2-10 attorneys	39%
Private practice 11-25 attorneys	6%
Private practice 26-50 attorneys	2%
Private practice 51-100 attorneys	3%
Business/industry	17%
Government	16%
Judicial clerkships	10%
Public interest	4%
Academic	2%
Military	2%

Faculty

The law school has 27 full-time and 37 part-time faculty members, of whom 24 are women. According to AAUP standards for Category IIA institutions, faculty salaries are above average. About 22% of full-time faculty have a graduate law degree in addition to the J.D. The ratio of full-time students to full-time faculty in an average class is 18 to 1; in a clinic, 8 to 1.

Students

About 47% of the student body are women; 14%, minorities; 9%, African American; 2%, Asian American; 3%, Hispanic; and 1%, Native American. The majority of students come from the Midwest (80%). The average age of entering students is 26; age range is 19 to 53. About 60% of students enter directly from undergraduate school and 7% have a graduate degree. About 10% drop out after the first year for academic or personal reasons; 86% remain to receive a law degree.

VANDERBILT UNIVERSITY

School of Law

Nashville, TN 37240

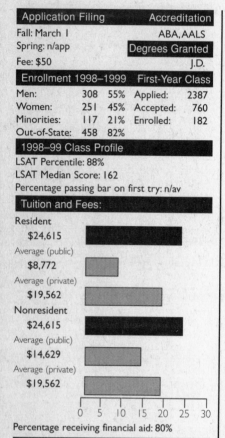

Application Filing

Fall: March 1
Spring: n/app
Fee: $50

Accreditation

ABA, AALS

Degrees Granted

J.D.

Enrollment 1998–1999   First-Year Class

Men:	308	55%	Applied:	2387
Women:	251	45%	Accepted:	760
Minorities:	117	21%	Enrolled:	182
Out-of-State:	458	82%		

1998–99 Class Profile

LSAT Percentile: 88%
LSAT Median Score: 162
Percentage passing bar on first try: n/av

Tuition and Fees:

Resident
$24,615

Average (public)
$8,772

Average (private)
$19,562

Nonresident
$24,615

Average (public)
$14,629

Average (private)
$19,562

0   5   10   15   20   25   30

Percentage receiving financial aid: 80%

ADMISSIONS

In the fall 1999 first-year class, 2387 applied, 760 were accepted, and 182 enrolled. Four transfers enrolled. The median LSAT percentile of the most recent first-year class was 88; the median GPA was 3.6 on a scale of 4.0. The lowest LSAT percentile accepted was 29; the highest was 99.

Requirements

Applicants must have a bachelor's degree from an accredited institution and take the LSAT. The most important admission factors include LSAT results, GPA, and academic achievement. No specific undergraduate courses are required. Candidates are interviewed.

Procedure

The application deadline for fall entry is March 1. Applicants should submit an application form, LSAT results, a nonrefundable application fee of $50, 2 letters of recommendation, and a personal statement. Notification of the admission decision is by April 1. The latest acceptable LSAT test date for fall entry is February. The law school uses the LSDAS.

Special

The law school recruits minority and disadvantaged students by means of on-campus recruiting, general mailings, and LSAC Forums. Transfer students must have one year of credit and have attended an ABA-approved law school.

Costs

Tuition and fees for the 1999-2000 academic year are $24,615 for all full-time students. On-campus room and board costs about $14,490 annually; and books and supplies run $1200.

Financial Aid

About 80% of current law students receive some form of aid. The average annual amount of aid from all sources combined, including scholarships, loans, and work contracts, is $25,500; maximum, $38,840. Awards are based on need and merit. The required financial statement is CSS Profile or the FAFSA. The aid application deadline for fall entry is March 1. First-year students are notified about their financial aid application at time of acceptance.

About the Law School

Vanderbilt University School of Law was established in 1874 and is a private institution. The campus is in an urban area 1½ mile west of downtown Nashville. The primary mission of the law school is to educate students to become effective lawyers in a wide range of professional areas. Students have access to federal, state, county, city, and local agencies, courts, correctional facilities, law firms, and legal aid organizations in the Nashville area. Facilities of special interest to law students are local, state, and federal courts in Nashville, the state capital. Housing for law students is available in off-campus and on-campus graduate facilities.

Calendar

The law school operates on a traditional semester basis. Courses for full-time students are offered days only and must be completed within 3 years. There is no part-time program. New students are admitted in the fall. There is no summer session. Transferable summer courses are not offered.

Programs

Students may take relevant courses in other programs and apply credit toward the J.D.; a maximum of 6 credits may be applied. The following joint degrees may be earned: J.D./M.B.A. (Juris Doctor/Master of Business Administration), J.D./M.T.S. (Juris Doctor/Master of Theological Studies), J.D./D.I.V. (Juris Doctor/Master of Divinity), J.D./M.A. (Juris Doctor/Master of Arts), and J.D./Ph.D. (Juris Doctor/Doctor of Philosophy).

Contact
Sonya Smith, Assistant Dean, 615-322-6452 for general inquiries; Derrick Dowell, Assistant Director of Admissions, for financial aid information.

Required
To earn the J.D., candidates must complete 88 total credits, of which 34 are for required courses. They must maintain a minimum GPA of 1.7 in the required courses. The following first-year courses are required of all students: Civil Procedure, Constitutional Law, Contracts, Criminal Law, Legal Writing and Introduction to Lawyering, Property, Torts, and Legal Process and Institutions of Lawmaking. Required upper-level courses consist of Professional Responsibility. The required orientation program for first-year students consists of an informal 2-day orientation to law school; there is no academic component.

Electives
Clinics, in the area of juvenile, criminal, and civil law, are elective 2- or 3-hour courses open to second- and third-year students. Many limited-enrollment seminars, worth 2- or 3 credit hours, are available to second- and third-year students. Internships are available with judges and legal organizations. Research programs consist of faculty research assistantships. Several lecture series are held each year. Students may participate in study-abroad programs sponsored by ABA-accredited law schools. Special writing assistance is available for first-year students who need tutoring. Special interest groups include Black Law Students Association and Asian Law Students Association.

Graduation Requirements
In order to graduate, candidates must have a GPA of 1.7 and have completed the upper-division writing requirement.

Organizations
Students edit the *Vanderbilt Law Review, Journal of Transnational Law,* and the newspaper *VLS Brief.* Organizations that participate in moot court competitions are the National Moot Court Team, the International Moot Court Team, and the Mock Trial Team. Two other traveling teams competed in 1996-97. Law student organizations include the Vanderbilt Bar Association, Environmental Law Society, and the Federalist Society. There are local chapters of ABA-Law Student Division and Phi Alpha Delta.

Library
The law library contains 207,887 hardcopy volumes and 417,126 microform volume equivalents, and subscribes to 4683 serial publications. Such on-line databases and networks as LEXIS, DIALOG, and WESTLAW are available to law students for research. Special library collections include a federal depository and the James Cullen Looney Medico-Legal Collection. Recently, the library expanded the building and became automated. The ratio of library volumes to faculty is 8916 to 1 and to students, 561 to 1. The ratio of seats in the library to students is 1 to 1.

Faculty
The law school has 36 full-time and 40 part-time faculty members, of whom 25 are women. According to AAUP standards for Category I institutions, faculty salaries are well above average. About 5% of full-time faculty have a graduate law degree in addition to the J.D.; about 1% of part-time faculty have one. The ratio of full-time students to full-time faculty in an average class is 17 to 1; in a clinic, 7 to 1. The law school has a regular program of bringing visiting professors and other distinguished lecturers and visitors to campus. There is a chapter of the Order of the Coif; 10 graduates are members.

Students
About 45% of the student body are women; 21%, minorities; 12%, African American; 7%, Asian American; and 1%, Hispanic. The majority of students come from the South (42%). The average age of entering students is 24; age range is 21 to 53. About 60% of students enter directly from undergraduate school and 40% have worked full-time prior to entering law school. About 2% drop out after the first year for academic or personal reasons; 98% remain to receive a law degree.

Placement

J.D.s awarded:	177
Services available through: separate law school placement center.	
Special features: n/av	
Full-time job interviews:	400 employers
Summer job interviews:	400 employers
Placement by graduation:	87% of class
Placement within 9 months:	98% of class
Average starting salary:	$62,000
Areas of placement:	
Private practice 51-100 attorneys	46%
Judicial clerkships	20%
Private practice 26-50 attorneys	15%
Private practice 11-25 attorneys	8%
Government	4%
Private practice 2-10 attorneys	3%
Academic	2%
Business/industry	2%
Public interest	1%

VERMONT LAW SCHOOL

P.O. Box 96, Chelsea Street
South Royalton, VT 05068-0096

Application Filing	Accreditation
Fall: February 1	ABA, AALS
Spring: November 1	**Degrees Granted**
Fee: n/av	J.D., M.S.E.L.

Enrollment 1998–1999		First-Year Class	
Men:	256 53%	Applied:	781
Women:	230 48%	Accepted:	574
Minorities:	39 8%	Enrolled:	179
Out-of-State:	413 85%		

1998–99 Class Profile
LSAT Percentile: 52%
LSAT Median Score: 151
Percentage passing bar on first try: 80%

Tuition and Fees:

Resident
$21,033

Average (public)
$8,772

Average (private)
$19,562

Nonresident
$21,033

Average (public)
$14,629

Average (private)
$19,562

0   5   10   15   20   25   30

Percentage receiving financial aid: 90%

ADMISSIONS
In the fall 1999 first-year class, 781 applied, 574 were accepted, and 179 enrolled. The median LSAT percentile of the most recent first-year class was 52; the median GPA was 3.02 on a scale of 4.0. The lowest LSAT percentile accepted was 7; the highest was 96.

Requirements
Applicants must have a bachelor's degree from an accredited institution and take the LSAT. The most important admission factors include academic achievement and LSAT results. No specific undergraduate courses are required. Candidates are interviewed.

Procedure
The application deadline for fall entry is February 1. Applicants should submit an application form, LSAT results, a nonrefundable application fee, 2 letters of recommendation, and 3 personal statements. Check with the school for current fee. Notification of the admission decision is on a rolling admission basis. The latest acceptable LSAT test date for fall entry is February. The law school uses the LSDAS.

Special
The law school recruits minority and disadvantaged students through the Council on Legal Education Opportunity (CLEO) program, direct mail through the Candidate Referral Service (CRS), and through participation in college minority student events and a diversity scholarship program. Transfer students must be in good academic standing and be eligible to return to the school from which they are transferring.

Costs
Tuition and fees for the 1999-2000 academic year are $21,033 for all full-time students. Books and supplies run $900.

Financial Aid
In a recent year, about 90% of current law students received some form of aid. The average annual amount of aid from all sources combined, including scholarships, loans, and work contracts, was $27,432; maximum, $31,220. Awards are based on need and merit. All institutional aid is need-based, though some awards have a merit component. The required financial statement is FAFSA. Check with the school for current aid application deadline. Special funds for minority or disadvantaged students include the Debevoise Family Scholarship Fund, which provides grants to qualified diverse applicants from traditionally underrepresented groups with demonstrated financial need. First-year students are notified about their financial aid application as early as possible after acceptance (usually late March).

About the Law School
Vermont Law School was established in 1972. The 10-acre campus is in a small town 70 miles southeast of Burlington, and 15 miles north. The primary mission of the law school is to provide a thorough understanding of the nature and function of law in society and to equip graduates to serve their communities in positions of leadership and responsibility. The school believes lawyers should be liberally educated, ethical, competent, and committed to improving the law and its administration. Students have access to federal, state, county, city, and local agencies, courts, correctional facilities, law firms, and legal aid organizations in the South Royalton area. The South Royalton Legal Clinic is located on campus and the Vermont General Assembly is located in nearby Montpelier, the state capital. A modern library was constructed in 1992 and a new classroom building was constructed in 1998. Nearby Hanover, New Hampshire, home of Dartmouth College, is a source of student cultural and social life. Child care is available on campus. Most students live in private houses, apartments, or rooms in the community or nearby towns. There is a copious supply of rental units in the area and the law school provides a listing to students.

Calendar
The law school operates on a traditional semester basis. Courses for full-time students are offered days only and must be completed within 4 years. There is no part-time programs. New full-time students are admitted in the fall and spring. There is an 8-week summer session. Transferable summer courses are offered.

Programs
In addition to the J.D., the law school offers the M.S.E.L. (Master of Studies in Environmental Law). Students may take relevant courses in other programs and apply credit toward the J.D.; a maximum of 9 credits may be applied. The following joint degrees may be earned: J.D./M.S.E.L. (Juris Doctor/Master of Studies in Environmental Law).

Phone: 802-763-8303
888-APPLY-VLS
Fax: 802-763-7071
E-mail: admiss@vermontlaw.edu
Web: www.vermontlaw.edu

Contact

Michelle D. Mason, Admissions Director, 802-763-8303, ext. 2239 or 888-APPLY-VLS for general inquiries; Director of Financial Aid, 802-763-8303, ext. 2235 or 888-APPLY-VLS for financial aid information.

Required

To earn the J.D., candidates must complete 84 total credits, of which 44 are for required courses. They must maintain a minimum GPA of 2.0 in the required courses. The following first-year courses are required of all students: Civil Procedure I and II, Contracts, Introduction to the Lawyering Process, Torts, Legal Reasoning, Writing, and Research, Constitutional Law I, Criminal Law, Property, and Dispute Resolution. Required upper-level courses consist of Legal Profession, Constitutional Law II, Appellate Advocacy, 1 perspective elective, 1 skills or clinical elective, and advanced writing project. All students must take clinical courses. The required orientation program for first-year students is 1 week of lectures and workshops on the legal process, court systems, and sources of law, and the analysis and briefing of cases. It also includes an orientation to the law library and its resources and support systems and meetings with faculty advisers.

Electives

The Vermont Law School offers concentrations in corporate law, criminal law, environmental law, family law, international law, labor law, litigation, tax law, and general practice; alternative dispute resolution; land use and real estate; and traditionally disadvantaged groups. In addition, clinics are open to second- and third-year students, but enrollment is limited. Clinics are Semester in Practice for 13 credits, Legislation Clinic for 6 credits, Environmental Semester in Washington, D.C. for 13 credits, and South Royalton Legal Clinic for 6 or 13 credits. About 20 seminars are offered annually on various topics to second- and third-year students for 2 or 3 credits each. Faculty-supervised internships are open to second- and third-year students. Credit varies and placement can be in a variety of legal settings, including private practice, government, nonprofit agencies, the judiciary, and business. Faculty-supervised research programs are open to second- and third-year students and culminates in a major piece of legal writing. Special lecture series include the Waterman Lectures and other lectures arranged by faculty and student organizations. There is an exchange program with McGill University, Faculty of Law in Montreal. Tutorial programs and the Program for Academic Success are offered. Workshops on topics such as time and stress management, case briefing, and

exam taking are held. Minority programs are offered through the Coalition for Diversity, BALSA, APALSA, NLALSA, Native American Law Society, and the office of The Dean of Student Services and Diversity. Special interest group programs are offered through the Alliance, Animal Law League, Environmental Law Society, and other groups. The most widely taken electives are environmental law, corporations, and estates.

Graduation Requirements

In order to graduate, candidates must have a GPA of 2.0, have completed the upper-division writing requirement, and Legal Profession course; 1 perspective elective; 1 skills or clinical elective.

Organizations

Students edit the *Vermont Law Review*, the *Environmental Law Journal*, a literary journal *Hearsay*, and the newspaper, *The Forum*. Moot court competitions include the annual Thomas M. Debevoise Moot Court, with finals argued before the Vermont Supreme Court, the annual Douglas M. Costle Environmental Moot Court, and various regional and national moot court competitions. Student organizations include the Jewish Students Group, Guardians ad Litem, and Coalition for Diversity. There are local chapters of Amnesty International, Association of Trial Lawyers of America, and Equal Justice Foundation. Campus clubs include the Barrister Bookshop, Law Partners, Chamber Music Group, Community Jazz Ensemble, Community Council, karate club, rugby club, soccer team, Ultimate Frisbee team, field hockey team, ice hockey team, basketball team, and softball team.

Library

The law library contains 215,000 hardcopy volumes and 95,000 microform volume equivalents, and subscribes to 1500 serial publications. Such on-line databases and networks as LEXIS, DIALOG, WESTLAW, NEXIS, ECONET, and EPIC are available to law students for research. Special library collections include environmental law, historic preservation, and alternative dispute resolution. In 1992, the 34,000 square foot Cornell Library, was built which includes a computer room, seminar rooms, and faculty study room. The ratio of library volumes to faculty is 6325 to 1 and to students, 450 to 1. The ratio of seats in the library to students is 1 to 100.

Placement

J.D.s awarded:	160

Services available through: A separate law school placement center.

Services: information regarding career alternatives

Special features: Letters of application are prepared for students from an employer database, leading to computerized matching of student interests and employers. Services are characterized by individual attention, with particulary strong public interest and environmental employer listings.

Full-time job interviews:	n/av
Summer job interviews:	n/av
Placement by graduation:	n/av
Placement within 9 months:	83% of class
Average starting salary:	$33,088 to $46,369

Areas of placement:

Private practice 2-10 attorneys	22%
Private practice 11-25 attorneys	5%
Private practice 26-50 attorneys	2%
Private practice 51-100 attorneys	3%
Government	19%
Business/industry	15%
Unknown	13%
Judicial clerkships	11%
Public interest	6%
Military	2%
Academic	2%

Faculty

The law school has 36 full-time and 36 part-time faculty members, of whom 22 are women. About 20% of full-time faculty have a graduate law degree in addition to the J.D.; about 15% of part-time faculty have one. The ratio of full-time students to full-time faculty in an average class is 45 to 1; in a clinic, 6 to 1.

Students

About 48% of the student body are women; 8%, minorities; 1%, African American; 3%, Asian American; 2%, Hispanic; and 1%, Native American. The majority of students come from the Northeast (50%). The average age of entering students is 26; age range is 20 to 60. About 25% of students enter directly from undergraduate school, 15% have a graduate degree, and 75% have worked full-time prior to entering law school. About 8% drop out after the first year for academic or personal reasons; 92% remain to receive a law degree.

School of Law

Garey Hall
Villanova, PA 19085

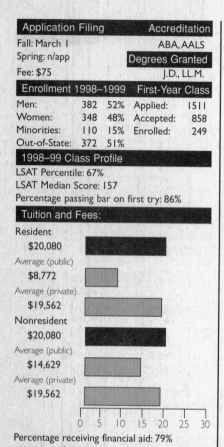

Application Filing	Accreditation
Fall: March 1	ABA, AALS
Spring: n/app	**Degrees Granted**
Fee: $75	J.D., LL.M.

Enrollment 1998–1999		First-Year Class	
Men:	382 52%	Applied:	1511
Women:	348 48%	Accepted:	858
Minorities:	110 15%	Enrolled:	249
Out-of-State:	372 51%		

1998–99 Class Profile
LSAT Percentile: 67%
LSAT Median Score: 157
Percentage passing bar on first try: 86%

Tuition and Fees:

Resident
$20,080

Average (public)
$8,772

Average (private)
$19,562

Nonresident
$20,080

Average (public)
$14,629

Average (private)
$19,562

0   5   10   15   20   25   30

Percentage receiving financial aid: 79%

ADMISSIONS

In the fall 1999 first-year class, 1511 applied, 858 were accepted, and 249 enrolled. Twelve transfers enrolled. The median LSAT percentile of the most recent first-year class was 67; the median GPA was 3.4 on a scale of 4.0. The lowest LSAT percentile accepted was 50; the highest was 99.

Requirements
Applicants must have a bachelor's degree from an accredited institution and take the LSAT. The most important admission factors include GPA, LSAT results, and a letter of recommendation. No specific undergraduate courses are required. Candidates are not interviewed.

Procedure
The application deadline for fall entry is March 1. Applicants should submit an application form, LSAT results, transcripts, a nonrefundable application fee. A deposit is required of students after acceptance. Notification of the admission decision is soon after the January 31 deadline. The latest acceptable LSAT test date for fall entry is February. The law school uses the LSDAS.

Special
The law school recruits minority and disadvantaged students at LSAC forums and through the various minority student groups on campus. Transfer students must have one year of credit and have attended an ABA-approved law school.

Costs

Tuition and fees for the 1999-2000 academic year are $20,080 for all full-time students. Books and supplies run $1000.

Financial Aid

about 79% of current law students receive some form of aid. In a recent year, the average annual amount of aid from all sources combined, including scholarships, loans, and work contracts, is $24,816; maximum, $41,500. Awards are based on need and merit. The required financial statement is FAFSA. Special funds for minority or disadvantaged students through scholarships. First-year students are notified about their financial aid application at soon after being admitted.

About the Law School

Villanova University School of Law was established in 1953 and is a private institution. The 250-acre campus is in a suburban area 15 miles west of Philadelphia. The primary mission of the law school is to provide the opportunity for students to develop an understanding of Anglo-American law in the common-law tradition as well as a knowledge of federal and state statutory and administrative developments required by the modern lawyer. The curriculum is broadly based and responsive to the needs of modern law practice. Students have access to federal, state, county, city, and local agencies, courts, correctional facilities, law firms, and legal aid organizations in the Villanova area. Facilities of special interest to law students is the library, which includes 88 Pentium computers and 21 486 computers connected to the law school network and the Internet, a microform center, and a separate facility containing the library's periodical collections. Housing for law students is in off-campus apartments and other facilities. Housing is not available through the school. The university's Director of Residence Life offers to assist students in finding housing. About 90% of the law school facilities are accessible to the physically disabled.

Calendar

The law school operates on a traditional semester basis. Courses for full-time students are offered days only and must be completed within 3 years. There is no part-time program. New full-time students are admitted in the fall. There is no summer session. Transferable summer courses are not offered.

Programs

In addition to the J.D., the law school offers the LL.M. The following joint degrees may be earned: J.D./Ph.D. (Juris Doctor/Doctor of Philosophy in psychology) and J.D./M.B.A. (Juris Doctor/Master of Business Administration).

Contact

Director of Admissions, 610-519-7010 for general inquiries; Wendy C. Barron, Director of Financial Aid, 610-519-7015 for financial aid information.

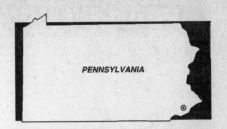

PENNSYLVANIA

Required

To earn the J.D., candidates must complete 87 total credits, of which 44 are for required courses. The following first-year courses are required of all students: Civil Procedure, Contracts, Criminal Law, Introduction to Legal Research, Legal Writing, Property, and Torts. Required upper-level courses consist of Constitutional Law I and II, Legal Profession, a research paper course, and a practical skills/writing course, plus selection from 3 category menus. The required orientation program for first-year students is a 2-day course, Introduction to Legal Analysis and Legal Studies.

Electives

clinical offerings include Juvenile Justice, Tax, and Community Legal Services I. Internships/externships include U.S. Attorney (Philadelphia, Delaware); EPA, IRS, Women Against Abuse, Police Barrio Project; NLRB; NJ Guardian; Philadelphia District Attorney; Judicare; and University Counsels Office. Research assistantships are available, including special research assistants to the Reuchlein Chair. Special lecture series include the Donald A. Giannella Memorial Lecture, Law Review Symposium, Environmental Law Symposium, and Sports and Entertainment Law Symposium. The school will accept up to 6 credits from an accredited American law school summer program abroad, provided it meets the standards of the school. Academic support is provided after the first semester to students at risk. Minority programs consist of summer orientation and support throughout the student's first year. The most widely taken electives are Decedents, Corporations, and Evidence.

Graduation Requirements

In order to graduate, candidates must have a GPA of 1.7 and have completed the upper-division writing requirement.

Organizations

Law students edit the *Villanova Law Review, Villanova Environmental Law Journal, Villanova Sports and Entertainment Law Journal,* and the student newspaper *The Docket.* Annually, the school sponsors the Reimel Moot Court Competition. Other competitions include the ABA Client Interviewing and Counseling Competition, Trial Practice, and numerous moot court and trial competitions. Law student organizations include the Moot Court Board, Honor Board, and Student Bar Association. There are local chapters of Phi Delta Phi, the Black Law Student Association, and the Federalist Society.

Library

The law library contains 450,304 hardcopy volumes and 138,811 microform volume equivalents, and subscribes to 3194 serial publications. Such on-line databases and networks as LEXIS, DIALOG, WESTLAW, CIS Congressional Universe and Legal Trac(periodial index) are available to law students for research. Special library collections include a collection devoted primarily to Anglo-American law and peripheral areas such as economics and criminology. Recently, the library became a member of OCLC, a computerized, bibliographic database providing on-line catalog information from nearly 100 major American law library collections. The ratio of library volumes to faculty is 10,234 to 1 and to students, 617 to 1. The ratio of seats in the library to students is 1 to 50.

Faculty

The law school has 44 full-time and 75 part-time faculty members, of whom 47 are women. According to AAUP standards for Category IIA institutions, faculty salaries are well above average. About 29% of full-time faculty have a graduate law degree in addition to the J.D. The ratio of full-time students to full-time faculty in an average class is 11 to 1; in a clinic, 6 to 1. The law school has a regular program of bringing visiting professors and other distinguished lecturers and visitors to campus. There is a chapter of the Order of the Coif; 35 faculty and 10 graduates are members.

Placement

J.D.s awarded:	234

Services available through: separate law school placement center.

Services: sponsors career seminars and job fairs and maintains a career development and research library as well as a formal alumni mentoring network.

Special features: Minority Internsip Program, 4-in-1 Interview Program, Public Interest Job Fairs, Careers for a Brighter Future Public Interest Job Fair, the Graduate Job Bulletin, and geographic location job fairs.

Full-time job interviews:	90 employers
Summer job interviews:	90 employers
Placement by graduation:	85% of class
Placement within 9 months:	87% of class
Average starting salary:	$35,000 to $105,000

Areas of placement:

Private practice 2-10 attorneys	16%
Private practice 11-25 attorneys	20%
Private practice 26-50 attorneys	57%
Private practice 51-100 attorneys	06%
Private practice 101+ attorneys	45%
Private practice-unknown firm size	8%
Judicial clerkships	19%
Government	13%
Business/industry	8%
Academic	7%
not seeking employment	2%

Students

About 48% of the student body are women; 15%, minorities; 4%, African American; 7%, Asian American; 3%, Hispanic; and 1%, Native American. The majority of students come from Pennsylvania (49%). The average age of entering students is 24; age range is 21 to 49. About 53% of students enter directly from undergraduate school, 7% have a graduate degree, and 47% have worked full-time prior to entering law school. About 1% drop out after the first year for academic or personal reasons; 99% remain to receive a law degree.

School of Law

P.O. Box 7206, Reynolda Station
Winston-Salem, NC 27109

Application Filing			Accreditation
Fall: March 15			ABA, AALS
Spring: n/app			**Degrees Granted**
Fee: $60			J.D., LL.M.

Enrollment 1998–1999			First-Year Class	
Men:	274	59%	Applied:	1391
Women:	191	41%	Accepted:	580
Minorities:	42	9%	Enrolled:	163
Out-of-State:	298	64%		

1998–99 Class Profile
LSAT Percentile: 86%
LSAT Median Score: 160
Percentage passing bar on first try: 90%

Tuition and Fees:

Resident
$21,250

Average (public)
$8,772

Average (private)
$19,562

Nonresident
$21,250

Average (public)
$14,629

Average (private)
$19,562

0 5 10 15 20 25 30

Percentage receiving financial aid: 78%

ADMISSIONS

In the fall 1999 first-year class, 1391 applied, 580 were accepted, and 163 enrolled. Eleven transfers enrolled. The median LSAT percentile of the most recent first-year class was 86; the median GPA was 3.3 on a scale of 4.0. The lowest LSAT percentile accepted was 26; the highest was 99.

Requirements
Applicants must have a bachelor's degree from an accredited institution and take the LSAT. The most important admission factors include LSAT results, GPA, and academic achievement. No specific undergraduate courses are required, but history, economics, English literature, logic, accounting, and philosophy are strongly recommended. Candidates are interviewed.

Procedure
The application deadline for fall entry is March 15. Applicants should submit an application form, LSAT results, transcripts, a nonrefundable application fee of $60, 2 letters of recommendation, and a dean's certification. Notification of the admission decision is on a rolling basis. The latest acceptable LSAT test date for fall entry is December. The law school uses the LSDAS.

Special
The law school recruits minority and disadvantaged students through collaboration with the Black Law Students Association (BLSA), which meets with admissions on a biweekly basis and calls accepted minority candidates to discuss the school and answer questions. BLSA and the school sponsor a minority recruitment day where students visit the campus, meet with enrolled students, and attend a mock class and a moot court presentation. Also, the Placement Office works with major law firms in the state to place minority candidates for summer employment and to expedite consideration of minority applicants. Transfer students must have one year of credit, have attended an ABA-approved law school, and have a letter of good standing from the dean of the law school and an official transcript of first-year grades.

Costs

Tuition and fees for the 1999-2000 academic year are $21,250 for all full-time students. There is no part-time program. Books and supplies run $700.

Financial Aid

About 78% of current law students receive some form of aid. The average annual amount of aid from all sources combined, including scholarships, loans, and work contracts, is $22,000; maximum, $32,240. Awards are based on need and merit. The required financial statement is FAFSA. The aid application deadline for fall entry is May 1. Special funds for minority or disadvantaged students consist of 2 full-tuition scholarships that are awarded in each entering class; candidates are eligible for all scholarships. First-year students are notified about their financial aid application at time of acceptance.

About the Law School

Wake Forest University School of Law was established in 1894 and is a private institution. The 340-acre campus is in an urban area 3 miles north of Winston-Salem. The primary mission of the law school is to graduate students eligible and qualified to practice law. Students have access to federal, state, county, city, and local agencies, courts, correctional facilities, law firms, and legal aid organizations in the Winston-Salem area. Clinical placements are with the district attorney, U.S. Attorney, Legal Aid, private practitioners, U.S. bankruptcy judge, and public defender. In addition, many upper-level students work for private practitioners. Housing for law students is available in approximately 5500 apartment units that are within a 2 1/2 mile radius of the campus. All law school facilities are accessible to the physically disabled.

Calendar

The law school operates on a traditional semester basis. Courses for full-time students are offered days only and must be completed within 3 years. There is no part-time program. New students are admitted in the fall. There are 2 5-week summer sessions. Transferable summer courses are offered.

Contact

Melanie E. Nutt, Admissions Director/Financial Aid Director, 336-758-5437 for general and financial aid information.

Programs

In addition to the J.D., the law school offers the LL.M. in American law (for foreign law school graduates only). The following joint degree may be earned: J.D./M.B.A. (Juris Doctor/Master of Business Administration).

Required

To earn the J.D., candidates must complete 89 total credits, of which 41 are for required courses. They must maintain a minimum grade average of 73 on a scale of 94 in the required courses. The following first-year courses are required of all students: Torts I and II, Contracts I and II, Property I and II, Civil Procedure I and II, Criminal Law I, Constitutional Law I, and Legal Research and Writing I and II. Required upper-level courses consist of Constitutional Law II, Evidence, Professional Responsibility, and Legal Writing III, plus 1 substantial writing project in an upper-level course. All students may take clinics in addition to the skill courses, Trial and Appellate Advocacy. The required orientation program for first-year students is a 1-week program before the beginning of classes devoted to the basics of legal research and writing.

Electives

The School of Law offers concentrations in corporate law, family law, international law, labor law, litigation, securities law, tax law, torts and insurance, and clinical law. In addition, to Trial and Appellate Advocacy, the school has 2 clinics. Both are upper-level client clinics and include classroom elements. One covers the civil-criminal law spectrum for 4 credit hours; the other is an in-house clinic with the medical school serving the indigent elderly for 3 credit hours. The Constitutional Lecture Series is an annual program featuring an address by a nationally prominent figure in the field of constitutional law. Two 5-week summer programs are offered, one in London, England, and the other in Venice, Italy. Enrollment is open to all students depending on availability. A tutorial program is offered to first-year students through the Dean's Office. The most widely taken electives are Trial Practice, Decedents' Estates, and Business Organizations.

Graduation Requirements

In order to graduate, candidates must have a grade average of 73, have completed the upper-division writing requirement, and have written a paper or a brief to the satisfaction of the instructor in a course approved by the faculty.

Organizations

Students edit the *Wake Forest Law Review*, the student newspaper *The Hearsay*, and *The Jurist*, an alumni magazine published in the spring and fall of each year. Moot court competitions include the Marshall competition in Chicago, National Moot Court competition, and Jessup International Moot Court competition. Student organizations include ABA-Law Student Division, Environmental Law Society, and the Federalist Society. There is a local chapter of the Inns of Court.

Library

The law library contains 341,653 hardcopy volumes and 800,000 microform volume equivalents, and subscribes to 5800 serial publications. Such on-line databases and networks as LEXIS, DIALOG, WESTLAW, and NEXIS, and CCALI are available to law students for research. Special library collections include a U.S. government documents depository. Recently, the library moved to a 43,000-square-foot facility, the Worrell Professional Center. It contains 438 carrels, all of which are networked. The ratio of library volumes to faculty is 9500 to 1 and to students, 700 to 1. The ratio of seats in the library to students is 1 to 1.

Faculty

The law school has 39 full-time and 28 part-time faculty members, of whom 20 are women. According to AAUP standards for Category IIA institutions, faculty salaries are well above average. About 22% of full-time faculty have a graduate law degree in addition to the J.D.; about 10% of part-time faculty have one. The ratio of full-time students to full-time faculty in an average class is 14 to 1; in a clinic, 12 to 1. The law school has a regular program of bringing visiting professors and other distinguished lecturers and visitors to campus. There is a chapter of the Order of the Coif.

Placement

J.D.s awarded:	158

Services available through: A separate law school placement center.

Special features: The Placement Office and Phi Alpha Delta law fraternity sponsor an Employment Fair that targets small North Carolina legal employers and the Southeastern Minority Job Fair.

Full-time job interviews:	122 employers
Summer job interviews:	122 employers
Placement by graduation:	n/av
Placement within 9 months:	96% of class
Average starting salary:	$22,000 to $100,000

Areas of placement:

Private practice 2-10 attorneys	20%
Private practice 11-25 attorneys	9%
Private practice 26-50 attorneys	6%
Private practice 51-100 attorneys	21%
Government	16%
Judicial clerkships	13%
Business/industry	12%
Military	2%
Public interest	1%

Students

About 41% of the student body are women; 9%, minorities; 7%, African American; 2%, Asian American; and 2%, Hispanic. The largest group of students come from North Carolina (36%). The average age of entering students is 24; age range is 20 to 47. About 50% of students enter directly from undergraduate school, 50% have a graduate degree, and 50% have worked full-time prior to entering law school. About 2% drop out after the first year for academic or personal reasons; 95% remain to receive a law degree.

School of Law

1700 College
Topeka, KS 66621

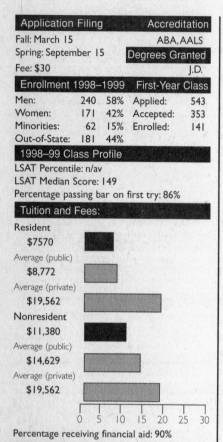

Application Filing		Accreditation
Fall: March 15		ABA, AALS
Spring: September 15		Degrees Granted
Fee: $30		J.D.

Enrollment 1998–1999		First-Year Class	
Men:	240 58%	Applied:	543
Women:	171 42%	Accepted:	353
Minorities:	62 15%	Enrolled:	141
Out-of-State:	181 44%		

1998–99 Class Profile
LSAT Percentile: n/av
LSAT Median Score: 149
Percentage passing bar on first try: 86%

Tuition and Fees:

Resident
$7570

Average (public)
$8,772

Average (private)
$19,562

Nonresident
$11,380

Average (public)
$14,629

Average (private)
$19,562

0 5 10 15 20 25 30

Percentage receiving financial aid: 90%

ADMISSIONS

In the fall 1999 first-year class, 543 applied, 353 were accepted, and 141 enrolled. Eight transfers enrolled. The median GPA of the most recent first-year class was 3.12.

Requirements
Applicants must have a bachelor's degree from an accredited institution and take the LSAT. No specific undergraduate courses are required. Candidates are not interviewed.

Procedure
The application deadline for fall entry is March 15. Applicants should submit an application form, a nonrefundable application fee of $30, at least 1 letter of recommendation (2 or 3 are recommended), and a personal statement, plus a credential evaluation if for a foreign bachelor's degree. Notification of the admission decision is January to May for the fall semester, September to November for the Spring Semester. The latest acceptable LSAT test date for fall entry is February. The law school uses the LSDAS.

Special
The law school recruits minority and disadvantaged students through CRS mailings; CLEO; law school forums in Chicago, Atlanta, New York, Dallas, Houston and accompanying workshops; law fairs at many colleges and universities; events in conjunction with BLSA, HALSA, AALSA, and NALSA; scholarships (merit and need); and through efforts with HBCU and Hispanic colleges and universities. Transfer students must have one year of credit, have a minimum GPA of 2.5, have attended an ABA-approved law school, and present a copy of the LSDAS report, official undergraduate degree transcript, a letter of good standing from the dean of the law school, an official transcript of law school grades, law school class rank, and 1 letter of recommendation from a law school professor. Preadmissions courses consist of the Prelegal Education Workshop for high school sophomores and juniors, a 3-day program each June. There is an academic support program orientation held immediately prior to enrollment for admitted students. There are no provisional-admit summer courses.

Costs

Tuition and fees for the 1999-2000 academic year are $7570 for full-time in-state students and $11,380 for out-of-state students. In-state full- or part-time students pay $251 per credit; all out-of-state students pay $378 per credit. On-campus room and board costs about $3200 annually; and books and supplies run $700.

Financial Aid

About 90% of current law students receive some form of aid. The maximum annual amount of aid for in-state students from the federal loan budget, from all sources combined, including scholarships, loans, and work contracts, is $19,334; the out-of-state maximum is $23,024. Scholarships are awarded based on need and merit. Federal loans up to $18,500 have no need or merit base. Factors that could increase the total award amount include number of dependents and other unusual expenses. All admitted applicants are automatically considered for academic scholarships. The required financial statement is CSS Profile or FAFSA. The aid application deadline for fall entry is April 1. Special funds for minority or disadvantaged students consist of need and academic scholarships. First-year students are notified about their financial

aid award at the time of application. Students are encouraged to apply for loans and need-based scholarships at the time of application. Academic and need scholarships are usually awarded at the time of admission. Loan awards begin April 1.

About the Law School

Washburn University School of Law was established in 1903 and is a public institution. The 160-acre campus is in an urban area 60 miles west of Kansas City. The primary mission of the law school is to provide a foundation in the theory, doctrine, and practice of law with a strong emphasis on professionalism in an atmosphere of cooperation and congeniality. Students have access to federal, state, county, city, and local agencies, courts, correctional facilities, law firms, and legal aid organizations in the Topeka area. Facilities of special interest to law students include a 4-story library, 3 computer laboratories with 73 work stations for students, group study rooms, individual study carrels, and a special collections room. Housing for law students is available in dormitories, but most students live in the many reasonably priced houses and apartments near the campus. All law school facilities are accessible to the physically disabled.

Calendar

The law school operates on a traditional semester basis. Courses for full- and part-time students are offered days only. Part-time students should complete their courses in no more than 5 years. New full- and part-time students are admitted in the fall and spring. There is 1 12-week, 2 6-week sessions, and a 6 week London summer session. Transferrable summer courses are offered.

Programs

The following joint degrees may be earned: J.D./M.B.A. (Juris Doctor/Master of Business Administration) and J.D./M.C.J. (Juris Doctor/Master of Criminal Justice).

Required
To earn the J.D., candidates must complete 90 total credits, of which 37 are for required courses. They must maintain a minimum GPA of 2.0 in the required courses. The following first-year courses are required of all students: Contracts I and II, Torts, Criminal Law, Property, Civil Procedure, Constitutional Law I, Legal Analysis, Research and Writing Seminar I and II, and Criminal Procedure. Required

Phone: 785-231-1185
888-WASHLAW
Fax: 785-232-8087
E-mail: admissions@washburnlaw.edu
Web: http://washburnlaw.edu

Contact

Director of Admissions, 785-231-1185 or 888-WASHLAW (888-927-4529) for general inquiries; Donna Winslow, scholarships; Jannell Harris, 785-231-1185, 785-231-1151, or 888-WASHLAW for financial aid information.

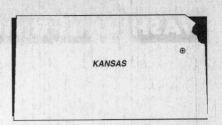

KANSAS

upper-level courses consist of Evidence, Professional Responsibility, and a Perspectives on Law course in which students choose from 12 listed courses, a writing requirement, and an oral presentation requirement. Students who have completed 50 credit hours, have a 2.0 GPA, are certified as a Legal Intern, and have completed or are concurrently enrolled in the Professional Responsibility course may enroll in the live client clinic, one of the oldest clinical programs in the country. The required orientation program for first-year students is 4 days for fall and 2 days for spring admittees, held immediately before classes begin. Orientation includes enrollment, introduction to the library, overview of the academic success program, and other informational and social activities.

Electives

Students must take 15 credits for certificate programs in their area of concentration. The School of Law offers concentrations in corporate law, criminal law, environmental law, family law, international law, litigation, tax law, torts and insurance. Certificate programs are offered in tax law, law and mental health, family law, environmental law and rural law which require 15 credits in the area of concentration and 96 total credits, rather than 90 credits, for graduation. In addition, clinics may be taken as an elective by third-year students. Directed clinic, available by permission, concentrates on one area of practice. Second- or third-year students may take seminars for 2 to 3 credit hours in areas such as civil liberties, civil rights, constitutional litigation, family law, negotiation and settlement, and rural law. An internship in the law library requires students to have an M.L.S. degree. There is also a U.S. Bankruptcy Court Internship and a Legislative Workshop Internship for 1 to 2 credit hours. There is a Kansas District Court Externship for 2 credit hours, a Tax Administrative Law Judge Externship for 1 to 2 credit hours, and a government or private attorney externship for 1 to 2 credit hours. A 6-credit-hour summer program, in comparative law is held at the Hampstead campus of King's College, London each year. All first-year students are included in the academic success program in 9 credit hours in the first year. Minority programs include the Frederick Douglass Moot Court Competition, President's scholarships, and active chapters of Black (BLSA), Asian (AALSA), Hispanic (HALSA), and Native American (NALSA) law student organizations. Spe-

cial interest group programs are offered at the Rural Law Center. In addition, there is a program in law and mental health with the world-renowned Menninger hospital. The most widely taken electives are Business Associations, Secured Transactions, and Decedents' Estates.

Graduation Requirements

In order to graduate, candidates must have a GPA of 2.0, completed the upper-division writing requirement, and upper-level oral presentation and at least 1 class from the list of 12 Perspectives on Law courses.

Organizations

The primary law review is the *Washburn Law Journal*. Students also solicit articles for and edit *The ABA Family Law Quarterly*. Students participate in 10 to 12 moot court competitions each year, including the John Marshall Privacy Law Competition, Jerome Prince Evidence Competition, the New York Bar's National Moot Court Competition, the Kansas Trial Lawyers, ABA Client Counseling, ABA Negotiations, Trial Advocacy, the BLSA Frederick Douglass Moot Court, and the NALSA Moot Court. The law student organizations include the Washburn Environmental Law Society, Washburn Society of International Law, and Washburn Sports and Entertainment Law Society. There are local chapters of the Black Law Students Association (BLSA), Hispanic Law Students Association (HALSA), Asian-American Law Students Association (AALSA), and Native American Law Students Association (NALSA). Law students may participate in campus intramural sports.

Library

The law library contains 321,470 hard-copy volumes and 141,744 microform volume equivalents, and subscribes to 3861 serial publications. Such on-line databases and networks as LEXIS, DIALOG, WESTLAW, and the Internet, Epic, OCLC, Compuserve, and FirstSearch are available to law students for research. Special library collections include U.S. documents, Kansas documents, and the Wolf Creek Collection, which is the Nuclear Regulatory Commission Depository. Recently, the library completed an addition that doubled its size. Three computer laboratories include 73 work stations for students. The ratio of library volumes to faculty is 11,085 to 1 and to students, 782 to 1. The ratio of library seats to students is 1 to 1.

Placement

J.D.s awarded:	155

Services available through: a separate law school placement center.

Services: presentations by employers and panels (e.g., U.S. Attorney's Office, Judicial Clerkships, alternative careers)

Special features: the Young Attorney's Association of Topeka conducts and critiques mock job interviews with students.

Full-time job interviews:	60 employers
Summer job interviews:	30 employers
Placement by graduation:	n/av
Placement within 9 months:	91% of class
Average starting salary:	$24,000 to $62,000

Areas of placement:

Private practice 2-10 attorneys	26%
Private practice 11-25 attorneys	5%
Private practice 26-50 attorneys	6%
Private practice 51-100 attorneys	5%
Private practice 100+ attorneys	2%
Solo practice	6%
Government	20%
Business/industry	13%
Pursuing advanced degree	6%
Judicial clerkships	5%
Public interest	4%

Faculty

The law school has 29 full-time and 36 part-time faculty members, of whom 16 are women. According to AAUP standards for Category IIA institutions, faculty salaries are above average. About 38% of full-time faculty have a graduate law degree in addition to the J.D. The ratio of full-time students to full-time faculty in an average class is 15 to 1; in a clinic, 5 to 1. The law school has a regular program of bringing visiting professors and other distinguished lecturers and visitors to campus.

Students

About 42% of the student body are women; 15%, minorities; 5%, African American; 4%, Asian American; 4%, Hispanic; and 1%, Native American. The majority of students come from Kansas (56%). The average age of entering students is 27; age range is 20 to 55. About 37% of students enter directly from undergraduate school, 11% have a graduate degree, and 48% have worked full-time prior to entering law school. About 7% drop out after the first year for academic or personal reasons; 86% remain to receive a law degree.

WASHINGTON AND LEE UNIVERSITY

School of Law

Lewis Hall
Lexington, VA 24450

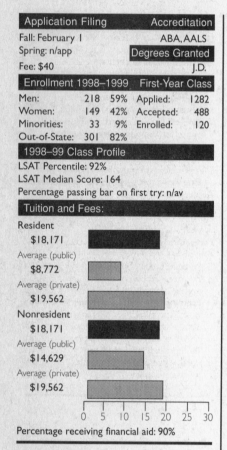

Application Filing		Accreditation
Fall: February 1		ABA, AALS
Spring: n/app		Degrees Granted
Fee: $40		J.D.

Enrollment 1998–1999		First-Year Class	
Men:	218 59%	Applied:	1282
Women:	149 42%	Accepted:	488
Minorities:	33 9%	Enrolled:	120
Out-of-State:	301 82%		

1998–99 Class Profile

LSAT Percentile: 92%

LSAT Median Score: 164

Percentage passing bar on first try: n/av

Tuition and Fees:

Resident
$18,171

Average (public)
$8,772

Average (private)
$19,562

Nonresident
$18,171

Average (public)
$14,629

Average (private)
$19,562

0 5 10 15 20 25 30

Percentage receiving financial aid: 90%

ADMISSIONS

In the fall 1999 first-year class, 1282 applied, 488 were accepted, and 120 enrolled. Five transfers enrolled. The median LSAT percentile of the most recent first-year class was 92; the median GPA was 3.4 on a scale of 4.0. The lowest LSAT percentile accepted was 26; the highest was 99.

Requirements

Applicants must have a bachelor's degree from an accredited institution and take the LSAT. All factors of a candidate's background are considered important. No specific undergraduate courses are required. Candidates are interviewed.

Procedure

The application deadline for fall entry is February 1. Applicants should submit an application form, LSAT results, transcripts, a nonrefundable application fee of $40, and 2 letters of recommendation. Notification of the admission decision is by April 1. The latest acceptable LSAT test date for fall entry is February. The law school uses the LSDAS.

Special

The law school recruits minority and disadvantaged students through regional law forums sponsored by LSDAS and college-sponsored forums, with interviews at institutions with a substantial proportion of minority students, with direct mail, and with an open house for applicants sponsored by the law school and the Black Law Students Association. Transfer students must have attended an ABA-approved law school.

Costs

Tuition and fees for the 1999-2000 academic year are $18,171 for all full-time students. On-campus room and board costs about $5300 annually; books and supplies run $750.

Financial Aid

About 90% of current law students receive some form of aid. The maximum annual amount of aid from all sources combined, including scholarships, loans, and work contracts, is $29,250. Awards are based on need and merit. The required financial statement is the FAFSA. The aid application deadline for fall entry is February 15. First-year students are notified about their financial aid application at time of acceptance.

About the Law School

Washington and Lee University School of Law was established in 1849 and is a private institution. The 322-acre campus is in a small town 3 hours southwest of Washington, D.C. The primary mission of the law school is to provide a rigorous, writing-intensive, and personalized legal education to each student as preparation for the legal profession; to do so in an atmosphere characterized by mutual respect, collegiality, and appreciation for the dignity of every person; and to inculcate in students a sense of the responsibility placed on lawyers and the ethical obligations of law practice. Students have access to federal, state, county, city, and local agencies, courts, correctional facilities, law firms, and legal aid organizations in the Lexington area. Housing for law students includes on-campus apartments adjacent to the law school building for single students; private apartments, rooms, and houses in Lexington and the surrounding area can also be found. All law school facilities are accessible to the physically disabled.

Calendar

The law school operates on a traditional semester basis. Courses for full-time students are offered days only and must be completed within 6 semesters. There is no part-time program. New students are admitted in the fall. There is no summer session. Transferable summer courses are not offered.

Programs

Required

To earn the J.D., candidates must complete 85 total credits, of which 37 are for required courses. They must maintain a minimum GPA of 1.0 in the required courses. The following first-year courses are required of all students: Criminal Law, Property, Contracts, Torts, Criminal Procedure, Civil Procedure I and II, and American Public Law Process. Required upper-level courses consist of Constitutional Law and Professional Responsibility. The required orientation program for first-year students is 3 days and includes social activities for the entire student body, an introduction to the case method and case briefing techniques, an introducton to legal research, an honor system orientation, and a university orientation.

Phone: 540-463-8504
Fax: 540-463-8586
E-mail: lawadm@wlu.edu
Web: www.wlu.edu

Contact

Susan Palmer, Assistant Dean, 540-463-8504 for general inquiries; McClain Stradtner, Associate Director of Financial Aid, 540-463-8729 for financial aid information.

Electives

Various clinics, open to second- and third-year students provide direct service to miners seeking black lung benefits, to patients at Western State Hospital, and to inmates of the Federal Correction Institution in Alderson, West Virginia. Credit ranges from 3 to 10 hours. Seminars, available to upper-level students, are worth 2 or 3 credits and are offered in a variety of areas. Upper-level students may perform internships with state trial court judges during the academic year for 4 graded credits or with government or nonprofit employers in the summer for 2 ungraded credits. Independent research projects may be undertaken by second- or third-year students. Credit varies. The Frances Lewis Law Center sponsors research fellowships for third-year students. Bain and Shepherd Fellowships provide stipends to support collaborative research projects between students and faculty. Special lecture series include the annual John Randolph Tucker Lecture and visiting lectures sponsored by the Frances Lewis Law Center and other law student organizations in areas of special interest to their members. The school offers no study-abroad program, but may accept credit for courses taken in programs offered by other ABA-approved law schools. Tutorials are offered to upper-class students in a variety of fields. The Academic Support Program offers a series of programs introducing the case method and legal analysis, and provides continuing academic support throughout the year. Special interest group programs include Women Law Students Organization, Black Law Students Association, Christian Legal Society, and Committee on Gay and Lesbian Legal Issues. The most widely taken electives are Federal Income Tax, Family Law, and Commercial Transactions.

Graduation Requirements

In order to graduate, candidates must have a GPA of 2.0 and have completed the upper-division writing requirement.

Organizations

Students edit the *Washington and Lee Law Review, Capital Defense Digest, Virginia Environmental Law Digest* sponsored by the Virginia State Bar, *Race and Ethnic Ancestry Law Digest*, and the newspaper *Law News*. Moot court competitions include Holderness Moot Court, John W. Davis Moot Court, and Jessup International Law Moot Court. Other competitions include National Mock Trial, Client Counseling, and Negotiation competitions. Law student organizations include the Student Bar Association, Federalist Society, and Environmental Law Forum. There are local chapters of Phi Alpha Delta, Phi Delta Phi, and Omicron Delta Kappa. Campus clubs and other organizations include Amnesty International, Habitat for Humanity, and Mock Convention.

Library

The law library contains 372,675 hardcopy volumes and 808,493 microform volume equivalents, and subscribes to 4638 serial publications. Such on-line databases and networks as LEXIS, DIALOG, WESTLAW, InfoTrac, OCLC, and First Search are available to law students for research. Special library collections include the Bankruptcy Revision Act 1978 (committee papers), the John W. Davis Collection of Records and Briefs, the Impeachment of President Nixon (committee papers), and the Lewis F. Powell, Jr. Archives. Recently, the library added graphic searching of the World Wide Web and upgraded the student computer laboratory to Pentiums. The ratio of library volumes to faculty is 9661 to 1 and to students, 878 to 1. The ratio of seats in the library to students is 1 to 1.

Faculty

The law school has 33 full-time and 18 part-time faculty members, of whom 8 are women. According to AAUP standards for Category IIB institutions, faculty salaries are well above average. About 12% of full-time faculty have a graduate law degree in addition to the J.D.; about 6% of part-time faculty have one. The ratio of full-time students to full-time faculty in an average class is 10 to 1; in a clinic, 10 to 1. The law school has a regular program of bringing visiting professors and other distinguished lecturers and visitors to campus. There is a chapter of the Order of the Coif; 32 faculty and 310 graduates are members.

Placement

J.D.s awarded:	118

Services available through: separate law school placement center.

Services: advice on networking, and programs on specific practice areas (e.g., corporate law, small firms, prosecution)

Special features: one-on-one work with students on resumes, cover letters, job search advice; a brochure for student use when applying to areas where school is less well-known; and students alumni interviews through the Alumni Placement Network

Full-time job interviews:	130 employers
Summer job interviews:	n/av
Placement by graduation:	76% of class
Placement within 9 months:	77% of class
Average starting salary:	$44,250 to $70,000

Areas of placement:

Private practice 2-10 attorneys	23%
Private practice 11-25 attorneys	6%
Private practice 26-50 attorneys	6%
Private practice 51-100 attorneys	21%
Judicial clerkships	27%
Business/industry	10%
Government	3%
Public interest	2%
Military	1%

Students

About 42% of the student body are women; 9%, minorities; 4%, African American; 3%, Asian American; 1%, Hispanic; 1%, Native American; and 1%, multiracial. The majority of students come from the South (31%). The average age of entering students is 25; age range is 20 to 47. About 46% of students enter directly from undergraduate school, 12% have a graduate degree, and 54% have worked full-time prior to entering law school. About 1% drop out after the first year for academic or personal reasons; 99% remain to receive a law degree.

School of Law

Box 1120, One Brookings Drive
St. Louis, MO 63130

Application Filing	Accreditation
Fall: March 1	ABA, AALS
Spring: n/app	**Degrees Granted**
Fee: $60	J.D., LL.M., J.S.D.

Enrollment 1998–1999		First-Year Class	
Men:	365 57%	Applied:	1961
Women:	270 43%	Accepted:	813
Minorities:	127 20%	Enrolled:	212
Out-of-State:	419 66%		

1998–99 Class Profile
LSAT Percentile: 83%
LSAT Median Score: 161
Percentage passing bar on first try: 89%

Tuition and Fees:

Resident
$24,280

Average (public)
$8,772

Average (private)
$19,562

Nonresident
$24,280

Average (public)
$14,629

Average (private)
$19,562

0 5 10 15 20 25 30

Percentage receiving financial aid: 70%

ADMISSIONS

In the fall 1999 first-year class, 1961 applied, 813 were accepted, and 212 enrolled. Eighteen transfers enrolled. The median LSAT percentile of the most recent first-year class was 83; the median GPA was 3.4 on a scale of 4.0. The lowest LSAT percentile accepted was 31; the highest was 99.

Requirements
Applicants must have a bachelor's degree from an accredited institution and take the LSAT. Minimum acceptable GPA is 2.0 on a scale of 4.0. The most important admission factors include LSAT results, GPA, and academic achievement. No specific undergraduate courses are required. Candidates are not interviewed.

Procedure
The application deadline for fall entry is March 1. Applicants should submit an application form, a nonrefundable application fee of $60, 2 letters of recommendation, and a personal statement. Notification of the admission decision is by April. The latest acceptable LSAT test date for fall entry is February. The law school uses the LSDAS.

Special
The law school recruits minority and disadvantaged students by means of a minority admissions counselor, specific mailings, scholarship programs, and visitation programs. Transfer students must have one year of credit and have attended an ABA-approved law school.

Costs

Tuition and fees for the 1999-2000 academic year are $24,280 for all full-time students. Books and supplies run $1120.

Financial Aid

About 70% of current law students receive some form of aid. The average annual amount of aid from all sources combined, including scholarships, loans, and work contracts, is $17,000; maximum, $32,000. Awards are based on need and merit. The required financial statement is FAFSA. The aid application deadline for fall entry is March 1. Special funds for minority or disadvantaged students are the Minority Scholars-in-Law program, Farmer Scholarship, and the Chancellor's Fellowship. First-year students are notified about their financial aid application between the time of acceptance and enrollment.

About the Law School

Washington University in St. Louis School of Law was established in 1867 and is a private institution. The 160-acre campus is in a suburban area in St. Louis. The primary mission of the law school is to provide an enduring foundation of legal education that is useful for whatever field of law is chosen. Students have access to federal, state, county, city, and local agencies, courts, correctional facilities, law firms, and legal aid organizations in the St. Louis area. Students have access to a congressional clinic and a federal administrative agency clinic in Washington, D.C. Facilities of special interest to law students include St. Louis-based national and international corporations. Housing for law students is available in surrounding neighborhoods; listings are available through an off-campus referral service. About 90% of the law school facilities are accessible to the physically disabled.

Calendar

The law school operates on a traditional semester basis. Courses for full-time students are offered days only. New students are admitted in the fall. There is no part-time program. There is a 5-week summer session. Transferable summer courses are offered.

Programs

In addition to the J.D., the law school offers the LL.M and J.S.D. Students may take relevant courses in other programs and apply credit toward the J.D.; a maximum of 9 credits may be applied. The following joint degrees may be earned: J.D./M.A. (Juris Doctor/Master of Arts in Asian studies, political scienc), J.D./M.S.W. (Juris Doctor/Master of Social Work), J.D./M.S. (Juris Doctor/Master of Science in economics and environmental policy), J.D./M.H.A. (Juris Doctor/Master of Health Administration), and J.D./M.B.A. (Juris Doctor/Master of Business Administration).

Phone: 314-935-4525
Fax: 314-935-6959
E-mail: admiss@walaw.wash.edu
Web: http://ls.wash.edu

Contact

Admissions Office, 314-935-4525 for general inquiries; JoAnn Eckrich, Associate Director, 314-935-4605 for financial aid information.

MISSOURI

Required

To earn the J.D., candidates must complete 85 total credits, of which 7 are for required courses. They must maintain a minimum average of 75 in the required courses. The following first-year courses are required of all students: Contracts, Criminal Law, Legal Research and Writing, Property, Torts, Civil Procedure, and Constitutional Law I. Required upper-level courses consist of Professional Responsibility-Legal Profession and 1 additional writing seminar. The required orientation program for first-year students runs for 3 days and focuses on academic, social, and administrative components of the school.

Electives

The School of Law offers concentrations in corporate law, criminal law, environmental law, family law, international law, labor law, litigation, securities law, tax law, and transactional (planning and drafting) courses. In addition, clinics are offered for 3 to 10 credit hours, including Congressional Clinic in Washington, D.C., Federal Administrative Agency in Washington, D.C., and Employment Law and Public Policy Clinic. Students may participate in research programs after the first year. Field work is performed as part of the clinics; recently, 8 clinics were offered. Special lectures include the Tyrrell Williams Memorial Lectures and the Public Interest Speakers Series. Tutorial programs are available on an individual basis. The Black Law Student Association organizes student study groups and visiting minority speakers. The most widely taken electives are Pretrial, Trial, and Evidence.

Graduation Requirements

In order to graduate, candidates must have completed the upper-division writing requirement.

Organizations

Students edit *The Washington University Law Quarterly* and the *Journal of Law and Policy*. The student newspaper is *The Devil's Advocate*. Moot court competitions include the Wiley Rutledge Moot Court program held in the fall and spring, Environmental Moot Court, and the Jessup International Law Moot Court. Other competitions include the National Mock Trial, National Client Counseling, the Negotiation, and the Intramural Client Counseling. Student organizations include the Student Bar Association, Environmental Law Society, and International Law Society. The Federalist Society, Phi Alpha Delta, and Phi Delta Phi have local chapters. There are numerous other campus organizations.

Library

The law library contains 563,292 hardcopy volumes and 847,000 microform volume equivalents, and subscribes to 5079 serial publications. Such on-line databases and networks as LEXIS, DIALOG, WESTLAW, and LEGISLATE are available to law students for research. Special library collections address congressional, British, and state administrative regulations. Recently, the library gained access to the INNOVALQ system. The ratio of library volumes to faculty is 12,105 to 1 and to students, 687 to 1. The ratio of seats in the library to students is 1 to 1.

Faculty

The law school has 47 full-time and 65 part-time faculty members, of whom 31 are women. According to AAUP standards for Category I institutions, faculty salaries are well above average. About 32% of full-time faculty have a graduate law degree in addition to the J.D.; about 27% of part-time faculty have one. The ratio of full-time students to full-time faculty in an average class is 14 to 1. The law school has a regular program of bringing visiting professors and other distinguished lecturers and visitors to campus. There is a chapter of the Order of the Coif; 17 faculty are members.

Placement

J.D.s awarded:	209
Services available through: A separate law school placement center.	
Special features: personalized services of 4 professionals who have practiced law.	
Full-time job interviews:	118 employers
Summer job interviews:	n/av
Placement by graduation:	n/av
Placement within 9 months:	95% of class
Average starting salary: $23,000 to $100,000	
Areas of placement:	
Private practice 2-10 attorneys	17%
Private practice 26-10 attorneys	25%
Business/industry	12%
Government	11%
Judicial clerkships	8%
Public interest	4%
Academic	3%
Military	1%

Students

About 43% of the student body are women; 20%, minorities; 10%, African American; 7%, Asian American; 2%, Hispanic; and 1%, Native American. The majority of students come from the Midwest (58%). The average age of entering students is 24; age range is 20 to 46. About 55% of students enter directly from undergraduate school and 45% have worked full-time prior to entering law school. About 7% drop out after the first year for academic or personal reasons; 92% remain to receive a law degree.

WAYNE STATE UNIVERSITY

Law School

468 W. Ferry Mall
Detroit, MI 48202

Application Filing		Accreditation
Fall: March 15		ABA, AALS
Spring: n/app		Degrees Granted
Fee: $20		J.D., LL.M.

Enrollment 1998–1999		First-Year Class	
Men:	393 52%	Applied:	910
Women:	361 48%	Accepted:	464
Minorities:	128 17%	Enrolled:	213
Out-of-State:	15 2%		

1998–99 Class Profile

LSAT Percentile: 65%
LSAT Median Score: 154
Percentage passing bar on first try: 81%

Tuition and Fees:

Resident
$7698

Average (public)
$8,772

Average (private)
$19,562

Nonresident
$15,828

Average (public)
$14,629

Average (private)
$19,562

0   5   10   15   20   25   30

Percentage receiving financial aid: 65%

ADMISSIONS

In the fall 1999 first-year class, 910 applied, 464 were accepted, and 213 enrolled. Nine transfers enrolled. The median LSAT percentile of the most recent first-year class was 65; the median GPA was 3.2 on a scale of 4.0.

Requirements

Applicants must have a bachelor's degree from an accredited institution and take the LSAT. The most important admission factors include LSAT results, GPA, and letter of recommendation. No specific undergraduate courses are required. Candidates are not interviewed.

Procedure

The application deadline for fall entry is March 15. Applicants should submit an application form, LSAT results, transcripts, a nonrefundable application fee of $20, 1 letter of recommendation, and a personal statement. Notification of the admission decision is on a rolling basis. The latest acceptable LSAT test date for fall entry is February. The law school uses the LSDAS.

Special

The law school recruits minority and disadvantaged students by means of an affirmative admission policy and by encouraging application, hosting a Minority Law Day, participating in Law Services' Atlanta Forum, and recruiting at historically black colleges and universities. Transfer students must have one year of credit, have a minimum GPA of 3.4, have attended an ABA-approved law school, have an official transcript sent from their current law school and their previous undergraduate institution, submit a letter of good standing from the dean, and submit a copy of the LSDAS report.

Costs

Tuition and fees for the 1999-2000 academic year are $7698 for full-time in-state students and $15,828 for out-of-state students. Tuition for part-time students is $4170 annually, or $252 per credit in-state and $8506, or $523 per credit out-of-state. On-campus room and board costs about $8970 annually; books and supplies run $800.

Financial Aid

About 65% of current law students receive some form of aid. The average annual amount of aid from all sources combined, including scholarships, loans, and work contracts, is $10,000; maximum, $21,416. Awards are based on need along with outside scholarship awards. The required financial statement is FAFSA. The aid application deadline for fall entry is April 30. Special funds for minority or disadvantaged students consist of Kenneth Cockerel, Wade McCree, and Law Alumni scholarships and fellowships. First-year students are notified about their financial aid application mid-April through summer, before fall enrollment.

About the Law School

Wayne State University Law School was established in 1927 and is a public institution. The campus is in an urban area in Detroit. The primary mission of the law school is to train lawyers for a wide variety of careers. Students have access to federal, state, county, city, and local agencies, courts, correctional facilities, law firms, and legal aid organizations in the Detroit area. Facilities of special interest to law students include the 3 buildings of the school, which house classrooms, seminar rooms, 2 practice courtrooms, the law library, and faculty and student offices. Housing for law students is available on campus, in the school vicinity, and throughout the metropolitan area. All law school facilities are accessible to the physically disabled.

Calendar

The law school operates on a traditional semester basis. Courses for full-time students are offered both day and evening and must be completed within 5 years. For part-time students, courses are offered both day and evening and must be completed within 6 years. New full- and part-time students are admitted in the fall. There is a 7-week summer session. Transferable summer courses are offered.

Programs

In addition to the J.D., the law school offers the LL.M and LL.M. in taxation, labor law, and corporate planning. Students may take relevant courses in other programs and apply credit toward the J.D.; a maximum of 8 credits may be applied. The following joint degrees may be earned: J.D./M.A. (Juris Doctor/Master of Arts in history, public policy and dispute resolution) and J.D./M.B.A. (Juris Doctor/Master of Business Administration).

Phone: 313-577-3937
Fax: 313-577-6000
E-mail: linda.sims@wayne.edu

Contact
Assistant Dean for Recruitment and Admissions, 313-577-3937 for general inquiries; Financial Aid Office, 313-577-5142 for financial aid information.

Required
To earn the J.D., candidates must complete 86 total credits, of which 36 are for required courses. They must maintain a minimum GPA of 2.0 in the required courses. The following first-year courses are required of all students: Civil Procedure, Contracts, Criminal Law, Legal Writing and Research, Property, and Torts. Required upper-level courses consist of Constitutional Law I and Professional Responsibility and the Legal Profession. The required orientation program for first-year students is 3 days for students in the day program and 5 days for students in the evening program, during which students begin their legal writing classes.

Electives
The Law School offers concentrations in criminal law, international law, labor law, tax law, and commercial law, and intellectual property. In addition, clinical experience is offered through the Student Trial Advocacy Program, Free Legal Aid Clinic, and the Criminal Appellate Practice Program in cooperation with the Michigan State Appellate Defender Office. There are some 28 seminars. Second- and third-year students have a choice of interning on a part-time basis with distinguished local judges in a variety of governmental and nonprofit agencies. Students earn 2 credits per semester in these internships. Special lecture series include I. Goodman Cohen Lecture in Trial Advocacy, Driker Forum for Excellence in the Law, and Bernard Gottfried Memorial Labor Law Symposium. There is a 6-week summer exchange program with the University of Warwick, England; students may also study for 1 semester in the London Law Programme of the University of Detroit-Mercy School of Law and at the Hague, Netherlands. The Supportive Services Program offers academic and related support to students. The Summer Institute Program allows minority students and other entering students to complete the Torts course before the regular academic year. The Intellectual Property Law Institute, a consortium with 2 other universities, offers additional intellectual property courses to law students. The most widely taken electives are Commercial Transactions, Taxation, and Evidence.

Graduation Requirements
In order to graduate, candidates must have a GPA of 2.0.

Organizations
Students edit the *Wayne State Law Review, The Journal of Law and Society*, and the newspaper *The Advocate*. Moot court competitions include Jerome Prince Evidence, Craven Constitutional, and National Product Liability competitions. Law student organizations include the Federalist Society, Environmental Law Society, and International Law Society. There are local chapters of National Lawyers Guild and ABA-Law Student Division.

Library
The law library contains 569,165 hardcopy volumes and 1,088,291 microform volume equivalents, and subscribes to 4844 serial publications. Such on-line databases and networks as LEXIS, DIALOG, WESTLAW, NEXIS, and Legal-Trac are available to law students for research. Special library collections include a U.S. government document depository, Michigan Supreme Court records and briefs, Michigan Probate Court opinions, and Michigan Superfund Sites Collection. Recently, the library upgraded the computer laboratory, including 20 Pentiums and 4 PowerMacs; added network printing; created a law library home page (http://www.lib.wayne.edu/lawlibrary/llhome.html); and renovated the cafe/vending area. The ratio of library volumes to faculty is 8084 to 1 and to students, 737 to 1. The ratio of seats in the library to students is 1 to 6.

Faculty
The law school has 35 full-time and 33 part-time faculty members, of whom 18 are women. According to AAUP standards for Category I institutions, faculty salaries are average. About 25% of full-time faculty have a graduate law degree in addition to the J.D.; about 31% of part-time faculty have one. The ratio of full-time students to full-time faculty in an average class is 26 to 1; in a clinic, 12 to 1. There is a chapter of the Order of the Coif; 35 faculty and approximately 300 graduates are members.

Placement

J.D.s awarded:	181
Services available through: A separate law school placement center.	
Services: offers a full placement service that provides career counseling	
Special features: Students are offered free use of fax, photocopier, and telephone	
Full-time job interviews:	n/av
Summer job interviews:	n/av
Placement by graduation:	50% of class
Placement within 9 months:	95% of class
Average starting salary:	n/av
Areas of placement:	
Private practice 2-100 attorneys	49%
Business/industry	20%
Unknown	19%
Judicial clerkships	4%
Government	4%
Academic	2%
Public interest	2%

Students
About 48% of the student body are women; 17%, minorities; 10%, African American; 5%, Asian American; 2%, Hispanic; and 1%, Native American. The majority of students come from Michigan (98%). The average age of entering students is 26; age range is 20 to 56. About 15% of students have a graduate degree. About 11% drop out after the first year for academic or personal reasons; 87% remain to receive a law degree.

WEST VIRGINIA UNIVERSITY

College of Law

P.O. Box 6130
Morgantown, WV 26506

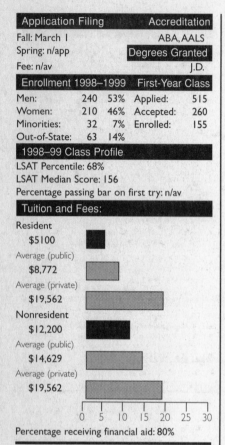

Application Filing		Accreditation
Fall: March 1		ABA, AALS
Spring: n/app		**Degrees Granted**
Fee: n/av		J.D.

Enrollment 1998–1999			First-Year Class	
Men:	240	53%	Applied:	515
Women:	210	46%	Accepted:	260
Minorities:	32	7%	Enrolled:	155
Out-of-State:	63	14%		

1998–99 Class Profile
LSAT Percentile: 68%
LSAT Median Score: 156
Percentage passing bar on first try: n/av

Tuition and Fees:

Resident
$5100

Average (public)
$8,772

Average (private)
$19,562

Nonresident
$12,200

Average (public)
$14,629

Average (private)
$19,562

0 5 10 15 20 25 30

Percentage receiving financial aid: 80%

ADMISSIONS

Information in the above capsule is approximate. In the fall 1999 first-year class, 515 applied, 260 were accepted, and 155 enrolled. Three transfers enrolled. The median LSAT percentile of the most recent first-year class was 68; the median GPA was 3.3 on a scale of 4.0.

Requirements
Applicants must have a bachelor's degree from an accredited institution and take the LSAT. The most important admission factors include LSAT results, academic achievement, and GPA. No specific undergraduate courses are required. Candidates are not interviewed.

Procedure
The application deadline for fall entry is March 1. Applicants should submit an application form, LSAT results, transcripts, (submitted by LSDAS), 3 letters of recommendation, and a personal statement. Check with the school for current application fee. Notification of the admission decision is rolling admissions. The latest acceptable LSAT test date for fall entry is February. The law school uses the LSDAS.

Special
The law school recruits minority and disadvantaged students through mailings, Minority Law Day, forums, and personal contacts from the school's Graduate Assistant for Minority Recruitment. Requirements are different for out-of-state students in that preference is given to West Virginia residents. Transfer students must have one year of credit and have attended an ABA-approved law school.

Costs

Tuition and fees for the 1999-2000 academic year are $5100 for full-time in-state students and $12,200 for out-of-state students. T;uition for part-time students is $235 per credit in state and $600 per credit out -of-state. Books and supplies run $1000.

Financial Aid

About 80% of current law students received some form of aid. The average annual amount of aid from all sources combined, including scholarships, loans, and work contracts, was $11,000; maximum, $16,431. Awards are based on need and merit. The required financial statement is check with the school for the current deadlines FAFSA. Special funds for minority or disadvantaged students include scholarships, and vocational-rehabilitation is offered to disabled and disadvantaged students. First-year students are notified about their financial aid application at the time of application.

About the Law School

West Virginia University College of Law was established in 1878 and is a public institution. The 1000-acre campus is in a small town 77 miles south of Pittsburgh, Pennsylvania. The primary mission of the law school is to prepare students for the practice of law and for public leadership through a curriculum that stresses basic legal principles, lawyering skills, and the responsibilities of the legal profession. Students have access to federal, state, county, city, and local agencies, courts, correctional facilities, law firms, and legal aid organizations in the Morgantown area. Facilities of special interest to law students are the Leo Carlin Computer Laboratory; the Marlyn E. Lugar Courtroom, a combination courtroom-auditorium; a mini courtroom; 3 conference-seminar rooms; 1 large courtroom; the law library; the Meredith Career Services Center with placement interview rooms; a student lounge; and a child-care cooperative. Housing for law students is available for both single and married students. The university housing office helps students find off-campus housing. All law school facilities are accessible to the physically disabled.

Phone: 304-293-5304
Fax: 304-293-6891
E-mail: lawaply@wvu.edu
Web: wvu.edu/~law/

Contact

Admissions Office, 304-293-5304 for general inquiries; Joanna Hastings, Financial Counselor, 304-293-5302 for financial aid information.

WEST VIRGINIA

Calendar

The law school operates on a traditional semester basis. Courses for full-and part-time students are offered days only and must be completed within 6 years. New full-and part-time students are admitted in the fall. There is no summer session. Transferable summer courses are not offered.

Programs

The following joint degrees may be earned: J.D./M.B.A. (Juris Doctor/Master of Business Administration, through the Department of Business and Economics) and J.D./M.P.A. (Juris Doctor/Master of Public Administration, through the Department of Public Administration).

Required

To earn the J.D., candidates must complete 93 total credits, of which 52 are for required courses. They must maintain a minimum GPA of 2.0 in the required courses. The following first-year courses are required of all students: Contracts I and II, Criminal Law, Property I and II, Torts, Legal Research and Writing I and II, Professional Responsibility, Civil Procedure I, and Constitutional Law. Required upper-level courses consist of Civil Procedure II, Appellate Advocacy, Evidence, Income Tax I, 2 perspective courses, a seminar, and Trial Advocacy or clinic. The required orientation program for first-year students is a 2 1/2-day program featuring mini classes covering legal writing, note taking, and exams; student panels discussing first-year life and financial aid information; a picnic with upper-class students and faculty, at which families are welcome; and a computer workshop for interested students.

Electives

approved upper-class students may earn 14 credit hours in a civil legal clinic. Students may also pursue independent study under faculty supervision. The most widely taken electives are Business Organizations, Property III, and Torts.

Graduation Requirements

In order to graduate, candidates must have a GPA of 2.0 and have completed the upper-division writing requirement.

Organizations

Students edit the *West Virginia Law Review*, the fourth oldest legal journal in the United States; the *Journal of College and University Law* in conjunction with the National Association of College and University Attorneys; and the newspaper *On-Point*. Moot court competitions include the Moot Court Board, Baker Cup Competition, held annually; Marlyn E. Lugar Trial Association Mock Trial Competition, held 4 times per year; and Gourley Cup Competition. Law student organizations include the Moot Court Board, Environmental Law Society, and Labor and Employment Law Association. There are local chapters of National Lawyers Guild, Student Bar Association, and Phi Delta Phi.

Library

The law library contains 246,532 hard-copy volumes and 355,617 microform volume equivalents, and subscribes to 2791 serial publications. Such on-line databases and networks as LEXIS, WESTLAW, and CALI are available to law students for research. Special library collections include a rare book room. Recently, the library purchased 8 486DX computers and a laser printer that will support computer-assisted legal instruction and temporary training centers in the Carlin laboratory, and installed a custom-built counter that accommodates 8 computers and 2 laser printers for student word processing. The ratio of library volumes to faculty is 6130 to 1 and to students, 395 to 1. The ratio of seats in the library to students is 1 to 2.

Faculty

The law school has 26 full-time and 11 part-time faculty members, of whom 11 are women. According to AAUP standards for Category I institutions, faculty salaries are below average. About 38% of full-time faculty have a graduate law degree in addition to the J.D.; about 10% of part-time faculty have one. The ratio of full-time students to full-time faculty in an average class is 18 to 1; in a clinic, 20 to 1. There is a chapter of the Order of the Coif; 4 faculty are members.

Placement

J.D.s awarded:	139

Services available through: separate law school placement center and the university placement center

Services: stress-management seminars, Myers-Briggs Type Indicator Administration and Interpretation, and individual counseling

Special features: The college has a close working relationship with the West Virginia State Bar.

Full-time job interviews:	24 employers
Summer job interviews:	29 employers
Placement by graduation:	80% of class
Placement within 9 months:	90% of class
Average starting salary:	$36,610 to $72,000

Areas of placement:

Private practice 2-10 attorneys	39%
Private practice 11-25 attorneys	10%
Private practice 26-50 attorneys	7%
Private practice 51-100 attorneys	6%
Government	18%
Business/industry	11%
Public interest	4%
Judicial clerkships	4%
Academic	1%

Students

About 46% of the student body are women; 7%, minorities; 5%, African American; 1%, Asian American; 1%, Hispanic; and 1%, Native American. The majority of students come from West Virginia (86%). The average age of entering students is 26; age range is 22 to 50. About 39% of students enter directly from undergraduate school and 13% have a graduate degree.

School of Law

1215 Wilbraham Road
Springfield, MA 01119

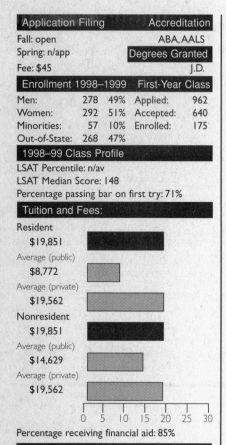

Application Filing		Accreditation
Fall: open		ABA, AALS
Spring: n/app		**Degrees Granted**
Fee: $45		J.D.

Enrollment 1998–1999		First-Year Class	
Men:	278 49%	Applied:	962
Women:	292 51%	Accepted:	640
Minorities:	57 10%	Enrolled:	175
Out-of-State:	268 47%		

1998–99 Class Profile
LSAT Percentile: n/av
LSAT Median Score: 148
Percentage passing bar on first try: 71%

Tuition and Fees:

Resident
$19,851

Average (public)
$8,772

Average (private)
$19,562

Nonresident
$19,851

Average (public)
$14,629

Average (private)
$19,562

0 5 10 15 20 25 30

Percentage receiving financial aid: 85%

ADMISSIONS

In the fall 1999 first-year class, 962 applied, 640 were accepted, and 175 enrolled. The median GPA of the most recent first-year class was 3.06 on a scale of 4.0. The lowest LSAT percentile accepted was 3; the highest was 93.

Requirements

Applicants must have a bachelor's degree from an accredited institution and take the LSAT. No specific undergraduate courses are required. Candidates are interviewed, but interviews are not required.

Procedure

The application deadline for fall entry is open. Applicants should submit an application form, LSAT results, transcripts, a non-refundable application fee of $45, 2 letters of recommendation, and a personal statement. Notification of the admission decision is as early as possible, usually 2 to 4 weeks after completion of the file. The latest acceptable LSAT test date for fall entry is June. The law school uses the LSDAS.

Special

The law school recruits minority and disadvantaged students by means of Law Services forums, attendance at historically black college recruiting events, mailings through the Candidate Referral Service, and limited scholarships. Transfer students must have one year of credit. The school receives approximately 10 to 15 transfer applications each year, of which less than half are generally accepted. There is no minimum law school GPA used as a cutoff.

Costs

Tuition and fees for the 1999-2000 academic year are $19,851 for all full-time students. Tuition for part-time students is $14,670 per year. Books and supplies run $833.

Financial Aid

About 85% of current law students receive some form of aid. The average annual amount of aid from all sources combined, including scholarships, loans, and work contracts, is $19,039; maximum, $27,116. Awards are based on need and merit. Limited merit and need-based scholarships are awarded by the law school admissions committee. The required financial statements are the FAFSA, the College's financial aid application, and tax returns with W2 statements for returning law students. The aid application deadline for fall entry is April 1. Special funds for minority or disadvantaged students are awarded to students who have overcome educational, cultural, economic, or physical barriers to achieve success at the undergraduate level. First-year students are notified about their financial aid application at time of acceptance.

About the Law School

Western New England College School of Law was established in 1919 and is a private institution. The 185-acre campus is in a suburban area 25 miles north of Hartford, and 90 miles west of Boston. The primary mission of the law school is to provide a practical and effective legal education in a humane and supportive environment, in which faculty and students work together in a rigorous yet rewarding educational process. Students have access to federal, state, county, city, and local agencies, courts, correctional facilities, law firms, and legal aid organizations in the Springfield area. Students have opportunities to work for federal and state judges and with government agencies and public interest organizations through the law school internship program, or by individually arranging internships. The Law School also offers a legal services clinic, discrimination law clinic, criminal law clinic, and disability law clinic. Facilities of special interest to law students include a 360,000 volume law library that contains computer laboratories exclusively for student use; a moot court room used for law trial simulation classes, moot court competitions, and semiannual visits by the Massachusetts appeals court; and the Healthful Living Center, a state-of-the-art athletic and recreation facility. Housing for law students is available in Springfield, which offers a variety of housing such as apartments in multifamily homes and in downtown apartment complexes. Limited on-campus housing is also available. All law school facilities are accessible to the physically disabled.

Calendar

The law school operates on a traditional semester basis. Courses for full-time students are offered both day and evening and must be completed within 4 years. For part-time students, courses are offered both day and evening and must be completed within 5 years. New full- and part-time students are admitted in the fall. There is an 8-week summer session. Transferable summer courses are not offered.

Programs

The following joint degrees may be earned: J.D./M.R.P. (Juris Doctor/Master of Regional Planning in conjunction with the University of Massachusetts-Amheurst) and J.D./M.S.W. (Juris Doctor/Master of Social work in conjunction with Springfield college).

MASSACHUSETTS

Phone: 413-782-1406
800-782-6665
Fax: 413-796-2067
E-mail: lawadmis@wnec.edu
Web: www.law.wnec.edu

Contact

Assistant Dean and Director of Admissions, 413-782-1406 or 800-782-6665 for general inquiries; Sandra Belanger, Financial Aid Specialist, 413-796-2080 for financial aid information.

Required

To earn the J.D., candidates must complete 88 total credits, of which 46 to 47 are for required courses. They must maintain a minimum grade average of 70 in the required courses. The following first-year courses are required of all students: Criminal Law, Constitutional Law, Contracts, Lawyering Process, Civil Procedure, Property, and Torts. Required upper-level courses consist of Business Organizations, Income Tax, Evidence, Qualified Writing, and Legal Profession. The required orientation program for first-year students is a 3-day program at which students meet faculty members, administrators, and representatives of various student organizations and attend Lawyering Process Orientation sessions.

Electives

Upper-level students may enroll in the Legal Services Clinic for 12 credits, Criminal Law Clinic for 6 credits, Disabilities Law Clinic for 6 credits, and Discrimination Law Clinic for 6 credits. There are a number of limited enrollment upper-level seminars and simulation courses offered in a broad range of subject-matter areas. Each is a three-credit course designed to satisfy the upper-class writing requirement. In independent study programs, a student may engage in advanced legal research for 2 to 3 credits, under the supervision of 2 faculty members. Students may take summer programs offered by other ABA-accredited law schools. Students may study in tutorials with a faculty member on a mutually agreed upon subject and earn 1 to 3 credits. Remedial programs consist of a Legal Education Assistance Program, which is voluntary and available to first-year and upper-class students. The goal of the program is to provide additional assistance in legal research, writing, reasoning, and examination taking skills. The most widely taken electives are Criminal Procedure, Trusts and Estates, and Secured Transactions.

Graduation Requirements

In order to graduate, candidates must have a grade average of 70 and have completed the upper-division writing requirement.

Organizations

Students edit the *Western New England Law Review, Lex Brevis*, the student newspaper, and *Lytae*, the student published yearbook. Annually, teams are sent to the National Moot Court, Jessup Moot Court International Law competitions, and Vale Corporate Moot Court. Other competitions include the ABA National Trial Competition and the Environmental Moot Court Competition. Organizations for law students include the Multi-Cultural Law Students Association, Women's Law Association, and Gay/Lesbian/Bisexual/Straight Alliance. Local chapters of national associations include Phi Alpha Delta, ABA-Law Student Division, and the Black Law Students Association. Other organizations include International Law Society, Environmental Law Coalition, and Sports and Entertainment Law Society.

Library

The law library contains 360,000 hard-copy volumes and 169,000 microform volume equivalents, and subscribes to 4513 serial publications. Such on-line databases and networks as LEXIS, DIALOG, WESTLAW, NEXIS, the Internet, LOIS, Index Master, Legal Trac, Wilson's Index to Legal Periodical Literature, State Universe, Social Law Library's Administrative database, CALI, and Congressional Universe are available to law students for research. Special library collections include a selective federal government document depository, publications of Massachusetts Continuing Legal Education, Inc., and a law and popular culture, print, video, and audio collection. Recently, the library added a second computer laboratory, installed a wireless network, and wired some carrels and added lights and electrical outlets to most carrel seating. The ratio of library volumes to faculty is 17,791 to 1 and to students, 534 to 1. The ratio of seats in the library to students is 1 to 1.

Faculty

The law school has 27 full-time and 38 part-time faculty members, of whom 21 are women. According to AAUP standards for Category IIA institutions, faculty salaries are well above average. About 22% of full-time faculty have a graduate law degree in addition to the J.D.; about 3% of part-time faculty have one. The ratio of full-time students to full-time faculty in an average class is 15 to 1; in a clinic, 10 to 1. The law school has a regular program of bringing visiting professors and other distinguished lecturers and visitors to campus.

Placement

J.D.s awarded:	160

Services available through: a separate law school placement center

Services: advice on alternative careers and practice in various areas of the law

Special features: networking functions, videotaped individual mock interviews, various panels and workshops presented on conducting the job search and on career options, a weekly Career Services newsletter containing part- and full-time job openings for students and alumni, articles of interest, and notices of writing competitions, summer study, study abroad, fellowships, clerkships, and internships. The school is an active member of 2 law school placement consortia, 1 state and 1 regional.

Full-time job interviews:	10 employers
Summer job interviews:	11 employers
Placement by graduation:	55% of class
Placement within 9 months:	92% of class
Average starting salary:	$18,000 to $95,000

Areas of placement:

Private practice 2-10 attorneys	24%
Private practice 11-25 attorneys	2%
Private practice 26-50 attorneys	2%
Private practice 51-100 attorneys	1%
Business/industry	32%
Government	19%
Judicial clerkships	10%
Academic	3%
Public interest	1%
Military	1%

Students

About 51% of the student body are women; 10%, minorities; 4%, African American; 2%, Asian American; 3%, Hispanic; and 1%, Native American. The majority of students come from Massachusetts (53%). The average age of entering students is 27; age range is 20 to 68. About 26% of students enter directly from undergraduate school. About 14% drop out after the first year for academic or personal reasons.

WESTERN STATE UNIVERSITY

College of Law

IIII North State College Blvd
Fullerton, CA 92831

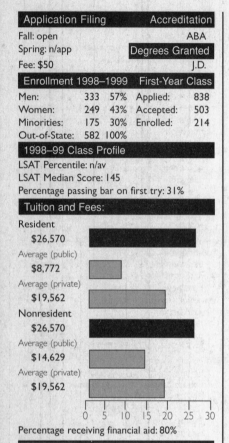

Application Filing			Accreditation
Fall: open			ABA
Spring: n/app			**Degrees Granted**
Fee: $50			J.D.

Enrollment 1998–1999		First-Year Class	
Men:	333 57%	Applied:	838
Women:	249 43%	Accepted:	503
Minorities:	175 30%	Enrolled:	214
Out-of-State:	582 100%		

1998–99 Class Profile

LSAT Percentile: n/av
LSAT Median Score: 145
Percentage passing bar on first try: 31%

Tuition and Fees:

Resident
$26,570

Average (public)
$8,772

Average (private)
$19,562

Nonresident
$26,570

Average (public)
$14,629

Average (private)
$19,562

0   5   10   15   20   25   30

Percentage receiving financial aid: 80%

ADMISSIONS

In the fall 1999 first-year class, 838 applied, 503 were accepted, and 214 enrolled. Fourteen transfers enrolled. The median GPA of the most recent first-year class was 2.9.

Requirements

Applicants must have a bachelor's degree from an accredited institution and take the LSAT. The most important admission factors include writing ability, GPA, and LSAT results. No specific undergraduate courses are required. Candidates are not interviewed.

Procedure

The application deadline for fall entry is open. Applicants should submit an application form, LSAT results, transcripts, a nonrefundable application fee of $50, and 2 letters of recommendation. Notification of the admission decision is 2 weeks after file is completed. The latest acceptable LSAT test date for fall entry is June. The law school uses the LSDAS.

Special

The law school recruits minority and disadvantaged students through a minority recruitment program and forums. Transfer students must have a minimum GPA of 2.0.

Costs

Tuition and fees for the 1999-2000 academic year are $26,570 for full-time students. Tuition for part-time students is $17,670 annually. On-campus room and board costs about $11,099 annually; books and supplies run $1080.

Financial Aid

About 80% of current law students receive some form of aid. The average annual amount of aid from all sources combined, including scholarships, loans, and work contracts, is $17,803; maximum, $37,054. Awards are based on need and merit. The required financial statement is FAFSA. The aid application deadline for fall entry is open. Special funds for minority or disadvantaged students consist of needs-based scholarships. First-year students are notified about their financial aid application at the time of acceptance.

About the Law School

Western State University College of Law was established in 1966 and is a private institution. The 4-acre campus is in a suburban area midway between Los Angeles and San Diego. The primary mission of the law school is to provide the highest quality legal education, based on an innovative program of studies designed to develop the tools of careful legal analysis and to foster a broad understanding of law, law practice, and legal theory. Students have access to federal, state, county, city, and local agencies, courts, correctional facilities, law firms, and legal aid organizations in the Fullerton area. Housing for law students is widely available in a university environment adjacent to Western State and California State University of Fullerton. About 98% of the law school facilities are accessible to the physically disabled.

Calendar

The law school operates on a traditional semester basis. Courses for full-time students are offered days only and must be completed within 5 years. For part-time students, courses are offered both day and evening and must be completed within 6 years. New full-time and part-time students are admitted in the fall and spring. There is a 8-plus 2-week summer sessions. Transferable summer courses are offered.

Phone: 714-738-1000, x2909
800-978-4529
Fax: 714-526-1062
E-mail: joel@wsulaw.edu
Web: wsulaw.edu

Contact

Joel Goodman, Director of Admissions, (714) 738-1000 Ext. 2911 for general inquiries.

Programs

Required

To earn the J.D., candidates must complete 88 credits, of which 58 are for required courses. They must maintain a minimum GPA of 2.0 in the required courses. The following first-year courses are required of all students: Criminal Law, Torts I and II, Civil Procedure I and II, Property I and II, Contracts, and Professional Skills I and II. Required upper-level courses consist of Criminal Procedure, Sales, Professional Responsibility, Advocacy, Constitutional Law, Evidence, Remedies, and Advanced Professional Skills. All students must take clinical courses. The orientation program for first-year students is mandatory.

Electives

The College of Law offers concentrations in entrepreneurial law and criminal law practice. In addition, research programs are available to all students for up to 2 credits. All students are eligible for externships (worth 5 to 8 credits) once prerequisites have been met. Study abroad is available to all students for a maximum of 6 credits. Non-credit tutorial and remedial programs are available to all students. There is an Academic Support Program for minority students. The most widely taken electives are First Amendment courses in the Entrepreneurial Law Center and the Criminal Law Practice Center.

Graduation Requirements

In order to graduate, candidates must have a GPA of 2.0 and complete the upper-division writing requirement and the Advocacy course.

Organizations

Students edit the *Western State University Law Review*, *The Dictum*, and the newspaper, *SBA Connections*. Moot court competitions include Ferguson Moot Court, Jessup Moot Court, and California Moot Court. Student organizations include Women's Law Association, Black Law Student Association, and Latino Law Student Association.

Library

The law library contains 158,966 hard-copy volumes and 370,000 microform volume equivalents, and subscribes to 846 serial publications. Such on-line databases and networks as LEXIS, DIALOG, and WESTLAW are available to law students for research. Recently, the library was expanded to 27,176 square feet and 312 networked connections. The ratio of library volumes to faculty is 6360 to 1 and to students, 261 to 1.

Faculty

The law school has 19 full-time and 21 part-time faculty members, of whom 11 are women. The law school has a regular program of bringing visiting professors and other distinguished lecturers and visitors to campus.

Students

About 43% of the student body are women; 30%, minorities; 6%, African American; 15%, Asian American; 3%, Hispanic; 1%, Native American; and 12%, Mexican-American.

Placement	
J.D.s awarded:	240
Services available through: A separate law school placement center.	
Special features: public service program, externship program, data terminals, alumni mentors	
Full-time job interviews:	10 employers
Summer job interviews:	10 employers
Placement by graduation:	n/av
Placement within 9 months:	92% of class
Average starting salary:	n/av
Areas of placement:	
Private practice 2-10 attorneys	27%
Private practice 11-25 attorneys	13%
Private practice 26-50 attorneys	5%
Private practice 51-100 attorneys	4%
Sole practice	7%
Business/industry	25%
Government	16%
Academic	1%
Judicial clerkships	1%
Public interest	1%

School of Law

3333 Harbor Blvd.
Costa Mesa, CA 92626

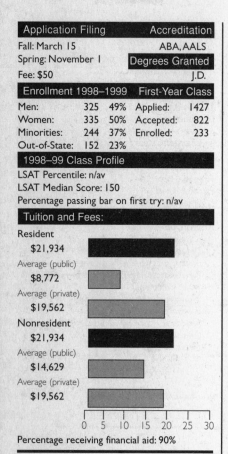

Application Filing	Accreditation
Fall: March 15	ABA, AALS
Spring: November 1	Degrees Granted
Fee: $50	J.D.

Enrollment 1998–1999		First-Year Class	
Men:	325 49%	Applied:	1427
Women:	335 50%	Accepted:	822
Minorities:	244 37%	Enrolled:	233
Out-of-State:	152 23%		

1998–99 Class Profile
LSAT Percentile: n/av
LSAT Median Score: 150
Percentage passing bar on first try: n/av

Tuition and Fees:

Resident
$21,934
Average (public)
$8,772
Average (private)
$19,562
Nonresident
$21,934
Average (public)
$14,629
Average (private)
$19,562

0 5 10 15 20 25 30

Percentage receiving financial aid: 90%

ADMISSIONS

In the fall 1999 first-year class, 1427 applied, 822 were accepted, and 233 enrolled. Ten transfers enrolled. The median GPA of the most recent first-year class was 3.0. The lowest LSAT percentile accepted was 8; the highest was 95.

Requirements
Applicants must have a bachelor's degree from an accredited institution and take the LSAT. Minimum acceptable GPA is 2.0 on a scale of 4.0. The most important admission factors include academic achievement, GPA, and LSAT results. No specific undergraduate courses are required. Candidates are not interviewed.

Procedure
The application deadline for fall entry is March 15. Applicants should submit an application form, LSAT results, transcripts, a nonrefundable application fee, and a personal statement; if foreign, the applicant must have his/her foreign degree reviewed by an evaluation service approved by the school. Check with the school for current fee. Moreover, transcripts must be presented at matriculation. Notification of the admission decision is as decisions are made. The latest acceptable LSAT test date for fall entry is June. The law school uses the LSDAS.

Special
The law school recruits minority and disadvantaged students by means of extensive fall recruiting, mass mailings targeted at minority groups, diversity scholarships, and the Summer Program. Transfer students must have one year of credit and have attended an ABA-approved law school.

Costs

Tuition and fees for the 1999-2000 academic year are $21,934 for all full-time students. Tuition for all part-time students is $13,174 per year. Books and supplies run $675.

Financial Aid

In a recent year, about 90% of current law students received some form of aid. The average annual amount of aid from all sources combined, including scholarships, loans, and work contracts, was $21,631; maximum, $35,233. Awards are based on need and merit. The required financial statement is FAFSA. Check with the school for current application deadline. Special funds for minority or disadvantaged students a limited number of diversity scholarships are available. First-year students are notified about their financial aid application at the time of acceptance.

About the Law School

Whittier College School of Law was established in 1975 and is a private institution. The 15-acre campus is in a suburban area in Costa Mesa, California. The Quaker tradition of Whittier College stresses concern for the individual student's intellectual and ethnic development. The Law School expresses this concern through a low student-to-faculty ratio, which allows for considerable interaction with students. Approximately 150 law firms exist within a 5-mile radius of campus. Orange County courts provide abundant opportunities for externships, clerkships, and other associations for students. Substantial resources are also available in nearby Los Angeles. Housing for law students is not available on campus but is available and affordable in surrounding areas. The Office of Student Affairs assists students seeking housing accommodations. All law school facilities are accessible to the physically disabled.

Calendar

The law school operates on a traditional semester basis. Courses for full-time students are offered both day and evening and must be completed within 5 years. For part-time students, courses are offered both day and evening and must be completed within 6 years. New full-time students are admitted in the fall and spring; part-time, fall. There is an 8-week summer session. Transferable summer courses are offered.

Programs

Students may take relevant courses in other programs and apply credit toward the J.D.; a maximum of 6 credits may be applied.

Phone: 714-444-4141, ext. 121
800-808-8188
Fax: 714-444-0250
E-mail: info@law.whittier.edu
Web: law.whittier.edu

Contact

Lorraine Physic, Director of Admissions, 714-444-4141, ext. 123 for general inquiries; 714-444-4141, ext. 203; 205, for financial aid information.

CALIFORNIA

Required

To earn the J.D., candidates must complete 87 total credits, of which 40 are for required courses. They must maintain a minimum grade average of 77 in the required courses. The following first-year courses are required of all students: Contracts, Torts, Criminal Law, Real Property, Civil Procedure, Legal Process, and Legal Skills/Legal Bibliography. Required upper-level courses consist of Constitutional Law and Professional Responsibility Practicum. All students must take clinical courses. The required orientation program for first-year is students an all-day program that includes introductions to and presentations by faculty, the administration, the library, financial aid office, and student organizations, plus a lecture entitled "How to Survive in Law School."

Electives

The School of Law offers concentrations in international law and health law, and a Center for Children's Rights Fellow Program. In addition, seminars are available including First Amendment, Health Law, and Adoption. Internships are permitted after the completion of 30 units. Students can earn up to 6 units working in the offices of county, state, city, and federal agencies and courts, such as the City Attorney's office, District Attorney's office, Small Business Administration, and the public defendant's office. Students may take up to 3 units of independent study with a full-time professor. Field Placements with various public and private non profit legal entities are available. Special Lecture series include International Law, Health Law, and Center for Children's Rights Fellow Program. The school does not offer classes abroad; however, students of law are permitted to enroll in ABA-approved study-abroad programs sponsored by other law schools for a maximum credit of 6 units. Each semester during the first year of law school, students are invited to attend extensive exam writing workshops. In addition, teaching assistants are available in most first-year classes for one-on-one and group tutorials. The school offers special remedial programs for entering students whose statistics place them in the lower quarter of the entering class. Participation is by invitation only and no units are given. No formalized minority program exists. The most widely taken electives are Criminal Procedure, Evidence, Wills and trusts.

Graduation Requirements

In order to graduate, candidates must have completed the upper-division writing requirement. Students are required to take a 4 unit Professional Responsibility Course that includes a 1-unit writing skills component.

Organizations

Students edit the *Whittier Law Review* and the student newspaper, *The Barrister*. Moot court teams are sent to the National Moot Court, National Criminal Procedure, and Jessup International competitions, among others. Law student organizations include the Alternative Dispute Resolution Group, Asian and Pacific Islander Law Students Association, Trial Advocacy Honors Board, and local chapters of Delta Theta Phi, Alpha Delta, and Phi Delta Phi.

Library

The law library contains 297,614 hardcopy volumes and 122,633 microform volume equivalents, and subscribes to 4689 serial publications. Such on-line databases and networks as LEXIS, DIALOG, WESTLAW, and NEXIS and all Internet databases are available to law students for research. Special library collections include a federal and a California state depository. Recently, the library was relocated to a completely new campus a building of 45,000 square feet with wired carrels and tables. The ratio of library volumes to faculty is 11,023 to 1 and to students, 476 to 1.

Faculty

The law school has 28 full-time and 32 part-time faculty members, of whom 20 are women. According to AAUP standards for Category IIB institutions, faculty salaries are well above average. About 21% of full-time faculty have a graduate law degree in addition to the J.D.; about 13% of part-time faculty have one. The ratio of full-time students to full-time faculty in an average class is 20 to 1; in a clinic, 15 to 1.

Placement

J.D.s awarded:	149

Services available through: a separate law school placement center.

Services: a mentor program, mock interviews, informational programs, and a comprehensive library of directories and other materials

Special features: member of Law School Career Advisors of Southern California (LSCA), a group of 9 law schools that sponsors career programs.

Full-time job interviews:	n/av
Summer job interviews:	n/av
Placement by graduation:	48% of class
Placement within 9 months:	92% of class
Average starting salary:	$25,000 to $110,000

Areas of placement:

Private practice 2-10 attorneys	46%
Private practice 11-25 attorneys	3%
Private practice 26-50 attorneys	6%
Private practice 51-100 attorneys	1%
Solo practice	6%
Unknown	2%
Business/industry	18%
Government	13%
Academic	2%
Judicial clerkships	2%
Public interest	1%

Students

About 50% of the student body are women; 37%, minorities; 6%, African American; 15%, Asian American; 9%, Hispanic; and 1%, Native American. The majority of students come from California (77%). The average age of entering students is 26; age range is 22 to 55. About 30% of students enter directly from undergraduate school and 9% have a graduate degree. About 5% drop out after the first year for academic or personal reasons; 95% remain to receive a law degree.

WIDENER UNIVERSITY

School of Law

4601 Concord Pike, P.O. Box 7474
Wilmington, DE 19803
and, 3800 Vartan Way
Harrisburg, PA

Application Filing	Accreditation
Fall: May 15	ABA, AALS
Spring: December 1	Degrees Granted
Fee: $60	J.D., LL.M., M.J.

Enrollment 1998–1999		First-Year Class	
Men:	768 53%	Applied:	1963
Women:	680 47%	Accepted:	1237
Minorities:	174 12%	Enrolled:	520
Out-of-State:	724 50%		

1998–99 Class Profile
LSAT Percentile: 32%
LSAT Median Score: 147
Percentage passing bar on first try: 61%

Tuition and Fees:

Resident
$19,550

Average (public)
$8,772

Average (private)
$19,562

Nonresident
$19,550

Average (public)
$14,629

Average (private)
$19,562

0 5 10 15 20 25 30

Percentage receiving financial aid: 85%

ADMISSIONS
In the fall 1999 first-year class, 1963 applied, 1237 were accepted, and 520 enrolled. Fifteen transfers enrolled. The median LSAT percentile of the most recent first-year class was 32; the median GPA was 3.0 on a scale of 4.0. The lowest LSAT percentile accepted was 4; the highest was 94.

Requirements
Applicants must have a bachelor's degree from an accredited institution and take the LSAT. The most important admission factors include LSAT results, GPA, and academic achievement. No specific undergraduate courses are required. Candidates are not interviewed.

Procedure
The application deadline for fall entry is May 15. Applicants should submit an application form, LSAT results, transcripts, and a non-refundable application fee of $60. Letters of recommendation and personal statement are strongly suggested. Notification of the admission decision is on a rolling basis. The latest acceptable LSAT test date for fall entry is February, although June test results will be considered based on seat availability. The law school uses the LSDAS.

Special
The law school recruits minority and disadvantaged students through making available significant scholarships to members of minority groups underrepresented in the bar. In addition, the Trial Admissions Program is designed to identify and assist qualified minority students. Transfer students must have attended an ABA-approved law school and submit a certified transcript and letter of good standing. A maximum of 35 qualified credits will be accepted in transfer. Preadmissions courses consist of Law and the Legal Profession, an intensive 2-week summer course for college students considering a career in law.

Costs
Tuition and fees for the 1999-2000 academic year are $19,550 for all full-time students. Tuition for part-time students is $14,670 annually. On-campus room and board costs about $7500 annually; books and supplies run $1000.

Financial Aid
About 85% of current law students receive some form of aid. The average annual amount of aid from all sources combined, including scholarships, loans, and work contracts, is $18,532; maximum, $31,520. Awards are based on need and merit. A number of substantial scholarships are awarded to outstanding applicants and continuing students under the Widener Scholars Program, as well as deferred tuition. Additional scholarships are awarded to applicants in conjunction with our partnership with the Pennsylvania State System of Higher Education. The required financial statement is FAFSA. Merit scholarships are available to minority and disadvantaged students. Deferred tuition loans are offered to students maintaining a satisfactory GPA. First-year students are notified about their financial aid application at the time of acceptance.

About the Law School
Widener University School of Law was established in 1971 and is a private institution. The 40-acre campus is in a suburban area in Delaware, 3 miles from downtown Wilmington; the Harrisburg, Pennsylvania campus is 7 miles from the Pennsylvania state capital. The primary mission of the law school is to emphasize the development of legal writing and practice skills through an extensive curriculum of traditional courses, skills training, clinics and externships, and specialized advanced seminars, with teaching as the highest priority. Students have access to federal, state, county, city, and local agencies, courts, correctional facilities, law firms, and legal aid organizations in the Wilmington area. In addition, students have access to the numerous resources available at the university's main campus. Both campuses provide extensive clinical and skills programs, moot court rooms, extensive law libraries, audiovisual centers, recreational facilities, and student dining centers. Housing in Wilmington consists of on-campus residence halls and townhouse apartments. In Harrisburg, several apartment complexes are within walking distance. About 90% of the law school facilities are accessible to the physically disabled.

Calendar
The law school operates on a traditional semester basis. Courses for full-time students are offered days only. Evening classes are offered on a space-available basis and must be completed within 5 years. For part-time students, courses are offered both day and evening as well as some Saturdays and must be completed within 6 years. New full- and part-time students are admitted in the fall. There is a 7-week summer session. Transferable summer courses are offered.

Programs
In addition to the J.D., the law school offers the LL.M and M.J. (Master of Jurisprudence). Students may take relevant courses in other programs and apply credit toward the J.D.; a maximum of 9 credits may be applied. The following joint degrees may be earned: J.D./M.B.A. (Juris Doctor/Master of Business Administration), J.D./Psy.D. (Juris Doctor/Doctor of Psychology in Law), and J.D./M.M.P. (Juris Doctor/Master of Marine Policy).

Phone: 302-477-2162 (DE); and
717-541-3903 (HBG)
1-888-WIDENER
Fax: 302-477-2224 (DE); and
717-541-3999 (HBG)
E-mail: law.admissions@law.widener.edu
Web: http://www.widener.edu/law/law.html

Contact

Barbara Ayars, Assistant Dean for Admissions, 302-477-2162 for general inquiries; Anthony Doyle, Assistant Dean for Financial Aid, 302-477-2272 for financial aid information.

Required

To earn the J.D., candidates must complete 87 total credits, of which 54 are for required courses. They must maintain a minimum GPA of 2.0 in the required courses. The following first-year courses are required of all students: Administrative Law, Civil Procedure, Contracts, Criminal Law, Introduction to Law or American Legal Systems, Legal Methods I/Analysis, Legal Methods II/Advocacy, Property, and Torts. Required upper-level courses consist of Business Organizations, Commercial Requirement-Sales and Leases, Secured Transactions, Constitutional Law, Criminal Procedure, Evidence, Federal Income Tax, and Professional Responsibility. The required orientation program for first-year students is 2 to 3 days including informational sessions on information technology, how to brief a case, library overview, and financial aid.

Electives

The School of Law offers concentrations in corporate law, criminal law, environmental law, family law, international law, juvenile law, labor law, litigation, securities law, tax law, torts and insurance, law and government, commercial, property and probate, and health law. In addition, clinics for up to 8 credits include Consumer Bankruptcy, Criminal Defense, and Domestic Violence. Clinical education also includes a comprehensive trial advocacy training program. Seminars are offered in most areas of concentration. There are extensive externship and judicial clerkship programs with legislative and state agencies, district attorneys, public defenders, legal aid societies, and courts. All students will complete a major research paper in a seminar. The Law School curriculum employs 10 full-time legal writing professors. The school's legal journals, moot court, trial advocacy program, the many institutes and organizations provide additional opportunities for scholarly research. Field work opportunities include the Wolcott Fellows Program, which places at least one student per academic year as a part-time clerk with each member of the Delaware Supreme Court. The Criminal Law and Procedure faculty has instituted a lecture series on selected timely criminal law topics. Widener has summer-abroad programs at Macquarie University in Sydney, Australia, the University of Nairobi in Kenya, and the Graduate Institute in Switzerland. Each campus has a full-time Academic Support Professor. In addition, specialized programs are provided through the Office of Career Planning and Placement and the Black Law Students Association for minority students. The most widely taken electives are advanced courses in Corporate and Business Law, Trial and Appellate Practice, Constitutional Law, Environmental Law, and Criminal Law.

Graduation Requirements

In order to graduate, candidates must have a GPA of 2.0 and have completed the upper-division writing requirement.

Organizations

The primary law reviews are *Delaware Journal of Corporate Law* (Wilmington), *Widener Journal of Public Law* (Harrisburg), and the *Widener Law Symposium Journal (Harrisburg)*. The student newspaper is *The Law Forum*. The Health Law Institute publishes the *Newsletter of the Society of Health Care Attorneys*. The Moot Court Honor Society sponsors the G. Fred DiBona Competition, the Delaware-Harrisburg Moot Court Competition, and Ruby R. Vale Interschool Corporate Moot Court Competition. The Moe Levine Trial Advocacy Society sponsors the Hugh B. Pearce Memorial Trial Advocacy Competition and qualifying competitions for the Gorby Moot Court and National Association of Criminal Defense Counsel. Student organizations include the Immigration Law Society, Land Use Planning and Real Property Development Society, Big Brothers/Big Sisters, and local chapters of Phi Delta Phi, Delta Theta Phi, and Phi Alpha Delta.

Library

The law library contains 314,170 hard-copy volumes and 296,560 microform volume equivalents, and subscribes to 3339 serial publications. Such on-line databases and networks as LEXIS, DIALOG, WESTLAW, CALI, Legal Resource Index, ProQuest, CIS Congressional Universal, and CCH Internet Tax Research Network are available to law students for research. Special library collections include state and federal depository materials, U.S. Supreme Court records and briefs, and CIS Congressional Library. The library has developed and maintains the Delaware Corporate Law Clearinghouse Website and has a Web-based catalog. The ratio of library volumes to faculty is 4189 to 1 and to students, 217 to 1. The ratio of seats in the library to students is 1 to 2.

Placement

J.D.s awarded:	443
Services available through: a separate law school placement center	
Services: career resource library that includes books, directories, periodicals, and videotapes; lists of all area judges	
Special features: Alumni-student mentor program; free faxing, photocopying and telephone usage; video-taped mock interviews; career panels on various career options; specialized programs for minority students; and a weekly e-mail alumni employment newsletter. All professional staff possess J.D. degrees	
Full-time job interviews:	21 employers
Summer job interviews:	80 employers
Placement by graduation:	57% of class
Placement within 9 months:	88% of class
Average starting salary:	$19,000 to $92,500
Areas of placement:	
Private practice 2-10 attorneys	22%
Private practice 11-25 attorneys	4%
Private practice 26-50 attorneys	2%
Private practice 51-100 attorneys	2%
Private practice, 100+ attorneys	3%
Business/industry	22%
Government	19%
Judicial clerkships	17%
Public interest	2%
Academic	1%

Faculty

The law school has 75 full-time and 91 part-time faculty members, of whom 57 are women. According to AAUP standards for Category IIA institutions, faculty salaries are average. About 24% of full-time faculty have a graduate law degree in addition to the J.D.; about 18% of part-time faculty have one. The ratio of full-time students to full-time faculty in an average class is 12 to 1; in a clinic, 10 to 1. The law school has a regular program of bringing visiting professors and other distinguished lecturers and visitors to campus.

Students

About 47% of the student body are women; 12%, minorities; 6%, African American; 1%, Asian American; and 1%, Hispanic. The majority of students come from the Northeast (91%). The average age of entering students is 25; age range is 21 to 76. About 28% of students enter directly from undergraduate school and 6% have a graduate degree. About 8% drop out after the first year for academic or personal reasons; 98% remain to receive a law degree.

College of Law

245 Winter Street S.E.
Salem, OR 97301

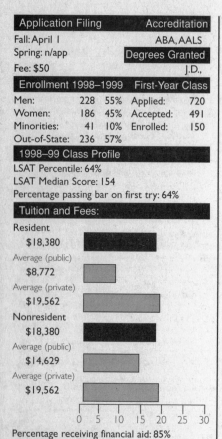

Application Filing	Accreditation
Fall: April 1	ABA, AALS
Spring: n/app	**Degrees Granted**
Fee: $50	J.D.,

Enrollment 1998–1999		First-Year Class	
Men:	228 55%	Applied:	720
Women:	186 45%	Accepted:	491
Minorities:	41 10%	Enrolled:	150
Out-of-State:	236 57%		

1998–99 Class Profile

LSAT Percentile: 64%
LSAT Median Score: 154
Percentage passing bar on first try: 64%

Tuition and Fees:

Resident
$18,380

Average (public)
$8,772

Average (private)
$19,562

Nonresident
$18,380

Average (public)
$14,629

Average (private)
$19,562

0 5 10 15 20 25 30

Percentage receiving financial aid: 85%

ADMISSIONS

In the fall 1999 first-year class, 720 applied, 491 were accepted, and 150 enrolled. Seven transfers enrolled. The median LSAT percentile of the most recent first-year class was 64; the median GPA was 3.2 on a scale of 4.0. The highest LSAT percentile was 97.

Requirements
Applicants must have a bachelor's degree from an accredited institution and take the LSAT. The most important admission factors include LSAT results, GPA, and academic achievement. No specific undergraduate courses are required. Candidates are not interviewed.

Procedure
The application deadline for fall entry is April 1. Applicants should submit an application form, LSAT results, transcripts, a nonrefundable application fee of $50, 2 letters of recommendation, and a personal statement. Notification of the admission decision is begun by March 15. The latest acceptable LSAT test date for fall entry is February. The law school uses the LSDAS.

Special
The law school recruits minority and disadvantaged students through programs, scholarships, and alumni contacts. Transfer students must have attended an ABA-approved law school and be in good standing academically, and be eligible to return to their current law school.

Costs

Tuition and fees for the 1999-2000 academic year are $18,380 for all full-time students. On-campus room costs about $6030 annually; books and supplies run $1250.

Financial Aid

About 85% of current law students receive some form of aid. The average annual amount of aid from all sources combined, including scholarships, loans, and work contracts, is $25,844; maximum, $37,840. Awards are based on need and merit. The required financial statement is FAFSA. The aid application deadline for fall entry is February 1. Special funds for minority or disadvantaged students include 2 full-tuition renewable waivers for qualified minority students in the entering class. First-year students are notified about their financial aid application approximately 2 weeks after acceptance.

About the Law School

Willamette University College of Law was established in 1883 and is a private institution. The 57-acre campus is in an urban area 45 miles south of Portland in Salem, the state capital. The primary mission of the law school is to provide legal training that is broad-based in content in an environment that promotes competition and encourages collaboration. Students have access to federal, state, county, city, and local agencies, courts, correctional facilities, law firms, and legal aid organizations in the Salem area. The college is located across the street from the state capitol and is within easy walking distance of the Tax Court, Oregon Supreme Court, the Supreme Court Library, the Oregon Court of Appeals, and virtually all state agencies and departments. In addition, several county and 2 federal courts are located within approximately 1 hour of Willamette University. Housing for law students consists of a limited number of on-campus single rooms. An apartment building on campus offers 1-bedroom apartments. Off-campus housing is easily attainable and reasonably priced. All law school facilities are accessible to the physically disabled.

Calendar

The law school operates on a traditional semester basis. Courses for full-time students are offered days only and must be completed within 3 years. There is no part-time program. New students are admitted in the fall. There is a 7-week summer session. Transferable summer courses are offered.

Programs

In addition to the J.D., the law school offers the Certificate in Dispute Resolution. Students may take relevant courses in other programs and apply credit toward the J.D.; a maximum of 6 credits may be applied. The following joint degree may be earned: J.D./M.M. (Juris Doctor/Master of Management).

Phone: 503-370-6282
Fax: 503-370-6375
E-mail: law-admission@willamette.edu

Contact

Lawrence Seno, Jr., Director of Admissions, 503-370-6282 for general inquiries; Leslie Limper, Financial Aid Director, 503-370-6273 for financial aid information.

OREGON

Required

To earn the J.D., candidates must complete 88 total credits, of which 39 are for required courses. They must maintain a minimum GPA of 2.0 in the required courses. The following first-year courses are required of all students: Civil Procedure, Property, Criminal Law, Contracts, Torts, Constitutional Law I and II, Dispute Resolution, and Legal Research and Writing. Required upper-level courses consist of Evidence, Professional Responsibility, and Constitutional Law II. The required orientation program for first-year students lasts 2 days and consists of an introduction to the law program and to legal research and writing.

Electives

The College of Law offers concentrations in corporate law, criminal law, environmental law, family law, international law, labor law, litigation, tax law, torts and insurance, and alternative dispute resolution, real estate finance and development, law and government, commercial law, and estate planning and elder law. In addition, there are live client clinics worth 3 hours of credit each. Seminars, worth 2 hours of credit, are offered to second- and third-year students on such topics as law and education, American Indian law, and state constitutional law. An externship program places students in civil or criminal practice environments under the supervision of the school's field instructors. There is an Annual Lecture Series, Dispute Resolution Series, and Paulus Lecture Series. A Summer in China study program, worth 5 hours of credit, is offered to second- and third-year students. In addition, individual students, with ABA approval, may spend a semester at a leading law school in Quito, Ecuador. Special student assistants are available for students in legal research and writing. Along with a pre-law school study program, the college of law has an active minority student organization that sponsors a Martin Luther King dinner involving the community at large. The college offers simulation courses on negotiations, mediation, arbitration, interviewing and counseling, and trial practice. The most widely taken electives are Negotiation, Mediation, and Arbitration.

Graduation Requirements

In order to graduate, candidates must have a GPA of 2.0 and have completed the upper-division writing requirement.

Organizations

Students edit the *Willamette Law Review* and the *Williamette Bulletin of International Law and Dispute Resolution*. Students participate in a number of moot court competitions, including the National Appellate Competition, the Jessup International, and the Labor Law Appellate Competition. The student-run Moot Court Board provides or assists with other competitions in trial and appellate practice. Law student organizations include Willamette Women's Law Caucus, National Lawyers Guild, and Oregon Trial Lawyers Association. There are local chapters of Phi Delta Phi, Phi Alpha Delta, and Inns of Court. Other campus clubs include the Student Bar Association, law class organizations, and the Joint Degree Students Organization.

Library

The law library contains 285,351 hard-copy volumes and 850,015 microform volume equivalents, and subscribes to 1313 serial publications. Such on-line databases and networks as LEXIS, DIALOG, WESTLAW, and NEXIS, Internet, campus networks, the university library online catalog, and Orbis (an online consortium of 14 Northwest academic institutions) are available to law students for research. Special library collections include a U.S. government depository, public international law, and labor and collections. Recently, the law school undertook a library construction and remodeling project. The library has doubled in size and is accessible to students 24 hours a day. Reference librarians are available evenings and weekends to help students. The ratio of library volumes to faculty is 10,568 to 1 and to students, 713 to 1. The ratio of seats in the library to students is 1 to 1.

Faculty

The law school has 21 full-time and 6 part-time faculty members, of whom 9 are women. According to AAUP standards for Category IIB institutions, faculty salaries are well above average. About 10% of full-time faculty have a graduate law degree in addition to the J.D. The ratio of full-time students to full-time faculty in an average class is 24 to 1; in a clinic, 12 to 1.

Placement

J.D.s awarded:	116

Services available through: A separate law school placement center.

Services: extensive mentor program with practicing attorneys; a first-year honors program; clerkship stipends; a fellowship program for minority students through the Oregon State Bar; and a separate Matching Funds program for public interest employment.

Special features: a director of career services, with special knowledge of the disabled. Services are coordinated for Joint Degree Students with Atkinson Graduate School of Management. There are career services newsletters with job hunting tips, workshop information, and job postings published every 2 weeks for students and monthly for alumni.

Full-time job interviews:	15 employers
Summer job interviews:	27 employers
Placement by graduation:	31% of class
Placement within 9 months:	87% of class
Average starting salary:	$16,800 to $80,000

Areas of placement:

Private practice 2-10 attorneys	24%
Private practice 11-25 attorneys	12%
Private practice 51-100 attorneys	3%
Private practice 100+ attorneys	14%
Private practice, firm size unknown	3%
Business/industry	16%
Government	16%
Judicial clerkships	8%
Military	3%

Students

About 45% of the student body are women; 10%, minorities; 2%, African American; 7%, Asian American; 1%, Hispanic; and 2%, Native American. Most of the students come from Oregon (43%). The average age of entering students is 26; age range is 21 to 53. About 12% drop out after the first year for academic or personal reasons; 88% remain to receive a law degree.

WILLIAM MITCHELL COLLEGE OF LAW

875 Summit Avenue
St. Paul, MN 55105-3076

Application Filing	Accreditation
Fall: June 30	ABA, AALS
Spring: November 1	Degrees Granted
Fee: $45	J.D.

Enrollment 1998–1999		First-Year Class	
Men:	491 48%	Applied:	972
Women:	528 52%	Accepted:	638
Minorities:	112 11%	Enrolled:	352
Out-of-State:	204 20%		

1998–99 Class Profile
LSAT Percentile: 56%
LSAT Median Score: 152
Percentage passing bar on first try: 88%

Tuition and Fees:

Resident
$18,120

Average (public)
$8,772

Average (private)
$19,562

Nonresident
$18,120

Average (public)
$14,629

Average (private)
$19,562

0 5 10 15 20 25 30

Percentage receiving financial aid: 90%

ADMISSIONS
In the fall 1999 first-year class, 972 applied, 638 were accepted, and 352 enrolled. Twenty-eight transfers enrolled. The median LSAT percentile of the most recent first-year class was 56; the median GPA was 3.22 on a scale of 4.0. The lowest LSAT percentile accepted was 13; the highest was 98.

Requirements
Applicants must have a bachelor's degree from an accredited institution and take the LSAT. The most important admission factors include academic achievement, LSAT results, and life experience. No specific undergraduate courses are required. Candidates are not interviewed.

Procedure
The application deadline for fall entry is June 30. Applicants should submit an application form, LSAT results, transcripts, TOEFL results if English is a second language, a nonrefundable application fee of $45, 2 (3 preferred) letters of recommendation, a personal essay, a resume, and a $150 nonrefundable deposit if accepted and planning to attend. Notification of the admission decision is on a rolling basis. The latest acceptable LSAT test date for fall entry is June. The law school uses the LSDAS.

Special
The law school recruits minority and disadvantaged students through a general policy of admissions that encourages diversity in the student body and through on-campus visits. Transfer students must have one year of credit, have a minimum GPA of 2.0, have attended an ABA-approved law school, and submit a letter of good standing from the dean of the previously attended school. Twenty-four credits must by completed at William Mitchell. Preadmissions courses consist of the Summer Partnership in Law (SPIL) for college sophomores and juniors. Introduction to Legal Theory is also taught.

Costs
Tuition and fees for the 1999-2000 academic year are $18,120 for all full-time students. Tuition for part-time students is $13,170 per year. Books and supplies run $694.

Financial Aid
About 90% of current law students receive some form of aid. The average annual amount of aid from all sources combined, including scholarships, loans, and work contracts, is $19,170. Awards are based on need and merit. The required financial statements are the FAFSA and Institutional Application. The aid application deadline for fall entry is March 16. Special funds for minority or disadvantaged students are available through the William Mitchell Access Scholarships and many named scholarships. First-year students are notified about their financial aid application at time of acceptance.

About the Law School
William Mitchell College of Law was established in 1900 and is a private institution. The 7-acre campus is in an urban residential area of St. Paul. The primary mission of the law school is to offer students a solid foundation on which to begin the practice of law by integrating the practical and the theoretical. The education is augmented by a strong clinical program and an adjunct faculty comprising the legal community of St. Paul/Minneapolis. Students have access to federal, state, county, city, and local agencies, courts, correctional facilities, law firms, and legal aid organizations in the St. Paul area. Facilities of special interest to law students are the Warren E. Burger Library, high-tech classrooms, and the Legal Practicum with model law-firm offices. Housing for law students is available in the neighborhood and elswehere in Minneapolis-St. Paul. About 98% of the law school facilities are accessible to the physically disabled.

Calendar
The law school operates on a traditional semester basis. Courses for full-time students are offered both day and evening and must be completed within 6 years. For part-time students, courses are offered both day and evening and must be completed within 6 years. New full- and part-time students are admitted in the fall. There is a summer institute offering short courses throughout the summer. Transferable summer courses are offered.

Programs
Students may take relevant courses in other programs and apply credit toward the J.D.; a maximum of 62 credits may be applied.

Phone: 651-290-6476
888-WMCL-LAW
Fax: 651-290-6414
E-mail: admissions@wmitchell.edu
Web: http://www.wmitchell.edu

Contact

Dr. James H. Brooks, Dean of Students, 651-290-6362 for general inquiries; Jeanette Maynard Nelson, Director of Financial Aid, 651-290-6358 for financial aid information.

Required

To earn the J.D., candidates must complete 86 total credits, of which 46 are for required courses. They must maintain a minimum GPA of 2.0 in the required courses. The following first-year courses are required of all students: Civil Procedure, Contracts, Legal Writing, Property I and II, and Torts I and II. Required upper-level courses consist of Constitutional Law-Powers, Constitutional Law-Liberties, Professional Responsibility, Lawyering, a skills course, and 2 statutory courses. The required orientation program for first-year students lasts 2 days and covers an introduction to law school, tours, the first class, and legal writing.

Electives

The William Mitchell College of Law offers concentrations in corporate law, criminal law, environmental law, family law, international law, labor law, litigation, securities law, tax law, torts and insurance, constitutional law, property, intellectual property, estates, jurisprudence, civil procedure, administrative and legislative process, and poverty law. In addition, there are clinics in administrative law, business law, and immigration law. Other opportunities are available for students as appellate and judicial interns working for the attorney general and by participating in an independent clinic, among others. Seminars are available in law and sexuality, biomedical eithics, and the First Amendment. Independent research projects are available for 1 to 4 credits; students may do a maximum of 2 projects. Study abroad consists of a summer program in London. A summer tutorial program allows students to benefit from introductory courses emphasizing the legal process. First-year-subject tutors are also available. Remedial programs include exam workshops. Minority programs are provided by the Black Law Students Association, Hispanic Law Students Association, Gay-Lesbian Student Association, and American Indian Law Student Association. Special interest group programs are provided by the Student Intellectual Property Association, Christian Law Fellowship, Jewish Law Society, Minnesota Public Interest Research Group, National Lawyers Guild, Minnesota Justice Foundation, and Women Law Students Association. The most widely taken electives are Criminal Law and Procedure, Evidence, and Intellectual Property Survey.

Graduation Requirements

In order to graduate, candidates must have a GPA of 2.0 and have completed the upper-division writing requirement.

Organizations

The primary law review is the *William Mitchell Law Review* and the student newspaper is the *Opinion*. Teams participate in the National Civil Rights Moot Court, Tax Moot Court, and Philip C. Jessup International Moot Court. Other competitions include Rosalie Wahl Moot Court, ABA Client Counseling, ABA Negotiations, and ATLA Trial Advocacy. Law student organizations include the Student Bar Association, WMCL Democrats, and Federalist Society. There are local chapters of Delta Theta Phi, Phi Alpha Delta, and Phi Delta Phi.

Library

The law library contains 296,813 hardcopy volumes and 132,535 microform volume equivalents, and subscribes to 2085 serial publications. Such on-line databases and networks as LEXIS, DIALOG, WESTLAW, NEXIS, OCLC, the Internet, and Congressional Universe are available to law students for research. The library is a federal depository library and has a comprehensive collection of federal government documents covering legal materials from the federal courts, U.S. government agencies, Congress, and the Executive Branch. There is also an extensive tax collection. Recently, the library added approximately 75 network access points at study tables and carrels. The ratio of library volumes to faculty is 8730 to 1 and to students, 291 to 1. The ratio of seats in the library to students is 1 to 66.

Faculty

The law school has 36 full-time and 115 part-time faculty members, of whom 48 are women. About 17% of full-time faculty have a graduate law degree in addition to the J.D. The ratio of full-time students to full-time faculty in an average class is 51 to 1; in a clinic, 5 to 1. The law school has a regular program of bringing visiting professors and other distinguished lecturers and visitors to campus.

Placement

J.D.s awarded:	292

Services available through: separate law school placement center

Services: career panels, resource library, out-of-state job-search resources, and on-line resources on the Web site

Special features: comprehensive career-planning program and "Graduate Bulletin" (newsletter) courtesy subscription to all recent graduates

Full-time job interviews:	23 employers
Summer job interviews:	60 employers
Placement by graduation:	80% of class
Placement within 9 months:	94% of class
Average starting salary:	$20,800 to $260,000

Areas of placement:

Private practice 2-10 attorneys	25%
Private practice 11-25 attorneys	5%
Private practice 26-50 attorneys	4%
Private practice 51-100 attorneys	2%
Private practice 100+ attorneys	7%
Business/industry	28%
Government	13%
Judicial clerkships	12%
Military	2%
Public interest	2%
Academic	1%

Students

About 52% of the student body are women; 11%, minorities; 4%, African American; 4%, Asian American; 2%, Hispanic; and 1%, Native American. The majority of students come from Minnesota (80%). The average age of entering students is 29; age range is 20 to 54. About 2% drop out after the first year for academic or personal reasons; 90% remain to receive a law degree.

Yale Law School

P.O. Box 208329
New Haven, CT 06520-8239

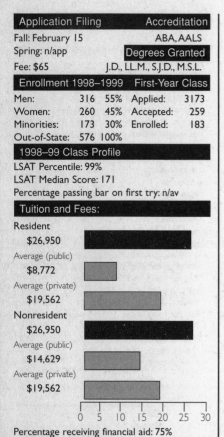

Application Filing	Accreditation
Fall: February 15	ABA, AALS
Spring: n/app	Degrees Granted
Fee: $65	J.D., LL.M., S.J.D., M.S.L.

Enrollment 1998–1999		First-Year Class	
Men:	316 55%	Applied:	3173
Women:	260 45%	Accepted:	259
Minorities:	173 30%	Enrolled:	183
Out-of-State:	576 100%		

1998–99 Class Profile

LSAT Percentile: 99%
LSAT Median Score: 171
Percentage passing bar on first try: n/av

Tuition and Fees:

Resident
$26,950

Average (public)
$8,772

Average (private)
$19,562

Nonresident
$26,950

Average (public)
$14,629

Average (private)
$19,562

0 5 10 15 20 25 30

Percentage receiving financial aid: 75%

ADMISSIONS

In the fall 1999 first-year class, 3173 applied, 259 were accepted, and 183 enrolled. Eleven transfers enrolled. The median LSAT percentile of the most recent first-year class was 99; the median GPA was 3.9 on a scale of 4.0. The lowest LSAT percentile accepted was 71; the highest was 99.

Requirements

Applicants must have a bachelor's degree from an accredited institution and take the LSAT. No specific undergraduate courses are required. Candidates are not interviewed.

Procedure

The application deadline for fall entry is February 15. Applicants should submit an application form, LSAT results, transcripts, a nonrefundable application fee of $65, 2 letters of recommendation, and an essay. Notification of the admission decision is on a rolling basis. The latest acceptable LSAT test date for fall entry is December. The law school uses the LSDAS.

Special

The law school recruits minority and disadvantaged students by means of Candidate Referral Services through Law Services. Transfer students must have one year of credit, have attended an ABA-approved law school, and have a weighted average of not less than B.

Costs

Tuition and fees for the 1999-2000 academic year are $26,950 for full-time in-state students. On-campus room and board plus books and supplies cost about $11,550 annually.

Financial Aid

About 75% of current law students receive some form of aid. The average annual amount of aid from all sources combined, including scholarships, loans, and work contracts, is $27,000; maximum, $45,000. Awards are based on need. The required financial statement is FAFSA. The aid application deadline for fall entry is March 15. First-year students are notified about their financial aid application at time of acceptance.

About the Law School

Yale University Law School was established in 1801 and is a private institution. The campus is in an urban area in New Haven on the block bounded by Grove, High, Wall and York streets. The primary mission of the law school is to train lawyers and leaders in the public and private sectors, and to encourage research in the law. The law school seeks to train lawyers for public service and teaching as well as for private practice, and to advance inquiry at the boundaries of the law as well as to inculate knowledge at the core. Facilities of special interest to law students include a newly renovated law library and computer facility; the Jerome W. Frank Legal Services Organization; the Orville H. Shell, Jr. Center for International Human Rights; the Center for Studies in Law, Economics, and Public Policy; numerous endowed lecture programs that bring distinguished speakers from around the world to Yale; and access to the university's 10.8 million-volume library system, and to its cultural, social, intellectual, and athletic facilities and activities. Limited space is available in the law school dormitories. The majority of students live in off-campus housing. Additionally, some family housing is available

from the university. The university also has a housing office that assists students in locating housing. About 85% of the law school facilities are accessible to the physically disabled.

Calendar

The law school operates on a traditional semester basis. Courses for full-time students are offered days only and must be completed within 6 terms. There is no part-time program. New full-time students are admitted in the fall. There is no summer session. Transferable summer courses are not offered.

Programs

In addition to the J.D., the law school offers the LL.M, S.J.D., and M.S.L, Master of Studies in Law, including fellowships in law for journalists. Students may take relevant courses in other programs and apply credit toward the J.D.; a maximum of 15 credits may be applied. The following joint degrees may be earned: J.D./M.Div. (Juris Doctor/Master of Divinity), J.D./M.A.R. (Juris Doctor/Master of Arts in religion), J.D./M.B.A. (Juris Doctor/Master of Business Administration), J.D./M.A. (Juris Doctor/Master of Arts), J.D./Ph.D. (Juris Doctor/Doctor of Philosophy), J.D./M.E.S. (Juris Doctor/Master of Environmental Studies), and J.D./M.D. (Juris Doctor/Doctor of Medicine).

Required

To earn the J.D., candidates must complete 82 total credits, of which 19 are for required courses. The following first-year courses are required of all students: Constitutional Law, Contracts, Procedure, and Torts. Required upper-level courses consist of Criminal Law and Administration, Supervised Analytic Writing Paper, and Professional Responsibility and Legal Ethics Reading Group. The optional orientation program for first-year students consists of a weekend prior to registration at which life at the law school and in New Haven is discussed.

Electives

The Yale Law School offers concentrations in corporate law, criminal law, entertainment law, environmental law, family law, international law, juvenile law, labor law, litigation, securities law, sports law, tax law, torts and insurance, administrative law,

Phone: 203-432-4995
E-mail: admissions.law@yale.edu
Web: www.law.yale.edu

Contact

Jean K. Webb, Director of Admissions, 203-432-4995 for general inquiries; Patricia Barnes, Associate Director of Financial Aid, 203-432-1688 for financial aid information.

CONNECTICUT

constitutional law, comparative law, legal history, torts, criminal procedure, bankruptcy, law and economics, employment discrimination, property, health law, antidiscrimination law, antitrust, evidence, federal jurisdiction, feminism, international business transactions, First Amendment, international human rights, the United Nations, and trusts and estates. In addition, clinical opportunities are offered through the Jerome N. Frank Legal Services Organization, which links law students with individuals in need of legal help who cannot afford private attorneys. Faculty-supervised students interview clients, write briefs, prepare witnesses, try cases, negotiate settlements, and argue appeals in state and federal courts, including the U.S. Court of Appeals for the Second Circuit and the Connecticut Supreme Court. There are 8 main projects: Advocacy for Parents and Children, Advocacy for People with Disabilities, Community Legal Services, Housing and Community Development, Immigration, Landlord/Tenant, Legal Assistance, and Prisons. Students also participate in independent projects at 2 local prosecutor's offices (the New Haven State Attorney and the U.S. Attorney) and at other public service law offices. Other clinics include the Environmental Protection Clinic and the Allard K. Lowenstein International Human Rights Law Clinic. In addition to the many seminars offered during the fall and spring terms, groups of 6 or more students may submit proposals for research and legislative drafting seminars. Also, fourth- and fifth-term students may elect to take the Intensive Semester Program. Research programs and independent reading may be undertaken after the first term with faculty permission. Numerous special lecture series are held annually, including the Timothy B. Atkeson Environmental Practitioner in Residence; the Cover Lecture in Law and Religion; the Ralph Gregory Elliot First Amendment Lecture; the Preiskel/Silverman Program on the Practicing Lawyer and the Public Interest; and the Robert L. Bernstein Lecture in International Human Rights. In the second term students may begin participation in programs managed primarily by students under the supervision of a faculty adviser. These include the Capital Defense Project, the Domestic Violence Temporary Restraining Order Project, the Greenhaven Prison Project, Street Law, Thomas Swan Barristers' Union, Morris Tyler Moot Court of Appeals, and numerous reviews and journals.

Graduation Requirements

In order to graduate, candidates must have completed the upper-division writing requirement.

Organizations

Student-edited publications include the *Yale Law Journal, Yale Journal of International Law, Yale Journal of Law and Feminism, Yale Journal of Law and Humanities, Yale Journal of Regulation, Yale Human Rights and Development Law Journal,* and *Yale Law and Policy Review.* Moot court competitions include the Thurman Arnold Appellate Competition Prize, the Benjamin N. Cardozo Prize, and the John Fletcher Caskey, John Currier Gallagher, Potter Stewart, and Harlan Fiske Stone prizes. Other competitions or prizes include the Albom, Brody Burkan Memorial, Cohen, Connecticut Attorneys' Title Insurance Company, Cullen, Egger, Emerson, Gherini, Gruter, Jewell, Khosla, Lemkin, Massey, Miller, Munson, Olin, Parker, Peres, Porter, Robbins Memorial, Scharps, Townsend, Wang, and Wayland. Law student organizations include the Asia Law Forum, the Initiative for Public Interest Law at Yale, and the Yale Law and Technolgy Society. There are local chapters of the Black Law Students Association, the Federalist Society, and the Native American Law Students Association.

Library

The law library contains 798,200 hardcopy volumes and 2583 microform volume equivalents, and subscribes to 9598 serial publications. Such on-line databases and networks as LEXIS, WESTLAW, ORBIS (Yale University catalog), and MORRIS (Yale Law School catalog) are available to law students for research. Special library collections include a 200,000-volume foreign and international law collection. Recently, the library underwent a major renovation as part of a comprehensive, $90 million renovation of the Sterling Law Building. The ratio of library volumes to faculty is 8583 to 1 and to students, 1285 to 1. The ratio of seats in the library to students is 2 to 3.

Placement	
J.D.s awarded:	194
Services available through: a separate law school placement center.	
Services: judicial clerkship counseling and programs, public interest counseling and programs, career counseling, publications, recruiting events, resource library	
Special features: a professional counseling staff, all of whom are attorneys; comprehensive individual career counseling; a program resource library; publications; and recruiting events.	
Full-time job interviews:	185 employers
Summer job interviews:	n/av
Placement by graduation:	97% of class
Placement within 9 months:	98% of class
Average starting salary:	$26,664 to $100,000
Areas of placement:	
Private practice	27%
Judicial clerkships	53%
Academic	6%
Public interest	4%
Business/industry	4%
Government	2%

Faculty

The law school has 58 full-time and 35 part-time faculty members, of whom 24 are women. According to AAUP standards for Category I institutions, faculty salaries are well above average. The ratio of full-time students to full-time faculty in an average class is 12 to 1. The law school has a regular program of bringing visiting professors and other distinguished lecturers and visitors to campus.

Students

About 45% of the student body are women; 30%, minorities; 10%, African American; 12%, Asian American; 7%, Hispanic; and 1%, Native American. The average age of entering students is 25. About 34% of students enter directly from undergraduate school and 17% have a graduate degree.

Benjamin N. Cardozo School of Law

55 Fifth Avenue
New York, NY 10003

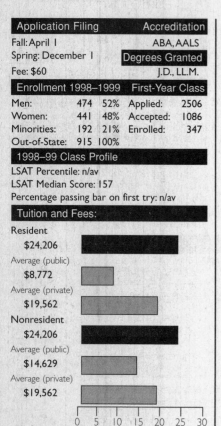

Application Filing	Accreditation
Fall: April 1	ABA, AALS
Spring: December 1	Degrees Granted
Fee: $60	J.D., LL.M.

Enrollment 1998–1999		First-Year Class	
Men:	474 52%	Applied:	2506
Women:	441 48%	Accepted:	1086
Minorities:	192 21%	Enrolled:	347
Out-of-State:	915 100%		

1998–99 Class Profile

LSAT Percentile: n/av
LSAT Median Score: 157
Percentage passing bar on first try: n/av

Tuition and Fees:

Resident
$24,206

Average (public)
$8,772

Average (private)
$19,562

Nonresident
$24,206

Average (public)
$14,629

Average (private)
$19,562

0   5   10   15   20   25   30

Percentage receiving financial aid: 80%

ADMISSIONS

In the fall 1999 first-year class, 2506 applied, 1086 were accepted, and 347 enrolled. Seven transfers enrolled. The median GPA of the most recent first-year class was 3.4.

Requirements

Applicants must have a bachelor's degree from an accredited institution and take the LSAT. No specific undergraduate courses are required. Candidates are not interviewed.

Procedure

The application deadline for fall entry is April 1. Applicants should submit an application form, LSAT results, transcripts, a nonrefundable application fee of $60, 2 letters of recommendation, a dean's certification form, and a personal statement. Notification of the admissions decision is on a rolling basis from October 1. The latest acceptable LSAT test date for fall entry is February. The law school uses the LSDAS.

Special

The law school recruits minority and disadvantaged students by means of Candidate Referral Service searches, special mailings, attendance at law fairs and receptions, and an Opportunities for Minority Students brochure. Transfer students must have one year of credit, and have attended an ABA-approved law school. Most of the emphasis in the admissions decision is placed on first-year performance.

Costs

Tuition and fees for the 1999-2000 academic year are $24,206 for all full-time students. Books and supplies run $960.

Financial Aid

About 80% of current law students receive some form of aid. The average annual amount of aid from all sources combined, including scholarships, loans, and work contracts, is $25,340; maximum, $43,299. Awards are based on need and merit. The required financial statements are FAFSA and Need Access. The aid application deadline for fall entry is April 15. Special funds for minority or disadvantaged students are available. First-year students are notified about their financial aid application at time of acceptance.

About the Law School

Yeshiva University Benjamin N. Cardozo School of Law was established in 1976 and is a private institution. The campus is in an urban area in the heart of Greenwich Village. The primary mission of the law school is to enhance the student's understanding of the legal profession and of the ethical dilemmas and professional responsibilities for a lawyer in today's society. Students have access to federal, state, county, city, and local agencies, courts, correctional facilities, law firms, and legal aid organizations in the New York area. Students benefit from the school's proximity to city, state, and federal bar associations and from reciprocal library privileges with numerous area law schools. Facilities of special interest to law students include the New York Stock Exchange, American Stock Exchange, the United Nations, and New York's many cultural institutions. Housing for law students is available through assistance from the Admissions Office, a housing booklet, and a newsletter. A residence hall is located 1 block from the law school. All law school facilities are accessible to the physically disabled.

Calendar

The law school operates on a traditional semester basis. Courses for full-time students are offered days only and must be completed within 7 semesters or 5 years. There is no part-time program. New full-time students are admitted in the fall, spring, and summer. There is a 13-week summer session. Transferable summer courses are offered.

Programs

In addition to the J.D., the law school offers the LL.M. Students may take relevant courses in other programs and apply credit toward the J.D.; a maximum of 12 credits may be applied. The following joint degrees may be earned: J.D./M.S.W (Juris Doctor/Master of Social Work) and J.D./M.A. (Juris Doctor/Master of Arts in social research).

Required

To earn the J.D., candidates must complete 84 total credits, of which 38 are for required courses. They must maintain a minimum GPA of 2.2 in the required courses. The following first-year courses are required of all students: Torts, Contracts, Property, Civil Procedure, Elements of the Law, Legal Writing and Moot Court, Criminal Law, and Constitutional Law. Required upper-level courses consist of Professional Responsibility, upper-level legal research, upper-level writing requirement, and distribution requirements. Clinics are offered, but are not required. The required orientation program for first-year students consists of 2 days of orientation activities.

Phone: 212-790-0274
Fax: 212-790-0482
E-mail: lawinfo@ymail.yu.edu
Web: www.cardozo.yu.edu/

Contact

Office of Admissions, 212-790-0274 for general inquiries; Thomas Curtin, Financial Aid Director, 212-790-0392 for financial aid information.

NEW YORK

Electives

The Benjamin N. Cardozo School of Law offers concentrations in corporate law, criminal law, entertainment, family law, international law, litigation, media law, tax law, and intellectual property law; commercial law; constitutional law; jurisprudence and legal history. In addition, clinical offerings include the Criminal Law Clinic at the Manhattan Criminal Court, the Criminal Appeals Clinic, in which students represent indigent appellants, the Innocence Project, in which students assist prisoners whose innocence may be proven through DNA testing, Prosecutor Practicum, in which students assist the Manhattan district attorney, Bet Tzedek Legal Services Clinic for the elderly and disabled, judicial clerkships through the Alexander Judicial Fellows Program, Mediation Center Clinic, which allows students to practice arbitration and mediation in social and personal conflicts, Tax Court Clinic, and Immigration Law Clinic. Special courses and seminars are offered in human rights, law and literature, sports law, federal regulation of the media, bioethics and the law, children, families, and the state, and international law. Additionally, the Intensive Trial Advocacy Program is taught by 175 trial attorneys and uses video training techniques. A wide variety of internships is offered during the academic year as well as through the Summer Institute. Research assistants are hired by professors. Field work is offered through the Criminal Law Clinics at the Manhattan Criminal Court, Brooklyn Mediation Center through the Mediation Clinic, and the U.S. Tax Court through the Tax Clinic. Many seminars and conferences are held each year. Study abroad is provided through the Uri and Caroline Bauer Israel Program at Hebrew University, a program in Budapest, Hungary, and at Oxford University, England. For students at risk, there is a Legal Methods program. Minority programs include activities of the Black, Asian, and Latino Law Student Association (BALLSA). There is an Intellectual Property Law Program, which encompasses traditional courses, unusual externships, and ground-breaking symposia and lectures, and the Samuel and Ronnie Heyman Center on Corporate Governance. The most widely taken electives are entertainment, communications, and corporate and tax law.

Graduation Requirements

In order to graduate, candidates must have a GPA of 2.2 and complete the upper-division writing requirement and the upper-level legal research and Professional Responsibility and distribution requirements.

Organizations

Students edit the *Cardozo Law Review, Arts and Entertainment Law Journal, Cardozo Women's Law Journal, Cardozo Journal of International and Comparative Law, Cardozo On-line Journal of Conflict Resolution, Cardozo Studies in Law and Literature, Estate Reporter,* and the newspaper *Forum.* Moot court competitions include the ABA-sponsored National, Jessup International, and Labor Law. Other competitions include the Advocacy and Monrad Paulsen competitions and the Cardozo/BMI Moot Court Competition in communications and entertainment law. Law student organizations include the Constitutional Law Society; Black, Asian, and Latino law student associations; and Arts and Entertainment Law Society. There are local chapters of Phi Alpha Delta, the Asian/Pacific Islander Law Students Association, and the National Lawyers Guild. Other organizations include the Family Law Cooperative, Federalist Society, and International Law Society.

Library

The law library contains 440,400 hard-copy volumes and 1,095,152 microform volume equivalents, and subscribes to 2268 serial publications. Such on-line databases and networks as LEXIS, DIALOG, WESTLAW, and OCLC are available to law students for research. Special library collections include the Louis and Ida Shlansky Family Foundation Library of Jewish and Israeli Law and a U.S. government depository. The ratio of library volumes to faculty is 9574 to 1 and to students, 481 to 1. The ratio of seats in the library to students is 1 to 2.

Placement

J.D.s awarded:	288

Services available through: a separate law school placement center.

Services: nationally renowned employment system and computerized data bases for student and alumni use, and organization of letters sent for clerkships

Special features: include mock video interviews, a summer institute combining an internship and seminar, extensive assistance with summer and postgraduate federal and state judicial clerkships, and separate career resource library.

Full-time job interviews:	126 employers
Summer job interviews:	n/av
Placement by graduation:	n/av
Placement within 9 months:	92% of class
Average starting salary:	$30,000 to $107,000

Areas of placement:

Private practice 2-10 attorneys	22%
Private practice 11-25 attorneys	7%
Private practice 26-50 attorneys	8%
Private practice 51-100 attorneys	7%
Private practice 101 to 500+ attorneys	20%
Business/industry	16%
Government	10%
Judicial clerkships	5%
Public interest	4%
Academic	1%

Faculty

The law school has 46 full-time and 92 part-time faculty members, of whom 36 are women. About 17% of full-time faculty have a graduate law degree in addition to the J.D. The ratio of full-time students to full-time faculty in an average class is 20 to 1; in a clinic, 8 to 1. The law school has a regular program of bringing visiting professors and other distinguished lecturers and visitors to campus. There is a chapter of the Order of the Coif; 16 faculty and 98 graduates are members.

Students

About 48% of the student body are women; 21%, minorities; 5%, African American; 10%, Asian American; and 5%, Hispanic. The average age of entering students is 23; age range is 20 to 74. About 50% of students enter directly from undergraduate school and 50% have worked full-time prior to entering law school. About 1% drop out after the first year for academic or personal reasons; 99% remain to receive a law degree.

CHAPTER 14

Law Schools Not Approved by the ABA

AN OVERVIEW

Although the vast majority of law school students attend institutions approved by the American Bar Association, a distinct minority attend schools that have not received ABA accreditation. Applicants frequently wonder whether it will make a difference if they attend a nonapproved school. The answer to this question requires an understanding of what it means for a law school to be accredited.

For nearly a century, the American Bar Association has developed educational standards for law schools, reviewed institutional adherence to those standards, and approved law schools that complied with the standards. The standards themselves have evolved out of the crucible of experience with input from legal educators, practitioners, and judges. The standards, while sometimes mystifying to those who do not understand legal education, represent well-reasoned statements of policy aimed at assuring that individuals who enter the practice of law undertake a rigorous curriculum in an intellectually demanding setting. Over the years the ABA approval process has established and maintained a basic set of standards for entry into the practice of law that is accepted by bar licensing authorities, practitioners, and the courts.

Recognizing the value of the accreditation process in upholding the quality of legal education and ultimately the legal profession, most states require candidates for the bar examination to have graduated from an ABA-approved law school. Some other states certify graduates of law schools located in the state but not approved by the ABA to sit for the bar exam in that state. It is virtually impossible for graduates of a nonapproved law school to take the bar outside the state where they attended law school.

The non-ABA schools generally fall into three groups: new schools seeking ABA approval, state-approved schools, and unapproved schools. New law schools seeking ABA accreditation must go through an initial review and provisional accreditation before becoming fully approved. During this period of several years the school undergoes strict scrutiny, and students who enroll run the risk that the institution may never meet ABA standards. In recent years, more than a few such schools have dissolved when they could not secure ABA approval. If this happens, students may lose all their law school credits, and, worse, find that they cannot take a bar examination anywhere. On the other hand, if the school gains ABA approval, the risk will turn out to have been worthwhile.

The differences between state-approved and unapproved schools may seem murky. In most states where graduates of non-ABA schools can take the bar, there are only one or two non-ABA schools. Whether these schools are accredited by a state accrediting agency or whether the graduates simply are certified by the bar examiners is probably immaterial to most students. In California, however, the distinction does have ramifications. Significantly, that state has the largest number of lawyers as well as the largest number of non-ABA schools. In California, the state approves law schools using a procedure similar to but different from the ABA. State-approved law schools are treated within the state much like ABA schools; outside California the graduates of these schools usually will be considered like graduates of any other non-ABA approved school. Schools in California that have not been approved by either the state or the ABA represent a separate group within that state, and graduates face additional restrictions on (but not prohibition from) bar admission.

Why would you choose to attend a non-ABA law school? The most common reason might be that you do not gain admission to an ABA school. There is definitely a pecking order among law schools from elite schools like Harvard or Yale down to the unapproved schools. Generally, the more prestigious the law school, the more competitive it will be, and, conversely, the lower the school's perceived ranking, the less stringent will be the admission standards. Legal educators frequently warn prelaw students to beware of law school rankings because they often are based on reputations decades old rather than the current state of legal education at the schools. Rankings also overlook distinctions among schools that make different schools the best choice for different students. In this sense you should evaluate the quality of education at an unapproved school the same way you would evaluate an approved school. The point here is that some students whose traditional qualifications (such as undergraduate GPA and LSAT percentile) will not get them into an approved school may be able to secure a seat at an unapproved one. Some candidates may decide not to attend law school at all if they are not accepted at an ABA school; others may want a law degree so much that they select one of the non-ABA institutions.

A second reason that some students give for attending an unapproved school is cost. Because they are not bound by ABA requirements, non-ABA schools frequently rely heavily on part-time instructors, who cost less than full-time professors. In addition, non-ABA schools may provide more spartan facilities (the library, for example). This bargain basement approach to education can mean tuition savings for students.

Because classes are taught by practitioners, non-ABA schools may offer a more practice-oriented education. There are tradeoffs learning from part-time instructors who have full-time jobs in law firms, government, or corporations. You may gain from the practical experiences of these teachers but miss the indepth attention that full-time teachers can provide.

On the negative side, attendance at a non-ABA law school will inevitably restrict the jurisdictions in which graduates may be licensed. Therefore, it is unwise to enroll in a non-ABA law school in a state where you are unwilling to live and practice. You should carefully check the bar admission requirements for all the jurisdictions you consider prior to entering any law school that is not fully approved by the ABA.

Those considering attending an unapproved law school should consider also the educational experience they will receive. Since many such schools provide a bare bones education,

applicants should scrutinize the academic program of the school at least as carefully as they would that of an ABA-approved school. While many non-ABA schools have existed for many years and maintain sound local reputations, other schools have less than solid foundations.

A final consideration that anyone contemplating attending a non-ABA-approved law school should address involves the career opportunities available to graduates. Not only is the bar passage rate lower at some non-ABA schools, thereby limiting career opportunities, but also the placement patterns of the graduates may be significantly different. The bottom line is that anyone considering law school should carefully investigate and research all aspects of each potential school before applying.

PROFILES OF SELECTED LAW SCHOOLS

Brief profiles of selected law schools not approved by the ABA appear on the following pages. The pros and cons of such law schools are discussed above. Only schools responding to our request for current information are included here.

Each profile begins with the name of the law school, its address and phone and fax numbers, and e-mail and Web addresses if provided. The capsule of basic information about the law school presents the following information.

Application Filing Fall and spring application deadlines and the application fee are given.

Accreditation Any professional accreditation is noted. (See **Abbreviations and Degrees** on page vii).

Degrees Granted Degrees are nearly always limited to the J.D.

Enrollment Enrollment breakdowns for 1999–2000 include men, women, minorities, and out-of-state students.

First-Year Class The applied, accepted, and enrolled figures refer to the number of students applying for the 1999–2000 entering class.

Class Profile This section includes the median LSAT percentile and the median LSAT score of freshmen in the 1999–2000 entering class, as well as the percentage of a recent graduating class that passed the bar on the first attempt.

Tuition and Fees Tuition and Fees figures given here are annual amounts, unless otherwise indicated. (NOTE: None of the schools featured in this edition are public institutions.) Because tuition charges change periodically, it is important to check with the school for current figures.

This section also features the percentage of current students receiving financial aid.

Contact The person or position to whom inquiries should be directed is given, along with appropriate phone numbers.

ABRAHAM LINCOLN UNIVERSITY SCHOOL OF LAW

3000 S. Robertson Blvd #420
Los Angeles, CA 90034

Phone: (310) 204-0222
Fax: (310) 204-7025
E-mail: info@alulaw.com
Web: www.alulaw.com

Application Filing	Accreditation
Fall: August 11	no
Spring: February 25	Degrees Granted
Fee: $50	J.D.

Enrollment 1998–1999			First-Year Class	
Men:	170	73%	Applied:	104
Women:	64	27%	Accepted:	104
Minorities:	178	76%	Enrolled:	92
Out-of-State:	9	4%		

1998–99 Class Profile
LSAT Percentile: n/av
LSAT Median Score: n/av
Percentage passing bar on first try: 100%

Tuition and Fees:

Resident
$5900 (P/T)

Average (public)
$8,772

Average (private)
$19,562

Nonresident
$5900 (P/T)

Average (public)
$14,629

Average (private)
$19,562

0   5   10   15   20   25   30

Percentage receiving financial aid: 2%

Contact
Dawn Monroe, Assistant Registrar, 310-204-0222 for general inquiries; Tracy Herreros, Assistant Academic Dean, 310-204-0222 for financial aid information.

AMERICAN COLLEGE OF LAW

1717 South State College
Boulevard #100
Anaheim, CA 92806

Phone: 714-634-3699
Fax: 714-634-3894
Web: www.aclaw.com

Application Filing	Accreditation
Fall: July 15	no
Spring: n/app	Degrees Granted
Fee: $25	J.D.

Enrollment 1998–1999			First-Year Class	
Men:	57	63%	Applied:	21
Women:	33	42%	Accepted:	19
Minorities:	10	11%	Enrolled:	19
Out-of-State:	90	100%		

1998–99 Class Profile
LSAT Percentile: 135%
LSAT Median Score: 135
Percentage passing bar on first try: 33%

Tuition and Fees:

Resident
$6630(P/T)

Average (public)
$8,772

Average (private)
$19,562

Nonresident
$6630(P/T)

Average (public)
$14,629

Average (private)
$19,562

0   5   10   15   20   25   30

Percentage receiving financial aid: n/av

Contact
Janice M. Meyers, Academics Administrator, 714-634-3699 for general inquiries; Janice Cowan, 704-634-3699 for financial aid information.

BARRY UNIVERSITY

Orlando School of Law

6441 East Colonial Drive
Orlando, FL 32807-3673

Phone: (407) 275-2000 ext. 237
Fax: (407) 275-2010
E-mail: lawinfo@mail.barry.edu

Application Filing	Accreditation
Fall: open	no
Spring: n/app	Degrees Granted
Fee: $50	J.D.

Enrollment 1998–1999			First-Year Class	
Men:	222	59%	Applied:	197
Women:	156	41%	Accepted:	137
Minorities:	102	27%	Enrolled:	64
Out-of-State:	95	25%		

1998–99 Class Profile
LSAT Percentile: 23%
LSAT Median Score: 144
Percentage passing bar on first try: n/av

Tuition and Fees:

Resident
$19,970 (F/T)

Average (public)
$8,772

Average (private)
$19,562

Nonresident
$19,970 (F/T)

Average (public)
$14,629

Average (private)
$19,562

0   5   10   15   20   25   30

Percentage receiving financial aid: 59%

Contact
Susan Bendlin, Director of Admissions, 407-275-2000 ext., 237 for general inquiries; Jack Agett, Director of Financial Services, 407-275-2000 ext., 264 for financial aid information.

CALIFORNIA NORTHERN

School of Law

1395 Ridgewood Drive, Suite 100
Chico, CA 95973

Phone: 530-891-6900
Fax: 530-891-3429
E-mail: info@calnorthern.edu
Web: www.calnorthern.edu

Application Filing	Accreditation
Fall: May 1	no
Spring: n/app	
Fee: $50	**Degrees Granted**
	J.D.

Enrollment 1998–1999			First-Year Class	
Men:	43	60%	Applied:	40
Women:	29	40%	Accepted:	29
Minorities:	n/av		Enrolled:	27
Out-of-State:	n/av			

1998–99 Class Profile
LSAT Percentile: n/av
LSAT Median Score: 145
Percentage passing bar on first try: n/av

Tuition and Fees:

Resident
$10,270 (P/T)

Average (public)
$8,772

Average (private)
$19,562

Nonresident
$10,270 (P/T)

Average (public)
$14,629

Average (private)
$19,562

0 5 10 15 20 25 30

Percentage receiving financial aid: n/av

Contact
530-891-6900 for general inquiries.

EMPIRE COLLEGE

Empire College School of Law

3033 Cleveland Avenue, Suite 102
Santa Rosa, CA 95403

Phone: 707-546-4000
Fax: 707-546-4058
E-mail: rhurd@empcol.com
Web: http://www.empcol.com

Application Filing	Accreditation
Fall: August 23	no
Spring: January 3	
Fee: $95	**Degrees Granted**
	J.D.

Enrollment 1998–1999			First-Year Class	
Men:	59	47%	Applied:	n/av
Women:	67	53%	Accepted:	n/av
Minorities:	4	3%	Enrolled:	n/av
Out-of-State:	0	0%		

1998–99 Class Profile
LSAT Percentile: 40%
LSAT Median Score: n/av
Percentage passing bar on first try: 57%

Tuition and Fees:

Resident
$3160(P/T)

Average (public)
$8,772

Average (private)
$19,562

Nonresident
$3160(P/T)

Average (public)
$14,629

Average (private)
$19,562

0 5 10 15 20 25 30

Percentage receiving financial aid: n/av

Contact
Pat Alley, Assistant to the Dean, 707-546-4000 for general inquiries; Patricia Spaeth, 707-546-4000 for financial aid information.

FAULKNER UNIVERSITY

Thomas Goode Jones School of Law

5345 Atlanta Highway
Montgomery, AL 36109

Phone: 334-386-7210
800-879-9816
Fax: 334-386-7223
E-mail: psmith@faulkner.edu

Application Filing	Accreditation
Fall: July 15	AALS
Spring: November 15	
Fee: $25	**Degrees Granted**
	J.D.

Enrollment 1998–1999			First-Year Class	
Men:	227	63%	Applied:	108
Women:	136	37%	Accepted:	83
Minorities:	44	12%	Enrolled:	63
Out-of-State:	7	2%		

1998–99 Class Profile
LSAT Percentile: 36%
LSAT Median Score: 147
Percentage passing bar on first try: 65%

Tuition and Fees:

Resident
$4950 (P/T)

Average (public)
$8,772

Average (private)
$19,562

Nonresident
$4950 (P/T)

Average (public)
$14,629

Average (private)
$19,562

0 5 10 15 20 25 30

Percentage receiving financial aid: 61%

Contact
Paul M. Smith, Admissions Director, 334-386-7210 for general inquiries; William E. Jackson, 334-386-7293 for financial aid information.

GLENDALE UNIVERSITY

Glendale University College of Law

220 North Glendale Avenue
Glendale, CA 91206

Phone: (818) 247-0770
Fax: (818) 247-0872
E-mail: admissions@glendalelaw.edu
Web: www.glendalelaw.edu

Application Filing	Accreditation
Fall: n/av	no
Spring: n/app	**Degrees Granted**
Fee: $40	J.D.

Enrollment 1998–1999		First-Year Class	
Men:	n/av	Applied:	n/av
Women:	n/av	Accepted:	n/av
Minorities:	n/av	Enrolled:	n/av
Out-of-State:	n/av		

1998–99 Class Profile

LSAT Percentile: n/av
LSAT Median Score: n/av
Percentage passing bar on first try: n/av

Tuition and Fees:

Resident
$256 (P/T) (PER CREDIT)

Average (public)
$8,772

Average (private)
$19,562

Nonresident
$256 (P/T) (PER CREDIT)

Average (public)
$14,629

Average (private)
$19,562

Percentage receiving financial aid: n/av

Contact
Darrin Greitzer, Director of Admissions, 818-247-0770 for general inquiries.

GUILD LAW SCHOOL

People's College of Law

660 South Bonnie Brae Street
Los Angeles, CA 90057

Phone: 213-483-0083
Fax: 213-483-0593
E-mail: people@peoplescollegeoflaw.edu
Web: http://peoplecollegeoflaw.edu

Application Filing	Accreditation
Fall: August 10	no
Spring: December 10	**Degrees Granted**
Fee: $30	J.D.

Enrollment 1998–1999		First-Year Class	
Men:	n/av	Applied:	n/av
Women:	n/av	Accepted:	n/av
Minorities:	n/av	Enrolled:	n/av
Out-of-State:	n/av		

1998–99 Class Profile

LSAT Percentile: n/av
LSAT Median Score: n/av
Percentage passing bar on first try: n/av

Tuition and Fees:

Resident
$3300

Average (public)
$8,772

Average (private)
$19,562

Nonresident
$3300

Average (public)
$14,629

Average (private)
$19,562

Percentage receiving financial aid: 0

Contact
Deborah Irving-Hunn, Administrator, 213-483-0083 for general inquiries.

HUMPHREYS COLLEGE

School of Law

6650 Inglewood Avenue
Stockton, CA 95207

Phone: 209-478-0800
Fax: 2089-478-8721
E-mail: ajohnson@humphreys.edu
Web: www.humphreys.edu

Application Filing	Accreditation
Fall: June 1	SBC, WASC
Spring: n/app	**Degrees Granted**
Fee: $50	J.D.

Enrollment 1998–1999			First-Year Class	
Men:	28	50%	Applied:	47
Women:	28	50%	Accepted:	27
Minorities:	14	25%	Enrolled:	23
Out-of-State:	0	0%		

1998–99 Class Profile

LSAT Percentile: 53%
LSAT Median Score: 151
Percentage passing bar on first try: n/av

Tuition and Fees:

Resident
$6021 (P/T)

Average (public)
$8,772

Average (private)
$19,562

Nonresident
$6021 (P/T)

Average (public)
$14,629

Average (private)
$19,562

Percentage receiving financial aid: 90%

Contact
209-478-0800 for general inquiries; Judi Johnston, Director of Financial Aid, 209-478-0800, ext. 122 for financial aid information.

JOHN F. KENNEDY UNIVERSITY

School of Law

547 Ygnacio Valley Road
Walnut Creek, CA 94596

Phone: 925-258-2322
Fax: 925-254-6964
E-mail: proginfo@jfku.edu
Web: www.jfku.edu

Application Filing		Accreditation
Fall: May 30		SBC, WASC
Spring: October 30		Degrees Granted
Fee: $50		J.D.

Enrollment 1998–1999			First-Year Class	
Men:	139	50%	Applied:	123
Women:	137	50%	Accepted:	103
Minorities:	88	32%	Enrolled:	87
Out-of-State:	0	0%		

1998–99 Class Profile

LSAT Percentile: 20%
LSAT Median Score: 142
Percentage passing bar on first try: N/AV

Tuition and Fees:

Resident
$8286 (P/T)

Average (public)
$8,772

Average (private)
$19,562

Nonresident
$8286 (P/T)

Average (public)
$14,629

Average (private)
$19,562

0 5 10 15 20 25 30

Percentage receiving financial aid: 60%

Contact
925-258-2322 for general inquiries; Mindy Bergeron, Director, 925-258-2385 for financial aid information.

LINCOLN LAW SCHOOL OF SACRAMENTO

3140 J Street
Sacramento, CA 95816

Phone: 916-446-1275
Fax: 916-446-5641
E-mail: lincolnlaw@lincolnlaw.edu
Web: www.lincolnlaw.edu

Application Filing		Accreditation
Fall: June 15		SBC
Spring: November 15		Degrees Granted
Fee: $30		J.D.

Enrollment 1998–1999			First-Year Class	
Men:	118	48%	Applied:	214
Women:	126	51%	Accepted:	158
Minorities:	37	15%	Enrolled:	124
Out-of-State:	0	0%		

1998–99 Class Profile

LSAT Percentile: 35%
LSAT Median Score: 145
Percentage passing bar on first try: 40%

Tuition and Fees:

Resident
$4900(P/T)

Average (public)
$8,772

Average (private)
$19,562

Nonresident
$4900(P/T)

Average (public)
$14,629

Average (private)
$19,562

0 5 10 15 20 25 30

Percentage receiving financial aid: 35%

Contact
Registrar, Admissions Office, 916-446-1275 for general inquiries; Melissa Fuller, Assistant Registrar, 916-446-1275 for financial aid information.

MASSACHUSETTS SCHOOL OF LAW

500 Federal Street
Andover, MA 01810

Phone: (978) 681-0800
Fax: (978) 681-6330
E-mail: pcolby@mslaw.edu
Web: www.mslaw.edu

Application Filing		Accreditation
Fall: open		no
Spring: open		Degrees Granted
Fee: $40		J.D., J.D./M.B.A.

Enrollment 1998–1999			First-Year Class	
Men:	270	60%	Applied:	225
Women:	180	40%	Accepted:	140
Minorities:	90	20%	Enrolled:	116
Out-of-State:	450	100%		

1998–99 Class Profile

LSAT Percentile: n/av
LSAT Median Score: n/av
Percentage passing bar on first try: 70%

Tuition and Fees:

Resident
$10,800 (F/T)

Average (public)
$8,772

Average (private)
$19,562

Nonresident
$10,800 (P/T)

Average (public)
$14,629

Average (private)
$19,562

0 5 10 15 20 25 30

Percentage receiving financial aid: 50%

Contact
Director of Admissions, 978-681-0800 for general inquiries; Lynn Bowab, Director of Financial Aid, 978-681-0800 for financial aid information.

NEW COLLEGE OF CALIFORNIA

New College of California School of Law

50 Fell Street
San Francisco, CA 94102

Phone: (415) 241-1314
Fax: (415) 241-1353
E-mail: lawinfo@newcollege.edu
Web: www.newcollege.edu

Application Filing			Accreditation
Fall: May 1			no
Spring: n/app			Degrees Granted
Fee: $45			J.D.

Enrollment 1998–1999			First-Year Class	
Men:	45	46	Applied:	n/av
Women:	52	54%	Accepted:	n/av
Minorities:	51	53%	Enrolled:	n/av
Out-of-State:	0	Null		

1998–99 Class Profile
LSAT Percentile: 39%
LSAT Median Score: n/av
Percentage passing bar on first try: n/av

Tuition and Fees:

Resident
$10,000 (F/T)

Average (public)
$8,772

Average (private)
$19,562

Nonresident
$7500 (P/T)

Average (public)
$14,629

Average (private)
$19,562

0 5 10 15 20 25 30

Percentage receiving financial aid: 90%

Contact
Jenie Chang, Assistant Dean Admissions, 415-241-1314 for general inquiries; Juanita Marshall-Bell, 415-241-1342 for financial aid information.

PRESIDENT'S COLLEGE

School of Law

123 S. Market Street
Wichita, KS 67202

Phone: (316) 267-9000
Fax: (316) 267-8825
E-mail: prescoll@wichita.infinet

Application Filing			Accreditation
Fall: August 1			no
Spring: December 1			Degrees Granted
Fee: $35			J.D.

Enrollment 1998–1999			First-Year Class	
Men:	29	71%	Applied:	7
Women:	12	29%	Accepted:	7
Minorities:	8	19%	Enrolled:	7
Out-of-State:	0	0%		

1998–99 Class Profile
LSAT Percentile: n/av
LSAT Median Score: n/av
Percentage passing bar on first try: n/av

Tuition and Fees:

Resident
$300 (P/T) (PER CREDIT)

Average (public)
$8,772

Average (private)
$19,562

Nonresident
$300 (P/T) (PER CREDIT)

Average (public)
$14,629

Average (private)
$19,562

0 5 10 15 20 25 30

Percentage receiving financial aid: 50%

Contact
Barbara McClintock, Registrar, 316-267-9000 for general inquiries; Thomas P. Laurino, Dean, 316-267-9000 for financial aid information.

SAN FRANCISCO LAW SCHOOL

20 Haight Street
San Francisco, CA 94102

Phone: 415-626-5550 ext. 121
Fax: 415-626-5584
E-mail: admin@sfls.edu
Web: sfls.edu

Application Filing			Accreditation
Fall: Null			no
Spring: n/app			Degrees Granted
Fee: n/av			J.D.

Enrollment 1998–1999			First-Year Class	
Men:	87	Null	Applied:	n/av
Women:	62	42%	Accepted:	n/av
Minorities:	n/av		Enrolled:	n/av
Out-of-State:	n/av			

1998–99 Class Profile
LSAT Percentile: n/av
LSAT Median Score: n/av
Percentage passing bar on first try: n/av

Tuition and Fees:

Resident
N/AV

Average (public)
$8,772

Average (private)
$19,562

Nonresident
N/AV

Average (public)
$14,629

Average (private)
$19,562

0 5 10 15 20 25 30

Percentage receiving financial aid: 62%

Contact
Ronda Shatara, Director of Admissions & Registrar, 415-626-5550 ext. 122 for general inquiries; Catherine Dawson, Associate Dean for Administration, 415-626-5550 for financial aid information.

Santa Barbara College of Law

20 E.Victoria Street
Santa Barbara, CA 93101

Phone: (805) 966-0010
Fax: (805) 966-7181
E-mail: sbcl@santabarbaralaw.edu
Web: www.sbcl@santabarbaralaw.edu

Application Filing		Accreditation
Fall: n/av		no
Spring: n/app		**Degrees Granted**
Fee: n/av		J.D.

Enrollment 1998–1999			First-Year Class	
Men:	53	48%	Applied:	69
Women:	57	52%	Accepted:	52
Minorities:	15	14%	Enrolled:	35
Out-of-State:	0	0%		

1998–99 Class Profile
LSAT Percentile: n/av
LSAT Median Score: n/av
Percentage passing bar on first try: n/av

Tuition and Fees:

Resident
4,355

Average (public)
$8,772

Average (private)
$19,562

Nonresident
4,355

Average (public)
$14,629

Average (private)
$19,562

0 5 10 15 20 25 30

Percentage receiving financial aid: n/av

Contact
Vicki Stevenson, Administrative Assistant, 805-966-0010 for general inquiries; Mary Osborne, Assistant Dean, 805-966-0010 for financial aid information.

Ventura College of Law

4475 Market Street
Ventura, CA 93003

Phone: 805-658-0511
Fax: 805-658-0529
E-mail: vcl@venturalaw.edu
Web: www.venturalaw.edu

Application Filing		Accreditation
Fall: June 1		SBC
Spring: December 1		**Degrees Granted**
Fee: $45		J.D.

Enrollment 1998–1999			First-Year Class	
Men:	51	47%	Applied:	69
Women:	57	53%	Accepted:	53
Minorities:	24	22%	Enrolled:	39
Out-of-State:	0	0%		

1998–99 Class Profile
LSAT Percentile: 41%
LSAT Median Score: n/av
Percentage passing bar on first try: n/av

Tuition and Fees:

Resident
$5135 (P/T)

Average (public)
$8,772

Average (private)
$19,562

Nonresident
$5135 (P/T)

Average (public)
$14,629

Average (private)
$19,562

0 5 10 15 20 25 30

Percentage receiving financial aid: n/av

Contact
Barbara Doyle, Assistant Dean, 805-658-0511 for general inquiries.

Southern New England School of Law

333 Faunce Corner Road
North Dartmouth, MA 02747-1252

Phone: 508-998-9400
800-213-0060
Fax: 508-998-9561
E-mail: nhebert@snesl.edu
Web: www.snesl.edu

Application Filing		Accreditation
Fall: June 30		no
Spring: n/app		**Degrees Granted**
Fee: $50		J.D.

Enrollment 1998–1999			First-Year Class	
Men:	149	66%	Applied:	152
Women:	77	34%	Accepted:	101
Minorities:	23	10%	Enrolled:	42
Out-of-State:	86	38%		

1998–99 Class Profile
LSAT Percentile: n/av
LSAT Median Score: 147
Percentage passing bar on first try: n/av

Tuition and Fees:

Resident
$18,156

Average (public)
$8,772

Average (private)
$19,562

Nonresident
$18,156

Average (public)
$14,629

Average (private)
$19,562

0 5 10 15 20 25 30

Percentage receiving financial aid: n/av

Contact
Nancy Fitzsimmons Herbert, Director of Admission, 508-998-9400 or 800-213-0060 for general inquiries; Sandra Leger Silva, Director of Financial Aid, 508-998-9600, ext. 112 for financial aid information.

TRINITY INTERNATIONAL UNIVERSITY

Trinity Law School

2200 North Grand Avenue
Santa Ana, CA 92705

Phone: (714) 796-7000
(800) 922-4748
Fax: (714) 796-7190
E-mail: tls@tiu.edu
Web: www.tls.edu

Application Filing	Accreditation
Fall: July 15	no
Spring: December 15	Degrees Granted
Fee: $30	J.D., M.A.

Enrollment 1998–1999			First-Year Class	
Men:	73	63%	Applied:	98
Women:	43	37%	Accepted:	70
Minorities:	59	51%	Enrolled:	43
Out-of-State:	5	4%		

1998–99 Class Profile

LSAT Percentile: 23%
LSAT Median Score: 144
Percentage passing bar on first try: n/av

Tuition and Fees:

Resident
$8810 (P/T)

Average (public)
$8,772

Average (private)
$19,562

Nonresident
$8810 (P/T)

Average (public)
$14,629

Average (private)
$19,562

Percentage receiving financial aid: 75%

Contact
Linda Ney, Admissions Counselor, 714-796-7100 for general inquiries; Rick Anderson, 714-796-7120 for financial aid information.

UNIVERSITY OF LA VERNE

College of Law San Fernendo Valley

21300 Oxnard Street,
CA 91367

Phone: 818-830-0529
830-0529
Fax: 818-883-8142
E-mail: murphy@ulv.edu
Web: www.ulv.edu/law/sfv

Application Filing	Accreditation
Fall: open	no
Spring: open	Degrees Granted
Fee: $45	J.D.

Enrollment 1998–1999			First-Year Class	
Men:	95	55%	Applied:	143
Women:	78	45%	Accepted:	84
Minorities:	42	24%	Enrolled:	45
Out-of-State:	3	2%		

1998–99 Class Profile

LSAT Percentile: 24%
LSAT Median Score: 141
Percentage passing bar on first try: 40%

Tuition and Fees:

Resident
$7530

Average (public)
$8,772

Average (private)
$19,562

Nonresident
$7530

Average (public)
$14,629

Average (private)
$19,562

Percentage receiving financial aid: 90%

Contact
Yvette Underdue Murph, Director of Admissions, 818-883-0529 for general inquiries; Michelle Stokes, Financial Aid Advisor, 909-593-3511, ext. 4138 for financial aid information.

UNIVERSITY OF WEST LOS ANGELES

School of Law

1155 Arbor Vitae Street
Inglewood, CA 90301-2902

Phone: 310-342-5254
Fax: 310-342-5295

Application Filing	Accreditation
Fall: July 31	SBC
Spring: December 31	Degrees Granted
Fee: $45	J.D.

Enrollment 1998–1999			First-Year Class	
Men:	159	53%	Applied:	147
Women:	140	47%	Accepted:	108
Minorities:	158	53%	Enrolled:	80
Out-of-State:	0	0%		

1998–99 Class Profile

LSAT Percentile: 31%
LSAT Median Score: n/av
Percentage passing bar on first try: n/av

Tuition and Fees:

Resident
$420 (PER CREDIT)

Average (public)
$8,772

Average (private)
$19,562

Nonresident
$420 (PER CREDIT)

Average (public)
$14,629

Average (private)
$19,562

Percentage receiving financial aid: 97%

Contact
Lynda Freeman, Admissions Counselor, 310-342-5254 for general inquiries; Roberto Quinones, Financial Aid Officer, 310-342-5268 for financial aid information.

INDEX

Entries set in roman type are law schools approved by the American Bar Association.
Entries set in italic type are law schools not approved by the American Bar Association.